SAFETY SYMBOLS	HAZARD	PRECAUTION	REMEDY
Disposal	Special disposal required	Dispose of wastes as directed by your teacher.	Ask your teacher how to dispose of laboratory materials.
Biological	Organisms that can harm humans	Avoid breathing in or skin contact with organisms. Wear dust mask or gloves. Wash hands thoroughly.	Notify your teacher if you suspect contact.
Extreme Temperature	Objects that can burn skin by being too cold or too hot	Use proper protection when handling.	Go to your teacher for first aid.
Sharp Object	Use of tools or glassware that can easily puncture or slice skin	Practice common sense behavior and follow guidelines for use of the tool.	Go to your teacher for first aid.
Fumes	Potential danger from smelling fumes	Must have good ventilation and never smell fumes directly.	Leave foul area and notify your teacher immediately.
Electrical	Possible danger from electrical shock or burn	Double-check setup with instructor. Check condition of wires and apparatus.	Do not attempt to fix electrical problems. Notify your teacher immediately.
Irritant	Substances that can irritate your skin or mucous membranes	Wear dust mask or gloves. Practice extra care when handling these materials.	Go to your teacher for first aid.
Chemical	Substances (acids and bases) that can react with and destroy tissue and other materials	Wear goggles and an apron.	Immediately flush with water and notify your teacher.
Toxic	Poisonous substance	Follow your teacher's instructions. Always wash hands thoroughly after use.	Go to your teacher for first aid.
Fire	Flammable and combustible materials may burn if exposed to an open flame or spark	Avoid flames and heat sources. Be aware of locations of fire safety equipment.	Notify your teacher immediately. Use fire safety equipment if necessary.

Eye Safety
This symbol appears when a danger to eyes exists.

Clothing Protection
This symbol appears when substances could stain or burn clothing.

Animal Safety
This symbol appears whenever live animals are studied and the safety of the animals and students must be ensured.

GLENCOE

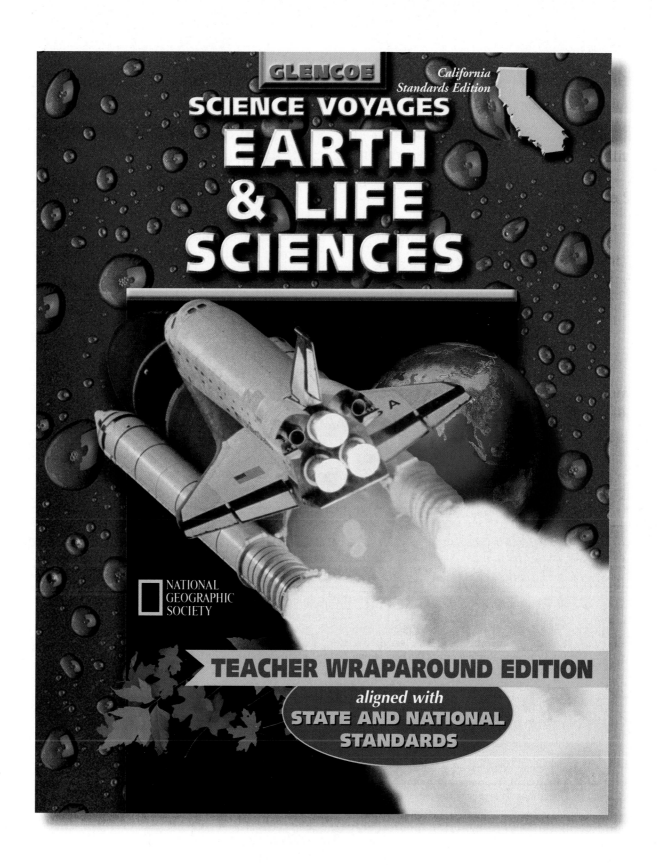

California Standards Edition

SCIENCE VOYAGES
EARTH & LIFE SCIENCES

NATIONAL GEOGRAPHIC SOCIETY

TEACHER WRAPAROUND EDITION

aligned with

STATE AND NATIONAL STANDARDS

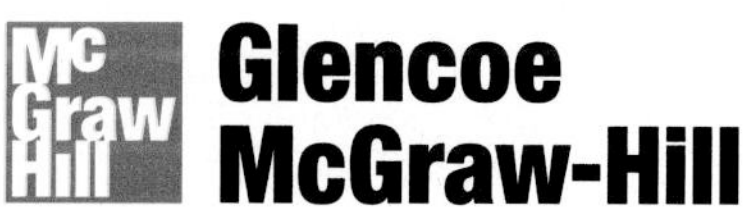

Glencoe McGraw-Hill

New York, New York   Columbus, Ohio   Woodland Hills, California   Peoria, Illinois

SCIENCE VOYAGES

Exploring the Life, Earth, and Physical Sciences

California Student Edition
California Teacher Wraparound Edition
Assessment
- Chapter Review
- California Science Content Standards Practice Questions
- Performance Assessment
- Assessment—Chapter Tests
- ExamView Test Bank Software
- Performance Assessment in the Science Classroom
- Alternate Assessment in the Science Classroom

Study Guide for Content Mastery, SE and TE
Chapter Overview Study Guide, SE and TE
Reinforcement
Enrichment
Critical Thinking/Problem Solving
Multicultural Connections
Activity Worksheets
Laboratory Manual, SE and TE
Science Inquiry Activities, SE and TE
California Home Involvement
Teaching Transparencies
Section Focus Transparencies
Science Integration Transparencies
Spanish Resources
California Lesson Plans
Lab and Safety Skills in the Science Classroom
Cooperative Learning in the Science Classroom
Exploring Environmental Issues
MindJogger Videoquizzes and Teacher Guide
English/Spanish Audiocassettes
Interactive Lesson Planner CD-ROM
Interactive CD-ROM
Internet Site
Using the Internet in the Science Classroom

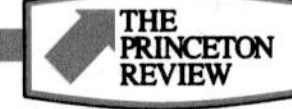

"Test-Taking Tip" and Test Practice features in this book were written by the Princeton Review, the nation's leader in test preparation. Through its association with McGraw-Hill, the Princeton Review offers the best way to help students excel on standardized assessments.

The Princeton Review is not affiliated with Princeton University or Educational Testing Service.

Glencoe/McGraw-Hill

A Division of The McGraw-Hill Companies

Send all inquiries to:

Glencoe/McGraw-Hill
8787 Orion Place
Columbus, OH 43240

ISBN 0-07-823977-X

Printed in the United States of America.

1 2 3 4 5 6 7 8 9 027/046 05 04 03 02 01 00

TEACHER GUIDE

TABLE of CONTENTS

AUTHORS

Alton Biggs is a Texas science teacher in Allen ISD. He has taught grades 7–12 for 25 years. He received his B.S. and M.S. degrees from Texas A&M University at Commerce. He is past president of the National Association of Biology Teachers and Texas Association of Biology Teachers, and an Honorary Member of both organizations.

John Burns teaches science at Ramona Junior High School, Chino, California. He received his B.S. in biology from California State University, Bakersfield, and M.A.T. Science from California State University, Fullerton. In 1992, he was a recipient of the Science and Mathematics Fellowship from the Council for Basic Education.

Lucille H. Daniel, Ed.D is a Rutherford County North Carolina science teacher with more than 38 years of experience. She has received the Presidential Award of Excellence in Mathematics and Science Teaching, the North Carolina Science Teachers Association Distinguished Service Award, and the Governor's Business Award for Excellence in Science Education.

Cathy Ezrailson is a Physics Teaching Resource Agent and field adjunct for the State of Texas. She is an active science writer, holding a B.S. from Ashland College and an M.S. from the University of Houston. She has been the Teacher of the Year in her region, and has received the Texas Presidential Award and the Tandy Scholars Award.

Ralph M. Feather, Jr., Ph.D. teaches Earth science, geology, and astronomy in Derry, Pennsylvania. He received his Ph.D. from the University of Pittsburgh in science education. Dr. Feather received the Presidential Award for Excellence in Science Teaching in 1991.

Patricia M. Horton is a mentor teacher and middle school science and math chairperson in the Etiwanda School District, California. She earned her master's degree at California State University San Bernadino in middle school grades education. She received the 1993 Commitment to Excellence in Education Award.

Thomas K. McCarthy, Ph.D. teaches physics and is the department chair at Saint Edward's School in Florida. He earned his bachelor's degree in physics from Loyola University in Chicago and his Ph.D. from the University of Texas at Dallas. He received the Presidential Scholar Distinguished Teacher Award in 1998.

Ed Ortleb is a science consultant and researcher in St. Louis, Missouri. He has advanced degrees from Washington University, and is a life member of NSTA. He served as NSTA president in 1978–79 and has received numerous awards for service to science education.

Susan L. Snyder teaches at Jones Middle School in Ohio. She received her B.S. from Miami University, Ohio, and M.S. in entomology from the University of Hawaii. She was the Ohio Teacher of the Year and a finalist for the National Teacher of the Year in 1987.

Eric Werwa, Ph.D. is a professor of physics at Otterbein College in Westerville, Ohio. Dr. Werwa received his B.S. in materials science and engineering from the University of Pennsylvania, and holds a Ph.D. in electronic materials from the Massachusetts Institute of Technology.

The National Geographic Society and Glencoe have joined forces to bring exciting new features and technologies to ***Science Voyages.*** By incorporating National Geographic's world-renowned photographs, illustrations, and content features, ***Science Voyages*** will engage students as never before.

Contributing Authors

Al Janulaw
Science Teacher
Creekside Middle School
Rohnert Park, California

Penny Parsekian
Science Writer
New London, Connecticut

Gerry Madrazo, Ph.D.
Mathematics and Science Education Network
University of North Carolina, Chapel Hill
Chapel Hill, North Carolina

Series Consultants

Chemistry

Douglas Martin, Ph.D.
Chemistry Department
Sonoma State University
Rohnert Park, California

Cheryl Wistrom, Ph.D.
Associate Professor of Chemistry
Saint Joseph's College
Rensselaer, Indiana

Earth Science

Tomasz K. Baumiller, Ph.D.
Museum of Paleontology
University of Michigan
Ann Arbor, Michigan

Maureen Allen
Science Resource Specialist
Irvine Unified School District
Laguna Hills, California

Connie Sutton, Ph.D.
Department of Geoscience
Indiana University
Indiana, Pennsylvania

Physics

Thomas Barrett, Ph.D.
Department of Physics
The Ohio State University
Columbus, Ohio

David Haase, Ph.D.
Professor of Physics
North Carolina State University
Raleigh, North Carolina

Life Science

William Ausich, Ph.D.
Department of Geological Sciences
The Ohio State University
Columbus, Ohio

Dennis Stockdale
Asheville High School
Asheville, North Carolina

Daniel Zeigler, Ph.D.
Director
Bacillus Genetic Stock Center
The Ohio State University
Columbus, Ohio

Reading

Nancy Farnan, Ph.D.
School of Teacher Education
San Diego State University
San Diego, California

Gary Kroesch
University of California
San Diego, California

Safety

Mark Vinciguerra
Lab Safety Instructor
Department of Physics
The Ohio State University
Columbus, Ohio

Curriculum

Tom Custer, Ph.D.
Maryland State Department of Education
Challenge/Reconstructed Schools
Baltimore, Maryland

Series Reviewers

Jhina Alvarado
Potrero Hill Middle School for the Arts
San Francisco, California

Richard Cheeseman
Bert Lynn Middle School
Torrance, California

Linda Cook
Rider High School
Wichita Falls, Texas

John B. Davis
Niagara-Wheatfield Central School
Sanborn, New York

Shirley Ann DeFilippo
Timothy Edwards Middle School
South Windsor, Connecticut

Janet Doughty
H J McDonald Middle School
New Bern, North Carolina

Jason Druten
Jefferson Middle School
Torrance, California

Lin Harp
Magellan Middle School
Raleigh, North Carolina

Doris Holland
West Cary Middle School
Raleigh, North Carolina

Deborah Huffine
Noblesville Intermediate School
Noblesville, Indiana

Paul Osborne
DeValls Bluff High School
DeValls Bluff, Arkansas

Erik Resnick
Robert E. Peary Middle School
Gardena, California

Robert Sirbu
Lowell Junior High School
Oakland, California

Michael Tally
Wake County Public Schools
Raleigh, North Carolina

Cindy Williamson
Whiteville City Schools
Whiteville, North Carolina

Maurice Yaggi
Middlebrook School
Wilton, Connecticut

Donna York
Anchorage School District
Anchorage, Alaska

Activity Testers

Clayton Millage
Science Teacher
Lynden Middle School
Lynden, Washington

Science Kit and Boreal Laboratories
Tonawanda, New York

CALIFORNIA SCIENCE CONTENT

Unit 1 • The Nature of Science

- ☑ **Chapter 1** The Nature of Science
- ☑ **Chapter 2** Measurement
- ☐ **Chapter 3** Rocks
- ☑ **Chapter 4** Resources
- ☑ **Chapter 5** Views of Earth

Unit 2 • Earth's Changing Surface

- ☑ **Chapter 6** Weathering and Soil
- ☑ **Chapter 7** Erosional Forces
- ☑ **Chapter 8** Water Erosion and Deposition

Unit 3 • Earth's Interior

- ☑ **Chapter 9** Plate Tectonics
- ☑ **Chapter 10** Earthquakes
- ☑ **Chapter 11** Volcanoes

Unit 4 • Change Through Time

- ☐ **Chapter 12** Clues to Earth's Past
- ☐ **Chapter 13** Geologic Time

Unit 5 • Earth's Air and Water

- ☑ **Chapter 14** Atmosphere
- ☑ **Chapter 15** Weather
- ☐ **Chapter 16** Climate
- ☑ **Chapter 17** Ocean Motion

Unit 6 • Astronomy

- ☐ **Chapter 18** The Sun-Earth-Moon System
- ☐ **Chapter 19** The Solar System
- ☐ **Chapter 20** Stars and Galaxies

Unit 1 • Interactions in the Living World

- ☑ **Chapter 1** The Nature of Science
- ☑ **Chapter 2** The Structure of Organisms
- ☑ **Chapter 3** Cell Processes
- ☑ **Chapter 4** Cell Reproduction
- ☑ **Chapter 5** Plant Reproduction
- ☑ **Chapter 6** Heredity
- ☑ **Chapter 7** Change Through Time

Unit 2 • Classifying Life

- ☑ **Chapter 8** Classifying LivingThings
- ☐ **Chapter 9** Bacteria
- ☐ **Chapter 10** Protists and Fungi
- ☐ **Chapter 11** Plants
- ☐ **Chapter 12** Invertebrate Animals
- ☐ **Chapter 13** Vertebrate Animals

Unit 3 • Ecology

- ☐ **Chapter 14** Life and the Environment
- ☐ **Chapter 15** Ecosystems

Unit 4 • The Human Body

- ☑ **Chapter 16** Bones, Muscles, and Skin
- ☑ **Chapter 17** Nutrients and Digestion
- ☑ **Chapter 18** The Circulatory System
- ☑ **Chapter 19** Respiration and Excretion
- ☑ **Chapter 20** The Nervous and Endocrine Systems
- ☑ **Chapter 21** Reproduction and Growth
- ☑ **Chapter 22** Immunity

Unit 1 • The Nature of Matter

- ☑ **Chapter 1** The Nature of Science
- ☑ **Chapter 2** Matter
- ☐ **Chapter 3** Energy
- ☑ **Chapter 4** States of Matter
- ☑ **Chapter 5** Inside the Atom
- ☑ **Chapter 6** The Periodic Table

Unit 2 • Chemical Interactions

- ☑ **Chapter 7** Chemical Bonds
- ☑ **Chapter 8** Chemical Reactions
- ☑ **Chapter 9** Solutions
- ☑ **Chapter 10** Carbon Chemistry

Unit 3 • Forces and Motion

- ☑ **Chapter 11** Motion
- ☑ **Chapter 12** Force and Newton's Laws
- ☐ **Chapter 13** Work and Simple Machines

Unit 4 • Interactions in the Physical World

- ☐ **Chapter 14** Waves
- ☐ **Chapter 15** Lights, Mirrors, and Lenses
- ☐ **Chapter 16** Electricity

STANDARDS CHECK ☑

Unit 7 • Ecology

- ☐ **Chapter 21** Classifying Living Things
- ☐ **Chapter 22** Diversity and Adaptations
- ☑ **Chapter 23** Life and the Environment
- ☑ **Chapter 24** Ecosystems

Unit 8 • Matter and Energy

- ☐ **Chapter 25** Matter
- ☑ **Chapter 26** Energy
- ☑ **Chapter 27** Waves

Unit 5 • Interactions in the Physical World

- ☑ **Chapter 23** Lights, Mirrors, and Lenses
- ☐ **Chapter 24** Motion and Forces
- ☑ **Chapter 25** Work and Simple Machines
- ☐ **Chapter 26** Electricity

Unit 6 • Earth Materials and Resources

- ☑ **Chapter 27** Rocks
- ☐ **Chapter 28** Resources and the Environment

Unit 7 • Change Through Time

- ☑ **Chapter 29** Clues to Earth's Past
- ☑ **Chapter 30** Geologic Time

Unit 5 • Astronomy

- ☑ **Chapter 17** Exploring Space
- ☑ **Chapter 18** The Sun-Earth-Moon System
- ☑ **Chapter 19** The Solar System
- ☑ **Chapter 20** Stars and Galaxies

Unit 6 • Life's Diversity

- ☐ **Chapter 21** Bacteria
- ☐ **Chapter 22** Protists and Fungi
- ☐ **Chapter 23** Plants
- ☐ **Chapter 24** Invertebrate Animals
- ☐ **Chapter 25** Vertebrate Animals

Unit 7 • You and the Environment

- ☐ **Chapter 26** Our Impact on Land
- ☐ **Chapter 27** Our Impact on Air and Water

GRADE EIGHT: FOCUS ON PHYSICAL SCIENCE

What are science content standards and why does California have them? Standards are guidelines for schools, students, and parents that describe the essential science concepts and skills for understanding the world in which we live. In 1999, The California State Board of Education established science content standards, and these standards will be the basis for state assessments that measure student achievement in science.

ADDITIONAL CONTENT STANDARDS FOR GRADE 8

- California Science Standards and Case Studies, found at the back of the book
- California Science Content Standards Assessment Practice booklets
- Chapter Assessments at the end of each chapter
- Science Voyages Website at www.glencoe.com/sec/science/ca

Motion

1. The velocity of an object is the rate of change of its position. As a basis for understanding this concept, students know:
   - **a.** position is defined relative to some choice of standard reference point and a set of reference directions.
     Sections 11-1, 17-2, 20-4, page 478
   - **b.** average speed is the total distance traveled divided by the total time elapsed. The speed of an object along the path traveled can vary.
     Sections 11-1, 17-1, 19-1, 19-2, page 478
   - **c.** how to solve problems involving distance, time, and average speed.
     Sections 11-1, 19-1, 19-2, page 479
   - **d.** to describe the velocity of an object, one must specify both direction and speed.
     Section 11-1, page 479
   - **e.** changes in velocity can be changes in speed, direction, or both.
     Sections 11-1, 11-2, page 480
   - **f.** how to interpret graphs of position versus time and speed versus time for motion in a single direction.
     Section 11-1, page 480

Forces

2. Unbalanced forces cause changes in velocity. As a basis for understanding this concept, students know:
   - **a.** a force has both direction and magnitude.
     Sections 5-1, 12-1, 12-2, 12-3, 12-4, 17-2, page 482
   - **b.** when an object is subject to two or more forces at once, the effect is the cumulative effect of all the forces.
     Sections 5-2, 12-1, 12-2, 24-4, 25-3, page 482
   - **c.** when the forces on an object are balanced, the motion of the object does not change.
     Sections 12-1, 12-4, 24-4, pages 482–483
   - **d.** how to identify separately two or more forces acting on a single static object, including gravity, elastic forces due to tension or compression in matter, and friction.
     Sections 12-1, 25-3, page 483
   - **e.** when the forces on an object are unbalanced, the object will change its motion (that is, it will speed up, slow down, or change direction).
     Sections 7-1, 12-1, 12-2, 12-3, 12-4, 17-2, 24-3, 25-3, page 483
   - **f.** the greater the mass of an object, the more force is needed to achieve the same change in motion.
     Sections 11-2, 12-2, 12-3, 19-2, page 484
   - **g.** the role of gravity in forming and maintaining planets, stars, and the solar system.
     Sections 17-2, 17-3, 18-2, 19-1, 19-2, 19-3, 19-4, 20-3, 20-4, page 484

Structure of Matter

3. Elements have distinct properties and atomic structure. All matter is comprised of one or more of over 100 elements. As a basis for understanding this concept, students know:
   - **a.** the structure of the atom and how it is composed of protons, neutrons, and electrons.
     Sections 5-1, 5-2, 7-1, 7-2, 9-2, 10-1, page 487
   - **b.** compounds are formed by combining two or more different elements. Compounds have properties that are different from the constituent elements.
     Sections 4-1, 4-2, 5-1, 7-2, 8-1, 9-1, 9-2, 10-1, 10-2, 10-3, page 487
   - **c.** atoms and molecules form solids by building up repeating patterns such as the crystal structure of NaCl or long chain polymers.
     Sections 4-1, 7-2, 10-3, pages 487–488
   - **d.** the states (solid, liquid, gas) of matter depend on molecular motion.
     Sections 4-1, 4-2, 4-3, pages 262–263
   - **e.** in solids the atoms are closely locked in position and can only vibrate, in liquids the atoms and molecules are more loosely connected and can collide with and move past one another, while in gases the atoms or molecules are free to move independently, colliding frequently.
     Sections 4-1, 4-2, 4-3, 9-1, pages 262–263
   - **f.** how to use the Periodic Table to identify elements in simple compounds.
     Sections 6-1, 6-2, 6-3, 7-1, 7-1, pages 488–489

Earth in the Solar System (Earth Science)

4. The structure and composition of the universe can be learned from the study of stars and galaxies, and their evolution. As a basis for understanding this concept, students know:
   - **a.** galaxies are clusters of billions of stars, and may have different shapes.
     Section 20-4, page 490
   - **b.** the sun is one of many stars in our own Milky Way galaxy. Stars may differ in size, temperature, and color.
     Sections 19-1, 19-3, 20-1, 20-2, 20-3, 20-4, page 490
   - **c.** how to use astronomical units and light years as measures of distance between the sun, stars, and Earth.
     Sections 19-2, 19-3, 20-1, 20-4, page 490

d. stars are the source of light for all bright objects in outer space. The moon and planets shine by reflected sunlight, not by their own light.
Sections 17-1, 18-2, 18-3, 19-1, 19-2, 20-3, pages 490–491

e. the appearance, general composition, relative position and size, and motion of objects in the solar system, including planets, planetary satellites, comets, and asteroids.
Sections 17-2, 17-3, 18-1, 18-2, 18-3, 19-1, 19-2, 19-3, 19-4, page 491

Reactions

5. Chemical reactions are processes in which atoms are rearranged into different combinations of molecules. As a basis for understanding this concept, students know:

a. reactant atoms and molecules interact to form products with different chemical properties.
Sections 8-1, 8-2, 9-3, 10-1, 10-2, 10-3, 22-2, 23-1, page 494

b. the idea of atoms explains the conservation of matter: in chemical reactions the number of atoms stays the same no matter how they are arranged, so their total mass stays the same.
Section 8-1, page 494

c. chemical reactions usually liberate heat or absorb heat.
Sections 8-1, 9-2, 26-2, page 494

d. physical processes include freezing and boiling, in which a material changes form with no chemical reaction.
Sections 4-1, 4-2, 8-1, 9-1, 9-2, page 495

e. how to determine whether a solution is acidic, basic or neutral.
Sections 9-3, 22-2, 27-1, page 496

Chemistry of Living Systems (Life Science)

6. Principles of chemistry underlie the functioning of biological systems. As a basis for understanding this concept, students know:

a. carbon, because of its ability to combine in many ways with itself and other elements, has a central role in the chemistry of living organisms.
Sections 6-2, 10-1, 10-2, 10-3, 21-1, 21-2, 22-2, 23-1, 26-2, page 498

b. living organisms are made of molecules largely consisting of carbon, hydrogen,nitrogen, oxygen, phosphorus and sulfur.
Sections 10-1, 10-2, 10-3, 21-2, 23-1, pages 498–499

c. living organisms have many different kinds of molecules including small ones such as water and salt, and very large ones such as carbohydrates, fats, proteins and DNA.
Sections 9-3, 10-1, 10-3, 23-1, 23-3, 24-4, pages 498–499

Periodic Table

7. The organization of the Periodic Table is based on the properties of the elements and reflects the structure of atoms. As a basis for understanding this concept, students know:

a. how to identify regions corresponding to metals, nonmetals and inert gases.
Sections 6-1, 6-2, 6-3, 7-2, page 501

b. elements are defined by the number of protons in the nucleus, which is called the atomic number. Different isotopes of an element have a different number of neutrons in the nucleus.
Sections 5-2, 6-1, page 501

c. substances can be classified by their properties, including melting temperature, density, hardness, heat, and electrical conductivity.
Sections 6-1, 6-2, 6-3, 7-1, page 502

Density and Buoyancy

8. All objects experience a buoyant force when immersed in a fluid. As a basis for understanding this concept, students know:

a. density is mass per unit volume.
Sections 1-2, 4-3, 18-1, pages 504–505

b. how to calculate the density of substances (regular and irregular solids, and liquids) from measurements of mass and volume.
Sections 1-2, 4-3, pages 504–506

c. the buoyant force on an object in a fluid is an upward force equal to the weight of the fluid it has displaced.
Sections 4-3, 25-1, pages 504–505

d. how to predict whether an object will float or sink.
Sections 1-2, 4-3, pages 504–505

Investigation and Experimentation

9. Scientific progress is made by asking meaningful questions and conducting careful investigations. As a basis for understanding this concept, and to address the content of the other three strands, students
should develop their own questions and perform investigations. Students will:

a. plan and conduct a scientific investigation to test a hypothesis.
Sections 1-1, 1-2, 4-2, 4-3, 5-1, 5-2, 6-2, 6-3, 7-1, 7-2, 8-1, 8-2, 9-2, 10-3, 11-1, 20-4, 21-1, 24-3, 25-4, 27-1, pages 127, 482, 483, 484, 486, 487, 489, 494, 495, 496, 507

b. evaluate the accuracy and reproducibility of data.
Sections 1-1, 5-1, 5-2, 6-3, 7-1, 8-1, 17-2, 21-1, 24-3, 25-4, pages 481, 483, 493, 495, 503

c. distinguish between variable and controlled parameters in a test.
Sections 1-1, 1-2, 6-3, 8-1, 8-2, 9-2, 11-2, 12-2, 18-1, 21-1, 21-2, 24-3, 25-4, 27-1, pages 481, 482, 483, 488, 494, 495, 497, 500, 503, 555

d. recognize the slope of the linear graph as the constant in the relationship y=kx and apply this to interpret graphs constructed from data.
Sections 11-1, 26-1, pages 479, 480, 498, 953–954, 978

e. construct appropriate graphs from data and develop quantitative statements about the relationships between variables.
Sections 1-1, 1-2, 4-1, 4-2, 5-2, 6-1, 9-2, 10-1, 25-1, 25-4, 26-1, pages 121, 149, 233, 479, 480, 498, 502, 978

f. apply simple mathematical relationships to determine one quantity given the other two (including speed = distance/time, density = mass/volume, force = pressure x area, volume = area x height).
Sections 1-1, 1-2, 4-1, 4-2, 4-3, 5-2, 7-1, 8-2, 9-2, 10-1, 10-3, 11-1, 11-2, 11-3, 12-4, 17-1, 17-2, 19-2, 21-2, 23-3, 26-1, 27-1, pages 324, 357, 479, 499, 505

g. distinguish between linear and nonlinear relationships on a graph of data.
Sections 1-1, 4-1, 4-2, 5-2, 10-1, 11-1, pages 325, 480, 491, 502, 953–954, 978

STUDENT EDITION

TABLE of CONTENTS

UNIT 5 Astronomy 608

Ch. 18

Chapter 19 The Solar System 666

Chapter 20 Stars and Galaxies 698

Table of Contents

UNIT 6 Life's Diversity 734

Science Connections

Reading & Writing in Science

Science & Society

History of Science

How it Works

Activities

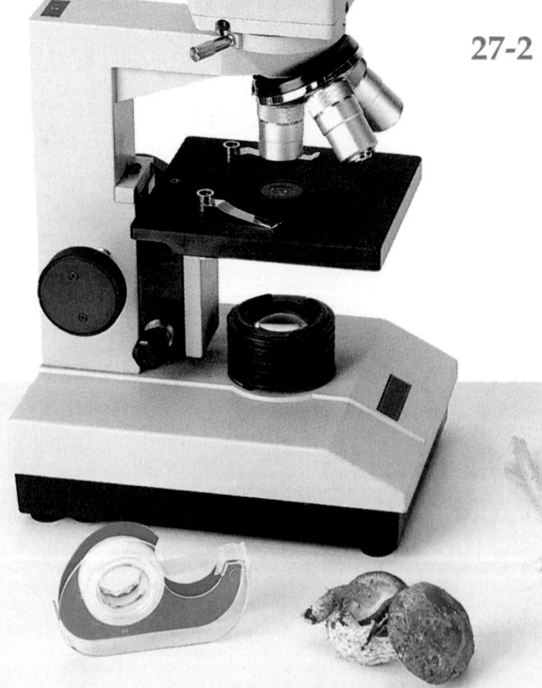

MiniLab

Try at Home MiniLab

Explore Activities

Table of Contents

Problem Solving

Skill Activities

Skill Builders

Benchmarks for Science Literacy

Benchmarks in Science Education

Students need to be aware of the science around them. They need to be science literate. Several programs have been proposed that have the goal of achieving science literacy for every student. Project 2061 is an example of one of these programs. Project 2061, developed by the American Association for Advancement of Science, proposes that the success of students can be measured by comparing their achievement at various benchmarks during their time in school. As stated in Project 2061's ***Benchmarks for Science Literacy,*** "benchmarks are statements of what all students should know or be able to do in science, mathematics, and technology by the end of grades 2, 5, 8, and 12." Benchmarks for students leaving the eighth grade describe what all middle school students should know before entering the ninth grade.

Benchmarks for Science Literacy proposes several ways to promote reform in science education. These guiding principles can be used by teachers as they develop new directions for their methods of science instruction.

Science Literacy

People who are science literate are defined in ***Benchmarks for Science Literacy*** as those who are "equipped with knowledge and skills they need to make sense of how the world works, to think critically and independently, and to lead interesting, responsible, and productive lives in a culture increasingly shaped by science and technology."

How does it work?

The benchmarks proposed by Project 2061 are not considered levels of achievement for an average student or an advanced student, but for all students. The number of technical terms learned by students is kept at a minimum.

What are the benefits?

Students and teachers can benefit from the reform proposals in ***Benchmarks for Science Literacy.*** Teachers have the opportunity to work with students as they explore for themselves. They also can work independently with students of varied abilities. Through activities, students develop skills in problem solving and critical thinking. This gives them the tools they need to make sense of how the world works. It provides them with science literacy.

Benchmarks and Science Voyages

In ***Science Voyages,*** subject core material is presented in a way that reduces the number of new science terms students must learn with each chapter. Concepts are presented in ways that help students understand the how and why of science, not just learn a number of facts that they commit to short-term memory. Students are shown how science concepts learned in class pertain to their daily experiences.

They experience activities of various designs that involve students in learning and applying scientific methods to practice thinking skills and construct scientific concepts. The table on page 24T shows how ***Science Voyages*** covers many of the topics in depth.

SCIENCE VOYAGES

Benchmark Correlation

The following table illustrates how the *Science Voyages* series addresses many of the Benchmarks for Science Literacy.

Benchmark	Level	Chapter(s)
4 The Physical Setting		
4A. The Universe	Red	18-20
	Blue	18–20
4B. The Earth	Red	4, 14–16, 18
	Blue	18, 26, 27
4C. Processes that Shape the Earth	Red	3, 4, 12, 13
	Green	27, 29, 30
	Blue	26
4D. Structure of Matter	Red	25, 26
	Blue	2–10
4E. Energy Transformation	Red	7, 14, 15, 17 20, 26, 27
	Green	16, 24, 25
	Blue	3, 11–14, 20
4F. Motion	Red	5, 10, 27
	Green	20, 23
	Blue	11, 12, 14, 15
4G. Forces of Nature	Red	7–9, 17, 18, 26
	Green	24, 25
	Blue	3, 12, 13, 18
5 The Living Environment		
5A. Diversity of Life	Red	21–23
	Green	2, 5, 6, 8–14
	Blue	21–25
5B. Heredity	Green	6, 21
5C. Cells	Green	2, 3, 11
	Blue	23
5D. Interdependence of Life	Red	23, 24
	Green	14, 15
5E. Flow of Matter and Energy	Red	23
	Green	3, 11, 14
	Blue	23
5F. Evolution of Life	Red	12, 13, 22
	Green	6, 7, 29, 30
6 The Human Organism		
6A. Human Identity	Red	12
	Green	3, 7, 17, 20–22, 29
6B. Human Development	Green	4, 21
6C. Basic Functions	Green	2, 3, 18–22
6D. Learning	Red	22
6E. Physical Health	Red	4, 23
	Green	14, 17, 22
6F. Mental Health	Green	2
8 The Designed World		
8C. Energy Sources and Use	Red	4, 26
	Green	26, 28
	Blue	3, 16
10 Historical Perspectives		
10A. Displacing the Earth from the Center of the Universe	Red	22
10F. Understanding Fire	Red	25
	Green	3, 6
	Blue	2
10G. Splitting the Atom	Red	4
10I. Discovering Germs	Green	9, 22
	Blue	21
12 Habits of Mind		
12A. Values and Attitudes	Red	1, 3, 4, 7, 8, 12–14, 16–21
	Green	1, 4, 7–10, 13, 17, 21, 22, 24, 26–30
	Blue	1, 5, 6, 9–11, 16–22, 25–27
12B. Computation and Estimation	Red	2–8, 12–24,
	Green	30
	Blue	1, 4–13, 15–27
12D. Communication skills	Red	All skill activities
	Green	All skill activities
	Blue	All skill activities

SCIENCE VOYAGES

NATIONAL SCIENCE EDUCATION STANDARDS

The *National Science Education Standards,* published by the National Research Council and representing the contribution of thousands of educators and scientists, offers a comprehensive vision of a scientifically literate society. The standards not only describe what students should know but also offers guidelines for science teaching and assessment. If you are using or plan to use the standards to guide changes in your science curriculum, you can be assured that ***Science Voyages*** aligns with the National Science Education Standards.

Science Voyages reflects how Glencoe's commitment to science education is changing the materials used in science classrooms today. ***Science Voyages*** is a program that provides numerous opportunities for students, teachers, and school districts to meet the National Science Education Standards.

Content Standards

The table on pages 26–28T shows the close alignment between ***Science Voyages*** and the grade-appropriate content standards. ***Science Voyages*** allows students to discover concepts within each of the content standards, giving them opportunities to make connections between the science disciplines. Our hands-on activities and inquiry-based lessons reinforce the science processes emphasized in the standards.

Teaching Standards

Alignment with the National Science Education Standards requires much more than alignment with the outcomes in the content standards. The way in which concepts are presented is critical to effective learning. The teaching standards within the National Science Education Standards recommend an inquiry-based program facilitated and guided by teachers. ***Science Voyages*** provides such opportunities through activities and discussions that allow students to discover critical concepts by inquiry and apply the knowledge they've constructed to their own lives. Throughout the program, students are building critical skills that will be available to them for lifelong learning. The ***Teacher Wraparound Edition*** helps you make the most of every instructional moment. It offers an abundance of effective strategies and suggestions for guiding students as they explore science.

Assessment Standards

The assessment standards are supported by many of the components that make up the ***Science Voyages*** program. ***The Teacher Wraparound Edition*** and ***Teacher Classroom Resources*** provide multiple chances to assess students' understanding of important concepts, as well as their ability to perform a wide range of skills. Ideas for portfolios, performance activities, written reports, and other assessment activities accompany every lesson. Rubrics and Performance Task Assessment Lists can be found in Glencoe's Professional Series booklet ***Performance Assessment in the Science Classroom.***

Program Coordination

The scope of the content standards requires students to meet the outcomes over the course of their education. The correlation on the following pages demonstrates the close alignment of this course of ***Science Voyages*** with the content standards.

NATIONAL SCIENCE EDUCATION STANDARDS

Correlation of Science Voyages, Level Blue, to the National Science Standards

Content Standard	Page Numbers
(UCP) Unifying Concepts and Processes	
1. Systems, order, and organization	36-48, 51-55, 101, 116, 203, 360, 361, 423, 463, 740, 788, 790, 794, 798, 802-804, 815, 817, 818, 821, 823-828, 832-836, 846, 848, 850, 856, 863, 864
2. Evidence, models, and explanation	12, 14-21, 25, 26, 28, 71, 72, 97, 98, 100, 101, 104-108, 113, 114, 116, 117, 128, 194, 214, 221, 249, 285, 289, 291, 309, 312, 316, 342, 343, 374, 423-425, 449, 450-454, 459, 462, 463, 469, 649, 687, 724, 725, 738, 751, 830, 831, 885, 919
3. Change, constancy, and measurement	13-16, 19-21, 25, 28, 71, 72, 101, 116, 215-217, 219, 223, 253-255, 302, 303, 305-308, 313, 314, 318, 319, 336, 338, 340, 351, 353, 362-364, 373, 374, 419, 429, 433, 458, 459, 466, 467, 613, 703, 704, 712, 719, 720
4. Evolution and equilibrium	101, 313, 329, 366, 367, 370, 758, 785, 787, 788
5. Form and function	25, 27, 28, 116, 366, 390-394, 417, 424, 431, 432, 436-438, 440, 451, 454, 615-618, 624, 655, 661, 673, 777, 789, 796, 804, 807, 816, 818, 821, 837, 839, 848, 857, 859, 862, 866-869, 892, 898
(A) Science as Inquiry	
1. Abilities necessary to do scientific inquiry	8, 10-21, 25, 26, 39, 42, 49, 53, 56, 57, 67, 71, 73, 82, 84, 85, 88, 101, 104, 110, 116, 141, 144, 145, 202, 214, 215, 218, 248, 348, 363, 372, 393, 399, 401, 404, 420, 422, 456, 618, 624, 648, 724, 725, 744, 751, 776, 777, 791, 796, 807, 818, 830, 831, 837, 839, 855, 884, 885, 892, 898, 912, 918, 927
2. Understandings about scientific inquiry	7, 9-13, 22, 23, 25, 27, 28, 56, 57, 84, 85, 104, 108, 117, 131-134, 188, 199, 220, 221, 309, 365, 376, 377, 399, 428, 434, 435, 460, 461, 470, 621, 623-625, 632, 633, 649, 655, 658-660, 673, 675-678, 680, 682, 684-686, 692, 706, 709, 714, 919
(B) Physical Science	
1. Properties and changes of properties in matter	28, 36-49, 51-57, 96-101, 103-107, 109, 110, 112, 114-117, 395-398, 418, 420-422, 430-432, 448, 451, 454

CORRELATION TO
NATIONAL SCIENCE EDUCATION STANDARDS

Content Standard	Page Numbers
2. Motions and forces	8, 20, 25, 96-98, 100, 101, 103-107, 109-113, 115-117, 360-363, 366-368, 371, 390-394, 419, 429
3. Transfer of energy	20, 64-89, 97, 98, 100, 101, 105-108, 112, 113, 366-370, 372, 373, 390-394, 400-406, 416, 419, 448-459, 462-467
(C) Life Science	
1. Structure and function in living systems	7, 225, 252, 256, 270, 279, 283, 284, 286-290, 346, 347, 715, 738-742, 744, 746-748, 750, 758-771, 784-794, 798-807, 814, 816-819, 821-828, 832-839, 846-860, 862-869
2. Reproduction and heredity	8, 741-743, 759, 766, 767, 772, 773, 776, 777, 790-794, 796, 798, 802, 818, 820, 822, 833, 848-850, 852, 854-856, 863, 865, 869
3. Regulation and behavior	158, 165, 166, 251, 653, 742, 743, 747, 762, 763, 765, 766, 773, 786-788, 814, 819, 821, 822, 826-828, 833, 835, 837-839, 846, 847, 849, 851-856, 860, 862, 868, 923
4. Populations and ecosystems	369, 740, 741-745, 758-761, 763, 764, 766, 767, 769-773, 785, 786, 788, 799-801, 814, 822, 826, 838, 849, 869, 881, 882, 888, 891, 894, 924, 925
5. Diversity and adaptations of organisms	742, 743, 747, 748, 759, 761, 768, 773, 774, 784-789, 792-795, 801, 832, 835, 837, 850, 851, 852, 854, 857, 859, 860, 866, 867
(D) Earth and Space Science	
1. Structure of the earth system	26, 113, 166, 200, 236, 237, 239, 240, 250, 255, 272, 311, 333, 615, 622-624, 640, 642, 707, 773, 791, 794, 795, 830, 892, 910, 911, 914
2. Earthís history	272, 655, 656, 690, 692, 758, 760, 767, 785, 792
3. Earth in the solar system	25, 99, 103, 104, 107, 306, 310, 328, 329, 334, 335, 346, 361, 450, 612, 613, 620, 621, 623-625, 628-630, 640, 641, 643-646, 648, 650-654, 656-658, 661, 668-671, 673, 676, 679, 682, 686-688, 690, 691, 701-705, 707, 708, 717, 719, 720, 723

Correlation to

NATIONAL SCIENCE EDUCATION STANDARDS

Content Standard	Page Numbers
(E) Science and Technology	
1. Abilities of technological design	8-10, 19, 23-25, 27, 141, 205, 369, 375, 425, 427, 430, 439, 455-458, 462, 464, 465, 619, 744, 797
2. Understandings about science and technology	7-10, 17, 22-27, 99, 114, 125-127, 129, 130, 132, 137, 139-141, 161-164, 166, 167, 169, 170, 172-174, 176, 205, 273, 274, 276, 303, 311, 352, 363, 369, 375, 439, 440, 454, 613-617, 619, 621, 623, 624, 628-633, 655, 658-660, 467-469, 672, 674-678, 680, 681, 683-685, 714, 746, 760, 762, 788, 793, 797, 805, 806, 827, 848, 858
(F) Science in Personal and Social Perspectives	
1. Personal health	9, 26-28, 249, 250, 252, 258, 259, 280, 283, 290, 432, 433, 648, 653, 709, 750, 769, 776, 807, 818, 830, 839, 898, 913, 918
2. Populations, resources, and environments	628, 880-898, 910-916, 918-923, 925
3. Natural hazards	22, 24, 467-469, 773, 913, 920
4. Risks and benefits	23, 24, 171, 250, 252, 290, 420, 468, 469
5. Science and technology in society	8, 143, 177, 205, 281, 321, 368, 427, 432, 433, 619, 693, 749, 775, 797, 881-883, 886, 890-892, 895, 899, 910, 911, 913-917, 920-923
(G) History and Nature of Science	
1. Science as a human endeavor	6-8, 11, 12, 19, 22-25, 27, 50, 114, 257, 330, 332, 335, 350, 362, 363, 368, 439, 440, 463, 471, 615, 616, 624, 625, 628-631, 633, 652, 668, 669, 689, 692, 710-712, 717, 720, 748, 774, 788, 829, 837, 861
2. Nature of science	11-19, 21, 23-25, 127, 129, 130, 330, 331, 361, 622, 631, 672, 723, 926
3. History of science	8, 27, 37, 39-42, 50, 124-128, 132, 152, 153, 159, 167, 173, 175, 202, 242, 257, 270, 310, 311, 317, 318, 330, 331, 335, 344, 362, 363, 368, 370, 372, 439, 440, 471, 617, 620, 622, 624, 625, 631, 640, 652, 654, 656, 668-670, 672, 681, 684, 688, 706, 712, 715, 741, 748, 774, 788, 827, 829, 861

PLANNING YOUR COURSE

Traditional Scheduling

Science Voyages provides flexibility in the selection of topics and content, which allows teachers to adapt the text to the needs of individual students and classes. In this regard, the teacher is in the best position to decide which topics to present, the pace at which to cover the content, and which material to emphasize.

Science Voyages may be used in a full-year, two-semester course that is comprised of 180 periods of approximately 45 minutes each.

Block Scheduling

To build flexibility into the curriculum, many schools are introducing a block-scheduling approach. Block scheduling often involves covering the same information in fewer days with longer class periods than with traditional scheduling. This approach allows curriculum supervisors and teachers to tailor the curriculum to meet students' needs while achieving local and/or state curriculum goals.

When following a block schedule, consider either combining lessons or eliminating certain topics and spending more time on the topics you do cover. *Science Voyages* also provides a wide variety of support materials that will help teachers and students, whether following a block schedule or full-year schedule.

Lesson Plans

The *Science Voyages* Lesson Plans include complete lesson planning guides for every numbered section. Program components are listed along with page numbers or other identifiers for easy reference. The Lesson Plans include schedules, objectives, and references to the ***Teacher Classroom Resources*** and strategies in the ***Teacher Wraparound Edition.***

Interactive Lesson Planner

The *Science Voyages* Interactive Lesson Planner integrates the ***Teacher Classroom Resources*** with an electronic lesson planner to make the teacher's job easier. The easy-to-use CD-ROM allows a teacher to plan daily, weekly, monthly, or year-long lessons in a versatile calendar format. Teachers can select a built-in plan, customize the built-in plan, or create a new plan. Lesson plans can be saved and printed.

An extensive list of resources, including all print components of the ***Teacher Classroom Resources,*** is accessible through a convenient pop-up menu. All pages can be printed easily—student pages and answer keys—from either the resource list or directly from the lesson plan.

Ron Chapple/FPG

California Science Content Standards and Case Studies Articles

The California Case Studies on pages 476 through 507 help make the California Science Content Standards relevant for your students. Each standard and its subsections for Grade Eight are described and include illustrations intended to draw out students' attention. Each part of a standard is discussed so that students are introduced to the standard as a whole. Following the discussion for each standard, a Case Study focuses on one part of that standard with examples and illustrations from California.

Using the Articles and Case Studies

The articles and case-study pages will add interest to your presentation of the California Science Content Standards required for Grade Eight. To help you focus your presentation, teaching strategies are presented in the Teacher Wraparound Edition. The case studies follow the same easy-to-teach, consistent, four-step lesson plan that is found in each chapter of the text. Topics and illustrations for the standards articles and case studies are California-centered. As a result, students may be familiar with one or more of the areas of the state discussed.

Reinforcing the Standards

In the Student Edition, each Standard for Grade Eight is spelled out, followed by a brief explanation of each standard. In many cases, an Investigation and Experimentation Activity is provided to help students practice their science-process skills. Strategies in the Teacher Wraparound Edition provide opportunities to draw on students' prior knowledge and to connect the science content to their everyday lives.

Inclusion strategies, Internet activities, and cross-curricular connections in the Teacher Wraparound Edition also help teachers meet the needs of all students.

Connecting and Relating to Chapter Content

The standards articles and the case studies can be used to introduce, reinforce, or close a lesson. At the end of each article, the "Going Further" box lists chapters and sections in the textbook that directly relate to the information covered in the article.

Investigation and Experimentation Activities

Short activities are included to help students practice science skills outlined in the standard for Investigation and Experimentation at each level of the California Science Content Standards. Within each standard's article or case study, these activities require students to apply problem solving or critical thinking skills, as well as plan and execute experiments.

Assessment

A variety of assessment strategies can be found in the Teacher Wraparound Edition. Performance assessment strategies, proficiency prep quizzes, writing opportunities, and strategies for helping students meet the California Math and Writing Competency Goals help you to assess your students' comprehension of the standards. Each California Science Content Standards article closes with a Content Standard Assessment that will help you test students' proficiency in a particular standard.

Visiting California Science Sites

Throughout the teacher margin, look for California Science Sites—interesting places in California that your students can visit. Some students may already be familiar with some of these sites, such as Lassen Volcanic National Park, the Living Desert, and the California Museum of Science and Industry. Each site listed includes a brief description of what the site has to offer.

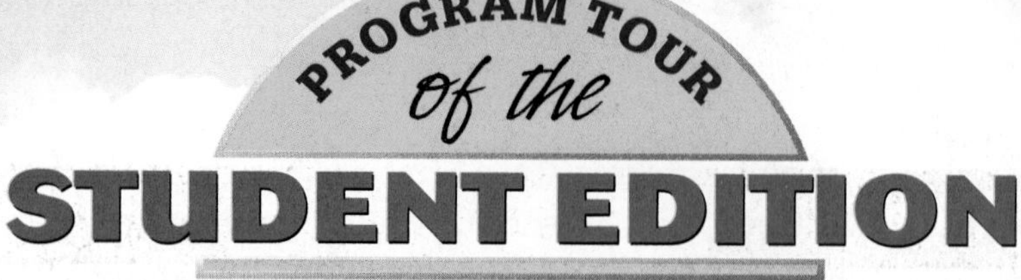

Helping you reach all students

This table will help you choose from many options available in the student edition of *Science Voyages.* Choose features that will assist you the most when you teach the chapter.

Feature Name	Where and How Many?	Suggestions For Use
Activities	• In every chapter • At the point where concept is taught	• Assign to groups in a lab setting. • Use to strengthen lab skills and understanding of science process.
Design Your Own Experiment	• At the point where concept is taught	• Assign to groups in a lab setting. • Open-ended activities help students learn science process. • Helps reinforce understanding of scientific methods
MiniLab	• In every chapter • At the point where concept is taught	• Do as a demonstration. • Assign to pairs or groups in lab setting. • Conduct these simple activities as short demonstrations. • Requires common inexpensive materials.
Try at Home MiniLab	• At the point where concept is taught	• Simple activities can be done at home or school • Assign as homework or class work.
On The Internet	• At the point where concept is taught	• Integrate the Internet into your class easily with these Internet activities. • Assign as homework or as a group project.
Explore Activity	• Begins each chapter • Focuses students' attention; stimulates curiosity for the chapter topic	• Do as a demonstration. • Assign as homework or class work. • Capture student's interest at the beginning of each chapter with these lesson launchers that use common, inexpensive materials.
Problem Solving	• One per chapter • At the point where concept is taught	• Assign as homework • Assign as a sponge activity after reading or other work. • Strengthens critical thinking skills with Problem Solving practice after reading or other work.
interNET CONNECTION	• In every chapter • At the point where concept is taught	• Assign as homework. • Assign as group project. • Focus student's Internet time with pre-determined links for each chapter related to chapter content • Assign as homework or during class to easily integrate the Internet into your classroom.

Feature Name	Where and How Many?	Suggestions For Use
Skill Builder	• Found at the end of every Section Assessment in each chapter	• Assign as homework or class work. • Go over in a group discussion. • Students feel comfortable with skills when practiced as an integral part of each lesson. Skill practice is easy when used often.
Science and Technology Skill Handbooks	• Aids student with specific science-related and technology skills	• Use to teach students how to organize information. • Use to teach students scientific processes. • Students always have skill assistance nearby with the skill handbook. • All skills are referenced to the handbook.
Skill Activity	• Found on pages 688–709 • One for each chapter	• Use as a demonstration. • Assign as homework or class work. • Further reinforce process skills with this bank of full-page activities.
Career Connection	• Found on the Reviewing Main Ideas Pages in select chapters	• Use to encourage students to pursue careers in science. • Use to show students that people of all ages, ethnicities, and educational training work in science.
National Geographic How it Works Reading & Writing in Science Science & Math History of Science Science & Society	• One per chapter • Found after the related section	• Use to show relationships between science and art, history, reading, and writing . • Use to illustrate how scientific concepts make things work.
Field Guide	• Periodically found at the end of the chapter	• Use to teach students how to use a key. • Assign as a group project or homework.
Reading Check	• At the beginning and end of every chapter • In every section	• Strategies for advancing reading skills • Focuses on important vocabulary and concepts
Reviewing Main Ideas	• One per chapter • Found at the end of the chapter	• Use as a review. • Use to preview the chapter content.

INVESTIGATION AND EXPERIMENTATION

Explore Activity

This photograph was taken by astronauts aboard the space shuttle *Endeavour.* It shows an area of the Pacific Ocean near the Hawaiian Islands. Other photographs of Earth in space are taken by cameras attached to satellites in orbit around our planet. These pictures show detailed features of Earth's surface, such as mountains and rivers. Scientists use these photos to make maps. In the activity below, you'll use a map or globe to explore Earth's surface.

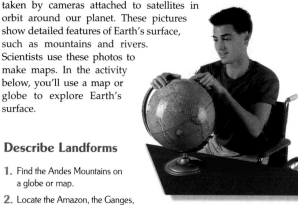

Describe Landforms

1. Find the Andes Mountains on a globe or map.
2. Locate the Amazon, the Ganges, and the Mississippi Rivers.
3. Locate the Indian Ocean, the Sea of Japan, and the Baltic Sea.
4. Now, find the continents of Australia, South America, and North America.
5. Locate your own country.

Science Journal

Choose one country on the globe or map and describe its major physical features in your Science Journal.

Explore Activity

Explore activities help you capture students' attention at the beginning of a chapter. These easy-to-manage activities ...

- set the stage for learning chapter content.
- require minimal equipment.
- promote inquiry learning.
- allow students to experience the natural world before they learn the content terms, symbols, or definitions.

MiniLab

MiniLabs occur within the chapter and help reinforce the concept that is being taught. These short labs ...

- allow students to experience the concept being taught.
- require few materials.
- occur two times in each chapter.
- contain numbered procedures.
- some can be done at home.

Try at Home MiniLab

Profiling the United States

Procedure

1. Place the bottom edge of a piece of paper across the middle of **Figure 6-2,** extending from the West Coast to the east coast.
2. Mark where different landforms are located along this edge.
3. Use a map of the United States and the descriptions of the landforms in Section 6-1 to help you draw a profile, or side view, of the United States. Use steep, jagged lines to represent mountains. Low, flat lines can represent plains.

Analysis

1. Describe how your profile changed shape as you moved from west to east.
2. Describe how the shape of your profile would be different if you moved from north to south.

Activity

One-page activities allow students to utilize scientific methods to obtain results.
Each one-page activity ...

- occurs at the end of the section where the concept is taught.
- requires a full period to perform.
- contains numbered procedures and data tables if necessary.
- asks students to conclude, analyze, and apply.

Using Scientific Methods

Activity 5•2

Making a Topographic Map

Have you ever wondered how topographic maps are made? Today, radar and remote-sensing devices aboard satellites collect data, and computers and graphic systems make the maps. In the past, surveyors and aerial photographers collected data. Then, maps were hand drawn by cartographers, or map-makers. In this activity, you can try your hand at cartography.

Materials

- Plastic model landform
- Water tinted with food coloring
- Transparency
- Clear, plastic storage box with lid
- Beaker
- Metric ruler
- Tape
- Transparency marker

What You'll Investigate

How is a topographic map made?

Goals

- **Make** a topographic map.
- **Compare and contrast** contour intervals.

Procedure

1. Using the ruler and the transparency marker, make marks up the side of the storage box 2 cm apart.
2. **Secure** the transparency to the outside of the box lid with tape.
3. Place the plastic model in the box. The bottom of the box will be zero elevation.
4. Using the beaker, **pour** water into the box to a height of 2 cm. Place the lid on the box.
5. Use the transparency marker to **trace** the top of the water line on the transparency.
6. Using the scale 2 cm = 10 m, **mark** the elevation on the line.
7. Remove the lid and **add** water until a depth of 4 cm is reached.
8. **Map** this level on the storage box lid and **record** the elevation.
9. Repeat the process of **adding** water and **tracing** until you have the hill **mapped.**
10. **Transfer** the tracing of the hill onto a sheet of white paper.

Conclude and Apply

1. What is the contour interval of this topographic map?
2. How does the distance between contour lines on the map show the steepness of the slope on the landform model?
3. **Determine** the total elevation of the hill.
4. How was elevation represented on your map?
5. How are elevations shown on topographic maps?
6. Must all topographic maps have a 0-m elevation contour line? **Explain.**
7. **Compare** the contour interval of an area of high relief with one of low relief on a topographic map.

5-3 Maps 147

INVESTIGATION AND EXPERIMENTATION

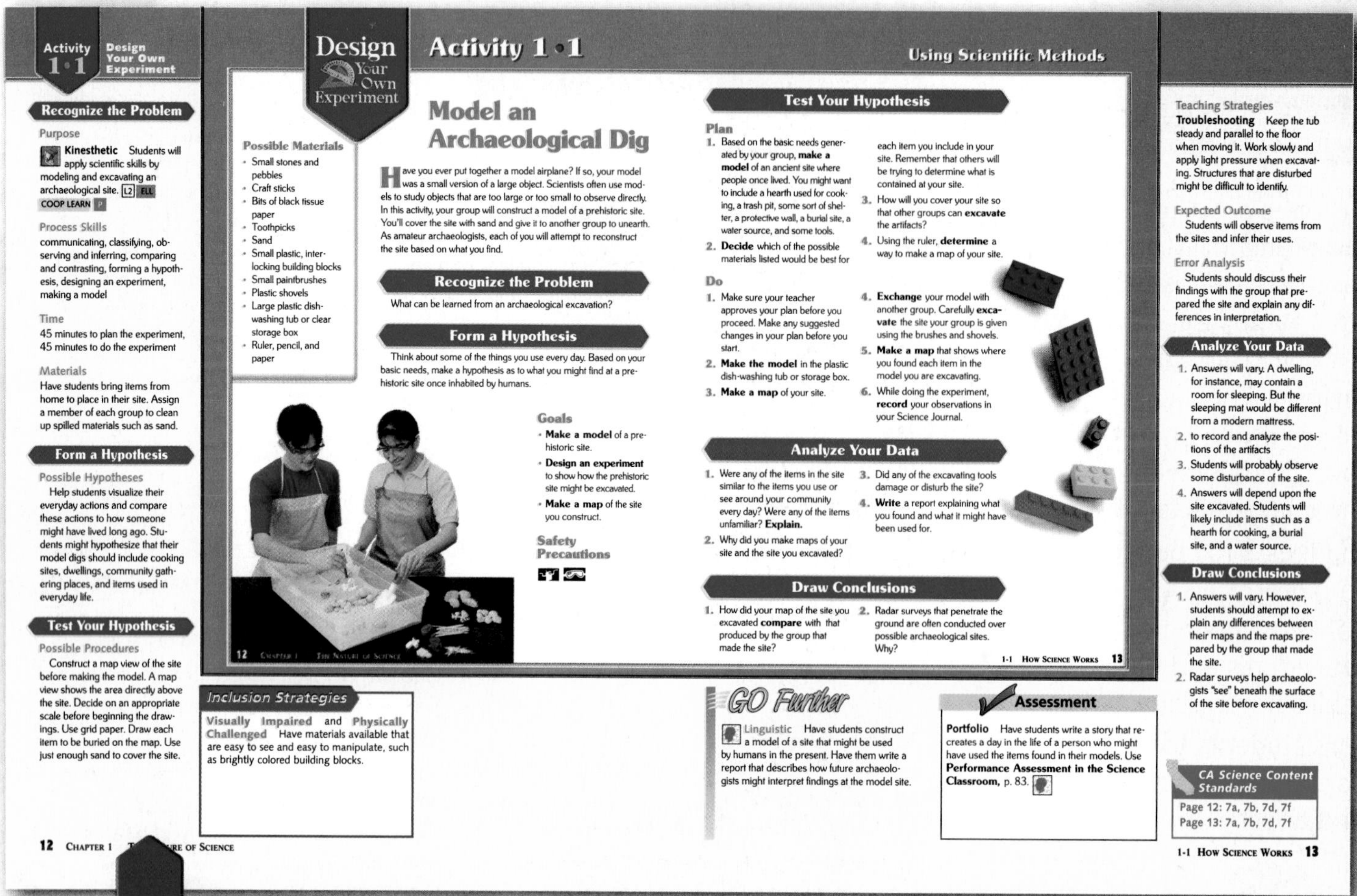

Activity 1•1 Design Your Own Experiment

Recognize the Problem

Purpose

Kinesthetic Students will apply scientific skills by modeling and excavating an archaeological site. L2 ELL COOP LEARN P

Process Skills

communicating, classifying, observing and inferring, comparing and contrasting, forming a hypothesis, designing an experiment, making a model

Time

45 minutes to plan the experiment, 45 minutes to do the experiment

Materials

Have students bring items from home to place in their site. Assign a member of each group to clean up spilled materials such as sand.

Form a Hypothesis

Possible Hypotheses

Help students visualize their everyday actions and compare these actions to how someone might have lived long ago. Students might hypothesize that their model digs should include cooking sites, dwellings, community gathering places, and items used in everyday life.

Test Your Hypothesis

Possible Procedures

Construct a map view of the site before making the model. A map view shows the area directly above the site. Decide on an appropriate scale before beginning the drawings. Use grid paper. Draw each item to be buried on the map. Use just enough sand to cover the site.

Design Your Own Experiment

Activity 1•1

Using Scientific Methods

Model an Archaeological Dig

Have you ever put together a model airplane? If so, your model was a small version of a large object. Scientists often use models to study objects that are too large or too small to observe directly. In this activity, your group will construct a model of a prehistoric site. You'll cover the site with sand and give it to another group to unearth. As amateur archaeologists, each of you will attempt to reconstruct the site based on what you find.

Possible Materials

- Small stones and pebbles
- Craft sticks
- Bits of black tissue paper
- Toothpicks
- Sand
- Small plastic, interlocking building blocks
- Small paintbrushes
- Plastic shovels
- Large plastic dishwashing tub or clear storage box
- Ruler, pencil, and paper

Recognize the Problem

What can be learned from an archaeological excavation?

Form a Hypothesis

Think about some of the things you use every day. Based on your basic needs, make a hypothesis as to what you might find at a prehistoric site once inhabited by humans.

Goals

- **Make a model** of a prehistoric site.
- **Design an experiment** to show how the prehistoric site might be excavated.
- **Make a map** of the site you construct.

Safety Precautions

12 Chapter 1 The Nature of Science

Test Your Hypothesis

Plan

1. Based on the basic needs generated by your group, **make a model** of an ancient site where people once lived. You might want to include a hearth used for cooking, a trash pit, some sort of shelter, a protective wall, a burial site, a water source, and some tools.
2. **Decide** which of the possible materials listed would be best for each item you include in your site. Remember that others will be trying to determine what is contained at your site.
3. How will you cover your site so that other groups can **excavate** the artifacts?
4. Using the ruler, **determine** a way to make a map of your site.

Do

1. Make sure your teacher approves your plan before you proceed. Make any suggested changes in your plan before you start.
2. **Make the model** in the plastic dish-washing tub or storage box.
3. **Make a map** of your site.
4. **Exchange** your model with another group. Carefully **excavate** the site your group is given using the brushes and shovels.
5. **Make a map** that shows where you found each item in the model you are excavating.
6. While doing the experiment, **record** your observations in your Science Journal.

Analyze Your Data

1. Were any of the items in the site similar to the items you use or see around your community every day? Were any of the items unfamiliar? **Explain.**
2. Why did you make maps of your site and the site you excavated?
3. Did any of the excavating tools damage or disturb the site?
4. **Write** a report explaining what you found and what it might have been used for.

Draw Conclusions

1. How did your map of the site you excavated **compare** with that produced by the group that made the site?
2. Radar surveys that penetrate the ground are often conducted over possible archaeological sites. Why?

1-1 How Science Works 13

Teaching Strategies

Troubleshooting Keep the tub steady and parallel to the floor when moving it. Work slowly and apply light pressure when excavating. Structures that are disturbed might be difficult to identify.

Expected Outcome

Students will observe items from the sites and infer their uses.

Error Analysis

Students should discuss their findings with the group that prepared the site and explain any differences in interpretation.

Analyze Your Data

1. Answers will vary. A dwelling, for instance, may contain a room for sleeping. But the sleeping mat would be different from a modern mattress.
2. to record and analyze the positions of the artifacts
3. Students will probably observe some disturbance of the site.
4. Answers will depend upon the site excavated. Students will likely include items such as a hearth for cooking, a burial site, and a water source.

Draw Conclusions

1. Answers will vary. However, students should attempt to explain any differences between their maps and the maps prepared by the group that made the site.
2. Radar surveys help archaeologists "see" beneath the surface of the site before excavating.

Inclusion Strategies

Visually Impaired and **Physically Challenged** Have materials available that are easy to see and easy to manipulate, such as brightly colored building blocks.

GO Further

Linguistic Have students construct a model of a site that might be used by humans in the present. Have them write a report that describes how future archaeologists might interpret findings at the model site.

Assessment

Portfolio Have students write a story that recreates a day in the life of a person who might have used the items found in their models. Use **Performance Assessment in the Science Classroom,** p. 83.

CA Science Content Standards

Page 12: 7a, 7b, 7d, 7f
Page 13: 7a, 7b, 7d, 7f

12 Chapter 1 The Nature of Science

1-1 How Science Works 13

Design Your Own Activity

Design Your Own activities allow students to construct their own activity. A topic and plan are provided, but students have the freedom of design. These activities ...

- occur in about half of the chapters.
- require a full period to perform.
- promote inquiry learning.
- ask students to conclude and apply.

Chapter 5

Skill Activity

Use After Section 5-3

Making Models

Background

Architects, builders, and designers often use detailed drawings as they plan their work. These are known as floorplans and represent a type of scale drawing. A scale drawing is a 2-dimensional model where an object's size and location are kept in the same proportions as in the actual object. For example, suppose a floorplan has a scale of 1 cm = 1 m. A room shown on this plan measures 10 cm × 15 cm. The actual room is 10 m × 15 m. A 1 m × 2 m desk in that room would be drawn as a rectangle 1 cm × 2 cm. The procedure below will help you make a scale drawing of your classroom.

Procedure

1. Measure the length and width of your classroom and decide on a scale to use that will allow your plan to cover most of your piece of paper. For example, if your paper is 25 cm × 36 cm and your room is 12 m × 15 m you could use a scale of 1 cm = 0.5 m. This would create a drawing of the classroom that measures 24 cm × 30 cm, which would fit on the paper.
2. Convert the dimensions of the room to your floorplan scale. Use a pencil and ruler to neatly draw the outline of the room on your paper.
3. Measure the width of the doorway and where it is located. Convert these measurements to your floorplan scale and draw the doorway on your plan.
4. Measure your teacher's desk and how far it is located from the walls. Use these measurements to accurately draw the desk in its proper position on your floorplan.
5. Repeat the procedure for any windows and other furniture in the classroom.
6. Title your classroom map and be sure to include your scale in the map key.

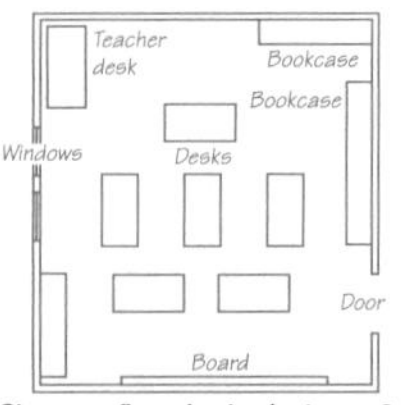

Classroom floor plan (scale: 1 cm = 2 m)

Practicing the SKILL

Imagine that your teacher has received two new computer work-stations. Each station has a desk that measures 1 m × 2 m. Use your scale drawing to determine where these work-stations might fit in the classroom. You may need to "move" some furniture on your map. Draw the workstations on your classroom floorplan.

For more skill practice, do the Chapter 5 Interactive Exploration on the **Science Voyages Level Red CD-ROM.**

698 SKILL ACTIVITY 5-3

Skill Activity

Skill activities give students extra practice with the skill used in science. There is one skill activity for each chapter and they ...

- occur at the back of the book after the Skill Handbook.
- require few materials.
- can usually be done by a single student.
- usually require less than one period.
- can be done as homework.

Internet Activity

Two-page Internet activities encourage students to use the Internet to explore concepts further. These activities ...

- occur at the point where the concept is being taught.
- can be used as homework or research projects.

On The Internet

Activity 24•2

Using Scientific Methods

Making a Paper Airplane

Materials

- Paper
- Measuring tape (50 m)
- Metric ruler
- Stopwatch
- Balance
- Tape
- Stapler
- Paper clips
- Scissors

When the Wright brothers set out to make the first powered airplane, they spent time researching flight and studying designs that had failed, as well as gliders that had been successful. They recognized the forces involved in flight, such as gravity, lift, thrust, and drag (a form of friction). If the lift is greater than gravity, then the plane will soar upward in the air. If the thrust is greater than the drag, then the plane will accelerate. Even today, these same forces must be considered when a new airplane is designed.

Recognize the Problem

How can a paper airplane that flies the longest time or the farthest distance be designed?

Form a Hypothesis

The design of the wing plays an important role in maximizing lift while reducing drag. An airfoil is the part of the wing responsible for controlling lift. The size, shape, angle, and cover material of the airfoil determine the lift and the drag that the wing will experience at a certain wind speed. **Form a hypothesis** about how your group can design a paper airplane that will either fly the longest period of time or go the farthest distance.

Goals

- **Research** paper airplane strategies.
- **Design** a paper airplane whose airfoil maximizes lift and minimizes drag.
- **Analyze** and **communicate** experimental results.

Safety Precautions

Data Sources

Visit the Glencoe Science Web Site at www.glencoe.com/sec/science/ca to find more information, hints, and data from other students.

Test Your Hypothesis

Plan

1. You may use a single sheet of any type of paper. You also may cut, fold, tape, glue, or staple the paper to form your airplane.
2. **Design** one or more types of paper airplanes. What type of paper will you use? What will be the shape of the wing?
3. **Sketch** your design. **Organize** the data you expect to collect in a table similar to the one below.
4. The testing area should be flat and open. Where will you test your designs?

Do

1. Be sure your teacher approves your plan before you begin.
2. **Build** your design. Record its mass in your data table.
3. **Experiment** with different ways of flying your airplane. Record your observations in your data table.
4. **Modify** your design as you think necessary. Remember to change only one variable at a time.
5. Tell your teacher when you have finished the airplane that you think will fly as long and as far as possible.
6. Hold a class contest to determine three categories: greatest time in the air, greatest distance flown from starting point, and the greatest overall flight.

Draw Conclusions

1. **Compare and contrast** the designs your class came up with. What features did the winning planes have?
2. How did the planes that flew long distances differ from the planes that flew for a long time?
3. Which design minimized drag? Maximized lift?
4. Post your design at the Glencoe Science Web Site. How do your designs compare with the designs other classes have posted ?

Flight Data

Trial	Mass (g)	Design change	Flight distance (m)	Flight time (s)

840 CHAPTER 24 MOTION AND FORCES

24-3 HOW DO THINGS MOVE? 841

Reading in the Content Area

Science Voyages is designed to increase science literacy. The techniques developed are active, constructive, and engaging and help improve reading comprehension and deepen students' understanding of ideas and concepts.

Several important strategies are recommended before reading and studying the chapter. For example, previewing the chapters' visuals, questions, vocabulary, and captions will set a purpose for reading the material for all students. Reading the introductory Explore Activity aloud or as a group helps engage students from the beginning of study.

While reading the chapter, periodic Reading Check questions will assist in comprehension of the material. In addition, a variety of learning strategies and engaging activities are found throughout each chapter, giving additional exposure to the material. These ideas include graphic organizers, creative responses, and journal writing.

In the Student Edition

Reading Check

Before you begin this chapter, write its headings and subheadings in an outline form
to see how the chapter is organized.

Reading Checks occur at the beginning, throughout, and at the end of each chapter. Reading checks at the chapter opener make students think about the chapter content before it is discussed.

Reading Check

What organelle releases energy for the cell?

In-text Reading Checks ask students questions about the content they just read. This reinforces the chapter text and vocabulary.

Reading Check

Variables, controls, and *trials* are used in scientific experiments. Compare the meaning of each word in this context with its meaning in a nonscientific context.

The Reviewing Main Ideas Reading Check has the students use their knowledge of the chapter content to perform a reading activity.

In the

Teacher Wraparound Edition

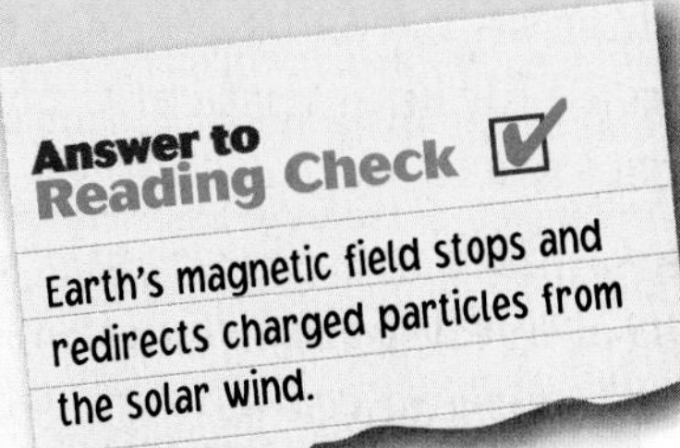

Answer to
Reading Check
Earth's magnetic field stops and redirects charged particles from the solar wind.

Answers to Reading Check questions are provided in the margin of the Teacher Wraparound Edition.

Guided Reading Strategy

Think-Pair Share This strategy encourages students to think first before discussing their ideas or thoughts about a topic. Students are asked to respond to a question by writing a response. After thinking for a few minutes, partners share responses to the question. Finally, the teacher asks the student to share responses with the class. Have students become involved in a Think-Pair Share about a topic in this section.

Guided Reading Strategies

Below and on the following pages are guided reading strategies found throughout the Teacher Wraparound Edition of Glencoe Science Voyages. These strategies cover a variety of learning styles.

- **Bubble Map** Using a bubble map helps students start ideas flowing about a given topic. Words are clustered to describe a topic or idea that is studied. Students can use the bubble map for a prewrite, to generate ideas before writing in their Journals, or to review for a test. Have students design a Bubble Map for a concept in this section.
- **Double Entry Journal** In this strategy, the student takes notes and adds his or her own reflections while reading the student text. Students are encouraged to explore ideas, make responses, and take risks in giving opinions about the reading. Have them divide the paper in half. On the left, identify a particular passage or quotation of significance in the reading. The reader records anything luminous, enigmatic, stimulating, or disturbing. On the right, the reader responds, questions, elaborates, makes personal connections, elaborates, makes personal connections, evaluates, reflects, analyzes or interprets. Have students make a Double Entry Journal for a passage in this section.
- **Metacognition** In this strategy, each student analyzes his or her own thought proceses. Have students divide the paper in half. On the left, have them record what they learned about a topic. On the right, have them record the reason they learned it. Have students write a Metacongition Journal about a concept in this section.
- **Learning Journa**l This strategy encourages students to interact with the reading, allowing personal responses. The left column entries can be research notes, lecture notes, or vocabulary terms. The right column entries are the student's response to, interpretation of, questions about, or analysis of the left column entries. Have students write a Learning Journal related to this section.
- **Problem Solution Journal** Have students divide a piece of paper in half. Label the left side "Problems" and the right side "Consequences of failing to resolve the problem." Through writing, the student identifies a problem, brainstorms possible alternatives, chooses a probable solution, an-

ticipates stumbling blocks, and proposes arguments. Have students write a Problem Solution Journal related to this section.

- **Double Bubble Map** This strategy uses two bubble maps to compare concepts. Each cluster has qualities that are unique to that idea. In the middle, connecting ideas are similar to both cluster ideas. This technique helps students list common qualities and unique qualities before writing or discussing a topic. Have students design a Double Bubble Map for a concept in this section.
- **Speculation about Effects/Prediction Journal** This strategy allows students to examine events and speculate about their possible long-term effects. Have students divide their papers in half. On the left side record "What happened." On the right, write "What might/should happen as a result of this." Have students write a Speculation about Effects/ Prediction Journal about an event in this section.
- **Synthesis Journal** In this strategy, students reflect on a project, a paper, or a performance in light of their own experiences and plan for personal application. Have each student divide a piece of paper into three sections. Have them record "What I did," "What I learned," and "How I can use it." Have students write a Synthesis Journal related to an activity in this section.
- **Reflective Journal** In this strategy, students identify activities and what they learned and record responses to the activities. Have students divide pieces of paper into several columns. Have them record their thoughts under headings such as "What I did," "What I learned," What questions do I have," "What surprises did I experience," and "Overall response." Have students write a Reflective Journal for an activity in this section.
- **Flow Chart** A flow chart helps students logically sequence events. Students will write major stages of the sequence in large rectangles and write substages in smaller rectangles under the larger rectangles. Have students design a Flow Chart for a concept in this section.
- **Pair of Pairs** This strategy encourages students as partners to respond to a question. They brainstorm together, recording on one paper their ideas. After a few minutes, they combine with another pair and share responses. Finally, the teacher asks the groups of four to share any responses. Have students use the Pair of Pairs strategy on a Thinking Critically question in a Section Assessment in this chapter.
- **Write-Draw-Discuss** This strategy encourages students to actively participate in reading and lectures, assimilating content creatively. Have students write about an idea, clarifying it, then make an illustration or drawing. Ask students to share responses with the class and display several examples. Have students Write, Draw, and Discuss about a concept in this section.
- **Four-Corner Discussion** This strategy encourages the class to debate a complex issue. Make four signs: Strongly Agree, Agree, Disagree, Strongly Disagree. Place one sign in each corner of the room. Write on the chalkboard a statement that will elicit a reaction from students. Have the students respond on paper to the statement. After several minutes, direct them to move to the corner whose sign most closely reflects their opinions. In the corners, students share responses. Each group then selects a spokesperson to report the opinions of the group. After all groups have reported, open the floor for debate. Allow students who have changed their opinions to change corners. Have students conduct a Four-Corner Discussion about some issue related to this chapter.
- **Quickwrites** This strategy, sometimes called freewrites, lets students use spontaneous writing to discover what they already know. Have students write a list of ideas about a topic then share these ideas with the class. Next, have students write freely in a paragraph their ideas without worrying about punctuation, spelling, and grammar. Have students use a Quickwrite to share ideas during or after a learning experience in this chapter.

- **Cause and Effect Chart** This strategy is used to focus on cause-effect reasoning. In the center, students will write the topic that they are trying to understand. To the left of center, write the apparent causes of the topic. On the right side, write the apparent effects of the topic. Have students design a Cause and Effect Chart for a concept in this section.
- **Jigsaw** In this collaborative learning technique, individuals become experts on a portion of a text and share their expertise with their small group, called their "home" group. Everyone shares responsibility for learning the assigned reading. Assign each person in each home group an "expert" number (1 through 5, for example). Have students gather into the expert groups that correspond to the number they were assigned. There, have them read, discuss, and master chapter concepts and determine how best to teach them to their home groups. Have students return to home groups and share the content they learned in their expert groups. Have students use the Jigsaw strategy with the student text for this section.
- **Buddy Interviews** This strategy helps students understand and clarify the reading. Have students interview one another to find out what helps them to understand what they are reading, how they find answers, and how they figure out new vocabulary terms. Have students use Buddy Interviews to help them master section concept.
- **Reciprocal Teaching** This strategy is designed to help construct meaning and apply reading skills. Have pairs of students begin by each partner silently reading a chunk of text. After several minutes of reading, one student retells the key points of what was read in his or her own words. The other student creates a question that can be answered directly from the text but could require inferences or evaluation. Continue the reading with each student alternating the questions and summaries. Consciously asking questions and summarizing content helps the reader attend deliberately to what is being read. Have students do Reciprocal Reading with a chunk of section content.
- **News Summary** This strategy helps students to explain and make connections to their study of science. Students are assigned the job of being television reporters. They are given several minutes to summarize or retell or analyze their investigation for their "television" audience. Have students do a News Summary for an application of a concept from this chapter.
- **Supporting Idea Chart** This strategy examines the relationship between a whole and its parts. Write the name of the whole object on the single line at the left. On the next set of lines to the right, write in major parts of the object. Finally, write in the sub-parts of each major part. Have students design a Supporting Idea Chart for a concept in this section.
- **ReQuest** To improve listening skills, have students listen carefully as the teacher reads an interesting piece or story aloud. After the reading, have students construct questions to be discussed with the teacher. The teacher can assign students to read the story and participate in the questioning with other students. Have students participate in a ReQuest with the chapter feature or another interesting piece related to chapter content.

***Guided Reading Strategies** provided by Gary Kroesch, University of California at San Diego.*

Concept maps

Helping students understand concepts through visuals

In science, concept maps make abstract information concrete and useful, improve retention of information, and show students that thought has shape.

Concept maps are visual representations or graphic organizers of relationships among particular concepts. Concept maps can be generated by individual students, small groups, or an entire class. *Science Voyages* develops and reinforces four types of concept maps—the **network tree, events chain, cycle concept map,** and **spider concept map**—that are most applicable to studying science. Students can learn how to construct each of these types of concept maps by referring to the **Skill Handbook.** To further develop concept mapping skills, each chapter of the *Study Guide for Content Mastery* in the *Teacher Classroom Resources* has a concept map.

Building Concept Mapping Skills

The **Developing Skills** section of the **Chapter Review** provides opportunities for practicing concept mapping. A variety of concept mapping approaches is also used throughout the text. Students may be directed to make a specific type of concept map and may be provided the terms to use. At other times, students may be given only general guidelines. For example, concept terms to be used may be provided and students may be required to select the appropriate model to apply, or vice versa. Finally, students may be asked to provide both the terms and type of concept map to explain relationships among concepts. Look for the conceptual strength of student responses, not absolute accuracy. You'll notice that most network tree maps provide connecting words that explain the relationships between concepts. We recommend that you require all students to supply these words, but many students may be challenged by this aspect.

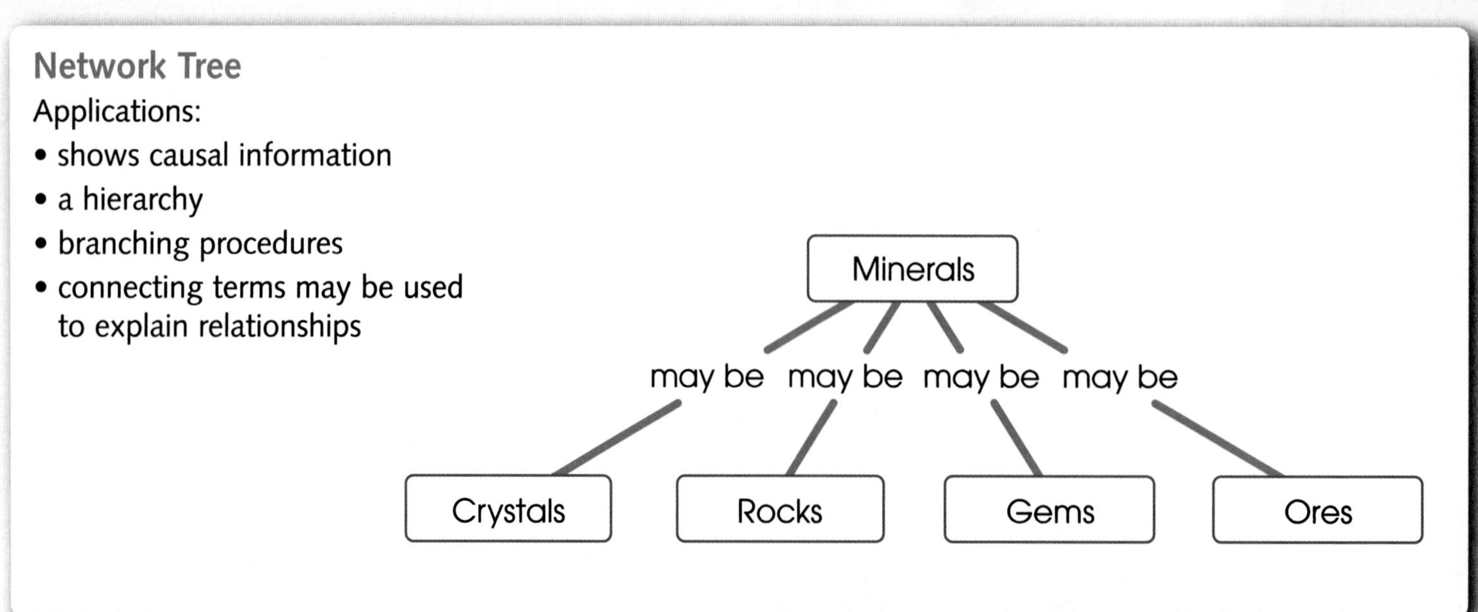

Network Tree
Applications:
• shows causal information
• a hierarchy
• branching procedures
• connecting terms may be used to explain relationships
Minerals
may be
may be
may be
may be
Crystals
Rocks
Gems
Ores

Study Guide for Content Mastery

The *Study Guide for Content Mastery* book of the *Teacher Classroom Resources,* too, provides a developmental approach for students to practice concept mapping.

As a teaching strategy, generating concept maps can be used to preview a chapter's content by visually relating the concepts to be learned and allowing the students to read with purpose. Using concept maps for previewing is especially useful when there are many new key science terms for students to learn. As an assessment and review strategy, constructing concept maps reinforces main ideas and clarifies their relationships. Construction of concept maps using cooperative learning strategies as described in this Teacher Guide will allow students to practice both interpersonal and process skills.

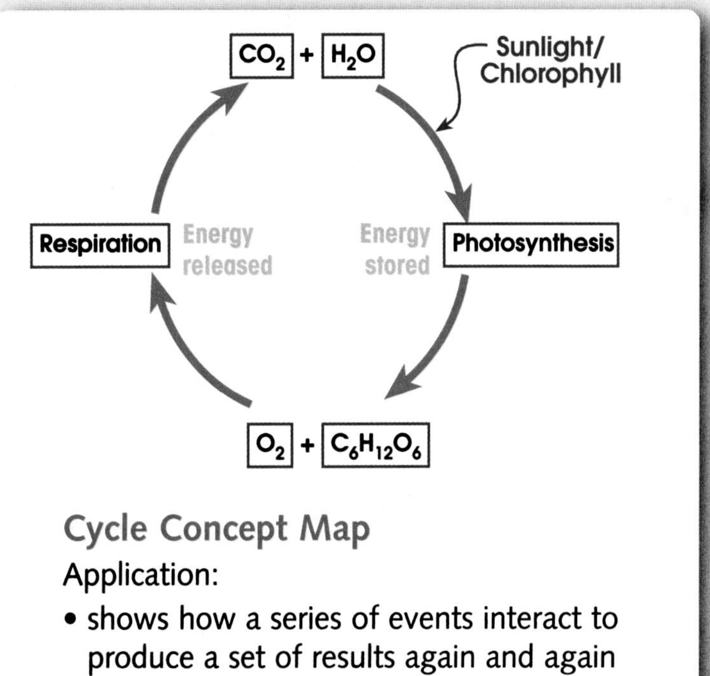

Cycle Concept Map

Application:

- shows how a series of events interact to produce a set of results again and again

Events Chain

Applications:

- describes the stages of a process
- the steps in a linear procedure
- a sequence of events

Initiating Event

Determine the problem.
↓
Make a hypothesis.
↓
Test your hypothesis.
↓
Analyze the results.
↓
Draw conclusions.

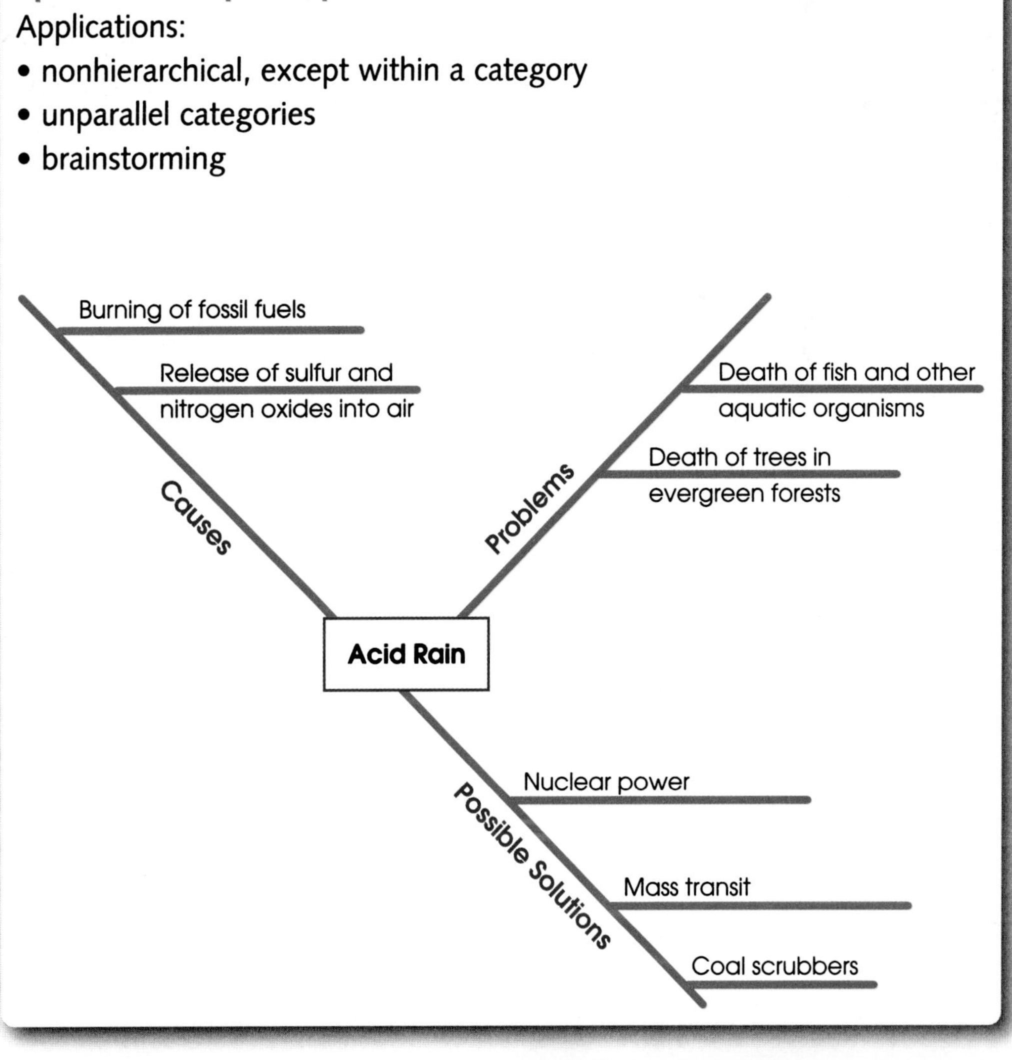

Spider Concept Map

Applications:

- nonhierarchical, except within a category
- unparallel categories
- brainstorming

Assessment

Science Voyages offers the Glencoe Assessment Advantage, a system of assessment options designed to give you the flexibility and tools to conduct standardized test preparation, content, and performance assessment.

Standardized Test Preparation

Glencoe is dedicated to helping you prepare students for success. Therefore, Glencoe provides a number of features designed to help you prepare students for state-mandated tests.

The Princeton Review is a nationally renowned company that specializes in preparing students for standardized assessments. For 15 years, they have been helping students prepare for the state and national tests that students are required to take. Glencoe has partnered with *The Princeton Review* in order to ensure that all of our materials meet the same tough standards that state and national testing agencies use themselves. This partnership has resulted in Student Edition **Test-Taking Tips** and **Test Practice** questions at the end of each **Chapter Assessment.**

Glencoe in association with *The Princeton Review* provides test practice booklets. The booklets contain questions that will assist you in preparing your students for success on standardized tests.

Content Assessment

Glencoe *Science Voyages* Student Edition contains numerous strategies and formative checkpoints for evaluating student progress toward mastery of science concepts.

Throughout the chapters, **Section Assessment** questions and application tasks are presented. A two-page **Reviewing Main Ideas** at the end of each chapter allows you to evaluate student responses and determine if reteaching is needed. The two-page **Chapter Assessment** is a useful tool for evaluating students' knowledge of scientific terminology, their understanding of scientific principles, and their ability to apply these principles.

MindJogger Videoquizzes offer interactive videos that provide a fun way for your students to review chapter concepts. You can extend the use of the videoquizzes by implementing them in a testing situation. The game-show format allows students to work as teams to answer questions and gain points. Questions are at three difficulty levels: basic, intermediate, and advanced.

The Interactive CD-ROM provides an interactive approach to quiz taking. The quizzes can be used as a whole-class presentation or as a review for individual students. The CD-ROM also is available on the *Science Voyages* Web Site.

Assessment—Chapter Tests present recognition and recall of vocabulary and facts in addition to interpretation of information. Students are asked to demonstrate their ability to determine relationships among facts, generalizations, definitions, and skills.

ExamView Test Bank Software for Macintosh and Windows makes creating, editing, and printing tests quick and easy. You can add your own questions and graphics to the tests.

Glencoe *Science Voyages* has been designed to provide you with a variety of assessment tools, both formal and informal, to help you develop a clearer picture of your students' progress.

Performance Assessment

Performance Assessment refers to the strategies used to assess students' level of science literacy. Performance assessment is based on judging the quality of a student's response to a performance task. A performance task is constructed to require the use of important concepts with supporting information, work habits important to science, and one or more of the elements of scientific literacy.

Performance Task Assessment Lists

Performance task assessment lists break the assessment criteria into several well-defined categories. Possible points for each category are assigned by the teacher. Both the teacher and the student assess the work and assign the number of points earned.

Science Voyages provides task assessment lists in Glencoe's ***Performance Assessment in the Science Classroom.*** These lists were developed for the summative and skill-performance tasks in the ***Performance Assessment*** book that accompanies the *Science Voyages* program.

Assessing Student Work with Rubrics

A rubric is a set of descriptions of the quality of a process and a product. The set of descriptions includes a continuum of quality from excellent to poor. Rubrics for various types of assessment products are in the Glencoe Professional Development Series booklet ***Performance Assessment in the Science Classroom.***

Portfolios

The **Portfolio** should help the student see the big picture of how he or she is performing in gaining knowledge and skills and how effective his or her work habits are. The process of assembling the portfolio should be both integrative (of process and content) and reflective. The performance portfolio is not a complete collection of all worksheets and other assignments but rather a collection that reflects the student's growth in concept attainment and skill development.

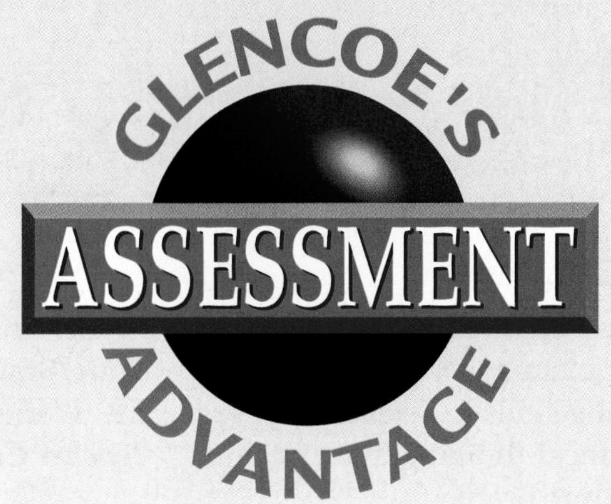

Group Assessment

Research has shown that a cooperative learning environment improves student-learning outcomes for students of all ability levels. An example, along with information about evaluating cooperative work, is provided in the booklet ***Alternate Assessment in the Science Classroom.***

The Science Journal

A Science Journal is intended to help the student organize his or her thinking. It is not a lecture or laboratory notebook. It is a place for students to make their thinking explicit in drawings and writing. It is the place to explore what makes science fun and what makes it hard.

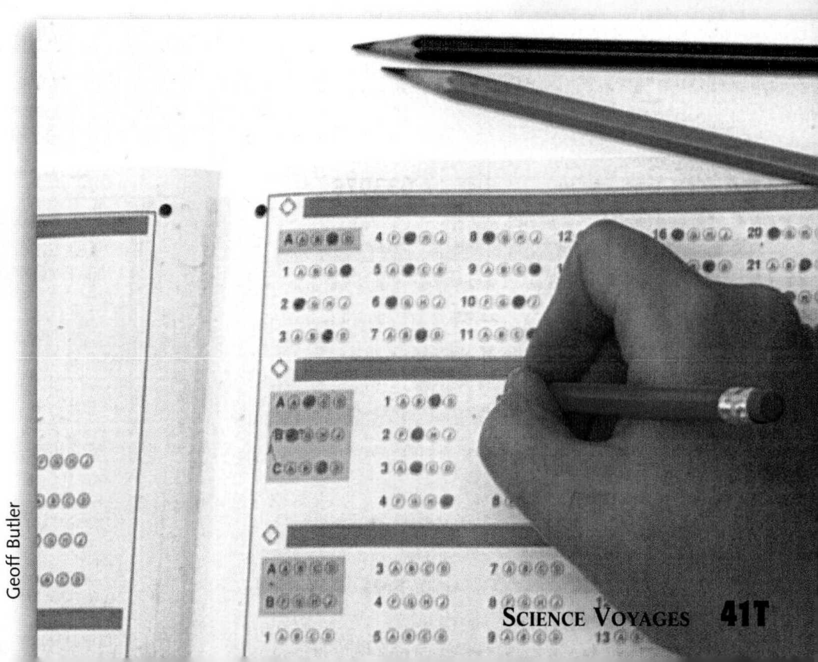

Geoff Butler

Flex Your Brain

A key element in the coverage of problem-solving and critical-thinking skills in *Science Voyages* is a critical-thinking matrix called **Flex Your Brain.**

Flex Your Brain provides students with an opportunity to explore a topic in an organized, self-checking way, and then identify how they arrived at their responses during each step of their investigation. The activity incorporates many of the skills of critical thinking. It helps students to consider their own thinking and learn about thinking from their peers.

Where is Flex Your Brain found?

Chapter 1, The Nature of Science, is an introduction to critical thinking and problem solving. **Flex Your Brain** accompanies the text section in the introductory chapter. A worksheet for **Flex Your Brain** appears on page 5 of the *Activity Worksheets* book and as a transparency (Teaching Transparency 1) in the *Teacher Classroom Resources.* The *Activity Worksheets* version provides spaces for students to write in their responses.

In the *Teacher Wraparound Edition,* suggested topics are given in each chapter for the use of **Flex Your Brain.** You can photocopy the worksheet master from the *Teacher Classroom Resources.*

Using Flex Your Brain

Flex Your Brain can be used as a whole-class activity or in cooperative groups, but is primarily designed to be used by individual students within the class. There are three basic steps.

1. Teachers assign a class topic to be investigated using **Flex Your Brain.**
2. Students use **Flex Your Brain** to guide them in their individual explorations of a topic.
3. After students have completed their explorations, teachers guide them in a discussion of their experiences with **Flex Your Brain,** bridging content and thinking processes.

Flex Your Brain

1 Topic: ______

2 What do I already know? 1. 2. 3. 4. 5.

3 Q: Ask a question

4 A: Guess an answer

5 How sure am I? (circle one)
Not sure 1 2 3 4 5 Very sure

6 How can I find out? 1. 2. 3. 4. 5.

7 EXPLORE

8 Do I think differently? yes no

9 What do I know now? 1. 2. 3. 4. 5.

10 SHARE 1. 2. 3.

Flex Your Brain can be used at many different points in the lesson plan.

Introduction: Ideal for introducing a topic, **Flex Your Brain** elicits students' prior knowledge and identifies misconceptions, enabling the teacher to formulate plans specific to student needs.

Development: **Flex Your Brain** leads students to find out more about a topic on their own, and develops their research skills while increasing their knowledge.

Review and Extension: **Flex Your Brain** allows teachers to check student understanding while allowing students to explore aspects of the topic that go beyond the material presented in class.

TEACHER WRAPAROUND EDITION

Helping you prepare for the lesson

This table will help you locate features of the Teacher Wraparound Edition that will help you develop your lesson plans. Choose those features that will assist you the most when you teach in the *Science Voyages* program.

Feature Name	Where and How Many?	Suggestions For Use
Chapter Organizers	• One per chapter, only in Teacher Wraparound Edition • Spans A, B, C, and D pages preceding each chapter	• Determine objectives. • Determine in which sections labs and other features occur. • Determine which materials are available from the TCR box for each section. • View list of transparencies to use for each section. • View list of materials for labs. **For C and D pages** • Note L1, L2, L3 coding to assist in planning for different levels of students.
Assessment Planner	• One per chapter • Found at the bottom of the Teacher Wraparound Edition on the first page of each chapter	• Use as a source of ideas for alternative assessments.
Multiple Learning Styles	• One per chapter • Found at the bottom of the Teacher Wraparound Edition opposite the first page of each chapter	• Use to develop teaching strategies for various learning styles or multiple intelligences.
Flex Your Brain	• One per chapter • Found in the margin of the Teacher Wraparound Edition	• Use to check for understanding. • Let students use as a self-assessment.
Key to Teaching Strategies	• On B pages of Chapter Organizers in the Teacher Wraparound Edition	• Use to select materials appropriate for different levels of learners.
Four-Step Teaching Cycle	• Steps are: **1 Motivate**, **2 Teach**, **3 Assess**, and **4 Close** • Repeated for each section in every chapter	• Great help for a first-year teacher • Great help for experienced teacher in the first year in a new program

How to use your

Teacher Wraparound Edition

Interleaf Pages E and F help you prepare for the lesson by giving you more information about each section. The information goes beyond the student text and can assist you with questions the students might ask.

The Teacher's Corner lists the products available from the National Geographic Society that can help teach the lesson.

Chapter 1 The Nature of Science

Helping You Prepare

What Science Is (Section 1-1)

Deep-sea refers to more than 150 m below the water's surface. Most submarines can dive only to a depth of about 400 m.

A submersible is a special underwater craft that can descend to depths of 6500 m. They are usually equipped with cameras, floodlights, baskets, and mechanical arms for collecting samples.

An unpiloted submersible is referred to as an ROV, or remotely operated vehicle. Scientists are developing autonomous underwater vehicles (AUV), which need no cable.

Form a Hypothesis (Section 1-1)

A hypothesis that holds up under many experiments by different scientists may become a theory. Scientific theories and laws are often confused, but they are not the same.

A law is a statement of what happens, such as Newton's third law of motion, which states that for every action force, there is an equal and opposite reaction force.

Theories explain why or how something happens. The theories of plate tectonics and continental drift explain how these phenomena take place on and within Earth. Keep in mind that no theory is completely proven. A theory is subject to correction as new facts or observations emerge.

GLENCOE TECHNOLOGY

Glencoe Science Voyages Interactive CD-ROM

Chapter Summaries

Use the Chapter Summary to introduce, teach, or review chapter material.

Controlled Experiments (Section 1-1)

Ideally, the experimental and the control group each should have several samples. This minimizes individual differences that cannot be controlled. This is particularly important when the independent variable is not changed but applied equally to all samples. An example is testing the effects of a new drug at a particular dosage for subjects in the experimental group.

Plan (Section 1-1)

A clinical trial is an experiment in which the subject is a human. Controlling variables is often difficult, particularly psychological variables. For example, volunteers who know they are receiving a new drug may allow this to influence how they feel.

NATIONAL GEOGRAPHIC — **Teacher's Corner**

Products Available from National Geographic Society

To order the following products for use with this chapter, call National Geographic Society at 1-800-368-2728:

Book

Everyday Science Explained

Video

Scientific Method

Index to National Geographic Magazine

The following articles may be used for research relating to this chapter:

"Making Sense of the Millennium," by Joel L. Swerdlow, January 1998.

4E CHAPTER 1 THE NATURE OF SCIENCE

These sample pages are not complete sections.

Interleaf Page F is a continuation of the content background found on the previous page.

A single-blind clinical trial is an experiment in which the subject does not know what treatment has been given. In a double-blind clinical trial, neither the subjects nor the investigators know which treatment has been given.

Using Technology (Section 1-2)

Robots range from having simple arms to being increasingly sophisticated "thinking" machines. Many robots have video-camera-based vision systems. Some robots even have smelling and tasting devices.

Some robots are programmed with a set of instructions and perform the same boring task repetitively. Some robots are much more sophisticated.

Sojourner, the first Mars rover, is a lightweight robotic machine on wheels. Sojourner is described as "thinking" because it is equipped with sophisticated laser eyes and can react to unplanned events on the surface of another planet.

Sojourner's intelligence is based on a mathematical model that emulates animal behavior. The ability for animals to avoid or flee from danger is a low-level reflex.

Sojourner was equipped with a spectrometer used to analyze the chemical composition of Martian rock and a camera that relayed images of the landscape back to Earth. Sojourner was carried to Mars via the space probe *Pathfinder,* which landed on Mars in July, 1997. This mission has been said to set the standard for twenty-first century space exploration. The Marie Curie rover is planned to be sent to Mars in 2001.

SCIENCE UPDATE

For current events or science in the news, access the Glencoe Science Web Site at **www.glencoe.com/sec/science/ca**

Space probes are designed to land on a surface or to orbit around a planet or moon. They can determine composition, temperature, and pressure of atmospheres; pick up radio emissions; probe magnetic fields around planets; and collect and analyze soil samples.

The largest, most complex, and most expensive interplanetary probe launched is *Cassini. Cassini's* four-year mission is to provide information about Saturn, its rings, and moons.

Most space shuttles are equipped with a remote manipulator system or RMS. The RMS resembles a human arm with a shoulder and elbow joint. It measures over 15 meters when extended. Because of its design and construction, it would collapse under its own weight if used on Earth. The end of the RMS does not have fingers. It looks like a canister and can grab only large, sturdy objects. Engineers still do not know how to construct robotic fingers that are skillful and light, yet strong.

Teacher to Teacher

"Before teaching a new topic, get students involved and help them recall prior knowledge. Using one set of index cards, write key vocabulary words and concepts. On a second set of cards, write the definition or information that the students will learn. Students work in pairs to try to match the cards."

Rebecca S. Buckingham
Rebecca S. Buckingham, Teacher
Lisbon Central School
Lisbon, NY

Teacher to Teacher consists of a teaching tip that directly relates to teaching chapter content or activities.

4F

These sample pages are not complete sections.

Easy-to-use **teaching cycle of Motivate, Teach, Assess,** and **Close** organizes all of the teacher material for each lesson into four easy steps.

Bellringer Activities suggest the use of **Section Focus Transparencies** to get your students' attention and help focus them on the day's lesson.

Resource Manager shows you exactly when to use Reproducible Masters, Color Transparencies, Multimedia, and other resources to support each lesson.

Tying to Previous Knowledge ties the current lesson to a previous lesson or experience.

SECTION 1•2

Prepare

Content Background

Refer to **Using Technology** on p. 4F.

Preplanning

Refer to the **Chapter Organizer** on pp. 4A–B.

1 Motivate

Bellringer

Before presenting the lesson, display **Section Focus Transparency 2** on the overhead projector. Use the accompanying **Focus Activity** worksheet. L2 ELL

SECTION FOCUS TRANSPARENCY

THE SCIENCE AND TECHNOLOGY CONNECTION

The study of technology doesn't just add to our understanding of our natural surroundings. It also allows us to make discoveries that help us. Science skills were used to create this and other robots commonly used in many industries.

1. How might scientific methods have been used to develop this technology?
2. What are some of the possible problems that the developers of this robot wanted to solve?
3. What are some ways technology helps us now? How many different ways can you think of?

Tying to Previous Knowledge

Ask students to recall ways that scientists have explored outer space without going there. This section will describe how scientists explore environments that are dangerous to humans.

1•2 Using Science to Explore

What You'll Learn

- How remotely operated vehicles help humans to explore
- How scientists use science skills in different ways

Vocabulary
technology
sequence
inference

Why It's Important

- Using science skills and technology helps you gather information about places that you cannot observe directly.

Using Technology

A week had passed since Mr. Hayes's assignment. The students were eager to share what they had found out.

Mr. Hayes opened the discussion. "Before we begin, who can tell us the difference between science and technology?"

Gabriella raised her hand. "Science is the process of trying to understand the world around you. **Technology** is the application of what has been learned through science."

"Excellent," Mr. Hayes said. "Why don't you go first, Gabriella?"

Gabriella stood. "The ocean is a frontier just waiting to be explored like the American West used to be. There's a difference, though. There are few places people may go underwater. It's too deep and the pressure is too great. That's what is known as a hostile environment—an environment in which the conditions are hazardous to people. People need technology to help them."

She continued, "Remotely operated vehicles, or ROVs, can withstand the pressure at several thousand feet. They have cameras and other instruments that gather data about things such as salinity (salt content) and currents. They have manipulators, or arms, that take samples."

Figure 1-14 This manned submersible, MIR I, is used to study and explore to a depth of 6000 m.

Resource Manager

The following **Teacher Classroom Resources** can be used with Section 1-2:

Reproducible Masters
- Activity Worksheets, pp. 3–4, 6 L2
- Critical Thinking/Problem Solving, p. 1 L2
- Enrichment, p. 2 L3
- Home Involvement, p. 28 L2
- Multicultural Connections, pp. 1–2 L2
- Reinforcement, p. 2 L2
- Study Guide, pp. 2–4 L1 ELL

Transparencies
- Teaching Transparency 2 L2
- Science Integration Transparency 1 L2

22 CHAPTER 1 THE NATURE OF SCIENCE

These sample pages are not complete sections.

"Volcanoes are another frontier on Earth," Jared volunteered. "I read about a spiderlike, walking robot that was designed to explore the inside of an active volcano."

Hiromi spoke next. "Space is another hostile environment," he said. "I read about a robot that NASA developed that's able to travel over rough terrain. They tested it in a desert that resembled the surface of the moon. Once on the moon, scientists would operate it from Earth. But, one thing that makes this robot different is that it has its own navigation system. Suppose it were going toward a cliff. It would take 2.5 seconds for the scientists to signal the robot on the moon, and by that time, the robot might have fallen off. But, this robot can determine what is safe and what is dangerous. It might even ignore the operator's commands if it detects a hazard."

Figure 1-15 The terrain of Mars was photographed and explored by this rover.

"That's the kind of technology I read about," said Kashanna. "Scientists are making robots to explore hostile environments that don't need someone giving them commands all the time. One robot is called STAR—that's the Spiral Track Autonomous Robot. It travels on two giant screws—that's the 'spiral' part—so it can turn around in tight spaces and climb steep terrain that other robots can't. It has an onboard computer system that allows it to make decisions—that's the 'autonomous' part."

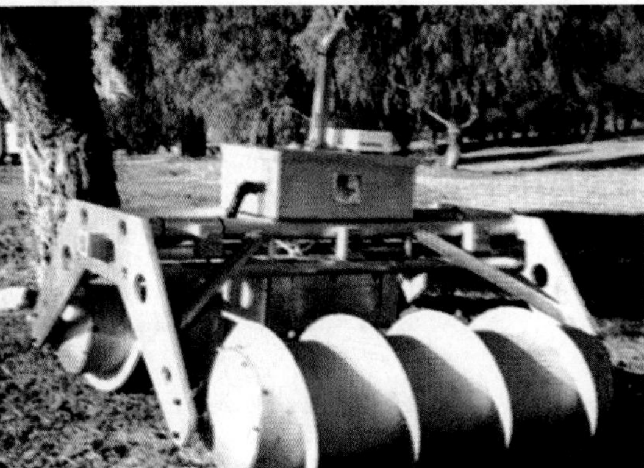

Figure 1-16 Technology, such as STAR, is developed to solve specific problems and explore unique environments.

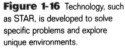

Content Background

JASON is a submersible that is linked by cables and video cameras to scientists at the surface. JASON can collect seafloor samples and delicate objects such as those from shipwrecks. It can dive as deep as 6100 m. A person who dives with scuba gear can safely dive only about 40 m.

2 Teach

Using Science Words

Robot comes from the Czech word *robota,* meaning "work" or "slavery." Karel Čapek invented the word for a play he wrote about a man who creates robots to work in his factory.

Content Background

The relative movements of the giant screws determine how STAR moves. The robot goes forward when the screws rotate in opposite directions. The robot goes sideways when they rotate in the same direction. The robot turns in place when one screw rotates while the other holds still.

Content Background provides additional information about a concept. This information is not in the student edition text.

Enrichment

Have students research for whom JASON was named and write a brief report about its namesake. How many other underwater vessels and spacecrafts can they find that were named after mythological characters? L2

GLENCOE TECHNOLOGY

Videodisc

The Infinite Voyage: Miracles by Design

Chapter 11 *"Smart Materials" and Their Construction* 3:00

Refer to the Teacher Guide for bar codes and teaching strategies.

These sample pages are not complete sections.

How to use your

Teacher Wraparound Edition

3 Assess

Check for Understanding

Using Science Words

Have students compare and contrast the ways in which scientists who design technology and scientists who explore use science skills. L2

Reteach

Have students list the hostile environments that are explored with robots or ROVs. Ask them to describe characteristics of the robots or ROVs that make it possible for them to function in hostile environments. L2

Extension

 For students who have mastered this section, use the **Reinforcement** and **Enrichment** masters.

Glencoe Technology and other multimedia references at point of use make it easy to integrate technology into every lesson.

GLENCOE TECHNOLOGY

Videodisc

The Infinite Voyage: To the Edge of the Earth

Chapter 5 *Exploring Volcanoes: To the Center of the Earth* 10:00

Refer to the Teacher Guide for bar codes and teaching strategies.

Glencoe Science Voyages Interactive Videodisc—Earth

Side 2, Lesson 8 *Space Exploration*

33975

36541

Refer to Videodisc Teacher Guide for additional bar codes.

Figure 1-18 When searching and exploring hostile environments, there are no right or wrong methods. Using your imagination and creativity, the world—and beyond—is yours to explore. **What might the researchers on this ocean-research vessel be studying in the Chukchi Sea (between Alaska and Russia)?**

Using Science Skills to Explore

From their assignment, the class decided that the scientists who explore hostile environments using technology do not necessarily follow step-by-step scientific methods. For example, scientists who explore the ocean, as in **Figure 1-18,** might not have a formal hypothesis. The question might be "What's down there?" But, the scientists still use a variety of science skills while following their particular method.

These skills might include observing (looking at the pictures transmitted), inferring (explaining what the pictures are), measuring (determining how much cable to use to lower the ROV in the water), interpreting (using meteorological data to forecast the weather at sea), and communicating (sharing information to position the ROV correctly).

Safe Science

Mr. Hayes emphasized that safety is an important reason for using technology to explore hostile environments. Having equipment become damaged is far less critical than risking a

Multiple Learning Styles Provide opportunities for all students. Look for learning styles logos throughout each Teacher Wraparound chapter.

Technology and Skills Have students think of a hostile environment they would like to explore that is not mentioned in the text. They should list the science skills they would use and the technology they would need. L2

Caption Answer

Figure 1-18 *Answers may vary. The researchers might be studying how the animals live in this cold climate. Or, they might be gathering information about the organisms that live in this part of the ocean. They might even be collecting meteorological data.*

26 CHAPTER 1 THE NATURE OF SCIENCE

These sample pages are not complete sections.

person's life. The class discussed safety rules to follow when conducting science activities or experiments. They designed a poster called SAFE TIPS.

Start a lab activity only with your teacher's permission.
Ask your teacher if you do not understand a procedure.
Follow all safety symbols. Wear goggles during labs.
Engage in responsible behavior.

Tell your teacher immediately of accidents or injuries.
Identify the location of emergency equipment.
Put away chemicals and supplies properly.
Slant test tubes away from you and others when heating.

The students also created the slogan NO TIDE. TIDE stands for **T**asting chemicals, **I**nhaling chemicals, **D**rinking, or **E**ating. This helps them to remember that they should never eat or drink anything in a laboratory. It also reminds them to be cautious around fumes or vapors that could be harmful.

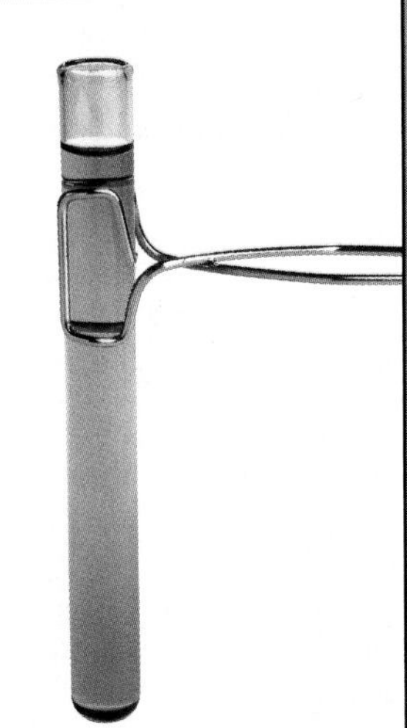

Figure 1-19 Lab equipment, like the test tube shown, must be handled properly.

Section Assessment

1. What are some ways technology is used to explore hostile environments?
2. What are some science skills scientists use to form a hypothesis about the design of an ROV or robot?
3. **Think Critically:** You have read about ways that scientists are like explorers. How are modern scientists different from explorers of the past?
4. **Skill Builder**
   Interpreting Data Suppose you have three plants that are supposed to bloom but are not blooming. You give one plant only water, another plant water and one type of plant fertilizer, and the third plant water and a different type of plant fertilizer. None of the plants bloom. How would you interpret your observations? If you need help, refer to Interpreting Data in the **Skill Handbook** on page 536.

Using Computers

Word Processing
Think of a problem faced by your community such as water pollution. Using a word processor, write a report describing how you would design a robot or an ROV to help solve the problem. If you need help, refer to page 544.

4. **Skill Builder**
   Answers may include that neither fertilizer helped the plants to bloom. Maybe too much or too little fertilizer was used. Or, maybe the plants need nutrients from another kind of fertilizer to bloom. More experiments need to be performed.

Assessment

Portfolio Have students design a poster that illustrates the importance of following a safety rule when performing science activities. Students may choose one or more rules. Use **Performance Assessment in the Science Classroom,** p. 133. P

4 Close

Proficiency Prep

Use this quiz to check students' recall of section content.

1. **What is the application of knowledge learned through science?** *technology*
2. **What are the two reasons that data are organized into tables and graphs?** *to help you analyze the results and draw conclusions*
3. **What should you do before starting any lab activity?** *get permission from your teacher*

Proficiency Prep questions develop and reinforce the chapter content.

Section Assessment

1. ROVs and robots are sent to sites of nuclear accidents, deep into the ocean, into volcanoes, into outer space, and into mines.
2. Answers could include using numbers, comparing, contrasting, sequencing, graphing, and communicating.
3. Think Critically Past explorers did not have the technology that scientists have today. Also, scientists today have access to a lot more information because of research done in the past.

The **Section Assessment** includes answers to review questions in the Student Edition assessment.

Using Computers

Answers will vary according to the community problem the student chooses to solve.

Answers are provided at point of use for student edition **Reading Check questions, Using Math, Internet Connections,** and **Using Computers.**

CA Science Content Standards
Page 26: 9a, 9b, 9c
Page 27: 9a, 9b, 9c

These sample pages are not complete sections.

How to use your
Teacher Wraparound Edition

Reviewing Main Ideas gives you activity ideas to use before, during, and after the lesson is taught.

Multiple Learning Styles Provide opportunities for all students. Look for learning styles logos throughout each Teacher Wraparound chapter.

Cultural Diversity gives a current or historical background on a custom or belief associated with a science concept.

Chapter 1 Reviewing Main Ideas

Reviewing Main Ideas can be used to preview, review, reteach, and condense chapter content.

Preview

Linguistic Have students try to answer the questions in their Science Journals. Use student answers as a source for discussion throughout the chapter.

Review

Interpersonal Have students answer the questions on separate pieces of paper and compare their answers with those of other students in the class.

Reteach

Visual-Spatial Have students look at the illustrations on these pages. Ask them to describe details that support the main ideas of the chapter found in the statement for each illustration.

OUT OF TIME?

Auditory-Musical If time does not permit teaching the entire chapter, use the information on these pages along with the chapter Audiocassettes to present the material in a condensed format.

Chapter 1 Reviewing Main Ideas

For a **preview** of this chapter, study this Reviewing Main Ideas before you read the chapter. After you have studied this chapter, you can use the Reviewing Main Ideas to **review** the chapter.

The Glencoe MindJogger, Audiocassettes, and CD-ROM provide additional opportunities for review.

Section 1-1 SCIENTIFIC PROBLEM SOLVING

A **scientific method** consists of steps taken to try to solve a problem. One step is to recognize a problem. A second step is to form a **hypothesis**—a prediction about a problem that can be tested. In another step, scientists test hypotheses by conducting controlled experiments or observational studies. In a controlled experiment, scientists change the **independent variable** and measure its effect on the **dependent variable.** Scientists who conduct observational studies do not change or control variables. They observe the relationships among variables. Another important step is to analyze data. Scientists organize data into tables or **graphs.** Often, the final step in a scientific method is to draw conclusions. A conclusion may or may not support the hypothesis. This does not necessarily mean the hypothesis is wrong. Sometimes, experiments are not designed correctly or unknown variables produce effects on the dependent variable. Scientists often must do many experiments and look at problems in different ways to find answers. ***Why should only one variable at a time be changed in a controlled experiment?***

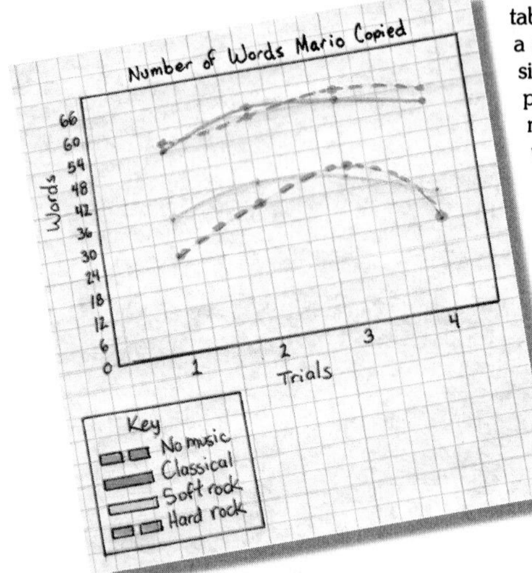

Cultural Diversity

Shamanic Medicine Principles of science are used to solve problems throughout the world. In the rain forests of Latin America, much of the healing is done by shamans, who are local people who use native plants for medicines. Today, researchers are working with shamans and investigating the medicinal value of the plants. Perhaps the cure to some diseases can be found in these plants.

30 CHAPTER 1 THE NATURE OF SCIENCE

These sample pages are not complete sections.

Reading Check ✓
Variables, controls, and *trials* are used in scientific experiments. Compare the meaning of each word in this context with its meaning in a nonscientific context.

Section **1-2** **USING SCIENCE TO EXPLORE**

A hostile environment is an environment in which the conditions are hazardous to people. Many places on Earth and in outer space cannot be explored directly by humans. Scientists have constructed robots and remotely operated vehicles, or ROVs, to go to sites of nuclear accidents, deep in the ocean, into volcanoes, into outer space, and into mines. People have increased their knowledge of hostile environments by analyzing data gathered through **technology.** Scientists who design technology to explore hostile environments use various approaches when forming a **scientific method** that will help them solve a particular problem. They design and conduct experiments to test models. Scientists who use technology to explore hostile environments use science skills. In both cases, scientists use science skills to solve a problem or to answer a question. *Does a scientist always have to follow certain steps in a scientific method? Why or why not?*

Career CONNECTION

John Swallow, Forest Technician

John Swallow works in South Dakota's Black Hills National Forest. He is an Oglala Sioux and a forest technician. John determines which trees in the forest can be safely cut down and which trees must be saved. Much of the cutting of trees is done for thinning—to reduce competition between trees for light and nutrients—thus promoting quicker growth. John also works to conserve sensitive or endangered plants in logging areas. *How can science help our understanding of the impact of logging on a forest?*

Answers to Questions

Section 1-1
Scientific Problem Solving
The scientist will know that any effect on the dependent variable was caused by the independent variable.

Section 1-2
Using Science to Explore
No, because following any scientific method step-by-step is not necessary to solve every problem or answer all questions.

GLENCOE TECHNOLOGY

CD-ROM

Glencoe Science Voyages Interactive CD-ROM

Chapter Summaries and Quizzes

Have students read the Chapter Summary then take the Chapter Quiz to determine whether they have mastered the chapter content.

Career CONNECTION

By using science skills, we can learn what methods are best to protect plants and trees in logging areas.

Answers are provided for the questions asked in **Reviewing Main Ideas.**

✓ Assessment

Portfolio Encourage students to place in their portfolios one or two items of what they consider to be their best work. Examples include:
- Across the Curriculum, pp. 14, 25
- Using Math, p. 19
- Assessment, p. 27 P

Performance Additional performance assessments may be found in **Performance Assessment** and **Science Integration Activities.** Performance Task Assessment Lists and rubrics for evaluating these activities can be found in Glencoe's **Performance Assessment in the Science Classroom.**

Assessment boxes tell you where to find additional assessment activities.

These sample pages are not complete sections.

How to use your Teacher Wraparound Edition

Chapter Assessment gives the answers to student edition questions.

Internet Connection tells you where to look on the Glencoe Science Voyages Web Site for reinforcement activities.

Chapter 1 Assessment

Using Vocabulary

1. k
2. e
3. i
4. b
5. c

interNET CONNECTION To reinforce chapter vocabulary, use the **Study Guide for Content Mastery** booklet. Also available are activities for **Glencoe Science Voyages** on the Glencoe Science Web Site. **www.glencoe.com/sec/science/ca**

Checking Concepts

6. A	11. B
7. C	12. A
8. D	13. B
9. C	14. A
10. D	15. B

Thinking Critically

16. Answers will vary. Answers might include that they would forget a step or that they would find it difficult to get ready on time.
17. The scientist wants to make sure it is the drug that is causing the effect.
18. Answers will vary. An example is observing the number and types of birds in their yards.
19. Following safety rules reduces the risk that someone could get injured.
20. Information helps scientist make better, educated guesses. They can base the hypothesis on what is already known.

Chapter 1 Assessment

Using Vocabulary

a. constant
b. control
c. dependent variable
d. graph
e. hypothesis
f. independent variable
g. inference
h. law
i. science
j. scientific method
k. sequence
l. technology
m. theory

Each of the following sentences is false. Make the sentence true by replacing the italicized word with a word from the list above.

1. A *control* is an approach taken to try to solve a problem.
2. An *inference* is a prediction about a problem that can be tested.
3. *Technology* is the process of trying to understand the world around you.
4. A *constant* is a standard to compare with.
5. The *independent variable* is the factor being measured in a controlled experiment.

Checking Concepts

Choose the word or phrase that best answers the question.

6. How is a hypothesis tested?
   A) experiment C) graph
   B) infer D) conclude
7. What will a scientist never do in an observational study?
   A) use technology C) control variables
   B) record data D) observe variables
8. What does a scientist use to reduce the effect of errors?
   A) observations C) hypotheses
   B) constants D) multiple trials
9. You decide to find out which of three cat foods your cat likes the best. What is the cat food that you try each time called?
   A) control C) independent variable
   B) dependent variable D) trial
10. How does a blind experiment differ from other experiments?
    A) Data are collected and interpreted.
    B) A hypothesis is formed after observations are made.
    C) Variables are changed to test the hypothesis.
    D) Some or all of the information is withheld from the subject.
11. What does it mean if an experiment does NOT support the hypothesis?
    A) The scientist has failed.
    B) The scientist has learned more.
    C) The scientist is not creative.
    D) The scientist did something wrong.
12. Why are ROVs and robots so useful?
    A) They gather information from hostile environments.
    B) They must follow commands from a person.
    C) They allow people to see hostile environments directly.
    D) They make all decisions on their own.
13. How do scientists who build ROVs use scientific methods?
    A) They test the effects of gravity.
    B) They work according to a sequence.
    C) They keep their data secret.
    D) They use every approach in the model.
14. What is a graph **NOT** used for?
    A) conducting an experiment
    B) interpreting data
    C) communicating information
    D) drawing conclusions
15. What is an explanation backed by experimental results?
    A) a control C) a law
    B) a theory D) a hypothesis

These sample pages are not complete sections.

Assessment

Thinking Critically

. You use the skill of sequencing when you get ready for school. What might happen if you changed the order of your actions?

7. A scientist wants to test a new drug that might relieve symptoms for a particular illness. Why is it important to use a control?

8. Give an example of an observational study you can do at home.

9. Why is it important to follow safety rules in the lab?

0. Why do scientists often do research before forming a hypothesis?

Developing Skills

you need help, refer to the **Skill Handbook.**

. **Concept Mapping:** Complete the events chain that shows the order in which science skills might be used in observational studies. Use these phrases: *analyze data, ask a question, draw conclusions, observe,* and *record data.*

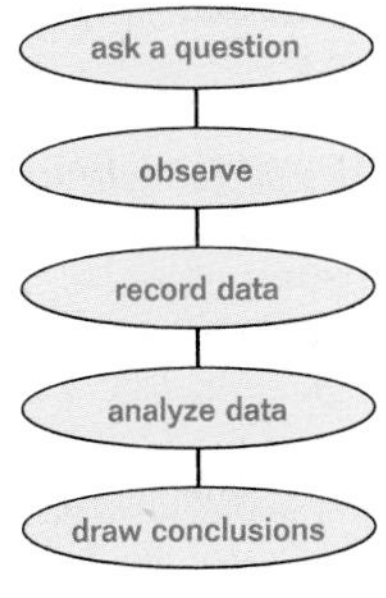

THE PRINCETON REVIEW

Test-Taking Tip

Beat the Clock and Then Go Back As you take a test, pace yourself to finish a few minutes early so you can go back and check over your work. You'll usually find a mistake or two. Don't worry. It's better to make corrections than to hand in a test with wrong answers.

Test Practice

Use these questions to test your Science Proficiency.

1. Michaela set up an experiment to find out if running would help her basketball game. Her basketball game did not improve. What can Michaela conclude from her results?
   A) Her hypothesis was wrong.
   B) Her results did not support the hypothesis.
   C) Running does not help a person do well in sports.
   D) A person who plays basketball should not run.
2. Alex eagerly arrived to science class early to begin his experiment. He set up the materials, popped a piece of gum into his mouth, and got right to work by himself, even though he wasn't quite sure of the procedure. What is the safety precaution that he ignored **FIRST?**
   A) He didn't put on goggles.
   B) He didn't ask questions about the correct procedure.
   C) He didn't get the teacher's permission to start the lab activity.
   D) He was eating during a lab activity.

THE PRINCETON REVIEW **Test Practice**

The Test-Taking Tip was written by The Princeton Review, the nation's leader in test preparation.

1. B

2. C

Developing Skills

21. See student page.

Bonus Question

Identify a problem or question that would best be answered by an observational study. *Answers will vary but may include the following: What are the mating behaviors of a particular animal? or What toys do infants prefer to play with?* **Identify a problem or question that would best be answered by a controlled experiment.** *Answers will vary but may include the following: How much medicine will supress a cough for four hours? or Which house paint holds up the best?*

Test Practice is designed to introduce standardized test format to the student.

Assessment Resources

The **Test Practice Workbook** provides students with practice in the format, concepts, and critical-thinking skills tested in standardized exams.

Reproducible Masters

Chapter Review, pp. 1–2 L2

Performance Assessment, p. 13 L2

Assessment, pp. 1–4 L2

Glencoe Technology

Chapter Review Software

Computer Test Bank

MindJogger Videoquiz

These sample pages are not complete sections.

Making Hypotheses
Students are given many opportunities to practice proposing hypotheses. Possible hypotheses are given. Make certain their hypotheses are always testable.

Activity 1•2

Purpose

Logical-Mathematical Students will compare densities of different liquids. L2 ELL COOP LEARN

Process Skills

communicating, making and using tables, making and using graphs, observing and inferring, measuring, using numbers, interpreting data, comparing and contrasting

Time

45 minutes

Materials

Students can use 4 g of table salt if the balance weighs only to the nearest gram.

Teaching Strategies

- Review correct use of the balance and how to read the scale.
- Designate separate graduated cylinders for each liquid and explain to students that any mixing could result in errors.

Answers to Questions

1. A ship would be able to carry more cargo in salt water because salt water is denser and will support more mass.
2. Oil is less dense than water so it will not support as much mass as water. The birds would have to expend more effort to stay afloat. The oil also would coat the feathers and make it more difficult for them to swim.

CA Science Content Standards
Page 28: 8a, 8b, 9a, 9b, 9c, 9e, 9f

Activity 1•2

Using Scientific Methods

Comparing Densities

Density is a physical property of a substance. It relates to how much material is contained within an object. In general, an object will float if its density is less than the density of the liquid. For example, ice floats in water because ice is less dense than water. How do the densities of various liquids compare?

Materials

- Graduated cylinder (100 mL)
- Balance and masses
- Water
- Cooking oil
- Table salt
- Paper cups
- Plastic spoons or stirrers
- Plastic beverage containers (to dispose of oil)

What You'll Investigate

How do the densities of liquids compare?

Goals

- **Infer** why objects float in some liquids but not in others.
- **Measure** liquids to determine their density.
- **Graph** the densities of the liquids.

Safety Precautions

Never taste anything during a lab activity. Wipe up any spills on the floor immediately.

Procedure

1. **Copy** the data table below for recording your measurements.
2. **Measure** the mass of a paper cup and record.
3. **Measure** 100 mL of water and pour it into the cup. Record the mass.
4. **Make** salt water by dissolving 3.5 g of table salt into 100 mL of tap water. Using a fresh paper cup each time, repeat steps 2 and 3 for the salt water and oil.
5. **Subtract** the mass of the cup to find the mass of the liquid. **Calculate** the density of each liquid using the formula, *density = mass/volume.* The unit used to express density is g/cm^3. One cubic centimeter occupies the same volume as one milliliter.
6. **Graph** your data using a bar graph. How does a graph help you analyze your results?

Conclude and Apply

1. Would a ship be able to carry more cargo in freshwater or salt water? Why?
2. Why might it be harder for aquatic birds to swim in an oil spill than in water?

Sample Data

Liquid's Measurement Data

Liquid	Mass of paper cup (g)	Mass of liquid in cup (g)	Mass of liquid only (g)	Volume of liquid (mL)	Density (g/cm^3)
Tap water	7	106	99	100	0.99
Salt water	6	110	104	100	1.04
Oil	6	98	92	100	0.92

Assessment

Performance Have students think of and perform another method for finding the relative densities of liquids. Use the **Performance Assessment in the Science Classroom,** p. 23.

These sample pages are not complete sections.

Meeting Individual Needs

Each student brings his or her own unique set of abilities, perceptions, and needs into the classroom. It is important that the teacher try to make the classroom environment as receptive to these differences as possible and to ensure a good learning environment exists for all students.

In an effort to provide all students with a positive science experience, this text offers a variety of ways for students to interact with materials so that they can utilize their preferred methods of learning the concepts.

Ability Levels

The activities are broken down into three levels to accommodate students of all ability levels. ***Science Voyages Teacher Wraparound Edition*** designates the activities as follows:

L1 Activities are basic activities designed to be within the ability range of lower-ability students. These activities reinforce the concepts presented.

L2 Activities are application activities designed for all students. These activities give students an opportunity for practical application of the concepts presented.

L3 Activities are challenging activities designed for the students who are able to go beyond the basic concepts presented. These activities allow students to expand their perspectives on the basic concepts.

English-Language Learners

In providing for the student with limited English proficiency, the focus needs to be on overcoming a language barrier. It is important not to confuse ability in speaking/reading English with academic ability or "intelligence." Look for this symbol ELL in the teacher margin for specific strategies for students with limited English proficiency.

Learning Styles

We at Glencoe believe it is our responsibility to provide you with a program that allows you to apply diverse instructional strategies to a population of students with diverse learning styles. A student with a kinesthetic style learns from touch, movement, and manipulating objects. Visual-spatial learners respond to images and illustrations. Using numbers and reasoning are characteristics of the logical-mathematical learner. A student with an interpersonal style has confidence in social settings, while a student with an intrapersonal style may prefer to learn on his or her own. Linguistic learning involves the use and understanding of words. Finally, auditory-musical learning involves listening to the spoken word and to tones and rhythms.

Any student may display any or all of these styles. The ***Student Edition*** and ***Teacher Wraparound Edition*** provide a number of strategies for encouraging students with diverse learning styles. These include **Using Math, Activities, MiniLabs,** and **Science Journal** features.

The chart on pages 60T–61T gives tips you may find useful in structuring the learning environment in your classroom to meet students' special needs.

Meeting Individual Needs

Tips for Instruction	With careful planning, the needs of all students can be met in the science clas
Learning Disabled	1. Provide support and structure; clearly specify rules, assignments, and duties. 2. Practice skills frequently. Use games and drills to help maintain student interest. 3. Allow students to record answers on tape and allow extra time to complete tests and assignments. 4. Provide outlines or tape lecture material. 5. Pair students with peer helpers, and provide class time for pair interaction.
Behaviorally Disordered	1. Provide a clearly structured environment with regard to scheduling, rules, room arrangement, and safety. 2. Clearly outline objectives and how you will help students obtain objectives. 3. Reinforce appropriate behavior and model it for students. 4. Do not expect immediate success. Instead, work for long-term improvement. 5. Balance individual needs with group requirements.
Physically Challenged	1. Openly discuss with the student any uncertainties you have about when to offer aid. 2. Ask parents or therapists and students what special devices or procedures are needed, and whether any special safety precautions need to be taken. 3. Allow physically disabled students to do everything their peers do, including participating in field trips, special events, and projects. 4. Help nondisabled students and adults understand physically disabled students.
Visually Impaired	1. Help the student become independent. Modify assignments as needed. 2. Teach classmates how to serve as guides. 3. Limit unnecessary noise in the classroom. 4. Provide tactile models whenever possible. 5. Describe people and events as they occur in the classroom. 6. Provide taped lectures and reading assignments. 7. Team the student with a sighted peer for laboratory work.
Hearing Impaired	1. Seat students where they can see your lip movements easily, and avoid visual distractions. 2. Avoid standing with your back to the window or light source. 3. Use an overhead projector to maintain eye contact while writing. 4. Seat students where they can see speakers. 5. Write all assignments on the board, or hand out written instructions. 6. If the student has a manual interpreter, allow both student and interpreter to select the most favorable seating arrangements.
English-Language Learners	1. Remember, students' ability to speak English does not reflect their academic abilities. 2. Try to incorporate the student's cultural experience into your instruction. The help of a bilingual aide may be effective. 3. Include information about different cultures in your curriculum to help build students' self-images. Avoid cultural stereotypes. 4. Encourage students to share their cultures in the classroom.
Gifted	1. Make arrangements for students to take selected subjects early and to work on independent projects. 2. Let students express themselves in art forms such as drawing, creative writing, or acting. 3. Make public services available through a catalog of resources, such as agencies providing free and inexpensive materials, community services and programs, and people in the community with specific expertise. 4. Ask "what if" questions to develop high-level thinking skills. Establish an environment safe for risk taking. 5. Emphasize concepts, theories, ideas, relationships, and generalizations.

Meeting Individual Needs

Multiple Learning Styles

People learn in many different ways. There are several different learning styles that help us approach and solve problems. Everyone possesses varying degrees of each of theses learning styles, but the ways in which they combine and blend are as varied as the personalities of the individuals. Glencoe's **Science Voyages** provides you with ways to accommodate students with these diverse learning styles.

Learning Style	Characteristics of Students	Activities in Student Edition
Linguistic	read regularly, write clearly, and easily understand the written word	**Science Journal** activities ask students to tell, write, and explain science concepts. Students express what they have learned in their Science Journals.
Logical–Mathematical	use numbers, logic, and critical thinking skills	Each clearly written **Explore Activity** presents an important concept and **Think Critically** questions, **Skill Builders,** and **Problem Solving** exercises encourage student to practice their logical thinking skills by using various strategies.
Visual–Spatial	think in terms of pictures and images	**Activities** and **Assessment** questions often ask students to draw or show science concepts through modeling, concepts maps, charts, graphs, and illustrations.
Auditory–Musical	remember spoken words and can produce rhythms and melodies	Multimedia software, such as the **Interactive CD-ROM, MindJogger Videoquizzes, and Interactive Videodiscs** can easily be incorporated into lessons.
Kinesthetic	learn from touch, movement, and manipulating objects	**Activities** and **Minilabs** provide for physical involvement in learning.
Interpersonal	understand and work well with other people	**Activities, Science Integrations, Internet Connections,** and **Minilabs** allow students to collaborate with others.
Intrapersonal	have a realistic understanding of their strengths and weaknesses	**Science Journals** and **Try at Home Minilabs** help students personalize science.
Naturalist	can distinguish among, classify, and use features of the environment	**National Geographic** features show students how science relates to the world around them.

As a science teacher, you may want to assign activities to students that accommodate their strongest learning styles, but frequently ask them to use their weakest learning styles. Additional activities are provided in the Teacher Wraparound Edition.

The resources available in **Science Voyages** guarantee that your classroom will be a multisensory environment, providing multiple paths for student learning.

TEACHER CLASSROOM RESOURCES

Technology helps you adapt your teaching methods to the needs of your students. Glencoe classroom technology products provide many pathways to help you match students' different learning styles. To make your lesson planning easier, all of the technology products listed below are correlated to the student text.

Assessment

- Chapter Review
- Standardized Test Practice
- Performance Assessment
- Assessment—Chapter and Unit Tests
- Performance Assessment in the Science Classroom
- Alternate Assessment in the Science Classroom

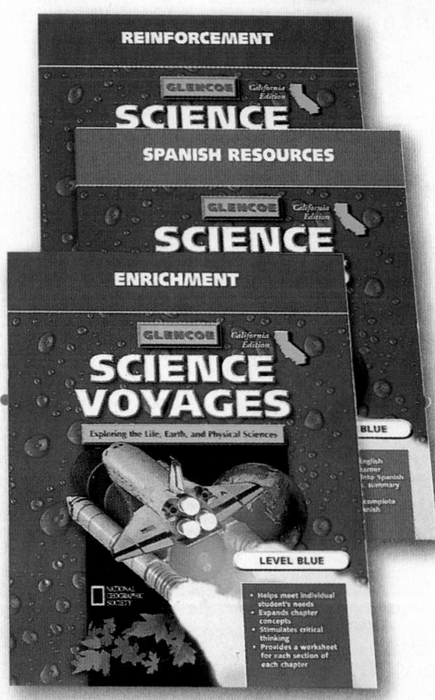

Meeting Individual Needs

- Study Guide for Content Mastery SE and TE
- Chapter Overview Study Guide, SE and TE
- Reinforcement
- Enrichment
- Spanish Resources

TEACHER CLASSROOM RESOURCES

Teacher Support and Planning
- Interactive Lesson Planner CD-ROM
- Lesson Plans

Transparencies
- Section Focus Transparencies
- Teaching/Integration Transparencies

Hands-On Activities
- Lab and Safety Skills in the Science Classroom
- Laboratory Manual, SE and TE
- Activity Worksheets
- Science Inquiry Activities, SE and TE

Extending Content
- Multicultural Connections
- Home Involvement
- Critical Thinking/Problem Solving
- Using the Internet in the Science Classroom
- Exploring Environmental Issues
- Cooperative Learning in the Science Classroom

Meeting Classroom

Interactive Lesson Planner CD-ROM
With Teacher Classroom Resources

- An electronic Lesson-Plan format
- Lesson Planners are designed to save you time
- Makes planning quick and easy

Help students with reading and comprehension with English and Spanish

Audiocassettes

- Available in English or Spanish
- Audiocassettes can be used as a supplement with the text for students who have difficulty reading.
- Students can use individually during class.
- Students can check out tapes and use them at home to reinforce what they have read.
- Use to review chapter before a test.

Reach visual learners with

Color Transparencies

- Teaching/Science Integration Transparencies
- Section Focus Transparencies
- Use a separate transparency as an introduction to each section
- Use as a review.
- Use to stimulate a classroom discussion.

Technology Needs

Videodiscs

- Videodiscs are designed to be used interactively in the classroom.
- Bar codes in this Teacher Wraparound Edition allow you to step through a program and pause to discuss and answer on-screen questions.

Have fun preparing students for Assessment with

MindJogger VideoQuizzes

- Chapter quizzes in video-game format
- Play with teams of four, as suggested on the tape.
- Run copies of questions on paper and have students answer for homework.
- Play as a pre-test or use as a review game.
- Each row forms a team. Every student records his or her answer on a card, then holds it up. Teacher pauses the tape while the row captain tallies points and writes updated scores on the board.

Infinite Voyage

Meeting Classroom

Interactive Videodiscs

- Videodiscs are designed to be used interactively in the classroom.
- Bar codes in this book allow you to step through the programs and pause to discuss and answer on-screen questions.
- Use as a review.

Make customized tests easily and quickly with

ExamView Test Bank Software

- Versions created for Macintosh and Windows.
- Makes creating, editing, and printing tests quick and easy
- You can also use it to edit questions or add your own favorite questions and graphics.
- On CD-ROM and floppy disc

Technology Needs

Interactive CD-ROM

Explorations and Quizzes

- Glencoe has an interactive CD-ROM for each of the textbooks in the ***Science Voyages*** series.
- Can be used as a library resource
- Use as a whole-class presentation.
- Use as a review for individual students.

Internet

- The Glencoe Science Web Site can be found at **http://www.glencoe.com/sec/science/ca**
- Use to extend textbook content.
- Use as a classroom resource.
- Use as an exploration tool for classroom projects.

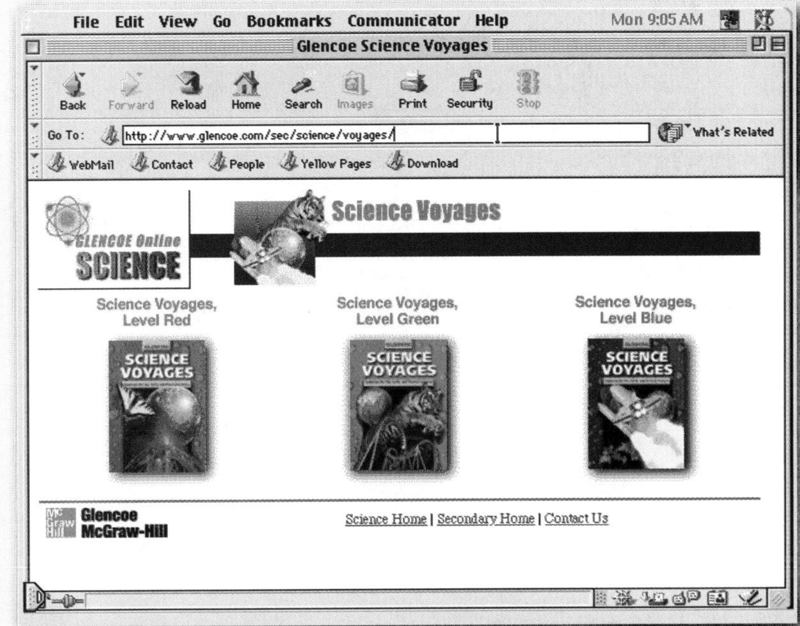

using the interNET

Getting Started

If you're already familiar with the Internet, skip to the next page. To read more about the **Science Voyages** Web Site, keep reading.

The Internet is an enormous reference library and a communication tool. You can use it to retrieve information quickly from computers around the globe. Like any good reference, it has an index to locate the right piece of information. An Internet index entry is called a Universal Resource Locator, or URL. Here's an example. It is the URL for Glencoe science products. **http://www.glencoe.com/sec/science/ca**

The first part of the URL tells the computer how to display the information. The second part, after the double slash, names the organization and tells the computer where the information is stored. The part after the first single slash tells the computer which directory to search and which file to retrieve. File locations change frequently. If you can't find what you're looking for, use the first part of the address only and follow links to what you need.

The World Wide Web

The World Wide Web (WWW), a subset of the Internet, began in 1992. Unlike regular text files, Web files can have links to other text files, images, and sound files. By clicking on a link, you can see or hear the linked information.

How do I get access?

To use the Internet, you need a computer, a modem, a telephone line, and a connection to the Internet. If your school doesn't have a connection, contact your local public library or a university; they often give free access to students and educators.

Glencoe Online Science

The **Science Voyages** Web Site at **www.glencoe.com/sec/science/ca** provides students and teachers with a wide range of materials. On the **Science Voyages** Web Site are links to other Web Sites on the Internet that provide more information on the topics students are studying. Internet projects give students an opportunity to research and share data with other students from around the country and even around the world. Professional development materials give teachers additional resources for teaching science.

Additional Information

You can obtain additional information about using the Internet from Glencoe's *Using the Internet in the Science Classroom,* a booklet that contains hints on how to safely use the Internet, as well as more detailed instructions on how to use it in the science classroom.

CAUTION: Contents may shift!

The sites referenced on any portion of Glencoe's Web Site are not under Glencoe's control. Therefore, Glencoe can make no representation concerning the content of these sites. To protect students, extreme care has been taken to provide only reputable links by using educational and government sites whenever possible. Internet searches have been conducted that, at this time and to Glencoe's knowledge, lead students to sites that contain no content intended for mature audiences.

Science Voyages Web Site Features

Web Links—Links to other previewed web sites that provide information on science topics

Interactive Tutor—Online worksheets and interactive games for study, practice, and review, along with answers

Skill Handbook—A handbook describing how to use basic science skills

Internet Activities—Internet-based projects, including additional information for teachers to help students carry out the projects

Teacher Corner—Professional Development

Activity Materials

Science Voyages has a variety of hands-on activities, short to long, directed and open ended. Many use common, inexpensive materials, making it easier for you to do activities in your classroom. They also are easy to manage with clearly numbered steps and illustrations that help students meet activity objectives. Our full-sized labs were bench-tested by Science Kit to ensure that they use the most common, inexpensive, and appropriate materials.

All MiniLabs have been teacher tested and all laboratory activities have been thoroughly reviewed for safety.

Science Voyages full-sized labs have been Bench-tested by Science Kit to ensure quality and safety.

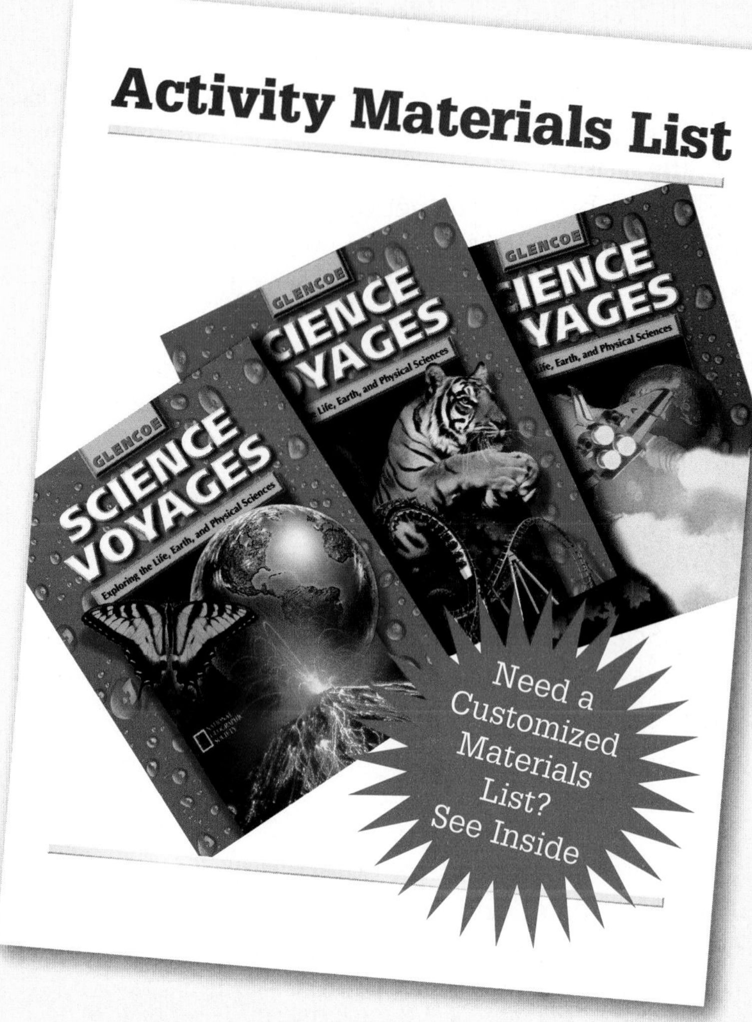

Get the materials you need quickly and easily!

Glencoe and Science Kit, Inc., have teamed up to make materials selection for *Science Voyages* easier with an activity-materials folder. This folder contains two convenient ways to order materials and equipment for the program: the **Activity Plan Checklist** and the **Activity Materials List** master.

Call Science Kit at 1-800-828-7777 to get your folder.

Materials Support Provided by

Science Kit® & Boreal® Laboratories
Your Classroom Resource
777 East Park Drive
Tonawanda, NY 14151-5003
800-828-7777; Fax Phone:/ 800-828-3299
www.sciencekit.com

Supplier Addresses

Scientific Suppliers

Carolina Biological Supply Co.
2700 York Road
Burlington, NC 27215
800-334-5551

Fisher Scientific Co.
1600 W. Glenlake
Itaska, IL 60143

Flinn Scientific Co.
P.O. Box 219
770 N. Raddant Road
Batavia, IL 60510
800-452-1261

Frey Scientific
100 Paragon Parkway
Mansfield, OH 44903
800-235-3739

Sargent-Welch Scientific Co.
P.O. Box 5229
911 Commerce Ct.
Buffalo Grove, IL 60089
800-727-4368

Science Kit & Boreal Laboratories
777 East Park Drive
Tonawanda, NY 14150-6748
800-828-7777

Ward's Natural Science Establishment, Inc.
P.O. Box 92912
Rochester, NY 14692
800-962-2660

Software Distributors

(AIT) Agency for Instructional Technology
Box A
Bloomington, IN 47402-0120
800-457-4509

Cambridge Development Laboratory, Inc.
86 West Street
Waltham, MA 02154

COMpress
P.O. Box 102
Wentworth, NH 03282

Earthware Computer Services
P.O. Box 30039
Eugene, OR 97403

Educational Activities, Inc.
1937 Grand Avenue
Baldwin, NY 11510
800-645-3739

Educational Materials and Equipment Company (EME)
P.O. Box 2805
Danbury, CT 06813-2805

GEMSTAR MEDIA, INC.
P.O. Box 50228
Staten Island, NY 10305

IBM Educational Systems
Department PC
4111 Northside Parkway
Atlanta, GA 30327
800-426-4968

McGraw-Hill Webster Division
1221 Avenue of the Americas
New York, NY 10020

Microphys
12 Bridal Way
Sparta, NJ 07871
800-832-6591

Queue, Inc.
338 Commerce Drive
Fairfield, CT 06432

School Division of The Learning Co.
6160 Summit Drive
Minneapolis, MN 55430

Texas Instruments, Data Systems Group
P.O. Box 1444
Houston, TX 77251

Ventura Educational Systems
910 Ramona, Suite E
Grover Beach, CA 93433

Audiovisual Distributors

Aims Multimedia
9710 Desoto Avenue
Chatsworth, CA 91311-4409
800-367-2467

BFA Educational Media
2349 Chaffee Dr.
St. Louis, MO 63146
800-221-1274

CRM Films
2215 Faraday Avenue
Carlsbad, CA 92008

Diversified Educational Enterprise
725 Main Street
Lafayette, IN 47901

Encyclopaedia Britannica Educational Corp. (EBEC)
310 S. Michigan Avenue
Chicago, IL 60604

Focus Media, Inc.
485 S. Broadway, Suite 12
Hicksville, NY 11801

Hawkill Associates, Inc.
125 E. Gilman Street
Madison, WI 53703
800-422-4295

Journal Films, Inc.
930 Pitner Avenue
Evanston, IL 60202

Lumivision
877 Federal Blvd.
Denver, CO 80204

National Earth Science Teachers Association
NESTA/MESTA Publications
C/O Lisa Bouda
2000 Florida Avenue, NW
Washington, DC 20009

National Geographic Society Education Services
17th and "M" Streets, NW
Washington, DC 20036-4688
800-368-2728

Phoenix Learning Group
2349 Chaffee Drive
St. Louis, MO 63146

Science Software Systems
11890 W. Pico Blvd.
Los Angeles, CA 90064

Society for Visual Education & Churchill Media
6677 N. Northwest Highway
Chicago, IL 60631-1304

Time-Life Videos
Time and Life Building
1271 Avenue of the Americas
New York, NY 10020

Universal Education & Visual Arts (UEVA)
100 Universal City Plaza
Universal City, CA 91608

Video Discovery
Suite 600
1700 Westlake Avenue, N
Seattle, WA 98109
800-548-3472

Lab Safety

Be Prepared

Safety is important in every classroom. However, the need for safety is even greater when science is taught. The activities in *Science Voyages* are designed to minimize dangers in the laboratory. Even so, there are no guarantees against accidents. Careful planning and preparation, as well as being aware of hazards, can keep accidents to a minimum. Many books and pamphlets are available on laboratory safety. In addition, the *Science Voyages* program provides safety guidelines in several forms. The ***Lab and Safety Skills*** booklet contains detailed guidelines, in addition to masters you can use to test students' lab and safety skills. The ***Student Edition*** and ***Teacher Wraparound Edition*** provide safety precautions and symbols designed to alert students to possible dangers. Know the rules of safety and what common violations occur. Know the **Safety Symbols** used in this book. Know where emergency equipment is stored and how to use it. Practice good laboratory housekeeping and management to ensure the safety of your students.

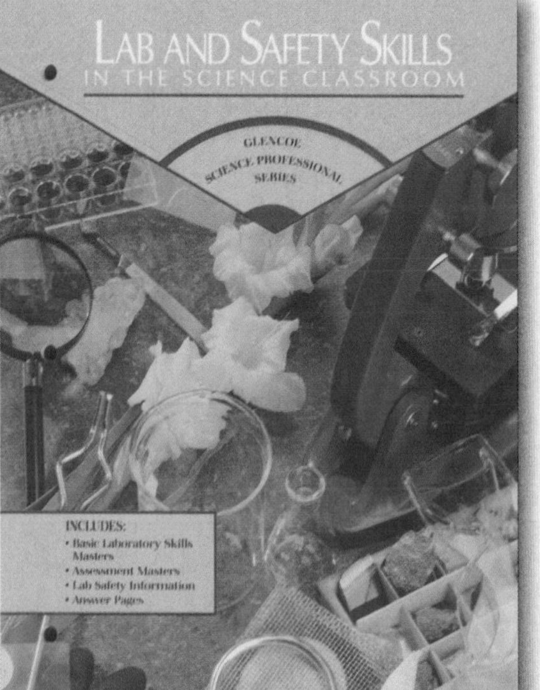

Using Chemicals in the Lab

It is most important to use safe laboratory techniques when handling all chemicals. Many substances may appear harmless but are, in fact, toxic, corrosive, or very reactive. Always check with the manufacturer. Chemicals should never be ingested. Be sure to use proper techniques to smell solutions or other agents. Always wear safety goggles, gloves, and an apron. The following general cautions should be used.

1. Poisonous/corrosive liquid and/or vapor. Use in the fume hood. Examples: ***acetic acid, hydrochloric acid, ammonia hydroxide, nitric acid.***
2. Poisonous and corrosive to eyes, lungs, and skin. Examples: ***acids, limewater, iron(III) chloride, bases, silver nitrate, iodine, potassium permanganate.***
3. Poisonous if swallowed, inhaled, or absorbed through the skin. Examples: ***glacial acetic acid, copper compounds, barium chloride, lead compounds, chromium compounds, lithium compounds, cobalt(II) chloride, silver compounds, and concentrated acids.***
4. Always add acids to water, never the reverse.
5. When sulfuric acid or sodium hydroxide is added to water, a large amount of thermal energy is released. Sodium metal reacts violently with water. Use extra care when handling any of these substances.

Preparation of Solutions

Unless otherwise specified, solutions are prepared by adding the solid to a small amount of distilled water and then diluting with water to the volume listed. For example, to make a 0.1*M* solution of aluminum sulfate, dissolve 34.2 g of $Al_2(SO_4)_3$ in a small amount of distilled water and dilute to a liter with water. If you use a hydrate that is different from the one specified in a particular preparation, you will need to adjust the amount of the hydrate to obtain the required concentration. Premixed solutions can be purchased from scientific supply houses in order to reduce the amount of chemicals that are on hand.

A major consideration for any school offering a science program is safety. Although posting safety guidelines and procedures has been held by recent court rulings an insufficient safety instruction, it should be done anyway. Post fire drill regulations and a chart of emergency procedures in a prominent place in the laboratory. Remind students of proper safety procedures at the beginning of each laboratory session.

Before each session, check all setups for proper assembly and make sure each student is wearing proper safety attire. Students must wear safety goggles and aprons when using any chemical, heat source, or hammer (to split rocks). Be sure that students with long hair secure it and avoid wearing loose-fitting clothing in the presence of an open flame. Wearing contact lenses, even with safety glasses, should not be permitted. Splashing chemicals could infuse under the lenses causing eye damage.

Familiarize yourself with each activity before the class session. Instruct students to follow directions carefully and not to take shortcuts or switch steps. (Such shortcuts may lead to an unsafe situation.) Allow for sufficient clean up time at the end of each laboratory session. At this time, inspect all materials and equipment. Always be present during the laboratory session. Do not allow students to work unsupervised. Familiarize yourself and your students with emergency and first aid procedures. The Red Cross frequently offers classes in first aid. Contact them to find out when they offer these classes. Demonstrate the parts and proper use of laboratory equipment before class. A sample laboratory contract is included below. You may wish to have each student fill out a contract for safety at the beginning of each semester.

STUDENT SAFETY CONTRACT

Date: ________________

I will:

- follow all instructions given by the teacher.
- protect eyes, face, hands, and body while conducting class activities.
- carry out good housekeeping practices.
- know the location of first aid and fire fighting equipment.
- conduct myself in a responsible manner at all times in a laboratory situation.

I,______________________________________, have read and agree to abide by the safety regulations as set forth above and also any additional printed instructions provided by the teacher and/or district. I further agree to follow all other written and verbal instructions given in class.

Signature ______________________________

Materials

Chemical Storage and Disposal

General Guidelines

Be sure to store all chemicals properly. The following are guidelines commonly used. Your school, city, county, or state may have additional requirements for handling chemicals. It is the responsibility of each teacher to become informed as to what rules or guidelines are in effect in his or her area.

1. Separate chemicals by reaction type. Strong acids should be stored together. Likewise, strong bases should be stored together and should be separated from acids. Oxidants should be stored away from easily oxidized materials, and so on.
2. Be sure all chemicals are stored in labeled containers indicating contents, concentration, source, date purchased (or prepared), any precautions for handling and storage, and expiration date.
3. Dispose of any outdated or waste chemicals properly according to accepted disposal procedures.
4. Do not store chemicals above eye level.
5. Wood shelving is preferable to metal. All shelving should be firmly attached to the wall and should have antiroll edges.
6. Store only those chemicals that you plan to use.
7. Hazardous chemicals require special storage containers and conditions. Be sure to know what those chemicals are and the accepted practices for your area. Some substances must even be stored outside the building.
8. When working with chemicals or preparing solutions, observe the same general safety precautions that you would expect from students. These include wearing an apron and goggles. Wear gloves and use the fume hood when necessary. Students will want to do as you do whether they admit it or not.
9. If you are a new teacher in a particular laboratory, it is your responsibility to survey the chemicals stored there and to be sure they are stored properly or disposed of. Consult the rules and laws in your area concerning what chemicals can be kept in your classroom. For disposal, consult up-to-date disposal information from the state and federal governments.

Disposal of Chemicals

Local, state, and federal laws regulate the proper disposal of chemicals. These laws should be consulted before chemical disposal is attempted. Although most substances encountered in biology can be flushed down the drain with plenty of water, it is not safe to assume that this is always true. It is recommended that teachers who use chemicals consult the following books from the National Research Council:

Prudent Practices for Handling Hazardous Chemicals in Laboratories. Washington, DC: National Academy Press, 1981.

Prudent Practices for Disposal of Chemicals from Laboratories. Washington, DC: National Academy Press, 1983.

Safety in Academic Chemistry Laboratories. Washington, DC: American Chemical Society, 1995.

Current laws in your area do, of course, supersede the information in these books.

Disclaimer

Glencoe/McGraw-Hill makes no claims to the completeness of this discussion of laboratory safety and chemical storage. The material presented is not all-inclusive, nor does it address all of the hazards associated with handling, storage, and disposal of chemicals, or with laboratory management.

UNIT 5

Astronomy

In this unit, students are introduced to the size, structure, and evolution of the universe. The unit is organized as an exploration outward from Earth, with chapters on exploring space, the sun-moon-Earth system, the solar system, and stars and galaxies. Students will learn about the energy that provides the intense heat inside stars and about interactions of objects orbiting stars. Students also will explore the immense nature of the universe and develop an understanding of Earth's place in it.

Unit Overview

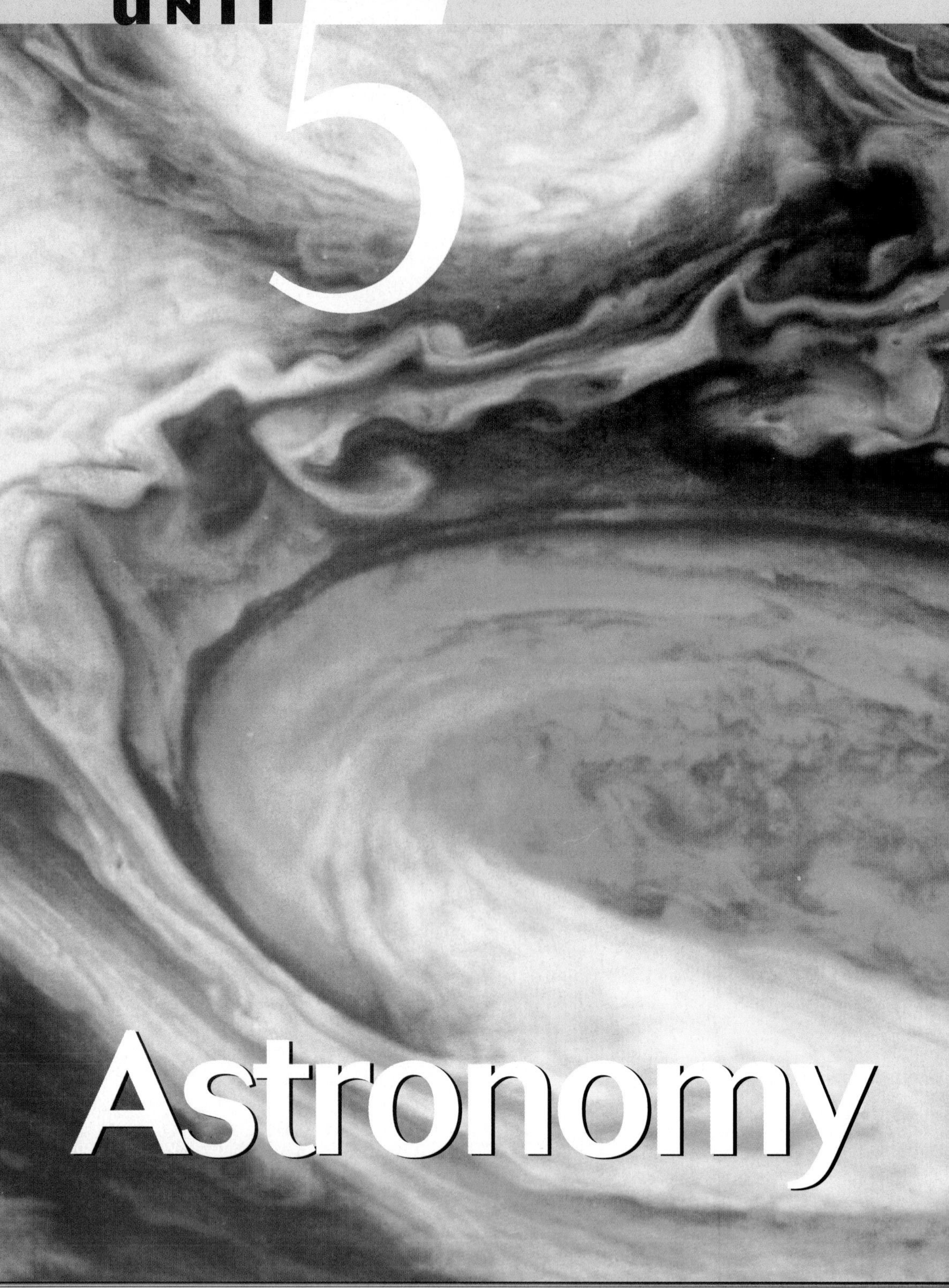

Science at Home

Patterns in the Sky Draw the Big Dipper and the Little Dipper on the chalkboard. Have students copy the pattern and try to locate it in the night sky. Ask them to note bright stars and any other unusual sights. For example, the faint blurred outline of a nova that exploded many years ago sometimes can be seen.

NATIONAL GEOGRAPHIC

What's Happening Here?

Much of the light you see twinkling in the night sky bears witness to a distant past. How so? If you peered at one of those stars through a powerful telescope, you would discover not how the star appears today but how it appeared millions of years ago. Likewise, if people on a distant planet were to aim a telescope at you, they would see Earth as it existed in the age of the dinosaurs! Outer space is so vast that light traveling at 300 000 kilometers a second takes millions of years to span the distance from a distant star to Earth. To grasp the subject of astronomy, you must expand your notion of distance to the unfathomable. In this unit, you will learn how the lure of this vastness has triggered a new age of exploration. En route into deep space, the *Voyager* probes launched in 1977 photographed Jupiter's Great Red Spot (left), a massive storm in the planet's outer gases. In 1996, this astronaut (inset) tested a minirocket backpack by flying solo above the space shuttle *Discovery*.

interNET CONNECTION

Explore the Glencoe Science Web Site at **www.glencoe.com/sec/science/ca** to find out more about topics found in this unit.

- Have students name as many objects and phenomena as they can that are found in outer space, such as galaxies, black holes, moons, and asteroids.

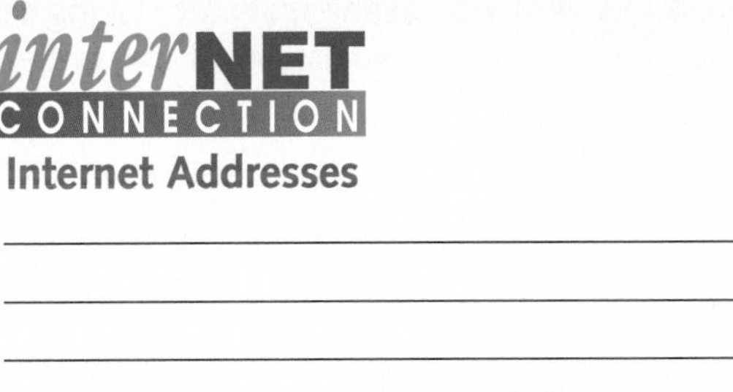

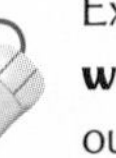

Explore the Glencoe Science Web Site at **www.glencoe.com/sec/science/ca** to find out more about topics found in this unit.

Introducing the Unit

What's happening here?

Have students read the text and examine the pictures. Ask students how many of them have seen photos of the surface of other planets taken by space probes. Point out that it takes years for these probes to reach other planets in our solar system, even though these other planets are relatively close to Earth.

Content Background

One project currently planned is Mars Surveyor 2001, scheduled for launch in April 2001. The first phase will use the atmosphere of Mars to slow down an orbiter and establish an orbit around the planet. This orbiter will use a spectrophotometer to determine the composition of the Martian surface. The lander will arrive soon after the orbiter and will perform actual tests on the Martian surface.

Previewing the Chapters

- Have students search for a figure that shows the relative sizes of all the planets in our solar system.
- Have students look for the names of space missions and tell whether they have heard about them in the news.

Tying to Previous Knowledge

- Ask students to speculate on how the collision of a large meteorite with Earth might have caused the extinction of ancient lifeforms. Many fires could be started by such a collision. Also, large amounts of dust could be thrown into the atmosphere, blocking light from the sun.

Chapter 17 Exploring Space

Section	Objectives	Activities/Features
Chapter Opener		**Explore Activity:** Observe White Light, p. 611
17-1 **Radiation from Space** 3½ Sessions 1½ Blocks	1. **Describe** the electromagnetic spectrum. 2. **Compare** and **contrast** refracting and reflecting telescopes. 3. **Compare** and **contrast** optical and radio telescopes.	**Physics Integration,** p. 613 **Problem Solving:** Interpreting Telescope Data, p. 615 **Skill Builder:** Sequencing, p. 617 **Using Math,** p. 617 **Activity 17-1:** Telescopes, p. 618 **How It Works:** Seeing in 3-D, p. 619
17-2 **Early Space Missions** 2 Sessions 1 Block	4. **Compare** and **contrast** natural and artificial satellites. 5. **Differentiate** between an artificial satellite and a space probe. 6. **Trace** the history of the race to the moon.	**Using Math,** p. 621 **Life Science Integration,** p. 623 **MiniLab:** Comparing the Effects of Light Pollution, p. 624 **Skill Builder:** Concept Mapping, p. 625 **Using Computers,** p. 625 **On the Internet:** Star Sightings, pp. 626–627
17-3 **Recent and Future Space Missions** 1 Session ½ Block	7. **Describe** the benefits of the space shuttle. 8. **Evaluate** the usefulness of orbital space stations. 9. **List** recent and future space missions.	**MiniLab:** Modeling Gravity, p. 630 **Skill Builder:** Making and Using Graphs, p. 633 **Science Journal,** p. 633

The number of recommended single-period sessions — The number of recommended blocks
One session and one-half block are allowed for chapter review and assessment.

Activity Materials

Explore	Activities	MiniLabs
p. 611 3 flashlights; white paper; colorless, green, blue, red cellophane paper	p. 618 candle, white cardboard, flashlight, hand lens, large glass, concave mirror, plane mirror, masking tape, convex mirror, empty paper towel tube, water	p. 624 empty paper towel tube, clear night sky p. 630 stereo record album, turntable, construction paper, masking tape, 3 marbles, scissors

Need Materials? Contact Science Kit at 1-800-828-7777 or at www.sciencekit.com on the Internet.
For alternate materials, see the activity on the listed page.

Standards		Reproducible Resources	Technology
National	State/Local	Test Practice Workbooks are available for use with each chapter.	English and Spanish audiocassettes are available for use with each section.
National Content Standards: UCP3, UCP5, A1, B2, B3, D1, D3, E2, G1, G3	California Science Content Standards: 1b, 4d, 4e, 9a, 9f	**Activity Worksheets,** pp. 95–96 **Enrichment,** p. 46 **Laboratory Manual,** pp. 111–112 **Laboratory Manual,** pp. 113–114 **Reinforcement,** p. 46 **Study Guide,** p. 65	**Section Focus Transparency 46** **Teaching Transparency 33** **Teaching Transparency 34** **Glencoe Science Voyages Interactive Videodisc—Earth** **The Infinite Voyage Series**
National Content Standards: UCP5, A1, A2, D1, D3, E2, G1, G2, G3	California Science Content Standards: 2a, 2e, 2g, 4e, 9a, 9b, 9f	**Activity Worksheets,** p. 97 **Enrichment,** p. 47 **Home Involvement,** p. 29 **Reinforcement,** p. 47	**Section Focus Transparency 47** **Science Integration Transparency 17** **Glencoe Science Voyages Interactive CD-ROM**
National Content Standards: A2, D3, E2, F2, G1, G2, G3	California Science Content Standards: 2g, 4e	**Activity Worksheets,** p. 98 **Critical Thinking/Problem Solving,** p. 17 **Enrichment,** p. 48 **Multicultural Connections,** pp. 33–34 **Reinforcement,** p. 48 **Study Guide,** pp. 66–68	**Section Focus Transparency 48** **Glencoe Science Voyages Interactive Videodisc—Earth** **Internet Connection,** p. 629

Key to Teaching Strategies

The following designations will help you decide which activities are appropriate for your students.

L1 Level 1 activities should be appropriate for students with learning difficulties.

L2 Level 2 activities should be within the ability range of all students.

L3 Level 3 activities are designed for above-average students.

ELL ELL activities should be within the ability range of English Language Learners.

COOP LEARN Cooperative Learning activities are designed for small group work.

P These strategies represent student products that can be placed into a best-work portfolio.

Multiple Learning Styles logos, as described on page 55T, are used throughout to indicate strategies that address different learning styles.

Assessment Resources

Chapter Review, pp. 33–34
Assessment, pp. 65–68
Performance Assessment in the Science Classroom (PASC)
MindJogger Videoquiz
Alternate Assessment in the Science Classroom
Performance Assessment, p. 17
Chapter Review Software
Computer Test Bank

Chapter 17 Exploring Space

This is a representation of key blackline masters available in the Teacher Classroom Resources. See Resource Manager boxes within the chapter for additional information.

Transparencies

Section Focus Transparencies

SECTION FOCUS TRANSPARENCY

LOOKING FOR LIGHT

This photograph shows stones that remain from Stonehenge, a structure built in England more than 3000 years ago. Many things about Stonehenge are still mysteries, but archaeologists hypothesize that the arrangement of stones had something to do with observing the skies. Ancient astronomers may have used these stones to help them keep accurate track of celestial movements much as we might use telescopes and other "high-tech" equipment today.

1. How do you think Stonehenge suggests that ancient people studied the skies?
2. Why do you think the people that built Stonehenge wanted to keep track of the movements of celestial objects such as the stars and planets?

L2

SECTION FOCUS TRANSPARENCY

REMOTE-CONTROLLED RESEARCH

Some things are impossible to see. They are too small, too dangerous, or too far away. How can people observe the universe? Telescopes help, but recently, scientists have also begun to use satellites and space probes to study the solar system and beyond.

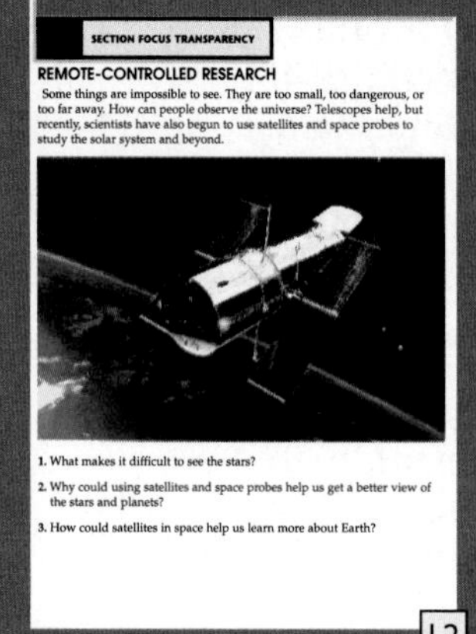

1. What makes it difficult to see the stars?
2. Why could using satellites and space probes help us get a better view of the stars and planets?
3. How could satellites in space help us learn more about Earth?

L2

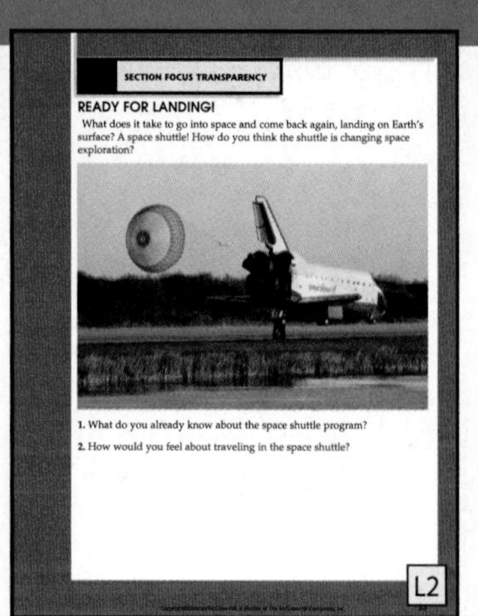

SECTION FOCUS TRANSPARENCY

READY FOR LANDING!

What does it take to go into space and come back again, landing on Earth's surface? A space shuttle! How do you think the shuttle is changing space exploration?

1. What do you already know about the space shuttle program?
2. How would you feel about traveling in the space shuttle?

L2

Science Integration Transparencies

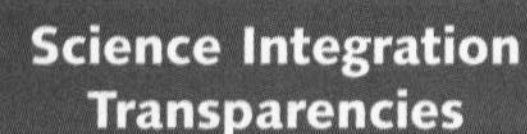

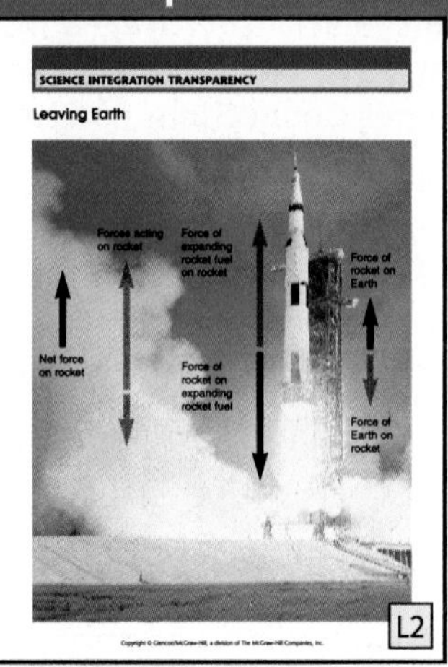

SCIENCE INTEGRATION TRANSPARENCY

Leaving Earth

L2

Teaching Transparencies

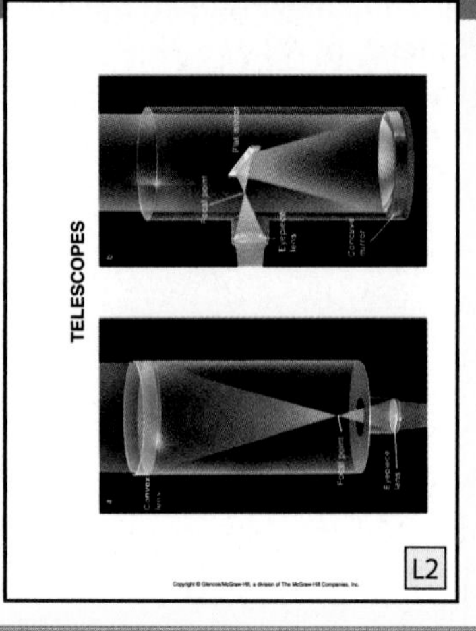

L2

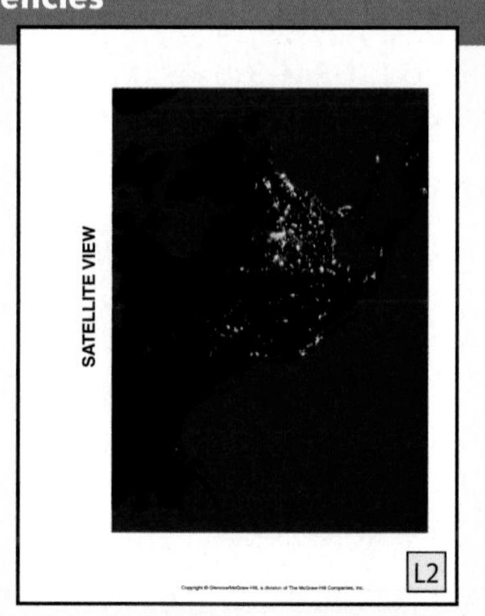

L2

Meeting Different Ability Levels

Study Guide for Content Mastery

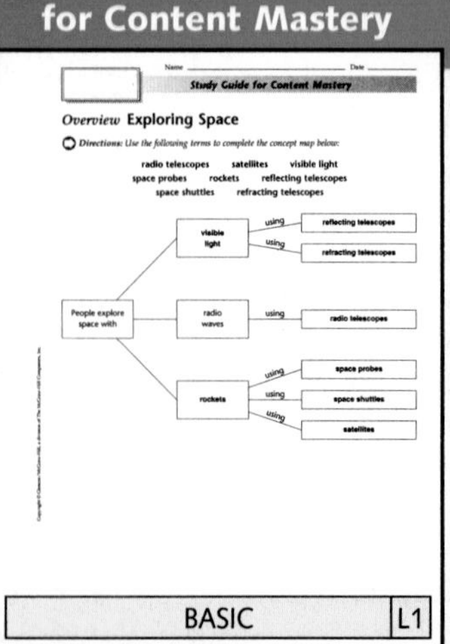

Name ____ Date ____

Study Guide for Content Mastery

Overview Exploring Space

Directions: Use the following terms to complete the concept map below:

radio telescopes, satellites, visible light, space probes, rockets, reflecting telescopes, space shuttles, refracting telescopes

BASIC L1

Reinforcement

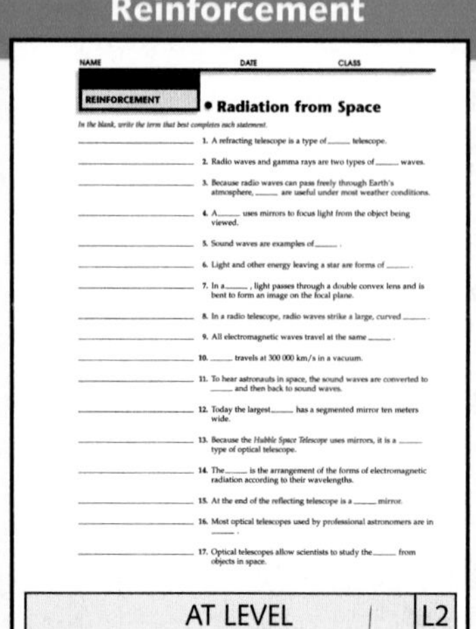

NAME ____ DATE ____ CLASS ____

REINFORCEMENT • **Radiation from Space**

In the blank, write the term that best completes each statement.

1. A refracting telescope is a type of ____ telescope.
2. Radio waves and gamma rays are two types of ____ waves.
3. Because radio waves can pass freely through Earth's atmosphere, ____ are useful under most weather conditions.
4. A ____ uses mirrors to focus light from the object being viewed.
5. Sound waves are examples of ____ .
6. Light and other energy leaving a star are forms of ____ .
7. In a ____ , light passes through a double convex lens and is bent to form an image on the focal plane.
8. In a radio telescope, radio waves strike a large, curved ____ .
9. All electromagnetic waves travel at the same ____ .
10. ____ travels at 300 000 km/s in a vacuum.
11. To hear astronauts in space, the sound waves are converted to ____ and then back to sound waves.
12. Today the largest ____ has a segmented mirror ten meters wide.
13. Because the *Hubble Space Telescope* uses mirrors, it is a ____ type of optical telescope.
14. The ____ is the arrangement of the forms of electromagnetic radiation according to their wavelengths.
15. At the end of the reflecting telescope is a ____ mirror.
16. Most optical telescopes used by professional astronomers are in ____ .
17. Optical telescopes allow scientists to study the ____ from objects in space.

AT LEVEL L2

Enrichment Worksheets

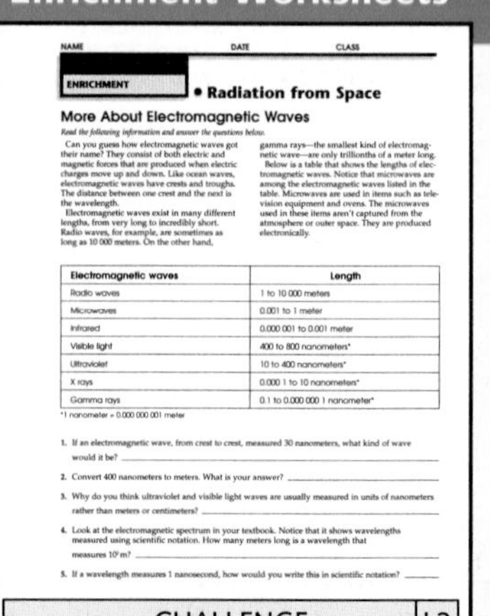

NAME ____ DATE ____ CLASS ____

ENRICHMENT • **Radiation from Space**

More About Electromagnetic Waves

Read the following information and answer the questions below.

Can you guess how electromagnetic waves got their name? They consist of both electric and magnetic forces that are produced when electric charges move up and down. Like ocean waves, electromagnetic waves have crests and troughs. The distance between one crest and the next is the wavelength.

Electromagnetic waves exist in many different lengths, from very long to incredibly short. Radio waves, for example, are sometimes as long as 10 000 meters. On the other hand, gamma rays—the smallest kind of electromagnetic wave—are only trillionths of a meter long.

Below is a table that shows the lengths of electromagnetic waves. Notice that microwaves are among the electromagnetic waves listed in the table. Microwaves are used in items such as television equipment and ovens. The microwaves used in these items aren't captured from the atmosphere or outer space. They are produced electronically.

Electromagnetic waves	Length
Radio waves	1 to 10 000 meters
Microwaves	0.001 to 1 meter
Infrared	0.000 001 to 0.001 meter
Visible light	400 to 800 nanometers*
Ultraviolet	10 to 400 nanometers*
X rays	0.000 1 to 10 nanometers*
Gamma rays	0.1 to 0.000 000 1 nanometer*

*1 nanometer = 0.000 000 001 meter

1. If an electromagnetic wave, from crest to crest, measured 30 nanometers, what kind of wave would it be? ____
2. Convert 400 nanometers to meters. What is your answer? ____
3. Why do you think ultraviolet and visible light waves are usually measured in units of nanometers rather than meters or centimeters? ____
4. Look at the electromagnetic spectrum in your textbook. Notice that it shows wavelengths measured using scientific notation. How many meters long is a wavelength that measures 10^9 m? ____
5. If a wavelength measures 1 nanosecond, how would you write this in scientific notation? ____

CHALLENGE L3

Hands-on Activities

Activity Worksheets

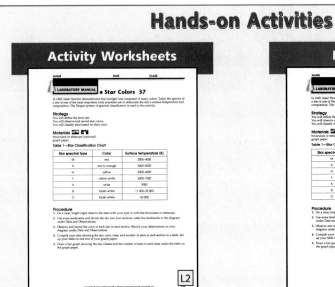

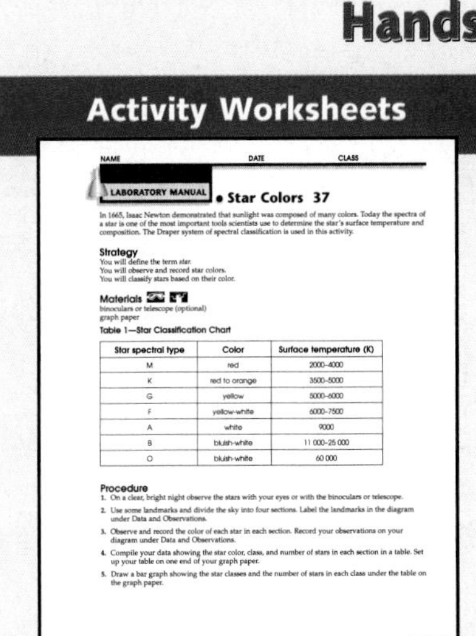

NAME DATE CLASS

LABORATORY MANUAL • **Star Colors 37**

In 1665, Isaac Newton demonstrated that sunlight was composed of many colors. Today the spectra of a star is one of the most important tools scientists use to determine the star's surface temperature and composition. The Draper system of spectral classification is used in this activity.

Strategy
You will define the term *star*.
You will observe and record star colors.
You will classify stars based on their color.

Materials
binoculars or telescope (optional)
graph paper

Table 1—Star Classification Chart

Star spectral type	Color	Surface temperature (K)
M	red	2000–4000
K	red to orange	3500–5000
G	yellow	5000–6000
F	yellow-white	6000–7500
A	white	9000
B	bluish-white	11 000–25 000
O	bluish-white	60 000

Procedure
1. On a clear, bright night observe the stars with your eyes or with the binoculars or telescope.
2. Use some landmarks and divide the sky into four sections. Label the landmarks in the diagram under Data and Observations.
3. Observe and record the color of each star in each section. Record your observations on your diagram under Data and Observations.
4. Compile your data showing the star color, class, and number of stars in each section in a table. Set up your table on one end of your graph paper.
5. Draw a bar graph showing the star classes and the number of stars in each class under the table on the graph paper.

L2

Lab Manual

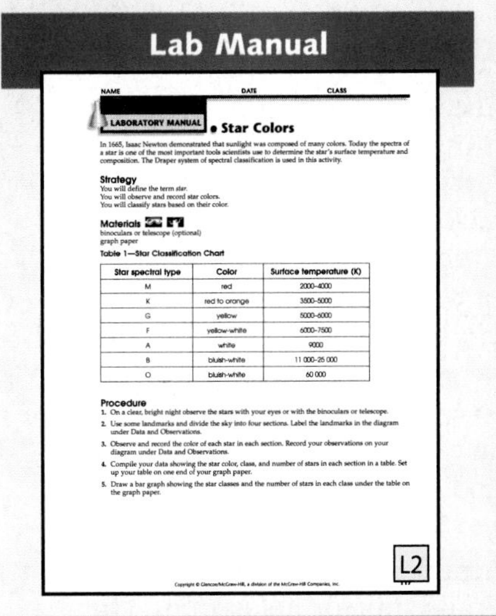

NAME DATE CLASS

LABORATORY MANUAL • **Star Colors**

In 1665, Isaac Newton demonstrated that sunlight was composed of many colors. Today the spectra of a star is one of the most important tools scientists use to determine the star's surface temperature and composition. The Draper system of spectral classification is used in this activity.

Strategy
You will define the term *star*.
You will observe and record star colors.
You will classify stars based on their color.

Materials
binoculars or telescope (optional)
graph paper

Table 1—Star Classification Chart

Star spectral type	Color	Surface temperature (K)
M	red	2000–4000
K	red to orange	3500–5000
G	yellow	5000–6000
F	yellow-white	6000–7500
A	white	9000
B	bluish-white	11 000–25 000
O	bluish-white	60 000

Procedure
1. On a clear, bright night observe the stars with your eyes or with the binoculars or telescope.
2. Use some landmarks and divide the sky into four sections. Label the landmarks in the diagram under Data and Observations.
3. Observe and record the color of each star in each section. Record your observations on your diagram under Data and Observations.
4. Compile your data showing the star color, class, and number of stars in each section in a table. Set up your table on one end of your graph paper.
5. Draw a bar graph showing the star classes and the number of stars in each class under the table on the graph paper.

L2

Accessibility

Spanish Resources

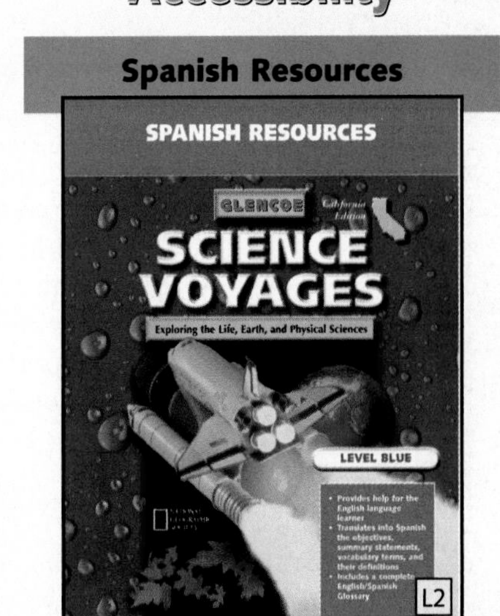

SPANISH RESOURCES
GLENCOE
SCIENCE VOYAGES
Exploring the Life, Earth, and Physical Sciences
LEVEL BLUE
• Provides help for the English language learner
• Translates into Spanish the objectives, summary statements, vocabulary terms, and their definitions
• Includes a complete English/Spanish Glossary
L2

Assessment

Performance Assessment

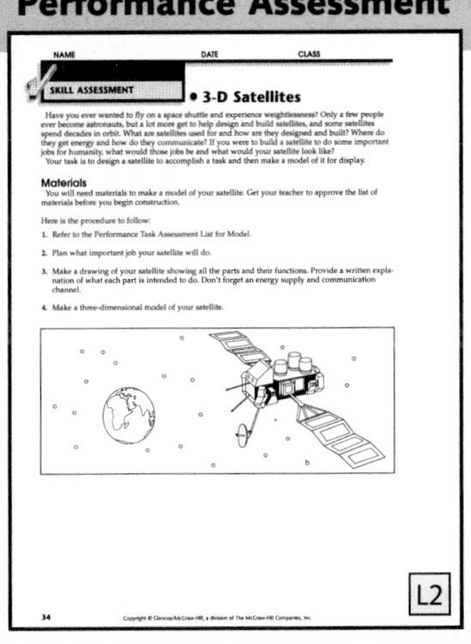

NAME DATE CLASS

SKILL ASSESSMENT • **3-D Satellites**

Have you ever wanted to fly on a space shuttle and experience weightlessness? Only a few people ever become astronauts, but a lot more get to help design and build satellites, and some satellites spend decades in orbit. What are satellites used for and how are they designed and built? Where do they get energy and how do they communicate? If you were to build a satellite to do some important jobs for humanity, what would those jobs be and what would your satellite look like?

Your task is to design a satellite to accomplish a task and then make a model of it for display.

Materials
You will need materials to make a model of your satellite. Get your teacher to approve the list of materials before you begin construction.

Here is the procedure to follow:
1. Refer to the Performance Task Assessment List for Model.
2. Plan what important job your satellite will do.
3. Make a drawing of your satellite showing all the parts and their functions. Provide a written explanation of what each part is intended to do. Don't forget an energy supply and communication channel.
4. Make a three-dimensional model of your satellite.

L2

Chapter Review

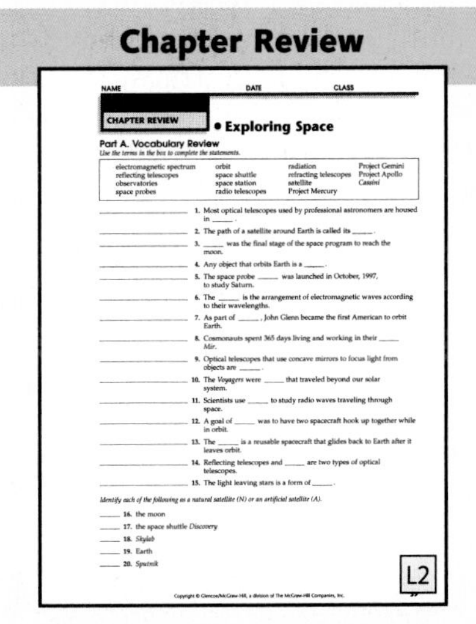

NAME DATE CLASS

CHAPTER REVIEW • **Exploring Space**

Part A. Vocabulary Review
Use the terms in the box to complete the statements.

electromagnetic spectrum	orbit	radiation	Project Gemini
reflecting telescopes	space shuttle	refracting telescopes	Project Apollo
observatories	space station	satellite	*Cassini*
space probes	radio telescopes	Project Mercury	

1. Most optical telescopes used by professional astronomers are housed in _____.
2. The path of a satellite around Earth is called its _____.
3. _____ was the final stage of the space program to reach the moon.
4. Any object that orbits Earth is a _____.
5. The space probe _____ was launched in October, 1997, to study Saturn.
6. The _____ is the arrangement of electromagnetic waves according to their wavelengths.
7. As part of _____, John Glenn became the first American to orbit Earth.
8. Cosmonauts spent 365 days living and working in their _____ *Mir*.
9. Optical telescopes that use concave mirrors to focus light from objects are _____.
10. The *Voyagers* were _____ that traveled beyond our solar system.
11. Scientists use _____ to study radio waves traveling through space.
12. A goal of _____ was to have two spacecraft hook up together while in orbit.
13. The _____ is a reusable spacecraft that glides back to Earth after it leaves orbit.
14. Reflecting telescopes and _____ are two types of optical telescopes.
15. The light leaving stars is a form of _____.

Identify each of the following as a natural satellite (N) or an artificial satellite (A).

16. the moon
17. the space shuttle *Discovery*
18. *Skylab*
19. Earth
20. *Sputnik*

L2

Assessment

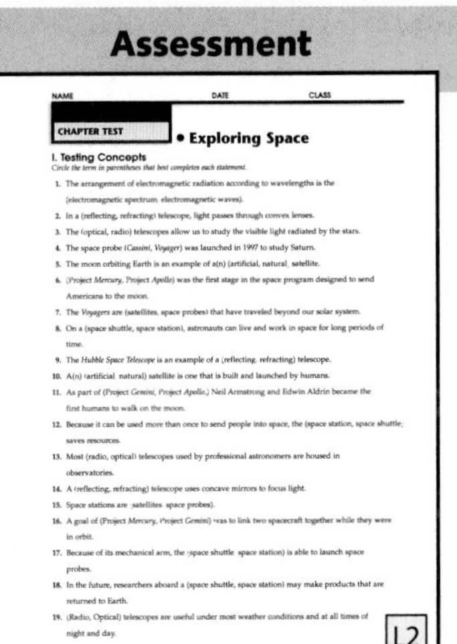

NAME DATE CLASS

CHAPTER TEST • **Exploring Space**

I. Testing Concepts
Circle the term in parentheses that best completes each statement.

1. The arrangement of electromagnetic radiation according to wavelengths is the (electromagnetic spectrum, electromagnetic waves).
2. In a (reflecting, refracting) telescope, light passes through convex lenses.
3. The (optical, radio) telescopes allow us to study the visible light radiated by the stars.
4. The space probe (*Cassini*, *Voyager*) was launched in 1997 to study Saturn.
5. The moon orbiting Earth is an example of a(n) (artificial, natural) satellite.
6. (Project *Mercury*, Project *Apollo*) was the first stage in the space program designed to send Americans to the moon.
7. The *Voyagers* are (satellites, space probes) that have traveled beyond our solar system.
8. On a (space shuttle, space station), astronauts can live and work in space for long periods of time.
9. The *Hubble Space Telescope* is an example of a (reflecting, refracting) telescope.
10. A(n) (artificial, natural) satellite is one that is built and launched by humans.
11. As part of (Project *Gemini*, Project *Apollo*,) Neil Armstrong and Edwin Aldrin became the first humans to walk on the moon.
12. Because it can be used more than once to send people into space, the (space station, space shuttle) saves resources.
13. Most (radio, optical) telescopes used by professional astronomers are housed in observatories.
14. A (reflecting, refracting) telescope uses concave mirrors to focus light.
15. Space stations are (satellites, space probes).
16. A goal of (Project *Mercury*, Project *Gemini*) was to link two spacecraft together while they were in orbit.
17. Because of its mechanical arm, the (space shuttle, space station) is able to launch space probes.
18. In the future, researchers aboard a (space shuttle, space station) may make products that are returned to Earth.
19. (Radio, Optical) telescopes are useful under most weather conditions and at all times of night and day.

L2

Test Practice Workbook

Extending Content

Critical Thinking/ Problem Solving

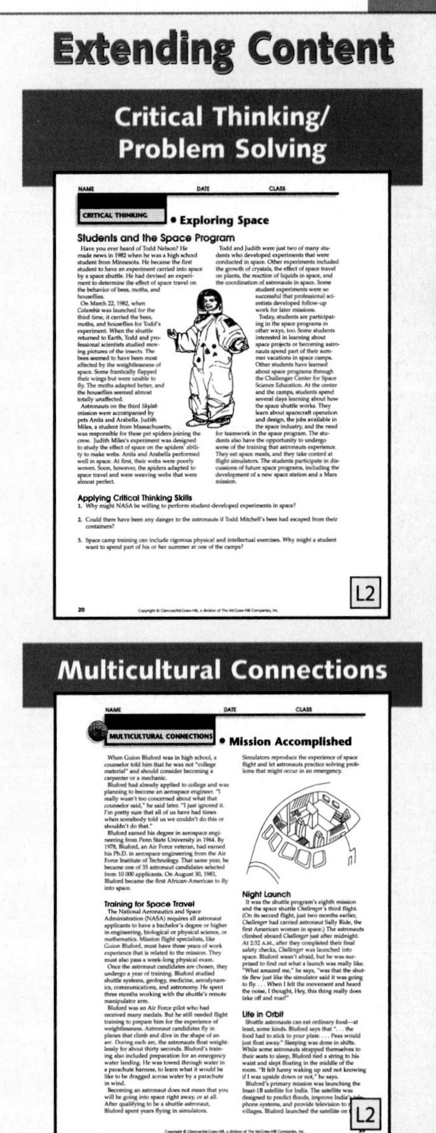

NAME DATE CLASS

CRITICAL THINKING • **Exploring Space**

Students and the Space Program

Have you ever heard of Todd Nelson? He made news in 1982 when he was a high school student from Minnesota. He became the first student to have an experiment carried into space by a space shuttle. He had devised an experiment to determine the effect of space travel on the behavior of bees, moths, and houseflies.

On March 22, 1982, when *Columbia* was launched for the third time, it carried the bees, moths, and houseflies for Todd's experiment. When the shuttle returned to Earth, Todd and professional scientists studied moving pictures of the insects. The bees seemed to have been most affected by the weightlessness of space. Some frantically flapped their wings but were unable to fly. The moths adapted better, and the houseflies seemed almost totally unaffected.

Astronauts on the third *Skylab* mission were accompanied by pets Anita and Arabella. Judith Miles, a student from Massachusetts, was responsible for these pet spiders joining the crew. Judith Miles's experiment was designed to study the effect of space on the spiders' ability to make webs. Anita and Arabella performed well in space. At first, their webs were poorly woven. Soon, however, the spiders adapted to space travel and were weaving webs that were almost perfect.

Todd and Judith were just two of many students who developed experiments that were conducted in space. Other experiments included the growth of crystals, the effect of space travel on plants, the reaction of liquids in space, and the coordination of astronauts in space. Some student experiments were so successful that professional scientists developed follow-up work for later missions.

Today, students are participating in the space programs in other ways, too. Some students interested in learning about space projects or becoming astronauts spend part of their summer vacations in space camps. Other students have learned about space programs through the Challenger Center for Space Science Education. At the center and the camps, students spend several days learning about how the space shuttle works. They learn about spacecraft operation and design, the jobs available in the space industry, and the need for teamwork in the space program. The students also have the opportunity to undergo some of the training that astronauts experience. They eat space meals, and they take control at flight simulators. The students participate in discussions of future space programs, including the development of a new space station and a Mars mission.

Applying Critical Thinking Skills
1. Why might NASA be willing to perform student-developed experiments in space?
2. Could there have been any danger to the astronauts if Todd Mitchell's bees had escaped from their containers?
3. Space camp training can include rigorous physical and intellectual exercises. Why might a student want to spend part of his or her summer at one of the camps?

L2

20

Multicultural Connections

NAME DATE CLASS

MULTICULTURAL CONNECTIONS • **Mission Accomplished**

When Guion Bluford was in high school, a counselor told him that he was not "college material" and should consider becoming a carpenter or a mechanic.

Bluford had already applied to college and was planning to become an aerospace engineer. "I really wasn't too concerned about what that counselor said," he said later. "I just ignored it. I'm pretty sure that all of us have had times when somebody told us we couldn't do this or shouldn't do that."

Bluford earned his degree in aerospace engineering from Penn State University in 1964. By 1978, Bluford, an Air Force veteran, had earned his Ph.D. in aerospace engineering from the Air Force Institute of Technology. That same year, he became one of 35 astronaut candidates selected from 10 000 applicants. On August 30, 1983, Bluford became the first African-American to fly into space.

Training for Space Travel

The National Aeronautics and Space Administration (NASA) requires all astronaut applicants to have a bachelor's degree or higher in engineering, biological or physical science, or mathematics. Mission flight specialists, like Guion Bluford, must have three years of work experience that is related to the mission. They must also pass a week-long physical exam.

Once the astronaut candidates are chosen, they undergo a year of training. Bluford studied shuttle systems, geology, medicine, aerodynamics, communications, and astronomy. He spent three months working with the shuttle's remote manipulator arm.

Bluford was an Air Force pilot who had received many medals. But he still needed flight training to prepare him for the experience of weightlessness. Astronaut candidates fly in planes that climb and dive in the shape of an arc. During each arc, the astronauts float weightlessly for about thirty seconds. Bluford's training also included preparation for an emergency water landing. He was towed through water in a parachute harness, to learn what it would be like to be dragged across water by a parachute in wind.

Becoming an astronaut does not mean that you will be going into space right away, or at all. After qualifying to be a shuttle astronaut, Bluford spent years flying in simulators. Simulators reproduce the experience of space flight and let astronauts practice solving problems that might occur in an emergency.

Night Launch

It was the shuttle program's eighth mission and the space shuttle *Challenger*'s third flight. (On its second flight, just two months earlier, *Challenger* had carried astronaut Sally Ride, the first American woman in space.) The astronauts climbed aboard *Challenger* just after midnight. At 2:32 A.M., after they completed their final safety checks, *Challenger* was launched into space. Bluford wasn't afraid, but he was surprised to find out what a launch was really like. "What amazed me," he says, "was that the shuttle flew just like the simulator said it was going to fly. . . . When I felt the movement and heard the noise, I thought, Hey, this thing really does take off and roar!"

Life in Orbit

Shuttle astronauts can eat ordinary food—at least, some kinds. Bluford says that ". . . the food had to stick to your plate. . . . Peas would just float away." Sleeping was done in shifts. While some astronauts strapped themselves to their seats to sleep, Bluford tied a string to his waist and slept floating in the middle of the room. "It felt funny waking up and not knowing if I was upside down or not," he says.

Bluford's primary mission was launching the Insat-1B satellite for India. The satellite was designed to predict floods, improve India's telephone systems, and provide television to villages. Bluford launched the satellite on

L2

Helping You Prepare

Large Telescopes (Section 17-1)

On April 21, 1998, the largest telescope on Earth captured light from its first star. The European Southern Observatory's Very Large Telescope (VLT) is located in Cerro Paranal, a mountaintop in the Chilean Andes. The VLT is composed of four identical 8.2-m individual telescopes and several movable 1.8-m telescopes.

Other large telescopes include the twin 10-m Keck reflecting telescopes on Mauna Kea in Hawaii. The primary mirror of each telescope has been constructed from 36 hexagonal glass segments, each 1.8 m in diameter.

The NASA Orbital Debris Observatory (NODO) uses a liquid mirror telescope. The objective mirror is made of a shallow container of the liquid element mercury. It is 3 m in diameter and is constantly spinning at one revolution every 6.02315 seconds. This spinning forces the liquid mercury to form a parabolic reflector. The telescope is kept level; thus, it only observes the sky's zenith. Its main mission is to locate and count orbital debris (space junk) as small as 1 cm in diameter.

The Very Large Array (VLA) of telescopes near Socorro, New Mexico, is composed of 27 radio telescopes. All 27 telescopes can be used at once to operate as one large telescope.

GLENCOE TECHNOLOGY

Glencoe Science Voyages Interactive CD-ROM

Chapter Summaries

Use the Chapter Summary to introduce, teach, or review chapter material.

Light Pollution (Section 17-1)

Light pollution is a glow in the sky caused by city lights. The glow makes it difficult to see dim stars.

In several U.S. cities, work has begun to reduce light pollution. Tucson, Arizona, located only 80 km from the Kitt Peak National Observatory, has replaced its streetlights with low-pressure sodium lamps. These lights shine at wavelengths that can be filtered out by astronomers.

Other cities have put hoods on billboards, parking-lot lights, and floodlights so they illuminate the object or the ground rather than the sky.

NATIONAL GEOGRAPHIC — Teacher's Corner

Products Available from National Geographic Society

To order the following products for use with this chapter, call National Geographic Society at 1-800-368-2728:

Books

Discover Mars

Mars: Uncovering the Secrets of the Red Planet

National Geographic Satellite Atlas of the World

Waves: The Electromagnetic Universe

Video

What We Learn About Earth from Space

Index to NATIONAL GEOGRAPHIC Magazine

The following articles may be used for research relating to this chapter:

"Return to Mars," by William R. Newcott, August 1998.

"New Eyes on the Universe," by Bradford A. Smith, January 1994.

"Satellite Rescue," by Thomas Y. Canby, November 1991.

"Mission to Mars," by Michael Collins, November 1988.

Satellites and Space Probes
(Section 17-2)

The first U.S. weather satellite, *Vanguard 2,* was launched in February 1959. Its mission was to take photographs of Earth's cloud patterns.

Evidence of possible water on the moon was first discovered by the *Clementine* space probe in 1994. Radio signals beamed from *Clementine* bounced off the moon and were received on Earth. Initial readings were similar to those produced by ice on Earth. In 1998, using data gathered by the *Lunar Prospector*, NASA mission scientists estimated that 6 billion tons of water are hidden in permanently shadowed regions of the moon's north and south poles.

Jupiter's moon, Europa, may contain water, too. Recent preliminary studies of Europa by the *Galileo* spacecraft indicate an ocean of water or ice under the moon's crustal layer of ice.

Space Spin-offs (Section 17-2)

Much of the technology developed by NASA to achieve its goals in space is now being used by people throughout the world. Technologies developed by NASA that are later used by the general public are called spin-offs.

NASA developed lightweight, compact breathing systems for astronauts to carry as they ventured out of their spacecraft and onto the moon. Today, firefighters use these breathing systems as well as fire-resistant uniforms originally designed as flight suits for NASA pilots. The lightweight material in the suits won't burn or crack.

A material designed for boots worn by astronauts on the moon is now found in some athletic shoes. Other materials have been incorporated into ski goggles, blankets, and bicycle seats.

People who are visually impaired also have benefited from spin-offs. One device vibrates ink on a printed page, enabling them to read materials that are not printed in Braille. Another device determines the denomination of currency and generates an audible signal.

Other spin-offs include pens that write without the help of gravity and sunglasses that adjust to various light levels.

International Space Station
(Section 17-3)

The International Space Station will be a permanently crewed satellite in which teams of astronauts from many nations will work cooperatively in space. Launch of materials and modules that are part of the International Space Station assembly began with the launch of the space shuttle *Endeavor.* It is believed that humans will find thousands of ways to use the space station that no one has even thought of yet.

SCIENCE UPDATE

For current events or science in the news, access the Glencoe Science Web Site at **www.glencoe.com/sec/science/ca**

Teacher to Teacher

"I encourage students to visit the media center to investigate how we continue to explore space. Ask students to use periodicals to investigate current NASA projects, or visit the NASA Web Site to gather and share information about current events."

Tracey L. Smeltzer, Library Media Specialist
Derry Area High School
Derry, PA

CHAPTER 17 Exploring Space

CHAPTER OVERVIEW

Section 17-1 This section discusses electromagnetic radiation and telescopes.

Section 17-2 Early artificial satellites and space probes are described.

Section 17-3 This section discusses recent and future space missions.

Chapter Vocabulary

electromagnetic spectrum
refracting telescope
reflecting telescope
observatory
radio telescope
satellite
orbit
space probe
Project Mercury
Project Gemini
Project Apollo
space shuttle
space station

Theme Connection

Energy/Scale and Structure The properties of electromagnetic radiation have enabled scientists to describe the scale and structure of our solar system and beyond.

00:00 OUT OF TIME?

If time does not permit teaching the entire chapter, use Reviewing Main Ideas on pp. 634–635.

CHAPTER 17 Exploring Space

Chapter Preview

Skills Preview

Skill Builders
- Sequence
- Map Concepts

MiniLabs
- Analyze Data
- Infer

Activities
- Draw Conclusions

Reading Check

As you read this chapter about space, write four or five questions that are answered in each section.

Multiple Learning Styles

Look for the following logos for strategies that emphasize different learning modalities.

Linguistic Science Journal, pp. 614, 615, 624; Using Science Words, p. 622; Activity, p. 623; Across the Curriculum, p. 631; Preview, p. 634

Visual-Spatial Explore Activity, p. 611; Reteach, pp. 616, 634; Multiple Learning Styles, p. 616; Activity, p. 618; MiniLab, p. 624; Quick Demo, p. 629; Inclusion Strategies, p. 629; Making a Model, p. 631

Auditory-Musical Out of Time, p. 634

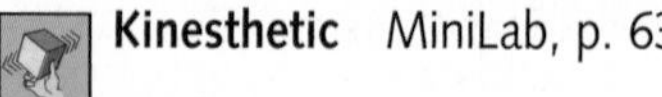

Kinesthetic MiniLab, p. 630

Interpersonal Discussion, p. 621; Reteach, p. 625; Review, p. 634

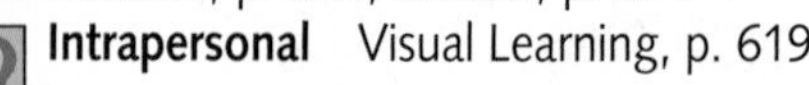

Intrapersonal Visual Learning, p. 619

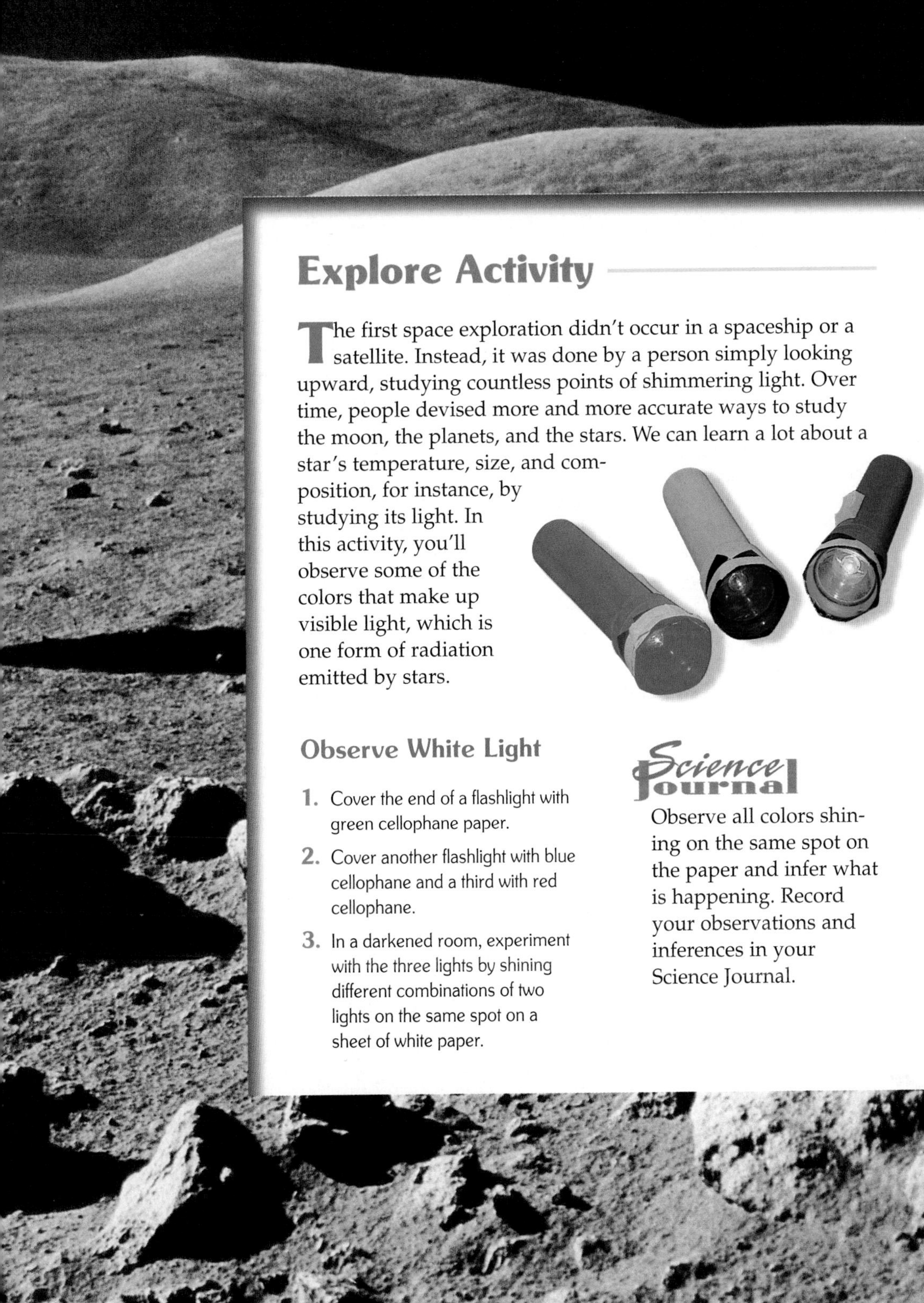

Explore Activity

The first space exploration didn't occur in a spaceship or a satellite. Instead, it was done by a person simply looking upward, studying countless points of shimmering light. Over time, people devised more and more accurate ways to study the moon, the planets, and the stars. We can learn a lot about a star's temperature, size, and composition, for instance, by studying its light. In this activity, you'll observe some of the colors that make up visible light, which is one form of radiation emitted by stars.

Observe White Light

1. Cover the end of a flashlight with green cellophane paper.
2. Cover another flashlight with blue cellophane and a third with red cellophane.
3. In a darkened room, experiment with the three lights by shining different combinations of two lights on the same spot on a sheet of white paper.

Science Journal

Observe all colors shining on the same spot on the paper and infer what is happening. Record your observations and inferences in your Science Journal.

Assessment Planner

Portfolio
Refer to p. 635 for suggested items that students might select for their portfolios.

Performance Assessment
See p. 635 for additional Performance Assessment options.
Skill Builder, pp. 617, 625, 633
MiniLab, pp. 624, 630
Activity 17-1, p. 618; 17-2, pp. 626–627

Content Assessment
Section Assessment, pp. 617, 625, 633
Chapter Assessment, pp. 636–637
Proficiency Prep, pp. 617, 625, 632

Explore Activity

Purpose

Visual-Spatial Use the Explore Activity to introduce students to the composition of white light. Inform students that they will be learning about electromagnetic radiation and how it can be used to study objects in space. L2 ELL COOP LEARN

Preparation

Have students bring in flashlights.

Materials

sheet of white paper; 3 flashlights; colorless, green, blue, and red cellophane sheets

Teaching Strategies

Troubleshooting The flashlights used by each group should be as close to identical as possible. Have students attach the cellophane to the flashlights with transparent tape. Make the room as dark as possible.

Science Journal The red and blue light created a new color when added together. As different-colored lights were combined, different colors were produced. When all colors were combined, white light was seen on the white paper.

Assessment

Oral As lights of different colors are added together on the white paper, ask students to explain what is happening. Use **Performance Assessment in the Science Classroom,** p. 71. P

SECTION 17•1

Prepare

Content Background

Refer to **Large Telescopes** and **Light Pollution** on p. 610E.

Preplanning

Refer to the **Chapter Organizer** on pp. 610A–B.

1 Motivate

Bellringer

Before presenting the lesson, display **Section Focus Transparency 46** on the overhead projector. Use the accompanying **Focus Activity** worksheet. L2 ELL

Section 17-1

SECTION FOCUS TRANSPARENCY

LOOKING FOR LIGHT

This photograph shows stones that remain from Stonehenge, a structure built in England more than 3000 years ago. Many things about Stonehenge are still mysteries, but archaeologists hypothesize that the arrangement of stones had something to do with observing the skies. Ancient astronomers may have used these stones to help them keep accurate track of celestial movements much as we might use telescopes and other "high-tech" equipment today.

1. How do you think Stonehenge suggests that ancient people studied the skies?
2. Why do you think the people that built Stonehenge wanted to keep track of the movements of celestial objects such as the stars and planets?

46

Tying to Previous Knowledge

Inform students that binoculars can be used to view large areas of the sky. Binoculars are actually two refracting telescopes side by side.

17•1 Radiation from Space

What You'll Learn

- The electromagnetic spectrum
- The differences between refracting and reflecting telescopes
- The differences between optical and radio telescopes

Vocabulary

electromagnetic spectrum
refracting telescope
reflecting telescope
observatory
radio telescope

Why It's Important

- You'll learn about the tools and methods used to study space.

Electromagnetic Waves

On a crisp, autumn evening, you take a break from your homework to gaze out the window at the many stars that fill the night sky. Looking up at the stars, it's easy to imagine future spaceships venturing through space and large space stations circling above Earth, where people work and live. But, when you look into the night sky, what you're really seeing is the distant past, not the future.

Light from the Past

When you look at a star, you see light that left the star many years ago. The light that you see travels fast. Still, the distances across space are so great that it takes years for the light to reach Earth—sometimes millions of years.

The light and other energy leaving a star are forms of radiation. Recall that radiation is energy that's transmitted from one place to another by electromagnetic waves. Because of the electric and magnetic properties of this radiation, it's called electromagnetic radiation. Electromagnetic waves carry energy through empty space as well as through matter.

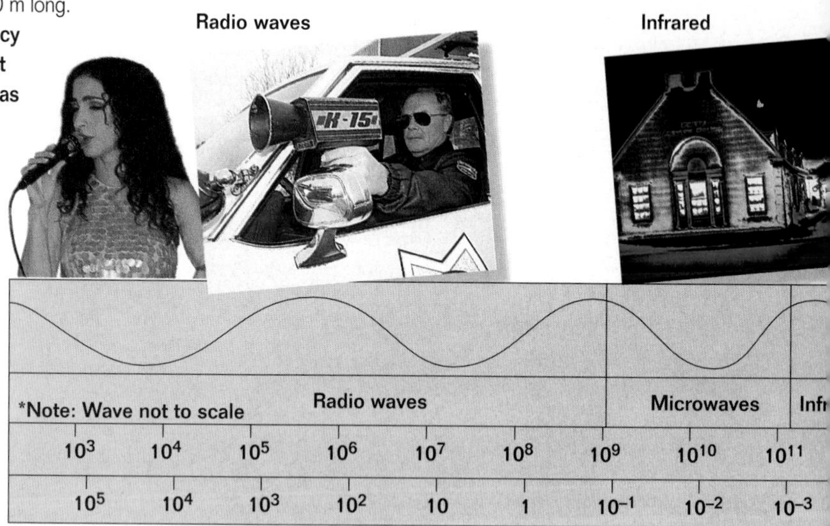

Figure 17-1 The electromagnetic spectrum ranges from gamma rays with wavelengths of less than 0.000 000 000 01 m to radio waves more than 100 000 m long. **What happens to frequency (the number of waves that pass a point per second) as wavelength shortens?**

Resource Manager

The following **Teacher Classroom Resources** can be used with Section 17-1:

Reproducible Masters

Activity Worksheets, pp. 95–96 L2
Enrichment, p. 46 L3
Laboratory Manual, pp. 111–112 L2
Laboratory Manual, pp. 113–114 L2
Reinforcement, p. 46 L2
Study Guide, p. 65 L1 ELL

Transparencies

Teaching Transparency 33 L2
Teaching Transparency 34 L2

Electromagnetic Radiation

Sound waves, a type of mechanical wave, can't travel through empty space. How do we hear the voices of the astronauts while they're in space? When they speak into a microphone, the sound is converted into electromagnetic waves called radio waves. The radio waves travel through space and through our atmosphere. They are then converted back into sound by electronic equipment and audio speakers.

Radio waves and visible light from the sun are just two types of electromagnetic radiation. The other types include gamma rays, X rays, ultraviolet waves, infrared waves, and microwaves. **Figure 17-1** shows these forms of electromagnetic radiation arranged according to their wavelengths. This arrangement of electromagnetic radiation is called the **electromagnetic spectrum.**

Although the various electromagnetic waves differ in their wavelengths, they all travel at the speed of 300 000 km/s in a vacuum. You're probably more familiar with this speed as the "speed of light." Visible light and other forms of electromagnetic radiation travel at this incredible speed, but the universe is so large that it takes millions of years for the light from some stars to reach Earth.

Once electromagnetic radiation from stars and other objects reaches Earth, we can use it to learn about the source of the electromagnetic radiation. What tools and methods do scientists use to discover what lies beyond our planet? One tool for observing electromagnetic radiation from distant sources is a telescope.

Bending Light

Pass a beam of white light through a prism. Note that different colors of light are bent, forming a spectrum. Infer how the white light and prism form a spectrum with violet on one end and red on the other.

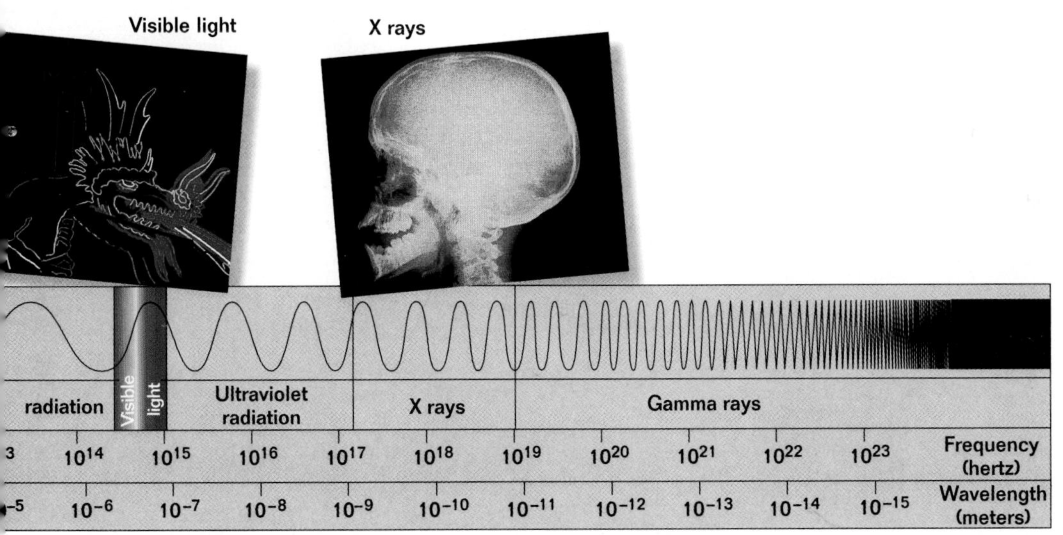

2 Teach

All colors in the visible spectrum, which have varying wavelengths, are bent through different angles, thus dispersing. Violet light, which has the shortest wavelength of light in the visible spectrum, is bent the most, whereas red light, which has the longest wavelength of light in the visible spectrum, is bent the least.

Caption Answer

Figure 17-1 *Because light of all wavelengths travels at the same speed, 300 000 km/s, shorter wavelengths have higher frequencies (more of the waves pass a particular point each second).*

Discussion

Which form of electromagnetic radiation has the highest frequency? *gamma rays*

GLENCOE TECHNOLOGY

Videodisc

Glencoe Science Voyages Interactive Videodisc—Earth

Side 2, Lesson 8 *Space Exploration*

36541

Refer to Videodisc Teacher Guide for additional bar codes.

Inclusion Strategies

Gifted Have students research the index of refraction. Have them relate what they learn to the use of lenses in a telescope. *The index of refraction of a substance is equal to the sine of the angle of incidence of light from a vacuum divided by the sine of the angle of refraction. The index of refraction of glass is used when determining how to shape the objective lens of a telescope.* L3

Integrating the Sciences

Physics Have students find out how concave and convex lenses affect the path of light that passes through them. Some students may wish to demonstrate the difference by using both types of lenses. L2

CA Science Content Standards

Page 612: 4d, 9f
Page 613: 4d

Teacher FYI

Hubble is so powerful that if you were in Washington, D.C., you could use it to read a newspaper headline in Missouri.

VISUAL Learning

Figure 17-2 Ask students to make a rough copy of each telescope design in their Science Journals. On the copy of each type of telescope, ask students to identify where the eyepiece, objective, focus (focal point or focal plane), and focal length would be. Then have students explain the difference in these two telescopes using the above-listed telescope parts. L2 ELL

Caption Answer

Figure 17-2 *reflecting*

GLENCOE TECHNOLOGY

Videodisc

The Infinite Voyage: Unseen Worlds

Chapter 3 *The Very Large Array: Monitoring Radio Waves* 3:30

Secrets from a Frozen World

Chapter 7 *Solar Ultraviolet Light and the Diminishing Ozone Layer* 3:00

Refer to the Teacher Guide for bar codes and teaching strategies.

Optical Telescopes

Optical telescopes produce magnified images of objects. Light is collected by an objective lens or mirror, which then forms an image at the focal point of the telescope. The eyepiece lens then magnifies the image. The two types of optical telescopes are shown in **Figure 17-2.**

In a **refracting telescope,** the light from an object passes through a double convex objective lens and is bent to form an image on the focal point. The image is then magnified by the eyepiece.

A **reflecting telescope** uses a mirror as an objective to focus light from the object being viewed. Light passes through the open end of a reflecting telescope and strikes a concave mirror at its base. The light is then reflected to the focal point to form an image. A smaller mirror is often used to reflect the light into the eyepiece lens so the magnified image can be viewed.

Using Optical Telescopes

Most optical telescopes used by professional astronomers are housed in buildings called **observatories.** Observatories often have a dome-shaped roof that opens up to let in light. However, not all telescopes are in observatories.

Figure 17-2 These diagrams show how each type of optical telescope collects light and forms an image.

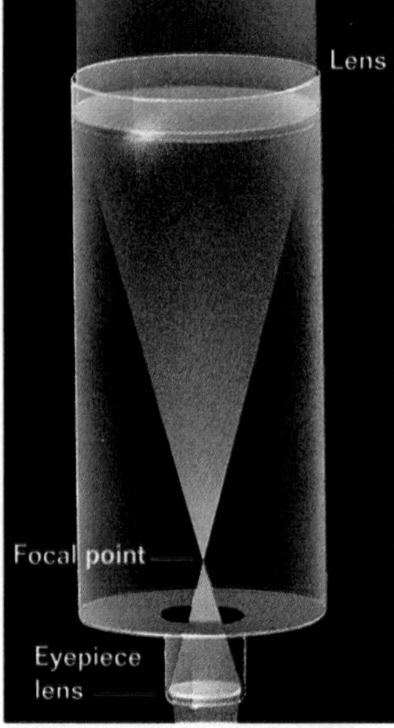

A In a refracting telescope, a double convex lens focuses light to form an image at the focal point.

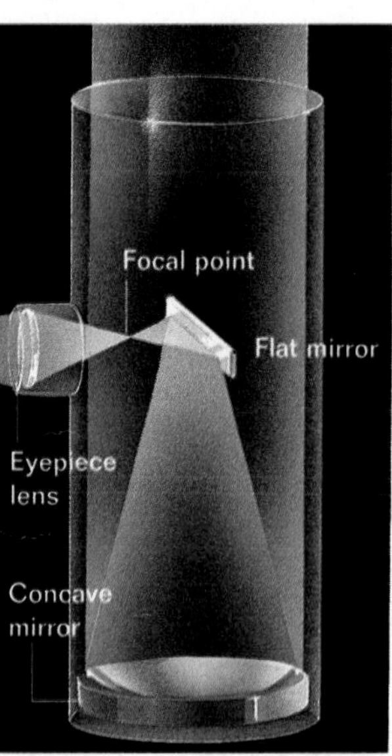

B In a reflecting telescope, a concave mirror focuses light to form an image at the focal point.

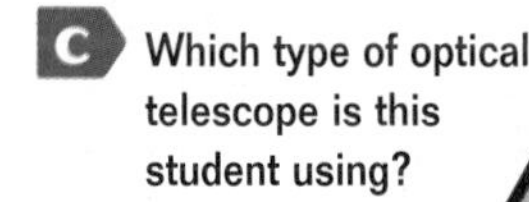

C **Which type of optical telescope is this student using?**

Telescopes Ask students to select one of the following questions and to write a brief paragraph in their Science Journals that answers the question selected.

- **How do reflecting and refracting telescopes differ in the way they form images?** *A reflecting telescope uses a concave mirror to reflect light to the focal plane, while a refracting telescope uses a convex lens to bend light to the focal plane.*
- **What advantage does a radio telescope have over optical telescopes?** *Radio telescopes can be used in almost all kinds of weather and at all times of the day and night. Radio telescopes can receive energy from objects that cannot be observed with optical telescopes.*

614 CHAPTER 17 EXPLORING SPACE

The *Hubble Space Telescope*, shown in **Figure 17-3,** was launched in 1990 by the space shuttle *Discovery*. Earth's atmosphere absorbs and distorts some of the energy received from space. Because *Hubble* didn't have to view space through our atmosphere, it should have produced clear images. However, when the largest mirror of this reflecting telescope was shaped, there was a mistake. Images obtained by the telescope were not as clear as expected. In December 1993, a team of astronauts repaired *Hubble's* telescope mirror and other equipment. Now, the clear images obtained by *Hubble Space Telescope* are changing scientists' ideas about space.

Figure 17-3 The *Hubble Space Telescope* was released from the cargo bay of the space shuttle *Discovery* on April 25, 1990. It's now orbiting Earth, sending back images and data about distant space objects.

Problem Solving

Interpreting Telescope Data

The magnifying power *(Mp)* of a telescope is determined by the focal lengths of the telescope's objective lens and eyepiece. Once built, you cannot easily change the objective lens, but you can easily change the eyepiece. That's why telescopes are often sold with three or four eyepieces—each with a different focal length. The magnifying power of a telescope is equal to the focal length of its objective lens divided by the focal length of its eyepiece.

Telescopes also have light-gathering power (LGP). Generally, the larger the diameter (aperture) of a telescope's objective, the more light the telescope can gather. Therefore, a telescope with an objective aperture of 125 mm will gather more light than a telescope with an objective aperture of 75 mm.

The following table lists the characteristics of two telescopes. Study the data about each telescope and interpret which has the greater magnifying power and which has the greater light-gathering power.

Telescope Data

Telescope	Aperture	Objective Focal Length	Eyepiece Focal Length
1	75 mm	1200 mm	9 mm, 12 mm
2	125 mm	900 mm	9 mm, 12 mm

Think Critically: Which telescope would you want to use to observe stars? Which telescope would you want to use to observe craters on the moon? Explain your selections.

Content Background

The largest radio telescope in the world is located near Arecibo, Puerto Rico. The curved dish, made of more than 38 400 aluminum panels, is 305 m in diameter.

Problem Solving

Review the equation for finding magnifying power (Mp). *Mp = focal length of the objective/focal length of the eyepiece* Make certain students understand that a telescope's magnifying power can vary, depending on the eyepiece used. For instance, using the 9-mm eyepiece, Telescope 1 has an Mp of 133. With the 12-mm eyepiece, Telescope 1 has an Mp of 100. By the same token, Telescope 2 has an Mp of 100 when equipped with the 9-mm eyepiece. With the 12-mm eyepiece, Telescope 2 has an Mp of 75.

Think Critically

Telescope 2, with an aperture of 125 mm, would be best for viewing stars—the larger the aperture, the more light the telescope can gather. Telescope 1 equipped with the 9-mm eyepiece would be best for viewing moon craters—it has the highest magnifying power.

Science Journal

Hubble Space Telescope Have students write about the space shuttle missions to repair the *Hubble Space Telescope. Aviation Week & Space Technology* (May 24, 1993) reports on one of the repair missions. One of its goals was to demonstrate the feasibility of in-orbit servicing of a complex satellite. L2

CA Science Content Standards

Page 614: 4d
Page 615: 4e, 9f

Caption Answer

Figure 17-4 *Being in space, it doesn't have the distorting effects of Earth's atmosphere.*

3 Assess

Check for Understanding

Enrichment

Have students research the issue of light pollution, which is a glow in the sky caused by city lights. Light pollution affects astronomers' abilities to view stars. Have students brainstorm possible solutions to light pollution.

Reteach

Visual-Spatial Show students labeled cross sections of refracting, reflecting, and radio telescopes. The cross sections should show the path of electromagnetic energy through the telescopes. Have students study the diagrams, then ask the class: **What is the function of the objective of each telescope?** *The objective is the lens, mirror, or dish antenna that collects visible light or radio waves and focuses them onto the focal plane.*

Extension

For students who have mastered this section, use the **Reinforcement** and **Enrichment** masters.

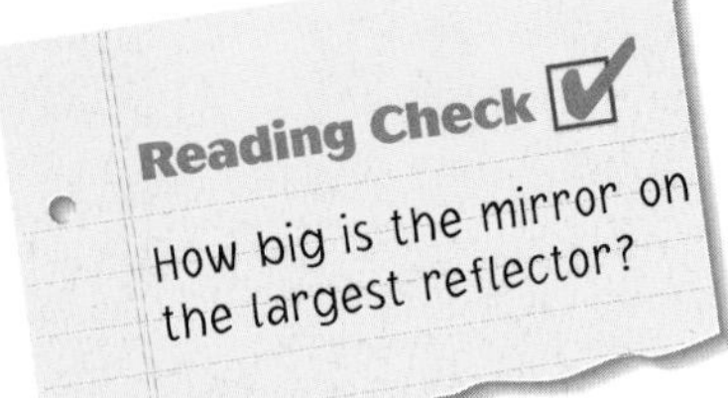

Reading Check
How big is the mirror on the largest reflector?

Active Optics

Since the early 1600s, when the Italian scientist Galileo Galilei first turned a telescope toward the stars, people have been searching for better ways to study what lies beyond our atmosphere, such as the twin Keck telescopes shown in **Figure 17-4.** Today, the largest reflector has a segmented mirror 10 m wide. The most recent innovations in optical telescopes involve active and adaptive optics. With active optics, a computer is used to compensate for changes in temperature, mirror distortions, and bad viewing conditions. Even more ambitious is adaptive optics, which uses a laser to probe the atmosphere and relay information to a computer about air turbulence. The computer then adjusts the telescope's mirror thousands of times per second, thus reducing the effects of atmospheric turbulence.

Figure 17-4 The twin Keck telescopes on Mauna Kea in Hawaii can be used together, more than doubling the resolving power. Each individual telescope has an objective mirror 10 m in diameter. To cope with the difficulty of building such a large mirror, this telescope design used several smaller mirrors positioned to work as one. **Although the Keck telescopes are much larger than the *Hubble Space Telescope*, the *Hubble* is able to achieve better resolution. Why?**

616 CHAPTER 17 EXPLORING SPACE

Multiple Learning Styles

Visual-Spatial Invite to class a person who rents or sells dish antennas for televisions. Ask him or her to explain how the dish antenna works and to show students a model of one. After students examine the model, ask them to compare and contrast dish antennas to radio telescopes. Explain to students that dish antennas and radio telescopes operate in the same basic way. Electromagnetic energy is collected by the dish and reflected to the receiver.

Radio Telescopes

As you know, stars and other objects radiate energy throughout the electromagnetic spectrum. A **radio telescope,** such as the one shown in **Figure 17-5,** is used to study radio waves traveling through space. Unlike visible light, radio waves pass freely through Earth's atmosphere. Because of this, radio telescopes are useful 24 hours a day under most weather conditions.

Radio waves reaching Earth's surface strike the large, curved dish of a radio telescope. This dish reflects the waves to a focal point where a receiver is located. The information allows scientists to detect objects in space, to map the universe, and to search for intelligent life on other planets.

In the remainder of this chapter, you'll learn about the instruments that travel into space and send back information that telescopes on Earth's surface cannot obtain.

Figure 17-5 This radio telescope is used to study radio waves traveling through space.

Section Assessment

1. What is the difference between radio telescopes and optical telescopes?
2. The frequency of electromagnetic radiation is the number of waves that pass a point in a specific amount of time. If red light has a longer wavelength than blue light, which would have a greater frequency?
3. **Think Critically:** It takes light from the closest star to Earth (other than the sun) about four years to reach us. If there were intelligent life on a planet circling that star, how long would it take for us to send them a radio transmission and for us to receive their reply?
4. **Skill Builder**
Sequencing Sequence these electromagnetic waves from longest wavelength to shortest wavelength: *gamma rays, visible light, X rays, radio waves, infrared waves, ultraviolet waves,* and *microwaves.* If you need help, refer to Sequencing in the **Skill Handbook** on page 950.

Using Math

The magnifying power (*Mp*) of a telescope is determined by dividing the focal length of the objective lens (FL_{obj}) by the focal length of the eyepiece (FL_{eye}) using the following equation.

$$Mp = \frac{FL_{obj}}{FL_{eye}}$$

If $FL_{obj} = 1200$ mm and $FL_{eye} = 6$ mm, what is the telescope's magnifying power?

4. **Skill Builder**
radio waves, microwaves, infrared waves, visible light, ultraviolet waves, X rays, gamma rays

Assessment

Content Assess students' abilities to sequence events by having them compare and contrast their sequences with those of other students. Use **Performance Assessment in the Science Classroom,** p. 97.

4 Close

Proficiency Prep

Use this quiz to check students' recall of section content.

1. **What type of telescope bends light to produce an image?** *refracting telescope*
2. **What type of telescope uses a mirror to focus light from the object being viewed?** *reflecting telescope*

Section Assessment

1. A radio telescope uses a curved dish antenna to collect and focus radio waves, whereas an optical telescope uses lenses or mirrors to collect and focus visible light.
2. More waves of light with a shorter wavelength would pass a point in a specific time period. Blue light would have a greater frequency.
3. **Think Critically** Assuming the message is understood and the intelligent life could send radio transmissions, it would take about eight years to receive the reply—four years for the message to reach them and four years for their reply to travel back to Earth.

Using Math

$$Mp = \frac{FL_{obj}}{FL_{eye}} =$$

1200 mm/6 mm = 200

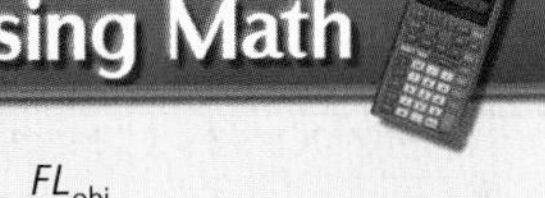

CA Science Content Standards

Page 616: 4d
Page 617; 4d, 4e, 9f

Activity 17•1

Purpose

Visual-Spatial Students will compare and contrast the paths taken by light in reflecting and refracting telescopes. L2 ELL COOP LEARN P

Process Skills

observing and inferring, communicating, comparing and contrasting, recognizing cause and effect, interpreting data, experimenting, defining operationally, separating and controlling variables

Time

50 to 60 minutes

Safety Precautions

Caution students to handle the hand lenses and mirrors with care. Caution them to keep hair and clothes away from the candle flame.

Answers to Questions

1. The focus of the lens is where the light from the candle is concentrated almost to a single point. The rays must have been bent to be concentrated to one point.
2. A concave mirror enlarges an image. The image in the convex mirror is smaller and farther away than the object. The image in a plane mirror is the same size and at the same distance as the object.
3. In both types of telescopes, light is directed to a focus. In refracting telescopes, light is bent to focus as it passes through a lens. Reflecting telescopes use a mirror to reflect light rays to a focus.
4. It collects incoming light and produces a small image at the focal point.

Activity 17•1 Using Scientific Methods

Telescopes

You have learned that optical telescopes use lenses and mirrors as objectives to collect light from an object. They use eyepiece lenses to magnify images of that object. Try this activity to see how the paths of light differ in reflecting and refracting telescopes.

Materials

- Candle
- White cardboard (50 cm × 60 cm)
- Flashlight
- Hand lens
- Large glass of water
- Concave mirror
- Plane mirror
- Masking tape
- Convex mirror
- Empty paper-towel tube

What You'll Investigate

In what way are paths of light affected by the lenses and mirrors in refracting and reflecting telescopes?

Goals

- **Observe** how different mirrors and lenses affect light and the appearance of objects.

Procedure

1. **Observe** your reflection in plane, convex, and concave mirrors.
2. Hold an object in front of each of the mirrors. **Compare** the size and position of the images.
3. **Darken** the room and hold the convex mirror in front of you at a 45° angle, slanting downward. Direct the flashlight toward the mirror. **Note** the size and position of the reflected light.
4. Repeat step 3 using a plane mirror. **Draw** a diagram to show what happens to the beam of light.
5. **Tape** the paper-towel tube to the flashlight so that the beam of light will pass through the tube. Direct the light into a glass of water, first directly from above, then from an angle 45° to the water's surface. **Observe** the direction of the light rays when viewed from the side of the glass.
6. **Light** a candle and set it some distance from the vertically held cardboard screen. **CAUTION:** *Keep hair and clothing away from the flame.* Using the hand lens as a convex lens, move it between the candle and the screen until you have the best possible image.
7. **Move** the lens closer to the candle. Note what happens to the size of the image. Move the cardboard until the image is in focus.

Conclude and Apply

1. How did you **determine** the position of the focal point of the hand lens in step 6? What does this tell you about the position of the light rays?
2. **Compare and contrast** the effect the three types of mirrors had on your reflection.
3. **Compare and contrast** the path of light in refracting and reflecting telescopes.
4. What is the purpose of the concave mirror in a reflecting telescope?

Assessment

Performance Provide each group of students with two lenses of different focal lengths. Ask students to design a working telescope using only the two lenses. Students should realize that if the lenses are lined up and held up to the eye with the lens of shortest focal length near the eye, a working telescope is built. Use **Performance Assessment in the Science Classroom,** p. 23.

How it Works

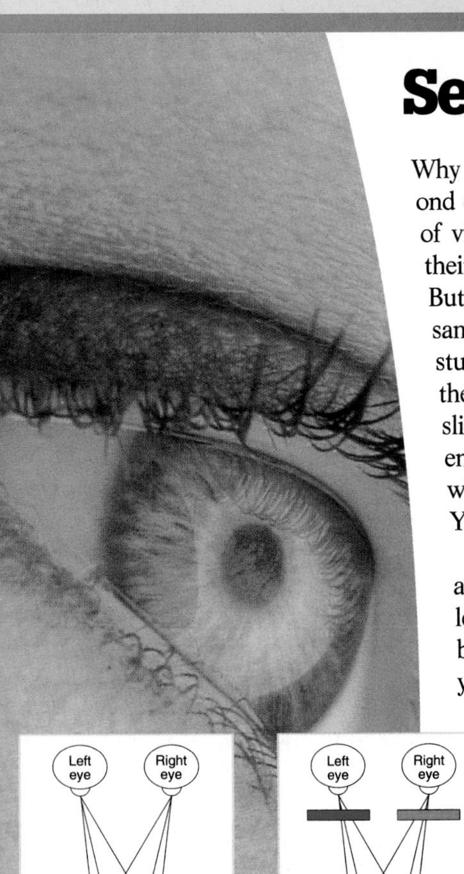

Seeing in 3-D

Why do humans have two eyes? One reason is that the second eye lets us see more of the world. It increases our field of view. Many animals have eyes set on opposite sides of their heads, so each eye sees a separate half of the world. But, human eyes are set closer together. They see almost the same scene but from a slightly different angle. Look at the student in front of you, first through only your right eye then only your left eye. You'll notice that each eye sees a slightly different view. But, your brain puts the two different views together, giving you the ability to figure out which object is closer to you and which is farther away. You see in three dimensions (3-D).

In the figure on the left, notice how the green block appears to the left of the yellow cylinder when seen by the left eye but to the right when seen by the right eye. Your brain interprets these two images, and you know that the yellow cylinder is in front of the green block.

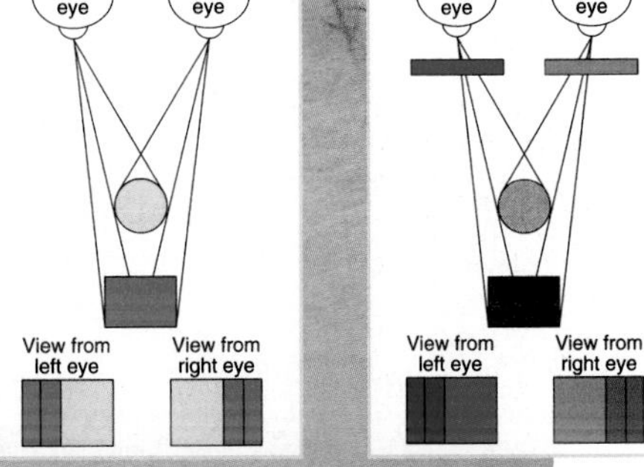

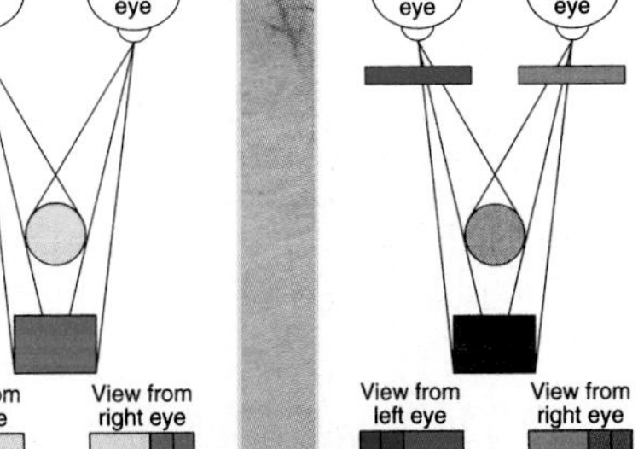

Movies and Television

How can you have a 3-D experience at the movies or on a TV? A camera with two lenses a few inches apart records the images on film or videotape. But, one lens has a red filter in front of it and the other a blue, as shown in the figure on the right. So, the image recorded by one lens is in shades of red, while the one recorded by the other lens is in shades of blue. The viewer watches the film through 3-D glasses that have the same color filters. Because the red filter allows only red light through it, only the image meant for that eye passes through that filter. The filters send the images meant for the right eye only to the right eye and the images meant for the left only to the left. The brain does the rest of the work. It combines the two colors, giving different shades of gray and interprets the slightly different images so that you can tell which object is in front and which is behind.

Career CONNECTION

Research how 3-D technology is being used in the latest computer animation software. Find out how the 3-D images used in computer animations are made.

NATIONAL GEOGRAPHIC

How it Works

Purpose

Students will gain an understanding of three-dimensional vision.

Content Background

The ability to judge distance and shape using two side-by-side eyes is called stereoscopic vision. Stereoscopic vision gives humans and many other animals depth perception. Predators in particular need this skill to hunt. However, the brain does not rely on stereoscopic vision alone to judge distance. It uses other learned techniques as well, such as perspective and parallax. Perspective causes an object to look big when it is close and small when it is far. Parallax makes close objects appear to move while more distant objects stay in place.

VISUAL Learning

Intrapersonal Have students test their 3-D vision by observing objects with one eye closed, then the other. Students should observe objects that are both near and far away.

Teaching Strategies

- If possible, obtain a model of a human eye and allow students to examine its parts.
- Help students make 3-D glasses. Obtain sheets of red and blue cellophane. Cut out small squares (approximately 6 cm by 6 cm) of each color. Cut eye holes in a rectangular piece of cardboard (roughly 8 cm by 16 cm), and paste the squares of red and blue cellophane over the holes.

Career CONNECTION

Computer graphic artists usually obtain at least a two-year degree, although many opt for four-year bachelor's degrees. Computer graphic artists work in a wide variety of fields ranging from film animation to newspaper design. Invite a computer graphic artist to speak to the class about training and job opportunities in his or her field.

CA Science Content Standards

Page 618: 9a
Page 619: 1b

SECTION 17•2

Prepare

Content Background

Refer to **Satellites and Space Probes** and **Space Spin-offs** on p. 610F.

Preplanning

Refer to the **Chapter Organizer** on pp. 610A–B.

1 Motivate

Bellringer

Before presenting the lesson, display **Section Focus Transparency 47** on the overhead projector. Use the accompanying **Focus Activity** worksheet. L2 ELL

Section 17-2

SECTION FOCUS TRANSPARENCY

REMOTE-CONTROLLED RESEARCH

Some things are impossible to see. They are too small, too dangerous, or too far away. How can people observe the universe? Telescopes help, but recently, scientists have also begun to use satellites and space probes to study the solar system and beyond.

1. What makes it difficult to see the stars?
2. Why could using satellites and space probes help us get a better view of the stars and planets?
3. How could satellites in space help us learn more about Earth?

47

Tying to Previous Knowledge

Blow up a balloon and release it. The balloon travels in the direction opposite from where the air is escaping. Rockets are propelled forward as gases escape from the nozzle at the back of the rocket.

17•2 Early Space Missions

What You'll Learn

- How to compare and contrast natural and artificial satellites
- The differences between artificial satellites and space probes
- The history of the race to the moon

Vocabulary

satellite
orbit
space probe
Project Mercury
Project Gemini
Project Apollo

Why It's Important

- Learning about space exploration will help you better understand the vastness of space.

The First Steps into Space

If you had your choice of watching your favorite sports team on television or from the stadium, which would you prefer? You would probably want to be as close as possible to the game so you wouldn't miss any of the action. Scientists feel the same way about space. Even though telescopes have taught them a great deal about the moon and planets, they want to learn more by actually going to those places or by sending spacecraft where they can't go.

Satellites

Space exploration began in 1957 when the former Soviet Union used a rocket to send *Sputnik I* into space. It was the first artificial satellite. A **satellite** is any object that revolves around another object. When an object enters space, it travels in a straight line unless a force such as gravity deflects it. When Earth's gravity pulls on a satellite, it falls toward Earth. The result of the satellite traveling forward while at the same time falling toward Earth is a curved path, called an **orbit,** around Earth. This is shown in **Figure 17-6.**

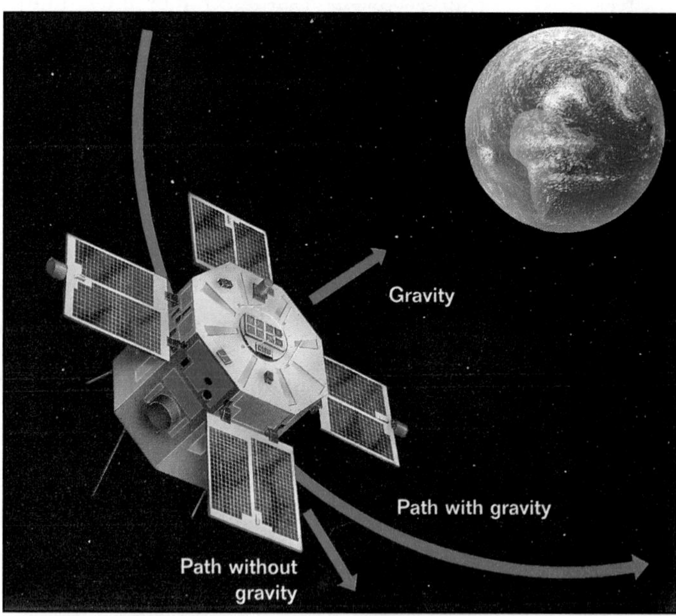

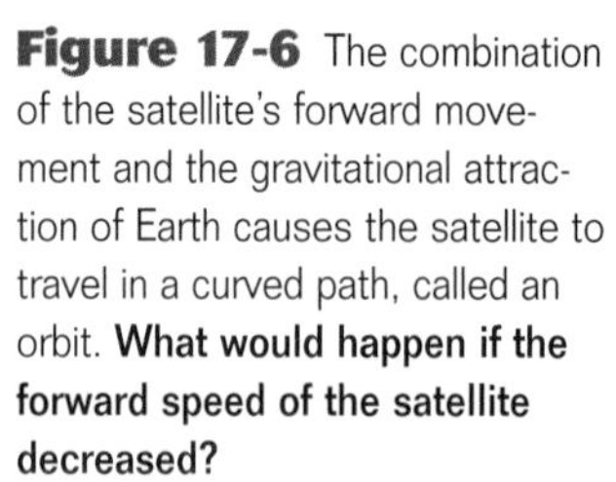

Figure 17-6 The combination of the satellite's forward movement and the gravitational attraction of Earth causes the satellite to travel in a curved path, called an orbit. **What would happen if the forward speed of the satellite decreased?**

Resource Manager

The following **Teacher Classroom Resources** can be used with Section 17-2:

Reproducible Masters

Activity Worksheets, p. 97 L2
Enrichment, p. 47 L3
Home Involvement, p. 29 L2
Reinforcement, p. 47 L2

Transparencies

Science Integration Transparency 17 L2

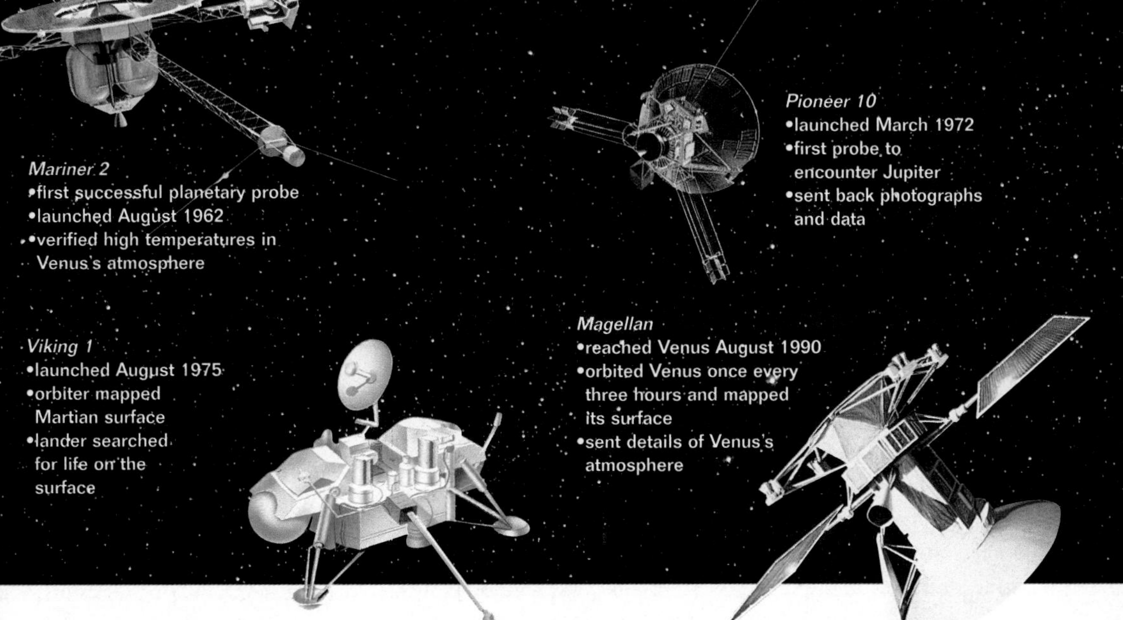

Mariner 2
•first successful planetary probe
•launched August 1962
•verified high temperatures in Venus's atmosphere
Pioneer 10
•launched March 1972
•first probe to encounter Jupiter
•sent back photographs and data
Viking 1
•launched August 1975
•orbiter mapped Martian surface
•lander searched for life on the surface
Magellan
•reached Venus August 1990
•orbited Venus once every three hours and mapped its surface
•sent details of Venus's atmosphere

Figure 17-7 Some early U.S. space probes and their missions provided much useful data.

Satellite Uses

The moon is a natural satellite of Earth. It completes one orbit every month. *Sputnik I* orbited Earth for 57 days before gravity pulled it back into the atmosphere, where it burned up. *Sputnik I* was an experiment to show that artificial satellites could be made. Today, thousands of artificial satellites orbit Earth.

Present-day communication satellites transmit radio and television programs to locations around the world. Other satellites gather scientific data that can't be obtained from Earth, and weather satellites constantly monitor Earth's global weather patterns.

Space Probes

Not all objects carried into space by rockets become satellites. Rockets also can be used to send instruments into space. A **space probe** is an instrument that gathers information and sends it back to Earth. Unlike satellites that orbit Earth, space probes travel far into the solar system. Some have even traveled out of the solar system. Space probes, like many satellites, carry cameras and other data-gathering equipment, as well as radio transmitters and receivers that allow them to communicate with scientists on Earth. **Figure 17-7** shows some of the early space probes launched by NASA (National Aeronautics and Space Administration).

Using Math

Suppose a spacecraft is launched at a speed of 40 200 km per hour. Express this speed in kilometers per second.

2 Teach

Discussion

Interpersonal Have pairs of students collaborate on a written report about information that could be obtained by artificial satellites in orbit around Earth. Then have the class discuss how this information could be used by humans on Earth's surface. To help students get started, list various types of artificial satellites: weather, communications, military, and astronomical. L2 COOP LEARN

Correcting Misconceptions

Many people think artificial satellites and space probes are identical. Explain that artificial satellites orbit other objects. Probes are spacecraft sent far into space by rockets. They don't orbit other objects. Both satellites and probes send information back to Earth.

Using Math

40 200 km/hr ÷ 3600 s/hr = 11.2 km/s

Using an Analogy

To help students understand the vast distances space probes travel, tell them that the *Cassini* probe, headed toward Saturn, must travel roughly 1.3 billion km, one way. That's nearly equivalent to walking around Earth along the equator more than 100 000 times.

Caption Answer

Figure 17-6 *The lower momentum would no longer balance the force of gravity, and the satellite would fall toward Earth.*

Guided Reading Strategy

Buddy Interviews This strategy helps students understand and clarify the reading. Have students interview one another to find out what helps them understand what they are reading, how they find answers, and how they figure out new vocabulary terms. Have students use Buddy Interviews to help them master section concept.

CA Science Content Standards

Page 620: 2e, 2g, 4e
Page 621: 4e, 9f

Using Science Words

Linguistic To help students better understand science words, ask them to list artificial objects and natural objects. Cars, for instance, are artificial objects, while trees are natural objects. Ask: **What is the difference between an artificial satellite and a natural satellite?** *Artificial satellites are made by humans. Natural satellites are made by natural processes.*

Enrichment

Help students understand why communication satellites should have a geostationary or synchronous orbit. Satellites that are not placed in a geostationary orbit pass over a particular location only once per orbit and for only a brief time. This limits their usefulness for communication purposes. A satellite that has a geostationary orbit circles Earth at a speed that matches Earth's rotational speed; thus, it appears to an Earth-based observer to be stationary. This keeps the satellite in the same location relative to Earth's surface.

GLENCOE TECHNOLOGY

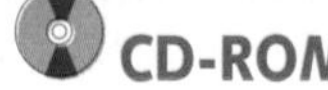

CD-ROM

Glencoe Science Voyages Interactive CD-ROM

Explorations

Have students do the interactive exploration *How does an artificial satellite stay in orbit?*

CA Science Content Standards

Page 622: 2g, 4e
Page 623: 2g, 4e

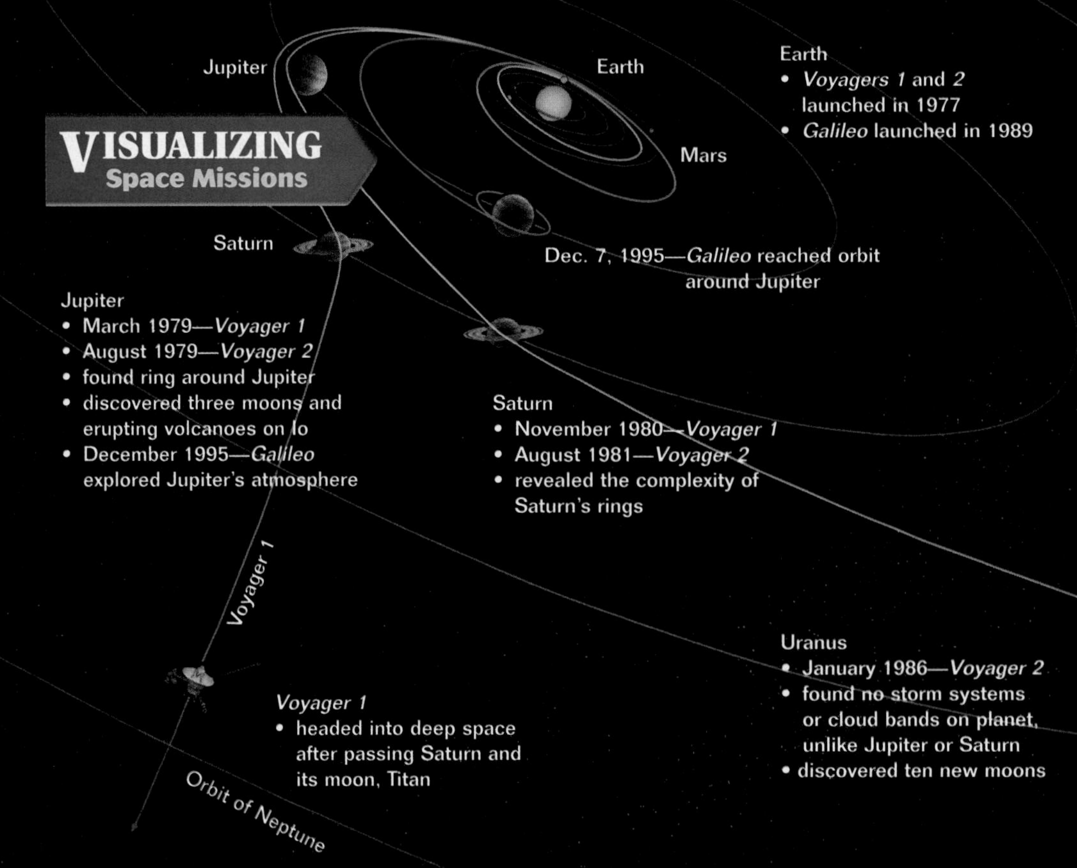

VISUALIZING
Space Missions
Jupiter
Earth
Mars
Saturn
Earth
• Voyagers 1 and 2 launched in 1977
• Galileo launched in 1989
Dec. 7, 1995—Galileo reached orbit around Jupiter
Jupiter
• March 1979—Voyager 1
• August 1979—Voyager 2
• found ring around Jupiter
• discovered three moons and erupting volcanoes on Io
• December 1995—Galileo explored Jupiter's atmosphere
Saturn
• November 1980—Voyager 1
• August 1981—Voyager 2
• revealed the complexity of Saturn's rings
Voyager 1
Uranus
• January 1986—Voyager 2
• found no storm systems or cloud bands on planet, unlike Jupiter or Saturn
• discovered ten new moons
Voyager 1
• headed into deep space after passing Saturn and its moon, Titan
Orbit of Neptune

Figure 17-8 The *Voyager* and *Galileo* spacecraft helped make many major discoveries.

You've probably heard of the space probes *Voyager 1* and *Voyager 2*. These two probes were launched in 1977 and are now heading toward deep space. *Voyager 1* flew past Jupiter and Saturn. *Voyager 2* flew past Jupiter, Saturn, Uranus, and Neptune. **Figure 17-8** describes some of what we've learned from the *Voyager* probes. Now, these probes are exploring beyond our solar system as part of the Voyager Interstellar Mission. Scientists expect these probes to continue to transmit data to Earth for at least 20 more years.

The fate of a probe is never certain, and not all probes are successful. In 1993, *Mars Observer* was only days away from entering orbit around Mars when it was lost. The problem was most likely a critical failure in the propulsion system.

Galileo, launched in 1989, reached Jupiter in 1995. In July 1995, *Galileo* released a smaller probe that began a five-month approach to Jupiter. The small probe took a parachute ride through Jupiter's violent atmosphere in December 1995.

Across the Curriculum

Social Studies Have students speculate on why so many developments occurred in the space program during the 1960s. Students should realize that the United States and the former Soviet Union were participating in a "race for space."

VISUAL Learning

Figure 17-8 Ask students to review the flights of *Voyager 1* and *Voyager 2.* Then ask students: **What was different about the flight paths of the two probes?** Voyager 2 *used the gravity of Saturn to give it the speed necessary to arrive at Uranus. It then used the gravity of Uranus to send it on to Neptune.*

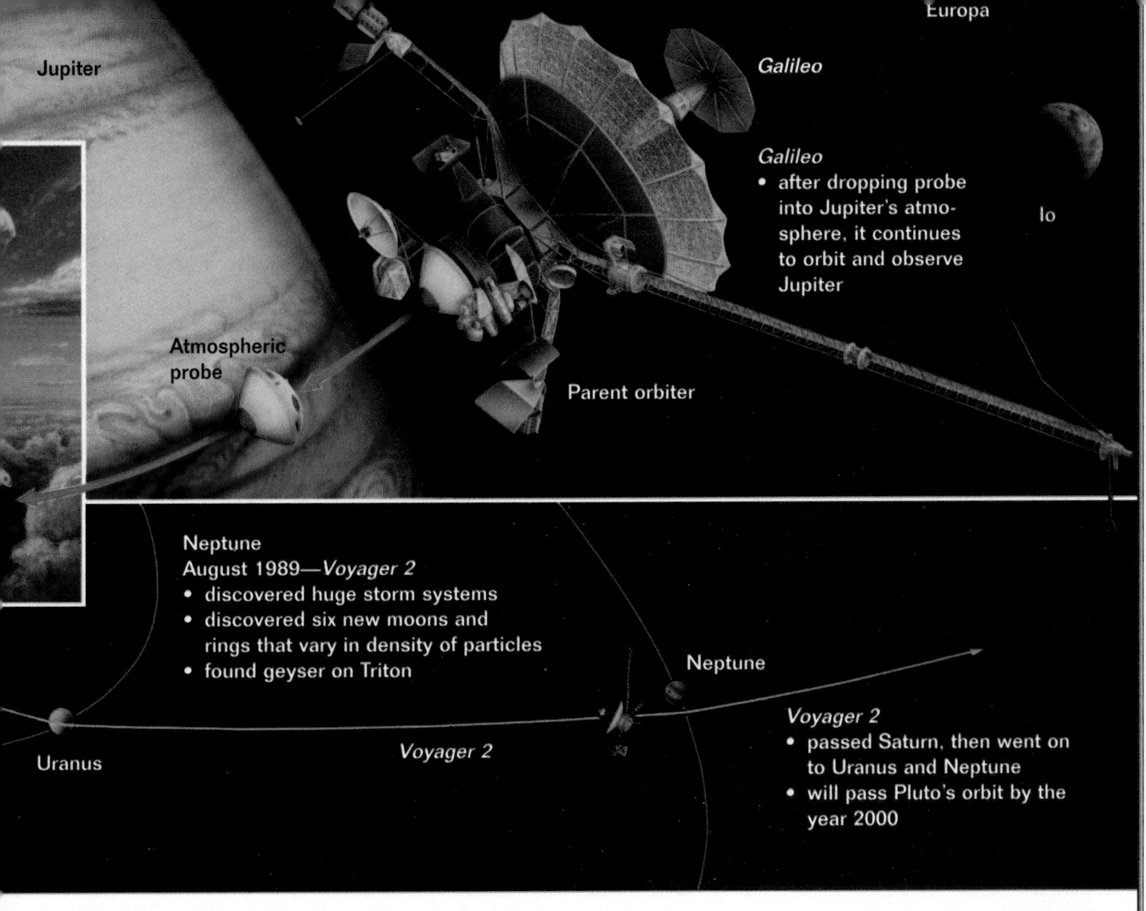

• discovered six new moons and rings that vary in density of particles
• found geyser on Triton

• will pass Pluto's orbit by the year 2000

Before being crushed by the atmospheric pressure, it transmitted information about Jupiter's composition, temperature, and pressure to the ship orbiting above. *Galileo* studied Jupiter's moons, rings, and magnetic fields and then relayed this information back to scientists who were eagerly waiting for it on Earth. ☑

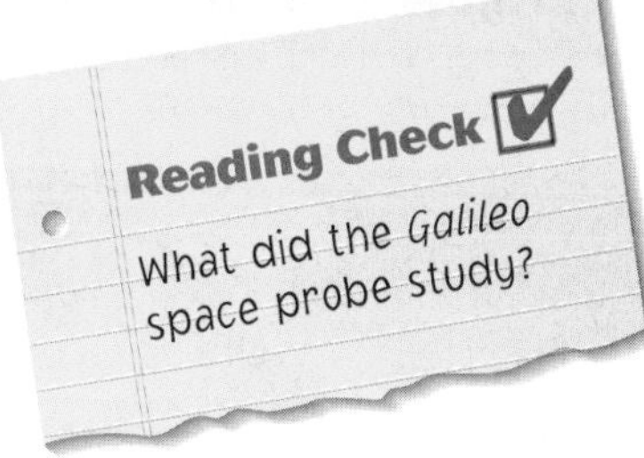

Reading Check
What did the Galileo space probe study?

Galileo
• after dropping probe into Jupiter's atmosphere, it continues to orbit and observe Jupiter
Parent orbiter

Recent studies of Jupiter's moon Europa by *Galileo* indicate that an ocean of water or ice may exist under the outer layer of ice that covers Europa's cracked surface. The cracks in the surface may be caused by geologic activity that heats the ocean underneath the surface. Sunlight penetrates these cracks, further heating the ocean and setting the stage for the possible existence of life on Europa. *Galileo* studied Europa through 1999. More advanced probes will be needed to determine whether molecular life actually does exist on this icy moon.

Answer to Reading Check
Jupiter and its moons

LIFE SCIENCE INTEGRATION

When searching for life elsewhere in space, scientists look for the presence of organic molecules—life as we know it is made up of these molecules. Titan, one of the satellites of Saturn, contains organic molecules. The molecules themselves aren't considered to be life, but they are thought to resemble the molecules from which life evolved on Earth. Given enough time—millions or billions of years—it's possible that the molecules on Titan may evolve into life as they did on Earth.

Activity

Linguistic Have pairs of students use the school library to research the original seven Project Mercury astronauts. Students should collaborate on a written report about the missions each astronaut performed in the Mercury and other space missions, and what these astronauts are doing now. L2 COOP LEARN

3 Assess

Check for Understanding

Enrichment

Have students research geostationary satellites to find out what these satellites are used for and how the term describes the type of orbit of such a satellite.

Inclusion Strategies

Gifted Have students research space junk. Space junk includes unused and nonfunctioning materials in orbit around Earth. It ranges from sand-grain-sized paint chips to large communication satellites. Students can write to NASA for more information. Students should discuss the growing threat space junk may pose to the safety of future crewed spaceflights. L3

Content Background

The most distant human-made object as of 1998 is the *Voyager 1* space probe. At that time, it was 10.4 billion km (70 AU) from Earth. *Voyager 1* is expected to continue to send information back to Earth until it runs out of electrical power, around 2020.

Try at Home

Mini Lab

Comparing the Effects of Light Pollution

Procedure

1. Obtain a cardboard tube from an empty roll of paper towels.
2. Select a night when clear skies are predicted. Go outside about two hours after sunset and look through the cardboard tube at a specific constellation decided upon ahead of time.
3. Count the number of stars you are able to see without moving the observing tube. Repeat this three times.
4. Determine the average number of observable stars at your location.

Analysis

1. Compare and contrast the number of stars visible from other students' homes.
2. Explain the cause and effect of differences in your observations.

The Race to the Moon

Throughout the world, people were shocked when they turned on their radios and television sets in 1957 and heard the radio transmissions from *Sputnik I* as it orbited over their heads. All that *Sputnik I* transmitted was a sort of beeping sound, but people quickly realized that putting a human into space wasn't far off.

In 1961, the Soviet cosmonaut Yuri A. Gagarin became the first human in space. He orbited Earth and then returned safely. Soon, President John F. Kennedy called for the United States to place people on the moon and return them to Earth by the end of that decade. The "race for space" had begun.

The U.S. program to reach the moon began with **Project Mercury.** The goals of Project Mercury were to orbit a piloted spacecraft around Earth and to bring it safely back. The program provided data and experience in the basics of space flight. On May 5, 1961, Alan B. Shepard became the first U.S. citizen in space. In 1962, *Mercury* astronaut John Glenn became the first U.S. citizen to orbit Earth. **Figure 17-9** shows Glenn preparing for liftoff. In 1998, Glenn returned to space aboard the space shuttle *Discovery.* You'll learn more about space shuttles in the next section.

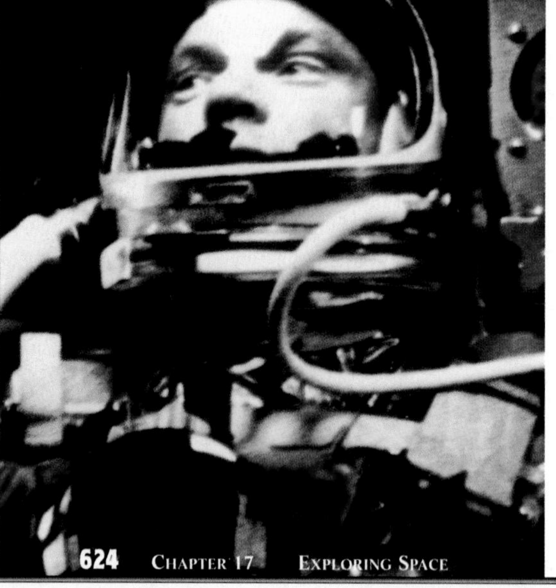

Figure 17-9 John Glenn was the first U.S. astronaut to orbit Earth.

Project Gemini

Project Gemini was the next step in reaching the moon. Teams of two astronauts in the same *Gemini* spacecraft orbited Earth. One *Gemini* team met and connected with another spacecraft in orbit—a skill that would be needed on a voyage to the moon.

Along with the *Mercury* and *Gemini* programs, a series of robotic probes was sent to the moon. *Ranger* proved we could get spacecraft to the moon. *Surveyor* landed gently on the moon's surface, indicating that the moon's surface could support spacecraft and humans. The mission of *Lunar Orbiter* was to take pictures of the moon's surface to help determine the best landing sites on the moon.

Try at Home

Mini Lab

For additional help doing this activity at home, see the corresponding pages in the **Home Involvement** booklet.

Purpose

Visual-Spatial Students will observe that light pollution affects the number of objects visible in the night sky. L2 ELL

Materials

cardboard tube from empty roll of paper towels

Teaching Strategies

Troubleshooting If all students live in the same area, have them call friends or relatives for additional star data.

Analysis

1. More stars should be visible in suburban than urban areas; even more stars should be visible in rural areas.
2. Because suburban and rural areas have less light pollution, more objects are visible in the sky.

Assessment

Process Have students list common sources of light pollution that they've probably taken for granted, such as lights at car dealerships and shopping centers, and streetlights. Use **Performance Assessment in the Science Classroom,** p. 17.

Science Journal

Project Apollo Use these questions as a starting point for student reports about Project Apollo: **How did the information gained in Project Gemini lead to success in the Apollo mission?** *Project Gemini provided the opportunity for astronauts to work in space. It also showed that two spacecraft could meet and rendezvous while in orbit.* **Why do you think Michael Collins remained in the command module while Neil Armstrong and Edwin Aldrin landed on the moon?** *It was considered safer to have a person in the command module in case of problems during the connection of the spacecraft.* L2

CA Science Content Standards

Page 624: 4e, 9a, 9b

Page 625: 2g, 4e

Project Apollo

The final stage of the U.S. program to reach the moon was **Project Apollo.** On July 20, 1969, *Apollo* 11 landed on the lunar surface. Neil Armstrong was the first human to set foot on the moon. His first words as he stepped onto its surface were, "That's one small step for man, one giant leap for mankind." Edwin Aldrin, the second of the three *Apollo* 11 astronauts, joined Armstrong on the moon, and they explored its surface for two hours. Michael Collins remained in the Command Module orbiting the moon, where Armstrong and Aldrin returned before beginning the journey home. A total of six lunar landings brought back more than 2000 samples of moon rock and soil for study before the program ended in 1972. **Figure 17-10** shows astronauts on the moon.

During the past three decades, most missions in space have been carried out by individual countries, often competing to be the first or the best. Today, there is much more cooperation among countries of the world to work together and share what each has learned. Projects are now being planned for cooperative missions to Mars and elsewhere. As you read the next section, you'll see how the U.S. program has progressed since the days of Project Apollo, and where it may be going in the future.

Figure 17-10 The Lunar Rover Vehicle was first used during the *Apollo 15* mission. Riding in the moon buggy, *Apollo 15, 16,* and *17* astronauts explored large areas of the lunar surface.

Section Assessment

1. Currently, no human-made objects are orbiting Neptune, yet Neptune has eight satellites. Explain.
2. *Galileo* was considered a space probe as it traveled to Jupiter. Once there, however, it became an artificial satellite. Explain.
3. **Think Critically:** Is Earth a satellite of any other body in space? Explain your answer.
4. **Skill Builder**
   Concept Mapping Make an events-chain concept map that lists the events in the U.S. space program to place people on the moon. If you need help, refer to Concept Mapping in the **Skill Handbook** on page 950.

Using Computers

Spreadsheet Use the spreadsheet feature on your computer to generate a table of recent successful satellites and space probes launched by the United States. Include a description of the craft, the date launched, and the mission. If you need help, refer to page 974.

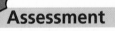

Reteach

Interpersonal Have pairs of students make outlines of the material presented in this section. Have partners quiz each other to review the material. L1 COOP LEARN

Extension

For students who have mastered this section, use the **Reinforcement** and **Enrichment** masters.

4 Close

Proficiency Prep

Use this quiz to check students' recall of section content.

1. **What object in space revolves around another object?** *satellite*
2. **Which space probe flew past Jupiter, Saturn, Uranus, and Neptune?** Voyager 2

Section Assessment

1. These eight satellites are natural satellites of the planet.
2. Once the probe arrived at Jupiter, it went into orbit around that planet and became an artificial satellite.
3. **Think Critically** Yes, Earth is a natural satellite of the sun.

Using Computers

NASA has information students can use to produce their spreadsheets. Also, several magazines—*Astronomy, Final Frontier,* and *Sky and Telescope*—provide information about recent satellites and space probes.

4. **Skill Builder**
   Students' concept maps may include the following events: President Kennedy calls for placing people on the moon; Project Mercury places people in orbit; Project Gemini has spacecraft meet and connect in space; probes are sent to the moon; Project Apollo places astronauts on the moon.

Assessment

Oral Use this Skill Builder to assess students' abilities to make concept maps. Have students make concept maps on the *Voyager 1* mission. Use **Performance Assessment in the Science Classroom,** p. 89.

Activity 17•2 On the Internet

Recognize the Problem

Students will use an astrolabe to make star sightings of Polaris. From their observations and data gathered off the Glencoe Science Web Site, students will determine the circumference of Earth. P

Form a Hypothesis

Internet

Students will use the Internet to learn more about stars and about astronomical instruments such as the astrolabe or sextant. Students will also post their data on the Internet as well as collect star-sighting information from other parts of the country.

Non-Internet Sources

Students should research the historical use of the astrolabe. Students can make repeated measurements of Polaris over time. If any class members are traveling north or south of your location, have them make star sightings while they are away and share their data with the class.

Time Required

one week

Activity 17•2

Star Sightings

For thousands of years, humans have used the stars to learn about the planet we live on. From star sightings, you can map the change of seasons, navigate the oceans, and even determine the size of Earth.

Polaris, or the North Star, has occupied an important place in human history. The location of Polaris is not affected by Earth's rotation. At any given observation point, it always appears at the same angle above the horizon. At Earth's north pole, Polaris appears directly overhead. At the equator, it is just above the northern horizon. Polaris provides a standard from which other locations can be measured. Such star sightings can be made using the astrolabe, an instrument used to measure the height of a star above the horizon.

Recognize the Problem

How can you determine the size of Earth?

Form a Hypothesis

Think about what you have learned about sightings of Polaris. How does this tell you that Earth is round? Knowing that Earth is round, **form a hypothesis** about whether you can estimate the circumference of Earth based on star sightings.

Goals

- **Record** your sightings of Polaris.
- **Share** the data with other students to **calculate** the circumference of Earth.

Safety Precautions

Do not use the astrolabe during the daytime to observe the sun.

Data Sources

Go to the Glencoe Science Web Site at www.glencoe.com/sec/science/ca to obtain instructions on how to make an astrolabe, for more information about the location of Polaris, and for data from other students.

626 CHAPTER 17 EXPLORING SPACE

Preparation

Internet Access the Glencoe Science Web Site at **www.glencoe.com/sec/science/ca** to run through the steps the students will follow.

Non-Internet Sources Find books concerning the history of astronomy. Bring them to class for students to use as references.

interNET CONNECTION

Internet Addresses

For Internet tips, see Glencoe's **Using the Internet in the Science Classroom.**

Test Your Hypothesis

Plan

1. Obtain an astrolabe or **construct** one using the instructions posted on the Glencoe Science Web Site.
2. **Design** a data table in your Science Journal similar to the one below.
3. Decide as a group how you will make your observations. Does it take more than one person to make each observation? When will it be easiest to see Polaris?

Do

1. Make sure your teacher approves your plan before you proceed.
2. Carry out your observations.
3. **Record** your observations in your data table.
4. **Average** your readings and post them in the table provided on the Glencoe Science Web Site.

Analyze Your Data

1. **Research** the names of cities that are at approximately the same longitude as your hometown. **Gather** astrolabe readings at the Glencoe Science Web Site from students in one of those cities.
2. **Compare** your astrolabe readings. **Subtract** the smaller reading from the larger one.
3. Determine the distance between your star sighting location and the other city.
4. To calculate the circumference of Earth, use the following relationship.

$$\text{Circumference} = \frac{(360°)(\text{distance between locations})}{\text{difference between readings}}$$

Draw Conclusions

1. How does the circumference of Earth that you calculated compare with the accepted value of 40 079 km?
2. What are some possible sources of error in this method of determining the size of Earth? What improvements would you suggest?

Polaris Observations		
Your location:		
Date	Time	Astrolabe Reading
Average astrolabe reading:		

Test Your Hypothesis

Teaching Strategies

- Have students make repeated star sightings of Polaris and other stars over a few nights and at different times. By doing repeated sightings of different stars, students will discover the unique nature of Polaris.
- After students have made a few observations, explain the circumference equation. Have them practice explaining the logic behind the circumference equation to a partner.

Troubleshooting Ask students why it is important that they obtain astrolabe readings from a town on the same longitude as they are. Use a globe to facilitate understanding.

Have students think about the fact that Earth is spinning on an axis. Have them consider how they might go about determining the speed at which they are spinning at their particular location on Earth. How might an astrolabe help in determining this speed?

References

- Turner, A.J., ed. *Time-Measuring Instruments, Part 1: Astrolabes, Astrolabe-Related Instruments.* Time Museum, 1986.
- Dickinson, Terence. *The Backyard Astronomer's Guide.* Camden House.

Assessment

Oral Have students work in groups to devise a method of determining the circumference of Earth if they lived in Australia, where Polaris is not visible. Have groups present their plans to the class.

CA Science Content Standards

Page 626: 4d, 4e, 9a, 9b, 9f

Page 627: 4d, 4e, 9a, 9b, 9f

SECTION 17•3

Prepare

Content Background

Refer to **International Space Station** on p. 610F.

Preplanning

Refer to the **Chapter Organizer** on pp. 610A–B.

1 Motivate

Bellringer

Before presenting the lesson, display **Section Focus Transparency 48** on the overhead projector. Use the accompanying **Focus Activity** worksheet. L2 ELL

Section 18-1

SECTION FOCUS TRANSPARENCY

LOOKING FOR LIGHT

This photograph shows stones that remain from Stonehenge, a structure built in England more than 3000 years ago. Many things about Stonehenge are still mysteries, but archaeologists hypothesize that the arrangement of stones had something to do with observing the skies. Ancient astronomers may have used these stones to help them keep accurate track of celestial movements much as we might use telescopes and other "high-tech" equipment today.

1. How do you think Stonehenge suggests that ancient people studied the skies?
2. Why do you think the people that built Stonehenge wanted to keep track of the movements of celestial objects such as the stars and planets?

48

Tying to Previous Knowledge

Ask students if they have watched the preparation, launch, and landing of a space shuttle. Show a film of a recent launch.

17•3 Recent and Future Space Missions

What You'll Learn

- The benefits of the space shuttle
- The usefulness of orbital space stations
- Future space missions

Vocabulary

space shuttle
space station

Why It's Important

- Many exciting things are planned for the future of space exploration.

The Space Shuttle

Imagine spending millions of dollars to build a machine, sending it off into space, and watching its 3000 metric tons of metal and other materials burn up after only a few minutes of work. That's exactly what NASA did for many years. The early rockets lifted a small capsule holding the astronauts into orbit. Sections of the rocket separated from the rest of the rocket body and burned as they reentered the atmosphere.

A Reusable Spacecraft

NASA administrators, like many others, realized that it would be less expensive and less wasteful to reuse resources. The reusable spacecraft that transports astronauts, satellites, and other materials to and from space is the **space shuttle.** The space shuttle is shown in **Figure 17-11.**

At launch, the space shuttle stands on end and is connected to an external liquid-fuel tank and two solid-fuel booster rockets. When the shuttle reaches an altitude of about 45 km, the emptied solid-fuel booster rockets drop off and parachute back to Earth. They are recovered and used again. The larger, external liquid-fuel tank eventually separates and falls back to Earth, but it isn't recovered.

Once the space shuttle reaches space, it begins to orbit Earth. There, astronauts perform many different tasks. The cargo bay can carry a self-contained laboratory, where astronauts conduct scientific experiments and determine the effects of space flight on the human body. On missions in which the cargo bay isn't used as a laboratory, the shuttle can launch, repair, and retrieve satellites.

To retrieve a satellite, a large mechanical arm in the cargo bay is extended. An astronaut inside the shuttle moves the arm by remote control. The arm grabs the satellite and pulls it back into the cargo bay. The doors are closed, and it is then returned to Earth.

Figure 17-11 The space shuttle is designed to make many trips into space.

Resource Manager

The following **Teacher Classroom Resources** can be used with Section 17-3:

Reproducible Masters

Activity Worksheets, p. 98 L2

Critical Thinking/Problem Solving, p. 17 L2

Enrichment, p. 48 L3

Multicultural Connections, pp. 33–34 L2

Reinforcement, p. 48 L2

Study Guide, pp. 66–68 L1 ELL

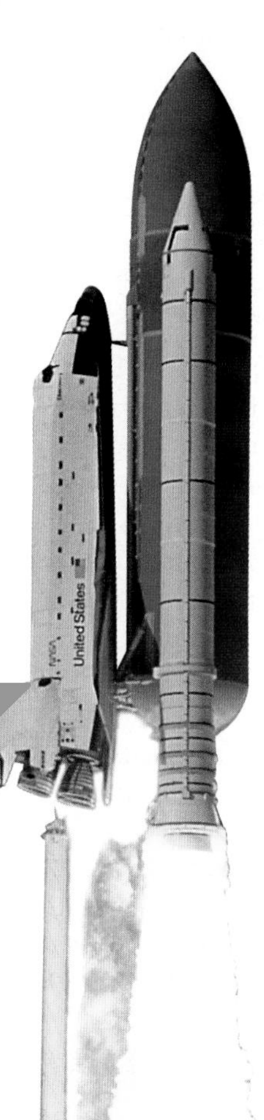

Similarly, the mechanical arm can be used to lift a satellite or probe out of the cargo bay and place it into space. In some cases, a defective satellite can be pulled in by the mechanical arm, repaired while in the cargo bay, and then placed into space once more.

After each mission is completed, the space shuttle glides back to Earth and lands like an airplane. A large landing field is needed because the gliding speed of the shuttle is 335 km/hr.

Space Stations

Astronauts can spend only a short time in space in the space shuttle. Its living area is small, and the crew needs more room to live, exercise, and work. A **space station** has living quarters, work and exercise areas, and all the equipment and support systems needed for humans to live and work in space.

The United States had such a station in the past. The space station *Skylab* was launched in 1973. Crews of astronauts spent up to 84 days in it performing experiments and collecting data on the effects that living in space had on humans. In 1979, the abandoned *Skylab* fell out of orbit and burned up as it entered Earth's atmosphere.

interNET CONNECTION

In 1962, John Glenn became the first U.S. citizen to orbit Earth. In 1998, Glenn returned to space aboard the space shuttle *Discovery.* Visit the Glencoe Science Web Site at **www.glencoe.com/sec/science/ca** for more information about the historical significance of Glenn's *Discovery* flight.

2 Teach

Quick Demo

Visual-Spatial If possible, obtain a working model of a space shuttle. Use the model to demonstrate how the cargo bay is used to carry satellites to and from Earth and how the mobile arm is used to place satellites into orbit and to bring them back into the cargo bay for repairs.

Flex Your Brain

Use the Flex Your Brain activity to have students explore THE INTERNATIONAL SPACE STATION.

GLENCOE TECHNOLOGY

Videodisc

Glencoe Science Voyages Inteactive Videodisc—Earth

Side 2, Lesson 8 *Space Exploration*

32923

Refer to Videodisc Teacher Guide for additional bar codes.

interNET CONNECTION

Internet Addresses

____

____

____

____

For Internet tips, see Glencoe's **Using the Internet in the Science Classroom.**

Inclusion Strategies

Hearing Impaired Assist students as they make models of space probes, space capsules, or space shuttles. Have them discuss some of the proposed future spacecraft and space stations. Students can draw or make models of their own ideas about future spacecraft. L2 ELL

CA Science Content Standards

Page 628: 4e
Page 629: 4e

Purpose

 **Kinesthetic** Students will simulate artificial gravity. L2 ELL COOP LEARN

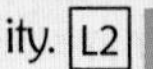

Materials

turntable, LP record, scissors, construction paper, masking tape, marbles

Teaching Strategies

Troubleshooting Inform students that only the slowest speed of the turntable should be used.

Safety Precautions Caution students to wear safety goggles in case marbles fly off the turntable.

Analysis

1. The marbles are accelerated outward from the center by forces generated by the rotation of the turntable. The inertia of the marbles causes them to continue to move outward. The surface of the paper exerts a force on the marbles and stops them from continuing their outward motion.
2. A space station could simulate artificial gravity by spinning slowly around a central axis of rotation.

Assessment

Oral Ask students: **What might happen if you partially filled a bucket with water and then swung it quickly over your head?** *No water would be spilled.* Have students relate their answers to their observations in the MiniLab. Use **Performance Assessment in the Science Classroom,** p. 71.

MiniLab

Modeling Gravity

Procedure

1. Locate a stereo record album and turntable you can use for this activity.
2. Fold 8-cm-wide strips of construction paper in half, then unfold them.
3. Wrap the strips along the fold around the circumference of the record so there is a 4-cm wall around the outside edge of the disc.
4. Securely tape the rest underneath the record.
5. Place the record on a turntable and place three marbles at its center.
6. Switch on the turntable.

Analysis

1. What did you observe about the movements of the marbles?
2. Hypothesize how what you've observed could be useful for simulating the effects of gravity on a space station.

Crews from the former Soviet Union have spent the most time in space aboard the space station *Mir.* Cosmonaut Dr. Valery Polyakov returned to Earth after 438 days in space studying the long-term effects of weightlessness.

Cooperation in Space

In 1995, the United States and Russia began an era of cooperation and trust in exploring space. Early in the year, Dr. Norman Thagard was launched into orbit aboard the Russian *Soyuz* spacecraft, along with two Russian cosmonaut crewmates. Dr. Thagard was the first U.S. astronaut launched into space by a Russian booster and the first American resident of the Russian space station *Mir*.

In June 1995, Russian cosmonauts rode into orbit aboard the space shuttle *Atlantis,* America's 100th crewed launch. The mission of *Atlantis* involved, among other studies, a rendezvous and docking with space station *Mir*. The cooperation that existed on this mission continued through

Figure 17-12 The proposed International Space Station is scheduled for completion in 2003.

Integrating the Sciences

Life Science When the United States and the former Soviet Union began their piloted space programs, humans were not the first to go into space. Ask students to find out what animals were used by each country and why these animals were used. Also ask students to describe how Project Mercury helped prepare the United States for future moon exploration. L2

Content Background

Space exploration is becoming a global endeavor. The International Space Station will draw on the resources of more than 16 nations. In addition, research and tracking facilities for the station are located in many countries around the globe.

CA Science Content Standards

Page 630: 2g, 4e
Page 631: 4e

eight more space shuttle-*Mir* docking missions. Each was an important step toward building and operating the International Space Station.

The International Space Station

The International Space Station (ISS) will be a permanent laboratory designed to use in long-term research. Diverse topics will be studied, such as researching the growth of protein crystals. This project will help scientists determine protein structure and function. This could enhance work on drug design and the treatment of diseases.

The space station will draw on the resources of more than 16 nations. Various nations will build units for the space station, which will then be transported into space aboard the space shuttle and Russian launch rockets. The station will be constructed in space. **Figure 17-12** shows what the completed station will look like.

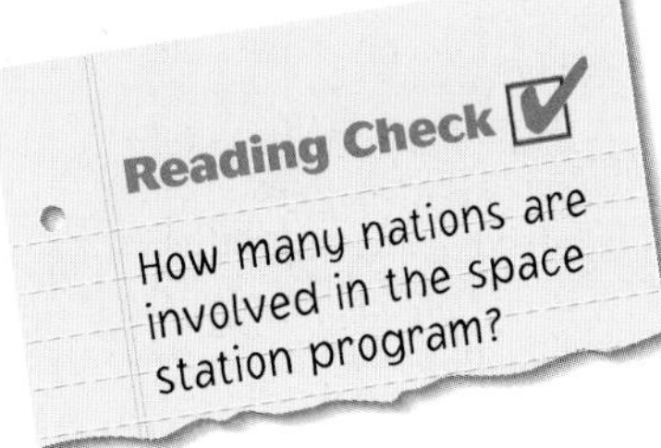

Reading Check
How many nations are involved in the space station program?

NASA is planning the space station program in three phases. Phase One, now concluded, involved the space shuttle-*Mir* docking missions. Phase Two began in 1998 with the launch of the Russian-built Functional Cargo Block, and will end with the delivery of a U.S. laboratory aboard the space shuttle. During Phase Two, a crew of three people will be delivered to the space station. This is expected to occur by January 2000.

Making a Model

Visual-Spatial Use the following model to help students understand how solid-fuel booster rockets help space shuttles go into space. Obtain a cardboard tube from an empty roll of paper towels. Attach two inflated balloons on either side of the tube. Attach a string to the ceiling, pull it tight, and place it through the tube. Have students help you open the closed nozzles of the balloons. Show students how the balloons act like the solid-fuel booster rockets attached to a space shuttle. The balloons will lift the cardboard tube like the solid-fuel rockets help to lift a space shuttle.

GLENCOE TECHNOLOGY

Videodisc

Glencoe Science Voyages Interactive Videodisc—Earth

Side 2, Lesson 8 *Space Exploration*

33168

Side 2, Lesson 8 *Space Exploration*

33975

Refer to Videodisc Teacher Guide for additional bar codes.

Across the Curriculum

Agriculture, Geography, Meteorology, and Medicine The space program has been used to benefit humans in many scientific fields. Ask interested students to pick a field of their choice and write a report in their Science Journals about what advancement has occurred in that particular field as a direct result of the space program. L2

3 Assess

Check for Understanding

Enrichment

Have students research the space shuttle *Challenger,* which exploded 75 seconds after its launch on Jan. 28, 1986. The explosion occurred when one of two solid-fuel booster rockets developed a leak. The hot gases burned through the main fuel tank, causing it to explode. All people on board were killed.

Reteach

Ask students to list some of the advantages of sharing space missions with other countries. *The cost of the space missions can be shared. Also, when data are shared by all nations, the number of repetitive missions can be reduced. This could provide funds for other space missions and research.* L2

Extension

For students who have mastered this section, use the **Reinforcement** and **Enrichment** masters.

4 Close

Proficiency Prep

Use this quiz to check students' recall of section content.

1. **What is a usable spacecraft that transports astronauts, satellites, and other materials to and from space?** *space shuttle*
2. **What is a space station?** *a spacecraft that has everything needed to live and work in space*

Figure 17-13 Using the space shuttle, scientists have already performed extensive experiments in the weightlessness of space.

Living in Space

The project will continue with Phase Three when the Japanese Experiment Module, the European Columbus Orbiting Facility, and another Russian lab will be delivered.

The U.S. hopes to deliver its Habitation module in 2003, although this date may be delayed. This will end Phase Three and make the International Space Station fully operational and ready for its permanent six- or seven-person crew. A total of 45 separate launches are required to take all components of ISS into space. NASA plans for crews of astronauts to stay on board the station for several months at a time. As shown in **Figure 17-13,** NASA has already conducted numerous tests to prepare astronauts for extended space missions. One day, the station could be a construction site for ships that will go to the moon and Mars.

Exploring Mars

Two of the most successful missions in recent years were the 1996 launchings of the Mars *Global Surveyor* and Mars *Pathfinder*. *Surveyor* orbited Mars, taking high-quality photos of the planet's surface. *Pathfinder* descended to the Martian surface, using rockets and a parachute system to slow its descent. Large balloons were used to absorb the shock of landing. *Pathfinder* carried technology to study the surface of the planet, including a remote-controlled robot rover called *Sojourner.* Using information gathered by the rover and photographs taken by *Surveyor*, scientists determined that areas of the planet's surface were once covered with water during Mars's distant past.

Content Background

The first space station placed into orbit by the United States was *Skylab.* When *Skylab* was launched in 1973, several problems occurred. It lost part of its outer protective covering and one of its solar panels. The other solar panel was not fully deployed and did not work. Temperatures inside the station were increasing and limited electrical power was being supplied from the solar panels. Astronauts first had to repair the station before they could occupy it. Once repairs were made, *Skylab* went on to complete a successful mission.

Exploring the Moon

Does water exist in the craters of the moon's poles? This is one question NASA intends to explore with data gathered from the *Lunar Prospector* spacecraft. Launched in 1998, the *Lunar Prospector's* one-year mission was to orbit the moon, taking photographs of the moon's surface for mapping purposes. Early data obtained from the spacecraft indicate that hydrogen is present in the rocks of the moon's poles. Hydrogen is one of the elements found in water. Scientists now theorize that ice on the floors of the moon's polar craters may be the source of this hydrogen.

Cassini

In October 1997, NASA launched the space probe *Cassini.* Destination: Saturn. *Cassini* will not reach its goal until 2004. At that time, the space probe will explore Saturn and surrounding areas for four years. One part of its mission is to deliver the European Space Agency's *Huygens* probe to Saturn's largest moon, Titan, as shown in **Figure 17-14.** Some scientists theorize that Titan's atmosphere may be similar to the atmosphere of early Earth.

Figure 17-14 *Cassini* will reach Saturn in 2004.

Section Assessment

1. What is the main advantage of the space shuttle?
2. Why were the space shuttle-*Mir* docking missions so important?
3. Describe Phase Three of the International Space Station program.
4. Recent space missions have been characterized by a spirit of cooperation. How does this compare and contrast with early space missions?
5. **Think Critically:** Why is the space shuttle more versatile than earlier spacecraft?
6. **Skill Builder** **Using Numbers** *Lunar Prospector* was placed in lunar orbit to photograph the moon's surface. Do the **Chapter 17 Skill Activity** on page 978 to learn more about satellites placed in orbit around Earth.

Science Journal Suppose you're in charge of assembling a crew for a new space station. Select 50 people you want for the station. Remember, you will need people to do a variety of jobs, such as farming, maintenance, scientific experimentation, and so on. In your Science Journal, explain whom you would select and why.

Section Assessment

1. It is a reusable spacecraft.
2. The space shuttle-*Mir* docking missions were a key initial step in the successful completion of the International Space Station. These missions also provided experience for sharing space technology among nations and worked to advance cooperation in space.
3. During Phase Three, the Japanese Experiment Module, the European Columbus Orbiting Facility, and another Russian lab will be delivered. Phase Three is currently scheduled to end with the delivery of the U.S. Habitation Module early in 2003.
4. Answers will vary, but students should realize that early space missions were marked by competition rather than cooperation.
5. **Think Critically** In addition to being reusable, it has a large cargo bay that enables it to carry satellites to and from Earth, it can be used to repair defective satellites, and it can land like an airplane.

Make sure students realize that the 50 people don't have to be known to them personally. Students' lists should include farmers, mechanics, writers, and so on.

Assessment

Process Use the Skill Builder to assess students' abilities to make graphs. Ask students to explain the benefits of creating a graph. Use **Performance Assessment in the Science Classroom,** p. 41.

CA Science Content Standards

Page 632: 4e
Page 633: 2g, 4e

Chapter 17 Reviewing Main Ideas

Reviewing Main Ideas can be used to preview, review, reteach, and condense chapter content.

Preview

Linguistic Have students try to answer the questions in their Science Journal. Use student answers as a source for discussion throughout the chapter.

Review

Interpersonal Have students answer the questions on separate pieces of paper and compare their answers with those of other students in the class.

Reteach

Visual-Spatial Have students look at the illustrations on these pages. Ask them to describe details that support the main ideas of the chapter found in the statement for each illustration.

00:00 OUT OF TIME?

Auditory-Musical If time does not permit teaching the entire chapter, use the information on these pages along with the chapter Audiocassettes to present the material in a condensed format.

Chapter 17 Reviewing Main Ideas

For a **preview** of this chapter, study this Reviewing Main Ideas before you read the chapter. After you have studied this chapter, you can use the Reviewing Main Ideas to **review** the chapter.

The Glencoe MindJogger, Audiocassettes, and CD-ROM provide additional opportunities for review.

Section 17-1 RADIATION FROM SPACE

Electromagnetic waves are arranged in the electromagnetic spectrum according to their wavelengths. Optical telescopes produce magnified images of objects. A **refracting telescope** bends light to form an image. A **reflecting telescope** uses mirrors to focus light to produce an image. **Radio telescopes** collect and record radio waves given off by some space objects. ***Why can radio telescopes be used during the day or night and in all types of weather?***

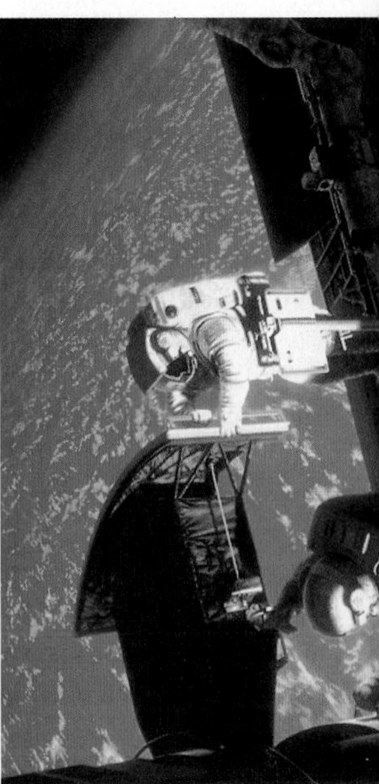

Section 17-2 EARLY SPACE MISSIONS

A **satellite** is an object that revolves around another object. The moons of planets are natural satellites. Artificial satellites are those made by people. An artificial satellite collects data as it **orbits** a planet. A **space probe** travels into the solar system, gathers data, and sends the information back to Earth. Some space probes become artificial satellites of the planet or other object they are sent to study. ***Why can the* Galileo *spacecraft be referred to both as a probe and as an artificial satellite of Jupiter?***

History Early standards for U.S. astronauts severely limited which Americans could participate in the program. For example, the earliest criteria required astronaut candidates (ASCANs) to be test pilots, but women were not allowed to train as test pilots until 1970. After a nine-year hiatus, ASCAN selection broadened in the late 1970s. The 1978 ASCAN group included six women, three African-American men, and an Asian-American. Three members of this group—Judith Resnick, Ronald McNair, and Ellison Onizuka—were killed in the 1986 *Challenger* explosion.

Reading Check

Review the space missions discussed in the chapter. Then, create a timeline that shows these discoveries in chronological order.

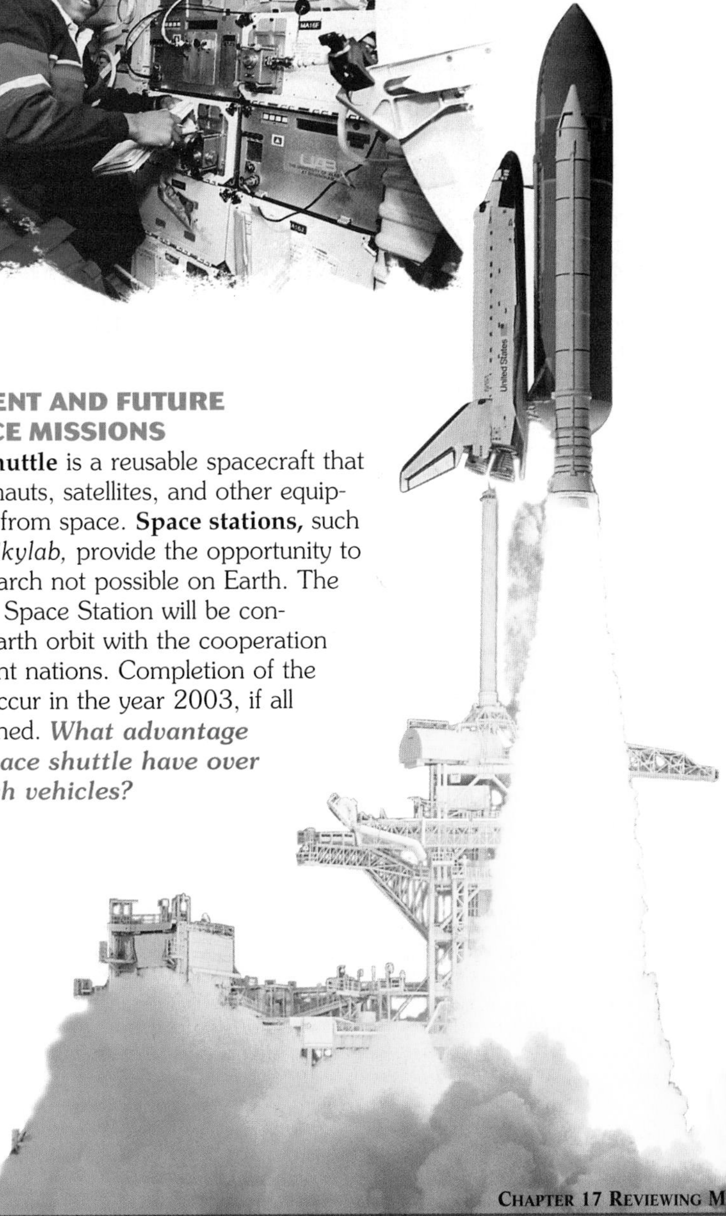

Section **17-3 RECENT AND FUTURE SPACE MISSIONS**

The **space shuttle** is a reusable spacecraft that carries astronauts, satellites, and other equipment to and from space. **Space stations,** such as *Mir* and *Skylab,* provide the opportunity to conduct research not possible on Earth. The International Space Station will be constructed in Earth orbit with the cooperation of 16 different nations. Completion of the ISS should occur in the year 2003, if all goes as planned. ***What advantage does the space shuttle have over other launch vehicles?***

Answers to Questions

Section 17-1

Radiation from Space Radio waves pass freely through Earth's atmosphere. They are not affected by most weather conditions and do not scatter during daylight hours.

Section 17-2

Early Space Missions The *Galileo* spacecraft was a space probe while traveling toward Jupiter. Once there and in orbit around Jupiter, it became a satellite of Jupiter.

Section 17-3

Recent and Future Space Missions The space shuttle is a reusable spacecraft that can carry astronauts, satellites, and other payloads to and from space. It can return damaged satellites, or astronauts can repair satellites from the cargo bay.

GLENCOE TECHNOLOGY

CD-ROM

Glencoe Science Voyages Interactive CD-ROM

Chapter Summaries and Quizzes

Have students read the Chapter Summary then take the Chapter Quiz to determine whether they have mastered chapter content.

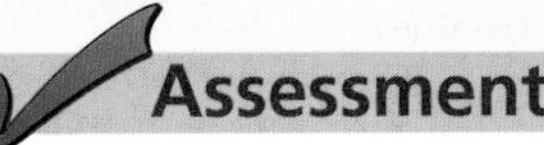

Assessment

Portfolio Encourage students to place in their portfolios one or two items of what they consider to be their best work. Examples include:

- Explore Activity, p. 611
- Activity 17-1, p. 618
- Activity 17-2, pp. 626–627 P

Performance Additional performance assessments may be found in **Performance Assessment** and **Science Integration Activities.** Performance Task Assessment Lists and rubrics for evaluating these activities can be found in Glencoe's **Performance Assessment in the Science Classroom.**

Using Vocabulary

1. h
2. j
3. f
4. l
5. a

interNET CONNECTION To reinforce chapter vocabulary, use the **Study Guide for Content Mastery** booklet. Also available are activities for **Glencoe Science Voyages** on the Glencoe Science Web Site. **www.glencoe.com/sec/science/ca**

Checking Concepts

6. D	11. A
7. D	12. C
8. B	13. C
9. A	14. B
10. B	15. D

Thinking Critically

16. Earth-based observations are obscured by the atmosphere. The atmosphere absorbs and distorts incoming radiation. Because the moon has no atmosphere, light and other forms of energy can reach its surface without distortion.
17. Most students should realize that the surface temperature of the sun and the immense heat that is radiated from it would make a space-probe encounter useless because the probe would burn up before getting close enough to gather data.
18. Answers will vary. Robotic space probes need fewer resources and can provide more data about the outer solar system and deep space. Spaceflights with people aboard provide information about living in space and also valuable technological data.
19. No, sound requires matter through which to travel. Space is a virtual vacuum.
20. When the probes crossed Pluto's orbit, Pluto was at another point in its orbit.

Chapter 17 Assessment

Using Vocabulary

a. electromagnetic spectrum
b. observatory
c. orbit
d. Project Apollo
e. Project Gemini
f. Project Mercury
g. radio telescope
h. reflecting telescope
i. refracting telescope
j. satellite
k. space probe
l. space shuttle
m. space station

The sentences below include italicized terms that have been used incorrectly. Change the incorrect terms so that the sentences read correctly. Underline your change.

1. A *reflecting telescope* uses lenses to bend light toward a focal point.
2. A *space probe* is an object that revolves around another object.
3. *Project Apollo* was the first piloted U.S. space program.
4. A *space station* carries people and tools to and from space.
5. In an *observatory*, electromagnetic waves are arranged according to their wavelengths.

Checking Concepts

Choose the word or phrase that best answers the question.

6. Which spacecraft has sent back images of Venus?
   A) *Voyager* C) *Apollo 11*
   B) *Viking* D) *Magellan*
7. Which telescope uses mirrors to collect light?
   A) radio C) refracting
   B) electromagnetic D) reflecting
8. *Sputnik I* was the first what?
   A) telescope C) observatory
   B) artificial satellite D) U.S. space probe
9. Which telescope can be used during day or night and during bad weather?
   A) radio C) refracting
   B) electromagnetic D) reflecting
10. When fully operational, the International Space Station will be crewed by up to how many people?
    A) 3 C) 15
    B) 7 D) 50
11. Which space mission had the goal to put a spacecraft in orbit and bring it back safely?
    A) Project Mercury C) Project Gemini
    B) Project Apollo D) *Viking I*
12. The space shuttle reuses which of the following?
    A) liquid-fuel tanks C) booster engines
    B) *Gemini* rockets D) *Saturn* rockets
13. What does the space shuttle use to place a satellite into space?
    A) liquid-fuel tank C) mechanical arm
    B) booster rocket D) cargo bay
14. What was *Skylab?*
    A) space probe C) space shuttle
    B) space station D) optical telescope
15. Which of the following is a natural satellite of Earth?
    A) *Skylab* C) the sun
    B) the space shuttle D) the moon

Thinking Critically

16. How would a moon-based telescope have advantages over the Earth-based telescopes being used today?
17. Would a space probe to the sun's surface be useful? Explain.
18. Which would you choose—space missions with people aboard or robotic space probes? Why?

19. Suppose two astronauts were outside the space shuttle, orbiting Earth. The audio speaker in the helmet of one astronaut quits working. The other astronaut is 1 m away, so she shouts a message to him. Can he hear her? Explain.
20. No space probes have visited the planet Pluto. Nevertheless, probes have crossed Pluto's orbit. How?

Developing Skills

If you need help, refer to the Skill Handbook.

21. **Measuring in SI:** Explain whether or not the following pieces of equipment could be used aboard the space shuttle as it orbits Earth: a balance, a meterstick, and a thermometer.
22. **Making and Using Tables:** Copy the table below. Use information in the chapter as well as news articles and other resources to complete your table.

U.S. Space Probes

Probe	Launch Date	Destinations	Planets or Objects Visited
Vikings 1 & 2	1975	Mars	Mars
Galileo	1989	Jupiter	Venus, Europa, Jupiter
Lunar Prospector	1998	Earth's moon	Earth's moon
Mars Pathfinder & Sojourner	996	Mars	Mars

23. **Classifying:** Classify the following as a satellite or a space probe: *Cassini, Sputnik I, Hubble Space Telescope, space shuttle,* and *Voyager 2.*

Test-Taking Tip

Best Times If your test is going to be timed, then practice under timed conditions. Try timing yourself on specific sections to see if you can improve your overall speed while maintaining accuracy.

Test Practice

Use these questions to test your Science Proficiency.

1. Large telescopes are usually reflectors. Which of the following statements **BEST** explains why this is true?
   A) Reflecting telescopes are easier to use and carry around.
   B) Reflecting telescopes have greater magnifying power.
   C) Reflecting telescopes are less expensive to build and maintain.
   D) In reflecting telescopes, the objective mirror can be supported from beneath and, therefore, can be made larger.
2. The *Lunar Prospector* was classified as a space probe when launched but is now classified as a satellite. What does this illustrate about this spacecraft's flight?
   A) The *Lunar Prospector* is in orbit around Earth.
   B) The *Lunar Prospector* was a space probe on its flight to the moon and became a satellite when it went into orbit around the moon.
   C) The *Lunar Prospector* is moving out of our solar system.
   D) The *Lunar Prospector* was launched from Earth, went into orbit around the moon, and landed on the moon.

Test Practice

The Test-Taking Tip was written by The Princeton Review, the nation's leader in test preparation.

1. D
2. B

Developing Skills

21. The balance couldn't be used because the objects and fluids to be measured wouldn't stay on the balance pans. However, distances and temperatures are not affected by the microgravity environment of space, so a meterstick and thermometer could be used.
22. See student page.
23. All are satellites except *Voyager 2,* which did not orbit any object and is therefore a probe.

Bonus Question

The *Cassini* spacecraft is presently traveling through space. Ask students to find out when it was launched, where it is heading, and when it is expected to arrive. Cassini *was launched in 1997, is heading for Saturn, and is expected to arrive in 2004.*

Assessment Resources

The **Test Practice Workbook** provides students with practice in the format, concepts, and critical-thinking skills tested in standardized exams.

Reproducible Masters

Chapter Review, pp. 33–34 L2

Performance Assessment, p. 17 L2

Assessment, pp. 65–68 L2

Glencoe Technology

Chapter Review Software

Computer Test Bank

MindJogger Videoquiz

Chapter 18 The Sun-Earth-Moon System

Section	Objectives	Activities/Features
Chapter Opener		Explore Activity: Model Seasons, p. 639
18-1 Planet Earth 3 Sessions 1½ Blocks	1. **Describe** Earth's shape and list physical data about Earth. 2. **Compare** and **contrast** the rotation and revolution of Earth. 3. **Demonstrate** how Earth's revolution and tilt causes seasons to change on Earth.	MiniLab: Comparing Spheres, p. 641 Physics Integration, p. 642 Skill Builder: Recognizing Cause and Effect, p. 646 Using Computers, p. 646 Reading and Writing in Science: A Brave and Startling Truth, p. 647 Activity 18-1: Tilt and Temperature, pp. 648–649
18-2 Earth's Moon 1 Session ½ Block	4. **Explain** how the moon's phases depend on the relative positions of the sun, the moon, and Earth. 5. **Describe** why eclipses occur, and compare solar and lunar eclipses. 6. **Hypothesize** what surface features of the moon tell us about its history.	Using Math, p. 651 MiniLab: Comparing the Sun and Moon, p. 652 Life Science Integration, p. 653 Problem Solving: Survival on the Moon, p. 655 Skill Builder: Interpreting Scientific Illustrations, p. 657 Science Journal, p. 657
18-3 Exploration of the Moon 2 Sessions 1 Block	7. **List** and **discuss** new information about the moon discovered by spacecraft. 8. **List** facts about the moon's poles that may be important to future space travel.	Skill Builder: Sequencing, p. 660 Using Math, p. 660 Activity 18-2: Moon Phases and Eclipses, p. 661

The number of recommended single-period sessions — The number of recommended blocks
One session and one-half block are allowed for chapter review and assessment.

Activity Materials

Explore	Activities	MiniLabs
p. 639 unshaded lamp, globe	pp. 648–649 tape, black construction paper, gooseneck lamp with 75-W bulb, thermometer, watch, protractor p. 661 unshaded light source, polystyrene ball, pencil, globe	p. 641 string, basketball or volleyball, ruler, protractor, calculator p. 652 chalk, string, meterstick

Need Materials? Contact Science Kit at 1-800-828-7777 or at www.sciencekit.com on the Internet.
For alternate materials, see the activity on the listed page.

Chapter Organizer

Standards		Reproducible Resources	Technology
National	State/Local	Test Practice Workbooks are available for use with each chapter.	English and Spanish audiocassettes are available for use with each section.
National Content Standards: A1, A2, B3, D1, D3, F1, G3	California Science Content Standards: 2d, 4e, 8a, 9a, 9b, 9c, 9e, 9f	**Activity Worksheets,** pp. 99–100, 103 **Critical Thinking/Problem Solving,** p. 18 **Enrichment,** p. 49 **Laboratory Manual,** pp. 115–116 **Laboratory Manual,** pp. 117–118 **Reinforcement,** p. 49 **Study Guide,** p. 69	**Section Focus Transparency 49** **Teaching Transparency 35** **Glencoe Science Voyages Interactive Videodisc—Earth** **National Geographic Society: STV** **Internet Connection,** p. 645 **Internet Connection,** p. 647 **The Infinite Voyage Series**
National Content Standards: UCP5, A2, C3, D2, D3, E2, F1, G1, G3	California Science Content Standards: 2g, 4d, 4e, 9f	**Activity Worksheets,** p. 104 **Enrichment,** p. 50 **Multicultural Connections,** pp. 35–36 **Reinforcement,** p. 50	**Section Focus Transparency 50** **Science Integration Transparency 18** **Teaching Transparency 36** **National Geographic Society: STV** **Internet Connection,** p. 655 **Glencoe Science Voyages Interactive CD-ROM**
National Content Standards: UCP5, A2, D3, E2	California Science Content Standards: 4d, 4e, 9a, 9b, 9e, 9f	**Activity Worksheets,** pp. 101–102 **Enrichment,** p. 51 **Reinforcement,** p. 51 **Study Guide,** pp. 70–72	**Section Focus Transparency 51**

Key to Teaching Strategies

The following designations will help you decide which activities are appropriate for your students.

L1 Level 1 activities should be appropriate for students with learning difficulties.

L2 Level 2 activities should be within the ability range of all students.

L3 Level 3 activities are designed for above-average students.

ELL ELL activities should be within the ability range of English Language Learners.

COOP LEARN Cooperative Learning activities are designed for small group work.

P These strategies represent student products that can be placed into a best-work portfolio.

Multiple Learning Styles logos, as described on page 55T, are used throughout to indicate strategies that address different learning styles.

Assessment Resources

Chapter Review, pp. 35–36
Assessment, pp. 69–72
Performance Assessment in the Science Classroom (PASC)
MindJogger Videoquiz
Alternate Assessment in the Science Classroom
Performance Assessment, p. 18
Chapter Review Software
Computer Test Bank

Chapter 18 The Sun-Earth-Moon System

This is a representation of key blackline masters available in the Teacher Classroom Resources. See Resource Manager boxes within the chapter for additional information.

Transparencies

Section Focus Transparencies

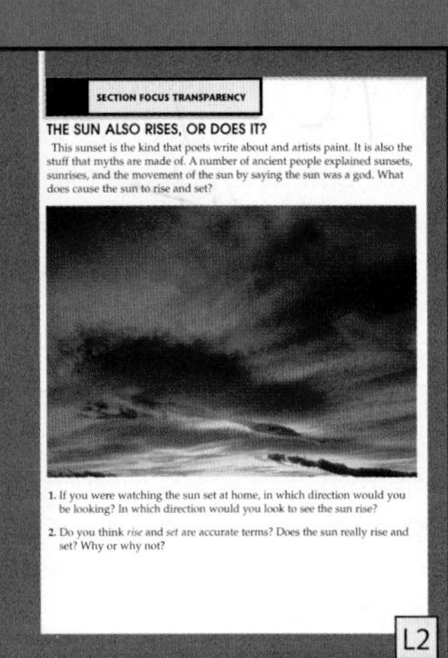

SECTION FOCUS TRANSPARENCY

THE SUN ALSO RISES, OR DOES IT?

This sunset is the kind that poets write about and artists paint. It is also the stuff that myths are made of. A number of ancient people explained sunsets, sunrises, and the movement of the sun by saying the sun was a god. What does cause the sun to rise and set?

1. If you were watching the sun set at home, in which direction would you be looking? In which direction would you look to see the sun rise?
2. Do you think *rise* and *set* are accurate terms? Does the sun really rise and set? Why or why not?

L2

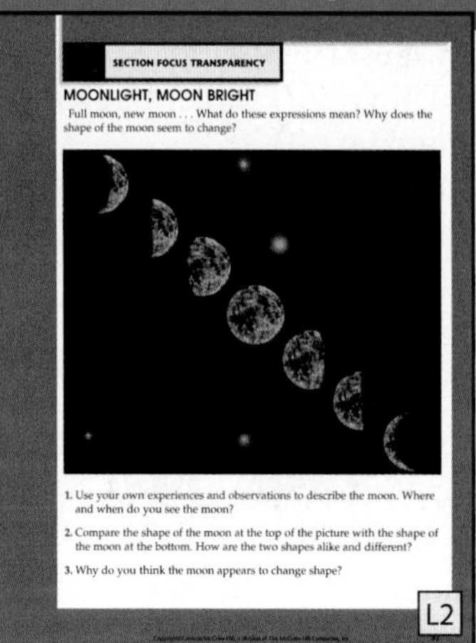

SECTION FOCUS TRANSPARENCY

MOONLIGHT, MOON BRIGHT

Full moon, new moon . . . What do these expressions mean? Why does the shape of the moon seem to change?

1. Use your own experiences and observations to describe the moon. Where and when do you see the moon?
2. Compare the shape of the moon at the top of the picture with the shape of the moon at the bottom. How are the two shapes alike and different?
3. Why do you think the moon appears to change shape?

L2

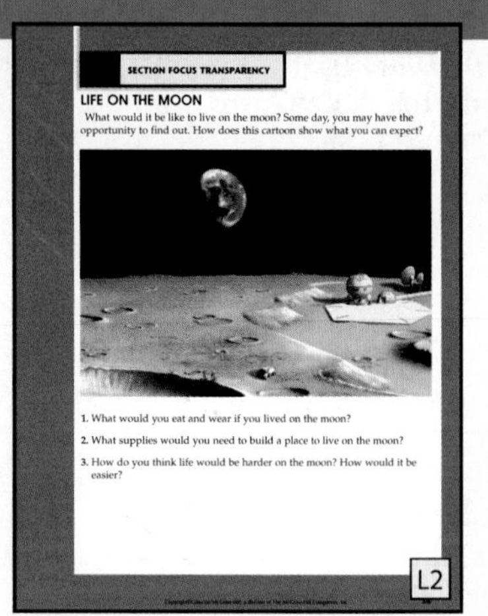

SECTION FOCUS TRANSPARENCY

LIFE ON THE MOON

What would it be like to live on the moon? Some day, you may have the opportunity to find out. How does this cartoon show what you can expect?

1. What would you eat and wear if you lived on the moon?
2. What supplies would you need to build a place to live on the moon?
3. How do you think life would be harder on the moon? How would it be easier?

L2

Science Integration Transparencies

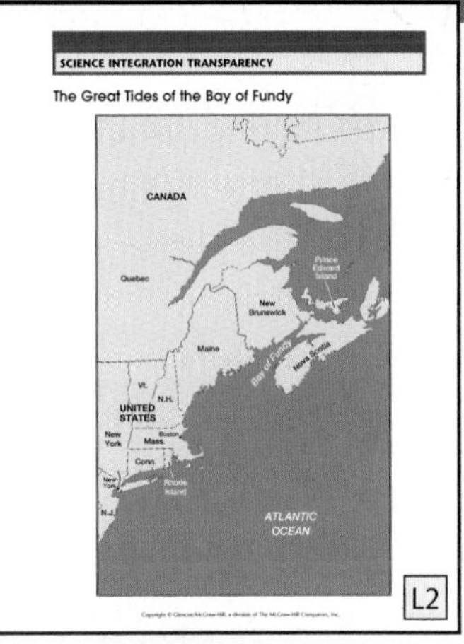

SCIENCE INTEGRATION TRANSPARENCY

The Great Tides of the Bay of Fundy

L2

Teaching Transparencies

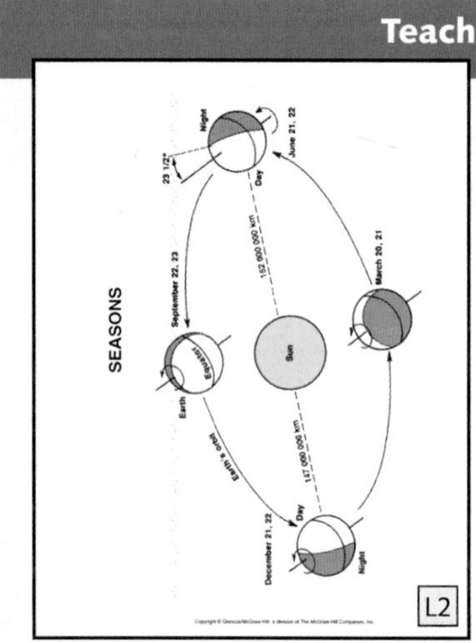

L2

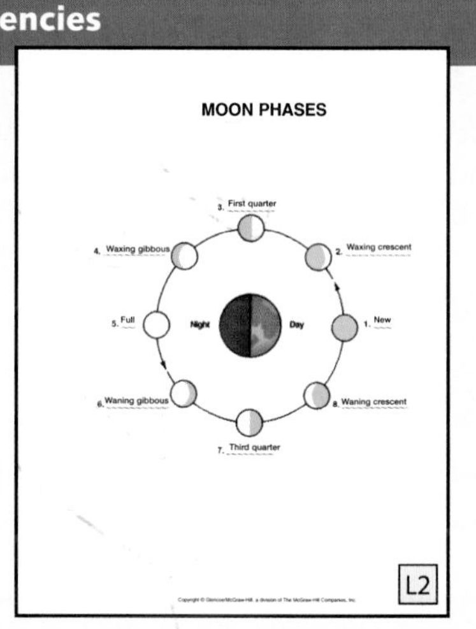

L2

Meeting Different Ability Levels

Study Guide for Content Mastery

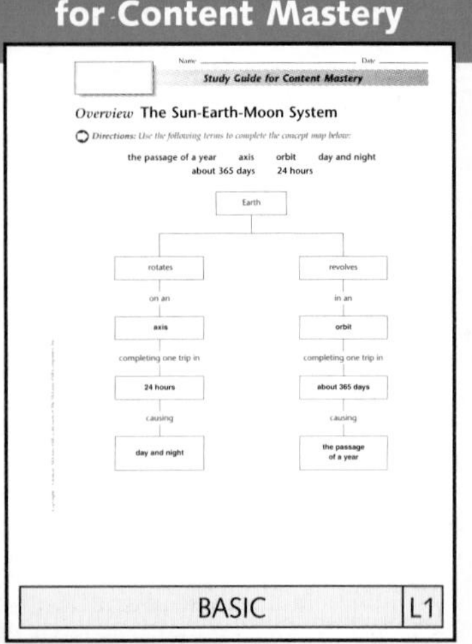

Name ____________ Date ______

Study Guide for Content Mastery

Overview The Sun-Earth-Moon System

Directions: Use the following terms to complete the concept map below:

the passage of a year   axis   orbit   day and night   about 365 days   24 hours

BASIC L1

Reinforcement

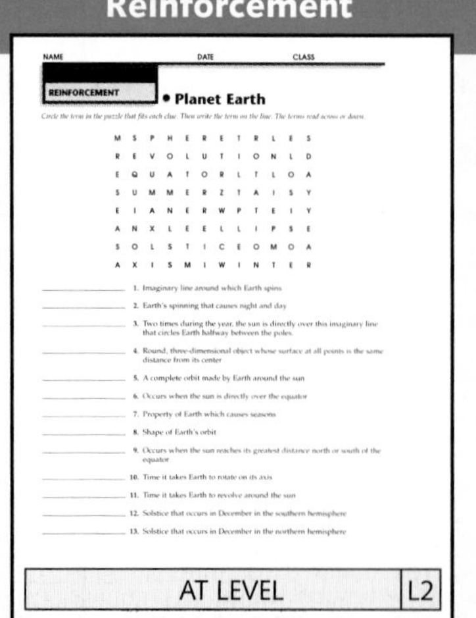

NAME ______ DATE ______ CLASS ______

REINFORCEMENT • Planet Earth

Circle the term in the puzzle that fits each clue. Then write the term on the line. The terms read across or down.

M S P H E R E T R L E S
R E V O L U T I O N L D
E Q U A T O R L T L O A
S U M M E R Z T A I S Y
E I A N E R W P T E I Y
A N X L E E L L I P S E
S O L S T I C E O M O A
A X I S M I W I N T E R

1. Imaginary line around which Earth spins
2. Earth's spinning that causes night and day
3. Two times during the year, the sun is directly over this imaginary line that circles Earth halfway between the poles.
4. Round, three-dimensional object whose surface at all points is the same distance from its center
5. A complete orbit made by Earth around the sun
6. Occurs when the sun is directly over the equator
7. Property of Earth which causes seasons
8. Shape of Earth's orbit
9. Occurs when the sun reaches its greatest distance north or south of the equator
10. Time it takes Earth to rotate on its axis
11. Time it takes Earth to revolve around the sun
12. Solstice that occurs in December in the southern hemisphere
13. Solstice that occurs in December in the northern hemisphere

AT LEVEL L2

Enrichment Worksheets

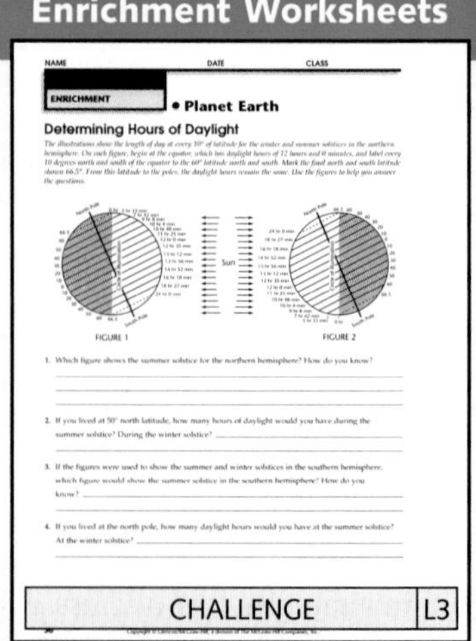

NAME ______ DATE ______ CLASS ______

ENRICHMENT • Planet Earth

Determining Hours of Daylight

The illustrations show the length of day at every 10° of latitude for the winter and summer solstices in the northern hemisphere. On each figure, begin at the equator, which has daylight hours of 12 hours and 0 minutes, and label every 10 degrees north and south of the equator to the 60° latitude north and south. Mark the final north and south latitude shown 66.5°. From this latitude to the poles, the daylight hours remain the same. Use the figures to help you answer the questions.

1. Which figure shows the summer solstice for the northern hemisphere? How do you know?
2. If you lived at 50° north latitude, how many hours of daylight would you have during the summer solstice? During the winter solstice?
3. If the figures were used to show the summer and winter solstices in the southern hemisphere, which figure would show the summer solstice in the southern hemisphere? How do you know?
4. If you lived at the north pole, how many daylight hours would you have at the summer solstice? At the winter solstice?

CHALLENGE L3

Resource Manager

Hands-on Activities

Activity Worksheets

NAME DATE CLASS

ACTIVITY 21-1 • Tilt and Temperature

Design Your Own Experiment

Lab Preview

Have you ever noticed how hot the surface of a blacktop driveway can get during the day? The sun's rays hit Earth more directly as the day progresses. Now consider the fact that Earth is tilted on its axis. How does this affect the amount of heat on an area on Earth receives from the sun?

Recognize the Problem

Form a Hypothesis

Goals

Possible Materials

Safety Precautions

Test Your Hypothesis

L2

Lab Manual

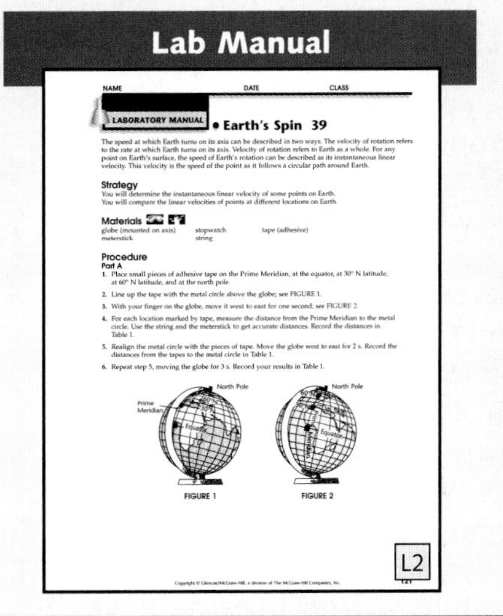

NAME DATE CLASS

LABORATORY MANUAL • Earth's Spin 39

Strategy

Materials

Procedure

FIGURE 1 FIGURE 2

L2

Accessibility

Spanish Resources

SPANISH RESOURCES

GLENCOE California Edition

SCIENCE VOYAGES

Exploring the Life, Earth, and Physical Sciences

LEVEL BLUE

L2

Assessment

Performance Assessment

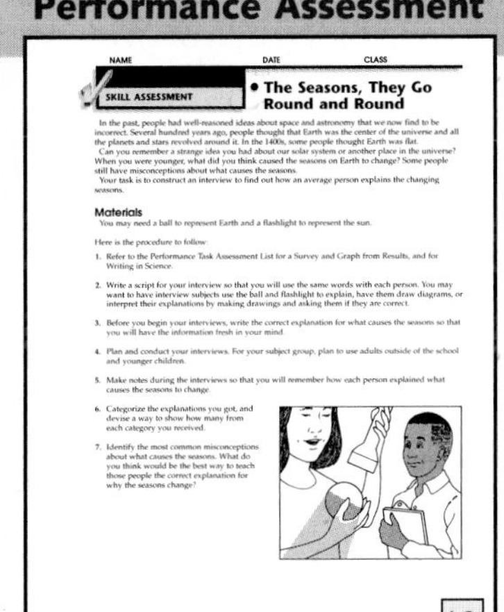

NAME DATE CLASS

SKILL ASSESSMENT • The Seasons, They Go Round and Round

Materials

L2

Chapter Review

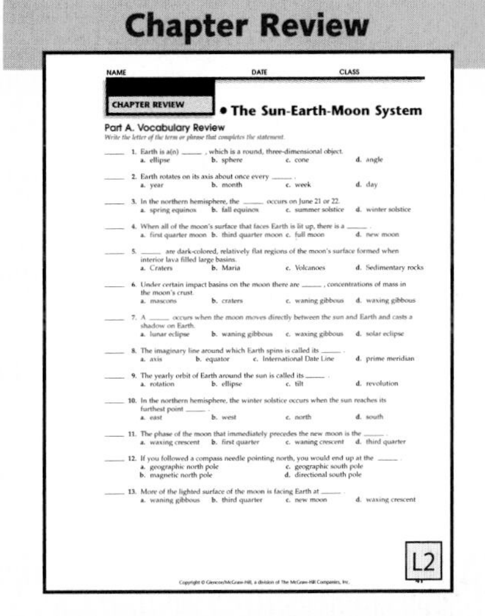

NAME DATE CLASS

CHAPTER REVIEW • The Sun-Earth-Moon System

Part A. Vocabulary Review

L2

Assessment

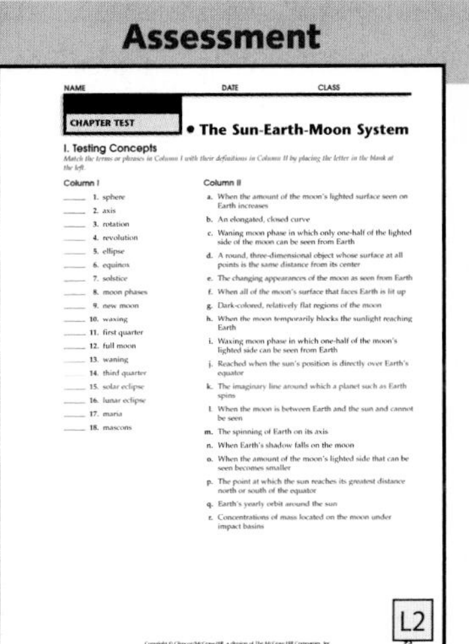

NAME DATE CLASS

CHAPTER TEST • The Sun-Earth-Moon System

I. Testing Concepts

Column I Column II

L2

Test Practice Workbook

CALIFORNIA SCIENCE CONTENT STANDARDS PRACTICE QUESTIONS STUDENT EDITION

GLENCOE California Edition

SCIENCE VOYAGES

Exploring the Life, Earth, and Physical Sciences

LEVEL BLUE

THE PRINCETON REVIEW

L2

Extending Content

Critical Thinking/ Problem Solving

NAME DATE CLASS

CRITICAL THINKING • The Sun-Earth-Moon System

Sick of Winter

Applying Critical Thinking Skills

L2

Multicultural Connections

NAME DATE CLASS

MULTICULTURAL CONNECTIONS • Eclipses, Legends, and Ancient Astronomers

Eclipse Legends

Early Astronomers

Solar Eclipse

Sun Moon Earth

Lunar Eclipse

Sun Earth Moon

L2

Helping You Prepare

Earth's Rotation (Section 18-1)

Atomic clocks measure time by recording the frequency of electromagnetic waves given off by atoms. Unlike conventional clocks, atomic clocks are not affected by changes in temperature or the wearing of their parts. They gain or lose less than one second in 200 000 years. Using these clocks, scientists have found that each successive day on Earth is getting longer.

Apparently, Earth's rotation has been slowing down for millions of years. By studying the growth lines on 375-million-year-old corals, scientists have determined that a year had 440 days at the time these corals were growing. Corals deposit monthly growth lines on their shells in much the same way trees develop yearly growth rings.

Atomic clocks and ancient corals indicate that Earth's rotation is slowing down. Scientists hypothesize that the gravitational attraction of the moon is dragging on Earth.

As this drag continues, the length of a day will increase. The length of a year will not be affected. Earth's period of revolution is not dependent on its period of rotation. This means that the number of days in a year will decrease, but the length of a year will not change.

GLENCOE TECHNOLOGY

CD-ROM

Glencoe Science Voyages Interactive CD-ROM

Chapter Summaries

Use the Chapter Summary to introduce, teach, or review chapter material.

Earth's Magnetic Field (Section 18-1)

Convection currents of molten iron deep in Earth's core produce huge electrical currents. These electrical currents, in turn, cause Earth's magnetic field. The orientation of the direction of Earth's magnetic field changes periodically over time. This is one of the bits of evidence that has been used to support the theories of seafloor spreading and plate tectonics. Scientists examine iron minerals in rocks such as basalt, which align themselves according to the magnetic field orientation at the time they form. When Earth's magnetic field is reversed, new iron minerals being formed reflect that magnetic reversal.

NATIONAL GEOGRAPHIC — **Teacher's Corner**

Products Available from National Geographic Society

To order the following products for use with this chapter, call National Geographic Society at 1-800-368-2728:

Poster

The Earth's Moon

Video

Sun, Earth, Moon

Index to National Geographic Magazine

"Physical World," by Joel L. Swerdlow, May 1998.

"Orbit: The Astronauts' View of Home," by Jay Apt, November 1996.

"The Darkness That Enlightens," by Jay M. Pasachoff, May 1992.

"The Moon's Racing Shadow," by Roger H. Ressmeyer, May 1992.

"Our Restless Planet Earth," by Rick Gore, August 1985.

Moon Craters (Section 18-2)

About 4 billion years ago, large meteorites created huge impact basins on the moon's surface. By 3.3 billion years ago, lava flows had filled in these impact basins, forming the large, relatively flat maria seen today. Although craters have formed on the maria and other areas of the moon since that time, its surface looks much as it did 3.3 billion years ago. It appears that meteorite impacts were much more frequent prior to the formation of maria.

Crater density is found by calculating the number of craters of different sizes found on an area of the moon's surface. Astronomers use crater density to determine the age of an area of the moon's surface. From this, they have been able to learn more about the history of the moon.

Origin of the Moon (Section 18-2)

Three early theories of the moon's origin were the capture, the condensation, and the fission theories.

The capture theory states that the moon formed in some other area of the solar system and was later captured by Earth as it passed by. In this theory, the compositions of Earth and the moon were different because they formed at different locations in the solar system. Although the compositions of the two objects are not the same, there are too many similarities in the makeup of their mantles for them to have formed totally apart. Also, it's highly unlikely that Earth's gravity could capture an object the size of the moon.

The condensation theory states that the moon and Earth formed at the same time from the same preformation materials. In this theory, Earth and the moon should have the same density and be made of similar materials. Because Earth and the moon do not have the same density and are composed of different materials, this theory has been largely discarded.

The fission theory states that the moon formed by splitting off of Earth. The Pacific Ocean is often mentioned as the area from which the moon split off. The problem with this theory is that it cannot explain how Earth could have thrown such a large portion of itself into a stable orbit.

The most recent theory of the moon's origin, the impact theory, was developed in part from data gathered by the *Apollo* space missions. The impact theory, which is described in detail in the student text, can be considered a hybrid of the capture and the fission theories.

Exploration of the Moon (Section 18-3)

Deviations in the lunar orbits of spacecraft led to the discovery of mascons, which are areas of high concentrations of mass. The presence of mascons indicates that the entire interior of the moon cannot be liquid. Enough crust must be present to support mascons.

SCIENCE UPDATE

For current events or science in the news, access the Glencoe Science Web Site at **www.glencoe.com/sec/science/ca**

Teacher to Teacher

"To help my students understand that the moon's phases are caused by the position of the moon in relation to Earth and the sun, I have them make observations of the moon at approximately the same time each day for three to four days."

Ralph M. Feather, Jr., Teacher
Derry Area High School
Derry, PA

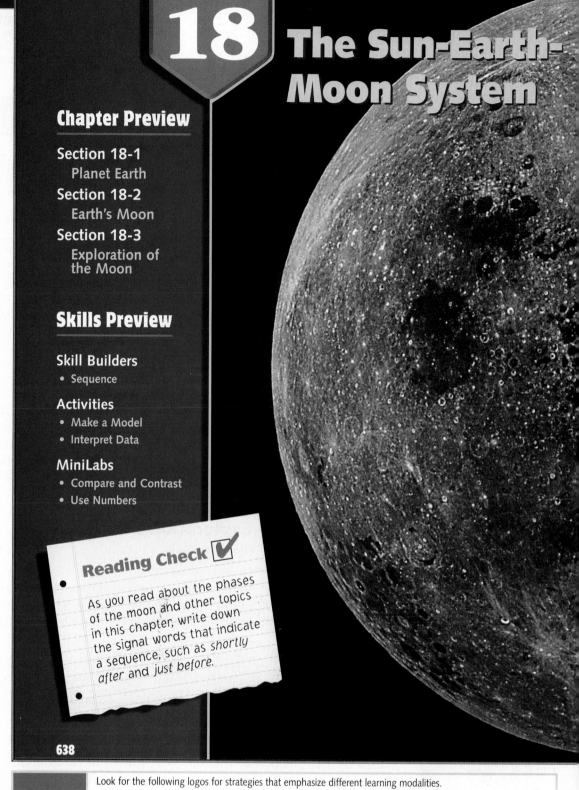

CHAPTER 18
The Sun-Earth-Moon System

CHAPTER OVERVIEW

Section 18-1 Physical data about Earth are presented. Seasons are explained in terms of Earth's position in space with respect to the sun and the tilt of Earth's axis.

Section 18-2 This section explains moon phases and eclipses. The structure and origin of the moon also are explored.

Section 18-3 Early and recent moon missions are described.

Chapter Vocabulary

sphere	waxing
axis	first quarter
rotation	full moon
revolution	waning
ellipse	third quarter
equinox	solar eclipse
solstice	lunar eclipse
moon phase	maria
new moon	mascon

Theme Connection

Systems and Interactions Earth's rotation and revolution cause daily and seasonal changes due to the interaction of the sun, the moon, and Earth. Phases of the moon occur monthly and also rely on the interaction among the sun, the moon, and Earth.

If time does not permit teaching the entire chapter, use Reviewing Main Ideas on pp. 662–663.

CHAPTER 18
The Sun-Earth-Moon System

Chapter Preview

Skills Preview

Skill Builders
- Sequence

Activities
- Make a Model
- Interpret Data

MiniLabs
- Compare and Contrast
- Use Numbers

Reading Check

As you read about the phases of the moon and other topics in this chapter, write down the signal words that indicate a sequence, such as *shortly after* and *just before.*

638

Multiple Learning Styles

Look for the following logos for strategies that emphasize different learning modalities.

Linguistic Science Journal, pp. 652, 656, 659; Integrating the Sciences, p. 656; Using Science Words, p. 659; Preview, p. 662

Logical-Mathematical MiniLab, p. 641; Activity, pp. 648–649

Visual-Spatial Explore Activity, p. 639; Reteach, pp. 645, 659, 662; Quick Demo, p. 654

Auditory-Musical Out of Time, p. 662

Kinesthetic Activity, p. 661

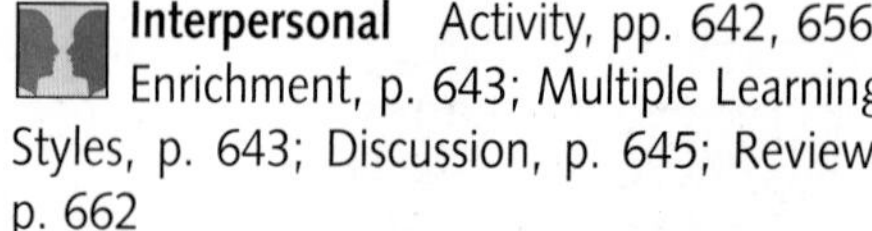
Interpersonal Activity, pp. 642, 656; Enrichment, p. 643; Multiple Learning Styles, p. 643; Discussion, p. 645; Review, p. 662

Explore Activity

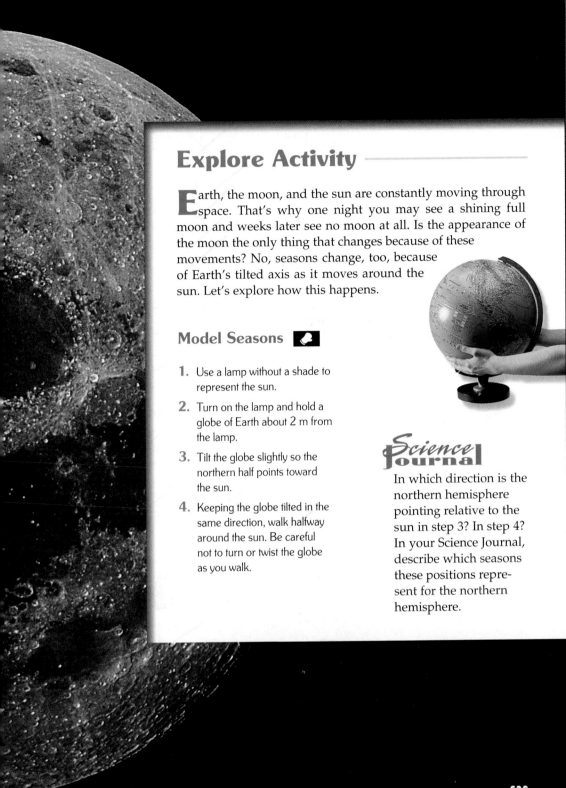

Earth, the moon, and the sun are constantly moving through space. That's why one night you may see a shining full moon and weeks later see no moon at all. Is the appearance of the moon the only thing that changes because of these movements? No, seasons change, too, because of Earth's tilted axis as it moves around the sun. Let's explore how this happens.

Model Seasons

1. Use a lamp without a shade to represent the sun.
2. Turn on the lamp and hold a globe of Earth about 2 m from the lamp.
3. Tilt the globe slightly so the northern half points toward the sun.
4. Keeping the globe tilted in the same direction, walk halfway around the sun. Be careful not to turn or twist the globe as you walk.

Science Journal

In which direction is the northern hemisphere pointing relative to the sun in step 3? In step 4? In your Science Journal, describe which seasons these positions represent for the northern hemisphere.

Assessment Planner

Portfolio

Refer to p. 663 for suggested items that students might select for their portfolios.

Performance Assessment

See p. 663 for additional Performance Assessment options.
Skill Builder, pp. 646, 657, 660
MiniLab, pp. 641, 652
Activity 18-1, pp. 648–649; 18-2, p. 661

Content Assessment

Section Assessment, pp. 646, 657, 660
Chapter Assessment, pp. 664–665
Proficiency Prep, pp. 646, 657, 660

Explore Activity

Purpose

Visual-Spatial Use the Explore Activity to introduce students to the causes of seasons. L2 ELL COOP LEARN

Preparation

Have students bring in small lamps from home. Also obtain several globes of Earth.

Materials

lamp without a shade, globe

Teaching Strategies

Put students into groups of three. As two students perform the activity, the third should record observations.

Safety Precautions Caution students to handle the lamp with care. The bulb will be hot.

Troubleshooting Be sure students understand that the orientation or "tilt" of the globe must remain constant.

In step 3, the northern hemisphere is pointing toward the sun. This represents summer in that hemisphere. In step 4, the northern hemisphere is pointing away from the sun. This represents winter in that hemisphere.

Assessment

Performance Ask students to determine the seasons for the southern hemisphere in steps 3 and 4. Use **Performance Assessment in the Science Classroom,** p. 17.

SECTION 18•1

Prepare

Refer to **Earth's Rotation** and **Earth's Magnetic Field** on p. 638E.

Preplanning

Refer to the **Chapter Organizer** on pp. 638A–B.

1 Motivate

Bellringer

Before presenting the lesson, display **Section Focus Transparency 49** on the overhead projector. Use the accompanying **Focus Activity** worksheet. L2 ELL

Section 18-1

SECTION FOCUS TRANSPARENCY

THE SUN ALSO RISES, OR DOES IT?

This sunset is the kind that poets write about and artists paint. It is also the stuff that myths are made of. A number of ancient people explained sunsets, sunrises, and the movement of the sun by saying the sun was a god. What does cause the sun to rise and set?

1. If you were watching the sun set at home, in which direction would you be looking? In which direction would you look to see the sun rise?
2. Do you think *rise* and *set* are accurate terms? Does the sun really rise and set? Why or why not?

49

Tying to Previous Knowledge

Have students recall that physical properties of matter can be measured without changing a substance into a new substance. Have students list some physical properties of Earth.

18•1 Planet Earth

What You'll Learn

- Physical data about Earth
- The difference between the rotation and revolution of Earth
- How Earth's revolution and tilt cause seasons to change on Earth

Vocabulary

sphere, ellipse, axis, equinox, rotation, solstice, revolution

Why It's Important

- The movements of Earth cause night and day.

Planet Earth Data

You rise early in the morning, while it's still dark outside. You sit by the window and watch the sun come up. Finally, day breaks, and the sun begins its journey across the sky. But, is the sun moving, or are you?

Today, we know that the sun appears to move across the sky because Earth is spinning as it travels around the sun. But, it wasn't long ago that people believed Earth was the center of the universe. They believed Earth stood still and the sun traveled around it.

As recently as the days of Christopher Columbus, some people also believed Earth was flat. They thought that if you sailed far out to sea, you eventually would fall off the edge of the world. How do you know this isn't true? How have scientists determined Earth's shape?

Earth's Shape

Space probes and artificial satellites have sent back images that show Earth is sphere-shaped. A **sphere** (SFIHR) is a round, three-dimensional object. Its surface at all points is the same distance from its center. Tennis balls and basketballs are examples of spheres. But, people had evidence of Earth's true shape long before cameras were sent into space.

Around 350 B.C., the Greek astronomer and philosopher Aristotle reasoned that Earth was spherical because it always casts a round shadow on the moon during an eclipse, as shown in **Figure 18-1.** Only a spherical object always produces a round shadow. If Earth were flat, it would cast a straight shadow.

Other evidence of Earth's shape was observed by early sailors. They watched as ships approached from across the ocean and saw that the top of the ship would come into view first. As they continued to watch the ship, more and more of it

Figure 18-1 If Earth were flat, its shadow during an eclipse would be straight on the moon, not curved, as shown.

Resource Manager

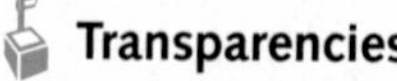

The following **Teacher Classroom Resources** can be used with Section 18-1:

Reproducible Masters

Activity Worksheets, pp. 99–100, 103 L2
Critical Thinking/Problem Solving, p. 18 L2
Enrichment, p. 49 L3
Home Involvement, p. 29 L2
Laboratory Manual, pp. 115–118 L2
Reinforcement, p. 49 L2
Study Guide, p. 69 L1 ELL

Transparencies

Teaching Transparency 35 L2

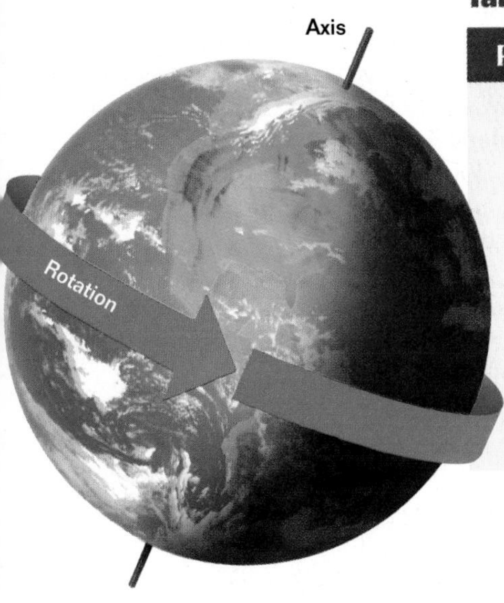

Table 18-1

Physical Properties of Earth	
Diameter (pole to pole)	12 714 km
Diameter (equator)	12 756 km
Circumference (poles)	40 008 km
Circumference (equator)	40 075 km
Mass	5.98×10^{27} g
Density	5.52 g/cm^3
Average distance to the sun	149 600 000 km
Period of rotation (1 day)	23 hr, 56 min
Period of revolution (1 year)	365 days, 6 hr, 9 min

would appear until they could see all of it. This was possible only if Earth was a sphere.

Today, we know that Earth is sphere-shaped, but it is not a perfect sphere. It bulges slightly at the equator and is somewhat flattened at the poles. The poles are located at the north and south ends of Earth's axis. Earth's **axis** is the imaginary line around which Earth spins. The spinning of Earth on its axis, called **rotation,** causes day and night to occur.

Earth's Rotation

As Earth rotates, the sun comes into view at daybreak. Earth continues to spin, making it seem as if the sun moves across the sky until it sets at night. During night, your area of Earth has spun away from the sun. Because of this, the sun is no longer visible. Earth continues to rotate steadily, and the sun eventually comes into view the next morning. One complete rotation takes about 24 hours, or one day. How many rotations does Earth complete during one year? As you can see in **Table 18-1,** it completes about 365 rotations during its journey around the sun.

Try at Home MiniLab

Comparing Spheres

Procedure 

1. Use a long piece of string to measure the circumference of a basketball or volleyball.
2. Measure the circumference of the ball at a right angle to your first measurement.
3. Determine the roundness ratio by dividing the larger measurement by the smaller one.
4. Compare these data with the roundness ratio data about Earth's circumference provided in **Table 18-1.**

Analysis

1. How round is Earth compared with the ball?
2. Is Earth larger through the equator or through the poles?
3. Explain how your observations support your answer.

2 Teach

Try at Home MiniLab

For additional help doing this activity at home, see the corresponding pages in the **Home Involvement** booklet.

Purpose

 **Logical-Mathematical** Students will compare spheres. L2 ELL COOP LEARN

Materials

string, ruler, basketball or volleyball, **Table 18-1**

Teaching Strategies

Troubleshooting Stress that precise measurements must be made because approximations will not produce accurate results.

Analysis

1. Measurements should confirm that the balls are actually less of a sphere than Earth is.
2. Earth is larger through the equator.
3. Measurements taken at right angles to other measurements will not be exactly equal, indicating that the balls are not perfect spheres.

Assessment

Performance Have students measure other kinds of balls. Have them arrange their data in a table and graph the results. Use **Performance Assessment in the Science Classroom,** p. 39. P

Across the Curriculum

Geography Help students recall how the length of day changes from winter to summer for the area in which they live. Encourage them to write letters to city or other government officials in other parts of the world (friends or relatives would work as well) to find out how much the number of daylight hours changes from winter to summer in those areas. Once the students collect data on the number of daylight hours in other parts of the world, have them produce a bar graph showing these data. Ask volunteers to select areas from the graph and discuss how living conditions might be affected by differences in the number of daylight and nighttime hours. L2

CA Science Content Standards

Page 640: 4e
Page 641: 4e, 8a, 9b, 9f

The movement of convection currents inside Earth's mantle generates an electromagnet similar to one created when an electrical current is passed through a coil of wire. Turns in the coil of wire (similar to convection currents inside Earth) cause increased overlapping of the magnetic force lines, intensifying the magnetic field.

Activity

 **Interpersonal** Have students demonstrate evidence of Earth's shape. First, put students into groups of two. Have one student in each pair hold a basketball at eye level, about 33 cm from his or her face. Have the second student slowly move a small object up and over the basketball from the opposite side. The first student should see the top of the object first, then the bottom. Have students reverse roles. Relate this to how the top of a ship is seen first when a ship at sea approaches shore. Then have students use a flashlight to cast shadows of a book and a ball against a wall. Have students relate this to the fact that Earth casts a curved shadow on the moon during a lunar eclipse. L2 ELL COOP LEARN

GLENCOE TECHNOLOGY

Videodisc

Glencoe Science Voyages Interactive Videodisc—Earth

Side 2, Lesson 8 *Space Exploration*

31965

Refer to Videodisc Teacher Guide for additional bar codes.

Earth's Magnetic Field

Convection currents inside Earth's mantle power the movement of tectonic plates. Scientists hypothesize that movement of material inside Earth along with Earth's rotation generates a magnetic field, as shown in **Figure 18-2.**

The magnetic field of Earth is much like that of a bar magnet. Earth has a north and a south magnetic pole, just as a bar magnet has opposite magnetic poles at its ends. **Figure 18-3** illustrates the effects of sprinkling iron shavings over a bar magnet. The shavings align with the magnetic field of the magnet. Earth's magnetic field is similar, almost as if Earth had a giant bar magnet in its core.

Magnetic North

When you observe a compass needle pointing toward the north, you are seeing evidence of Earth's magnetic field. Earth's magnetic axis, the line joining its north and south magnetic poles, does not align with its rotational axis. The magnetic axis is inclined at an angle of 11.5° to the rotational axis. If you followed a compass needle pointing north, you would end up at the magnetic north pole rather than the geographic (rotational) north pole.

Earth's magnetic field and other physical properties affect us every day. What occurrences can you explain in terms of Earth's physical properties and movement in space?

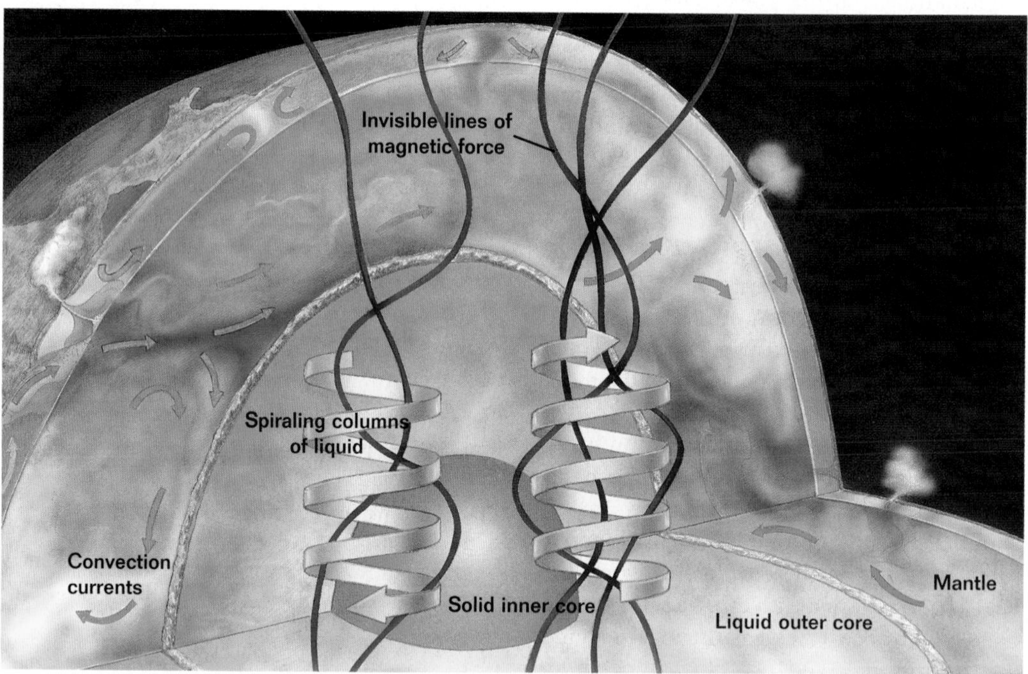

Figure 18-2 Heat and pressure within Earth cause the liquid outer core to move continuously. Driven by Earth's rotation and convection currents deep within Earth, the molten liquid forms spiraling columns. These spirals generate mechanical energy, which in turn generates electricity that creates the magnetic field.

Integrating the Sciences

Physics Make a sketch of Earth on an overhead transparency. Label the geographic poles. Place the transparency over a bar magnet on an overhead projector. Rotate the figure so that the magnet makes an 11.5° angle with the rotational axis of Earth. Sprinkle iron shavings over the transparency and tap it lightly. Have a volunteer relate this demonstration to Earth's magnetic field.

Figure 18-3 Particles in the solar wind streaming through space from the sun distort Earth's magnetic field. As a result, Earth's magnetic field isn't symmetrical. It doesn't have the same shape as a magnetic field surrounding a bar magnet, which is symmetrical.

Seasons

Autumn is coming, and each day it gets colder outside. Dawn comes later each morning, and the sun appears lower in the sky. A month ago, it was light enough to ride your bike at 8:00 P.M. Now, it's dark at 8:00 P.M. What is causing this change?

Earth's Revolution

You learned earlier that Earth's rotation causes day and night. Another important motion of Earth is its **revolution,** or yearly orbit around the sun. Just as the moon is a satellite of Earth, Earth is a satellite of the sun. If Earth's orbit were a circle and the sun were at the center of the circle, Earth would maintain a constant distance from the sun. However, this is not the case. Earth's orbit is an **ellipse** (ee LIHPS), which is an elongated, closed curve. As **Figure 18-4** shows, the sun is offset from the center of the ellipse. Because of this, the distance between Earth and the sun changes during Earth's yearlong orbit. Earth gets closest to the sun—about 147 million km away—around January 3. The farthest point in Earth's orbit is about 152 million km away from the sun and is reached around July 4. 

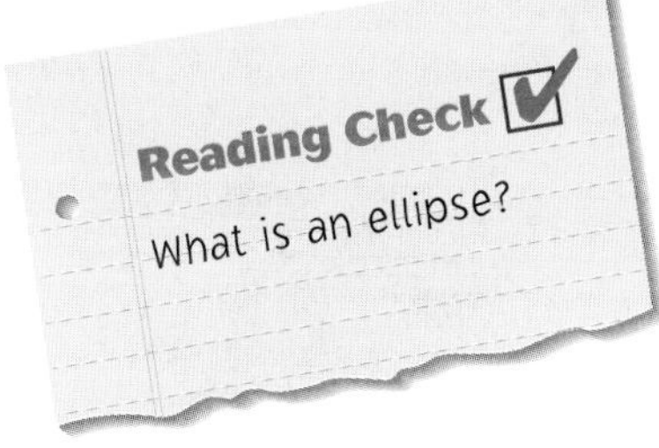

Does this elliptical orbit cause seasonal temperatures on Earth? If it did, you would expect the warmest days in January. You know this isn't the case in the northern hemisphere. Something else causes the change.

Even though Earth is closest to the sun in January, the overall amount of energy Earth receives from the sun changes little throughout the year. However, the amount of energy any one place on Earth receives can vary greatly.

Enrichment

Interpersonal Separate students into groups of four. Ask each group to devise a method to demonstrate the difference between Earth's rotation and revolution. Once finished, groups can demonstrate their ideas to other groups. L2 ELL COOP LEARN

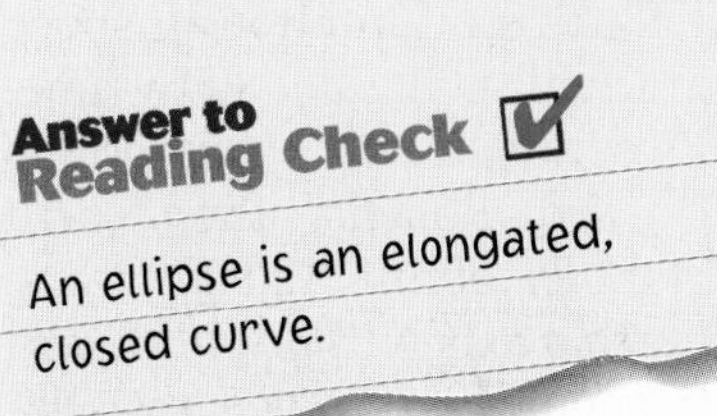

Answer to Reading Check
An ellipse is an elongated, closed curve.

Flex Your Brain

Use the Flex Your Brain activity to have students explore SEASONS.

GLENCOE TECHNOLOGY

Videodisc

The Infinite Voyage: The Living Clock

Chapter 6 *How Living Things Convert Light into Time* 5:30

Chapter 8 *Mental Health and the Biological Clock* 5:30

Refer to the Teacher Guide for bar codes and teaching strategies.

Multiple Learning Styles

Interpersonal Celebrate the seasons by having students work with elementary students to select a special day for each season. On this day, students can decorate the school halls, library, cafeteria, and other areas where the younger students congregate. Invite administrative personnel to planning sessions. L2

CA Science Content Standards

Page 642: 2d, 2e
Page 643: 2d, 2e

Caption Answers

Figure 18-4 *No, if it were, we would have the warmest temperatures in January when Earth is closest to the sun.*

Figure 18-5 *During summer in either hemisphere, Earth's axis is tilted toward the sun. The hemisphere tilted toward the sun receives more energy.*

Teacher FYI

Earth's orientation in space gradually changes with time. Presently, Earth's axis points toward Polaris, the North Star. In about 12 000 years, Earth's axis will point toward the star Vega in the constellation Lyra. This change is the result of Earth's "wobbling" on its axis.

Videodisc

STV: Solar System

Unit 1 *The Big Picture, Rotation and Revolution* 0:33

05295-06309

Refer to the Teacher Guide for additional bar codes and teaching strategies.

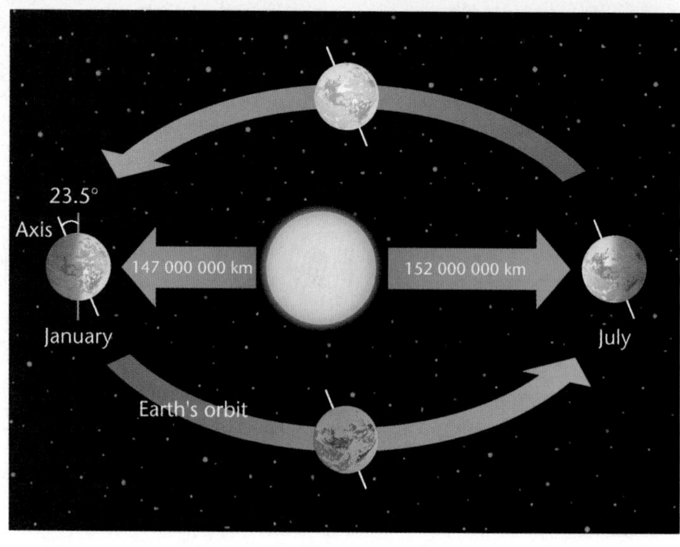

Figure 18-4 The northern hemisphere experiences summer when Earth is farthest from the sun. It experiences winter when Earth is closest to the sun. **Is the change of seasons caused by Earth's elliptical orbit? Explain your answer.**

Earth's Tilted Axis

Earth's axis is tilted 23.5° from a line perpendicular to its orbit. This tilt causes the seasons. Daylight hours are longer for the hemisphere tilted toward the sun. Think of how early it gets dark in the winter compared to the summer. As shown in **Figure 18-4,** the hemisphere tilted toward the sun receives more hours of sunlight than the hemisphere tilted away from the sun.

Earth's tilt also causes the sun's radiation to strike the hemisphere tilted toward it at a higher angle than it does the other hemisphere. Because of this, the hemisphere tilted toward the sun receives more electromagnetic radiation per unit area than the hemisphere tilted away. In other words, if you measured the amount of radiation received in a 1-km^2 area in the northern hemisphere and, at the same time, measured it for 1 km^2 in the southern hemisphere, you would find a difference. The hemisphere tilted toward the sun would be receiving more energy.

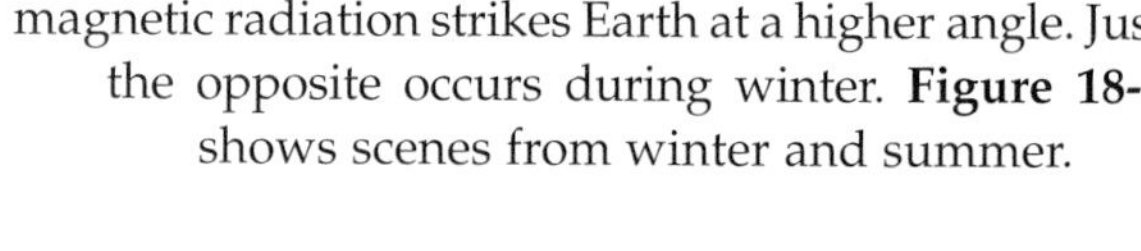

A summer season results when the sun's electromagnetic radiation strikes Earth at a higher angle. Just the opposite occurs during winter. **Figure 18-5** shows scenes from winter and summer.

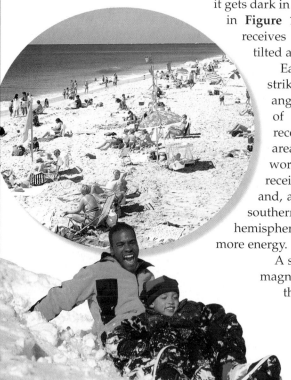

Figure 18-5 Temperatures during summer are warmer than those during winter. **Why?**

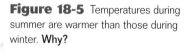

Across the Curriculum

Geography Arrange students into groups of four. Supply each group with a globe of Earth and a flashlight. Instruct them to shine the flashlight directly on the Tropics of Cancer and Capricorn to illustrate why the areas within the Arctic and Antarctic Circles are called the lands of the midnight sun during summer solstice. L2 COOP LEARN

Content Background

The slowing of Earth's rotation has been documented by Babylonian records of solar eclipses. The recorded dates of the eclipses could have occurred only if Earth were rotating slightly faster in the past.

Equinoxes and Solstices

Because of the tilt of Earth's axis, the sun's position relative to Earth's equator constantly changes. Most of the time, the sun is north or south of the equator. Two times during the year, however, the sun is directly over the equator.

Equinox

Look at **Figure 18-6.** When the sun reaches an **equinox** (EE kwuh nahks), it is directly above Earth's equator, and the number of daylight hours equals the number of nighttime hours all over the world. At that time, neither the northern nor the southern hemisphere is tilted toward the sun. In the northern hemisphere, the sun reaches the spring equinox on March 20 or 21 and the fall equinox on September 22 or 23. In the southern hemisphere, the equinoxes are reversed. Spring occurs in September and fall occurs in March.

Solstice

The **solstice** is the point at which the sun reaches its greatest distance north or south of the equator. In the northern hemisphere, the sun reaches the summer solstice on June 21 or 22, and the winter solstice occurs on December 21 or 22. Just the opposite is true for the southern hemisphere. When the sun is at the summer solstice, there are more daylight

Visit the Glencoe Science Web Site at **www.glencoe.com/sec/science/ca** for more information about seasons.

Figure 18-6 At summer solstice in the northern hemisphere, the sun is directly over the Tropic of Cancer, 23.5° north latitude at noon. At winter solstice, the sun is directly over the Tropic of Capricorn, 23.5° south latitude at noon. At both fall and spring equinoxes, the sun is directly over the equator at noon.

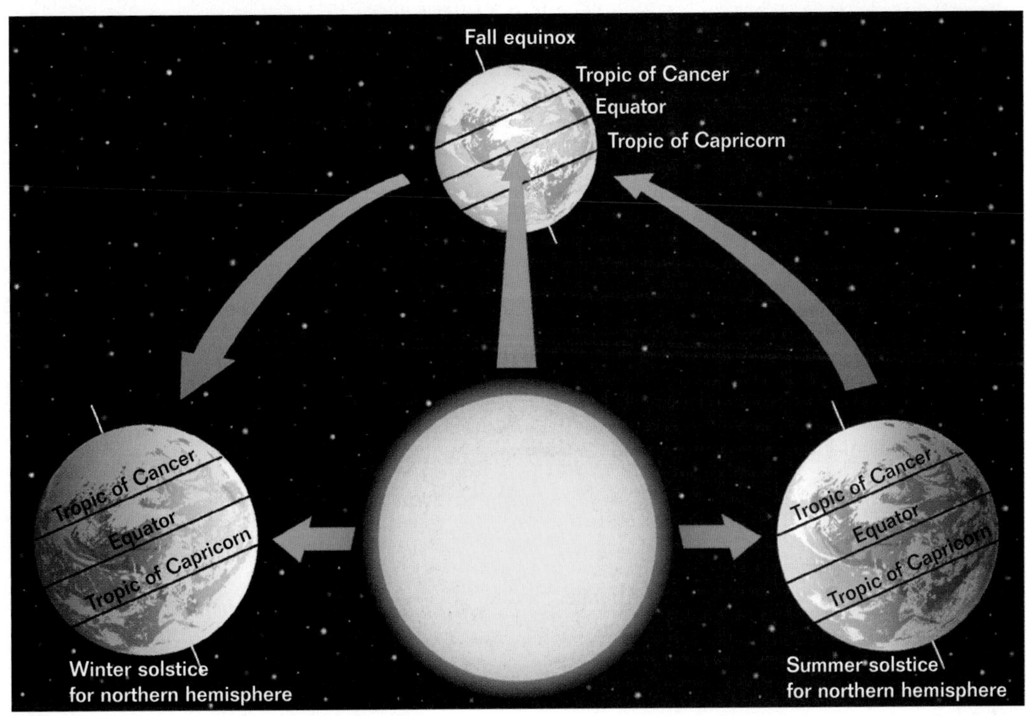

Internet Addresses

For Internet tips, see Glencoe's **Using the Internet in the Science Classroom.**

3 Assess

Check for Understanding

Discussion

Interpersonal Arrange students into groups of four. Have each group discuss what they like best about each season. When finished, conduct a class discussion about the pros and cons of each season. Encourage students to be creative and to describe specific characteristics about their favorite seasons. L1 COOP LEARN

Reteach

Visual-Spatial Darken the room and place a globe of Earth next to a light source. Tilt the globe 23.5°. Hold the globe so that its axis points toward and then away from the light. Slowly spin the globe to demonstrate how the amount of light striking each hemisphere of the globe changes. Help students conclude that days are shorter in the northern hemisphere when Earth's axis is tilted away from the sun, and longer when Earth's axis is tilted toward the sun.

Content Background

Earth's magnetic poles are not located in the same location as Earth's geographic poles. The difference in location between the two different poles, measured in degrees, is declination. Magnetic compass directions can be corrected to true geographic directions by either adding or subtracting the declination value listed on a map. If the declination is east, the value is subtracted from the compass reading. If the declination is west, the value is added. Many cars today are built with electronic compasses. The compasses must be adjusted for the local declination before they will show a correct reading.

CA Science Content Standards

Page 644: 4e, 4f
Page 645: 4e

Extension

For students who have mastered this section, use the **Reinforcement** and **Enrichment** masters.

4 Close

Proficiency Prep

Use this quiz to check students' recall of section content.

1. **What is the imaginary line around which Earth spins?** *axis*
2. **What is Earth's rotation.** *the spinning of Earth on its axis*
3. **What type of currents deep inside Earth are thought to generate its magnetic field?** *convection currents*
4. **What is the yearly orbit of Earth around the sun called?** *revolution*

Section Assessment

1. rotation
2. Light from the sun strikes Earth's surface at a higher angle, and the days are longer.
3. **Think Critically** Earth's orbit around the sun is an ellipse. Thus, its distance from the sun varies.

Using Computers

Student tables of Earth's physical data should include the information listed in **Table 18-1.**

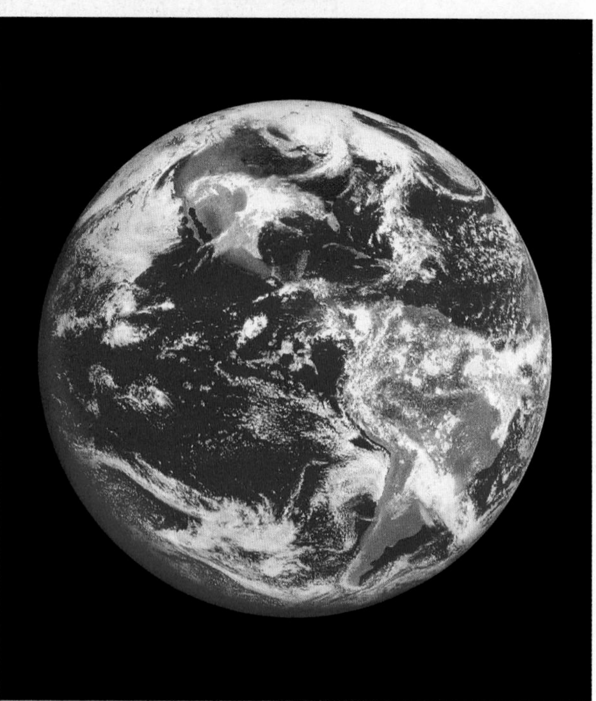

hours than during any other day of the year. When it's at the winter solstice, on the shortest day of the year, the most nighttime hours occur.

Earth Data Review

Earth, shown in **Figure 18-7,** is an imperfect sphere that bulges very slightly at the equator and is somewhat flattened at the poles. The rotation of Earth causes day and night. Earth's tilted axis is responsible for the seasons you experience, and our revolution around the sun marks the passing of a year. In the next section, you will read how Earth's nearest neighbor, the moon, is also in constant motion and how you observe this motion each day.

Figure 18-7 In this photo, Earth appears to be nearly a perfect sphere. In reality, its diameter is 42 km larger at the equator than at the poles.

Section Assessment

1. Which Earth motion causes night and day?
2. Why does summer occur in Earth's northern hemisphere when Earth's north pole is tilted toward the sun?
3. **Think Critically: Table 18-1** lists Earth's distance from the sun as an average. Why isn't there one exact measurement of this distance?
4. **Skill Builder**
   Recognizing Cause and Effect
   Answer these questions about the sun-Earth-moon relationship. If you need help, refer to Recognizing Cause and Effect in the **Skill Handbook** on page 957.
   a. What causes seasons on Earth?
   b. What causes winter?
   c. Earth is closest to the sun in January. What effect does this have on seasons?

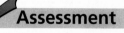

Using Computers

Spreadsheet Using the table or spreadsheet capabilities of a computer program, generate a table of Earth's physical data showing its diameter, mass, period of rotation, and other data. Then, write a description of the planet based on the table you have created. If you need help, refer to page 974.

4. **Skill Builder**
   a. the tilt of Earth's axis
   b. The sun's radiation strikes Earth at a low angle.
   c. It has little effect. The seasons are primarily due to the tilt of Earth on its axis, not its distance from the sun.

Assessment

Oral Use this Skill Builder to assess students' abilities to recognize cause and effect. Ask students to identify the cause of Earth's magnetic field and the effect this field has on a compass needle. Use **Performance Assessment in the Science Classroom,** p. 71.

A Brave and Startling Truth by Maya Angelou

In this chapter, you have learned some of the physical characteristics of our planet. Now, find out how one poet, Maya Angelou, uses Earth-science imagery to describe the human race and the quest for world peace. Below are several excerpts, or parts, from her poem "A Brave and Startling Truth."

We, this people, on a small and lonely planet
Traveling through casual space
Past aloof stars, across the way of indifferent suns
To a destination where all signs tell us
It is possible and imperative that we learn
A brave and startling truth...

When we come to it
Then we will confess that not the Pyramids
With their stones set in mysterious perfection
Nor the Gardens of Babylon
Hanging as eternal beauty
In our collective memory
Not the Grand Canyon
Kindled into delicious color
By Western sunsets
These are not the only wonders of the world...

When we come to it
We, this people, on this wayward, floating body
Created on this earth, of this earth
Have the power to fashion for this earth
A climate where every man and every woman
Can live freely without sanctimonious piety
And without crippling fear

When we come to it
We must confess that we are the possible
We are the miraculous, the true wonder of this world
That is when, and only when
We come to it.

interNET CONNECTION

Visit the Glencoe Science Web Site at **www.glencoe.com/sec/science/ca** to learn more about Maya Angelou and her works. Do her other books and poems also contain Earth-science imagery? Using your knowledge of Earth science, write a short poem that uses Earth-science imagery to describe a social issue important to you.

Content Background

Maya Angelou is probably best known as a poet. This Pulitzer prize winner, however, is also a playwright, director, actor, and producer, and is recognized as an important social voice in America. In the 1960s, Dr. Martin Luther King, Jr. made her the northern coordinator of the Southern Christian Leadership Conference. Gerald Ford chose her to be on the American Revolution Advisory Bicentennial Council. She was appointed to the National Commission on the Observance of International Women's Year by Jimmy Carter. President Bill Clinton requested that she write and deliver a poem at his 1993 presidential inauguration. Ms. Angelou is currently Reynolds professor of American Studies at Wake Forest University in North Carolina. She holds positions in many professional organizations including the board of trustees of the American Film Institute and the Director's Guild.

Teaching Strategies

Have a volunteer state some of the physical characteristics of Earth—its diameter, mass, volume, and so on. Lead a discussion that contrasts these measurements with Angelou's descriptions of the planet (small, miniscule, mote of matter). Make sure students realize that our planet is in fact but a speck in the universe.

For Additional Information

Angelou, Maya. *A Brave and Startling Truth.* New York: Random House, 1995.

interNET CONNECTION

Internet Addresses

____

____

____

____

For Internet tips, see Glencoe's **Using the Internet in the Science Classroom.**

CA Science Content Standards

Page 646: 4e, 9e
Page 647: 4e

Activity 18•1 Design Your Own Experiment

Recognize the Problem

Purpose

Logical-Mathematical To design and carry out an experiment to show how the angle at which sunlight strikes an area of Earth's surface determines the amount of heat received by that area. L2 ELL COOP LEARN

Process Skills

communicating, making and using tables, observing and inferring, comparing and contrasting, recognizing cause and effect, designing an experiment, measuring in SI, hypothesizing, separating and controlling variables, interpreting data, formulating models

Time

one class period

Alternate Materials A desk lamp held at the proper angle can be used instead of a gooseneck lamp.

Safety Precautions

The lightbulb and shade may be hot for some time after the lamp is turned off.

Form a Hypothesis

Possible Hypotheses

When light strikes a surface area from directly above, the area will receive more heat per unit area than when the light strikes the same surface area at a glancing angle.

Design Your Own Experiment

Activity 18•1

Tilt and Temperature

Possible Materials

- Tape
- Black construction paper (one sheet)
- Gooseneck lamp with 75-watt bulb
- Celsius thermometer
- Watch
- Protractor

Have you ever noticed how hot the surface of a blacktop driveway can get during the day? The sun's rays hit Earth more directly as the day progresses. Now, consider the fact that Earth is tilted on its axis. How does this affect the amount of heat an area on Earth receives from the sun?

Recognize the Problem

How is the angle at which light strikes an area on Earth related to the changing of the seasons?

Form a Hypothesis

State a hypothesis about how the angle at which light strikes an area affects the amount of heat energy received by that area.

Goals

- **Measure** the amount of heat generated by a light as it strikes a surface at different angles.
- **Describe** how light striking a surface at different angles is related to the changing of the seasons on Earth.

Safety Precautions

Do not touch the lamp without safety gloves. The lightbulb and shade can be hot even when the lamp has been turned off. Handle the thermometer carefully. If it breaks, do not touch anything. Inform your teacher immediately.

648 CHAPTER 18 THE SUN-EARTH-MOON SYSTEM

Test Your Hypothesis

Possible Procedures

Fold the black construction paper in half lengthwise. Tape the short edges together to form an envelope. Use this envelope to hold the thermometer. As an independent variable, set the lamp so that light shines directly down on the envelope containing the thermometer, and then change the angle to 45°. Select a specific time period for recording the temperature (for example, every three to nine minutes).

Test Your Hypothesis

Plan

1. As a group, agree upon and write out your hypothesis statement.
2. As a group, **list the steps** you need to take to test your hypothesis. Be specific, describing exactly what you will do at each step. List your materials.
3. **Make a list** of any special properties you expect to observe or test.
4. Read over your entire experiment to make sure that all steps are in a logical order.
5. **Identify** any constants, variables, and controls in the experiment.
6. Will you **summarize** data in a graph, table, or some other format?
7. How will you **determine** whether the length of time the light is turned on affects heat energy?
8. How will you **determine** whether the angle at which light strikes an area causes changes in heat and energy?

Do

1. Make sure your teacher approves your plan before you proceed.
2. **Carry out** the experiment as planned.
3. **Complete** the data table in your Science Journal.

Analyze Your Data

1. **Describe** your experiment, including how you used independent variables to test your hypothesis.
2. What happened to the temperature of the area being measured as you modified your variables?
3. **Identify** the dependent variable in your experiment.

Draw Conclusions

1. Did your experiment support your hypothesis? **Explain.**
2. If not, **determine** how you might change the experiment in order to retest your hypothesis. How might you change your hypothesis?

Teaching Strategies

Troubleshooting Remind students to allow the thermometer to return to room temperature before each use.

Expected Outcome

Students should realize that the surface area heats up more quickly when light hits it from a more direct angle. They should also realize that this causes the warmer temperatures of summer.

Error Analysis

Ask students if they believe they would receive more energy from the sun when it is high in the sky or when it is low in the sky. Ask students to compare air temperatures at noon and at dusk.

Analyze Your Data

1. Descriptions will vary, but students should mention that they varied the angle at which light struck the thermometer.
2. Answers will vary, but students should note that when light strikes a surface at an angle, temperature increases more slowly.
3. Temperature is the dependent variable.

Draw Conclusions

1. Answers will vary depending on student hypotheses.
2. Answers will vary. Students may say that they need to change the angles of the light source or record temperatures at a different rate.

GO Further

Predict how the absorption of heat would be affected by changing your independent variable. Try your experiment with different values for your independent variable. Students should realize that lowering the angle should cause less of a temperature rise, and increasing the angle to a greater amount should cause the temperature to rise more quickly.

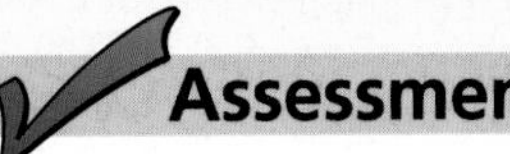

Assessment

Process Ask students to explain in writing why temperatures rise faster when light hits a surface area at a more direct angle. Use **Performance Assessment in the Science Classroom,** p. 87. P

CA Science Content Standards

Page 648: 4e, 9a, 9b, 9c, 9e
Page 649: 4e, 9a, 9b, 9c, 9e

SECTION 18•2

Prepare

Refer to **Moon Craters** and **Origin of the Moon** on p. 638F.

Preplanning

Refer to the **Chapter Organizer** on pp. 638A–B.

1 Motivate

Bellringer

Before presenting the lesson, display **Section Focus Transparency 50** on the overhead projector. Use the accompanying **Focus Activity** worksheet. L2 ELL

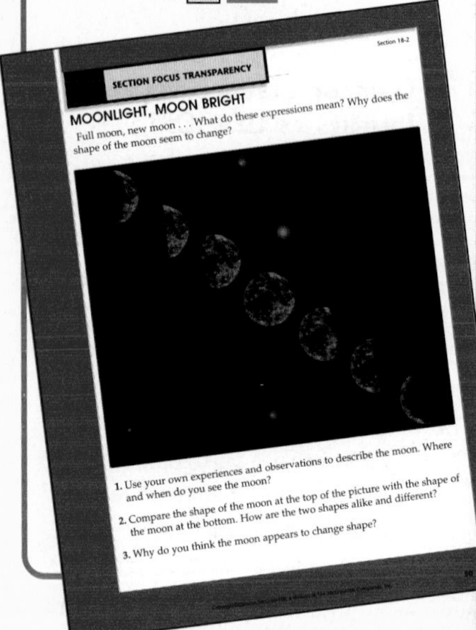

Section 18-2

SECTION FOCUS TRANSPARENCY

MOONLIGHT, MOON BRIGHT

Full moon, new moon . . . What do these expressions mean? Why does the shape of the moon seem to change?

1. Use your own experiences and observations to describe the moon. Where and when do you see the moon?
2. Compare the shape of the moon at the top of the picture with the shape of the moon at the bottom. How are the two shapes alike and different?
3. Why do you think the moon appears to change shape?

Tying to Previous Knowledge

Help students recall the cause of tides from their earlier studies. Also, help students recall that large tidal ranges occur when Earth, the sun, and the moon are lined up.

18•2 Earth's Moon

What You'll Learn

- How the moon's phases depend on the relative positions of the sun, the moon, and Earth
- Why eclipses occur and how solar and lunar eclipses compare
- What the surface features of the moon may tell us about its history

Vocabulary

moon phase, new moon, waxing, first quarter, full moon, waning, third quarter, solar eclipse, lunar eclipse, maria

Why It's Important

- The moon is our closest neighbor in space.

Motions of the Moon

You have probably noticed how the moon's apparent shape changes from day to day. Sometimes, just after sunset, you can see a full, round moon low in the sky. Other times, only half of the moon is visible, and it's high in the sky at sunset. Sometimes, the moon is visible during the day. Why does the moon look the way it does? What causes it to change its appearance and position in the sky?

The Moon's Rotation and Revolution

Just as Earth rotates on its axis and revolves around the sun, the moon rotates on its axis and revolves around Earth. The moon's revolution causes changes in its appearance. If the moon rotates on its axis, why don't we see it spin around in space? The moon rotates on its axis once every 27.3 days. It takes the same amount of time to revolve once around Earth. As **Figure 18-8** shows, because these two motions take the same amount of time, the same side of the moon always faces Earth.

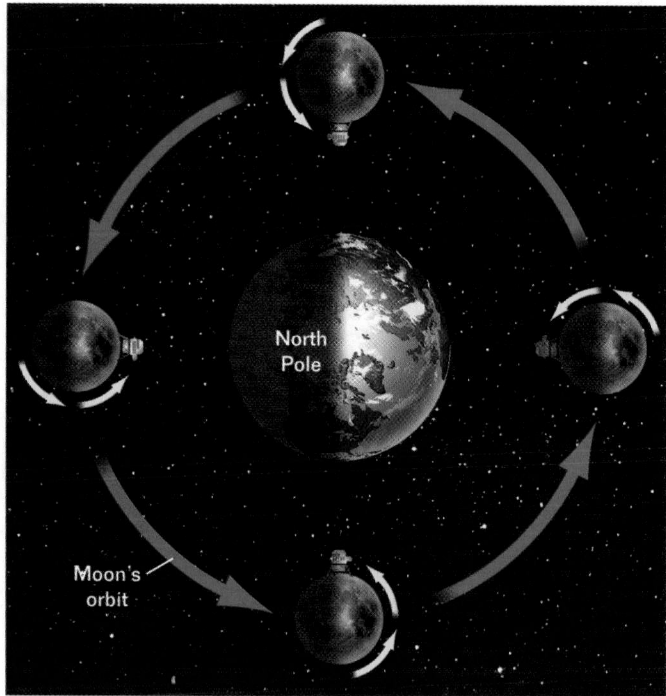

Figure 18-8 In about one month, the moon orbits Earth. It also completes one rotation on its axis during the same period. **Does this affect which side of the moon faces Earth? Explain.**

Resource Manager

The following **Teacher Classroom Resources** can be used with Section 18-2:

Reproducible Masters

Activity Worksheets, p. 104 L2

Enrichment, p. 50 L3

Multicultural Connections, pp. 35–36 L2

Reinforcement, p. 50 L2

Transparencies

Science Integration Transparency 18 L2

Teaching Transparency 36 L2

Figure 18-9 The phases of the moon are: (A) new moon, (B) waxing crescent, (C) first quarter, (D) waxing gibbous, (E) full moon, (F) waning gibbous, (G) third quarter, and (H) waning crescent.

You can show this by having a friend hold a ball in front of you. Instruct your friend to move the ball around you while keeping the same side of it facing you. Everyone else in the room will see all sides of the ball. You will see only one side.

Why the Moon Shines

The moon shines because it reflects sunlight from its surface. Just as half of Earth experiences day as the other half experiences night, half of the moon is lighted while the other half is dark. As the moon revolves around Earth, you see different portions of its lighted side, causing the moon's appearance to change. **Moon phases,** as shown in **Figure 18-9,** are the changing appearances of the moon as seen from Earth. The phase you see depends on the relative positions of the moon, Earth, and the sun.

Phases of the Moon

A new moon occurs when the moon is between Earth and the sun. During a **new moon,** the lighted half of the moon is facing the sun and the dark side faces Earth. The moon is in the sky, but it cannot be seen.

Waxing Phases

Shortly after a new moon, more and more of the moon's lighted side becomes visible—the phases are **waxing.** About 24 hours after a new moon, you can see a thin slice of the side of the moon that is lighted by the sun. This phase is called the waxing crescent. About a week after a new moon, you can see half of the lighted side, or one-quarter of the moon's surface. This phase is **first quarter.**

The phases continue to wax. When more than one-quarter is visible, it is called waxing gibbous. A **full moon** occurs when all of the moon's surface that faces Earth is lit up.

Using Math

Earth rotates through an angle of 360° in one day. How many degrees does Earth rotate in one hour?

2 Teach

Caption Answer

Figure 18-8 *Yes, because the moon's rotation and revolution take the same amount of time, the same side of the moon always faces Earth.*

Correcting Misconceptions

Some students may think that the far side of the moon is not seen because it is dark. Explain that this side of the moon receives as much light as the side that faces Earth. The far side is not seen because it always faces away from Earth.

Using Math

360°/24 hrs = 15°/hr

GLENCOE TECHNOLOGY

CD-ROM

Glencoe Science Voyages Interactive CD-ROM

Explorations

Have students do the interactive exploration *How do Earth and the moon interact to cause the moon's phases?*

Inclusion Strategies

Gifted Have students work in pairs to make time-lapse videos of the phases of the moon. Every night, the partners should videotape the moon for a few seconds. They should do this for one month. A regular 35-mm camera can be used if a video camera is not available. L2 COOP LEARN

Behaviorally Disordered Have students research myths about the full moon. After gathering the information, encourage students who have difficulty working within normal classroom constraints to perform skits that illustrate some of the myths. L2 COOP LEARN

CA Science Content Standards

Page 650: 4d, 4e
Page 651: 4d, 4e, 4f

Purpose

Students will compare the sizes of the sun, the moon, and Earth.

Materials

chalk, string, meterstick

Teaching Strategies

This activity works best in a large, open, paved area. Make sure students have at least 4 m of string with which to draw their circles.

Analysis

1. The sun is more than 400 times the size of the moon.
2. & 3. The sun's diameter is approximately 109 times greater than Earth's. The diameters of new circles representing the sun and Earth would be 109 cm and 1 cm, respectively.

Performance Tell students that the moon's diameter is 3476 km. Have them draw two new circles representing the relative sizes of Earth and the moon. Use **Performance Assessment in the Science Classroom,** p. 29.

Videodisc

STV: Solar System

Unit 1 *The Big Picture, Landing on the Moon* 1:41

08780-11815

Refer to the Teacher Guide for additional bar codes and teaching strategies.

Comparing the Sun and Moon

Procedure

1. Find an area where you can make a chalk mark on pavement or another surface.
2. Tie a piece of chalk to one end of a string that's 400 cm long.
3. Hold the other end of the string to the pavement.
4. Have a friend pull the string tight and walk around you, leaving a mark on the pavement as he or she circles you.
5. Draw a circle with a 1-cm diameter in the middle of the large circle.

Analysis

1. The small circle represents the moon, and the larger circle represents the sun. How big is the sun compared to the moon?
2. The diameter of the sun is 1.39 million km. The diameter of the Earth is 12 756 km. Draw two new circles modeling the sizes of the sun and Earth.
3. What are the diameters of your two new circles?

Figure 18-10 The orbit of the moon is not in the same plane as Earth's orbit around the sun. If it were, we would experience a solar eclipse each month during the new moon. The plane of the moon's orbit is tilted about 5° to the plane of Earth's orbit.

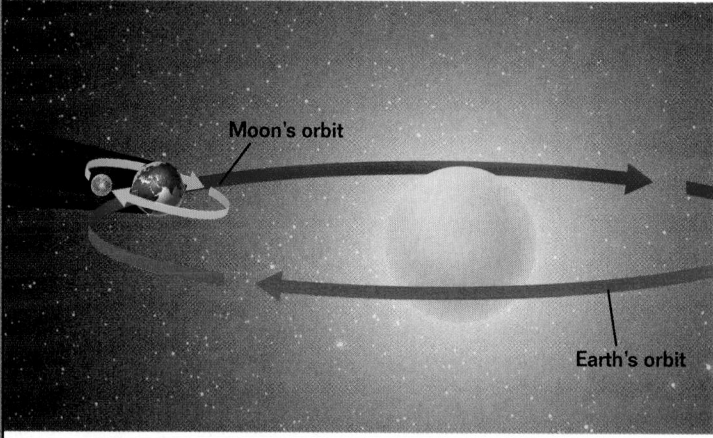

Waning Phases

After a full moon, the amount of the moon's lighted side that can be seen becomes smaller. The phases are said to be **waning.** Waning gibbous begins just after a full moon. When you can see only half of the lighted side, the **third-quarter** phase occurs. The amount of the moon that can be seen continues to become smaller. Waning crescent occurs just before another new moon. Once again, you can see a small slice of the lighted side of the moon.

The complete cycle of the moon's phases takes about 29.5 days. Recall that it takes about 27.3 days for the moon to revolve around Earth. The discrepancy between these two numbers is due to Earth's revolution. It takes the moon about two days to "catch up" with Earth's advancement around the sun.

Eclipses

Imagine yourself as one of your ancient ancestors, living 10 000 years ago. You are out foraging for nuts and other fruit in the bright afternoon sun. Gradually, the sun disappears from the sky, as if being swallowed by a giant creature. The darkness lasts only a short time, and the sun soon returns to full brightness. You realize something unusual has happened, but you don't know what caused it. It will be almost 8000 years before anyone can explain the event that you just experienced.

The event just described was a total solar eclipse (ih KLIPS). Today, we know what causes such eclipses, but for our early ancestors, they must have been terrifying events. Many animals act as if night has come. Cows return to their barns, and chickens go to sleep. What causes the day to suddenly change into night and then back into day?

Phases of the Moon Ask students to spend five to ten minutes writing freely in their Science Journals about everything they now know about the moon's phases. Have them use their free-writing exercise to formulate questions that will teach them information they still need or want to know. L2

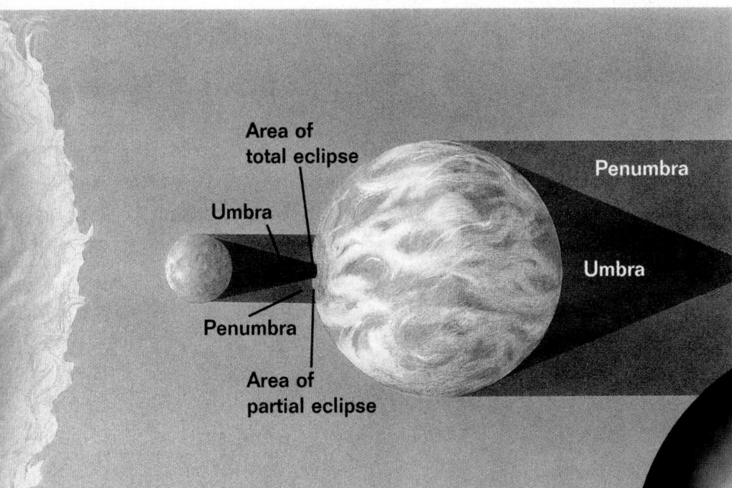

Figure 18-11 Only a small area of Earth experiences a total solar eclipse during the eclipse event. Only the outer portion of the sun's atmosphere is visible during a total solar eclipse. Distances are not drawn to scale.

The Cause of Eclipses

Revolution of the moon causes eclipses. Eclipses occur when Earth or the moon temporarily blocks the sunlight reaching the other. Sometimes, during a new moon, a shadow cast by the moon falls on Earth and causes a solar eclipse. During a full moon, a shadow of Earth can be cast on the moon, resulting in a lunar eclipse.

Eclipses can occur only when the sun, the moon, and Earth are lined up perfectly. Look at **Figure 18-10.** Because the moon's orbit is not in the same plane as Earth's orbit around the sun, eclipses happen only a few times each year.

Solar Eclipses

A **solar eclipse,** such as the one in **Figure 18-11,** occurs when the moon moves directly between the sun and Earth and casts a shadow on part of Earth. The darkest portion of the moon's shadow is called the umbra (UM bruh). A person standing within the umbra experiences a total solar eclipse. The only portion of the sun that is visible is part of its atmosphere, which appears as a pearly white glow around the edge of the eclipsing moon.

Surrounding the umbra is a lighter shadow on Earth's surface called the penumbra (puh NUM bruh). Persons standing in the penumbra experience a partial solar eclipse. **CAUTION:** *Regardless of where you are standing, never look directly at a solar eclipse. The light can permanently damage your eyes.*

Changing Seasons

Suppose that Earth's rotation took twice the time that it presently does. Write a report on how conditions such as global temperatures, work schedules, plant growth, and other factors might be different.

Answers will vary but may include the fact that daytime temperatures would be higher, whereas nighttime temperatures would be lower. With longer daytime hours, work schedules might be more flexible. Plants would adapt to a longer cycle of food production based on photosynthesis.

Content Background

Eclipses can occur only if the moon, the sun, and Earth are in a straight line, which is a state known as *syzygy.* Also, eclipses occur only when the moon is at new-moon or full-moon stage and is located near a node (a point where the moon's path crosses the ecliptic). In the case of solar eclipses, the moon needs to be close to perigee (its closest approach to Earth). The closer the moon is to perigee (and the closer Earth is to aphelion), the more likely it is that a total solar eclipse will occur and the longer it will last.

Using an Analogy

Tell students to imagine they are sitting on the couch, watching television. Ask them how their view of the television screen would change if someone stood between the television and the couch. Compare this analogy to the positions of the moon or Earth during eclipses.

CA Science Content Standards

Page 652: 4d, 4e, 9f
Page 653: 4d, 4e

Guided Reading Strategy

Reciprocal Teaching This strategy is designed to help construct meaning and apply reading skills. Have pairs of students begin by each partner silently reading a chunk of text. After several minutes of reading, one student retells the key points of what was read in his or her own words. The other student creates a question that can be answered directly from the text but could require inferences or evaluation. Continue the reading with each student alternating questions and summaries. Consciously asking questions and summarizing content helps the reader focus on what is being read. Have students do Reciprocal Reading with a chunk of section content.

Enrichment

Help students realize that the word *month* comes from the same root as the word *moon*. Month describes the period of time that can be measured by the movement of the moon. A sidereal month is 27.3 days long, which is the actual period of the moon's revolution around Earth. A synodic month, the time between successive phases, is 29.5 days long. The discrepancy is due to Earth's revolution. It takes the moon about two days to catch up with Earth's advancement around the sun.

Quick Demo

Visual-Spatial Obtain a globe of the moon, or use a volleyball to represent the moon. Darken the room, and place three overhead projectors across the front of the room with their lights aimed toward the back of the room at an angle above students' heads. Have students cluster near the center of the room. Inform students that the projectors represent the sun, and the globe or ball represents the moon. The students represent observers on Earth. Keep the same side of the moon facing the students as you revolve the moon around them. Students should be able to see the moon go through phases beginning with new moon. Point out that the side of the moon that we aren't able to see is lighted during new moon. After the demonstration of lunar phases, position the moon properly during new and full moon to demonstrate how light is blocked out during solar and lunar eclipses. ELL COOP LEARN

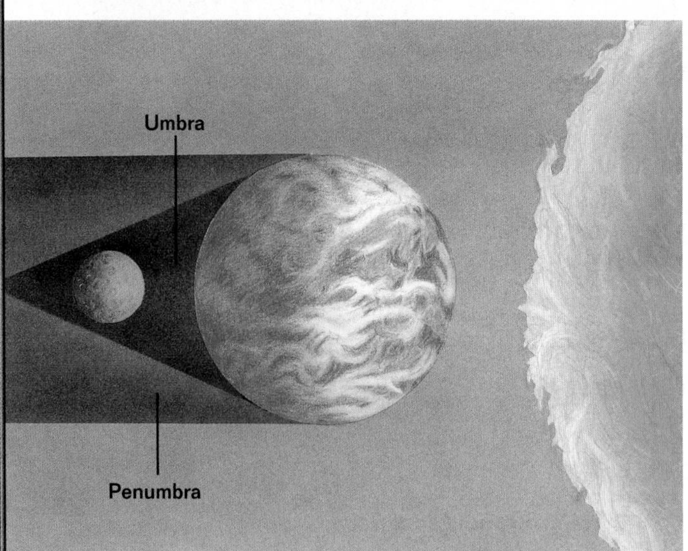

Figure 18-12 During a total lunar eclipse, Earth's shadow blocks light coming from the sun.

Lunar Eclipses

When Earth's shadow falls on the moon, a **lunar eclipse** like the one shown in **Figures 18-12** and **18-13** occurs. A lunar eclipse begins when the moon moves into Earth's penumbra. As the moon continues to move, it enters Earth's umbra and you see a curved shadow on the moon's surface. It was from this shadow that Aristotle concluded that Earth's shape was spherical. When the moon moves completely into Earth's umbra, the moon becomes dark red because light from the sun is refracted by Earth's atmosphere onto the moon. A total lunar eclipse has occurred.

A partial lunar eclipse occurs when only a portion of the moon moves into Earth's umbra. The remainder of the moon is in Earth's penumbra and, therefore, receives some direct sunlight.

A total solar eclipse occurs up to two times every year, yet most people live their entire lives without witnessing one. You may not be lucky enough to see a total solar eclipse, but it is almost certain you will have a chance to see a total lunar eclipse in your lifetime. The reason it is so difficult to view a total solar eclipse is that only those people in the small region where the moon's umbra strikes Earth can witness one. In contrast, anyone on the nighttime side of Earth can see a total lunar eclipse.

Figure 18-13 These photographs show the moon moving from right to left into Earth's umbra, then out again.

654 CHAPTER 18 THE SUN-EARTH-MOON SYSTEM

Cloudless Moon Have students research and write a one-page report in their Science Journals about why the moon does not have an atmosphere and whether it ever did have one. *The moon's gravitational force is not strong enough to hold gases at its surface. When sunlight falls on the moon, the moon's surface becomes intensely hot. Thus, the molecules that make up air travel fast enough to escape the moon's force of gravity. Atmospheric gases have probably been released by volcanic activity on the moon's surface in the past, but they have escaped into space.* L3

Structure of the Moon

When you look at the moon, you can see many of its larger surface features. The dark-colored, relatively flat regions are called **maria.** Maria formed when ancient lava flows from the moon's interior filled large basins on the moon's surface. The basins formed early in the moon's history.

Craters

Many depressions on the moon were formed by meteorites, asteroids, and comets, which strike the surfaces of planets and their satellites. These depressions are called craters. During impact, cracks may have formed in the moon's crust, allowing lava to reach the surface and fill in the large craters, forming maria. The igneous rocks of the maria are 3 to 4 billion years old. They are the youngest rocks found on the moon thus far.

The Moon's Interior

Seismographs left on the moon by *Apollo* astronauts have enabled scientists to study moonquakes. The study of earthquakes allows scientists to map Earth's interior. Likewise, the study of moonquakes has led to a model of the moon's interior. One model of the moon shows that its crust is about 60 km thick on the side facing Earth and about 150 km thick on the far side. Below the crust, a solid mantle may extend to a depth of 1000 km. A partly molten zone of the mantle extends farther down. Below this may be an iron-rich, solid core.

interNET CONNECTION

Visit the Glencoe Science Web Site at **www.glencoe.com/sec/science/ca** to learn more about the *Apollo* space missions.

Problem Solving

Survival on the Moon

You and your crew have crash-landed on the moon, far from your intended landing site at the moon colony. It will take one day to reach the colony on foot. The side of the moon that you are on will be facing away from the sun during your entire trip back. You manage to salvage the following items from your wrecked ship: food, rope, solar-powered heating unit, battery-operated heating unit, three 70-kg oxygen tanks, map of the constellations, magnetic compass, oxygen-burning signal flares, matches, 8 L of water, solar-powered radio receiver and transmitter, three flashlights and extra batteries, signal mirror, and binoculars. Keep in mind that the moon's gravity is about one-sixth that of Earth's, and it lacks a magnetic field. Determine which items will be of no use to you. Determine which items to take with you on your journey to the colony.

Think Critically: Based on what you have learned about the moon, describe why each of the salvaged items is useful or not useful.

1. How did the moon's physical properties affect your decisions?
2. How did the lack of sunlight affect your decisions?

Problem Solving

Help students understand that items necessary for survival on Earth may not be important for survival on the moon.

Think Critically

Food and water will be needed. A battery-operated heating unit is also necessary because of the low temperatures on the moon's nightside. Oxygen tanks are the most important items to bring. A map of the constellations may help if the crew becomes lost. A flashlight is absolutely necessary. Binoculars will be useless unless you transverse into the daytime side. Rope may be needed to cross rough terrain. The solar-powered heating unit and radio and the signal mirror are useless without sunlight. Signal flares and matches cannot be used in the oxygen-free environment.

1. The moon's rough terrain, lack of oxygen, and low temperatures determine many of the objects selected.
2. The signal mirror, solar-powered heating unit, radio, and binoculars are left behind because they are useless without sunlight. By the same token, the flashlight is essential.

interNET CONNECTION

Internet Addresses

For Internet tips, see Glencoe's **Using the Internet in the Science Classroom.**

CA Science Content Standards

Page 654: 4d, 4e
Page 655: 4d, 4e

VISUAL Learning

Figure 18-14 Have students research the moons of other planets such as Jupiter or Mars. Have them compare and contrast the various moons.

Answer to Reading Check

The impact theory states that the moon was formed about 4.6 billion years ago when a Mars-sized object collided with Earth, throwing gas and debris into orbit, some of which later formed the moon.

3 Assess

Check for Understanding

Activity

Interpersonal Put students into groups of four. Provide each group with a map of the moon's surface which can be found in astronomy field guides and reference books. Have students find and describe key surface features and explain how each feature might have formed. L2 COOP LEARN

Reteach

Using a globe of Earth, a tennis ball, and a large beach ball, simulate solar and lunar eclipses with the help of volunteers.

Extension

For students who have mastered this section, use the **Reinforcement** and **Enrichment** masters.

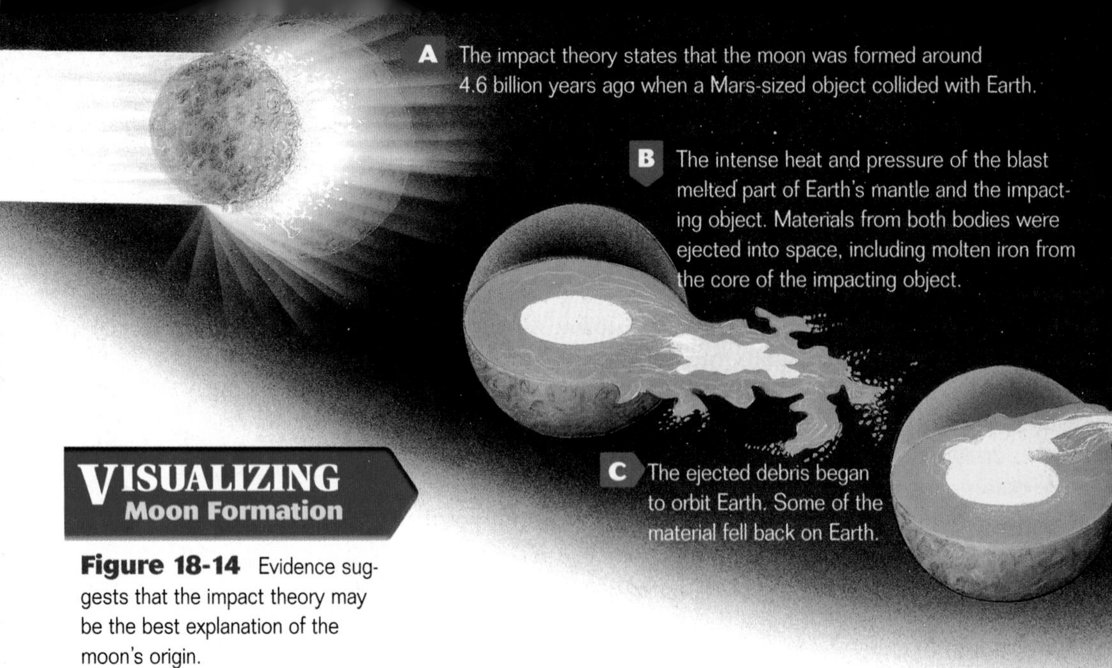

A The impact theory states that the moon was formed around 4.6 billion years ago when a Mars-sized object collided with Earth.
B The intense heat and pressure of the blast melted part of Earth's mantle and the impacting object. Materials from both bodies were ejected into space, including molten iron from the core of the impacting object.
C The ejected debris began to orbit Earth. Some of the material fell back on Earth.

VISUALIZING Moon Formation

Figure 18-14 Evidence suggests that the impact theory may be the best explanation of the moon's origin.

Origin of the Moon

Prior to the data obtained from the *Apollo* space missions, there were three theories about the moon's origin. The first was that the moon was captured by Earth's gravity. It had formed elsewhere and wandered into Earth's vicinity. The second theory was that the moon condensed from loose material surrounding Earth during the early formation of the solar system. The last theory was that a blob of molten material was ejected from Earth while Earth was still in its early molten stage.

Impact Theory

The data gathered by the *Apollo* missions have led many scientists to support a new impact theory. According to the impact theory, the moon was formed about 4.6 billion years ago when a Mars-sized object collided with Earth, throwing gas and debris into orbit. The gas and debris then condensed into one large mass, forming the moon. **Figure 18-14** illustrates the impact theory.

Reading Check What is the impact theory of the moon's origin?

Regardless of the moon's true origin, it has played an important role in our history. It was a source of curiosity for many early astronomers. Studying the phases of the moon and eclipses led people to conclude that Earth and the moon were in motion around the sun. Earth's shadow on the moon proved that Earth's shape was spherical. When Galileo first turned his telescope to the moon, he found a surface scarred by craters

Moon Observations Have students keep a two-week log of moon observations, including the moon phase, the time it was observed, the moon's altitude above the horizon, and a brief description of sky conditions. The width of a fist when held at arm's length is approximately equal to 10° of altitude. L2

Integrating the Sciences

Seismology Have students write a report in their Science Journals about the kinds of equipment left behind on the moon and how these instruments have given scientists a better understanding of the moon's structure and history. L3

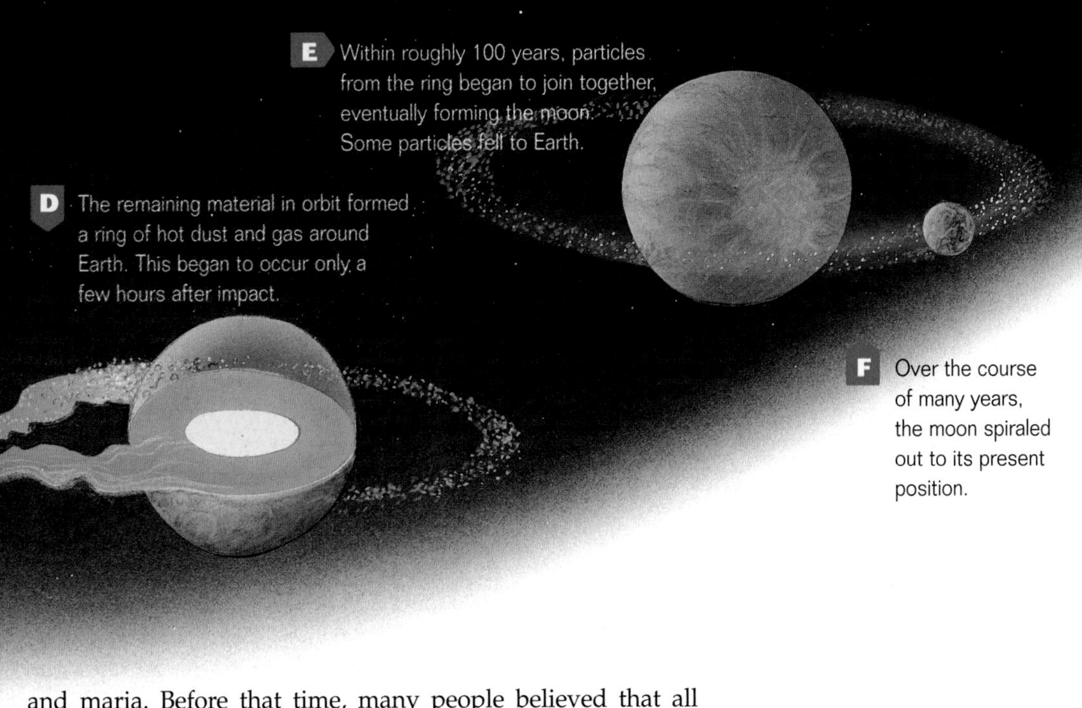

and maria. Before that time, many people believed that all planetary bodies were perfect, without surface features.

E Within roughly 100 years, particles from the ring began to join together, eventually forming the moon. Some particles fell to Earth.
D The remaining material in orbit formed a ring of hot dust and gas around Earth. This began to occur only a few hours after impact.
F Over the course of many years, the moon spiraled out to its present position.

By studying the moon, we can learn about ourselves and the planet we live on. As you will read in the next section, not only is the moon important as an object from our past, but it is important to our future, as well.

Section Assessment

1. What are the relative positions of the sun, the moon, and Earth during a full moon?
2. Why does a lunar eclipse occur only during a full moon?
3. Compare and contrast umbra and penumbra.
4. **Think Critically:** What provides the force necessary to form craters on the moon?
5. **Skill Builder** **Interpreting Scientific Illustrations** By tracking the changing positions of the sun, Earth, and the moon, scientists can predict solar eclipses. Do the **Chapter 18 Skill Activity** on page 979 to see when and where future solar eclipses will occur.

Research the moon's origin in astronomy books and magazines. In your Science Journal, write a report about the various theories, including the theory about a Mars-sized object colliding with Earth. Make a drawing of each theory.

Assessment

Performance Assess students' abilities to interpret scientific illustrations by having them draw the impact theory of the moon's formation. Use **Performance Assessment in the Science Classroom,** p. 55.

4 Close

Proficiency Prep

Use this quiz to check students' recall of section content.

1. **Which type of eclipse occurs when the moon moves directly between Earth and the sun?** *solar eclipse*
2. **Which type of eclipse occurs when Earth's shadow falls on the moon?** *lunar eclipse*
3. **What are maria and how did they form?** *Maria are dark-colored, relatively flat areas on the moon that formed when lava filled large basins on the surface of the moon.*

Section Assessment

1. Earth is between the sun and the moon.
2. In order for a lunar eclipse to occur, the moon must be within Earth's shadow. This happens only during full moon.
3. The darkest part of the moon's or Earth's shadow during an eclipse is the umbra. The lighter, broader shadow is the penumbra.
4. Think Critically the collision of meteorites into the moon's surface

Answers should relate to the theories of capture, condensation, fission, and impact.

CA Science Content Standards

Page 656: 2g, 4e
Page 657: 2g, 4d, 4e

SECTION 18•3

Prepare

Content Background

Refer to **Exploration of the Moon** on p. 638F.

Preplanning

Refer to the **Chapter Organizer** on p. 638A–B.

1 Motivate

Bellringer

Before presenting the lesson, display **Section Focus Transparency 51** on the overhead projector. Use the accompanying **Focus Activity** worksheet. L2 ELL

Section 18-3

SECTION FOCUS TRANSPARENCY

LIFE ON THE MOON

What would it be like to live on the moon? Some day, you may have the opportunity to find out. How does this cartoon show what you can expect?

1. What would you eat and wear if you lived on the moon?
2. What supplies would you need to build a place to live on the moon?
3. How do you think life would be harder on the moon? How would it be easier?

Tying to Previous Knowledge

Help students recall that humans first landed on the moon in 1969 and that a total of six *Apollo* missions have explored the moon with crews on its surface.

18•3 Exploration of the Moon

What You'll Learn

- Recent information about the moon discovered by spacecraft
- Facts about the moon's poles that may be important to future space travel

Vocabulary

mascon

Why It's Important

- Future missions to the moon may lead to important discoveries about Earth's origin.

Early Moon Missions

For centuries, astronomers have studied the moon for clues to its makeup and origin. In 1958, the former Soviet Union took studies of the moon into space with the launching of the *Luna* spacecraft. Three years later, the United States launched the first *Ranger* spacecraft, beginning its own lunar space exploration program.

Early U.S. moon missions, such as those involving the uncrewed *Ranger* and later the *Lunar Orbiter* spacecraft, focused on taking detailed photographs of the moon's surface. The *Lunar Orbiter* missions were followed by the *Surveyor* missions, wherein seven *Surveyor* spacecraft landed on the moon in preparation for the ultimate goal: to land astronauts on the moon. In 1969, this goal was realized with the launching of *Apollo 11*. By 1972 when the *Apollo* missions ended, 12 U.S. astronauts had walked on the moon.

Return to the Moon

More than 20 years passed before the United States resumed its studies of the moon from space. In 1994, the *Clementine* spacecraft was placed into lunar orbit to conduct a two-month survey of the moon's surface. *Clementine's* mission was to test new sensors for tracking cold objects, such as satellites, in space.

Figure 18-15 This false-color photograph, taken by cameras on the *Clementine* spacecraft, shows the moon, the sun, and the planet Venus.

Resource Manager

The following **Teacher Classroom Resources** can be used with Section 18-3:

Reproducible Masters

Activity Worksheets, pp. 101–102 L2

Enrichment, p. 51 L3

Reinforcement, p. 51 L2

Study Guide, pp. 70–72 L1 ELL

658 CHAPTER 18 THE SUN-EARTH-MOON SYSTEM

In addition, *Clementine* was placed in lunar orbit to take high-resolution photographs in order to compile a detailed map of the moon's surface. **Figure 18-15** shows a photograph taken by *Clementine. Clementine's* four cameras were able to resolve features as small as 200 m across, enhancing our knowledge of the moon's surface.

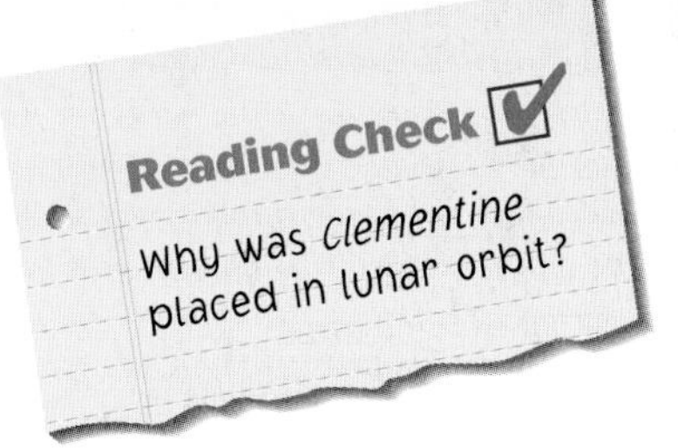
Reading Check
Why was Clementine placed in lunar orbit?

The Moon's South Pole

The South Pole-Aitken Basin is the oldest identifiable impact feature on the moon's surface. It is also the largest and deepest impact basin or depression found thus far anywhere in the solar system, measuring 12 km in depth and 2500 km in diameter. Data returned by *Clementine* gave scientists the first set of high-resolution photographs of this area of the moon. Much of this depression stays in shadow throughout the moon's rotation, forming a cold area where ice deposits from impacting comets may have collected. Radio signals reflected from *Clementine* to Earth indicated the presence of ice at the moon's south pole. Also, a large plateau that is always in sunlight was discovered in this area. If there truly is ice near the plateau, this would be an ideal location for a moon colony powered by solar energy.

Figure 18-16 is a global map showing the moon's crustal thickness based on *Clementine* data. According to the data, the moon's crust thins under impact basins. Also, the moon's crust on the side facing Earth is much thinner than on the far side. Such maps show the location of **mascons,** which are concentrations of mass. Mascons are located under impact basins. Data collected by *Clementine* also provided information on the mineral content of moon rocks. In fact, this part of its mission was instrumental in naming the spacecraft. Clementine was the daughter of a miner in the ballad "My Darlin' Clementine."

Figure 18-16 This computer-enhanced map based on *Clementine* data indicates the thickness of the moon's crust. The crust of the side of the moon facing Earth, shown mostly in red, is thinner than the crust on the far side of the moon.

The Lunar Prospector

The success of *Clementine* at a relatively low cost opened the door for further moon missions. In 1998, NASA launched the *Lunar Prospector* spacecraft. Its mission was to orbit the moon, taking photographs of the lunar surface for mapping purposes. These maps confirmed the *Clementine* data. The

2 Teach

Answer to Reading Check

to take photographs to compile a detailed map of the moon's surface

3 Assess

Check for Understanding

Using Science Words

Linguistic Ask students to research and write about cold objects in space. Student reports should explain why objects such as satellites, warheads, and near-Earth asteroids are referred to as cold objects, and why scientists need to track such objects. L3

Reteach

Visual-Spatial Obtain photographs of the moon from early crewed and uncrewed missions to the moon and from the recent *Clementine* and *Lunar Prospector* spacecraft. Help students decide which photographs show more detail and would best be used for mapmaking. Contact NASA for photographs. L2 ELL COOP LEARN

Extension

For students who have mastered this section, use the **Reinforcement** and **Enrichment** masters.

Content Background

One of the first scientists to recognize possible causes of craters on the moon and Earth was Grove K. Gilbert (1843–1918). His explanation of impact cratering on the moon led to our current understanding of the evolution of terrestrial planets.

Science Journal

The Back of the Moon Show students maps of the back of the moon and have them list the names of some of the larger features found there. Ask them to also write a report on which lunar missions were responsible for providing the first photographs of these features. L2

CA Science Content Standards

Page 658: 4e
Page 659: 4e

4 Close

Proficiency Prep

Use this quiz to check students' recall of section content.

1. **The former Soviet Union launched the study of the moon with which spacecraft?** *Luna 1*
2. **Which U.S. spacecraft soft-landed on the moon in preparation for landing astronauts on the moon?** *Surveyor*

Section Assessment

1. the presence of ice at the moon's poles, a sunlit plateau near the moon's south pole, thinning of the moon's crust under impact basins, location of mascons, information on mineral content of moon rocks
2. to orbit the moon, take photos of its surface, and search for clues to its origin and makeup
3. Countries began to study the moon from space.
4. **Think Critically** With the possibility of water from the ice, the large plateau near the moon's south pole would be an ideal location for a moon colony. Also, oxygen and hydrogen from the water could be used to produce fuel for future space flights.

Using Math

Lunar Prospector also was scheduled to conduct a detailed study of the moon's surface, searching for clues as to the origin and makeup of the moon.

Icy Poles

Early data obtained from the *Lunar Prospector* indicate that hydrogen is present in the rocks found in the craters at the moon's poles, as shown in **Figure 18-17.** Hydrogen is one of the elements that make up water. These data, combined with data from *Clementine,* have led scientists to theorize that ice may exist in the floors of the craters at both of the moon's poles. These craters are deep and cold. Sunlight never reaches their floors, where temperatures are as low as –233°C—definitely cold enough to have preserved any ice that may have collected in the craters from colliding comets or meteorites.

Based on the *Lunar Prospector* data, scientists estimate that 6 billion tons of ice lie under the surface of the moon's poles. The ice may be buried under about 40 cm of crushed rock. Data from *Lunar Prospector* also have enabled scientists to conclude that the moon has a small, iron-rich core about 600 km across.

Figure 18-17 Data from *Lunar Prospector* indicate the presence of twice as much ice at the moon's north pole as at its south pole.

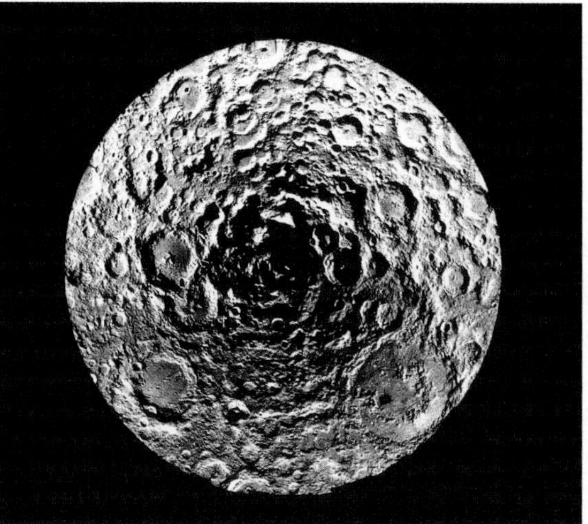

Section Assessment

1. List two discoveries about the moon made by the *Clementine* spacecraft.
2. What was the main mission of the *Lunar Prospector?*
3. How did studies of the moon change after the 1950s?
4. **Think Critically:** Why would the discovery of ice at the moon's poles be important to future space flights?
5.  **Skill Builder**
   Sequencing Sequence the following moon missions in the order in which they occurred: *Surveyor, Lunar Prospector, Apollo, Lunar Orbiter, Ranger,* and *Clementine.* If you need help, refer to Sequencing in the **Skill Handbook** on page 950.

Using Math

The moon's orbit is tilted at an angle of about 5° to Earth's orbit around the sun. Using a protractor, draw an angle of 5°. Draw a model of the moon's orbit around Earth.

5.  **Skill Builder**
   Ranger, Lunar Orbiter, Surveyor, Apollo, Clementine, and *Lunar Prospector*

Assessment

Performance Assess student understanding of moon studies by asking them which missions landed on the moon and which orbited the moon. Surveyor *and* Apollo *landed on the moon; and* Lunar Orbiter, Clementine, *and* Lunar Prospector *orbited the moon.* Use **Performance Assessment in the Science Classroom,** p. 103.

Moon Phases and Eclipses

Materials

- Light source (unshaded)
- Polystyrene ball on pencil
- Globe

You know that moon phases and eclipses result from the relative positions of the sun, the moon, and Earth. In this activity, you will demonstrate the positions of these bodies during certain phases and eclipses. You also will see why only people on a small portion of Earth's surface see a total solar eclipse.

What You'll Investigate

Can a model be devised to show the positions of the sun, the moon, and Earth during various phases and eclipses?

Goals

- **Model** moon phases.
- **Model** solar and lunar eclipses.

Procedure 

1. Review the illustrations of moon phases and eclipses shown in Section 18-2.
2. **Use** the light source as a model sun and a polystyrene ball on a pencil as a model moon. **Move** the model moon around the globe to duplicate the exact position that would have to occur for a lunar eclipse to take place.
3. **Move** the model moon to the position that would cause a solar eclipse.
4. **Place** the model moon at each of the following phases: first quarter, full moon, third quarter, and new moon. **Identify** which, if any, type of eclipse could occur during each phase. Record your data.
5. **Place** the model moon at the location where a lunar eclipse could occur. **Move** it slightly toward Earth, then away from Earth. Note the amount of change in the size of the shadow causing the eclipse. Record this information.
6. **Repeat** step 5 with the model moon in a position where a solar eclipse could occur.

Conclude and Apply

1. During which phase(s) of the moon is it possible for an eclipse to occur?
2. **Describe** the effect that a small change in the distance between Earth and the moon has on the size of the shadow causing the eclipse.
3. As seen from Earth, how does the apparent size of the moon **compare** with the apparent size of the sun? How can an eclipse be used to confirm this?
4. **Infer** why a lunar and solar eclipse do not occur every month.
5. Suppose you wanted to more accurately model the movement of the moon around Earth. **Explain** how your model moon moves around the globe. Would it always be in the same plane as the light source and the globe?
6. Why have only a few people seen a total solar eclipse?

Moon Phase Observations

Moon Phase	Observations
first quarter	
full	
third quarter	
new	

Purpose

Kinesthetic Students will formulate a model and demonstrate the relative positions of Earth and the moon during lunar phases. L2 ELL COOP LEARN P

Process Skills

communicating, sequencing, observing and inferring, recognizing and using spatial relationships, comparing and contrasting, recognizing cause and effect

Time

30 to 40 minutes

Safety Precautions

Caution students to handle the light source with care.

Teaching Strategies

Troubleshooting Point out that the distance between the moon and Earth is not constant.

Answers to Questions

1. Lunar eclipses occur at full moon. Solar eclipses occur during new moon.
2. It has little effect. During solar eclipses, the closer the two bodies, the larger the moon's shadow on Earth and the longer the duration of the eclipse.
3. The moon and sun appear similar in size. During a solar eclipse, the moon seems to exactly fit the solar disk being eclipsed.
4. Eclipses are possible only when the moon is crossing Earth's orbital plane around the sun. Except for a few minutes each month, the moon is always located either above or below Earth's orbital plane.
5. In order to model lunar motions around Earth, the moon must be located either above or below Earth's orbital plane. It will move slightly away from and closer to Earth during its elliptical orbit.
6. If the sun, the moon, and Earth are not lined up perfectly, the umbra of the moon's shadow will not fall on Earth. When the umbra does fall on Earth, it covers only a small band across Earth's surface.

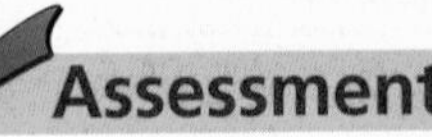

Assessment

Performance To further assess students' understanding of moon phases and eclipses, have students repeat the activity using themselves as the model of Earth. Have one student move the moon model around another student so that the class can observe all phases and eclipses. Use **Performance Assessment in the Science Classroom,** p. 25.

CA Science Content Standards

Page 660: 4e, 9f
Page 661: 4d, 4e, 9a, 9b, 9e

Reviewing Main Ideas can be used to preview, review, reteach, and condense chapter content.

Preview

Linguistic Have students try to answer the questions in their Science Journals. Use student answers as a source for discussion throughout the chapter.

Review

Interpersonal Have students answer the questions on separate pieces of paper and compare their answers with those of other students in the class.

Reteach

Visual-Spatial Have students look at the illustrations on these pages. Ask them to describe details that support the main ideas of the chapter found in the statement for each illustration.

00:00 OUT OF TIME?

Auditory-Musical If time does not permit teaching the entire chapter, use the information on these pages along with the chapter Audiocassettes to present the material in a condensed format.

Chapter 18 Reviewing Main Ideas

For a **preview** of this chapter, study this Reviewing Main Ideas before you read the chapter. After you have studied this chapter, you can use the Reviewing Main Ideas to **review** the chapter.

The Glencoe MindJogger, Audiocassettes, and CD-ROM provide additional opportunities for review.

Section

18-1 PLANET EARTH

Earth is a **sphere** that is slightly flattened at its poles. Earth **rotates** once each day and **revolves** around the sun in a little more than 365 days. Seasons on Earth are due to the amount of solar radiation received by a hemisphere at a given time. The tilt of Earth on its **axis** causes the amount of solar energy to vary. ***How does Earth's interior act like an electromagnet?***

Section

18-2 EARTH'S MOON

Earth's moon goes through **phases** that depend on the relative positions of the sun, the moon, and Earth. Eclipses occur when Earth or the moon temporarily blocks sunlight from the other. A **solar eclipse** occurs when the moon moves directly between the sun and Earth. A **lunar eclipse** occurs when Earth's shadow falls on the moon. The moon's **maria** are the result of ancient volcanism. Craters on the moon's surface formed from impacts with meteorites, asteroids, and comets. ***If the moon is between Earth and the sun for each new moon, why are there only one or two solar eclipses each year?***

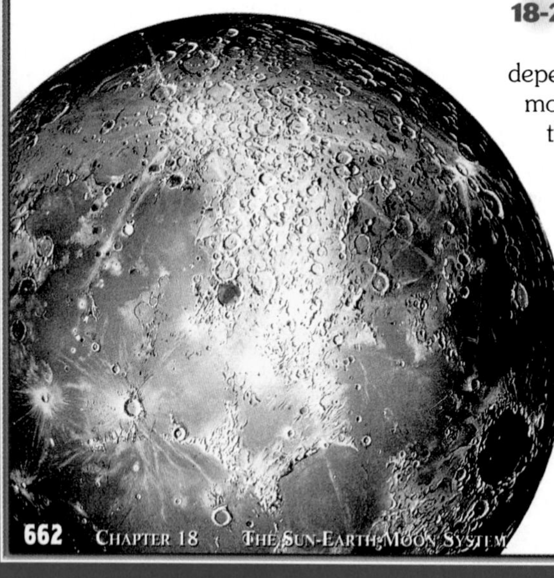

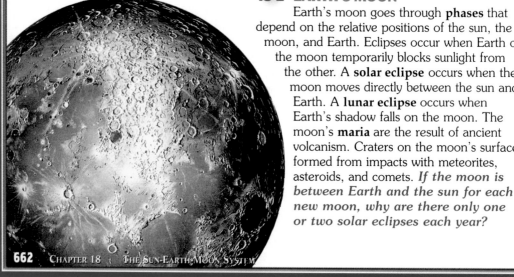

662 CHAPTER 18 THE SUN-EARTH-MOON SYSTEM

Cultural Diversity

Social Studies For some groups, time defines activities. For others, activities define time. Many Americans do certain activities on certain months of the year—we celebrate Independence Day because it is July 4. But for the Nuer, a group of seminomadic pastoralists living in East Africa, months are defined by activities. The Nuer base their yearly cycle on a system of full moons. Each moon is named after the activities associated with it. *Kur,* for example, is a time to make the first fishing dams and build the first cattle camps. It is part of *mai* (the dry season). *Dwat* is the month when they break camp and return to their village. It is part of *tot* (the wet season). Two transitional seasons, *rwil* and *jiom* (meaning "wind"), are recognized as seasons of rapid change.

Reading Check

Use these words in sentences that do not relate to the sun, Earth, or moon: *sphere, axis, rotation, revolution, ellipse, waxing,* and *waning.*

Section

18-3 EXPLORATION OF THE MOON

The *Clementine* spacecraft took detailed, high-resolution photographs of the moon's surface. Data from *Clementine* indicate that the moon's South Pole-Aitken Basin may contain ice deposits that could supply water for a moon colony. The *Clementine* spacecraft also noted that **mascons** occur beneath impact basins on the moon. NASA has returned to exploring the moon with its latest spacecraft, the *Lunar Prospector.* Data from *Lunar Prospector* seem to support the ice theory and also indicate that the moon's north pole may contain twice as much ice as the south pole. ***How did the* Clementine *spacecraft get its name?***

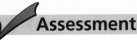

Career CONNECTION

Gibor Barsi, Astronomer

Gibor Barsi is an astronomer who works with the Keck Telescopes on Mauna Kea, Hawaii. The summit of Mauna Kea is considered the world's premier site for astronomical observation. Gibor is interested in answering the questions, "How many planets are there around other stars, what are they like, and how do they form?" He feels that the next generation of astronomers and technology will answer these questions. ***Why do you suppose astronomers are interested in finding new planets?***

Answers to Questions

Section 18-1

Planet Earth Convection currents of molten iron in Earth's core produce electrical currents, which cause Earth's magnetic field.

Section 18-2

Earth's Moon The moon is not always on the ecliptic during new-moon phase. Usually, the moon is above or below the plane of Earth's orbit around the sun.

Section 18-3

Exploration of the Moon Part of the mission of the *Clementine* spacecraft was to provide information on the mineral content of moon rocks. This was instrumental in naming the spacecraft *Clementine.* Clementine was the daughter of a miner in the ballad, "My Darlin' Clementine."

Career CONNECTION

to explore the possibility of life on other planets and to learn more about how planets form

GLENCOE TECHNOLOGY

 **CD-ROM**

Glencoe Science Voyages Interactive CD-ROM

Chapter Summaries and Quizzes

Have students read the Chapter Summary then take the Chapter Quiz to determine whether they have mastered chapter content.

Assessment

Portfolio Encourage students to place in their portfolios one or two items of what they consider to be their best work. Examples include:

- MiniLab, p. 641
- Activity 18-1, pp. 648–649
- Activity 18-2, p. 661 P

Performance Additional performance assessments may be found in **Performance Assessment** and **Science Integration Activities.** Performance Task Assessment Lists and rubrics for evaluating these activities can be found in Glencoe's **Performance Assessment in the Science Classroom.**

Using Vocabulary

1. rotation
2. equinox
3. full moon
4. solar eclipse
5. mascon

interNET CONNECTION To reinforce chapter vocabulary, use the **Study Guide for Content Mastery** booklet. Also available are activities for **Glencoe Science Voyages** on the Glencoe Science Web Site. **www.glencoe.com/sec/science/ca**

Checking Concepts

6. C
7. A
8. C
9. D
10. D
11. B
12. A
13. B
14. D
15. B

Thinking Critically

16. If the moon moved between the observer and the sun, phases would be observed. The specific phases would depend on the relative positions of the observer, the moon, and the sun.
17. Earth bulges at the equator. The gravitational attraction there is less than that at the poles. Thus, a person weighs less at the equator.
18. During full and new moons, Earth, the sun, and the moon align; thus, the gravitational attraction is greatest then. High tides are the highest and low tides are the lowest during these two phases.
19. The moon does not have a magnetic field. Star charts could be used to navigate, but a compass could not.
20. The changing position of the moon from night to night is a real motion because the moon is orbiting Earth. The moon appears to move westward across the sky due to Earth's rapid rotation. Although the moon is progressing eastward in its revolution around Earth, its trip across the sky in a single night is due to Earth's rotation. Seeing the same side of the moon seems to indicate a lack of rotation. This is an apparent motion because the moon's period of rotation equals its period of revolution.

Chapter 18 Assessment

Using Vocabulary

a. axis	j. new moon
b. ellipse	k. revolution
c. equinox	l. rotation
d. first quarter	m. solar eclipse
e. full moon	n. solstice
f. lunar eclipse	o. sphere
g. maria	p. third quarter
h. mascon	q. waning
i. moon phase	r. waxing

Each phrase below describes a science term from the list. Write the term that matches the phrase describing it.

1. causes day and night to occur on Earth
2. occurs when the sun's position is directly above the equator
3. moon phase in which all of the lighted side of the moon is seen
4. eclipse that occurs when the moon is between Earth and the sun
5. concentration of mass on the moon located under an impact basin

Checking Concepts

Choose the word or phrase that completes the sentence.

6. How long does it take for the moon to rotate?
   A) 24 hours C) 27.3 hours
   B) 365 days D) 27.3 days
7. Where is Earth's circumference greatest?
   A) equator C) poles
   B) mantle D) axis
8. During an equinox, the sun is directly over what part of Earth?
   A) southern hemisphere
   B) northern hemisphere
   C) equator
   D) pole
9. Why does the sun appear to rise and set?
   A) Earth revolves.
   B) The sun moves around Earth.
   C) Earth rotates.
   D) Earth orbits the sun.
10. How long does it take for the moon to revolve?
    A) 24 hours C) 27.3 hours
    B) 365 days D) 27.3 days
11. As the lighted portion of the moon appears to get larger, what is it said to be?
    A) waning C) rotating
    B) waxing D) crescent shaped
12. During what kind of eclipse is the moon directly between the sun and Earth?
    A) solar C) full
    B) new D) lunar
13. What is the darkest part of the shadow during an eclipse?
    A) waxing gibbous C) waning gibbous
    B) umbra D) penumbra
14. What are depressions on the moon called?
    A) eclipses C) phases
    B) moonquakes D) craters
15. What fact do data gathered from the *Clementine* spacecraft support?
    A) The moon rotates once in 29.5 days.
    B) The moon has a thinner crust on the side facing Earth.
    C) The moon revolves once in 29.5 days.
    D) The moon has a thicker crust on the side facing Earth.

Thinking Critically

16. How would the moon appear to an observer in space during its revolution? Would phases be observable? Explain.
17. Would you weigh more at Earth's equator or at the north pole? Explain.

664 CHAPTER 18 THE SUN-EARTH-MOON SYSTEM

18. Tides occur due to the gravitational attraction among the sun, the moon, and Earth. During which phases of the moon are tides the highest? Explain.
19. If you were lost on the moon's surface, why would it be more beneficial to have a star chart rather than a compass?
20. Which of the moon's motions are real? Which are apparent? Explain.

Developing Skills

If you need help, refer to the Skill Handbook.

21. **Hypothesizing:** Why do locations near Earth's equator travel faster during one rotation than places near the poles?
22. **Using Variables, Constants, and Controls:** Describe a simple activity to show how the moon's rotation and revolution work to keep one side facing Earth at all times.
23. **Comparing and Contrasting:** Compare and contrast a waning moon with a waxing moon.
24. **Concept Mapping:** Copy and complete the cycle map shown on this page. Show the sequences of the moon's phases.

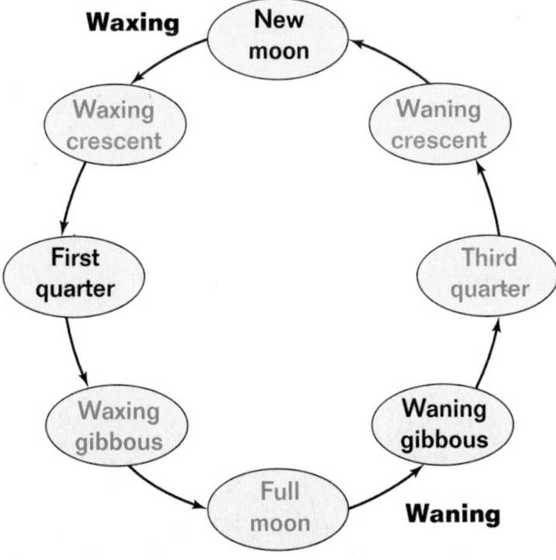

Test-Taking Tip

Practice, Practice, Practice Practice to improve *your* performance. Don't compare yourself with anyone else.

Test Practice

Use these questions to test your Science Proficiency.

1. As the moon revolves around Earth, it keeps the same side facing Earth. Which of the following statements **BEST** explains why this is so?
   A) The moon rotates once on its axis as it makes one complete revolution around Earth.
   B) The moon does not rotate as it revolves.
   C) The speed of rotation for the moon exactly equals its speed of revolution.
   D) The speed of revolution for the moon is constant and therefore keeps one side facing Earth at all times.
2. More craters are on the far side of the moon than on the side facing Earth. Which of the following statements would **BEST** explain this fact?
   A) A greater number of volcanoes occur on the far side of the moon.
   B) Earth's gravity attracts more of the objects that would produce craters on the side of the moon facing Earth.
   C) Earth blocks the paths of any objects that would collide with the side of the moon facing Earth.
   D) The far side of the moon is always facing away from the sun.

Assessment Resources

The **Test Practice Workbook** provides students with practice in the format, concepts, and critical-thinking skills tested in standardized exams.

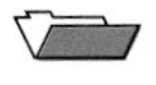

Reproducible Masters

Chapter Review, pp. 35–36 L2
Performance Assessment, p. 18 L2
Assessment, pp. 69–72 L2

Glencoe Technology

Chapter Review Software
Computer Test Bank
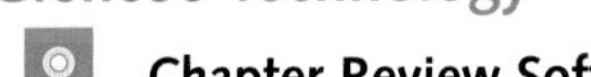
MindJogger Videoquiz

The Test-Taking Tip was written by The Princeton Review, the nation's leader in test preparation.

1. A
2. B

Developing Skills

21. The circumference of Earth is greater at low latitudes than at high latitudes. Thus, locations near the equator have a greater distance to travel to complete one rotation than do locations near the poles.
22. Place an X on a basketball. As you walk around a classmate, keep the X pointed toward him or her. You must turn the ball to keep the X facing him or her as you walk. As the ball revolves once, it rotates once.
23. At both times, the moon's apparent size is changing. A waxing moon is one that appears to get larger each night. A waning moon appears to get smaller each night.
24. See student page.

Bonus Question

How might your life be different if you lived in the southern hemisphere? Mention the seasons and how they compare with those in the northern hemisphere. *Answers will vary but should reference the fact that summer would begin in December and winter would begin in June. Also, the seasons of spring and fall would begin in September and March, respectively.*

Chapter 19 The Solar System

Section	Objectives	Activities/Features
Chapter Opener		**Explore Activity:** Model Comet Collisions, p. 667
19-1 **The Solar System** 2½ Sessions 1 Block	1. **Compare** and **contrast** the sun-centered and Earth-centered models of the solar system. 2. **Describe** current models of the formation of the solar system.	**Physics Integration,** p. 672 **Skill Builder:** Concept Mapping, p. 672 **Using Math,** p. 672 **Activity 19-1:** Planetary Orbits, p. 673
19-2 **The Inner Planets** 1 Session ½ Block	3. **List** the inner planets in their relative order from the sun. 4. **Identify** important characteristics of each inner planet. 5. **Compare** and **contrast** Venus and Earth.	**Using Math,** p. 675 **Problem Solving:** Interpret Planetary Data, p. 676 **MiniLab: Inferring Effects of Gravity,** p. 677 **Life Science Integration,** p. 678 **Skill Builder:** Interpreting Data, p. 679 **Science Journal,** p. 679
19-3 **The Outer Planets** 3 Sessions 1½ Blocks	6. **List** the major characteristics of Jupiter, Saturn, Uranus, and Neptune. 7. **Recognize** how Pluto differs from the other outer planets.	**MiniLab:** Modeling Planets, p. 682 **Skill Builder:** Recognizing Cause and Effect, p. 685 **Using Computers,** p. 685 **Activity 19-2:** Solar System Distance Model, pp. 686–687
19-4 **Other Objects in the Solar System** 1 Session ½ Block	8. **Explain** where a comet comes from and describe how a comet develops as it approaches the sun. 9. **Differentiate** among comets, meteoroids, and asteroids.	**Skill Builder:** Inferring, p. 692 **Science Journal,** p. 692 **Science and Society:** Mission to Mars, p. 693

The number of recommended single-period sessions — The number of recommended blocks
One session and one-half block are allowed for chapter review and assessment.

Activity Materials

Explore	Activities	MiniLabs
p. 667 flour, cake pan, cement mix, various-sized objects, metric ruler	p. 673 thumbtacks, metric ruler, string, cardboard, paper pp. 686–687 meterstick, scissors, string	p. 677 Appendix A p. 682 drawing compass, metric ruler, paper, pencil

Need Materials? Contact Science Kit at 1-800-828-7777 or at www.sciencekit.com on the Internet.
For alternate materials, see the activity on the listed page.

Chapter Organizer

Standards		Reproducible Resources	Technology
National	State/Local	Test Practice Workbooks are available for use with each chapter.	English and Spanish audiocassettes are available for use with each section.
National Content Standards: UCP5, A2, B1, B3, D3, G1, G2, G3	California Science Content Standards: 1b, 1c, 2g, 4e, 9a, 9f	**Activity Worksheets,** pp. 105–106 **Enrichment,** p. 52 **Multicultural Connections,** pp. 37–38 **Reinforcement,** p. 52 **Study Guide,** p. 73	Section Focus Transparency 52 Teaching Transparency 37 Teaching Transparency 38 Science Integration Transparency 19
National Content Standards: A2, D3, E2	California Science Content Standards: 1b, 1c, 2f, 2g, 4c, 4e, 5a, 9b, 9f	**Activity Worksheets,** p. 109 **Enrichment,** p. 53 **Home Involvement,** p. 28 **Laboratory Manual,** pp. 119–122 **Reinforcement,** p. 53	Section Focus Transparency 53 National Geographic Society: STV Glencoe Science Voyages Interactive CD-ROM
National Content Standards: UCP2, A2, B1, D3, E2, G3	California Science Content Standards: 2g, 4c, 4e, 8d, 9a, 9b, 9e, 9f	**Activity Worksheets,** pp. 107–108, 112 **Enrichment,** p. 54 **Home Involvement,** p. 37 **Laboratory Manual,** pp. 123–124 **Reinforcement,** p. 54	Section Focus Transparency 54 National Geographic Society: STV **Internet Connection,** p. 683 The Infinite Voyage Series
National Content Standards: A2, B2, D2, D3, G1, G3	California Science Content Standards: 2g, 4e	**Critical Thinking/Problem Solving,** p. 19 **Enrichment,** p. 55 **Reinforcement,** p. 55 **Study Guide,** pp. 74–76	Section Focus Transparency 55 National Geographic Society: STV **Internet Connection,** p. 689 **Internet Connection,** p. 690

Key to Teaching Strategies

The following designations will help you decide which activities are appropriate for your students.

L1 Level 1 activities should be appropriate for students with learning difficulties.

L2 Level 2 activities should be within the ability range of all students.

L3 Level 3 activities are designed for above-average students.

ELL ELL activities should be within the ability range of English Language Learners.

COOP LEARN Cooperative Learning activities are designed for small group work.

P These strategies represent student products that can be placed into a best-work portfolio.

Multiple Learning Styles logos, as described on page 55T, are used throughout to indicate strategies that address different learning styles.

Assessment Resources

Chapter Review, pp. 37–38
Assessment, pp. 73–76
Performance Assessment in the Science Classroom (PASC)
MindJogger Videoquiz
Alternate Assessment in the Science Classroom
Performance Assessment, p. 19
Chapter Review Software
Computer Test Bank

Chapter 19 The Solar System

This is a representation of key blackline masters available in the Teacher Classroom Resources. See Resource Manager boxes within the chapter for additional information.

Transparencies

Section Focus Transparencies

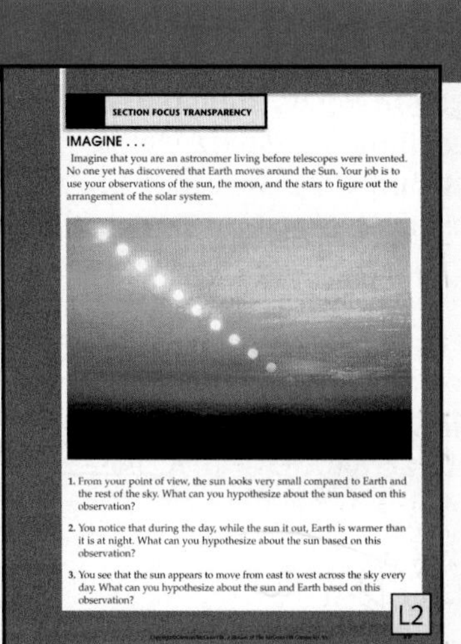

SECTION FOCUS TRANSPARENCY

IMAGINE . . .

Imagine that you are an astronomer living before telescopes were invented. No one yet has discovered that Earth moves around the Sun. Your job is to use your observations of the sun, the moon, and the stars to figure out the arrangement of the solar system.

1. From your point of view, the sun looks very small compared to Earth and the rest of the sky. What can you hypothesize about the sun based on this observation?
2. You notice that during the day, while the sun it out, Earth is warmer than it is at night. What can you hypothesize about the sun based on this observation?
3. You see that the sun appears to move from east to west across the sky every day. What can you hypothesize about the sun and Earth based on this observation?

L2

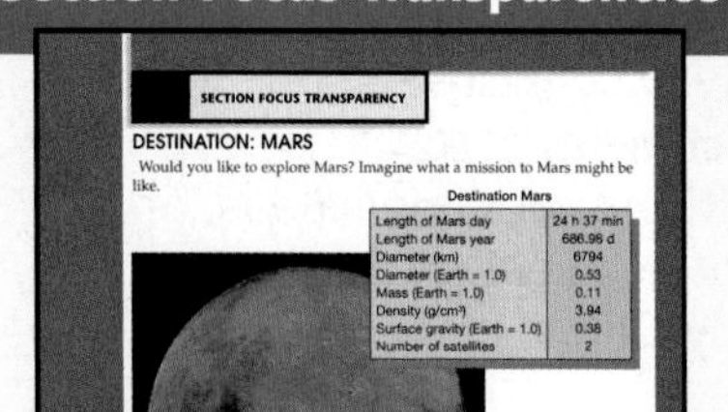

SECTION FOCUS TRANSPARENCY

DESTINATION: MARS

Would you like to explore Mars? Imagine what a mission to Mars might be like.

Destination Mars

Length of Mars day	24 h 37 min
Length of Mars year	686.98 d
Diameter (km)	6794
Diameter (Earth = 1.0)	0.53
Mass (Earth = 1.0)	0.11
Density (g/cm³)	3.94
Surface gravity (Earth = 1.0)	0.38
Number of satellites	2

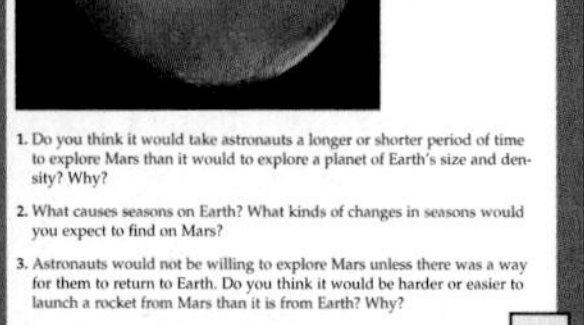

1. Do you think it would take astronauts a longer or shorter period of time to explore Mars than it would to explore a planet of Earth's size and density? Why?
2. What causes seasons on Earth? What kinds of changes in seasons would you expect to find on Mars?
3. Astronauts would not be willing to explore Mars unless there was a way for them to return to Earth. Do you think it would be harder or easier to launch a rocket from Mars than it is from Earth? Why?

L2

SECTION FOCUS TRANSPARENCY

FOUR MOONS RISING

Have you ever watched Earth's moon rising? Imagine what it would be like to watch two, four, sixteen or even twenty moons tracing a path around the sky. Most of the outer planets have many moons.

1. Jupiter is shown here with four of its sixteen moons. Try to imagine what Jupiter might be like. What questions would you have to answer in order to describe Jupiter?
2. The outer planets are much further from the sun than Earth is. Knowing only that, what can you hypothesize about them?

L2

Science Integration Transparencies

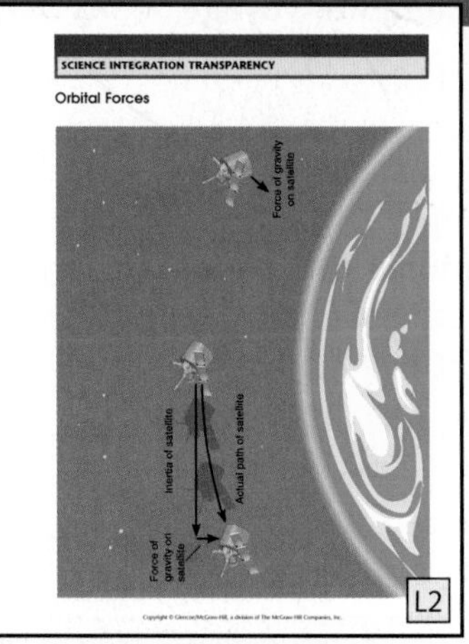

SCIENCE INTEGRATION TRANSPARENCY

Orbital Forces

L2

Teaching Transparencies

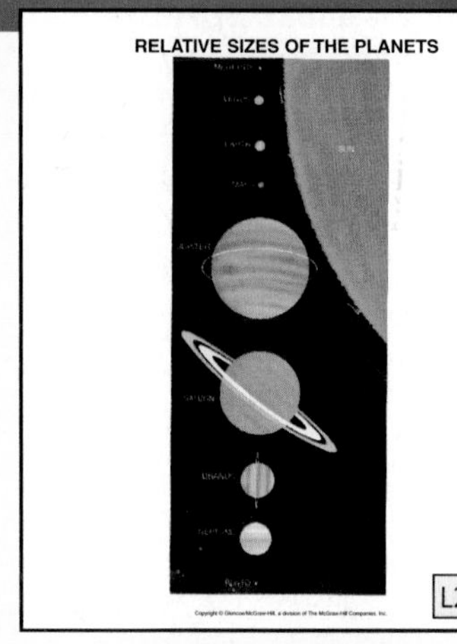

RELATIVE SIZES OF THE PLANETS

L2

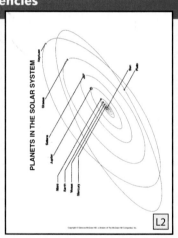

PLANETS IN THE SOLAR SYSTEM

Neptune, Uranus, Saturn, Jupiter, Mars, Earth, Venus, Mercury, Sun, Pluto

L2

Meeting Different Ability Levels

Study Guide for Content Mastery

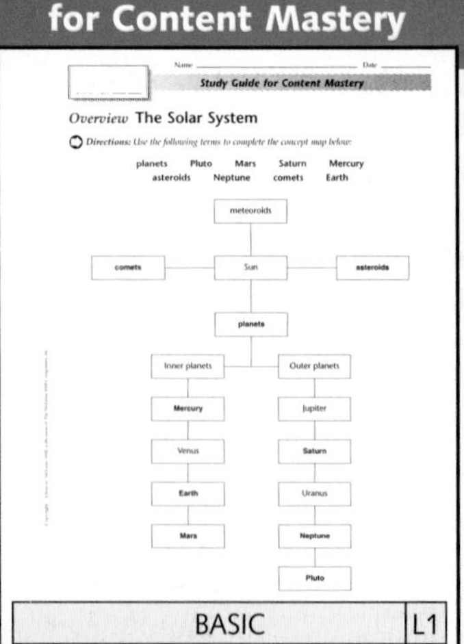

Study Guide for Content Mastery

Overview The Solar System

Directions: Use the following terms to complete the concept map below:

planets, Pluto, Mars, Saturn, Mercury, asteroids, Neptune, comets, Earth

meteoroids — Sun — comets — asteroids — planets — Inner planets: Mercury, Venus, Earth, Mars — Outer planets: Jupiter, Saturn, Uranus, Neptune, Pluto

BASIC L1

Reinforcement

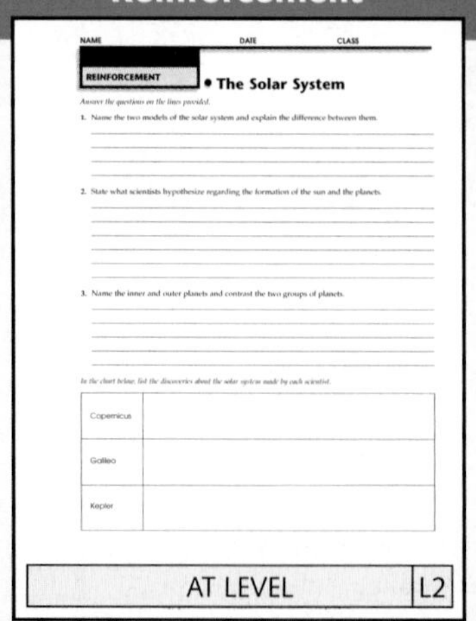

REINFORCEMENT • The Solar System

Answer the questions on the lines provided.

1. Name the two models of the solar system and explain the difference between them.
2. State what scientists hypothesize regarding the formation of the sun and the planets.
3. Name the inner and outer planets and contrast the two groups of planets.

In the chart below, list the discoveries about the solar system made by each scientist.

Copernicus	
Galileo	
Kepler	

AT LEVEL L2

Enrichment Worksheets

ENRICHMENT • The Solar System

Is there a tenth planet?

1. Why were five of the planets discovered thousands of years ago?
2. What invention made it possible to discover Uranus?
3. Why do you think Pluto wasn't discovered before Uranus or Neptune?
4. Why do you think astronomers believe that Pluto is too small to affect Uranus's and Neptune's orbits?

CHALLENGE L3

Resource Manager

Hands-on Activities

Activity Worksheets

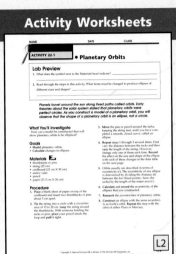

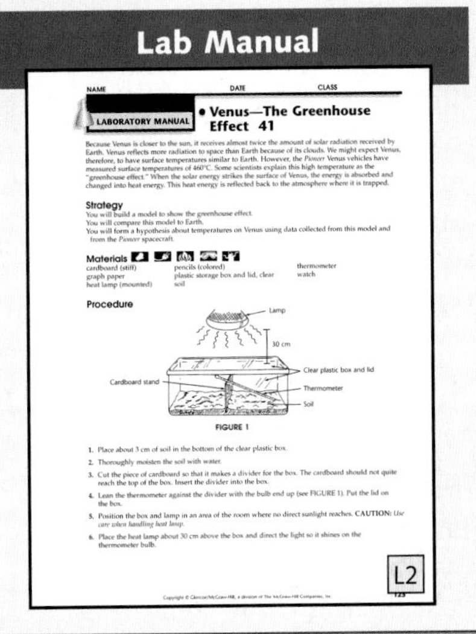

Lab Manual

NAME DATE CLASS

LABORATORY MANUAL • Venus—The Greenhouse Effect 41

Strategy

Materials

Procedure

FIGURE 1

L2

Accessibility

Spanish Resources

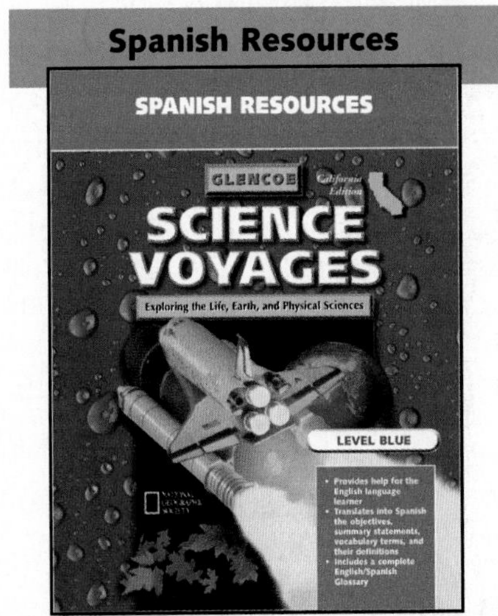

SPANISH RESOURCES
GLENCOE
SCIENCE VOYAGES
Exploring the Life, Earth, and Physical Sciences
LEVEL BLUE

Assessment

Performance Assessment

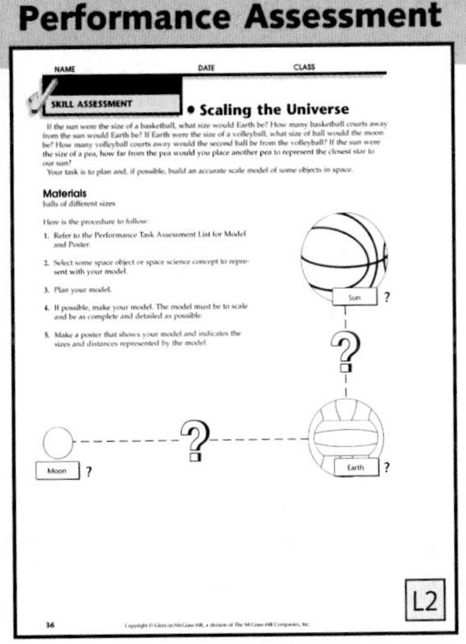

NAME DATE CLASS

SKILL ASSESSMENT • Scaling the Universe

Materials

L2

Assessment

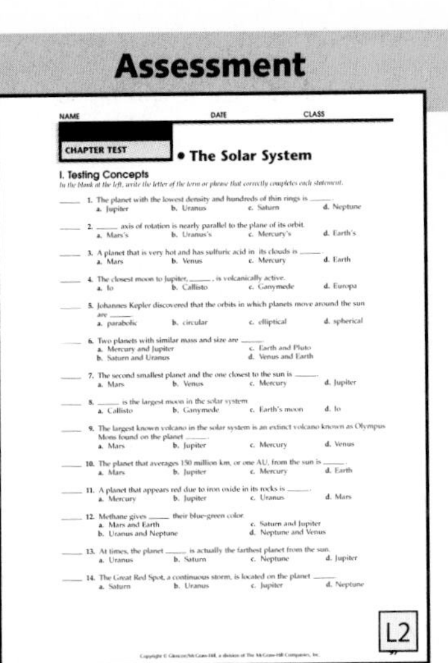

NAME DATE CLASS

CHAPTER TEST • The Solar System

I. Testing Concepts

L2

Chapter Review

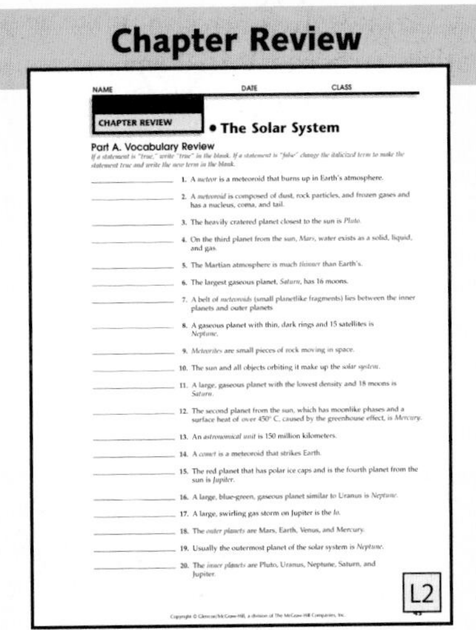

NAME DATE CLASS

CHAPTER REVIEW • The Solar System

Part A. Vocabulary Review

L2

Test Practice Workbook

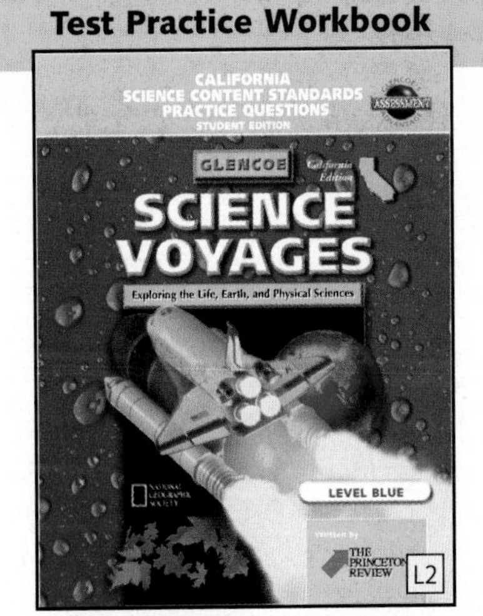

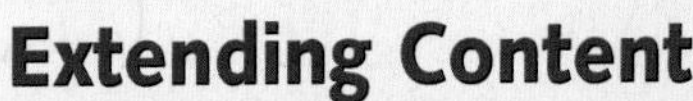

Extending Content

Critical Thinking/ Problem Solving

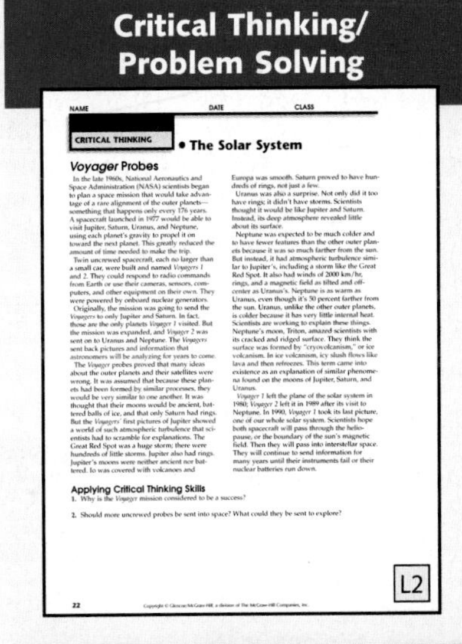

NAME DATE CLASS

CRITICAL THINKING • The Solar System

Voyager Probes

Applying Critical Thinking Skills

L2

Multicultural Connections

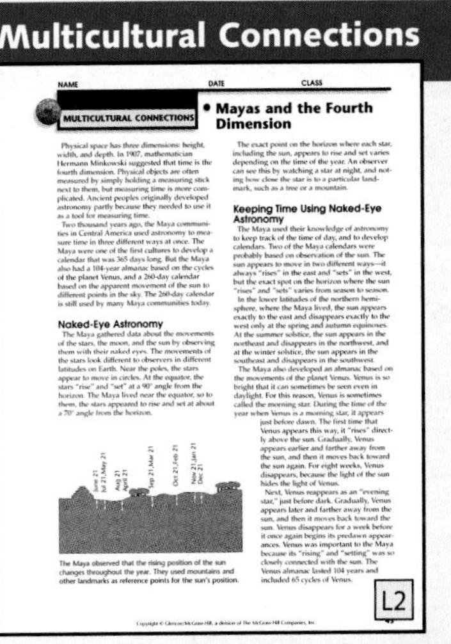

NAME DATE CLASS

MULTICULTURAL CONNECTIONS • Mayas and the Fourth Dimension

Keeping Time Using Naked-Eye Astronomy

Naked-Eye Astronomy

L2

Helping You Prepare

Sun-Centered Model (Section 19-1)

Most objects in the solar system rotate and revolve toward the east. Any motion different from this eastward motion is called retrograde motion. The retrograde motion of Mars was one piece of evidence used by Copernicus to support his sun-centered model of the solar system.

Solar System Formation (Section 19-1)

Several modern theories attempt to explain the formation of our solar system. One hypothesis suggests that a nearby star may have exploded, sending shock waves through the resulting cloud, or nebula. The shock waves caused the particles in the cloud to condense, leading to the formation of the solar system. Other scientists propose that the movement of one of the arms of the Milky Way Galaxy through the nebula started the formation process. Most scientists agree that something provided the shock that started the motions within the nebula that eventually formed the solar system.

Earth's Atmosphere (Section 19-2)

Carbon dioxide dissolves in water; therefore, much of the carbon dioxide in Earth's atmosphere has been removed by rain. If it weren't for the presence of liquid water on Earth, the amount of carbon dioxide in the air would probably be similar to that in Venus's atmosphere, causing a tremendous increase in the greenhouse effect on Earth.

Planet Classification (Section 19-2)

All planets except Earth can be classified as inferior or superior. Inferior planets—Mercury and Venus—have orbits that are inside Earth's orbit. Superior planets have orbits that lie outside Earth's orbit. These include Mars, Jupiter, Saturn, Uranus, Neptune, and Pluto.

GLENCOE TECHNOLOGY

Glencoe Science Voyages Interactive CD-ROM

Chapter Summaries

Use the Chapter Summary to introduce, teach, or review chapter material.

NATIONAL GEOGRAPHIC — Teacher's Corner

Products Available from Glencoe

To order the following products for use with this chapter, call Glencoe at 1-800-334-7344:

CD-ROM

NGS PictureShow: Solar System

Transparency Set

NGS PicturePack: Solar System

Videodisc

STV: Solar System

Products Available from National Geographic Society

To order the following products for use with this chapter, call National Geographic Society at 1-800-368-2728:

Poster

Solar System/Celestial Family

Video

Comets and Asteroids

Index to National Geographic Magazine

The following articles may be used for research relating to this chapter:

"The Age of Comets," by William R. Newcott, December 1997.

"Venus Revealed," by William R. Newcott, February 1993.

"Neptune: Voyager's Last Picture Show," by Rick Gore, August 1990.

"Halley's Comet 1986," by Rick Gore, December 1986.

Outer Planets (Section 19-3)

The atmospheres of Jupiter and Saturn contain three distinct layers. The upper layer is composed of ammonia ice, the second layer is composed of ammonium hydrosulfide ice, and the lowest layer is composed mostly of water ice.

Most of the material in Saturn's rings lies below the Roche distance for that planet. The Roche distance is the distance from an object below which other objects would be torn apart by gravitational forces.

Uranus doesn't appear to have an internal heat source. Some scientists believe a collision with another object may have turned Uranus on its side and destroyed its heat source.

Pluto (Section 19-3)

Pluto is very different from the other outer planets. Hypotheses suggest it may not have formed in the orbit it now occupies, or that Pluto and its moon Charon are large cometary members of the Kuiper belt.

In 1996, the *Hubble Space Telescope* sent back new images of Pluto showing 12 distinct areas on the planet's surface. Some of these areas are more than 1000 km across—some are bright; others are dark.

Based on current knowledge of the outer solar system, it appears that Pluto and Neptune's moon Triton are more similar to each other than any other two objects in the solar system. Some scientists believe the retrograde (backward) revolution of Triton indicates it was captured by the gravity of Neptune and could once have been a planet of the sun, just like Pluto. This line of thinking supports the idea that Pluto, and perhaps Triton, are two of many icy, dwarf planets that may have formed far from the sun.

Discovery of the Kuiper belt further supports this idea. This area, which begins about 30 to 50 AU from the sun, is littered with icy, dwarf planets; comets; and other debris.

SCIENCE UPDATE

For current events or science in the news, access the Glencoe Science Web Site at **www.glencoe.com/sec/science/ca**

Comets (Section 19-4)

Comets appear to orbit the sun in the Oort Cloud some 50 000 AU from the sun. Some comets take more than a million years to complete one orbit.

Another area of comets, the Kuiper belt, is thought to extend outward from the orbit of Neptune to a distance of 100 AU from the sun. Formerly, it was probably much larger than it is today, but it was cleared out by the large gravitational field of Neptune. The Kuiper belt may represent an area of the solar system where the formation of a large planet failed.

Teacher to Teacher

"When studying our solar system's planets, I give students the assignment of developing an ad campaign for selling one of the planets. They develop and present to the class a bumper sticker, a poster, and an ad that contains ten facts and the historical significance of the planet's name."

John E. Burns

John E. Burns, Teacher
Ramona Junior High School
Chino, CA

CHAPTER 19 The Solar System

CHAPTER OVERVIEW

Section 19-1 This section describes the sun-centered model of the solar system and the formation of the solar system.

Section 19-2 Characteristics of the inner planets are described. Information about Mars gathered from recent space missions is presented.

Section 19-3 This section describes the outer planets. Information gathered from the *Voyager* space probes is presented.

Section 19-4 Comets, meteoroids, asteroids, meteors, and meteorites are compared and contrasted.

Chapter Vocabulary

solar system	Great Red Spot
inner planet	Saturn
outer planet	Uranus
Mercury	Neptune
Venus	Pluto
Earth	comet
astronomical unit	Oort Cloud
Mars	meteor
Jupiter	meteorite
	asteroid

Theme Connection

Scale and Structure The theme of this chapter is the scale and structure of the solar system. All objects in this system are compared and contrasted according to size and composition.

00:00 OUT OF TIME?

If time does not permit teaching the entire chapter, use Reviewing Main Ideas on pp. 694–695.

CHAPTER 19 The Solar System

Chapter Preview

Section 19-1
The Solar System

Section 19-2
The Inner Planets

Section 19-3
The Outer Planets

Section 19-4
Other Objects in the Solar System

Skills Preview

Skill Builders
- Map Concepts

Activities
- Make a Model

MiniLabs
- Observe and Infer

Reading Check

As you read this chapter, identify and describe the cause-effect relationships that control the structure of the solar system.

Multiple Learning Styles

Look for the following logos for strategies that emphasize different learning modalities.

Linguistic Science Journal, pp. 669, 678, 684; Using an Analogy, p. 670; Enrichment, p. 675; Preview, p. 694

Logical-Mathematical Activity pp. 673, 686–687; Across the Curriculum, pp. 675, 677; MiniLab, p. 677; Reteach, p. 691

Visual-Spatial Making a Model, p. 669; Reteach, pp. 671, 694; Activity, p. 676; Multiple Learning Styles, p. 681; Across the Curriculum, p. 682

Auditory-Musical Out of Time, p. 694

Kinesthetic Explore Activity, p. 667; MiniLab, p. 682

Interpersonal Activity, pp. 669, 681; Inclusion Strategies, p. 670; Reteach, pp. 678, 684; Review, p. 694

Intrapersonal Enrichment, p. 684

Explore Activity

The planets of our solar system are our neighbors in space. But to us on Earth, they look like tiny points of light among the thousands of others visible on a clear night. With the help of telescopes and space probes, the points of light become giant colorful spheres, some with rings, others pitted with countless craters. This false-color image of Mars shows the space rover *Sojourner* exploring the planet's surface. Mars has two heavily cratered moons. In this activity, you'll explore how craters are made on the surfaces of planets and moons.

Model Comet Collisions

1. Place fine white flour into a cake pan to a depth of 3 cm, completely covering the bottom of the pan.
2. Cover the flour with 1 cm of fine, gray, dry cement mix, or try different colors of gelatin powder.
3. From different heights ranging from 10 cm to 25 cm, drop various-sized objects into the pan. Use marbles, lead weights, bolts, and nuts.

In your Science Journal, draw what happened to the surface of the powder in the pan when each object was dropped from different heights.

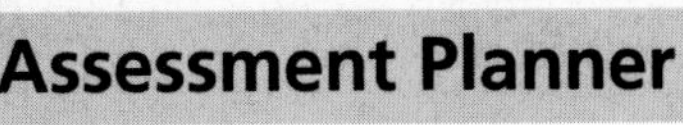

Assessment Planner

Portfolio

Refer to p. 695 for suggested items that students might select for their portfolios.

Performance Assessment

See p. 695 for additional Performance Assessment options.
Skill Builder, pp. 672, 679, 685, 692
MiniLab, pp. 677, 682
Activity 19-1, p. 673; 19-2, pp. 686–687

Content Assessment

Section Assessment, pp. 672, 679, 685, 692
Chapter Assessment, pp. 696–697
Proficiency Prep, pp. 672, 679, 685, 692

Explore Activity

Purpose

Kinesthetic Use the Explore Activity to introduce students to the cause and effect of comet impacts on planetary surfaces. L2 ELL COOP LEARN

Preparation

Prior to beginning this chapter, obtain flat pans or ask students to bring in flat pans from home.

Materials

flat pans; metric ruler; white flour; gray, dry cement mix (or colored, powdered gelatin); and objects such as marbles, lead weights, bolts, and nuts

Teaching Strategies

Troubleshooting Have students place the pans on large sheets of newspaper.

Safety Precautions Caution students to wear safety goggles while dropping objects.

The white powder splashes out over the darker powdered surface. A crater forms as the object is buried in the powder. Craters are deeper when the objects are dropped from greater distances. Craters on Mars and the moon probably formed in the same way.

Assessment

Performance Let groups examine each other's pans. Have students determine which craters were caused by big objects. Ask them to determine which craters formed first. Use **Performance Assessment in the Science Classroom,** p. 17.

SECTION 19•1

Prepare

Content Background

Refer to **Sun-Centered Model** and **Solar System Formation** on p. 666E.

Preplanning

Refer to the **Chapter Organizer** on pp. 666A–B.

1 Motivate

Bellringer

Before presenting the lesson, display **Section Focus Transparency 52** on the overhead projector. Use the accompanying **Focus Activity** worksheet. L2 ELL

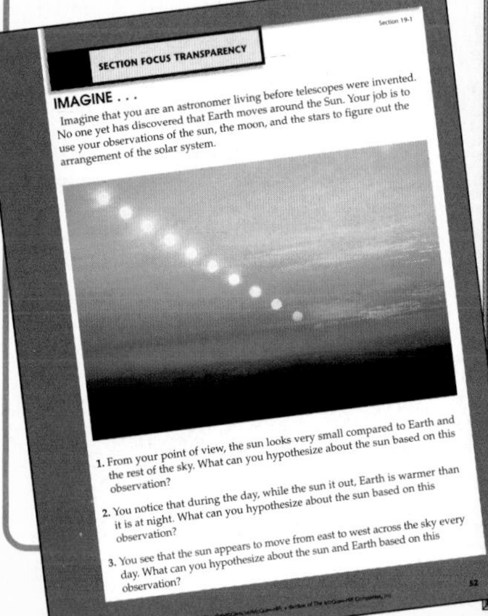

Section 19-1

SECTION FOCUS TRANSPARENCY

IMAGINE . . .

Imagine that you are an astronomer living before telescopes were invented. No one yet has discovered that Earth moves around the Sun. Your job is to use your observations of the sun, the moon, and the stars to figure out the arrangement of the solar system.

1. From your point of view, the sun looks very small compared to Earth and the rest of the sky. What can you hypothesize about the sun based on this observation?
2. You notice that during the day, while the sun it out, Earth is warmer than it is at night. What can you hypothesize about the sun based on this observation?
3. You see that the sun appears to move from east to west across the sky every day. What can you hypothesize about the sun and Earth based on this observation?

52

Tying to Previous Knowledge

Remind students that the "rising" and "setting" of the sun are caused by Earth's rotation. Ask students why people once thought that Earth was the center of the solar system. L2

19•1 The Solar System

What You'll Learn

- The sun-centered and Earth-centered models of the solar system
- Current models of the formation of the solar system

Vocabulary

solar system
inner planet
outer planet

Why It's Important

- You'll learn how views of the solar system have changed over time.

Early Ideas About the Solar System

Imagine yourself on a warm, clear summer night lying in the grass and gazing at the stars and the moon. The stars and the moon seem so still and beautiful. You may even see other planets in the solar system, thinking they are stars. Although the planets are different from the stars, they blend in with the stars and are usually hard to pick out.

Earth-Centered Model

It is generally known today that the sun and the stars appear to move through the sky because Earth is moving. This wasn't always an accepted fact. Many early Greek scientists thought the planets, the sun, and the moon were embedded in separate spheres that rotated around Earth. The stars were thought to be embedded in another sphere that also rotated around Earth. Early observers described moving objects in the night sky using the term *planasthai,* which means "to wander." The word *planet* comes from this term.

This model is called the Earth-centered model of the solar system. It included Earth, the moon, the sun, five planets—Mercury, Venus, Mars, Jupiter, and Saturn—and the sphere of stars.

Figure 19-1 Each of the nine planets in the solar system is unique. The sizes of the planets and sun are drawn to scale but the distances between the planets and sun are not to scale.

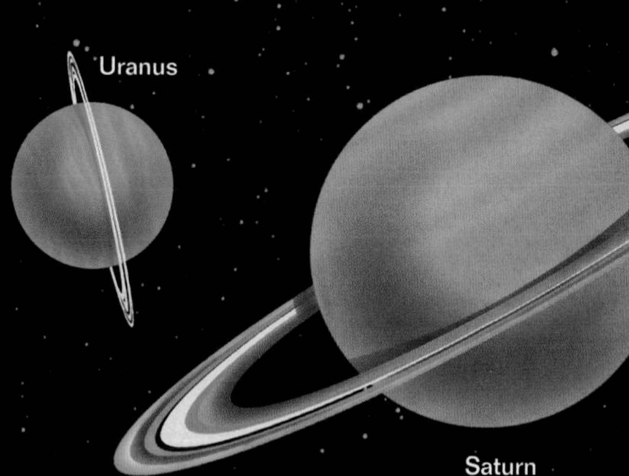

Resource Manager

The following **Teacher Classroom Resources** can be used with Section 19-1:

Reproducible Masters

Activity Worksheets, pp. 105–106 L2
Enrichment, p. 52 L3
Multicultural Connections, pp. 37–38 L2
Reinforcement, p. 52 L2
Study Guide, p. 73 L1 ELL

Transparencies

Teaching Transparency 37 L2
Teaching Transparency 38 L2
Science Integration Transparency 19 L2

Sun-Centered Model

The idea of an Earth-centered solar system was held for centuries until the Polish astronomer Nicholas Copernicus published a different view in 1543. Using an idea proposed by an early Greek scholar, Copernicus stated that the moon revolved around Earth, which was a planet. Earth, along with the other planets, revolved around the sun. He also stated that the daily movement of the planets and the stars was due to Earth's rotation. This is the sun-centered model of the solar system.

Using his telescope, the Italian astronomer Galileo Galilei found evidence that supported the ideas of Copernicus. He discovered that Venus went through phases like the moon's. These phases could be explained only if Venus were orbiting the sun. From this, he concluded that Venus revolves around the sun and that the sun is the center of the solar system.

Modern View of the Solar System

We now know that the **solar system** is made up of the nine planets, including Earth, and many smaller objects that orbit the sun. The sizes of the nine planets and the sun are shown to scale in **Figure 19-1.** However, the distances between the planets are not to scale. The dark areas on the sun are sunspots, which you will learn about later. Notice how small Earth is compared with some of the other planets and the sun, which is much larger than any of the planets.

The solar system includes a vast territory extending billions of kilometers in all directions from the sun. The sun contains 99.86 percent of the mass of the whole solar system. Because of its gravitational pull, the sun is the central object around which other objects of the solar system revolve.

2 Teach

Activity

Interpersonal Have pairs of students make flash cards of the planets in the solar system. They can draw the planet on one side of the card and write anything they know about it on the other side. Students should keep their flash cards handy so they can correct or update their information as they read this chapter. L2

Making a Model

Visual-Spatial Have volunteers compare and contrast the sun-centered model of the solar system with the Earth-centered model by making sketches on the chalkboard. As one student draws the models, have a partner point out how the two models are similar and how they are different. L2 COOP LEARN

Content Background

The Earth-centered model of the solar system is known as the geocentric model and the sun-centered model is known as the heliocentric model. A combination of the two, called the hybrid model, was proposed by Tycho Brahe (1546–1601). In this model, the sun and moon went around Earth and everything else went around the sun.

Solar System Models Have students write a report that describes what evidence led Copernicus to propose the sun-centered model of the solar system. Ask students to explain how this evidence refuted the Earth-centered model. They should list which scientists discovered the evidence used by Copernicus. L3

CA Science Content Standards

Page 668: 4e
Page 669: 2g, 4e

Using Science Words

Assess students' understanding of astronomical terms by asking the following questions. **What was Johannes Kepler's contribution to the sun-centered solar system model?** *He used mathematics to determine the shapes of the orbits and to calculate that the sun was not at the center of the elliptical paths.* **How do the planets' revolutions support the idea that the cloud that formed the solar system spun faster as it contracted?** *The inner planets revolve faster than the outer planets.*

Using an Analogy

Linguistic Ask students why ice skaters pull their arms toward their bodies as they spin. *to increase their rotational speed* Compare this analogy to the rotational speed of the cloud from which the solar system formed, which spun faster as more material was pulled toward its center.

VISUAL Learning

Figure 19-2 Scientists have recently discovered planetary systems in orbit around stars other than the sun. Have students research the planetary systems of the stars 51 Pegasi, 47 Ursae Majoris, and 16 Cygni B. Using **Figure 19-2,** have them compare and contrast these systems to our solar system.

Figure 19-2 Through careful observations, astronomers have found clues that help explain how our solar system may have formed.

B As gravity pulled matter inward, the cloud began to contract and spin. The densely packed matter grew extremely hot.

A About 4.6 billion years ago, a large cloud of gas, ice, and dust occupied our place in space.

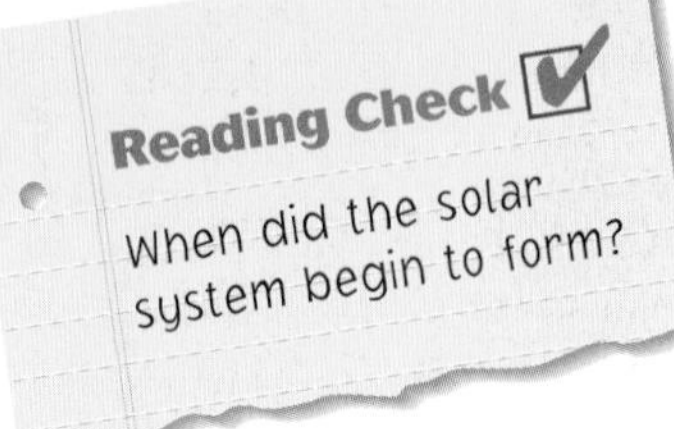

Reading Check
When did the solar system begin to form?

How the Solar System Formed

Scientists hypothesize that the sun and the solar system formed from a cloud of gas, ice, and dust about 4.6 billion years ago. **Figure 19-2** illustrates how this may have happened. This cloud was slowly rotating in space. A nearby star may have exploded, and the shock waves from this event may have caused the cloud to start contracting. At first, the cloud was rotating slowly. As it contracted, the matter in the cloud was squeezed into less space. The cloud's density became greater and the increased attraction of gravity pulled more gas and dust toward the cloud center. This caused the cloud to rotate faster, which in turn caused it to flatten into a disk with a dense center.

As the cloud contracted, the temperature began to increase. Eventually, the temperature in the core of the cloud reached about 10 million °C and nuclear fusion began. A star was born—this was the beginning of our sun. Nuclear fusion occurs when atoms with low mass, such as hydrogen, combine to form heavier elements, such as helium. The new, heavy element contains slightly less mass than the sum of the light atoms that formed it. The lost mass is converted into energy.

Not all of the nearby gas, ice, and dust were drawn into the core of the cloud. Remaining gas, ice, and dust particles

Inclusion Strategies

Gifted Have students research famous astronomers. Students can work in groups of five or six to write plays in which these astronomers are brought together in time to discuss their ideas. Students can perform the plays for the class. L3 COOP LEARN

Physically Challenged Have students work in small groups to make mobiles of the solar system to display in class. Place physically challenged students in groups where they can contribute their knowledge and ideas. On the back side of each model planet, students should include pertinent facts, such as temperature extremes, atmospheric conditions (or lack of atmosphere), length of orbit, number of moons, and so on. L2 COOP LEARN

C The center of the rotating disk continued to heat. Meanwhile, gas and dust particles in the outer rim clumped together, forming larger objects.

D The larger clumps continued to grow as more objects collided.

collided and stuck together, forming larger objects that in turn attracted more particles because of the stronger pull of gravity. Close to the sun, the temperature was hot, and the easily vaporized elements could not condense into solids. This is why light elements are more scarce in the planets closer to the sun than in planets farther out in the solar system. Instead, the inner solar system is dominated by small, rocky planets with iron cores.

The **inner planets**—Mercury, Venus, Earth, and Mars—are the solid, rocky planets closest to the sun. The **outer planets**—Jupiter, Saturn, Uranus, Neptune, and Pluto—are those farthest from the sun. Except for Pluto, which is made of rock and ice, the outer planets are made mostly of lighter elements such as hydrogen, helium, methane, and ammonia.

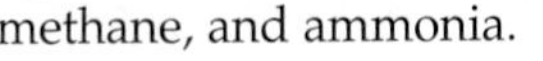

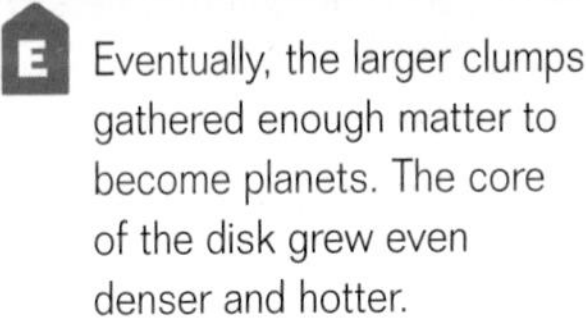

E Eventually, the larger clumps gathered enough matter to become planets. The core of the disk grew even denser and hotter.

F Nuclear fusion began in the core, and the sun became a star. Some of the smaller objects became moons and rings around the planets.

PHYSICS INTEGRATION

Planetary motion is discussed on the following page. Have students research and write about Kepler's three laws of planetary motion. Students should describe the steps that led Kepler to devise the laws. L3

Flex Your Brain

Use the Flex Your Brain activity to have students explore FORMATION OF THE SOLAR SYSTEM.

Teacher FYI

Clouds of gas, ice, and dust in space that form into planetary systems such as our solar system are called nebulae.

3 Assess

Check for Understanding

Reteach

Visual-Spatial Have students compare and contrast labeled photographs or illustrations of the planets. Have students divide the planets into two groups based on size alone. Discuss where Pluto fits in this classification. L2

Extension

For students who have mastered this section, use the **Reinforcement** and **Enrichment** masters.

Guided Reading Strategy

News Summary This strategy helps students explain and make connections to their study of science. Students are assigned the job of being television reporters. They are given several minutes to summarize, retell, or analyze their investigation for their "television" audience. Have students do a News Summary for an application of a concept from this chapter.

CA Science Content Standards

Page 670: 2g, 4e
Page 671: 2g, 4e

4 Close

Proficiency Prep

Use this quiz to check students' recall of section content.

1. **What model of the solar system did Copernicus propose in 1543?** *sun-centered*
2. **What do the sun, nine planets, their moons, and many smaller objects make up?** *solar system*
3. **Which planets are small and rocky and have iron cores?** *inner*
4. **Which planets, except for Pluto, are composed mostly of lighter elements?** *outer*

Section Assessment

1. In the sun-centered model, all objects orbit the sun. In the Earth-centered model, the sun, planets, and other objects moved around Earth.
2. About 4.6 billion years ago, a large cloud of gas, ice, and dust began to condense. The center of the cloud formed the sun. The planets and other objects in the solar system formed from outer portions of the cloud.
3. Temperatures are too low for water to exist as a liquid.
4. Think Critically It would be longer because Uranus's orbit is much longer than Earth's. One year on Uranus equals 84 years on Earth.

Using Math

Mercury orbits at a speed of 47.89 km/s and Earth orbits at a speed of 29.79 km/s. 47.89 km/s divided by 29.79 km/s = 1.6 times faster.

Motions of the Planets

When Nicholas Copernicus developed his sun-centered model of the solar system, he thought that the planets orbited the sun in circles. In the early 1600s, the German mathematician Johannes Kepler began studying the orbits of the planets. He discovered that the shapes of the orbits are not circular, but elliptical. He also calculated that the sun is not at the center of the ellipse but is offset from the center.

Kepler also discovered that the planets travel at different speeds in their orbits around the sun. By studying these speeds, you can see that the planets closer to the sun travel faster than planets farther away from the sun. As a result, the outer planets take much longer to orbit the sun than the inner planets do.

Copernicus's ideas, considered radical at the time, led to the birth of modern astronomy. Early scientists didn't have technology such as space probes to learn about the planets. They used instruments such as the one shown in **Figure 19-3.** Nevertheless, they developed theories about the solar system that we still use today. In the next section, you'll learn about the inner planets—our nearest neighbors in space.

Figure 19-3 This instrument, called an astrolabe, was used for a variety of astronomical calculations.

Section Assessment

1. What is the difference between the sun-centered and the Earth-centered models of the solar system?
2. How do scientists hypothesize the solar system formed?
3. The outer planets are rich in water, methane, and ammonia—the materials needed for life. Yet life is unlikely on these planets. Explain.
4. **Think Critically:** Would a year on the planet Uranus be longer or shorter than an Earth year? Explain.
5. **Skill Builder**
   Concept Mapping Make a concept map that compares and contrasts the Earth-centered model with the sun-centered model of the solar system. If you need help, refer to Concept Mapping in the **Skill Handbook** on page 950.

Using Math

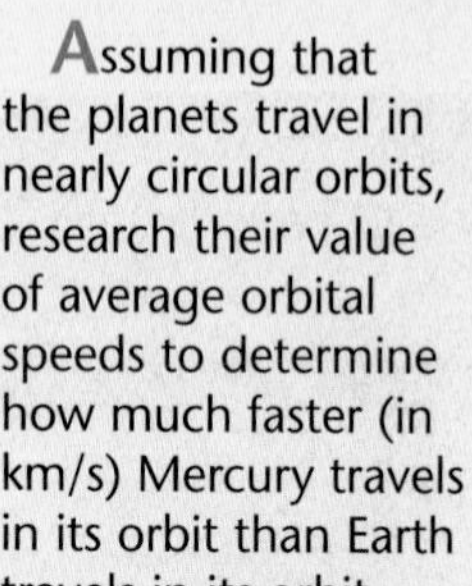

Assuming that the planets travel in nearly circular orbits, research their value of average orbital speeds to determine how much faster (in km/s) Mercury travels in its orbit than Earth travels in its orbit.

5. **Skill Builder**

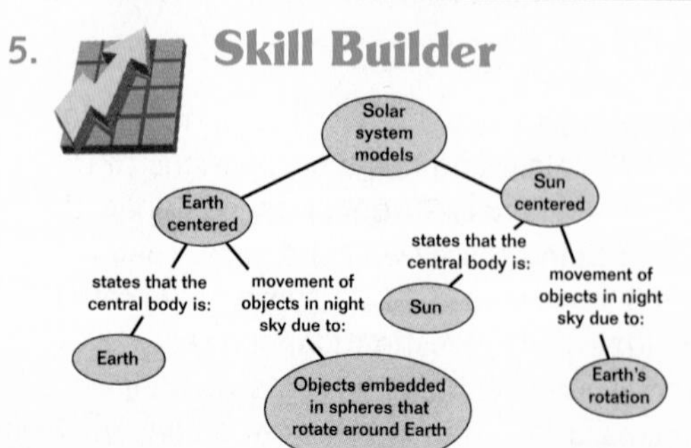

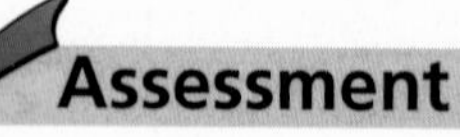

Assessment

Content Use this Skill Builder to assess students' understanding of concept maps. Ask students to compare how the sun is handled in the two models shown in their concept maps. Use **Performance Assessment in the Science Classroom,** p. 89.

Planetary Orbits

Planets travel around the sun along fixed paths called orbits. Early theories about the solar system stated that planetary orbits were perfect circles. As you construct a model of a planetary orbit, you will observe that the shape of planetary orbits is an ellipse, not a circle.

Materials

- Thumbtacks or pins
- Metric ruler
- String (25 cm)
- Pencil
- Cardboard (23 cm × 30 cm)
- Paper (21.5 cm × 28 cm)

What You'll Investigate

How can a model be constructed that will show planetary orbits to be elliptical?

Goals

- **Model** planetary orbits.
- **Calculate** changes in ellipses.

Procedure

1. **Place** a blank sheet of paper on top of the cardboard and insert two thumbtacks or pins about 3 cm apart.
2. **Tie** the string into a circle with a circumference of 15 to 20 cm. **Loop** the string around the thumbtacks. With someone holding the tacks or pins, **place** your pencil inside the loop and **pull** it tight.

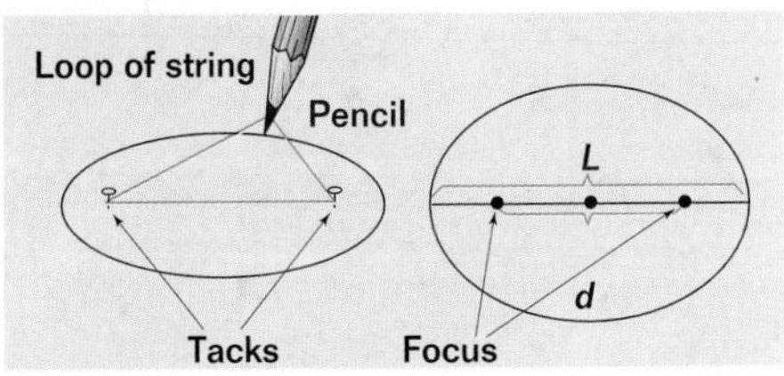

3. **Move** the pencil around the tacks, keeping the string tight, until you have completed a smooth, closed curve, called an ellipse.
4. **Repeat** steps 1 through 3 several times. First, **vary** the distance between the tacks, then **vary** the length of the string. However, change only one of these each time. Make a data table to record the changes in the sizes and shapes of the ellipses.
5. Orbits usually are described in terms of eccentricity (e). The eccentricity of any ellipse is determined by dividing the distance (d) between the foci (fixed points—here, the tacks) by the length of the major axis (L). See the diagram at left.
6. **Calculate** and **record** the eccentricity of the ellipses that you constructed.
7. **Research** the eccentricities of planetary orbits.
8. **Construct** an ellipse with the same eccentricity as Earth's orbit. **Repeat** this step with the orbit of either Pluto or Mercury.

Conclude and Apply

1. **Analyze** the effect a change in the length of the string or the distance between the tacks has on the shape of the ellipse.
2. **Hypothesize** what must be done to the string or placement of tacks to decrease the eccentricity of a constructed ellipse.
3. **Describe** the shape of Earth's orbit. Where is the sun located within the orbit?
4. **Identify** the planets that have the most eccentric orbits.
5. **Describe** the path of an orbit with an eccentricity of zero.

Data and Observations

Eccentricity of Ellipses	d (cm)	L (cm)	e (d/L)
# 1	3	15.6	0.19
# 2	5	13.5	0.37
# 3	5	8.7	0.57
Earth's orbit	0.48	28	0.017
Mercury's orbit			0.206
Pluto's orbit			0.248

Assessment

Oral Based on this activity, ask students to describe what must be true to obtain a circular orbit. What conditions would provide a more elliptical orbit? Use **Performance Assessment in the Science Classroom,** p. 71.

Activity 19•1

Purpose

Logical-Mathematical Students will describe a model that best represents the shape of planetary orbits. L2 ELL COOP LEARN

Process Skills

measuring in SI, observing, inferring, using numbers, comparing and contrasting, forming operational definitions, and making and using tables

Time

40 minutes

Safety Precautions

Caution students to handle thumbtacks or pins with care.

Teaching Strategies

Provide students with several values for d and L for imaginary ellipses and allow them to solve for e.

Troubleshooting If students have a problem with the equation $e = d/L$, relate the equation to known numbers such as $3 = 6/2$ or $3 = 12/4$.

Answers to Questions

1. Increasing the length of the string or decreasing the distance between the tacks makes the ellipse more circular. Decreasing the string's length or increasing the distance between foci makes the shape more elliptical.
2. lengthen the string or move the tacks closer to each other
3. Although it appears to be circular, Earth's orbit is an ellipse with the sun at one of the foci.
4. Pluto (0.248), Mercury (0.206), and Mars (0.093)
5. circular

CA Science Content Standards

Page 672: 1b, 1c, 2f, 2g, 4e, 9f

Page 673: 4e, 9a, 9f

SECTION 19•2

Prepare

Content Background

Refer to **Earth's Atmosphere** and **Planet Classification** on p. 666E.

Preplanning

Refer to the **Chapter Organizer** on pp. 666A–B.

1 Motivate

Bellringer

Before presenting the lesson, display **Section Focus Transparency 53** on the overhead projector. Use the accompanying **Focus Activity** worksheet. L2 ELL

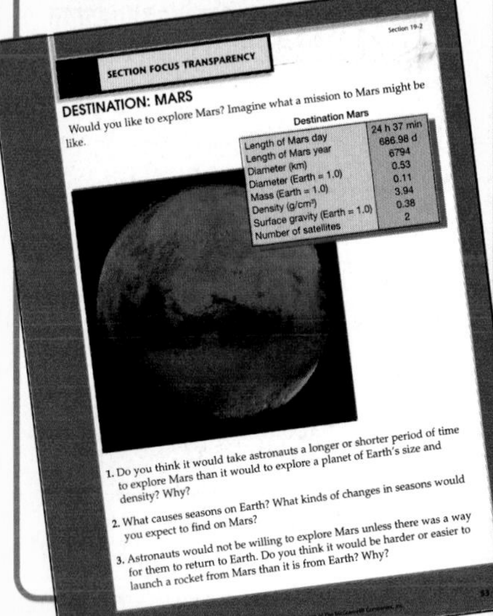

Section 19-2

SECTION FOCUS TRANSPARENCY

DESTINATION: MARS

Would you like to explore Mars? Imagine what a mission to Mars might be like.

Destination Mars	
Length of Mars day	24 h 37 min
Length of Mars year	686.98 d
Diameter (km)	6794
Diameter (Earth = 1.0)	0.53
Mass (Earth = 1.0)	0.11
Density (g/cm³)	3.94
Surface gravity (Earth = 1.0)	0.38
Number of satellites	2

1. Do you think it would take astronauts a longer or shorter period of time to explore Mars than it would to explore a planet of Earth's size and density? Why?
2. What causes seasons on Earth? What kinds of changes in seasons would you expect to find on Mars?
3. Astronauts would not be willing to explore Mars unless there was a way for them to return to Earth. Do you think it would be harder or easier to launch a rocket from Mars than it is from Earth? Why?

Tying to Previous Knowledge

Remind students that much of what we know about the solar system has been sent back to Earth by space probes.

19•2 The Inner Planets

What You'll Learn

- The inner planets in their relative order from the sun
- Important characteristics of each inner planet
- How Venus and Earth compare and contrast

Vocabulary

Mercury, Venus, Earth, astronomical unit, Mars

Why It's Important

- Other planets have characteristics that are different from those of Earth.

Inner Planets

We have learned much about the solar system since the days of Copernicus and Galileo. Advancements in telescopes allow astronomers to observe the planets from Earth. The planets shine by sunlight reflected from their surfaces. In addition, space probes have explored much of our solar system, adding greatly to the knowledge we have about the planets. Let's take a tour of the solar system through the "eyes" of the space probes.

Mercury

The closest planet to the sun is **Mercury.** It is also the second-smallest planet. The first and only American spacecraft mission to Mercury was in 1974-1975 by *Mariner 10,* which flew by the planet and sent pictures back to Earth. *Mariner 10* photographed only 45 percent of Mercury's surface—we do not know what the other 55 percent looks like. What we do know is that the surface of Mercury has many craters and looks much like our moon. It also has cliffs as high as 3 km on its surface, as seen in **Figure 19-4.** These cliffs may have formed when Mercury apparently shrank about 2 km in diameter.

Why did Mercury apparently shrink? Scientists think the answer may lie inside the planet. *Mariner 10* detected a weak magnetic field around Mercury, indicating that the planet has a large iron core. Some scientists hypothesize that the crust of Mercury solidified while the iron core was still hot and

Figure 19-4 Giant cliffs on Mercury, like the one marked by the arrow, suggest that the planet might have shrunk.

Resource Manager

The following **Teacher Classroom Resources** can be used with Section 19-2:

Reproducible Masters

Activity Worksheets, p. 109 L2

Enrichment, p. 53 L3

Home Involvement, p. 28 L2

Laboratory Manual, pp. 119–122 L2

Reinforcement, p. 53 L2

molten. Then, as the core cooled and solidified, it contracted, causing the planet to shrink. The large cliffs may have resulted from breaks in the crust caused by this contraction, similar to what happens when an apple dries out and shrivels up.

Because of Mercury's small size and low gravitational pull, most gases that could form an atmosphere escape into space. Mercury's thin atmosphere is composed of hydrogen, helium, sodium, and potassium. The sodium and potassium may diffuse upward through the crust. The thin atmosphere and the nearness of Mercury to the sun cause this planet to have large extremes in temperature. Mercury's surface temperature can reach 450°C during the day and drop to –170°C at night.

Using Math

The average distance from the sun to Earth is 150 million km. How many minutes does it take light traveling at 300 000 km/s to reach Earth? Use the equation

$$\text{Time} = \frac{\text{distance}}{\text{speed}}$$

Venus

The second planet outward from the sun is **Venus.** Venus is sometimes called Earth's twin because its size and mass are similar to Earth's. One major difference is that the entire surface of Venus is blanketed by a dense atmosphere. The atmosphere of Venus, which has 96 times the surface pressure of Earth's at sea level, is mostly carbon dioxide. The clouds in the atmosphere contain droplets of sulfuric acid, which gives them a slightly yellow color.

Clouds on Venus are so dense that only two percent of the sunlight that strikes the top of the clouds reaches the planet's surface. The solar energy that reaches the surface is trapped by the carbon dioxide gas and causes a greenhouse effect similar to but more intense than Earth's greenhouse effect. Due to this intense greenhouse effect, the temperature on the surface of Venus is 470°C.

The former Soviet Union led the exploration of Venus. Beginning in 1970 with the first *Venera* probe, the Russians have photographed and mapped the surface of Venus using radar and surface probes. Between 1990 and 1994, the *U.S. Magellan* probe used its radar to make the most detailed maps yet of Venus's surface. *Magellan* revealed huge craters, faultlike cracks, and volcanoes with visible lava flows, as seen in **Figure 19-5.**

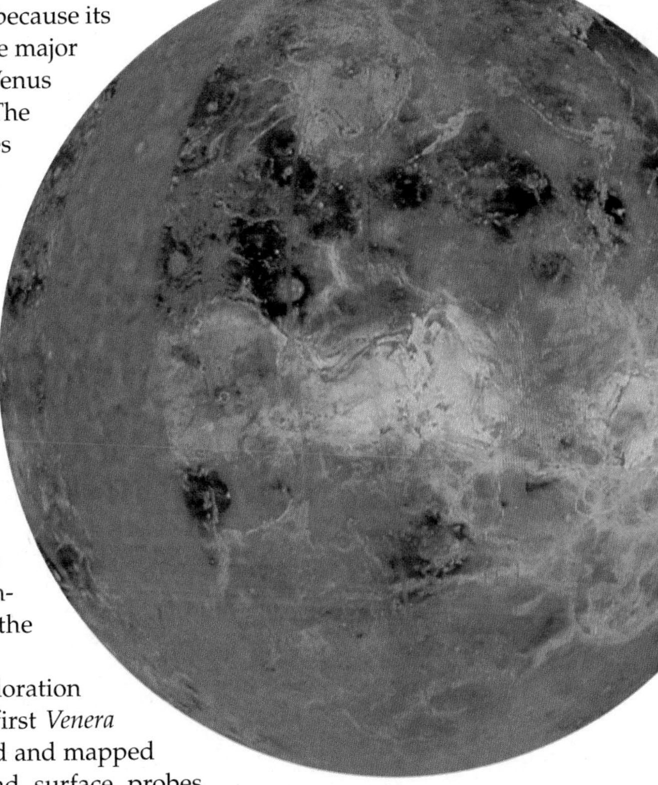

Figure 19-5 Although Venus is similar to Earth, there are important differences. **How could studying Venus help us learn more about Earth?**

2 Teach

Enrichment

Linguistic Encourage students to make up sentences that help them to remember the planets in order from the sun. For example, My Very Exceptional Mother Just Served Us Nutritious Pizza. L2

Using Math

150 million km ÷ 300 000 km/s = 500 s; 500 s ÷ 60 s = 8.3 minutes

Caption Answer

Figure 19-5 *Studying processes that occur on Venus allows us to learn about similar processes that may have occurred on Earth during our planet's early history.*

NATIONAL GEOGRAPHIC

Videodisc

STV: Solar System

Unit 1 *The Big Picture, The Nine Planets* 0:56

03600-05294

Refer to the Teacher Guide for additional bar codes and teaching strategies.

Content Background

Venus's yellow color is due to the sulfuric acid in its clouds. Earth's oceans of liquid water give it a distinctive blue color. Mars, the red planet, gets its color from iron oxide in weathered rocks on its surface. The composition of particular parts of each planet produces each planet's unique color.

Across the Curriculum

Mathematics Have students compute the volumes of the inner planets using the equation $V = 0.166\pi d^3$, where V is the volume and d is the diameter of each planet. Students can use astronomical books to research the volumes of the inner planets. L3

CA Science Content Standards

Page 674: 2g, 4e

Page 675: 1b, 1c, 2g, 4e, 9f

Activity

Visual-Spatial Have students research and list sizes of the inner planets and surface conditions. Have student volunteers draw each planet to scale on the chalkboard. Using colored chalk, have the volunteers illustrate at least one important characteristic of each planet's surface. Encourage all students to do the same in their Science Journals. L2 ELL COOP LEARN

Problem Solving

Normally, one would expect planets closer to the sun to be hotter than those farther away. However, if the more distant planet has an atmosphere that can trap heat, conditions on that planet's surface can be quite different from what is expected. The atmosphere of a planet can trap heat on the planet's surface just as the glass of a greenhouse traps heat inside the greenhouse.

Think Critically

The thick atmosphere of Venus absorbs solar energy and prevents it from rapidly radiating back into space. Mercury, which has little atmospheric gas, loses energy rapidly from its surface. Even though Venus is farther from the sun than Mercury, its atmosphere holds and circulates solar energy to a much greater extent. P

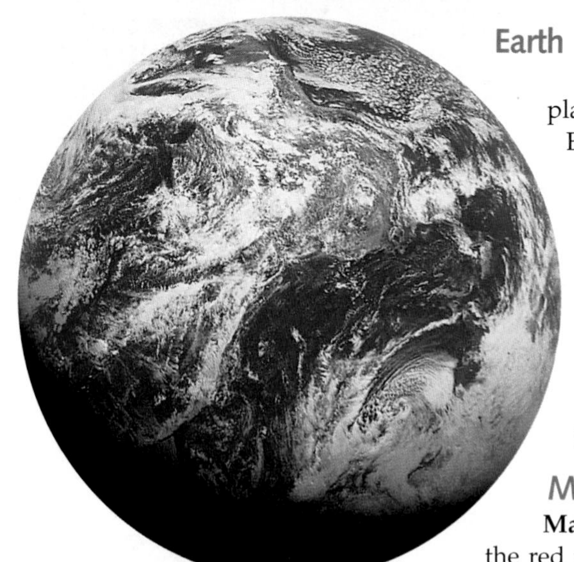

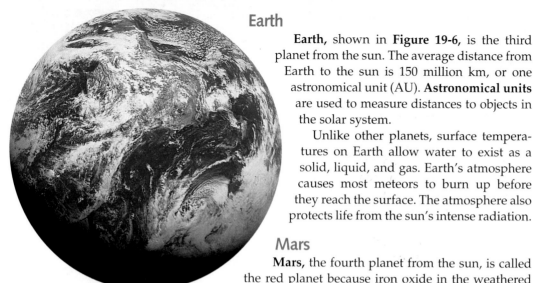

Figure 19-6 More than 70 percent of Earth's surface is covered by liquid water. **What is unique about surface temperatures on Earth?**

Earth

Earth, shown in **Figure 19-6,** is the third planet from the sun. The average distance from Earth to the sun is 150 million km, or one astronomical unit (AU). **Astronomical units** are used to measure distances to objects in the solar system.

Unlike other planets, surface temperatures on Earth allow water to exist as a solid, liquid, and gas. Earth's atmosphere causes most meteors to burn up before they reach the surface. The atmosphere also protects life from the sun's intense radiation.

Mars

Mars, the fourth planet from the sun, is called the red planet because iron oxide in the weathered rocks on its surface gives it a reddish color, as seen in **Figure 19-7.** Other features of Mars visible from Earth are its polar ice caps, which get larger during the Martian winter and shrink during the summer. The ice caps are made mostly of frozen carbon dioxide and frozen water.

Most of the information we have about Mars came from the *Mariner 9, Viking* probes, *Mars Global Surveyor*, and *Mars Pathfinder*. *Mariner 9* orbited Mars in 1971–1972. It revealed long channels on the planet that may have been carved by

Problem Solving

Interpret Planetary Data

Your teacher asks you to determine which planet's surface is hotter, Mercury or Venus. You must also explain the temperature difference. You decide that this assignment is going to be easy. Of course, Mercury has to be hotter than Venus because it is much closer to the sun. Venus is almost twice as far away as Mercury. You write your answer and turn in your paper. Later, when you receive your paper back, you find out that your assumptions were evidently wrong. Your teacher suggests that you research the question further, using the table on this page as a guide. As a further hint, your teacher tells you to consider how a greenhouse works to keep it warmer inside than outside and to relate this to what might happen to a planet with a thick atmosphere.

Data for Mercury and Venus

	Mercury 0.39 AU from sun	Venus 0.72 AU from sun
Surface Temperature (High)	450°	470°
Atmosphere Density	very thin	very dense
Atmosphere Compostion	potassium, sodium, hydrogen, helium	carbon dioxide sulfuric acid

Think Critically: What causes Venus to have a higher surface temperature than Mercury? Explain.

676 CHAPTER 19 THE SOLAR SYSTEM

GLENCOE TECHNOLOGY

CD-ROM

Glencoe Science Voyages Interactive CD-ROM

Explorations

Have students do the interactive exploration *How do planets in our solar system differ?*

Caption Answer

Figure 19-6 *They allow water to exist as a solid, liquid, and gas.*

Integrating the Sciences

Chemistry Mars is commonly known as the red planet. Ask students to research the composition of surface rocks on Mars. Based on their research, have them explain the chemical reaction in the Martian soil responsible for the planet's red color. *Iron in the Martian soil may have reacted with oxygen in the ancient Martian atmosphere, forming iron oxide.* L3

flowing water. *Mariner 9* also discovered the largest volcano in the solar system, Olympus Mons. Like all Mars's volcanoes, Olympus Mons is extinct. Large rift zones that formed in the Martian crust were also discovered. One such rift, Valles Marineris, is shown in **Figure 19-7.**

The Viking probes

In 1976, the *Viking 1* and *2* probes arrived at Mars. Each spacecraft consisted of an orbiter and a lander. The *Viking 1* and *2* orbiters photographed the entire surface of Mars from orbit, while the *Viking 1* and *2* landers touched down on the planet's surface to conduct meteorological, chemical, and biological experiments. The biological experiments found no evidence of life in the soil. The *Viking* landers also sent back pictures of a reddish-colored, barren, rocky, and windswept surface.

Inferring Effects of Gravity

Procedure

1. Suppose you are a crane operator who is sent to Mars to help build a Mars colony.
2. You know that your crane can lift 44 500 N on Earth, but the gravity on Mars is only 40 percent of Earth's gravity.
3. Using Appendix B, determine how much mass your crane could lift on Mars.

Analysis

1. How can what you have discovered be an advantage over construction on Earth?
2. In what ways might construction advantages change the overall design of the Mars colony?

Figure 19-7 Valles Marineris is more than 4000 km long, up to 240 km wide, and more than 6 km deep.

Try at Home **Mini Lab**

For additional help doing this activity at home, see the corresponding pages in the **Home Involvement** booklet.

Purpose

Logical-Mathematical Students will study gravity and mass on Mars. L2

Teaching Strategies

- Remind students that force equals mass times acceleration due to gravity: $F = ma$.
- Mars's gravity is 40 percent that of Earth's. To determine the acceleration due to gravity on Mars, multiply Earth's acceleration due to gravity by 0.4. Earth's acceleration due to gravity, a, is 9.8 m/s^2. Acceleration due to gravity on Mars is 0.4×9.8 m/s^2, or 3.92 m/s^2.
- $F_e = ma_e$; $m = F_e/a_e$
  $m = 44\,500$ N/9.8 m/s^2
  $= 4541$ kg on Earth
  $F_m = ma_m$; $m = F_m/a_m$
  $m = 44\,500$ N/3.92 m/s^2
  $= 11\,352$ kg on Mars

Analysis

1. The crane could lift more material on Mars and thus speed up construction.
2. The structure could be made of larger sections. Massive objects could be lifted higher.

Assessment

Performance To further assess students' understanding of conditions on Mars, have them calculate how much mass they could lift on the planet. Use **Performance Assessment in the Science Classroom,** p. 29.

Across the Curriculum

Mathematics Tell students that the average distance between the orbits of Earth and Mars is 78 million km. Have them calculate how many years it would take to travel from Earth's orbit to Mars's orbit, if they were traveling at 88 km/hr, the average highway speed of a car. *The trip would take about 100 years.* L2

CA Science Content Standards

Page 676: 2g, 4c, 4e
Page 677: 2f, 2g, 4e, 9b, 9f

Answer to Reading Check
It has distinct layers similar to the Grand Canyon.

LIFE SCIENCE INTEGRATION

Iron oxide in the weathered rocks gives Mars its reddish color.

3 Assess

Check for Understanding

Teacher FYI

Biological tests conducted on Mars by *Viking 1* and *2* were inconclusive as to whether any life is present in the Martian soil. One test gave a reading that could have indicated a biological reaction, but the same readings can be achieved by chemical reactions. Current theory leans toward the chemical rather than the biological reaction.

Reteach

Interpersonal Use the following question to reinforce data on the inner planets. **Why isn't Earth's surface marked by many craters like Mercury and the moon?** *Earth's atmosphere causes most meteors to burn up before they reach the surface.*

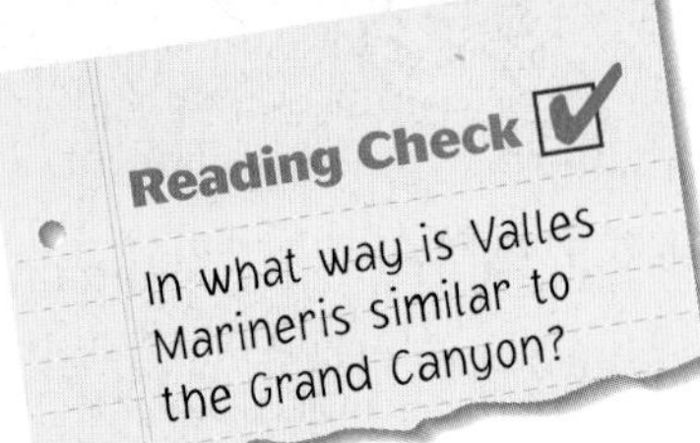

Reading Check
In what way is Valles Marineris similar to the Grand Canyon?

CHEMISTRY INTEGRATION

Mars has always been known as the red planet. Research the composition of surface rocks on Mars. Describe the chemical reaction in the Martian soil responsible for the planet's red color.

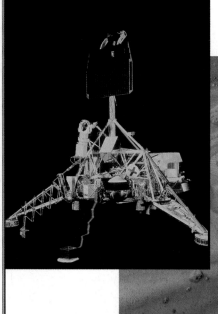

Global Surveyor and Pathfinder

The *Mars Pathfinder,* shown in **Figure 19-8,** gathered data that indicated that iron in Mars's crust may have been leached out by groundwater. In addition, high-quality cameras on board *Global Surveyor* showed that the walls of Valles Marineris have distinct layers similar to the Grand Canyon on Earth. *Global Surveyor* also noticed that a vast flat region, similar to a dried-up seabed or mudflat, covers a large area of Mars's northern hemisphere. This evidence, combined with evidence gathered from *Mariner 9,* indicates that large amounts of water were once present on the planet. Where has all the water gone? Many believe it is frozen into Mars's crust at the poles, shown in **Figure 19-9,** or has soaked into the ground.

The Martian atmosphere is much thinner than Earth's and is composed mostly of carbon dioxide, with some nitrogen and argon. The thin atmosphere does not filter out harmful rays from the sun as Earth's atmosphere does. Surface temperatures range from 35°C to –170°C. The temperature difference between day and night sets up strong winds on the planet, which can cause global dust storms during certain seasons.

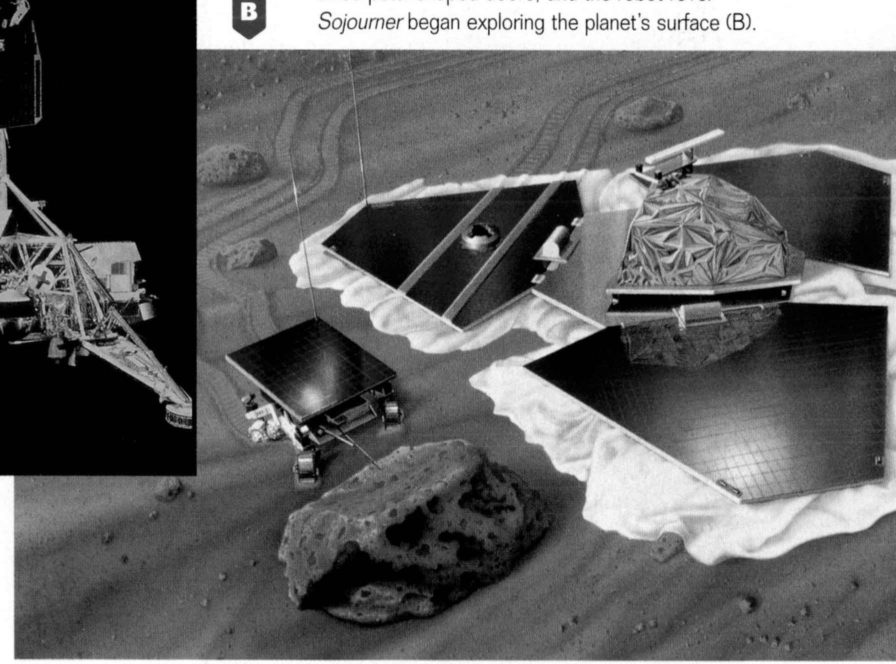

Figure 19-8 *Mars Pathfinder* (A) arrived at Mars in 1997. Upon landing, the craft opened its three petal-shaped doors, and the robot rover *Sojourner* began exploring the planet's surface (B).

Water on Mars Have students research the recent *Mars Global Surveyor* and *Pathfinder* missions for information on whether Mars may once have had liquid water on its surface. Have students write a one-page summary in their Science Journals about the data they discover. L2

Extension

For students who have mastered this section, use the **Reinforcement** and **Enrichment** masters.

CA Science Content Standards

Page 678: 4e, 5a
Page 679: 2g, 4e

Figure 19-9 These photos show two features of Mars.

A Olympus Mons is the largest volcano in the solar system.

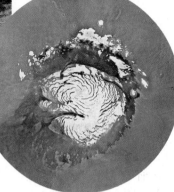

B Water that flowed on Mars long ago may now be frozen in polar ice caps.

Martian Moons

Mars has two small, heavily cratered moons. Phobos is 25 km in diameter, and Deimos is 13 km in diameter. Phobos's orbit is slowly spiraling inward toward Mars. Phobos is expected to impact the Martian surface in about 50 million years.

As you toured the inner planets using the "eyes" of the space probes, you saw how each planet is unique. Mercury, Venus, Earth, and Mars are different from the outer planets, which you'll explore in the next section.

Section Assessment

1. How are Mercury and Earth's moon similar?
2. List one important characteristic of each inner planet.
3. Although Venus is often called Earth's twin, why would life as we know it be unlikely on Venus?
4. Name the inner planets in order from the sun.
5. **Think Critically:** Do the closest planets to the sun always have the hottest surface temperatures? Explain your answer.
6. **Skill Builder**
   Interpreting Data Using the information in this section, explain how Mars is like Earth. How are they different? If you need help, refer to Interpreting Data in the **Skill Handbook** on page 960.

Science Journal

Use textbooks and NASA materials to investigate NASA's missions to Mars. In your Science Journal, report on the possibility of life on Mars and the tests that have been conducted to see whether life is there.

6. **Skill Builder**

Answers should include that both are inner planets. The processes of volcanism and weathering helped to form each planet. Both have polar ice caps. Liquid water is common on Earth's surface now, and may once have been present on Mars.

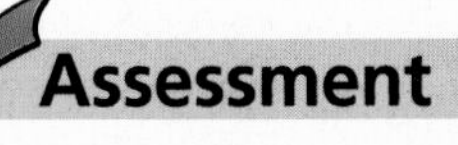

Assessment

Performance Use this Skill Builder to assess students' abilities to interpret data. Ask students to explain what equipment they would need in order to live on Mars's surface. Use **Performance Assessment in the Science Classroom,** p. 27.

4 Close

Proficiency Prep

Use this quiz to check students' recall of section content.

1. **Which planet is closest to the sun?** *Mercury*
2. **Which planet is considered to be Earth's twin?** *Venus*

Section Assessment

1. The surfaces of both are heavily cratered. The amount of light reflected from both objects is low because of the dark-colored surfaces.
2. Answers might include: Mercury is heavily cratered; Venus has a dense cloud cover; water on Earth exists in three states; and Mars appears red due to iron oxide.
3. The greenhouse effect raises surface temperatures on Venus to 470°C.
4. Mercury, Venus, Earth, Mars
5. **Think Critically** No, because of its intense greenhouse effect, Venus has a hotter surface temperature than Mercury, which is closer to the sun.

Science Journal

Viking landers: Gas Exchange Experiment, Pyrolytic Release Experiment, and Labeled Release Experiment; *Pathfinder* and *Sojourner:* geologic studies of the Martian surface and meteorological studies. Several spacecraft have studied the planet from orbit.

19-2 THE INNER PLANETS 679

SECTION 19•3

Prepare

Content Background

Refer to **Outer Planets** and **Pluto** on p. 666F.

Preplanning

Refer to the **Chapter Organizer** on pp. 666A–B.

1 Motivate

Bellringer

Before presenting the lesson, display **Section Focus Transparency 54** on the overhead projector. Use the accompanying **Focus Activity** worksheet. L2 ELL

Section 19-3

SECTION FOCUS TRANSPARENCY

FOUR MOONS RISING

Have you ever watched Earth's moon rising? Imagine what it would be like to watch two, four, sixteen or even twenty moons tracing a path around the sky. Most of the outer planets have many moons.

1. Jupiter is shown here with four of its sixteen moons. Try to imagine what Jupiter might be like. What questions would you have to answer in order to describe Jupiter?
2. The outer planets are much further from the sun than Earth is. Knowing only that, what can you hypothesize about them?

Tying to Previous Knowledge

Voyager 1 and *2* have sent back information about the outer planets. *Galileo* has sent back information about Jupiter and its moons.

19•3 The Outer Planets

What You'll Learn

- The major characteristics of Jupiter, Saturn, Uranus, and Neptune
- How Pluto differs from the other outer planets

Vocabulary

Jupiter, Great Red Spot, Saturn, Uranus, Neptune, Pluto

Why It's Important

- You'll learn about the planets in our solar system that differ most from Earth.

Outer Planets

You have learned that the inner planets are small, solid, rocky bodies in space. By contrast, the outer planets, except for Pluto, are large, gaseous objects.

You may have heard or read about the *Voyager* and *Galileo* spacecraft. Although they were not the first probes to the outer planets, they have uncovered a wealth of new information about Jupiter, Saturn, Uranus, and Neptune. Let's follow the spacecraft on their journeys to the outer planets of the solar system.

Jupiter

In 1979, *Voyager 1* and *Voyager 2* flew past **Jupiter,** the largest planet and the fifth planet from the sun. *Galileo* reached Jupiter in 1995. The major discoveries of the probes include new information about the composition and motion of Jupiter's atmosphere and the discovery of three new moons. *Voyager* probes also discovered that Jupiter has faint dust rings around it and that one of its moons has volcanoes on it.

Jupiter is composed mostly of hydrogen and helium, with some ammonia, methane, and water vapor as well. Scientists theorize that the atmosphere of hydrogen and helium gradually changes to a planetwide ocean of liquid hydrogen and helium toward the middle of the planet. Below this liquid layer may be a solid rocky core. The extreme pressure and temperature, however, make the core different from any rock on Earth.

You've probably seen pictures from the probes of Jupiter's colorful clouds. Its atmosphere has bands of white, red, tan, and brown clouds, as shown in **Figure 19-10.** Continuous storms of swirling, high-pressure gas have been observed on Jupiter. The **Great Red Spot** is the most spectacular of these storms. Lightning also has been observed within Jupiter's clouds.

Jupiter

A

B

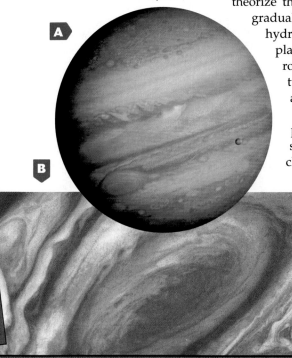

Figure 19-10 Jupiter (A) is the largest planet in our solar system, containing more mass than all of the other planets combined. The Great Red Spot (B) is a giant storm about 12 000 km from top to bottom.

Resource Manager

The following **Teacher Classroom Resources** can be used with Section 19-3:

Reproducible Masters

Activity Worksheets, pp. 107–108, 110 L2

Enrichment, p. 54 L3

Home Involvement, p. 37 L2

Laboratory Manual, pp. 123–124 L2

Reinforcement, p. 54 L2

Moons of Jupiter

Sixteen moons orbit Jupiter. The four largest, shown in **Table 19-1,** were discovered by Galileo in 1610. Io is the closest large moon to Jupiter. Jupiter's tremendous gravitational force and the gravity of Europa pull on Io. This force heats up Io, causing it to be the most volcanically active object in the solar system. The next large moon is Europa. It is composed mostly of rock with a thick, smooth crust of ice, which may indicate the presence of an ocean under the ice. Next is Ganymede, which is the largest moon in the solar system. It's larger than the planet Mercury. Callisto, the last of the large moons, is composed of ice and rock. Studying these moons and events such as the comet collision shown in **Figure 19-11** further our knowledge of the solar system.

Saturn

The next planet surveyed by the *Voyager* probes was Saturn, in 1980 and 1981. **Saturn** is the sixth planet from the sun and is also known as the ringed planet. Saturn is the second-largest planet in the solar system but has the lowest density. Its density is so low that the planet would float on water.

Table 19-1

Large Moons of Jupiter	
Io The most volcanically active object in the solar system; sulfur lava gives it its distinctive red and orange color; has a thin oxygen, sulfur, and sulfur dioxide atmosphere.	
Europa Rocky interior is covered by a 100-km-thick ice crust, which has a network of cracks, indicating tectonic activity; has a thin oxygen atmosphere.	
Ganymede Has an ice crust about 100 km thick, covered with grooves; crust may surround a mantle of water or slushy ice; has a rocky core and a thin hydrogen atmosphere.	
Callisto Has a heavily cratered, ice-rock crust several hundred kilometers thick; crust may surround a salty ocean around a rock core; has a thin atmosphere of hydrogen, oxygen, and carbon dioxide.	

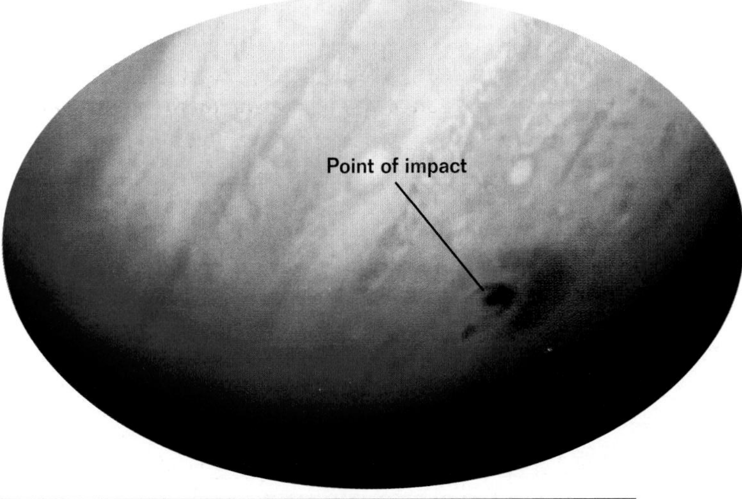

Figure 19-11 In 1994, comet Shoemaker-Levy 9 collided into Jupiter causing a series of spectacular explosions. Information from this impact gives us clues about what might happen if such an impact occurred on Earth.

2 Teach

Activity

Interpersonal Form groups of four students. Have students play "Planet Jeopardy" by reading statements from this section and the previous section and calling on a student to form an appropriate question. Award points for every correct question by a group. L2 COOP LEARN

VISUAL Learning

Table 19-1 Ask students why the four moons shown in the table are called the Galilean satellites of Jupiter. *They were discovered by Galileo.* Ask them also to list the moons in their Science Journals and to write a brief description of the characteristics of each moon. L2

GLENCOE TECHNOLOGY

Videodisc

The Infinite Voyage: Sail On, Voyager

Chapter 4 *Jupiter's Atmosphere* 1:30

Chapter 5 *Jupiter's Moons and Unexpected Volcanoes* 6:00

Chapter 7 *The Rings of Saturn* 3:30

Refer to the Teacher Guide for bar codes and teaching strategies.

Multiple Learning Styles

Visual-Spatial If a local organization of sky observers exists in your area, invite one of its members to talk to the class about nighttime observations. Perhaps one of the members has searched for and found a comet at some time. If no organization exists locally, organize a nighttime observation with students. Students may wish to invite their parents or guardians to participate in a session to observe Jupiter or Saturn. Use planet observations to support in-class discussions on the solar system.

CA Science Content Standards

Page 680: 4e
Page 681: 2g, 4e, 8d

Try at Home MiniLab

For additional help doing this activity at home, see the corresponding pages in the **Home Involvement** booklet.

Purpose

 **Kinesthetic** Students will formulate models of the solar system. L2 ELL P

Materials

metric rulers, drawing compass, pencil, paper

Teaching Strategies

Safety Precautions Caution students to handle drawing compasses carefully.

Troubleshooting Have students determine a scale for Earth first. The scale for each planet will be the product of the scale for Earth times the other planet's multiple of true Earth size. For example, Jupiter is 11.19 times larger than Earth. If model Earth were 2 cm in diameter, model Jupiter would be 2 cm × 11.19 or 22.38 cm in scale diameter.

Analysis

1. & 2. Answers will vary depending on the scale used. Have students compute their answers by multiplying Earth's scale diameter by 11 728, which is the number of Earth diameters in 1 AU.
3. At 1 AU = 2 m, the sun would be 19 mm in diameter. Model Earth would be considerably smaller—0.18 mm or 0.018 cm.

Assessment

Performance To further assess students' understanding of scale models, have them formulate models of each planet out of balls of crumpled newspaper. Use **Performance Assessment in the Science Classroom,** p. 51.

Figure 19-12 Saturn's rings are composed of pieces of rock and ice.

Similar to Jupiter, Saturn is a large, gaseous planet with a thick outer atmosphere composed mostly of hydrogen and helium. Saturn's atmosphere also contains ammonia, methane, and water vapor. As you go deeper into Saturn's atmosphere, the gases gradually change to liquid hydrogen and helium. Below its atmosphere and liquid ocean, Saturn may have a small rocky core.

The *Voyager* probes gathered new information about Saturn's ring system and its moons. The *Voyager* probes showed that Saturn has several broad rings, each of which is composed of thousands of thin ringlets. Each ring is composed of countless ice and rock particles ranging in size from a speck of dust to tens of meters across, as shown in **Figure 19-12.** This makes Saturn's ring system the most complex of all the outer gaseous planets.

At least 20 moons orbit Saturn. That's more than any other planet in our solar system. The largest of these, Titan, is larger than Mercury. It has an atmosphere of nitrogen, argon, and methane. Thick clouds prevent us from seeing the surface of Titan.

Modeling Planets

Procedure

1. Research the planets to determine how the sizes of the planets in the solar system compare with each other.
2. Select a scale for the diameter of Earth based on the size of your paper.
3. Make a model by drawing a circle with this diameter on paper.
4. Using Earth's diameter as 1.0, draw each of the other planets to scale.

Analysis

1. At this scale, how far would your model Earth need to be located from the sun?
2. What would 1 AU be equal to in this model?
3. Using a scale of 1 AU = 2 m, how large would the sun and Earth models have to be to remain in scale?

Across the Curriculum

Mathematics Supply students with the following diameters of the larger moons in the solar system: Earth's moon (3476 km), Io (3630 km), Europa (3138 km), Ganymede (5262 km), Callisto (4800 km), Titan (5150 km), and Triton (2720 km). Have students compare and contrast the sizes of these moons with the sizes of the inner planets. Using a scale of 1 mm = 100 km, have students draw to scale the inner planets and moons listed above. Students should note that some of the moons are larger than Mercury.

  L2

Uranus

After touring Saturn, *Voyager 2* flew by Uranus in 1986. **Uranus,** shown in **Figure 19-13,** is the seventh planet from the sun and wasn't discovered until 1781. It is a large, gaseous planet with 17 satellites and a system of thin, dark rings.

Voyager revealed numerous thin rings and ten moons that had not been seen earlier. *Voyager* also detected that the planet's magnetic field is tilted 55 degrees from its rotational poles.

The atmosphere of Uranus is composed of hydrogen, helium, and some methane. The methane gives the planet its blue-green color. Methane absorbs the red and yellow light, and the clouds reflect the green and blue. No cloud bands and few storm systems are seen on Uranus. Evidence suggests that under its atmosphere, Uranus has a mantle of liquid water, methane, and ammonia surrounding a rocky core.

One of the most unique features of Uranus is that its axis of rotation is tilted on its side compared with the other planets. The axes of rotation of the other planets, except Pluto, are nearly perpendicular to the planes of their orbits. Uranus, however, has a rotational axis nearly parallel to the plane of its orbit, as shown in **Figure 19-14.** Some scientists believe a collision with another object turned Uranus on its side.

Figure 19-13 The atmosphere of Uranus gives the planet its distinct blue-green color.

*inter***NET** CONNECTION

Visit the Glencoe Science Web Site at **www.glencoe.com/sec/science/ca** for more information about the *Voyager* space probes.

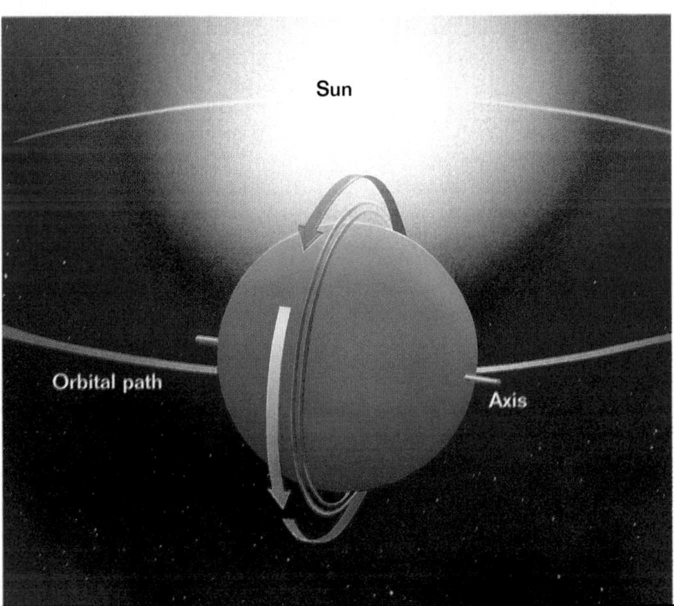

Figure 19-14 Uranus rotates on an axis nearly parallel to the plane of its orbit. During its revolution around the sun, one of the poles, at times, points almost directly at the sun.

*inter***NET** CONNECTION

Internet Addresses

For Internet tips, see Glencoe's **Using the Internet in the Science Classroom.**

NATIONAL GEOGRAPHIC

Videodisc

STV: Solar System

Unit 3 *Outer Planets* 6:33

24512-36610

Refer to the Teacher Guide for additional bar codes and teaching strategies.

GLENCOE TECHNOLOGY

Videodisc

The Infinite Voyage: Sail On, Voyager

Chapter 10 *Voyager 2: Uranus* 7:00

Refer to the Teacher Guide for bar codes and teaching strategies.

Content Background

Voyager 2 has provided astronomers with data about the composition of the atmospheres of the gaseous giant planets. Also, using data from the *Hubble Space Telescope,* the sizes of the gaseous giants, their moons, Pluto, and Charon have been determined to a much better degree. These data have enabled scientists to produce more detailed models of the solar system's scale and structure.

CA Science Content Standards

Page 682: 4c, 4e, 9f
Page 683: 4e

GLENCOE TECHNOLOGY

Videodisc

The Infinite Voyage: Sail On, Voyager

Chapter 21 *Voyager 2: Neptune* 8:00

Refer to the Teacher Guide for bar codes and teaching strategies.

3 Assess

Check for Understanding

Enrichment

Intrapersonal Have each student compile a list of the physical properties of all known moons orbiting the outer planets. Suggest students use data available from the *Voyager* and *Galileo* missions. L3

Reteach

Interpersonal Have pairs of students sketch each outer planet on a separate flash card. On the reverse side of the card, instruct students to write down the characteristics of each planet. Partners can then test each other using the flash cards. L1 COOP LEARN

Extension

For students who have mastered this section, use the **Reinforcement** and **Enrichment** masters.

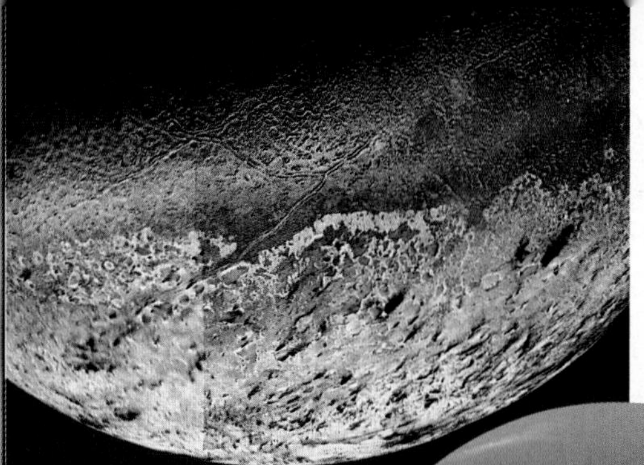

Figure 19-15 Triton, above, is Neptune's largest moon.

Neptune

Neptune

From Uranus, *Voyager 2* traveled on to Neptune, a large, gaseous planet. Discovered in 1846, **Neptune** is usually the eighth planet from the sun. However, Pluto's orbit crosses inside Neptune's during part of its voyage around the sun. Between 1979 and 1998, Pluto was closer to the sun than Neptune. In 1999, Pluto once again became the farthest planet from the sun.

Neptune's atmosphere is similar to that of Uranus. The methane content gives Neptune, shown in **Figure 19-15,** its distinctive blue-green color, just as it does for Uranus.

Neptune has dark-colored, stormlike features in its atmosphere that are similar to the Great Red Spot on Jupiter. One discovered by *Voyager* is called the Great Dark Spot.

Under its atmosphere, Neptune is thought to have liquid water, methane, and ammonia. Neptune probably has a rocky core.

Voyager 2 detected six new moons, so the total number of Neptune's known moons is now eight. Of these, Triton is the largest. Triton, shown in **Figure 19-15,** has a diameter of 2700 km and a thin atmosphere composed mostly of nitrogen. *Voyager* detected methane geysers erupting on Triton. *Voyager* also detected that Neptune has rings that are thin in some places and thick in other places. Neptune's magnetic field is tilted 47 degrees from its rotational axis. In comparison, Earth's magnetic field is tilted only 11.5 degrees from its rotational axis.

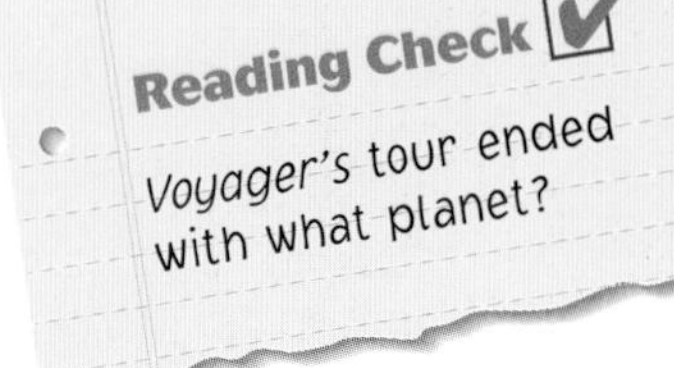

Reading Check
Voyager's tour ended with what planet?

Voyager ended its tour of the solar system with Neptune. Both *Voyager* probes are now beyond the orbits of Pluto and Neptune. They will continue into space, studying how far the sun's power reaches into the outer limits of our solar system.

Pluto

The smallest planet in our solar system, and the one we know the least about, is Pluto. Because **Pluto** is farther from the sun than Neptune during most of its orbit around the sun, it is considered the ninth planet from the sun. Pluto is not like the other outer planets. It's surrounded by only a

Galileo Have students write a report about new information gathered by *Galileo* about Jupiter, its moons, and its rings. Ask students to discuss how NASA used gravity assists to power the space probe during its long flight to Jupiter. L2

thin atmosphere, and it's the only outer planet with a solid, icy-rock surface.

Pluto's only moon, Charon, has a diameter about half the size of Pluto's. Charon orbits close to Pluto. Pluto and Charon are shown in **Figure 19-16.** Because of their close size and orbit, they are sometimes considered to be a double planet.

Recent data from the *Hubble Space Telescope* indicate the presence of a vast disk of icy comets near Neptune's orbit, called the Kuiper belt. Some of the ice comets are hundreds of kilometers in diameter. Are Pluto and Charon members of this belt? Are they escaped moons of one of the larger gaseous giants, or did they simply form at the distance they are? Maybe planets at that distance from the sun should be small and composed of icy rock. We may not find out until we send a probe to Pluto.

With the *Voyager* probes, we entered a new age of knowledge about the solar system. The space probe *Galileo*, which arrived at Jupiter in 1995, and the *Cassini* probe, which will arrive at Saturn in 2004, will continue to extend our understanding of the solar system.

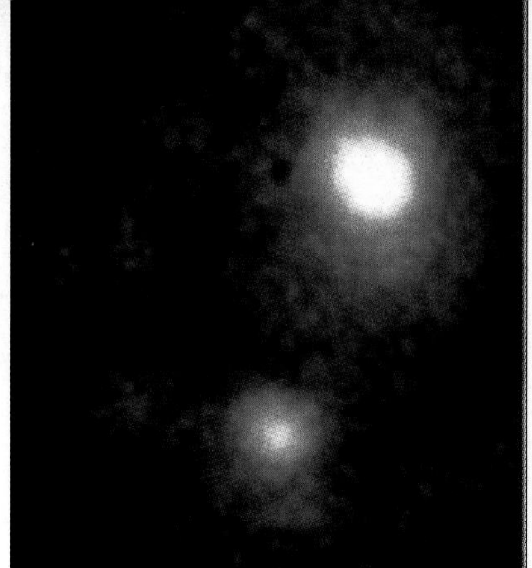

Figure 19-16 The *Hubble Space Telescope* gave astronomers their first clear view of Pluto and Charon as distinct objects.

Section Assessment

1. What are the differences between the outer planets and the inner planets?
2. Are any moons in the solar system larger than planets? If so, which ones?
3. How does Pluto differ from the other outer planets?
4. **Think Critically:** Why is Neptune sometimes the farthest planet from the sun?
5. **Skill Builder**
   Recognizing Cause and Effect
   Answer the following questions about Jupiter. If you need help, refer to Recognizing Cause and Effect in the **Skill Handbook** on page 957.
   a. What causes Jupiter's surface color?
   b. How is the Great Red Spot affected by Jupiter's atmosphere?
   c. How does Jupiter's mass affect its gravitational force?

Using Computers

Spreadsheet Design a table using spreadsheet software of the nine planets. Compare their characteristics, such as size, distance from the sun, orbital speed, and number of satellites. If you need help, refer to page 974.

4 Close

Proficiency Prep

Use this quiz to check students' recall of section content.

1. **Which planet is the largest?** *Jupiter*
2. **Which planet has the most complex ring system?** *Saturn*

Section Assessment

1. The outer planets are large, gaseous objects, except for Pluto. The inner planets are small, solid, rocklike bodies in space.
2. Yes, Ganymede and Titan are larger than Mercury. Several moons are larger than Pluto: Earth's moon, Io, Europa, Ganymede, Callisto, Titan, and Triton.
3. Pluto is small and rocky; the other outer planets are large gaseous giants.
4. **Think Critically** Pluto's orbit is more elliptical than the orbits of other planets. This causes Pluto to come closer to the sun than Neptune for about 20 years of its orbit. This most recently occurred between 1979 and 1999.

Using Computers

Student spreadsheets will vary, but should include size, distance from the sun, orbital speed, and number of satellites.

5.  **Skill Builder**
   a. bands of red, tan, and brown clouds
   b. High pressure causes the gases in the storm to flow inward toward its center.
   c. Jupiter is the most massive planet and thus has the greatest gravitational force of the nine planets.

Assessment

Oral Assess students' abilities to recognize cause and effect by asking the following question: **What causes Io to be so volcanically active?** Use **Performance Assessment in the Science Classroom,** p. 17.

CA Science Content Standards

Page 684: 2g, 4e
Page 685: 2g, 4c, 4e, 9e

Activity 19·2 Design Your Own Experiment

Recognize the Problem

Purpose

Logical-Mathematical Students will model distances between the sun and the planets. L2 ELL COOP LEARN P

Process Skills

measuring in SI, using numbers, sequencing, formulating a hypothesis, separating and controlling variables, interpreting data, and making models

Time

one class period

Safety Precautions

Caution students to handle scissors with care.

Form a Hypothesis

Possible Hypotheses

Students will select a scale to represent distances in AU. The mean distances to planets in AU will be obtained and adjusted by the selected scale. The scale distances will be placed on a data chart, and a scale model of planet distances will be constructed from string.

Test Your Hypothesis

Possible Procedures

Use research materials to obtain the mean distance from the sun to each planet in AU. Record these values in a data table. Determine a scale for making a model of the solar system from string. Use paper to make planets. Design a method for placing the planets in proper positions on the solar system model.

Design Your Own Experiment

Activity 19·2

Solar System Distance Model

Distances between the planets of the solar system are large. Can you design a model that will demonstrate the large distances between and among the sun and planets in the solar system?

Possible Materials

- Meterstick
- Scissors
- Pencil
- String (several meters)
- Paper (several sheets of notebook paper)

Recognize the Problem

How can a model be designed that will show the relative distances between and among the sun and planets of the solar system?

Form a Hypothesis

State a hypothesis about how a model with scale dimensions of the solar system can be constructed.

Goals

- **Make a table** of scale distances that will represent planetary distances to be used in a model of the solar system.
- **Research** planetary distances.
- **Make a model** of the distances between the sun and planets of the solar system.

Safety Precautions

Take care when handling scissors.

Planetary Distances

Planet	Distance to Sun (km)	Distance to Sun (AU)	Scale Distance (1 AU = 10 cm)	Scale Distance (1 AU = 2 m)
Mercury	5.8×10^7	0.38	3.9 cm	77.4 cm
Venus	1.08×10^8	0.72	7.2 cm	1.45 m
Earth	1.50×10^8	1.00	10.0 cm	2.00 m
Mars	2.28×10^8	1.52	15.2 cm	3.05 m
Jupiter	7.80×10^8	5.20	52.0 cm	10.40 m
Saturn	1.43×10^9	9.54	95.4 cm	19.08 m
Uranus	2.88×10^9	19.18	191.8 cm	38.40 m
Neptune	4.51×10^9	30.06	300.6 cm	60.10 m
Pluto	5.92×10^9	39.44	394.4 cm	78.90 m

Teaching Strategies

Tying to Previous Knowledge Remind students of the dimensions of distances between inner planets. Tell them that distances between outer planets are much larger.

Troubleshooting Some students will need help in choosing a scale to use for their models. If necessary, suggest that they use a scale of 1 AU = 10 cm. Sample data have been provided for this scale. Some students may also need help with the math.

Test Your Hypothesis

Plan

1. As a group, **agree** upon and write out your hypothesis statement.
2. **List** the steps that you need to take in making your model to **test** your hypothesis. Be specific, describing exactly what you will do at each step.
3. **Make** a list of the materials that you will need to complete your model.
4. **Make a table** of scale distances you will use in your model.
5. **Write** a description of how you will **build** your model, **explaining** how it will demonstrate relative distances between and among the sun and planets of the solar system.

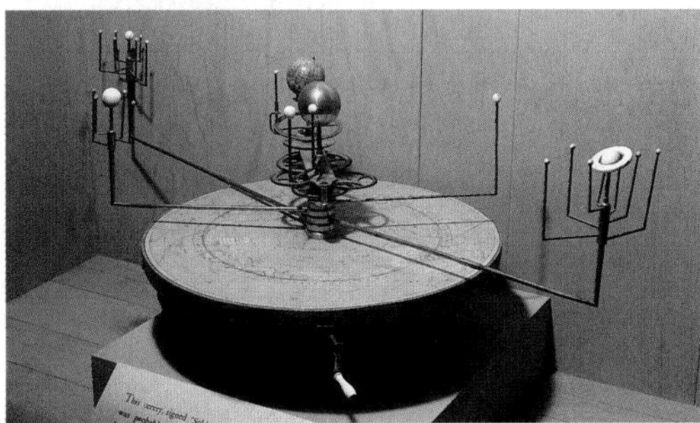

Do

1. Make sure your teacher approves your plan before you proceed.
2. **Construct the model** as planned using your scale distances.
3. While constructing the model, **write** down any observations that you or other members of your group make and complete the data table in your Science Journal.
4. **Calculate** the scale distance that would be used in your model if 1 AU = 2 m.

Analyze Your Data

1. **Explain** how a scale distance is determined.
2. How much string would be required to construct a model with a scale distance 1 AU = 2 m?

Draw Conclusions

1. Was it possible to work with your scale? **Explain** why or why not.
2. Proxima Centauri, the closest star to our sun, is about 270 000 AU from the sun. Based on your scale, how much string would you need to place this star on your model?

Expected Outcome

Some students will begin with a scale that is too large. They should realize that their scale will require great lengths of string. Other scales will not be large enough to show individual planet orbits. Students should realize that a scale that allows Pluto to be placed on the string will work for all planets.

Error Analysis

If students' models are not working, review their scale. Using their scale, have them compute the distance to Pluto. This will indicate if their scale is too large.

Analyze Your Data

1. Scale distance is determined by multiplying the AU-distance of each planet by the scale selected.
2. 78.94 m or any answer near 80 m

Draw Conclusions

1. Answers will vary depending upon the scale chosen. Students may say that their scale was too large to include all planets or too small to show individual planet orbits.
2. Answers will vary, but for a scale of 1 AU = 10 cm, Proxima Centauri would be about 27 km away from the model sun.

GO Further

Have students summarize distances between and among inner and outer planets. Inner planets are closer to the sun and closer to one another. Outer planets are farther from the sun and farther apart from one another.

Assessment

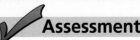

Performance Using the same scale selected for their solar system models, have students place the asteroid Ceres in their models. The orbit of Ceres lies 2.77 AU from the sun. Use **Performance Assessment in the Science Classroom,** p. 29.

CA Science Content Standards

Page 686: 4c, 4e, 9a

Page 687: 4c, 4e, 9a, 9b, 9f

SECTION 19•4

Prepare

Refer to **Comets** on p. 666F.

Preplanning

Refer to the **Chapter Organizer** on pp. 666A–B.

1 Motivate

Bellringer

Before presenting the lesson, display **Section Focus Transparency 55** on the overhead projector. Use the accompanying **Focus Activity** worksheet. L2 ELL

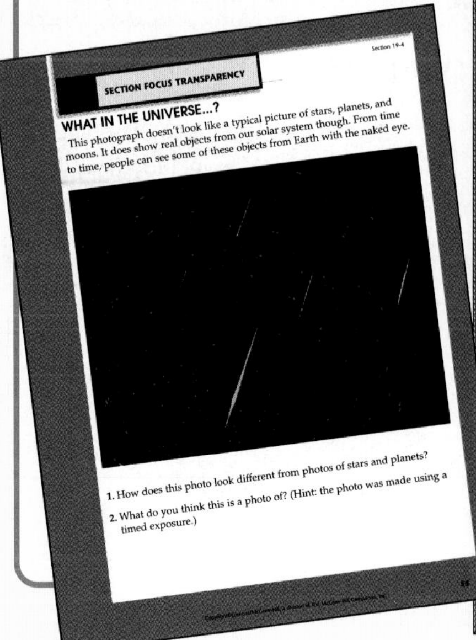

Section 19-4

SECTION FOCUS TRANSPARENCY

WHAT IN THE UNIVERSE...?

This photograph doesn't look like a typical picture of stars, planets, and moons. It does show real objects from our solar system though. From time to time, people can see some of these objects from Earth with the naked eye.

1. How does this photo look different from photos of stars and planets?
2. What do you think this is a photo of? (Hint: the photo was made using a timed exposure.)

55

Tying to Previous Knowledge

Remind students that the moon's surface is heavily cratered. Tell them that most craters on the moon probably formed from meteorite impacts.

Other Objects in the Solar System

What You'll Learn

- Where a comet comes from and how a comet develops as it approaches the sun
- Comets, meteoroids, and asteroids

Vocabulary

comet	meteorite
Oort Cloud	asteroid
meteor	

Why It's Important

- Comets, meteoroids, and asteroids may be composed of material that formed early in the history of the solar system.

Comets

Although the planets and their moons are the most noticeable members of the sun's family, many other objects orbit the sun. Comets, meteoroids, and asteroids are other objects in the solar system.

You've probably heard of Halley's comet. A **comet** is composed of dust and rock particles mixed in with frozen water, methane, and ammonia. Halley's comet was last seen from Earth in 1986. English astronomer Edmund Halley realized that comet sightings that had taken place about every 76 years were really sightings of the same comet. This comet, which takes about 76 years to orbit the sun, was named after him. Halley's comet is just one example of the many other objects in the solar system besides the planets. The Dutch astronomer Jan Oort proposed the idea that a large collection of comets lies in a cloud that completely surrounds the solar

Figure 19-17 Comet Hale-Bopp was visible in March and April 1997.

Resource Manager

The following **Teacher Classroom Resources** can be used with Section 19-4:

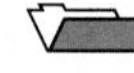 **Reproducible Masters**

Critical Thinking/Problem Solving, p. 19 L2

Enrichment, p. 55 L3

Reinforcement, p. 55 L2

Study Guide, pp. 74–76 L1 ELL

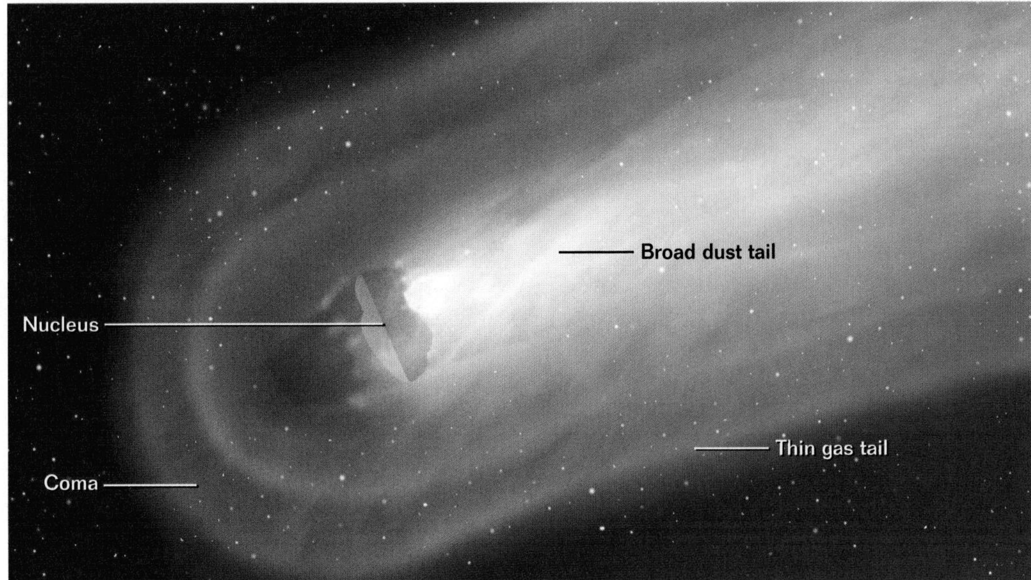

Figure 19-18 A comet consists of a nucleus, a coma, and a tail.

system. This cloud is located beyond the orbit of Pluto and is called the **Oort Cloud.** Evidence suggests that the gravity of the sun and nearby stars interacts with comets in the Oort Cloud. Comets either escape from the solar system or get captured into much smaller orbits. As mentioned earlier, another belt of comets, called the Kuiper belt, may exist near the orbit of Neptune.

On July 23, 1995, two backyard astronomers made an exciting discovery—a new comet was headed toward the sun. This comet, Comet Hale-Bopp, is larger than most that approach the sun and was the brightest comet visible from Earth in 20 years. Shown in **Figure 19-17,** it was at its brightest in March and April 1997.

Structure of Comets

The structure of a comet, shown in **Figure 19-18,** is like a large, dirty snowball or a mass of frozen ice and rock. But as the comet approaches the sun, it develops a distinctive structure. Ices of water, methane, and ammonia begin to vaporize because of the heat from the sun. Dust and bits of rock are released. The vaporized gases and released dust form a bright cloud called a coma around the nucleus, or solid part, of the comet. The solar wind pushes on the gases and released dust in the coma. These particles form a tail that always points away from the sun.

After many trips around the sun, most of the frozen ice in a comet has vaporized. All that is left are small particles that spread throughout the orbit of the original comet.

Visit the Glencoe Science Web Site at **www.glencoe.com/sec/science/ca** for more information about comets.

2 Teach

interNET CONNECTION

Internet Addresses

For Internet tips, see Glencoe's **Using the Internet in the Science Classroom.**

Discussion

When students have read about comets in the text, use the following questions to guide a class discussion on comets. **What is a comet?** *an object made of dust; rocks; and frozen water, methane, and ammonia* **What is the Oort Cloud and where is it located?** *The Oort Cloud is a large collection of comets that orbits beyond Pluto.* **What is the Kuiper belt?** *a belt of comets that may exist near the orbit of Neptune*

STV: Solar System

Unit 4 *Smaller Objects* 3:17

21955-24475

Refer to the Teacher Guide for additional bar codes and teaching strategies.

Comet Studies Have students research the last approach of Halley's comet to Earth in 1986. Ask them to write about the five space probes sent to study the comet up close. What did these probes learn? *Five space probes were launched to study Halley's comet: the Soviet* Vega 1 *and* Vega 2; *the Japanese* Suisei *and* Sakigake; *and the European Space Agency's* Giotto. Giotto *traveled closest to the comet's nucleus. Data sent back by the probes indicate that the nucleus is black, about 15 km in length and 8 km in width, and rotates once every two days. The coma contains boulder-size rocks as well as fine dust particles.* L2

CA Science Content Standards

Page 688: 2g, 4e
Page 689: 2g, 4e

VISUAL Learning

Figure 19-19 Have students draw pictures of a meteoroid traveling through space, a meteor entering Earth's atmosphere, and a meteorite striking Earth's surface. Student drawings should be labeled.

Flex Your Brain

Use the Flex Your Brain activity to have students explore COMETS.

Answer to Reading Check

A meteorite is a meteoroid (a small, rocklike body) that strikes Earth's surface.

Using Science Words

Help students practice using science words by asking them the following questions. **What causes a meteor shower?** *A meteor shower occurs when Earth passes within the orbit of a comet that has broken apart or has left material in its orbit from passing close to the sun.* **What do meteorites tell us about the solar system?** *Meteorites come from comets or asteroids; thus, they provide data about the material that formed the solar system.* **Where else in the solar system besides the asteroid belt can asteroids be found?** *Some of the larger asteroids may have been thrown out of the belt and are scattered throughout the solar system. Some may have been captured by planets as moons.*

VISUALIZING Meteorites

Figure 19-19 Meteorites strike the surface of a moon or planet.

A A large meteorite struck Arizona 50 000 years ago.

interNET CONNECTION

Visit the Glencoe Science Web Site at **www.glencoe.com/sec/science/ca** for more information about meteor craters.

Reading Check
What is a meteorite?

Meteoroids, Meteors, and Meteorites

You learned that comets tend to break up after they have passed close to the sun several times. The small pieces of the comet nucleus spread out into a loose group within the original orbit of the broken comet. These small pieces of rock moving through space are then called meteoroids.

When the path of a meteoroid crosses the position of Earth, it enters our atmosphere at between 15 and 70 km/s. Most meteoroids are so small that they are completely vaporized in Earth's atmosphere. A meteoroid that burns up in Earth's atmosphere is called a **meteor.** People often see these and call them shooting stars.

Each time Earth passes through the loose group of particles within the old orbit of a comet, many small particles of rock and dust enter the atmosphere. Because more meteors than usual are seen, this is called a meteor shower.

If the meteoroid is large enough, it may not completely burn up in Earth's atmosphere. When it strikes Earth, it is called a **meteorite.** Meteor Crater in Arizona, shown in **Figure 19-19A,** was formed when a large meteorite struck Earth about 50 000 years ago. Most meteorites are probably debris from asteroid collisions or broken-up comets, but some are from the moon and Mars.

Content Background

Evidence indicates that a large meteorite or asteroid collided with Earth about 66 million years ago. The collision, which occurred on what is now the Yucatan Peninsula in Mexico near the town of Chicxulub, caused tremendous destruction on a global scale. Dust, water vapor, and carbon dioxide would have been released into the air worldwide. This may have blocked the sun's rays for an extended period of time, which in turn may have caused the extinction of many organisms, including dinosaurs.

B This crater made by a meteorite is on the moon.

C A meteoroid that burns up in Earth's atmosphere is called a meteor.

Asteroids

An **asteroid** is a piece of rock similar to the material that formed into the planets. Most asteroids are located in an area between the orbits of Mars and Jupiter called the asteroid belt, shown in **Figure 19-20.** Why are they located there? The gravity of Jupiter may have kept a planet from forming in the area where the asteroid belt is now located.

Other asteroids are scattered throughout the solar system—they may have been thrown out of the belt by gravity. Some may have since been captured as moons around other planets.

Figure 19-20 The asteroid belt lies between the orbits of Mars and Jupiter.

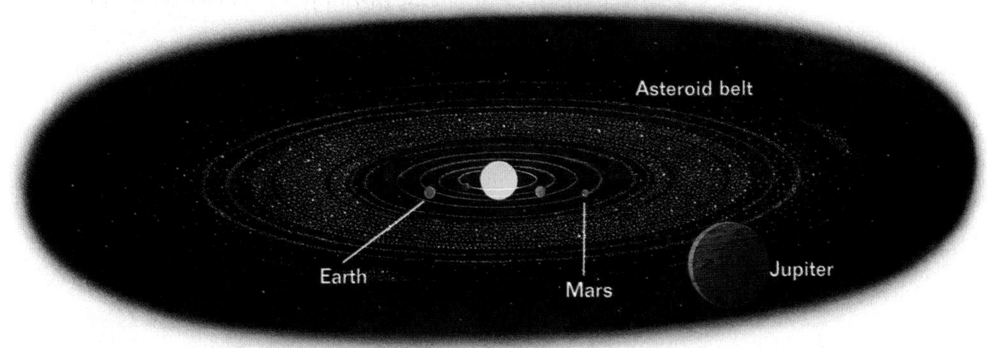

Quick Demo

Use a small fan and strips of paper fastened to a rubber ball to demonstrate why a comet's tail always points away from the sun. The wind generated by the fan is analogous to the solar wind.

3 Assess

Check for Understanding

Correcting Misconceptions

Many people incorrectly refer to meteors as shooting stars. Explain that meteors are relatively small, rocklike bodies that enter Earth's atmosphere. Stars, however, are enormous balls of gas that tend to remain in their places in space.

Reteach

Logical-Mathematical Provide students with metric rulers. Have student pairs contrast the sizes of the larger asteroids, Earth, and the moon, using a scale of 1 mm = 100 km. Have students use these data: Earth (12 756 km), the moon (3476 km), Ceres (940 km), Pallas (540 km), Vesta (510 km), and Hygeia (410 km). L2

Extension

For students who have mastered this section, use the **Reinforcement** and **Enrichment** masters.

interNET CONNECTION

Internet Addresses

For Internet tips, see Glencoe's **Using the Internet in the Science Classroom.**

Across the Curriculum

Economics Have students research the nickel mines of Sudbury Basin in Ontario, Canada. About 2 billion years ago, an asteroid 6 km in diameter collided with Earth at this location. The collision caused the formation of rich deposits of nickel, cobalt, and platinum. L2

CA Science Content Standards

Page 690: 2g, 4e
Page 691: 2g, 4e

4 Close

Proficiency Prep

Use this quiz to check students' recall of section content.

1. **What is a comet?** *an object in space composed of dust and rock particles mixed with frozen water, methane, and ammonia*
2. **What do we call the large collection of comets beyond Pluto's orbit?** *Oort Cloud*
3. **What does a meteoroid become when it burns up in Earth's atmosphere?** *meteor*

Section Assessment

1. As a comet approaches the sun, thermal energy causes some of the comet to vaporize. Solar wind pushes on these gases to form a tail on the comet.
2. a crater
3. Comets are collections of frozen gas and rocky particles that generally travel in elliptical orbits around the sun. Meteoroids are usually small fragments of rock that move independently through space. Asteroids generally orbit the sun between Mars and Jupiter. Their sizes can range from small particles to objects as large as 1000 km in diameter.
4. Think Critically dust and rock particles mixed with ice, methane, and ammonia; outer planets

Asteroid Size

The sizes of the asteroids in the asteroid belt range from tiny particles to 940 km. Ceres is the largest and the first one discovered. The next three in size are Pallas (523 km), Vesta (501 km), and Juno (244 km). Two asteroids, Gaspra and Ida, were photographed by *Galileo* on its way to Jupiter, as shown in **Figure 19-21.**

Comets, meteoroids, and asteroids are probably composed of material that formed early in the history of the solar system. Scientists study the structure and composition of these space objects in order to better understand what the solar system may have been like long ago. Understanding what the early solar system was like could help scientists to better understand the formation of Earth and its relationship to other objects in the solar system.

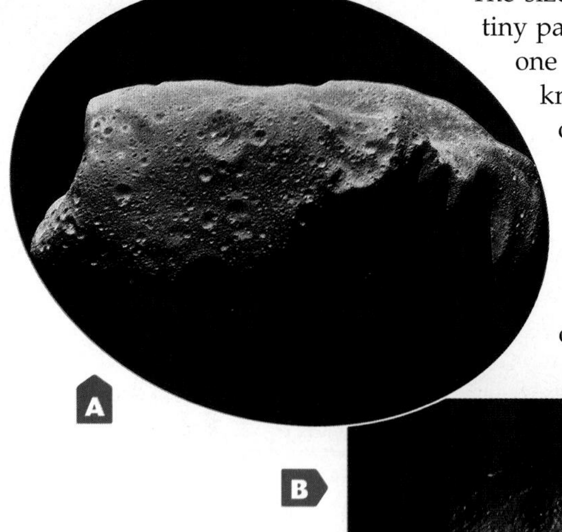

Figure 19-21 The asteroid Ida (A) is about 56 km long. Gaspra (B) is about 20 km long.

Section Assessment

1. How does a comet's tail form as it approaches the sun?
2. What type of feature might be formed on Earth if a large meteorite reached its surface?
3. Describe differences among comets, meteoroids, and asteroids.
4. **Think Critically:** What is the chemical composition of comets? Are comets more similar to the inner or the outer planets?
5. **Skill Builder**
   Inferring Scientists can learn a lot about a planet's history by studying its impact craters. Do the **Chapter 19 Skill Activity** on page 980 to infer how scientific illustrations can be used to determine the ages of impact craters.

The asteroid belt contains many objects—from tiny particles to objects 940 km in diameter. In your Science Journal, describe how mining the asteroids for valuable minerals might be accomplished.

Encourage students to be as creative as possible but to include ideas that are scientifically reasonable and possible to accomplish.

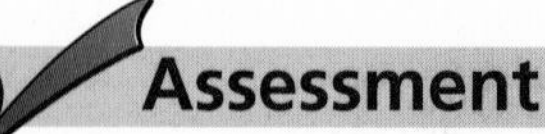

Assessment

Oral Assess students' abilities to infer. Ask students to explain why a comet tail points away from the sun. Use **Performance Assessment in the Science Classroom,** p. 17.

692 CHAPTER 19 THE SOLAR SYSTEM

Science & Society

Mission to Mars

Scientists are currently developing plans for further exploration of Mars. But even at its closest, Mars is 55 million km away from Earth, a distance that would take astronauts three years to travel round-trip. Given the long flight, not to mention conditions astronauts would face living on Mars, a journey to the Red Planet would be full of risks. This raises a question: Should humans or robots be sent to explore Mars?

Risks to Humans

Getting to and from Mars would take a toll on the human body. In the near-zero gravity of outer space, bones lose calcium and gradually become weaker. Muscles lose their strength as well, because they don't have to work against gravity to support and move body parts. Furthermore, in a weightless environment, body fluids don't flow downward as they do on Earth. Unusual circulation of body fluids can interfere with kidney function and lead to dehydration.

Assuming humans survived the long flight to Mars in good health, they would face other challenges upon arrival. To explore Mars properly, a team of astronauts would probably have to live on the planet for months, even years. The NASA painting, left, shows a module that could house explorers. Such a structure would have to withstand the Martian environment and protect astronauts from high levels of solar radiation.

The Case for Robots

Because of the many risks a Mars mission would pose for humans, some scientists suggest sending specialized robots that could operate equipment and carry out scientific experiments. These robots would be equipped with artificial senses that would allow researchers on Earth to experience the planet's surface in a way second only to being there in person. However, radio signals sent back and forth between robots on Mars and operators on Earth would take up to 20 minutes to travel each way. Scientists are working to solve this problem in the hope that extensive exploration of Mars will soon be a reality—by people or by machines.

Science JOURNAL

How do you think Mars should be further explored? Write a proposal to your class explaining how you would explore Mars.

NATIONAL GEOGRAPHIC

Science & Society

Teaching Strategies

Have students research the achievements and problems experienced by former Soviet cosmonauts, current Russian cosmonauts, and American astronauts aboard the *Mir* space station.

Science JOURNAL Answers will vary. Students may note that if humans travel to Mars, they could be protected from radiation with extra shielding on the spacecraft. Also, one large shield could be deployed in space to protect astronauts from solar radiation. Bone and muscle weakening could be reduced by producing an artificial gravity field in the spacecraft.

If robots are sent, they could continually search the surface of Mars for signs of life or past life and send information to the orbiting mother ship. If certain rocks appear to contain evidence of current or past life, samples could be loaded on a robotic ship and sent back to Earth orbit, where they could be retrieved by the space shuttle.

For More Information

Refer to *The Case for Mars* by Robert Zubrin (1996), Touchstone (Simon & Schuster).

Content Background

If implemented, the Mars Direct plan for a crewed mission to Mars will begin with the launch of an uncrewed Earth return vehicle (ERV) to Mars. Once there, the ERV would produce fuel (methane and oxygen) from the Martian atmosphere for the return trip. Next a piloted habitation module would be sent to Mars. Once there, astronauts would live and work in the habitation module, and return to Earth in the ERV. When the first humans arrive on Mars, a new ERV would be sent along to start producing fuel for the next piloted landing.

CA Science Content Standards

Page 692: 4e
Page 693: 2g, 4e

Chapter 19 Reviewing Main Ideas

Reviewing Main Ideas can be used to preview, review, reteach, and condense chapter content.

Preview

Linguistic Have students try to answer the questions in their Science Journals. Use student answers as a source for discussion throughout the chapter.

Review

Interpersonal Have students answer the questions on separate pieces of paper and compare their answers with those of other students in the class.

Reteach

Visual-Spatial Have students look at the illustrations on these pages. Ask them to describe details that support the main ideas of the chapter found in the statement for each illustration.

00:00 OUT OF TIME?

Auditory-Musical If time does not permit teaching the entire chapter, use the information on these pages along with the chapter Audiocassettes to present the material in a condensed format.

Chapter 19 Reviewing Main Ideas

For a **preview** of this chapter, study this Reviewing Main Ideas before you read the chapter. After you have studied this chapter, you can use the Reviewing Main Ideas to **review** the chapter.

The Glencoe MindJogger, Audiocassettes, and CD-ROM provide additional opportunities for review.

Section 19-1 THE SOLAR SYSTEM

Early astronomers thought that the planets, the moon, the sun, and the stars were embedded in separate spheres that rotated around Earth. The sun-centered model of the **solar system** states that the sun is the center of the solar system. Using a telescope, Galileo discovered evidence that supported the sun-centered model. Later, Kepler discovered that the planets orbit the sun in elliptical orbits, not circles. ***What type of evidence did Galileo discover that indicated the sun-centered model was correct?***

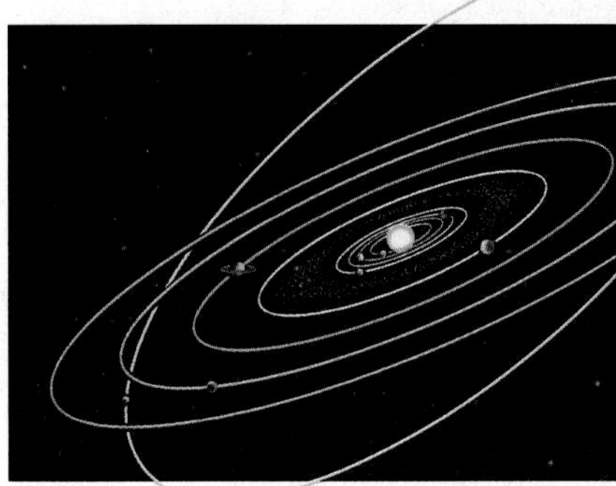

Section 19-2 THE INNER PLANETS

The **inner planets,** in increasing distance from the sun are Mercury, Venus, Earth, and Mars. The moonlike **Mercury** has craters and cliffs on its surface. **Venus** has a dense atmosphere of carbon dioxide and sulfuric acid. On **Earth,** water exists in three states. **Mars** appears red due to the iron oxide content of its weathered rocks. Recent studies by *Pathfinder* indicate that Mars's surface once had large amounts of water flowing over it. ***Venus and Earth are similar in size and mass. Why, then, are their surface characteristics so different?***

694 CHAPTER 19 THE SOLAR SYSTEM

Cultural Diversity

Planetary Wisdom Some of the planets are visible in Earth's night sky and have been used to explain or chart the course of life on Earth. Many early sky watchers interpreted planets appearing in conjunction (appearing to move close to each other) as an important sign. In ancient India, periodic destruction of the universe by flooding or conflagration was marked by the conjunction of Jupiter and Saturn. Jupiter passes Saturn in the night sky every 20 years. The Chaldeans believed that if all seven planets were in conjunction in Cancer, the universe would end in deluge. If all seven conjoined in Capricorn, the universe would end in fire.

Reading Check ✓

Locate a legend, myth, or folktale from another culture that explains the origin of all or part of the solar system. Share it with the class.

Section

19-3 THE OUTER PLANETS

Faint rings and 16 moons orbit the gaseous **Jupiter.** Jupiter's Great Red Spot is a high-pressure storm generated by huge thunderstorms in Jupiter's atmosphere. **Saturn** is made mostly of gas and has pronounced rings. **Uranus** is a large, gaseous planet with many moons and several rings. **Neptune** is similar to Uranus in size, composition, and stormlike features. **Pluto** has a thin, changing atmosphere, and its surface is icy rock. ***Why would the average densities of the four large, outer planets be so low when compared with the average densities of the inner planets?***

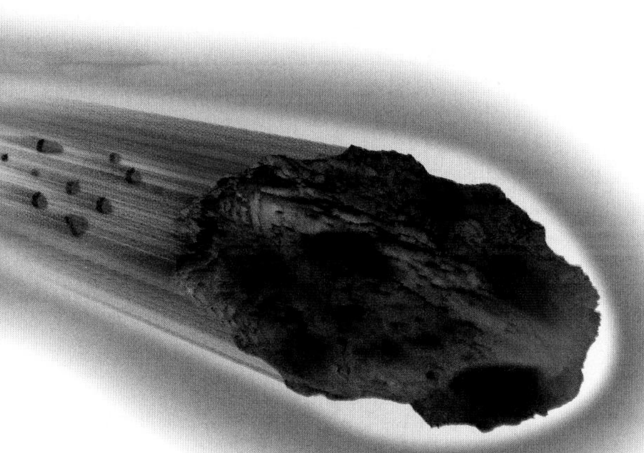

Section

19-4 OTHER OBJECTS IN THE SOLAR SYSTEM

As a **comet** approaches the sun, vaporized gases form a bright coma around the comet's nucleus and solar wind forms a tail that points away from the sun. Meteoroids form when asteroids collide, when comets break up, or when **meteorites** collide with the moon or other planets. An **asteroid** is a piece of rock usually found in the asteroid belt. ***Why does the tail of a comet always point away from the sun?***

Answers to Questions

Section 19-1

The Solar System Using a telescope, Galileo discovered that Venus goes through phases indicating that it orbits the sun.

Section 19-2

The Inner Planets Venus's entire surface is blanketed by dense clouds made up mostly of CO_2. This and other gases led Venus to develop a "runaway" greenhouse effect, raising its surface temperature to 470°C.

Section 19-3

The Outer Planets The four large, outer planets are composed mainly of gases. Even though these planets have solid rocky cores, most of their size is composed of gas. This produces a low average density.

Section 19-4

Other Objects in the Solar System The tail of a comet is made of gas and dust from the comet's coma which has been pushed outward away from the sun by solar wind.

GLENCOE TECHNOLOGY

CD-ROM

Glencoe Science Voyages Interactive CD-ROM

Chapter Summaries and Quizzes

Have students read the Chapter Summary then take the Chapter Quiz to determine whether they have mastered chapter content.

Assessment

Portfolio Encourage students to place in their portfolios one or two items of what they consider to be their best work. Examples include:

- Problem Solving, p. 676
- MiniLab, p. 682
- Activity 19-2, pp. 686–687 P

Performance Additional performance assessments may be found in **Performance Assessment** and **Science Integration Activities.** Performance Task Assessment Lists and rubrics for evaluating these activities can be found in Glencoe's **Performance Assessment in the Science Classroom.**

Chapter 19 Assessment

Using Vocabulary

1. An asteroid is a rock similar to the material that formed the planets. A comet is composed of dust and rock particles mixed with ice, methane, and ammonia.
2. The inner planets—Mercury, Venus, Earth, and Mars—are closest to the sun. The outer planets—Jupiter, Saturn, Uranus, Neptune, and Pluto—are farthest from the sun.
3. Meteors are meteoroids—small pieces of rock—that burn up in Earth's atmosphere. Meteorites are meteoroids that strike Earth's surface.
4. The Great Red Spot is a storm in Jupiter's atmosphere. The Oort Cloud is a collection of comets located beyond the orbit of Pluto.
5. Neptune is usually the eighth planet from the sun. Uranus is the seventh planet.

interNET CONNECTION To reinforce chapter vocabulary, use the **Study Guide for Content Mastery** booklet. Also available are activities for **Glencoe Science Voyages** on the Glencoe Science Web Site. **www.glencoe.com/sec/science/ca**

Checking Concepts

6. B	11. C
7. C	12. C
8. B	13. B
9. D	14. A
10. D	15. B

Thinking Critically

16. The greenhouse effect on Venus is much greater than that on Earth because the clouds on Venus are very dense and the amount of carbon dioxide in the air is greater. The CO_2 retains the heat.
17. In general, more massive planets have more satellites.
18. The extreme heat and the dense, gaseous atmospheres would probably destroy any space probe before it could reach either of the planets' surfaces.
19. Iron contained in the weathered rocks combines with oxygen in the presence of water to produce iron oxide. Channels appear to have been carved by flowing water. Cavern walls show layering of rock. The northern ice cap is composed partly of ice.
20. Any planet orbiting the sun inside the orbit of the planet you are observeing from appears to go through phases. The orbit of Venus is inside the orbit of Earth.

Chapter 19 Assessment

Using Vocabulary

a. asteroid
b. astronomical unit
c. comet
d. Earth
e. Great Red Spot
f. inner planet
g. Jupiter
h. Mars
i. Mercury
j. meteor
k. meteorite
l. Neptune
m. Oort Cloud
n. outer planet
o. Pluto
p. Saturn
q. solar system
r. Uranus
s. Venus

Distinguish between the terms in each of the following pairs.

1. asteroid, comet
2. inner planet, outer planet
3. meteor, meteorite
4. Great Red Spot, Oort Cloud
5. Neptune, Uranus

Checking Concepts

Choose the word or phrase that best answers the question.

6. Who proposed a sun-centered solar system?
A) Ptolemy C) Galileo
B) Copernicus D) Oort
7. How does the sun produce energy?
A) magnetism C) nuclear fusion
B) nuclear fission D) the greenhouse effect
8. What is the shape of planetary orbits?
A) circles C) squares
B) ellipses D) rectangles
9. Which planet has extreme temperatures because it has essentially no atmosphere?
A) Earth C) Mars
B) Jupiter D) Mercury
10. Water is a solid, liquid, and gas on which planet?
A) Pluto C) Saturn
B) Uranus D) Earth
11. Where is the largest known volcano in the solar system?
A) Earth C) Mars
B) Jupiter D) Uranus
12. What do scientists call a rock that strikes Earth's surface?
A) asteroid C) meteorite
B) comet D) meteoroid
13. Which planet has a complex ring system made of hundreds of ringlets?
A) Pluto C) Uranus
B) Saturn D) Mars
14. Which planet has a magnetic pole tilted 60 degrees?
A) Uranus C) Jupiter
B) Earth D) Pluto
15. How does the tail of a comet always point?
A) toward the sun C) toward Earth
B) away from the sun D) away from the Oort Cloud

Thinking Critically

16. Why is the surface temperature on Venus so much higher than that on Earth?
17. Describe the relationship between the mass of a planet and the number of satellites it has.
18. Why are probe landings on Jupiter or Saturn unlikely events?
19. What evidence suggests that water is or once was present on Mars?
20. An observer on Earth can watch Venus go through phases much like Earth's moon does. Explain why this is so.

Developing Skills

If you need help, refer to the Skill Handbook.

21. Concept Mapping: Complete the concept map on this page to show how a comet changes as it travels through space.

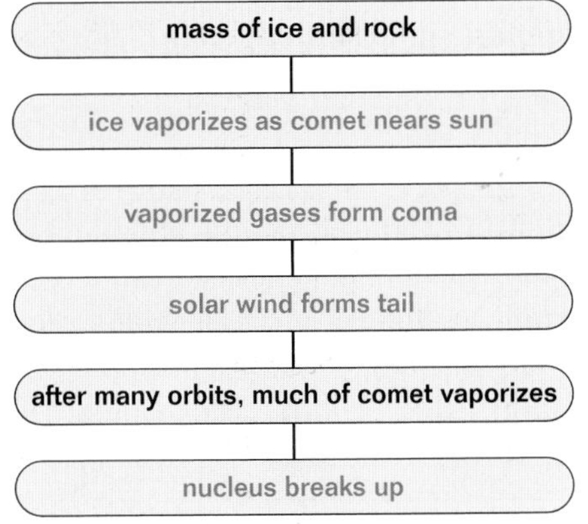
mass of ice and rock
ice vaporizes as comet nears sun
vaporized gases form coma
solar wind forms tail
after many orbits, much of comet vaporizes
nucleus breaks up

22. Hypothesizing: Mercury is the closest planet to the sun, yet it does not reflect much of the sun's light. What can you say about Mercury's color?

23. Sequencing: Arrange the following planets in order from the planet with the most natural satellites to the one with the fewest: Earth, Jupiter, Saturn, Neptune, Uranus, and Mars.

24. Making and Using Tables: Make a table that summarizes the main characteristics of each planet in the solar system.

25. Measuring in SI: The Great Red Spot of Jupiter is about 40 000 km long and about 12 000 km wide. What is its approximate area in km^2?

THE PRINCETON REVIEW

Test-Taking Tip

Get to the Root of Things If you don't know a word's meaning, you can still get an idea of its meaning if you focus on its roots, prefixes, and suffixes. For instance, words that start with *non-*, *un-*, *a-*, *dis-*, and *in-* generally reverse what the rest of the word means.

Test Practice

Use these questions to test your Science Proficiency.

1. Earth is probably the only planet in our solar system on which life exists. Which of the following statements **BEST** explains why this is true?
   A) Earth is the only planet on which water exists in all three states.
   B) Earth has frozen ice caps at its poles.
   C) Earth has carbon dioxide in its atmosphere.
   D) Earth has an atmosphere.
2. Both Copernicus and Kepler proposed a model of the solar system. What was the major difference between the two models?
   A) Copernicus's model had the sun in the center. Kepler's model had Earth in the center.
   B) Copernicus's model included Saturn. Kepler's model did not.
   C) Copernicus's model included circular orbits for the planets. Kepler's model included elliptical orbits for the planets.
   D) Copernicus's model showed the moon as a planet. Kepler's model showed the moon as a satellite of Earth.

THE PRINCETON REVIEW

Test Practice

The Test-Taking Tip was written by The Princeton Review, the nation's leader in test preparation.

1. A
2. C

Developing Skills

21. See student page.
22. Mercury is dark in color, and it doesn't reflect much of the light that reaches its surface.
23. Saturn, Uranus, Jupiter, Neptune, Mars, Earth
24. Student tables should include number of satellites, type of atmospheres, and other planetary characteristics.
25. area = length × width = 40 000 km × 12 000 km = 480 000 000 km^2

Bonus Question

Planetary orbits are ellipses, not circles. Based on the models of planetary orbits developed in Activity 19-1, how would you draw an orbit that is extremely elliptical? *Using one nail, stretch the string to a distance equal to the radius of the circular orbit. To draw an extremely elliptical orbit, place two nails far apart.*

Assessment Resources

The **Test Practice Workbook** provides students with practice in the format, concepts, and critical-thinking skills tested in standardized exams.

Reproducible Masters

Chapter Review, pp. 37–38 L2
Performance Assessment, p. 19 L2
Assessment, pp. 73–76 L2

Glencoe Technology

Chapter Review Software
Computer Test Bank
MindJogger Videoquiz

Chapter 20 Stars and Galaxies

Section	Objectives	Activities/Features
Chapter Opener		**Explore Activity:** Model the Universe, p. 699
20-1 Stars 1 Session ½ Block	1. **Explain** why the positions of the constellations change throughout the year. 2. **Compare** and **contrast** absolute magnitude and apparent magnitude. 3. **Describe** how parallax is used to determine distance.	**Problem Solving:** Star Light, Star Bright, p. 702 **MiniLab:** Observing Star Patterns, p. 703 **Skill Builder:** Recognizing Cause and Effect, p. 704 **Using Computers,** p. 704
20-2 The Sun 3½ Sessions 1½ Blocks	4. **Describe** how energy is produced in the sun. 5. **Recognize** that sunspots, prominences, and solar flares are related. 6. **Explain** why our sun is considered an average star and how it differs from stars in binary systems.	**Skill Builder:** Interpreting Scientific Illustrations, p. 708 **Science Journal,** p. 708 **Activity 20-1:** Sunspots, p. 709
20-3 Evolution of Stars 1 Session ½ Block	7. **Diagram** how stars are classified. 8. **Relate** the temperature of a star to its color. 9. **Outline** the evolution of a star.	**Physics Integration,** p. 712 **Chemistry Integration,** p. 713 **Skill Builder:** Sequencing, p. 715 **Using Math,** p. 715 **Reading and Writing in Science:** Dreamtime Down Under, p. 716
20-4 Galaxies and the Universe 3½ Sessions 1½ Blocks	10. **List** the three main types of galaxies. 11. **Identify** several characteristics of the Milky Way Galaxy. 12. **Relate** how the big bang theory explains the observed Doppler shifts of galaxies.	**MiniLab:** Measuring Distance in Space, p. 720 **Skill Builder:** Predicting, p. 723 **Science Journal,** p. 723 **Activity 20-2:** Measuring Parallax, pp. 724–725 **Field Guide to Astronomy,** pp. 726–729

The number of recommended single-period sessions. The number of recommended blocks.
One session and one-half block are allowed for chapter review and assessment.

Activity Materials

Explore	Activities	MiniLabs
p. 699 balloon, clothespin, felt-tip marker, string, ruler,	p. 709 books, cardboard, clipboard, drawing paper, small refracting telescope, small tripod, scissors pp. 724–725 meterstick, metric ruler, masking tape, pencil	p. 703 no materials needed p. 720 metric ruler, drawing compass, paper, pencil

Need Materials? Contact Science Kit at 1-800-828-7777 or at www.sciencekit.com on the Internet.
For alternate materials, see the activity on the listed page.

Chapter Organizer

Standards		Reproducible Resources	Technology
National	State/Local	Test Practice Workbooks are available for use with each chapter.	English and Spanish audiocassettes are available for use with each section.
National Content Standards: UCP3, B1, B3, D3	California Science Content Standards: 4a, 4b, 4c	**Activity Worksheets,** p. 115 **Enrichment,** p. 56 **Home Involvement,** p. 28 **Laboratory Manual,** pp. 125–126 **Laboratory Manual,** pp. 127–130 **Reinforcement,** p. 56 **Study Guide,** p. 77	**Section Focus Transparency 56** **Glencoe Science Voyages Interactive CD-ROM**
National Content Standards: A2, B3, D1, D3, F1, G3	California Science Content Standards: 4a, 4b, 4c	**Activity Worksheets,** pp. 111–112 **Enrichment,** p. 57 **Multicultural Connections,** pp. 39–40 **Reinforcement,** p. 57	**Section Focus Transparency 57** **Science Integration Transparency 20** **Internet Connection,** p. 707
National Content Standards: UCP3, A2, B1, B3, C1, E2, G1, G3	California Science Content Standards: 2g, 4a, 4b, 4c	**Critical Thinking/Problem Solving,** p. 20 **Enrichment,** p. 58 **Reinforcement,** p. 58	**Section Focus Transparency 58** **Teaching Transparency 39** **Teaching Transparency 40**
National Content Standards: UCP2, UCP3, A1, B1, B2, D3, G1, G2	California Science Content Standards: 1a, 2g, 4a, 4b, 4c, 9a	**Activity Worksheets,** pp. 113–114, 116 **Enrichment,** p. 59 **Reinforcement,** p. 59 **Study Guide,** pp. 78–80	**Section Focus Transparency 59** **National Geographic Society: STV** **Internet Connection,** p. 721 **Internet Connection,** p. 727 **The Infinite Voyage Series**

Key to Teaching Strategies

The following designations will help you decide which activities are appropriate for your students.

L1 Level 1 activities should be appropriate for students with learning difficulties.

L2 Level 2 activities should be within the ability range of all students.

L3 Level 3 activities are designed for above-average students.

ELL ELL activities should be within the ability range of English Language Learners.

COOP LEARN Cooperative Learning activities are designed for small group work.

P These strategies represent student products that can be placed into a best-work portfolio.

Multiple Learning Styles logos, as described on page 55T, are used throughout to indicate strategies that address different learning styles.

Assessment Resources

Chapter Review, pp. 39–40
Assessment, pp. 77–80
Performance Assessment in the Science Classroom (PASC)
MindJogger Videoquiz
Alternate Assessment in the Science Classroom
Performance Assessment, p. 20
Chapter Review Software
Computer Test Bank

Chapter 20 Stars and Galaxies

This is a representation of key blackline masters available in the Teacher Classroom Resources. See Resource Manager boxes within the chapter for additional information.

Transparencies

Section Focus Transparencies

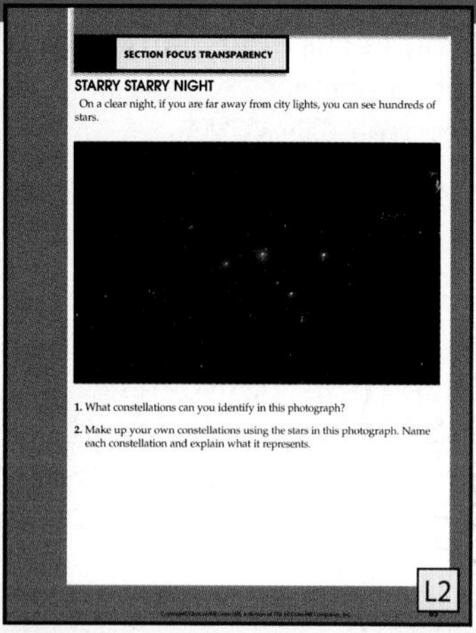

SECTION FOCUS TRANSPARENCY

STARRY STARRY NIGHT

On a clear night, if you are far away from city lights, you can see hundreds of stars.

1. What constellations can you identify in this photograph?
2. Make up your own constellations using the stars in this photograph. Name each constellation and explain what it represents.

L2

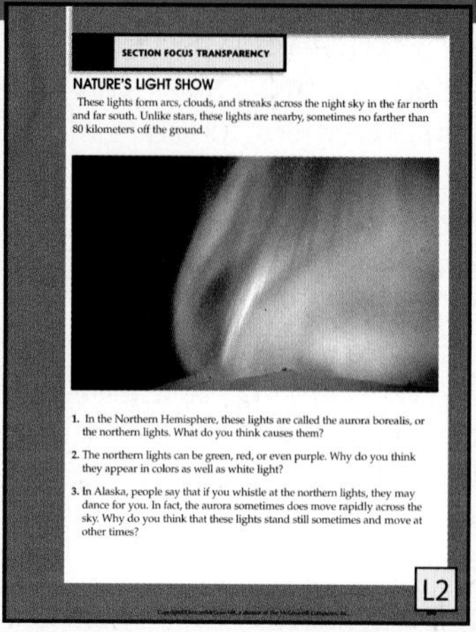

SECTION FOCUS TRANSPARENCY

NATURE'S LIGHT SHOW

These lights form arcs, clouds, and streaks across the night sky in the far north and far south. Unlike stars, these lights are nearby, sometimes no farther than 80 kilometers off the ground.

1. In the Northern Hemisphere, these lights are called the aurora borealis, or the northern lights. What do you think causes them?
2. The northern lights can be green, red, or even purple. Why do you think they appear in colors as well as white light?
3. In Alaska, people say that if you whistle at the northern lights, they may dance for you. In fact, the aurora sometimes does move rapidly across the sky. Why do you think that these lights stand still sometimes and move at other times?

L2

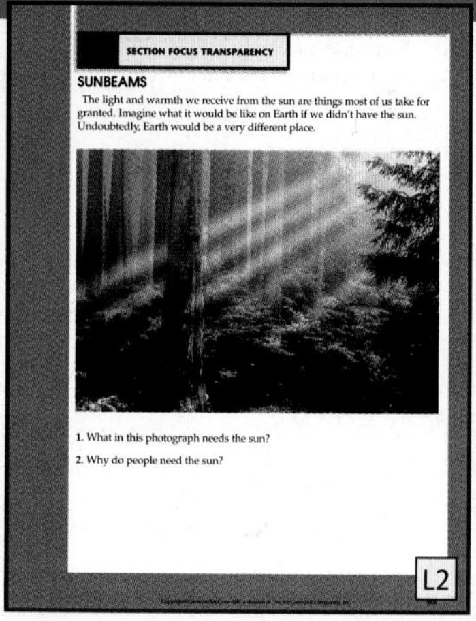

SECTION FOCUS TRANSPARENCY

SUNBEAMS

The light and warmth we receive from the sun are things most of us take for granted. Imagine what it would be like on Earth if we didn't have the sun. Undoubtedly, Earth would be a very different place.

1. What in this photograph needs the sun?
2. Why do people need the sun?

L2

Science Integration Transparencies

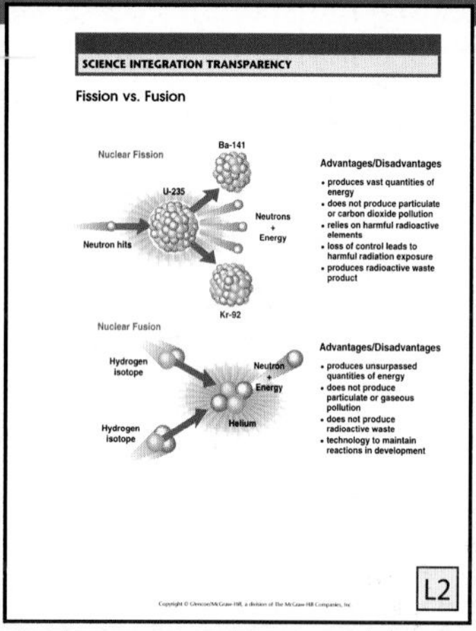

SCIENCE INTEGRATION TRANSPARENCY

Fission vs. Fusion

Nuclear Fission

Ba-141, U-235, Neutron hits, Neutrons + Energy, Kr-92

Advantages/Disadvantages
- produces vast quantities of energy
- does not produce particulate or carbon dioxide pollution
- relies on harmful radioactive elements
- loss of control leads to harmful radiation exposure
- produces radioactive waste product

Nuclear Fusion

Hydrogen isotope, Hydrogen isotope, Neutron + Energy, Helium

Advantages/Disadvantages
- produces unsurpassed quantities of energy
- does not produce particulate or gaseous pollution
- does not produce radioactive waste
- technology to maintain reactions in development

L2

Teaching Transparencies

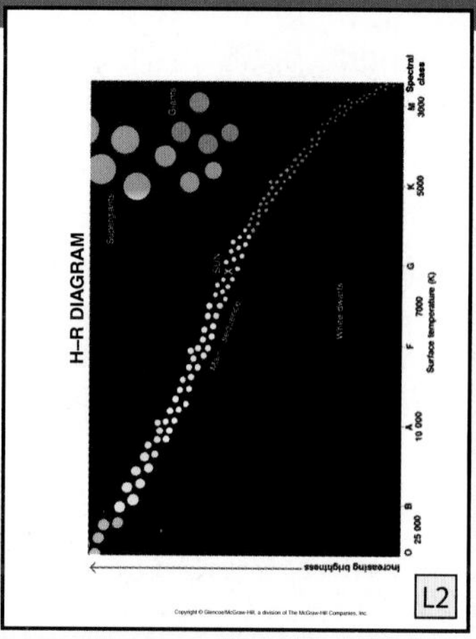

H–R DIAGRAM

Increasing brightness

Spectral class: O 25 000, B, A 10 000, F, G 7500, K 5000, M 3000

Surface temperature (K)

L2

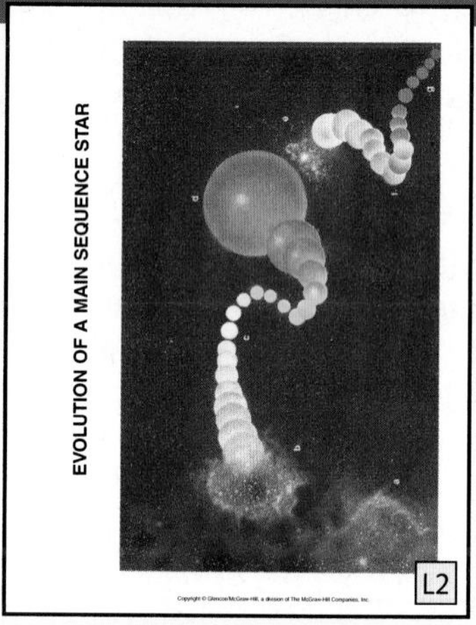

EVOLUTION OF A MAIN SEQUENCE STAR

L2

Meeting Different Ability Levels

Study Guide for Content Mastery

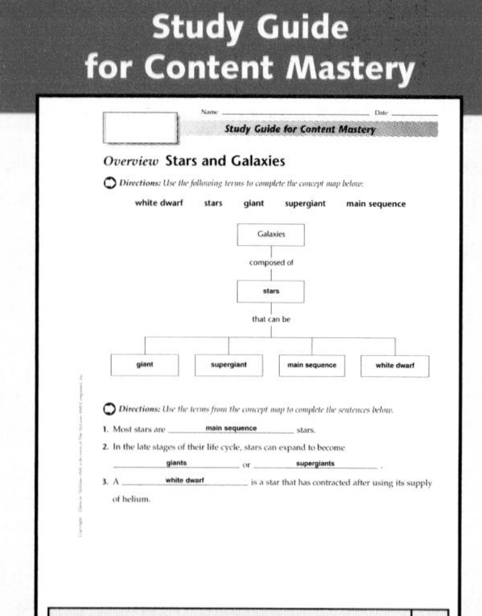

Name ______ Date ______

Study Guide for Content Mastery

Overview **Stars and Galaxies**

Directions: *Use the following terms to complete the concept map below:*

white dwarf stars giant supergiant main sequence

Galaxies — composed of — stars — that can be — giant, supergiant, main sequence, white dwarf

Directions: *Use the terms from the concept map to complete the sentences below.*

1. Most stars are main sequence stars.
2. In the late stages of their life cycle, stars can expand to become giants or supergiants.
3. A white dwarf is a star that has contracted after using its supply of helium.

BASIC L1

Reinforcement

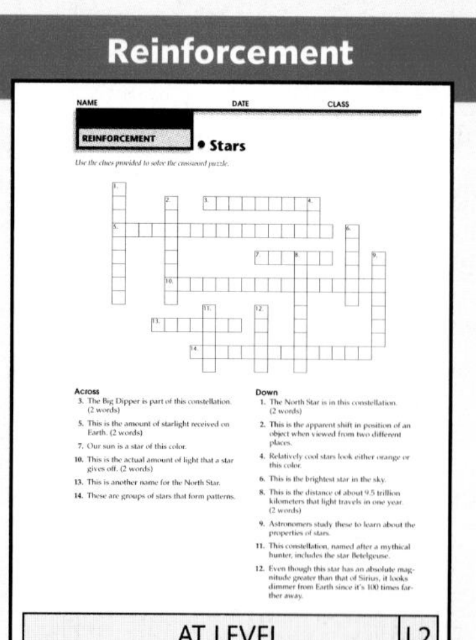

NAME DATE CLASS

REINFORCEMENT • **Stars**

Use the clues provided to solve the crossword puzzle.

Across

3. The Big Dipper is part of this constellation. (2 words)
5. This is the amount of starlight received on Earth. (2 words)
7. Our sun is a star of this color.
10. This is the actual amount of light that a star gives off. (2 words)
13. This is another name for the North Star.
14. These are groups of stars that form patterns.

Down

1. The North Star is in this constellation. (2 words)
2. This is the apparent shift in position of an object when viewed from two different places.
4. Relatively cool stars look either orange or this color.
6. This is the brightest star in the sky.
8. This is the distance of about 9.5 trillion kilometers that light travels in one year. (2 words)
9. Astronomers study these to learn about the properties of stars.
11. This constellation, named after a mythical hunter, includes the star Betelgeuse.
12. Even though this star has an absolute magnitude greater than that of Sirius, it looks dimmer from Earth since it's 100 times farther away.

AT LEVEL L2

Enrichment Worksheets

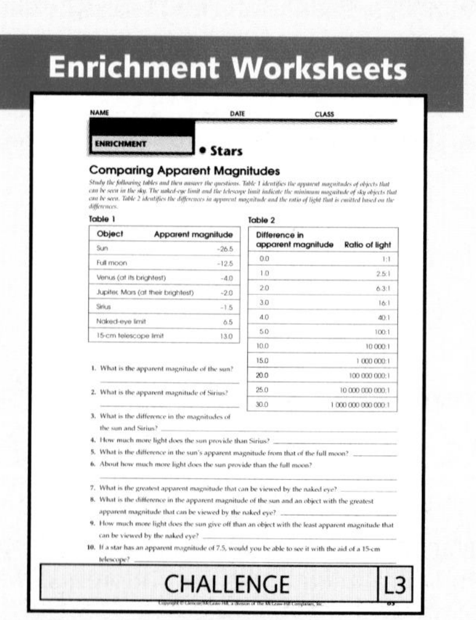

NAME DATE CLASS

ENRICHMENT • **Stars**

Comparing Apparent Magnitudes

Study the following tables and then answer the questions. Table 1 identifies the apparent magnitudes of objects that can be seen in the sky. The naked-eye limit and the telescope limit indicate the minimum magnitude of sky objects that can be seen. Table 2 identifies the differences in apparent magnitude and the ratio of light that is emitted based on the differences.

Table 1

Object	Apparent magnitude
Sun	-26.5
Full moon	-12.5
Venus (at its brightest)	-4.0
Jupiter, Mars (at their brightest)	-2.0
Sirius	-1.5
Naked-eye limit	6.5
15-cm telescope limit	13.0

Table 2

Difference in apparent magnitude	Ratio of light
0.0	1:1
1.0	2.5:1
2.0	6.3:1
3.0	16:1
4.0	40:1
5.0	100:1
10.0	10 000:1
15.0	1 000 000:1
20.0	100 000 000:1
25.0	10 000 000 000:1
30.0	1 000 000 000 000:1

1. What is the apparent magnitude of the sun?
2. What is the apparent magnitude of Sirius?
3. What is the difference in the magnitudes of the sun and Sirius?
4. How much more light does the sun provide than Sirius?
5. What is the difference in the sun's apparent magnitude from that of the full moon?
6. About how much more light does the sun provide than the full moon?
7. What is the greatest apparent magnitude that can be viewed by the naked eye?
8. What is the difference in the apparent magnitude of the sun and an object with the greatest apparent magnitude that can be viewed by the naked eye?
9. How much more light does the sun give off than an object with the least apparent magnitude that can be viewed by the naked eye?
10. If a star has an apparent magnitude of 7.5, would you be able to see it with the aid of a 15-cm telescope?

CHALLENGE L3

Resource Manager

Hands-on Activities

Activity Worksheets

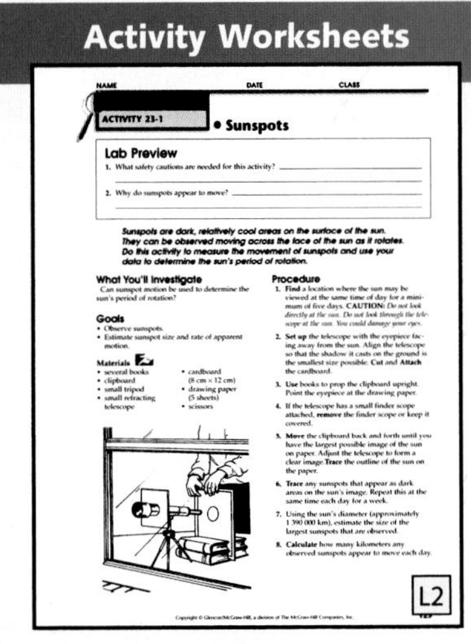
ACTIVITY 23-1 • Sunspots

L2

Lab Manual

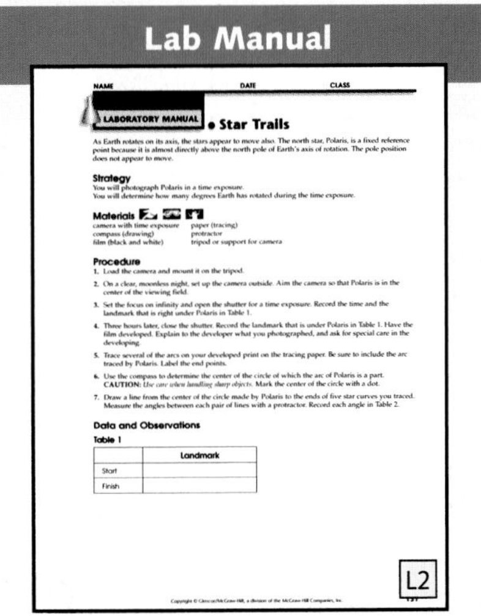
LABORATORY MANUAL • Star Trails

L2

Accessibility

Spanish Resources

SPANISH RESOURCES
GLENCOE
SCIENCE VOYAGES
Exploring the Life, Earth, and Physical Sciences
LEVEL BLUE
• Provides help for the English language learner
• Translates into Spanish the objectives, summary statements, vocabulary terms, and their definitions
• Includes a complete English/Spanish Glossary
L2

Assessment

Performance Assessment

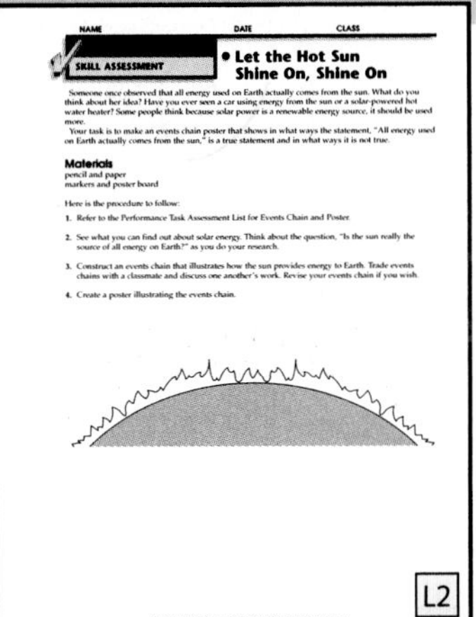
SKILL ASSESSMENT • Let the Hot Sun Shine On, Shine On

L2

Chapter Review

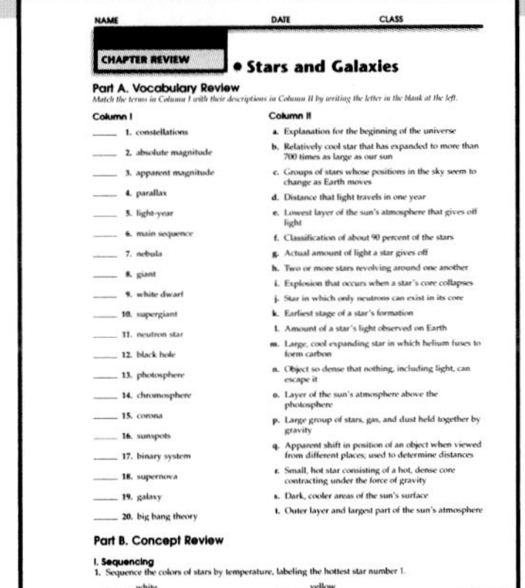
CHAPTER REVIEW • Stars and Galaxies

L2

Assessment

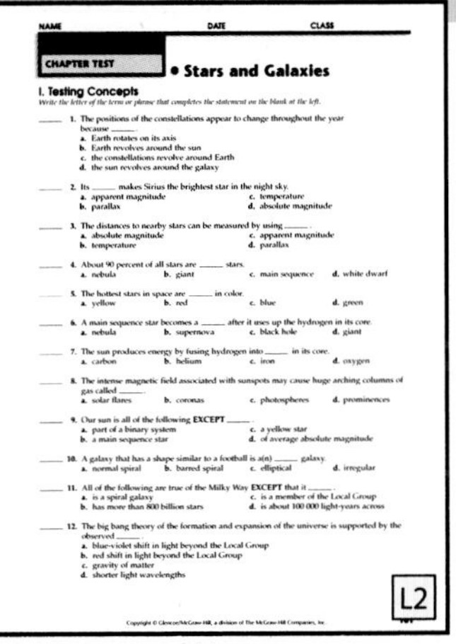
CHAPTER TEST • Stars and Galaxies

L2

Test Practice Workbook

Extending Content

Critical Thinking/ Problem Solving

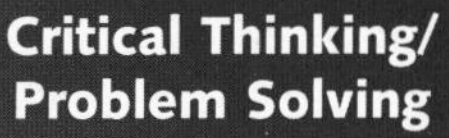
CRITICAL THINKING • Stars and Galaxies

Archaeoastronomy

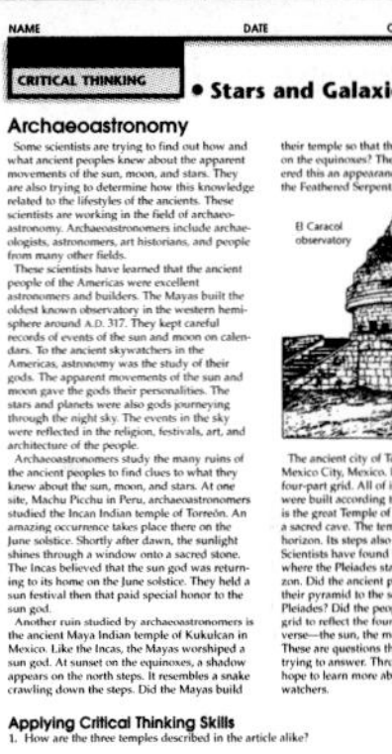
El Caracol observatory

L2

Multicultural Connections

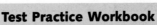

MULTICULTURAL CONNECTIONS • Adriana Ocampo—Space Scientist

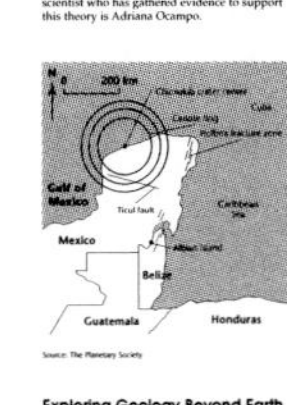

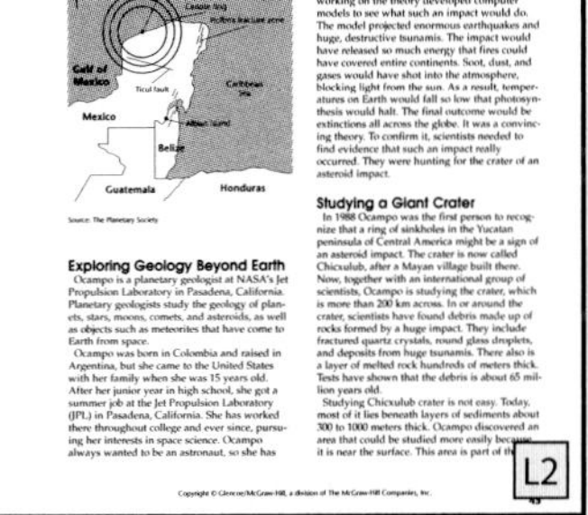
Exploring Geology Beyond Earth

Studying a Giant Crater

L2

Chapter 20 Stars and Galaxies

Helping You Prepare

Stars (Section 20-1)

The absolute magnitude of a star is affected by its size and its temperature. The apparent magnitude of a star is affected by its size, its temperature, and its distance. If the absolute and apparent magnitudes of a star are known, its distance from Earth can be determined.

Clouds of gas and dust in space, called nebulas, can obscure starlight, reducing a star's apparent magnitude. Interstellar nebulas make stars in large sections of our galaxy, the Milky Way, so low in apparent magnitude that they cannot be seen. The gas and dust also make stars appear more reddish. The interstellar material tends to be opaque to light of shorter wavelengths, allowing longer wavelengths of red light to pass through.

Surface of the Sun (Section 20-2)

Granulation on the surface of the sun was first seen by Galileo. He thought the phenomena resembled grains of wheat and thus called the features granules. Granules on the sun's surface are the tops of large convection cells that extend deep into the sun. The presence of these granules is evidence that convection currents do exist inside the sun, just under the photosphere. Each granule measures about 1000 km across. They form as hot gases are forced upward by surrounding denser gases. The hot gases flow toward the surface, emit energy, cool, and sink back toward the sun's interior.

GLENCOE TECHNOLOGY

CD-ROM

Glencoe Science Voyages Interactive CD-ROM

Chapter Summaries

Use the Chapter Summary to introduce, teach, or review chapter material.

Solar Activity (Section 20-2)

Solar activity affects the circulation of Earth's atmosphere. Thus, there appears to be a correlation between the sun's 22-year activity cycle (magnetic reversals occur with each 11-year activity cycle; thus, the total cycle is 22 years) and droughts on Earth. Solar activity can affect Earth's climate over a long period of time. The Little Ice Age that occurred in northern Europe during the late 1600s occurred during the Maunder minimum, a time when the sun had very few sunspots.

NATIONAL GEOGRAPHIC — **Teacher's Corner**

Products Available from Glencoe

To order the following products for use with this chapter, call Glencoe at 1-800-334-7344:

CD-ROM

NGS PictureShow: Stars and Galaxies

Transparency Set

NGS PicturePack: Stars and Galaxies

Products Available from National Geographic Society

To order the following products for use with this chapter, call National Geographic Society at 1-800-368-2728:

Videos

Stars and Constellations

Sun: Earth's Star

Index to National Geographic Magazine

The following articles may be used for research relating to this chapter:

"New Eyes on the Universe," by Bradford A. Smith, January 1994.

"Orion: Where Stars Are Born," by James Reston, Jr., December 1995.

Evolution of Stars (Section 20-3)

Not all stars shine with a steady light. Stars that change in brightness are called variable stars. Stars may vary because the outer layers of the star expand and contract, causing a change in the temperature and the absolute magnitude of the star.

One class of variable star, called a Cepheid variable, is important to the study of the universe. These stars vary regularly, and their period of variation is an indication of their absolute magnitudes. Because of this, they can be used to determine distances to faraway clusters and galaxies. If two Cepheid variables have the same period of pulsation, they are the same average size and have the same average absolute magnitude. Any difference noted in the apparent magnitudes of the two stars is caused by a difference in the distances to the stars. Polaris is a Cepheid variable.

Exoplanets (Section 20-3)

Scientists are closely studying Fomalhaut, Beta Pictoris, HR 4796A, and Vega—four stars with dust rings. The dust may possibly form into planets, allowing scientists to observe the formation of new solar systems.

Exoplanets—planets outside our solar system—recently have been discovered orbiting at least nine stars other than the sun. What astronomers have found has surprised them. The exoplanets show diverse orbital characteristics when compared to those in our solar system. The star 51 Pegasi has at least one planet with a mass that may exceed 50 percent of Jupiter's.

Black Holes (Section 20-4)

New infrared studies of the center of our galaxy, the Milky Way, provide more evidence for a supermassive black hole at the core of the Milky Way. The total output of energy from the object at the Milky Way's core is more than 1 million times that of the sun. This object, called Sgr A*, appears to contain between 1 and 2 million solar masses.

New Galaxies (Section 20-4)

A new galaxy of the dwarf spheroidal type has been found just 50 000 light-years from the Milky Way's nucleus. It lies on the opposite side of the Milky Way from Earth. Researchers hypothesize that within another 100 million years, the stars from this small galaxy will be incorporated into our own Milky Way. This corresponds to a theory that states that large galaxies, such as the Milky Way, are formed, in part, by incorporating smaller galaxies. Larger galaxies are built up from smaller galaxies.

SCIENCE UPDATE

For current events or science in the news, access the Glencoe Science Web Site at **www.glencoe.com/sec/science/ca**

Teacher to Teacher

"While studying the stars, my students build a planetarium from a 50-foot square of plastic film. The final product will be 30 feet in diameter and 16 feet tall. Plans are available in *The Science Teacher*, vol. 64, no. 7, October 1997."

Dennis L. Stockdale

Dennis L. Stockdale, Teacher
Asheville High School
Asheville, NC

CHAPTER 20
Stars and Galaxies

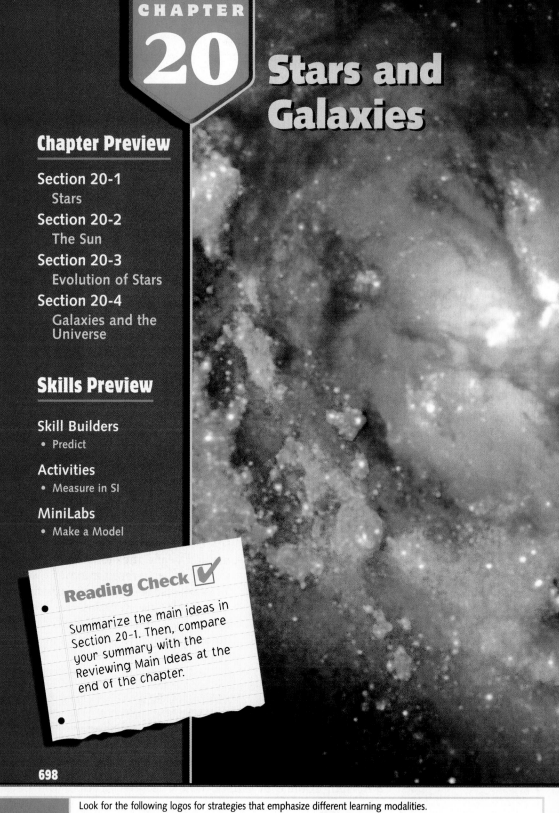

CHAPTER OVERVIEW

Section 20-1 This section discusses constellations and compares the absolute and apparent brightnesses of stars. Other properties of stars also are presented.

Section 20-2 The structure and surface features of the sun are discussed in this section.

Section 20-3 The evolution of stars is presented. Energy production in stars is also discussed.

Section 20-4 This section illustrates different types of galaxies. The big bang theory of the evolution of the universe is also presented.

Chapter Vocabulary

constellation
absolute magnitude
apparent magnitude
parallax
light-year
photosphere
chromosphere
corona
sunspot
binary system
main sequence
nebula
giant
white dwarf
supergiant
neutron star
black hole
galaxy
big bang theory

Theme Connection

Scale and Structure/Stability and Change The major themes of this chapter deal with the vast scale and structure of the universe and how the universe and the matter that makes up the universe change.

00:00 OUT OF TIME?

If time does not permit teaching the entire chapter, use Reviewing Main Ideas on pp. 730–731.

CHAPTER
20 Stars and Galaxies

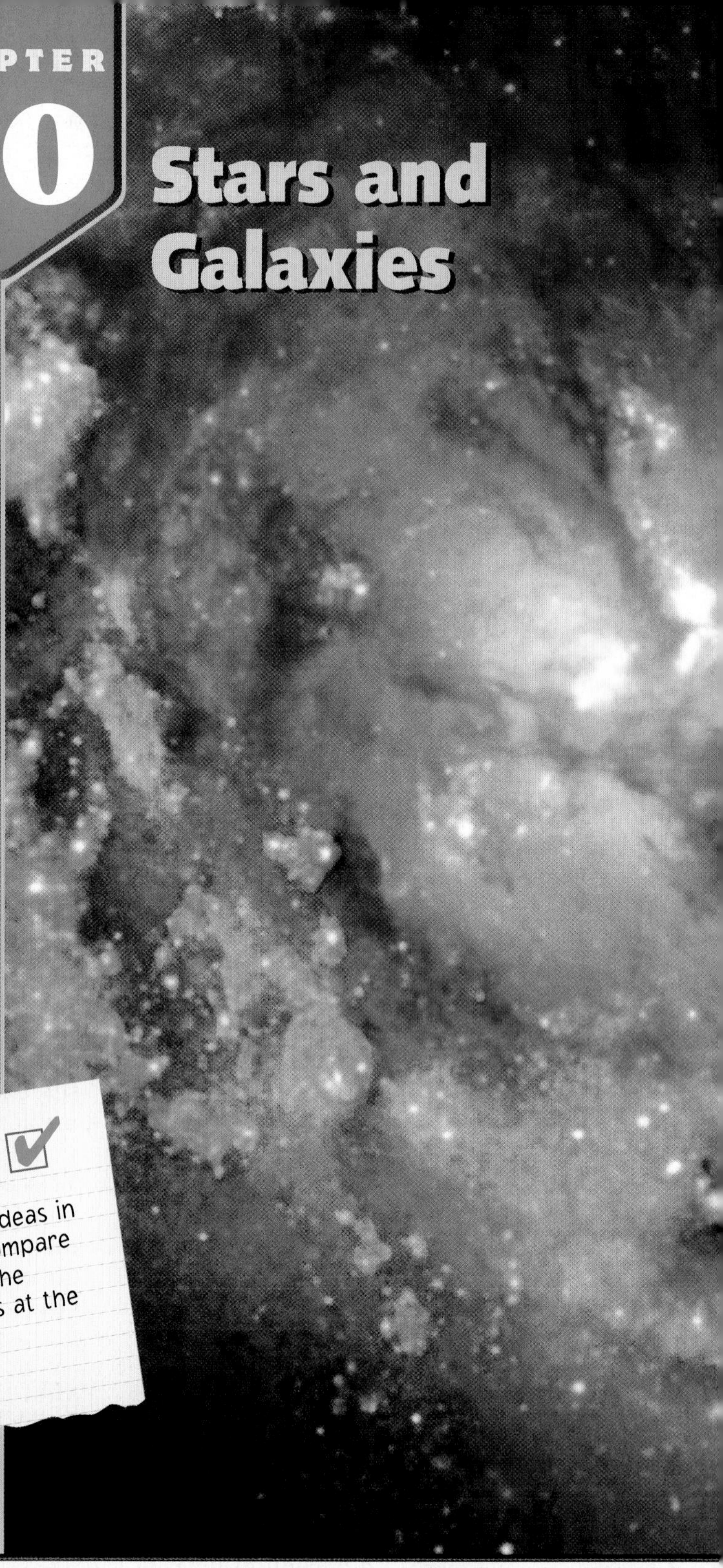

Chapter Preview

Skills Preview

Skill Builders
- Predict

Activities
- Measure in SI

MiniLabs
- Make a Model

Reading Check

Summarize the main ideas in Section 20-1. Then, compare your summary with the Reviewing Main Ideas at the end of the chapter.

698

Multiple Learning Styles

Look for the following logos for strategies that emphasize different learning modalities.

Linguistic Using Science Words, p. 711; Enrichment, p. 713; Science Journal, pp. 719, 721; Preview, p. 730

Logical-Mathematical Activity, pp. 724–725

Visual-Spatial Multiple Learning Styles, p. 701; Activity, pp. 702, 709; MiniLab, pp. 703, 720; Using an Analogy, p. 706; Reteach, pp. 707, 722, 730; Quick Demo, p. 712

Auditory-Musical Quick Demo, p. 721; Out of Time, p. 730

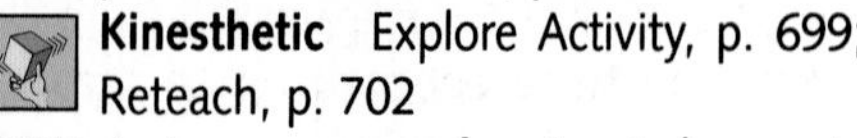
Kinesthetic Explore Activity, p. 699; Reteach, p. 702

Interpersonal Enrichment, p. 711; Discussion, p. 714; Activity, p. 718; Inclusion Strategies, p. 722; Review, p. 730

Intrapersonal Assessment, p. 715

Explore Activity

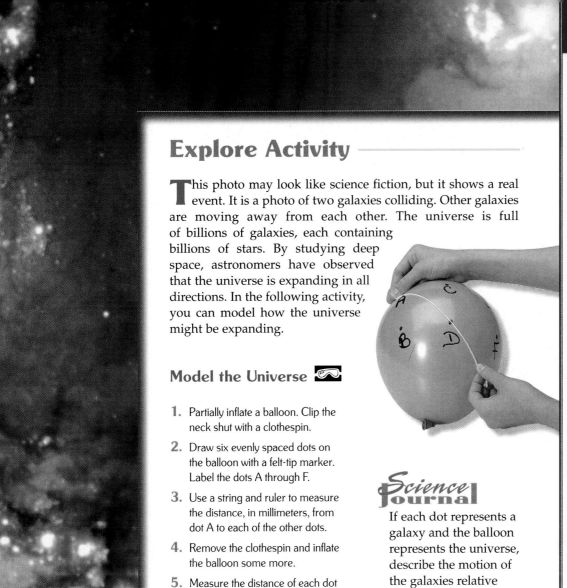

This photo may look like science fiction, but it shows a real event. It is a photo of two galaxies colliding. Other galaxies are moving away from each other. The universe is full of billions of galaxies, each containing billions of stars. By studying deep space, astronomers have observed that the universe is expanding in all directions. In the following activity, you can model how the universe might be expanding.

Model the Universe

1. Partially inflate a balloon. Clip the neck shut with a clothespin.
2. Draw six evenly spaced dots on the balloon with a felt-tip marker. Label the dots A through F.
3. Use a string and ruler to measure the distance, in millimeters, from dot A to each of the other dots.
4. Remove the clothespin and inflate the balloon some more.
5. Measure the distance of each dot from A again.
6. Inflate the balloon again, tie the neck shut, and take new measurements.

Science Journal

If each dot represents a galaxy and the balloon represents the universe, describe the motion of the galaxies relative to one another. Is the universe expanding? Explain.

Assessment Planner

Portfolio
Refer to p. 731 for suggested items that students might select for their portfolios.

Peformance Assessment
See p. 731 for additional Performance Assessment options.
Skill Builder, pp. 704, 708, 709, 715, 723
MiniLab, pp. 703, 720
Activity 20-1, p. 709; 20-2, pp. 724–725

Content Assessment
Section Assessment, pp. 704, 708, 715, 723
Chapter Assessment, pp. 732–733
Proficiency Prep, pp. 704, 708, 714, 723

Explore Activity

Purpose

Kinesthetic Use the Explore Activity to introduce students to the concept of an expanding universe.

Preparation

Several days before you begin this chapter, have students bring in large, round balloons and clothespins.

Materials

one balloon, one clothespin, one felt-tip marker, string, and a metric ruler for each group

Teaching Strategies

Form students into groups of four. Assign appropriate student roles. One student should blow up the balloon and clip it shut. Another should draw the dots on the balloon. The other two students should measure the distance between the dots.

Safety Precautions Caution students not to blow up the balloons to the breaking point.

The galaxy clusters are moving away from each other. This type of motion implies that the universe is expanding.

Assessment

Process Have students illustrate the motion of the galaxy clusters. Their drawings should indicate that the universe is expanding. Use **Performance Assessment in the Science Classroom,** p. 55.

Prepare

Refer to **Stars** on p. 698E.

Preplanning

Refer to the **Chapter Organizer** on pp. 698A–B.

1 Motivate

Bellringer

Before presenting the lesson, display **Section Focus Transparency 56** on the overhead projector. Use the accompanying **Focus Activity** worksheet. L2 ELL

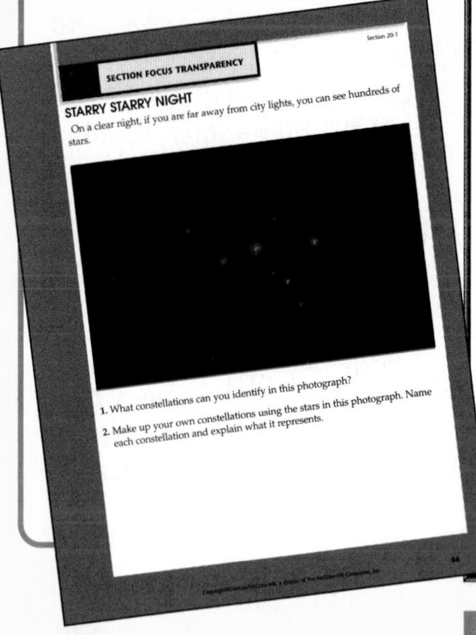

Section 20-1

SECTION FOCUS TRANSPARENCY

STARRY STARRY NIGHT

On a clear night, if you are far away from city lights, you can see hundreds of stars.

1. What constellations can you identify in this photograph?
2. Make up your own constellations using the stars in this photograph. Name each constellation and explain what it represents.

Tying to Previous Knowledge

Ask students if they have seen the Big Dipper. Draw the stars of the Big Dipper on the chalkboard and show why it's called a dipper.

20•1 Stars

What You'll Learn

- Why the positions of the constellations change throughout the year
- Absolute magnitude and apparent magnitude
- How parallax is used to determine distance

Vocabulary
constellation
absolute magnitude
apparent magnitude
parallax
light-year

Why It's Important

- You'll learn to recognize groups of stars found in the night sky.

Constellations

Have you ever watched clouds drift by on a summer day? It's fun to look at the clouds and imagine they have shapes familiar to you. One may look like a face. Another might resemble a rabbit or a bear. People long ago did much the same thing with patterns of stars in the sky. They named certain groups of stars, called **constellations,** after animals, characters in mythology, or familiar objects.

From Earth, a constellation looks like a group of stars that are relatively close to one another. In most cases, the stars in a constellation have no relationship to each other in space.

The position of a star in the sky can be given as a specific location within a constellation. For example, you can say that the star Betelgeuse (BEE tul jooz) is in the shoulder of the mighty hunter Orion. Orion's faithful companion is his dog, Canis Major. The brightest star in the sky, Sirius, is in the constellation Canis Major. Orion and Canis Major are shown in **Figure 20-1.**

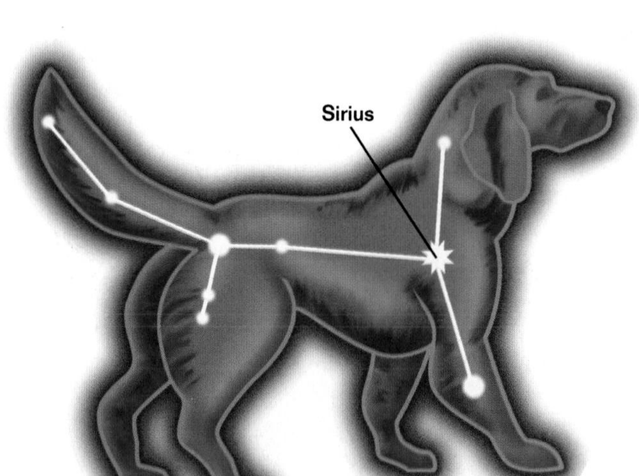

Figure 20-1 Groups of stars can form patterns that look like familiar objects or characters.

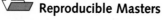

Resource Manager

The following **Teacher Classroom Resources** can be used with Section 20-1:

Reproducible Masters

Activity Worksheets, p. 115 L2
Enrichment, p. 56 L3
Home Involvement, p. 28 L2
Laboratory Manual, pp. 125–126 L2
Laboratory Manual, pp. 127–130 L2
Reinforcement, p. 56 L2
Study Guide, p.77 L1 ELL

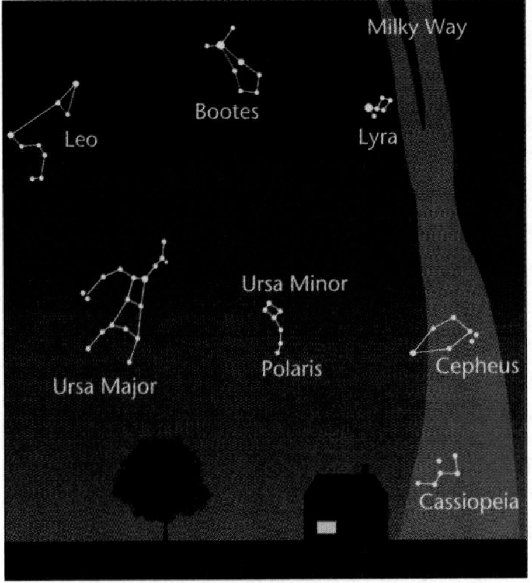

Summer

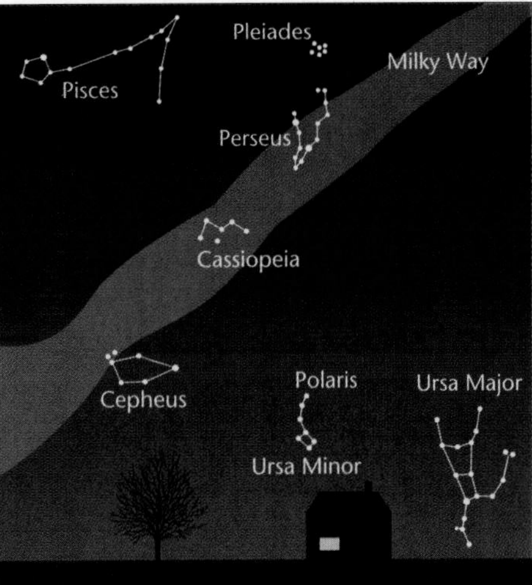

Winter

Figure 20-2 Some constellations are visible only during certain seasons of the year. Others, such as those close to Polaris, are visible year-round.

Early Greek astronomers named many constellations. Modern astronomers used many of these names to divide the sky into 88 constellations. You may already know some of them. Have you ever tried to find the Big Dipper? It's part of the constellation Ursa Major, shown in **Figure 20-2.** Notice how the front two stars of the Big Dipper point directly at the star Polaris. Polaris, also known as the North Star, is located at the end of the Little Dipper in the constellation Ursa Minor. Polaris is almost directly over Earth's north pole. You'll learn how to locate Polaris and constellations in the **Field Guide to Backyard Astronomy** at the end of this chapter.

Circumpolar Constellations

As Earth rotates, you can watch Ursa Major, Ursa Minor, and other constellations in the northern sky circle around Polaris. Because these constellations circle Polaris, they are called circumpolar constellations.

All of the constellations appear to move because Earth is moving. Look at **Figure 20-3.** The stars appear to complete one full circle in the sky in just under 24 hours as Earth rotates on its axis. The stars also appear to change positions in the sky throughout the year as Earth revolves around the sun.

Circumpolar constellations are visible all year long, but other constellations are not. As Earth orbits the sun, different constellations come into view while others disappear. Orion, which is visible in the winter in the northern hemisphere, can't be seen in the summer because the daytime side of Earth is facing it.

Figure 20-3 This photograph shows the path of circumpolar stars over several hours. Polaris is almost directly over the north pole. **Does Polaris appear to move as Earth rotates? Explain.**

2 Teach

Correcting Misconceptions

Many students may think that stars within one constellation are close to one another in space. Explain that two stars that appear side by side may be separated by hundreds of light-years.

Caption Answer

Figure 20-3 *Because Polaris is almost directly over the north pole, it does not appear to move as Earth rotates.*

Content Background

The magnitude scale was first defined and used by Hipparchus, and later refined by Ptolemy. In the 1850's Pogson and Herschel discovered that a first magnitude star is 100 times brighter than a sixth magnitude star. (The brighter the star, the smaller the value of the magnitude.) In turn, a one magnitude difference corresponds to a factor of 2.512 in brightness. ($100^{1/5} = 2.512$) Apparent magnitude is the brightness of a star as seen from Earth. But since distance affects this measurement, absolute magnitude is defined as the brightness of a star if it was located 10 parsecs (32.6 light-years) away from Earth.

Multiple Learning Styles

Visual-Spatial Have students cut black construction paper into 4-cm squares. On each square, put pinholes to form major constellations. Place a constellation square at one end of a cardboard tube. Point the tube toward a light source to view the constellations. L2

Constellations from Mythology Have students research and write a report in their Science Journals about a well-known constellation of their choice. Students should name the stars in the constellation and describe the mythological character or story that gave the constellation its name.

CA Science Content Standards

Page 700: 4b, 4d
Page 701: 1a, 4b, 4e

Answer to Reading Check

Absolute magnitude is a measure of the amount of light a star actually gives off.

Problem Solving

Apparent brightness is the amount of light received from an object. Because a light meter measures the light received from a light source, it measures apparent brightness. As distance from a light meter is doubled, the light intensity is cut to $\frac{1}{4}$ of what it had been. As distance is tripled, the light intensity is cut to $\frac{1}{9}$ of what it had been.

Think Critically

The relationship between light intensity and distance can be expressed as 1 divided by the square of how many times distance is increased. At 100 cm, the light intensity will be decreased to $\frac{1}{25}$ of its original intensity.

Absolute and Apparent Magnitudes

When you look at constellations, you'll notice that some stars are brighter than others. Sirius looks much brighter than Rigel. But is Sirius actually a brighter star, or is it just closer to Earth, which makes it appear to be brighter? As it turns out, Sirius is 100 times closer to Earth than Rigel. If Sirius and Rigel were the same distance from Earth, Rigel would appear much brighter in the night sky than would Sirius.

When you refer to the brightness of a star, you can refer to either its absolute magnitude or its apparent magnitude. The **absolute magnitude** of a star is a measure of the amount of light it actually gives off. A measure of the amount of light received on Earth is called the **apparent magnitude.** A star that's actually rather dim can appear bright in the sky if it's close to Earth. A star that's actually bright can appear dim if it's far away. If two stars are the same distance away, what factors might cause one of them to be brighter than the other?

Reading Check

What is absolute magnitude?

You can experience the effect of distance on apparent magnitude when driving in a car at night. Observe the other cars' headlights as they approach. Which cars' headlights are brighter—those that are closer to you or those that are farther away?

Problem Solving

Star Light, Star Bright

Mary conducted an experiment to determine the relationship between distance and the brightness of stars. She used a meterstick, a light meter, and a lightbulb. The bulb was mounted at the zero end of the meterstick. Mary placed the light meter at the 20-cm mark on the meterstick and recorded the distance and the light-meter reading in the data table below. Readings are in luxes, which are units for measuring light intensity. Mary doubled and tripled the distance and took more readings.

Effect of Distance on Light

Distance (cm)	Meter Reading (luxes)
20	4150.0
40	1037.5
60	461.1
80	259.4

Think Critically: What happened to the amount of light recorded when the distance was increased from 20 cm to 40 cm? From 20 cm to 60 cm? What does this indicate about the relationship between light intensity and distance? What would the light intensity be at 100 cm?

702 CHAPTER 20 STARS AND GALAXIES

3 Assess

Check for Understanding

Activity

Visual-Spatial Supply students with unlabeled star charts. Ask students to make up their own constellations using the charts. Have students explain their star patterns. L2 ELL

Reteach

Kinesthetic Take students to an open field to demonstrate parallax. Give one student a compass with a sighting mirror. Have this student stand 50 m from another student and determine the exact compass heading to the other student. Repeat this activity, varying the distances between students. L2 ELL COOP LEARN

CA Science Content Standards

Page 702: 4b, 9a
Page 703: 1a, 4b, 4c, 9b

How far are stars?

How do we know when a star is close to our solar system? One way is to measure its parallax. **Parallax** is the apparent shift in the position of an object when viewed from two different positions. You are already familiar with parallax. Hold your hand at arm's length and look at one finger first with your left eye closed and then with your right eye closed. Your finger appears to change position with respect to the background. Now, try the same experiment with your finger closer to your face. What do you observe? The nearer an object is to the observer, the greater its parallax.

We can measure the parallax of relatively close stars to determine their distances from Earth, as shown in **Figure 20-4.** When astronomers first realized how far away stars actually are, it became apparent that a new unit of measure would be needed to record their distances. Measuring star distances in kilometers would be like measuring the distance between cities in millimeters.

Distances in space are measured in light-years. A **light-year** is the distance that light travels in one year. Light travels at 300 000 km/s, or about 9.5 trillion km in one year. The nearest star to Earth, other than the sun, is Proxima Centauri. Proxima Centauri is 4.2 light-years away, or about 40 trillion km.

Observing Star Patterns

Procedure

1. On a clear night, go outside after dark and study the stars. Take an adult with you and see if you can help each other find constellations.
2. Let your imagination go to work and try to see any patterns of stars in the sky that look like something with which you are familiar.
3. Draw the stars you see, where they are in the sky, and include a drawing of what you think the star pattern resembles.

Analysis

1. How do your constellations compare with those observed by your classmates?
2. How do you think recognizing star patterns could be useful?

Figure 20-4 Parallax can be seen if you observe the same star while Earth is at two different points during its orbit around the sun (A). The star's position relative to more-distant background stars will appear to change (B and C).

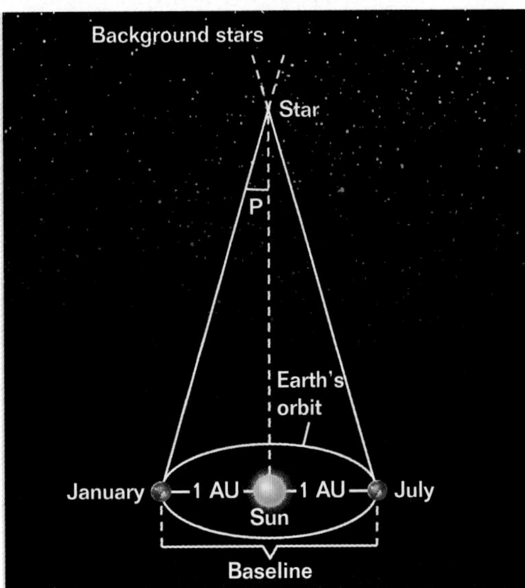

B

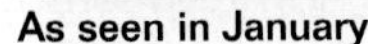

As seen in January

C

As seen in July

Extension

For students who have mastered this section, use the **Reinforcement** and **Enrichment** masters.

For additional help doing this activity at home, see the corresponding pages in the **Home Involvement** booklet.

Purpose

Visual-Spatial Students will place stars in patterns. L2 P

Teaching Strategies

Troubleshooting As preparation for this MiniLab, first perform the activity on p. 702 in the teacher's edition.

Analysis

1. Answers will vary depending on student drawings.
2. Answers will vary. Students may say that constellations can be used to find direction.

Performance Have students write a mythological story describing one of the star drawings they made while studying the night sky. Use **Performance Assessment in the Science Classroom,** p. 83.

GLENCOE TECHNOLOGY

CD-ROM

Glencoe Science Voyages Interactive CD-ROM

Explorations

Have students do the interactive exploration *How does the composition of stars determine their classification?*

Inclusion Strategies

Gifted Students should perform this activity away from city lights. Place a single lens reflex camera on a tripod. Aim the camera so that the North Star is in the center of the viewfinder. Use fast film, such as ASA 1000. Open the shutter for 30 minutes and have the aperture wide open. As Earth rotates, the starlight will expose the film and appear as circular streaks.

Caption Answer

Figure 20-5 *elements in a star's atmosphere*

4 Close

Proficiency Prep

Use this quiz to check students' recall of section content.

1. **What term describes the distance light travels during one year?** *light-year*
2. **What does the color of a star indicate?** *temperature*

Section Assessment

1. As Earth revolves around the sun, the nighttime side of Earth faces different directions in space. As a result, different constellations are visible.
2. Because both stars give off the same amount of light, they have the same absolute magnitude. If one star looks brighter than the other, it's probably closer to Earth.
3. Its atmosphere is similar to the sun's.
4. Think Critically Because the nearest stars are mostly invisible when viewed from Earth, their absolute magnitudes aren't very bright.

Using Computers

Charts will vary depending on the season chosen. Reference points should be included in all charts. P

CA Science Content Standards

Page 704: 1a, 4b, 4c, 4d, 4e, 9e
Page 705: 4b

Figure 20-5
These star spectra were made by placing a prism over a telescope's objective lens. **What causes the lines in spectra?**

How hot are stars?

The color of a star indicates its temperature. For example, hot stars are a blue-white color. A relatively cool star looks orange or red. Stars the temperature of our sun have a yellow color.

Astronomers learn about other properties of stars by studying their spectra. They use spectrographs to break visible light from a star into its component colors. If you look closely at the spectrum of a star, such as the ones shown in **Figure 20-5,** you will see dark lines in it. The lines are caused by elements in the star's atmosphere.

As light radiated from a star passes through the star's atmosphere, some of it is absorbed by elements in the atmosphere. The wavelengths of visible light that are absorbed appear as dark lines in the spectrum. Each element absorbs certain wavelengths, producing a certain pattern of dark lines. The patterns of lines can be used to identify which elements are in a star's atmosphere.

Section Assessment

1. Explain how Earth's revolution affects constellations that are visible throughout the year.
2. If two stars give off the same amount of light, what might cause one to look brighter than the other?
3. If the spectrum of another star shows the same absorption lines as the sun, what can be said about its composition?
4. **Think Critically:** Only about 700 stars can be studied using parallax. Most stars are invisible to the naked eye. What does this indicate about their apparent magnitudes?
5. **Skill Builder**
   Recognizing Cause and Effect
   Suppose you viewed Proxima Centauri through a telescope. How old were you when the light that you see left Proxima Centauri? Why might Proxima Centauri look dimmer than the star Betelgeuse, a large star 310 light-years away? If you need help, refer to Recognizing Cause and Effect in the **Skill Handbook** on page 957.

Using Computers

Graphics Use drawing software on a computer to make a star chart of major constellations visible from your home during the current season. Include reference points to help others find the charted constellations. If you need help, refer to page 970.

5. **Skill Builder**
Proxima Centauri is 4.2 light-years away. Ages will vary but should equal the students' ages minus 4.2 years. Proxima Centauri is close, but it doesn't give off much light. Both the absolute and apparent magnitudes of Betelgeuse are brighter than Proxima Centauri's.

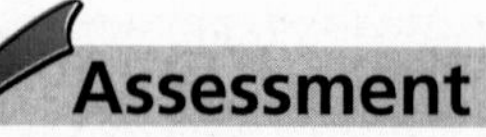

Assessment

Performance To further assess students' abilities to recognize cause and effect, ask them to explain in writing why Deneb appears so bright and yet is more than 1400 light-years away. Use **Performance Assessment in the Science Classroom,** p. 17.

The Sun

20•2

Layers of the Sun

More than 99 percent of all of the matter in our solar system is in the sun. The sun is the center of our solar system, and it makes life possible on Earth. But in the grand scheme of the universe, our sun is just another star in the sky.

The sun is an average, middle-aged star. Its absolute magnitude is about average and it shines with a yellow light. Like other stars, the sun is an enormous ball of gas, producing energy by fusing hydrogen into helium in its core. **Figure 20-6** is a model of the sun's interior and atmosphere.

The Sun's Atmosphere

The lowest layer of the sun's atmosphere and the layer from which light is given off is the **photosphere.** The photosphere is often called the surface of the sun. Temperatures there are around 6000 K. Above the photosphere is the **chromosphere.** This layer extends upward about 2000 km above the photosphere. A transition zone occurs between 2000 and 10 000 km above the photosphere. Above the transition zone is the **corona.** This is the largest layer of the sun's atmosphere and extends millions of kilometers into space. Temperatures in the corona are as high as 2 millionK. Charged particles continually escape from the corona and move through space as solar wind.

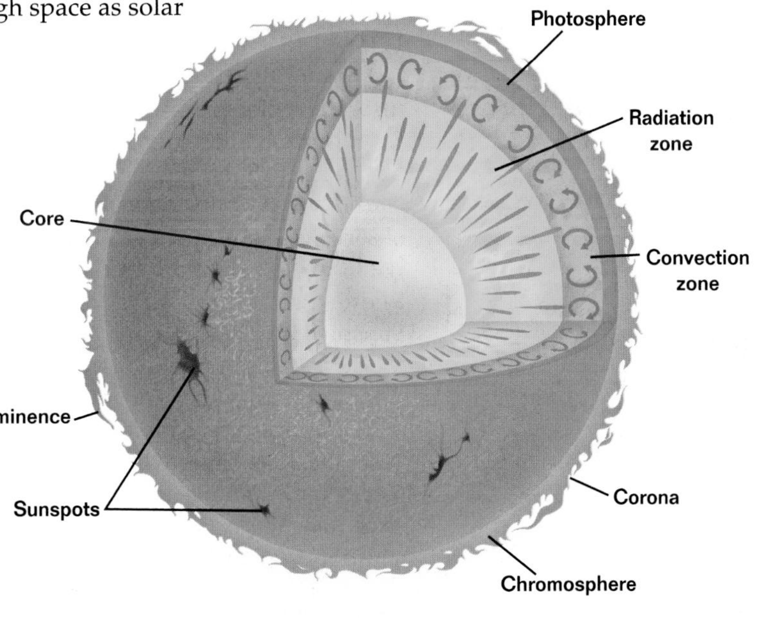

Figure 20-6 Energy produced by fusion in the sun's core travels outward by radiation and convection. The sun's atmosphere, composed of the photosphere, the chromosphere, and the corona, is illuminated by the energy produced in the core.

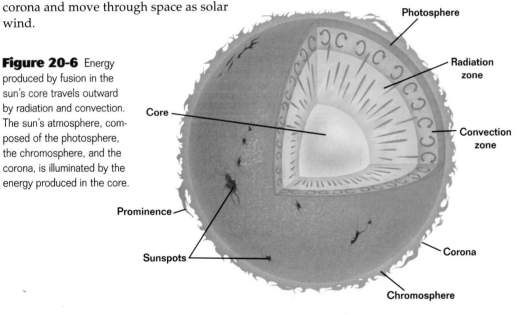

What You'll Learn

- How energy is produced in the sun
- That sunspots, prominences, and solar flares are related
- Why our sun is considered an average star and how it differs from stars in binary systems

Vocabulary

photosphere
chromosphere
corona
sunspot
binary system

Why It's Important

- The sun is the source of most energy on Earth.

SECTION 20•2

Prepare

Refer to **Surface of the Sun** and **Solar Activity** on p. 698E.

Preplanning

Refer to the **Chapter Organizer** on pp. 698A–B.

1 Motivate

Bellringer

Before presenting the lesson, display **Section Focus Transparency 57** on the overhead projector. Use the accompanying **Focus Activity** worksheet. L2 ELL

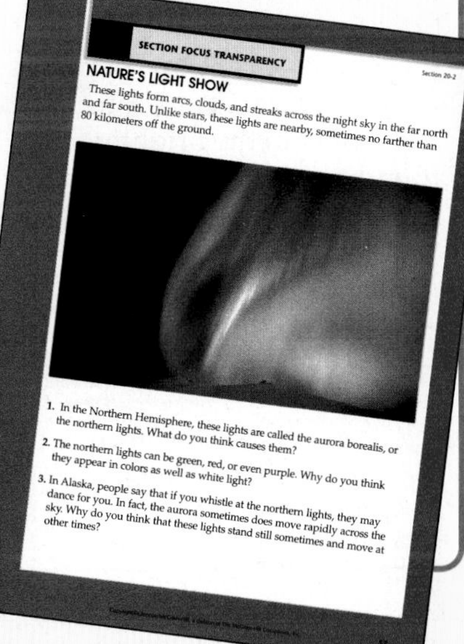
SECTION FOCUS TRANSPARENCY

Section 20-2

NATURE'S LIGHT SHOW

These lights form arcs, clouds, and streaks across the night sky in the far north and far south. Unlike stars, these lights are nearby, sometimes no farther than 80 kilometers off the ground.

1. In the Northern Hemisphere, these lights are called the aurora borealis, or the northern lights. What do you think causes them?
2. The northern lights can be green, red, or even purple. Why do you think they appear in colors as well as white light?
3. In Alaska, people say that if you whistle at the northern lights, they may dance for you. In fact, the aurora sometimes does move rapidly across the sky. Why do you think that these lights stand still sometimes and move at other times?

57

Tying to Previous Knowledge

Remind students that interactions of air, water, and energy from the sun cause Earth's weather.

Resource Manager

The following **Teacher Classroom Resources** can be used with Section 20-2:

 **Reproducible Masters**

Activity Worksheets, pp. 111–112 L2

Enrichment, p. 57 L3

Multicultural Connections, pp. 39–40

Reinforcement, p. 57 L2

Transparencies

Science Integration Transparency 20 L2

2 Teach

Answer to Reading Check

areas of the sun's surface that appear to be dark because they are cooler than surrounding areas

Using an Analogy

Visual-Spatial To help students understand why sunspots look dark even though they are quite bright, use the following analogy. Show students an overhead projector screen without the projector on. Ask them what color it is. Students will note that it is white. Now, place a transparency with white printing on the projector and turn on the projector. Students will now see that black lines appear to have been drawn on the screen. The lines are white, but next to the brighter white of the screen, they look black. A similar phenomena occurs on the sun—next to the brighter surrounding areas of the sun's surface, sunspots look dark.

Content Background

Sunspots are caused by intense magnetic storms on the sun. As the sun rotates, magnetic field lines wrap around it. These lines dip into the sun's interior and then out, forming sunspots. This explains why many sunspots occur in pairs and why each one of the pair has a magnetic sign opposite that of its partner.

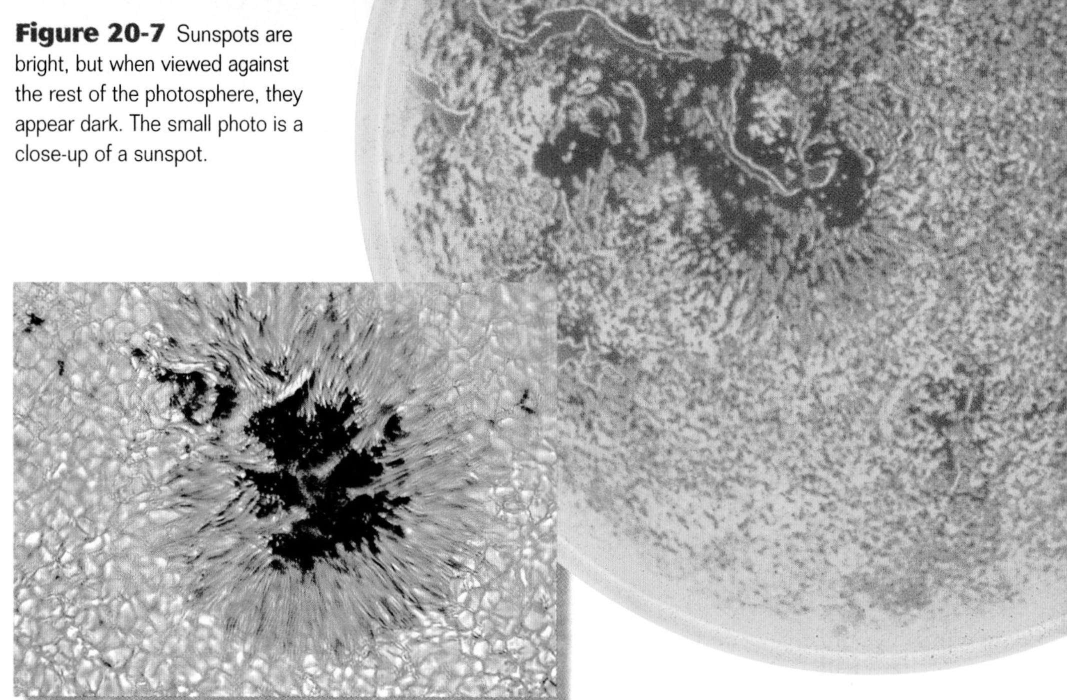

Figure 20-7 Sunspots are bright, but when viewed against the rest of the photosphere, they appear dark. The small photo is a close-up of a sunspot.

Surface Features of the Sun

Because the sun is a ball of hot gas, it's hard to imagine its surface as anything but a smooth layer. In reality, the sun's surface has many features, including sunspots, prominences, and flares.

Sunspots

Areas of the sun's surface that appear to be dark because they are cooler than surrounding areas are called **sunspots.** Ever since Galileo identified sunspots like those in **Figure 20-7,** scientists have been studying them. One thing we've learned by studying sunspots is that the sun rotates. We can observe the movement of individual sunspots as they move with the sun's rotation. The sun doesn't rotate as a solid body, as does Earth. It rotates faster at its equator than at its poles. Sunspots near the equator take about 27 days to go around the sun. At higher latitudes, they take 31 days.

Reading Check What are sunspots?

Sunspots aren't permanent features on the sun. They appear and disappear over a period of several days, weeks, or months. Also, there are times when there are many large sunspots—a sunspot maximum—and times when there are only a few small sunspots or none at all—a sunspot minimum. Periods of sunspot maximum occur about every 11 years.

Across the Curriculum

Math Using the table below, have student groups plot a graph of sunspot activity. Have each group describe any trend the group observes. L2 COOP LEARN

Year	Sunspots
1969	105
1970	104
1971	67
1972	69
1973	38
1974	35
1975	16
1976	13
1977	28
1978	93
1979	155
1980	155
1981	140
1982	116
1983	67
1984	46
1985	18
1986	14
1987	29
1988	100
1989	159
1990	147
1991	145
1992	94
1993	54
1994	31
1995	18

Prominences and Flares

Sunspots are related to several features on the sun's surface. The intense magnetic field associated with sunspots may cause prominences, which are huge arching columns of gas. Some prominences blast material from the sun into space at speeds ranging from 600 km/s to more than 1000 km/s.

Gases near a sunspot sometimes brighten up suddenly, shooting gas outward at high speed. These violent eruptions from the sun, shown in **Figure 20-8,** are called solar flares.

Ultraviolet light and X rays from solar flares can reach Earth and cause disruption of radio signals. Solar flares make communication by radio and telephone difficult at times. High-energy particles emitted by solar flares are captured by Earth's magnetic field, disrupting communication equipment. These particles also interact with Earth's atmosphere near the polar regions and create light. This light is called the aurora borealis, or northern lights, when it occurs in the northern hemisphere. In the southern hemisphere, it is called the aurora australis.

Visit the Glencoe Science Web Site at **www.glencoe.com/sec/science/ca** for more information about sunspots, solar flares, and prominences.

Figure 20-8 Features such as solar flares (A) and solar prominences (B) can reach hundreds of thousands of kilometers into space. **How big is this compared with the size of Earth?**

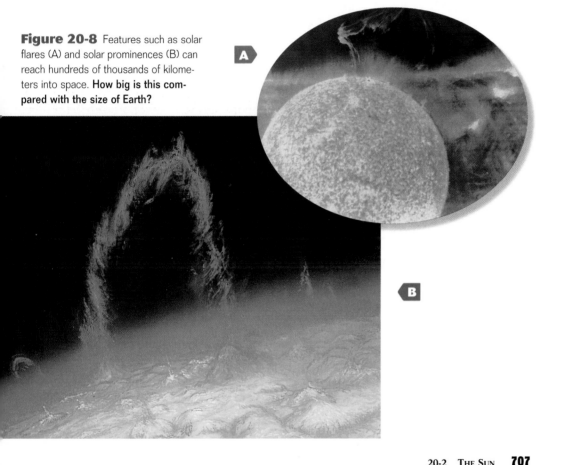

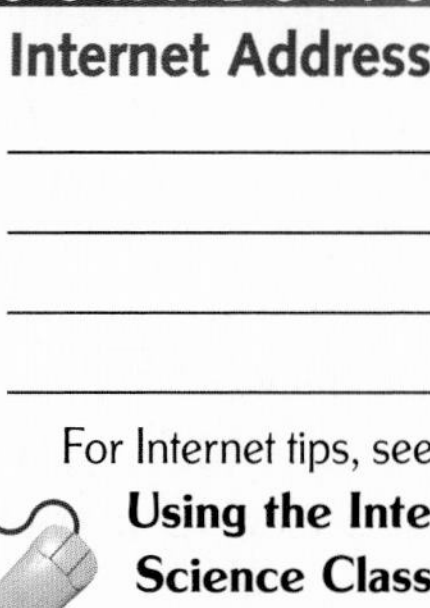

Internet Addresses

For Internet tips, see Glencoe's **Using the Internet in the Science Classroom.**

Caption Answer

Figure 20-8 *The flares can extend to a distance equal to several tens of Earth diameters.*

3 Assess

Check for Understanding

Activity

Have students research the relationship between sunspot activity and Earth's weather and climate. Have interested students research the Maunder minimum, a period from 1645 through 1715 when few sunspots were observed. During this time, Europe experienced record low temperatures, and severe droughts occurred in the western United States. L3

Reteach

Visual-Spatial Have students illustrate how the light and heat from the sun are produced. L2 ELL

Extension

For students who have mastered this section, use the **Reinforcement** and **Enrichment** masters.

Guided Reading Strategy

Supporting Idea Chart This strategy examines the relationship between a whole and its parts. Write the name of the whole object on the single line at the left. On the next set of lines to the right, write in major parts of the object. Finally, write in the subparts of each major part. Have students design a Supporting Idea Chart for a concept in this section.

Sample Chart:

- Atomic structure
  - Electrons
  - Nucleus
    - Neutrons
    - Protons

CA Science Content Standards

Page 706: 1a, 4b
Page 707: 4b, 9f

20-2 THE SUN 707

4 Close

Proficiency Prep

Use this quiz to check students' recall of section content.

1. **Which layer of the sun's atmosphere gives off light?** *photosphere*
2. **What are cooler, dark areas on the sun's surface called?** *sunspots*

Section Assessment

1. Magnetic fields near a sunspot can cause huge arching columns of gas called prominences. Gases near sunspots can become concentrated and shoot outward from the sun as a solar flare.
2. The sun's size, temperature, and absolute magnitude are similar to other yellow stars' on the main sequence. The sun is unlike many stars because it's not part of a binary system.
3. Think Critically Answers will vary. Students may say that our sun could have been a member of a cluster or multiple-star system that spread out across the galaxy or that the cloud from which our sun formed may not have contained enough matter for more than one star.

Science Journal

Fusion reactions in the sun's core change hydrogen into helium. Student hypotheses will vary. Some may know that when the sun exhausts its hydrogen supply, it will begin to fuse helium in its core.

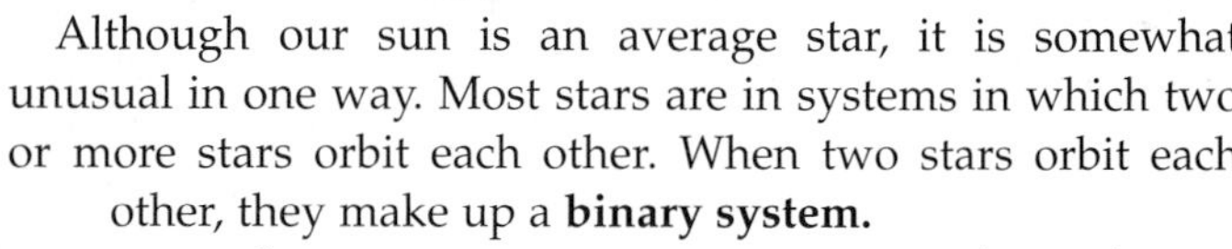

Our Sun—A Typical Star?

Although our sun is an average star, it is somewhat unusual in one way. Most stars are in systems in which two or more stars orbit each other. When two stars orbit each other, they make up a **binary system.**

In some cases, astronomers can detect binary systems because one star occasionally eclipses the other. The total amount of light from the star system becomes dim and then bright again on a regular cycle. Algol in Perseus is an example of this.

In many cases, stars move through space together as a cluster. In a star cluster, many stars are relatively close to one another and are gravitationally attracted to each other. The Pleiades star cluster, shown in **Figure 20-9,** can be seen in the constellation of Taurus in the winter sky. On a clear, dark night, you may be able to see seven of the stars of this cluster. Most star clusters are far from our solar system and appear as a fuzzy patch in the night sky.

Figure 20-9 Pleiades is a cluster of stars that are gravitationally bound to each other.

Section Assessment

1. How are sunspots, prominences, and solar flares related?
2. What properties does the sun have in common with other stars? What property makes it different from most other stars?
3. **Think Critically:** Because most stars are found in multiple-star systems, what might explain why the sun is a single star?
4. **Skill Builder**
   Interpreting Scientific Illustrations Use **Figure 20-6** to answer the questions below. If you need help, refer to Interpreting Scientific Illustrations in the **Skill Handbook** on page 962.
   a. Which layers make up the sun's atmosphere?
   b. What process occurs in the sun's convection zone that enables energy produced in the core to reach the surface?

Write a brief description in your Science Journal that explains how the sun generates energy. Hypothesize what might happen to the sun when it exhausts the supply of hydrogen in its core.

4. 
Skill Builder
a. photosphere, chromosphere, corona
b. Gases heated at the bottom of the convection zone are forced upward by denser surrounding gases. The hot gases release energy, cool, and sink. This process creates convection currents.

Assessment

Oral To further assess students' abilities to interpret scientific illustrations, have them hypothesize what is causing the glow around the stars in **Figure 20-9.** Use **Performance Assessment in the Science Classroom,** p. 17.

Sunspots

Sunspots are dark, relatively cool areas on the surface of the sun. They can be observed moving across the face of the sun as it rotates. Do this activity to measure the movement of sunspots, and use your data to determine the sun's period of rotation.

Materials

- Several books
- Cardboard (about 8 cm × 12 cm)
- Clipboard
- Drawing paper (5 sheets)
- Small refracting telescope
- Small tripod
- Scissors

What You'll Investigate

Can sunspot motion be used to determine the sun's period of rotation?

Goals

- **Observe** sunspots.
- **Estimate** sunspot size and rate of apparent motion.

Procedure

1. **Find** a location where the sun may be viewed at the same time of day for a minimum of five days. **CAUTION:** *Do not look directly at the sun. Do not look through the telescope at the sun. You could damage your eyes.*
2. **Set up** the telescope with the eyepiece facing away from the sun, as shown below. Align the telescope so that the shadow it casts on the ground is the smallest size possible. **Cut** and **attach** the cardboard as shown in the photo.
3. **Use** books to prop the clipboard upright. Point the eyepiece at the drawing paper.
4. If the telescope has a small finder scope attached, **remove** the finder scope or keep it covered.
5. **Move** the clipboard back and forth until you have the largest possible image of the sun on the paper. Adjust the telescope to form a clear image. **Trace** the outline of the sun on the paper.
6. **Trace** any sunspots that appear as dark areas on the sun's image. Repeat this step at the same time each day for a week.
7. Using the sun's diameter (approximately 1 390 000 km), **estimate** the size of the largest sunspots that you observed.
8. **Calculate** how many kilometers any observed sunspots appear to move each day.
9. At the rate determined in step 8, **predict** how many days it will take for the same group of sunspots to return to about the same position in which you first observed them.

Conclude and Apply

1. What was the average number of sunspots observed each day?
2. What was the estimated size and rate of apparent motion of the largest sunspots?
3. **Infer** how sunspots can be used to determine that the sun's surface is not solid like Earth's.

Assessment

Content To further assess students' understanding of sunspots, ask them to hypothesize about sunspot movement on the hemisphere they did not observe. How might sunspots on the opposite hemisphere (north or south) move compared to those plotted in this activity? Use **Performance Assessment in the Science Classroom,** p. 21.

Activity 20•1

Purpose

Visual-Spatial Students will observe sunspots and estimate their size and rate of motion across the sun's photosphere. L3 ELL COOP LEARN

Process Skills

observing and inferring, interpreting data, using numbers

Time

10 minutes each day for five days

Safety Precautions

Caution students not to look directly at the sun. Do not allow them to look through the telescope at the sun.

Alternate Materials If a telescope isn't available, use binoculars with one eyepiece covered. Set the binoculars on a stack of books on the window ledge.

Teaching Strategies

Troubleshooting

- If the apparatus must be taken down or moved, ensure correct alignment by marking the exact position of the telescope, books, and clipboard.
- If no sunspots are visible, keep the setup in place until some are sighted. Check to see if you are observing the sun during a sunspot minimum.

Answers to Questions

1. & 2. Answers will vary depending on solar activity. However, the answers of each group should be approximately the same.
3. Sunspots near the sun's equator move at different rates than those near the poles.

CA Science Content Standards

Page 708: 4a, 4b
Page 709: 1a, 4b, 9a, 9f

SECTION 20•3

Prepare

Refer to **Evolution of Stars** and **Exoplanets** on p. 698F.

Preplanning

Refer to the **Chapter Organizer** on pp. 698A–B.

1 Motivate

Bellringer

Before presenting the lesson, display **Section Focus Transparency 58** on the overhead projector. Use the accompanying **Focus Activity** worksheet. L2 ELL

SECTION FOCUS TRANSPARENCY

SUNBEAMS

The light and warmth we receive from the sun are things most of us take for granted. Imagine what it would be like on Earth if we didn't have the sun. Undoubtedly, Earth would be a very different place.

1. What in this photograph needs the sun?
2. Why do people need the sun?

Tying to Previous Knowledge

Tell students that stars are composed of matter in the plasma state. Have them describe what happens to matter in the plasma state.

20•3 Evolution of Stars

What You'll Learn

- How stars are classified
- How the temperature of a star relates to its color
- How a star evolves

Vocabulary

main sequence, nebula, giant, white dwarf, supergiant, neutron star, black hole

Why It's Important

- The evolution of stars helps explain the theory for the evolution of the universe.

The H-R Diagram

In the early 1900s, Ejnar Hertzsprung and Henry Russell noticed that for most stars, the higher their temperatures, the brighter their absolute magnitudes. They developed a graph to show this relationship.

Hertzsprung and Russell placed the temperatures of stars across the bottom of the graph and the absolute magnitudes of stars up one side. A graph that shows the relationship of a star's temperature to its absolute magnitude is called a Hertzsprung-Russell (H-R) diagram. **Figure 20-10** shows a variation of an H-R diagram.

The Main Sequence

As you can see, stars seem to fit into specific areas of the chart. Most stars fit into a diagonal band that runs from the upper left to the lower right of the chart. This band, called the **main sequence,** contains hot, blue, bright stars in the upper left and cool, red, dim stars in the lower right. Yellow, medium-temperature, medium-brightness stars fall in between. The sun is a yellow main sequence star.

About 90 percent of all stars are main sequence stars, most of which are small, red stars found in the lower right of the H-R diagram. Among main sequence stars, the hottest stars generate the most light and the coolest generate the least. But,

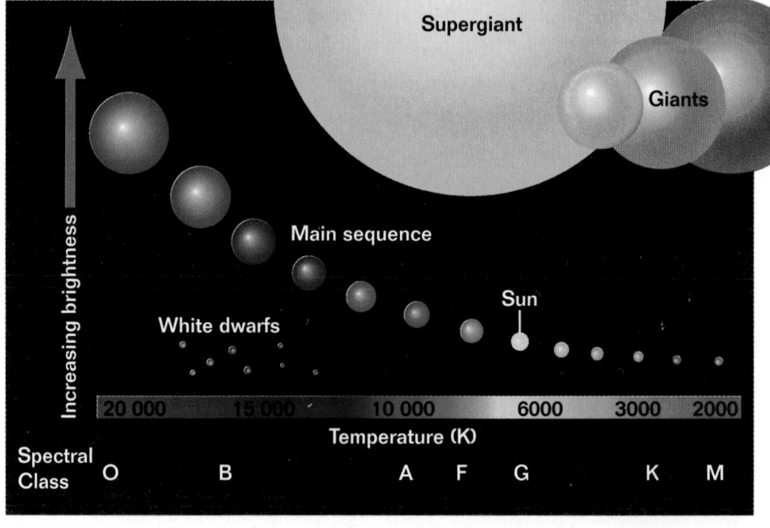

Figure 20-10 This variation of a Hertzsprung-Russell diagram shows the relationships among a star's color, temperature, and brightness. Stars in the main sequence run from hot, bright stars in the upper-left corner of the diagram to cool, faint stars in the lower-right corner. **What type of star shown in the diagram is the coolest, brightest star?**

Resource Manager

The following **Teacher Classroom Resources** can be used with Section 20-3:

Reproducible Masters

Critical Thinking/Problem Solving, p. 20 L2

Enrichment, p. 58 L3

Reinforcement, p. 58 L2

Transparencies

Teaching Transparency 39 L2

Teaching Transparency 40 L2

what about the remaining ten percent? Some of these stars are hot but not bright. These small stars are located on the lower left of the H-R diagram and are called white dwarfs. Other stars are extremely bright but not hot. These large stars on the upper right of the H-R diagram are called giants, or red giants because they are usually red in color. The largest giants are called supergiants. The relative sizes of stars are shown in **Figure 20-11.**

Fusion

When the H-R diagram was developed, scientists didn't know what caused stars to shine. Hertzsprung and Russell developed their diagram without knowing what produced the light and heat of stars.

For centuries, people had been puzzled by the question of what stars were and what made them shine. It wasn't until the early part of the twentieth century that scientists began to understand how a star could shine for billions of years. Until that time, many had estimated that Earth was only a few thousand years old. The sun could have been made of coal and shined for that long. But what material could possibly burn for billions of years?

Generating Energy

In 1920, one scientist hypothesized that temperatures in the center of the sun must be high. Another scientist then suggested that with these high temperatures, hydrogen could fuse to make helium in a reaction that would release tremendous amounts of energy. **Figure 20-12** on the next page illustrates how four hydrogen nuclei could combine to create one helium nucleus. The mass of one helium nucleus is less than the mass of four hydrogen nuclei, so some mass is lost in the reaction. In the 1930s, scientists hypothesized that carbon could be used as a catalyst in fusion reactions. This explained the energy production in hotter stars.

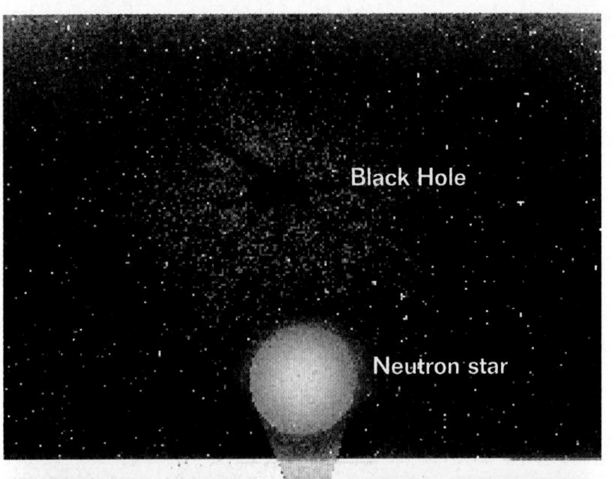

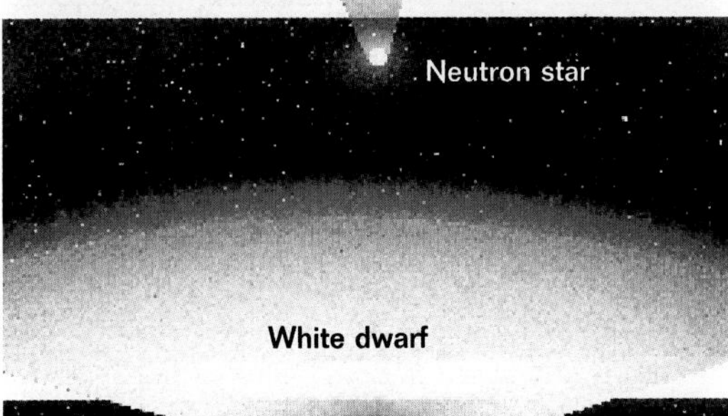

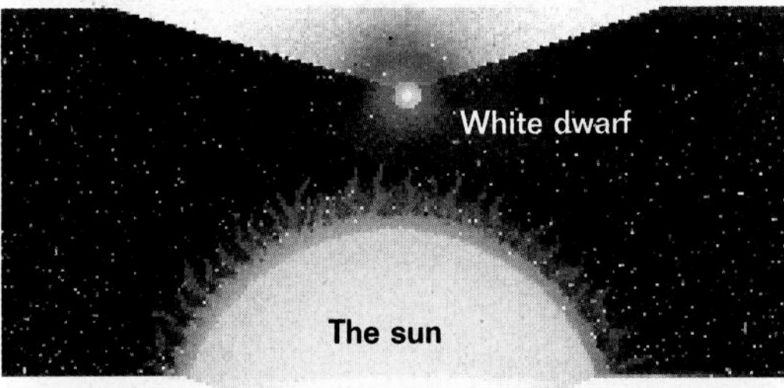

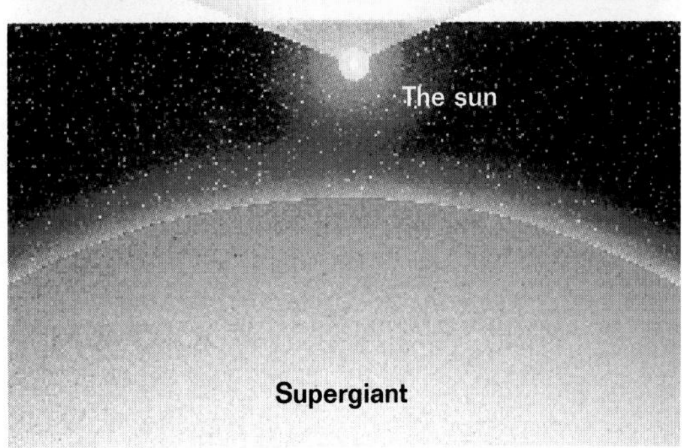

Figure 20-11 The relative sizes of stars range from supergiants as much as 800 times larger than the sun to neutron stars and black holes possibly 30 km or less across. The relative sizes of a supergiant, the sun, a white dwarf, a neutron star, and a black hole are shown.

2 Teach

Caption Answer

Figure 20-10 *giants*

Using Science Words

Linguistic Help students practice the use of science words by asking the following questions. **What properties of stars are plotted on the H-R diagram?** *Absolute magnitude is plotted against temperature or stellar classification.* **What process generates energy in the core of a star?** *Fusion generates energy in the core of a star. Four hydrogen atoms fuse to become one helium atom. Mass lost in the reaction is changed to energy.* L2

Content Background

A group of astronomers has devised a new class of stars, stellar class L. Stars of this class are relatively cool—1500 K to 2000 K. (Kelvin scale temperatures are expressed as kelvins, K, not as degrees.) Stars of this newly proposed classification have spectra that show the presence of iron hydride (FeH) and chromium hydride (CrH). Alkali metals such as sodium, potassium, and cesium are also found in the spectra of L-class stars. As with M-class stars, L-class stars are dwarfs.

Enrichment

Interpersonal Have pairs of students prepare and display a bulletin board version of a Hertzsprung-Russell (H-R) diagram. Have them use **Figure 20-10** as a guide. L2 COOP LEARN

Integrating the Sciences

Physics Refer students to "The Eagle's Nest" by Samantha Parker in *Sky & Telescope*, February 1996, pp. 32–34. After students have read the article, show them illustrations of the Eagle nebula (M16). Ask them why scientists are interested in this nebula. *Data gathered by the* Hubble Space Telescope *indicate that the evaporating gaseous globules (EGGs) found in this nebula are forming into stars.*

CA Science Content Standards

Page 710: 4b
Page 711: 4b, 6a

Stars evolve and change into other types of stars because of what is happening inside the star. As a star uses up one element as fuel, conditions change inside the star. If the star can attain high enough temperatures, new, heavier elements can be used as fuel for the fusion process to continue at the star's core. Ask students what property of the star determines what can be used as fuel for fusion at the star's core. *stellar mass*

Answer to Reading Check
a large cloud of gas and dust in space

Quick Demo

Visual-Spatial Using tongs, hold the end of a wire over the flame of a Bunsen burner until it begins to glow. Ask students to record the color of the glowing wire. Continue to hold the wire over the flame. Ask students to record any changes they see in the wire as it's heated. Ask one student to summarize what happened to the wire. *As the wire was heated, it started to glow and gradually changed from reddish-orange to yellowish-white as it became hotter.* **CAUTION:** *Wear goggles and safety gloves. Handle the hot wire carefully.* L2

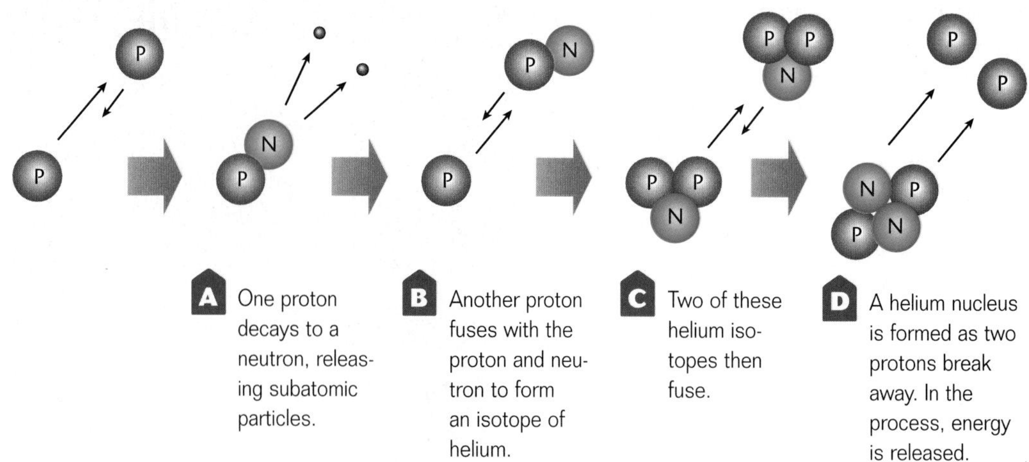

P
N
A One proton decays to a neutron, releasing subatomic particles.
B Another proton fuses with the proton and neutron to form an isotope of helium.
C Two of these helium isotopes then fuse.
D A helium nucleus is formed as two protons break away. In the process, energy is released.

Figure 20-12 In a star's core, fusion begins as two hydrogen nuclei (protons) are forced together. **What happens to the "lost" mass during this process?**

Years earlier, in 1905, Albert Einstein had proposed a theory stating that mass can be converted into energy. This was stated as the famous equation $E = mc^2$, where E is the energy produced, m is the mass, and c is the speed of light. The small amount of mass "lost" when hydrogen atoms fuse to form a helium atom is converted to a large amount of energy.

Fusion occurs in the cores of stars. Only in the core are temperatures and pressures high enough to cause atoms to fuse. Normally, they would repel each other, but in the core of a star, atoms are forced close enough together that their nuclei fuse together.

The Evolution of Stars

The H-R diagram and other theories explained a lot about stars. But they also led to more questions. Many wondered why some stars didn't fit in the main sequence group and what happened when a star exhausted its supply of hydrogen fuel. Today, we have a theory of how stars evolve, what makes them different from one another, and what happens when they die. **Figure 20-13** illustrates the lives of different types of stars.

Nebula

Stars begin as a large cloud of gas and dust called a **nebula.** The particles of gas and dust exert a gravitational force on each other, and the nebula begins to contract. Gravitational forces cause instability within the nebula. The nebula can fragment into smaller pieces. Each will eventually collapse to form a star.

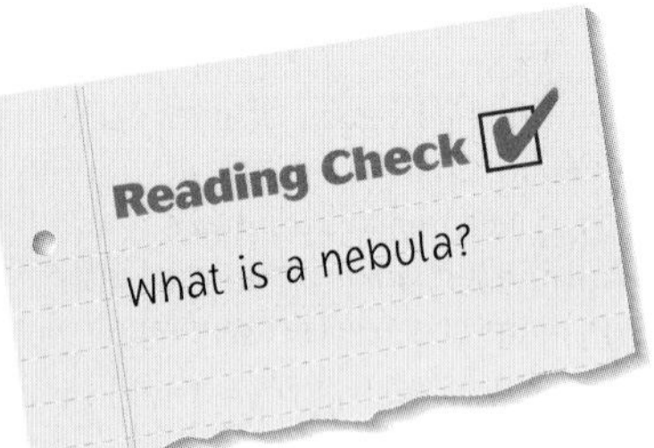

Content Background

Based on observed evidence, most stars form inside clouds of gas and dust at the same time that other stars are forming from the same cloud. In the Orion nebula (M42), a star nursery located 1500 light-years away, hundreds of stars have already formed and many more will follow.

Caption Answers

Figure 20-12 *It is converted to a large amount of energy.*

Figure 20-13 *They become white dwarfs.*

Figure 20-14 *Iron forms in the core of a supergiant. Fusion can no longer occur and the core collapses violently. Outer layers of the star fall in and "bounce" off the core, and then expand quickly outward like an explosion.*

As the particles in the smaller clouds move closer together, the temperatures in each nebula increase. When temperatures inside each nebula reach 10 millionK, fusion begins. The energy released radiates outward through the condensing ball of gas. As the energy radiates into space, stars are born.

CHEMISTRY INTEGRATION

Star Spectrum
The spectrum of a star shows absorption lines of helium and hydrogen and is bright in the blue end. Describe as much as you can about the star's composition and surface temperature.

Main Sequence to Giant Stars

In the newly formed star, the heat from fusion causes pressure that balances the attraction due to gravity, and the star becomes a main sequence star. It continues to use up its hydrogen fuel.

When hydrogen in the core of the star is exhausted, there is no longer a balance between pressure and gravity. The core contracts, and temperatures inside the star increase. This causes the outer layers of the star to expand. In this late stage of its life cycle, a star is called a **giant.**

Once the core temperature reaches 100 millionK, helium nuclei fuse to form carbon in the giant's core. By this time, the star has expanded to an enormous size, and its outer layers are much cooler than they were when it was a main sequence star. In about 5 billion years, our sun will become a giant.

Figure 20-13 The life of a star depends greatly on its mass. Massive stars eventually become neutron stars, or possibly black holes. **What happens to stars the size of our sun?**

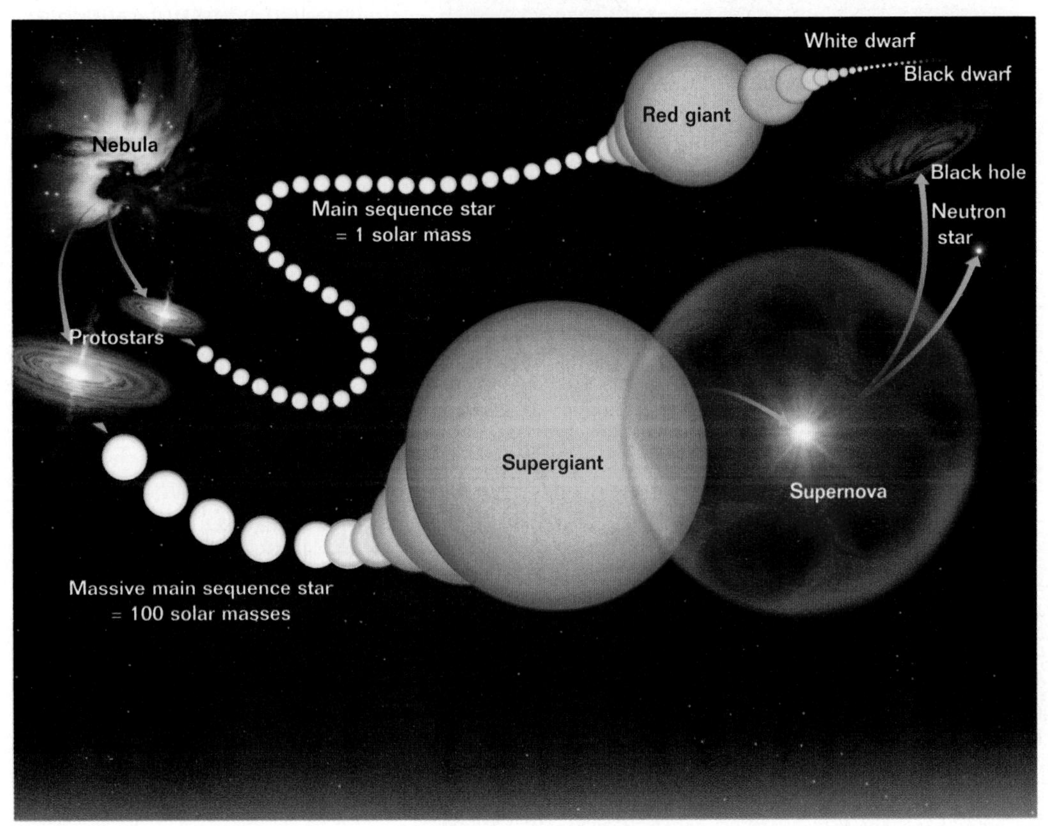

Flex Your Brain

Use the Flex Your Brain activity to have students explore EVOLUTION OF STARS.

CHEMISTRY INTEGRATION

The star's atmosphere contains helium and hydrogen. Its surface has a high temperature.

Enrichment

Linguistic Have students use astronomy books and magazine articles to research the Horsehead and Orion nebulas, located in the constellation Orion. Have them determine why the Horsehead nebula is a dark nebula and the Orion nebula is a bright nebula. Also, have them explain the relationship between the brightness of the nebulas and the star-formation processes occurring within them. L3

Teacher FYI

In a star with a mass similar to our sun's, outer layers become unstable and begin escaping into space when the core runs out of hydrogen fuel. The escaping gases form a shell around the star, producing a planetary nebula. The Ring nebula in the constellation Lyra is an example of this process.

Integrating the Sciences

Physics Assess students' understanding of how physics relates to the study of star evolution by asking the following questions. **Why does a star become unstable when its hydrogen fuel is used up?** *The outward force caused by fusion is reduced and no longer balances the inward force of gravity.* **If the temperature inside a star's contracting core heats up, why does the outer layer of the star turn reddish in color?** *The increased heat inside the star causes the outer layers of the star to expand. As the outer layers expand, the gases contained in them cool down, thus becoming reddish in color.* L2

CA Science Content Standards

Page 712: 2g, 4b
Page 713: 2g, 4b

3 Assess

Check for Understanding

Discussion

Interpersonal Refer students to **Figure 20-10. What is true about the absolute magnitude and temperature of supergiants?** *Supergiants have high absolute magnitudes but relatively low temperatures.* **Based on their name, what can you infer about the size of supergiants?** *Supergiants are large compared with other stars.*

Reteach

Refer students to **Figure 20-10** and ask the following question as a means of initiating a class discussion. **Why do the stars located in the upper-left portion of the diagram have such a high absolute magnitude?** *These stars are fairly large and have high temperatures.*

Extension

For students who have mastered this section, use the **Reinforcement** and **Enrichment** masters.

4 Close

Proficiency Prep

Use this quiz to check students' recall of section content.

1. **Stars begin as large clouds of gas and dust called what?** *nebulas*
2. **Once the outer layers of a star like our sun escape into space, what is left behind?** *white dwarf*

CA Science Content Standards

Page 714: 2g, 4a, 4b

Page 715: 2g, 4b, 4e, 6a, 9f

White Dwarfs

After the star's core uses up its supply of helium, it contracts even more. As the core of a star like the sun runs out of fuel, its outer layers escape into space. This leaves behind the hot, dense core. The core contracts under the force of gravity. At this stage in a star's evolution, it is a **white dwarf.** A white dwarf is about the size of Earth.

Supergiants and Supernovas

In stars that are over ten times more massive than our sun, the stages of evolution occur more quickly and more violently. The core heats up to much higher temperatures. Heavier and heavier elements form by fusion. The star expands into a **supergiant.** Eventually, iron forms in the core. Fusion can no longer occur once iron forms. The core collapses violently, sending a shock wave outward through the star. The outer portion of the star explodes, producing a supernova like the one shown in **Figure 20-14.** A supernova can be billions of times brighter than the original star.

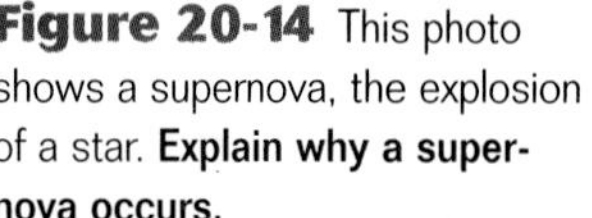

Figure 20-14 This photo shows a supernova, the explosion of a star. **Explain why a supernova occurs.**

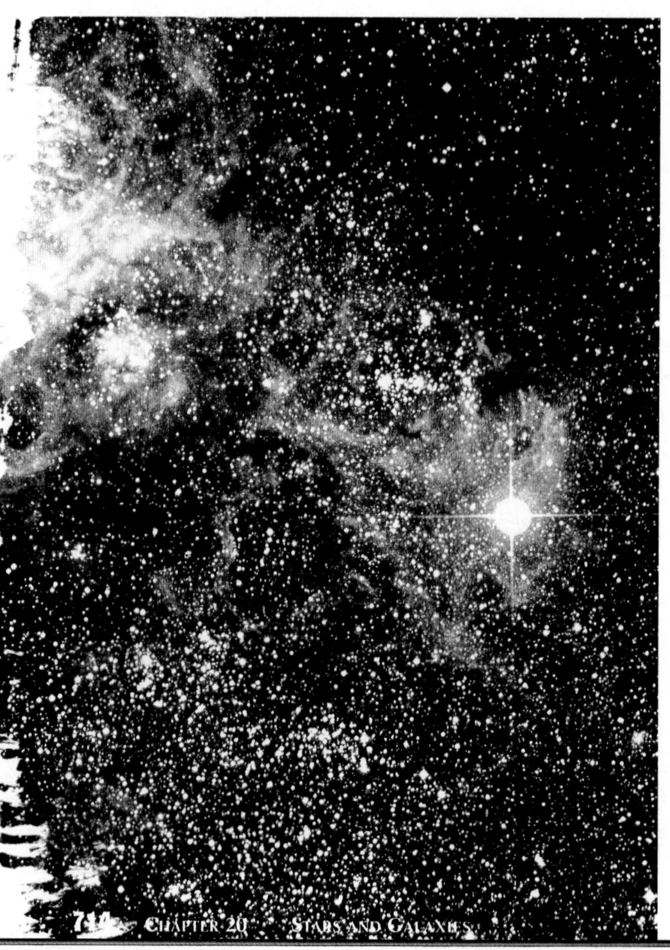

Neutron Stars

The collapsed core of a supernova shrinks to about 10 km to 15 km in diameter. Only neutrons can exist in the dense core, and the supernova becomes a **neutron star.**

If the remaining dense core is more than two times more massive than the sun, probably nothing can stop the core's collapse. It quickly evolves into a **black hole**—an object so dense that nothing can escape its gravity field.

Black Holes

If you could shine a flashlight on a black hole, the light wouldn't illuminate the black hole. The light would simply disappear into it. So, how do scientists locate black holes? Matter being pulled into a black hole can collide with other material, generating X rays. Astronomers have located X-ray sources around possible black holes. Extremely massive black holes probably exist in the centers of galaxies.

Star Evolution Have students construct concept maps in their Science Journals showing the evolution of a star. Then ask the following questions. **After a supernova, what type of object forms if the remaining dense core collapses?** *a black hole* **If black holes can't be seen, how do astronomers locate them?** *Astronomers hypothesize that as matter is drawn into a black hole, large amounts of X rays are given off. Astronomers have found several strong X-ray sources that appear to have high masses but which can't be seen.*

What are nebulas?

A star begins its life as a nebula, shown in **Figure 20-15.** But where does the matter in a nebula come from? Nebulas form partly from the matter that was once in other stars. A star ejects enormous amounts of matter during its lifetime. This matter can be incorporated into other nebulas, which can evolve into new stars. The matter in stars is recycled many times.

What about the matter created in the cores of stars? Are elements such as carbon and iron recycled also? Some of these elements do become parts of new stars. In fact, spectrographs have shown that our sun contains some carbon, iron, and other such elements. Because the sun is a main sequence star, it is too young to have created these elements itself. Our sun condensed from material that was created in stars that died many billions of years ago.

Some elements condense to form planets and other bodies rather than stars. In fact, your body contains many atoms that were fused in the cores of ancient stars. Evidence suggests that the first stars formed from hydrogen and helium and that all the other elements have formed in the cores of stars.

Figure 20-15 Stars are forming in the Crescent Nebula.

Section Assessment

1. Explain why giants are not in the main sequence on the H-R diagram. How do their temperatures and absolute magnitudes compare with those of main sequence stars?
2. What can be said about the absolute magnitudes of two equal-sized stars whose colors are blue and yellow?
3. Outline the history and probable future of our sun.
4. **Think Critically:** Why doesn't the helium currently in the sun's core undergo fusion?
5. **Skill Builder** **Sequencing** Sequence the following in order of most evolved to least evolved: *main sequence star, supergiant, neutron star,* and *nebula.* If you need help, refer to Sequencing in the **Skill Handbook** on page 950.

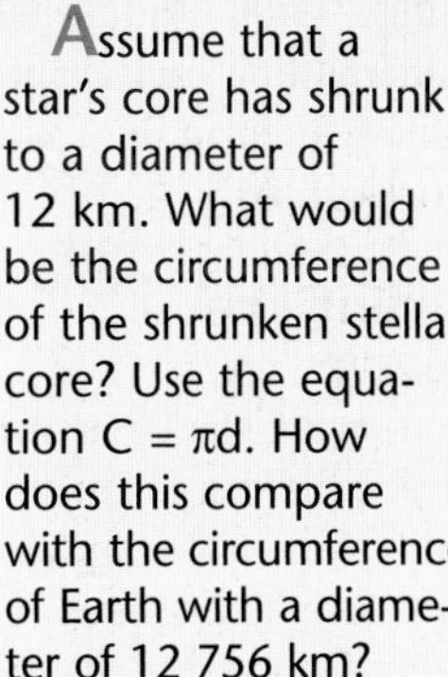

Using Math

Assume that a star's core has shrunk to a diameter of 12 km. What would be the circumference of the shrunken stellar core? Use the equation $C = \pi d$. How does this compare with the circumference of Earth with a diameter of 12 756 km?

5.  **Skill Builder**
neutron star, supergiant, main sequence star, nebula

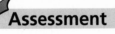

Assessment

Content Have students share their star sequences with another student. Use **Performance Assessment in the Science Classroom,** p. 97.

Section Assessment

1. Giants are large but relatively cool stars. Their temperatures compare with small main sequence stars, but their absolute magnitudes compare with the larger main sequence stars.
2. Because the blue star is hotter, its absolute magnitude would be brighter than that of the yellow star.
3.
   - I. Nebula
     - A. Cloud contracts
     - B. Heated to 10 000 000 K
     - C. Fusion in cloud center
   - II. Main sequence star
     - A. Energy of fusion balances gravity
     - B. Hydrogen fuel exhausted
   - III. Giant
     - A. Fuses helium
     - B. Outer layers escape
   - IV. White dwarf
     - A. Exhausts fuel supply
     - B. Core contracts
4. **Think Critically** The sun still has a supply of hydrogen for fusion. This keeps the core from collapsing and temperatures from rising. Currently, the sun's core is not hot enough to fuse significant amounts of helium.

Using Math

$C = \pi d$

$C = (3.14)(12 \text{ km}) = 37.7 \text{ km}$

$C = (3.14)(12\,756 \text{ km}) = 40\,054 \text{ km}$

The circumference of Earth is 1062 times larger than the shrunken stellar core.

Reading & Writing in Science

Content Background

As with many modern theories about the origin of the universe, early beliefs about the universe's origin attempt to show how the order we see today emerged from disorder. Many early beliefs state that Earth formed, at first, as a bare object void of water, plants, animals, and people. This is how the Australian Aborigines picture the beginning of Earth. Earth was first a featureless plain. The Aborigines believe that during Dreamtime supernatural beings emerged and created all the features now seen on Earth. Supernatural beings were linked to specific features on Earth. Recall that the same is true for constellations.

Science Journal

Encourage creativity in student poems. Emphasize that they are writing about what they think happened.

Reading & Writing in Science

Dreamtime Down Under

The Aborigines of Australia believe that the world began long ago—before anyone can remember—when Dreamtime began. At first, Earth was cold and dark, and the spirit Ancestors slept underground.

When the Ancestors awoke, they moved to Earth's surface and created the sun for warmth and light. Some Ancestors became people. Others became plants, animals, clouds, or stars. As the Ancestors moved over Earth, they sang, and their singing created hills, rivers, and other features.

Leaving a Path

The movement of the Ancestors left Dreaming Tracks that the Aborigines still treasure. When the Ancestors tired, they returned underground. The bodies of some Ancestors remain on Earth's surface as rock outcroppings, trees, islands, and other natural features, such as the formation in the inset, below right.

Ancient Aborigines drew maps to show where the Ancestors came out, walked, and returned underground. Drawings with traditional dot patterns (see bark painting, far right) form the basis of Aboriginal art.

Dreaming the Big Bang

Some compare the Dreamtime forces that shaped Earth to the big bang theory—huge fields of energy interacting and forming planets. Later, more energy—more Dreaming—created today's continents, including Australia.

Today, Aborigines are struggling to maintain ancient traditions while living in modern Australia. They believe that the Ancestors still live in the land and that Dreamtime continues with no foreseeable end.

Science JOURNAL

In your Science Journal, write a poem that expresses your own view of our relationship to nature and to the land.

Teaching Strategies

Reading Encourage students to read about modern theories of the origin of the universe, such as the big bang theory. Obtain copies of the February 1998 issue of *Astronomy* magazine. It contains several articles about the origin of the universe. L2

Writing Have students write a description of the sand drawing shown on the student page. L2

For Additional Information

- Holder, Robyn. *Aborigines of Australia.* Vero Beach, FL: Rourke, 1987.
- Lawlor, Robert. *Voices of the First Day: Awakening in the Aboriginal Dreamtime.* Rochester, VT: Inner Traditions, 1991.
- Nile, Richard. *Australian Aborigines.* Austin, TX: Steck-Vaughn, 1993.

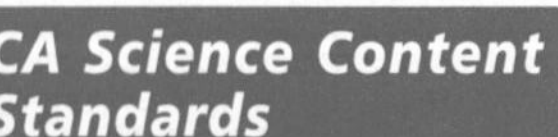

CA Science Content Standards

Page 716: 4e

Page 717: 4a, 4b, 4c

Galaxies and the Universe

Galaxies

One reason to study astronomy is to learn about your place in the universe. Long ago, people thought they were at the center of the universe and everything revolved around Earth. Today, you know this isn't the case. But, do you know where you are in the universe?

You are on Earth, and Earth orbits the sun. But does the sun orbit anything? How does it interact with other objects in the universe? The sun is one star among many in a galaxy. A **galaxy** is a large group of stars, gas, and dust held together by gravity. Our galaxy, called the Milky Way, is shown in **Figure 20-16.** It contains about 200 billion stars, including the sun. Galaxies are separated by huge distances—often millions of light-years.

Just as stars are grouped together within galaxies, galaxies are grouped into clusters. The cluster the Milky Way belongs to is called the Local Group. It contains about 30 galaxies of various types and sizes.

What You'll Learn

- The three main types of galaxies
- Several characteristics of the Milky Way Galaxy
- How the big bang theory explains the observed Doppler shifts of galaxies

Vocabulary
galaxy
big bang theory

Why It's Important

- You'll explore theories about how the universe may have formed.

Figure 20-16 The Milky Way Galaxy is usually classified as a normal spiral galaxy. Its spiral arms, composed of stars and gas, radiate out from an area of densely packed stars called the nucleus.

Resource Manager

The following **Teacher Classroom Resources** can be used with Section 20-4:

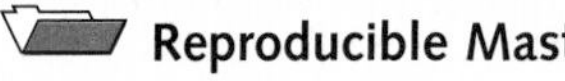
Reproducible Masters

Activity Worksheets, pp. 113–114, 116 L2

Enrichment, p. 59 L3

Reinforcement, p. 59 L2

Study Guide, pp. 78–80 L1 ELL

SECTION 20•4

Prepare

Refer to **Black Holes** and **New Galaxies** on p. 698F.

Preplanning

Refer to the **Chapter Organizer** on pp. 698A–B.

1 Motivate

Bellringer

Before presenting the lesson, display **Section Focus Transparency 59** on the overhead projector. Use the accompanying **Focus Activity** worksheet. L2 ELL

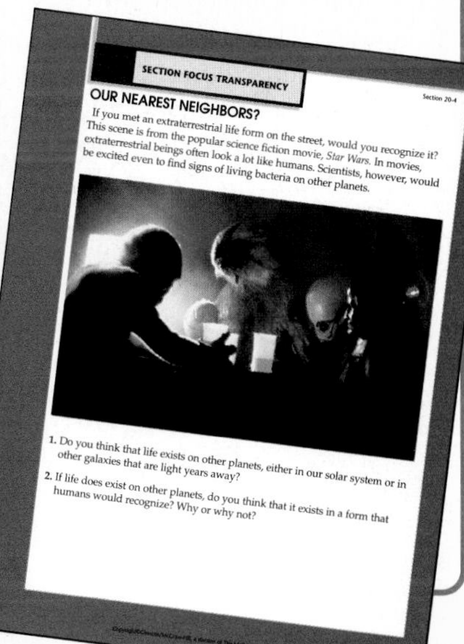

SECTION FOCUS TRANSPARENCY

Section 20-4

OUR NEAREST NEIGHBORS?

If you met an extraterrestrial life form on the street, would you recognize it? This scene is from the popular science fiction movie, *Star Wars.* In movies, extraterrestrial beings often look a lot like humans. Scientists, however, would be excited even to find signs of living bacteria on other planets.

1. Do you think that life exists on other planets, either in our solar system or in other galaxies that are light years away?
2. If life does exist on other planets, do you think that it exists in a form that humans would recognize? Why or why not?

Tying to Previous Knowledge

Ask students if they have ever observed the night sky far from city lights. If so, they may have seen the band of stars that stretches across the sky—the Milky Way, our home galaxy.

2 Teach

Activity

Interpersonal Have pairs of students make flash cards of the types of galaxies. Have them draw the galaxy type on one side and write its name on the reverse. Partners can then test each other using the flash cards. Next, have the partners draw ten to 20 images of the Milky Way Galaxy on separate cards. Have them place the sun at slightly different positions around the galaxy on each card. When finished, partners can demonstrate the movement of the sun around the galaxy by flipping the cards. L2 ELL COOP LEARN

VISUAL Learning

Figures 20-17, 20-18, and 20-20 Ask students to compare and contrast the three major classifications of galaxies. *Students should mention differences in size and shape, as well as similarities in formation and composition.*

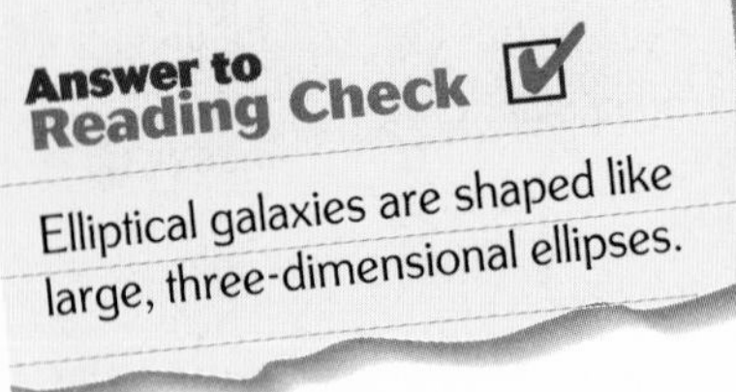

Caption Answers

Figure 20-17 *the Local Group*
Figure 20-18 *spiral and irregular*

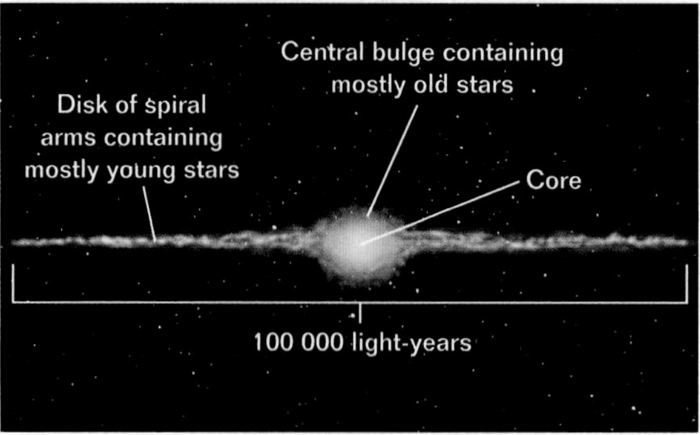

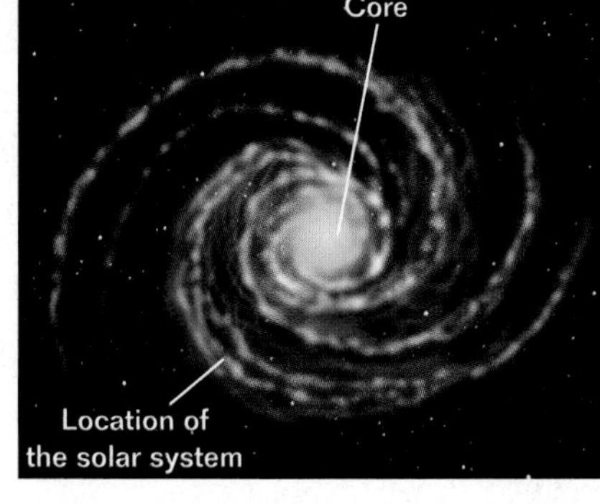

Figure 20-17 These illustrations show a side view and an overhead view of the Milky Way. **The Milky Way is part of what group of galaxies?**

Spiral Galaxies

The three major types of galaxies are elliptical, spiral, and irregular. Spiral galaxies have spiral arms that wind outward from inner regions. The Milky Way is a spiral galaxy, as shown in **Figure 20-17.** Its spiral arms are made up of bright stars and dust. The fuzzy patch you can see in the constellation of Andromeda is actually a spiral galaxy. It's so far away that you can't see its individual stars. Instead, it appears as a hazy spot in our sky. The Andromeda Galaxy is a member of the Local Group. It is about 2.2 million light-years away.

Arms in a normal spiral start close to the center of the galaxy. Barred spirals have spiral arms extending from a large bar of stars and gas that passes through the center of the galaxy.

Elliptical Galaxies

Probably the most common type of galaxy is the elliptical galaxy, shown in **Figure 20-18.** These galaxies are shaped like large, three-dimensional ellipses. Many are football-shaped, but others are round. Some elliptical galaxies are small, while some are so large that the entire Local Group of galaxies would fit inside one of them. **Figure 20-19** shows the Local Group and its relation to the solar system, the Milky Way, and large galaxy clusters.

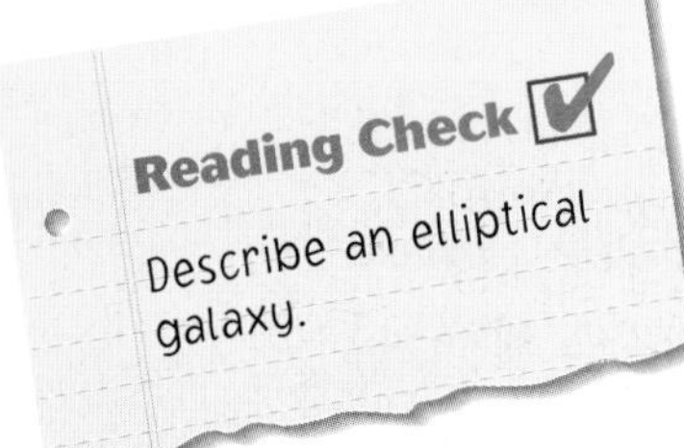

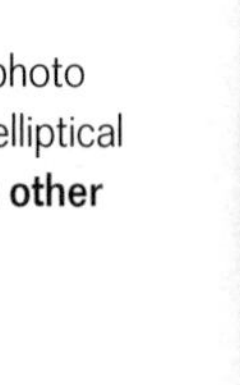

Figure 20-18 This photo shows an example of an elliptical galaxy. **What are the two other types of galaxies?**

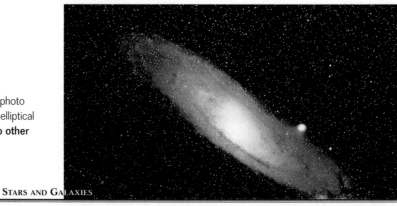

Content Background

Brown dwarfs are stars that never generated fusion in their cores. They did not reach the mass necessary to initiate fusion of hydrogen into helium. The mass needed for this to occur is about 8 percent of the sun's mass. Brown dwarfs are very dim. They are found by observing the movement of a more easily seen star. The path through space by a single star would be a nearly straight line. However, the path of a star with a brown dwarf in orbit around it would show a distinct wobble. This wobble is used to locate brown dwarfs in much the same way it has been used to locate exoplanets.

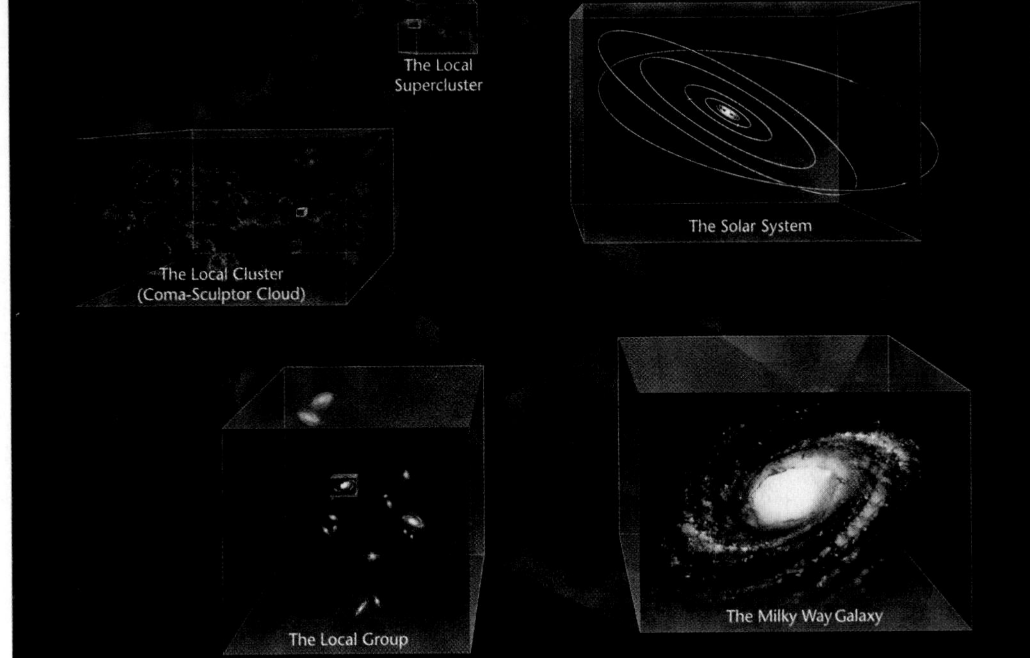

Figure 20-19 There may be more than 100 billion galaxies in the universe, and nearly all of them seem to be organized into clusters.

Irregular Galaxies

The third type of galaxy, irregular, includes most of those galaxies that don't fit into the other classifications. Irregular galaxies have many different shapes and are smaller and less common than the other types. Two irregular galaxies called the Clouds of Magellan orbit the Milky Way. The Large Magellanic Cloud is shown in **Figure 20-20.**

Figure 20-20 The Large Magellanic Cloud is an irregular galaxy. It's a member of the Local Group, and it orbits our own galaxy.

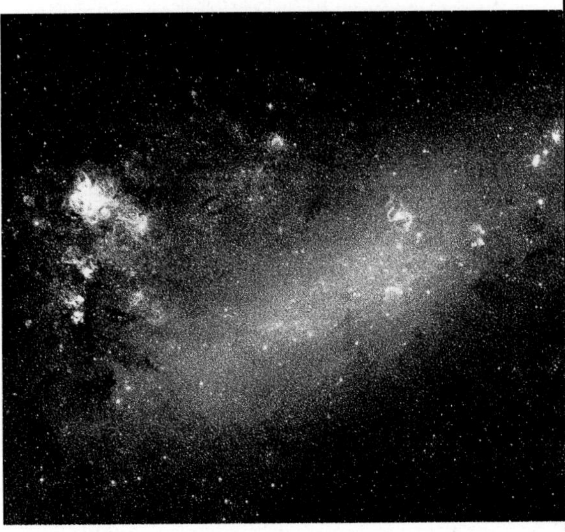

The Milky Way Galaxy

The Milky Way contains more than 200 billion stars. The visible disk of stars is about 100 000 light-years across, and the sun is located about 30 000 light-years out from its center. In our galaxy, all stars orbit around a central region. Based on a distance of 30 000 light-years and a speed of 235 km/s, the sun orbits around the center of the Milky Way once every 240 million years.

The Milky Way is usually classified as a normal spiral galaxy. However, recent evidence suggests that it might be a barred spiral. It is difficult to know for sure because we can never see our galaxy from the outside.

You can't see the normal spiral or barred shape of the Milky Way because you are

Discussion

What are the Clouds of Magellan? *irregular galaxies orbiting the Milky Way* **How far away is the Andromeda Galaxy?** *2.2 million light-years* **Recent evidence indicates that the Milky Way may be what type of galaxy?** *a barred spiral*

 **Videodisc**

STV: Solar System

Unit 1 *The Big Picture, Studying the Sun* 1:17

06338-08660

Refer to the Teacher Guide for additional bar codes and teaching strategies.

The Ring Galaxy Have students research the Cartwheel Galaxy in "A Galaxy of News," by David Bruning in *Astronomy,* June 1995, pp. 40–41. Ask them to write about the results of their research in their Science Journals. L2

CA Science Content Standards

Page 718: 4a, 4b, 4c
Page 719: 1c, 4a, 4c

Purpose

Visual-Spatial Students will develop a scale showing the vastness of space.

Materials

large sheet of paper, metric ruler or meterstick, compass

Teaching Strategies

Troubleshooting Help students conceptualize the vast scale of their model. If our sun were represented by a dot, the circle representing the distance to Proxima Centauri would be nearly within that same dot.

Analysis

1. Answers will vary.
2. Whatever the scale used, the distance to the Andromeda Galaxy would be about 22 times the diameter of the student's Milky Way model. This can be determined by dividing the distance to the Andromeda Galaxy (2.2million light-years) by the diameter of the Milky Way (100 000 light-years).

Assessment

Content Have students determine the scale distance to the Large Magellanic Cloud. Its true distance is about 169 000 light-years. Use the **Performance Assessment in the Science Classroom,** p. 29.

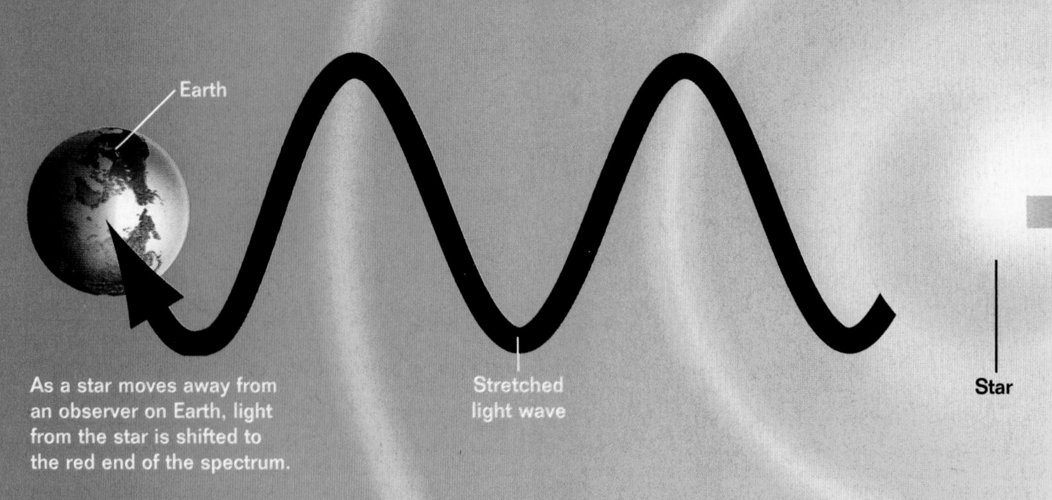

Earth
As a star moves away from an observer on Earth, light from the star is shifted to the red end of the spectrum.
Stretched light wave
Star

Figure 20-21 The Doppler shift causes the wavelengths of light coming from starts and galaxies to be compressed or stretched.

located within one of its spiral arms. You can see the Milky Way stretching across the sky as a faint band of light. All of the stars you can see in the night sky belong to the Milky Way Galaxy.

Measuring Distance in Space

Procedure

1. On a large sheet of paper, draw an overhead view of the Milky Way Galaxy. If necessary, refer to **Figure 20–17.** Choose a scale to show distance in light-years.
2. Mark the approximate location of our solar system, about two-thirds of the way out on one of the spiral arms.
3. Draw a circle around the sun indicating the 4.2 light-year distance of the next closest star to the sun, Proxima Centauri.

Analysis

1. What scale did you use to represent distance on your model?
2. At this scale, interpret how far away the next closest spiral galaxy—the Andromeda Galaxy—would be located.

Expansion of the Universe

What does it sound like when a car is blowing its horn while it drives past you? The horn has a high pitch as the car approaches you, then the horn seems to drop in pitch as the car drives away. This effect is called the Doppler shift. The Doppler shift occurs with light as well as with sound. **Figure 20-21** shows how the Doppler shift causes changes in the light coming from distant stars and galaxies. If a star is moving toward us, its wavelengths of light are pushed together. If a star is moving away from us, its wavelengths of light are stretched.

The Doppler Shift

Look at the spectrum of a star in **Figure 20-22A.** Note the position of the dark lines. How do they compare with the lines in **Figures 20-22B** and **C?** They have shifted in position. What caused this shift? As you just learned, when a star is moving toward Earth, its wavelengths of light are

720 CHAPTER 20 STARS AND GALAXIES

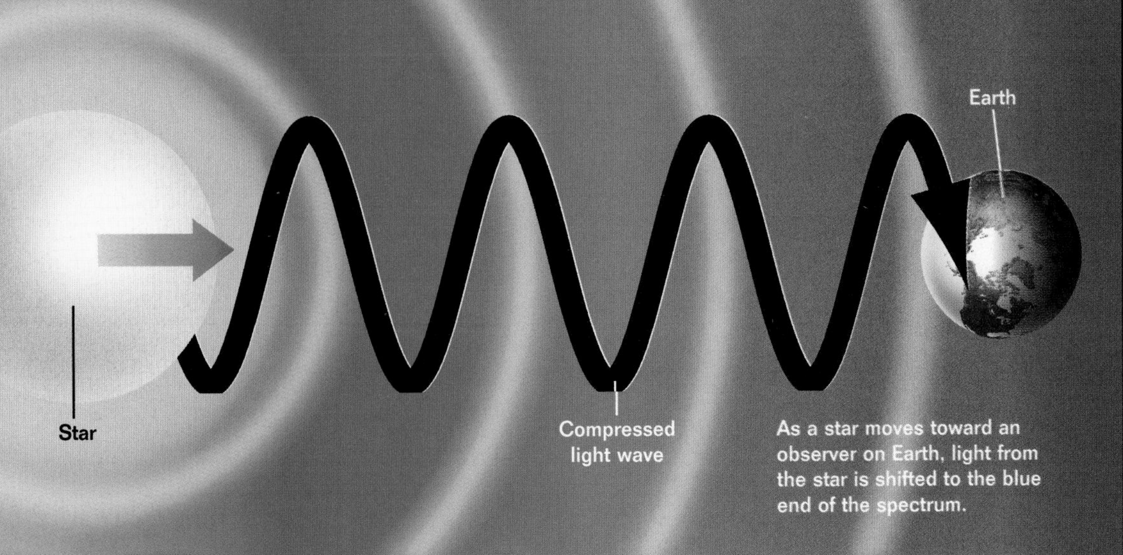
Earth
Star
Compressed light wave
As a star moves toward an observer on Earth, light from the star is shifted to the blue end of the spectrum.

pushed together, just as the sound waves from the car's horn are. This causes the dark lines in the spectrum to shift toward the blue-violet end of the spectrum. A red shift in the spectrum occurs when a star is moving away from Earth. In a red shift, the dark lines shift toward the red end of the spectrum.

In the early twentieth century, scientists noticed an interesting fact about the light coming from most galaxies. When a spectrograph is used to study light from galaxies beyond the Local Group, there is a red shift in the light. What does this red shift tell you about the universe?

Because all galaxies beyond the Local Group show a red shift in their spectra, they must be moving away from Earth. If all galaxies outside the Local Group are moving away from Earth, this indicates that the entire universe must be expanding. Think of the Explore Activity at the beginning of the chapter. The dots on the balloon moved apart as the model universe expanded. Regardless of which dot you picked, all the other dots moved away from it. Galaxies beyond the Local Group move away from us just as the dots moved apart on the balloon.

interNET CONNECTION

Visit the Glencoe Science Web Site at **www.glencoe.com/sec/science/ca** for more information about the Doppler shift.

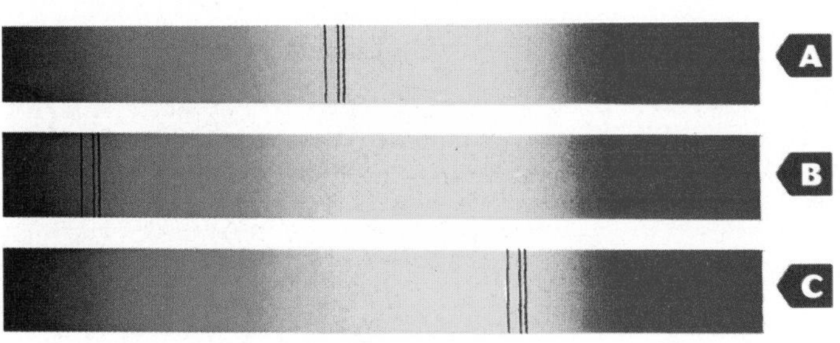
A
B
C

Figure 20-22 The dark lines in the spectra (A) are shifted toward the blue-violet end when a star is moving toward Earth (B). A red shift (C) indicates that a star is moving away from Earth.

interNET CONNECTION

Internet Addresses

For Internet tips, see Glencoe's **Using the Internet in the Science Classroom.**

Quick Demo

Auditory-Musical Ask students if they have ever experienced the Doppler shift of sound waves. Remind them of train whistles from approaching and receding trains and the siren of a fire truck as it drives by. Securely tie a cord to an alarm clock and gently twirl the clock around as the alarm is sounding. Students will hear the changing pitch as the clock approaches them and then recedes.

GLENCOE TECHNOLOGY

Videodisc

The Infinite Voyage: Unseen Worlds

Chapter 5 *Evolution of the Universe Is Traced* 3:30

Refer to the Teacher Guide for bar codes and teaching strategies.

Science Journal

The Great Wall Have students research and write about the work of Margaret Geller and John Huchra, of the Harvard-Smithsonian Center for Astrophysics, on mapping the universe. The work of these astronomers has led to the realization that great voids and large concentrations of galaxies alternate throughout the universe. For more information, refer students to "A Cross Section of the Universe" by Jeff Kanipe, *Astronomy*, November 1989, p. 44; "Beyond the Big Bang" by Jeff Kanipe, *Astronomy*, April 1992, pp. 30–37; "COBE's Big Bang" by R. Talcott, *Astronomy*, August 1992, pp. 42–44; and recent astronomy textbooks.

CA Science Content Standards

Page 720: 1a, 4a, 4c, 9f
Page 721: 1a, 4a

VISUAL Learning

Figure 20-23 Have students describe the big bang theory in their own words.

3 Assess

Check for Understanding

Discussion

Why are some galaxies classified as irregular in shape? *Irregular galaxies don't have regular shapes.* **Why can't you see the spiral shape of the Milky Way Galaxy?** *In order to see the spiral shape of the Milky Way, you would have to be located above or below the plane of the galaxy. Earth, in orbit around the sun, is located in one of the spiral arms.*

Reteach

Visual-Spatial Show students one loaf of raisin bread before baking. Have students measure the distance between the raisins in the unbaked bread. Send the loaf to the home economics or domestic arts department to be baked. When the loaf is returned, have students measure the distance between the raisins again. Have students explain why the raisins are farther apart after baking. Have them relate this to the expansion of the universe. L1

Extension

 For students who have mastered this section, use the **Reinforcement** and **Enrichment** masters.

GLENCOE TECHNOLOGY

Videodisc

The Infinite Voyage: Unseen Worlds

Chapter 4 *Astronomers Use Radio Waves to Examine Galaxies* 7:00

Refer to the Teacher Guide for bar codes and teaching strategies.

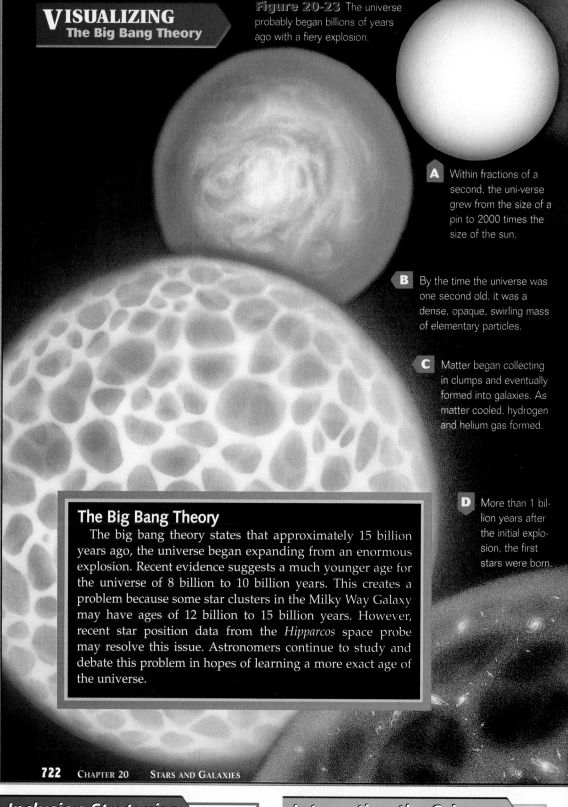

VISUALIZING The Big Bang Theory

Figure 20-23 The universe probably began billions of years ago with a fiery explosion.

A Within fractions of a second, the uni-verse grew from the size of a pin to 2000 times the size of the sun.

B By the time the universe was one second old, it was a dense, opaque, swirling mass of elementary particles.

C Matter began collecting in clumps and eventually formed into galaxies. As matter cooled, hydrogen and helium gas formed.

D More than 1 billion years after the initial explosion, the first stars were born.

The Big Bang Theory

The big bang theory states that approximately 15 billion years ago, the universe began expanding from an enormous explosion. Recent evidence suggests a much younger age for the universe of 8 billion to 10 billion years. This creates a problem because some star clusters in the Milky Way Galaxy may have ages of 12 billion to 15 billion years. However, recent star position data from the *Hipparcos* space probe may resolve this issue. Astronomers continue to study and debate this problem in hopes of learning a more exact age of the universe.

Inclusion Strategies

Behaviorally Disabled Match behaviorally disabled students with other students. Ask each student group to come up with original ideas on how to develop a model that would demonstrate the big bang theory. L2 

Integrating the Sciences

Physics To help students understand how physics is integrated with the study of astronomy, ask the following question. **What will determine whether the universe keeps on expanding or begins to contract?** *If enough mass exists in the universe, it may eventually slow and begin to collapse.*

The Big Bang Theory

When scientists determined that the universe was expanding, they realized that galaxy clusters must have been closer together in the past. The leading theory about the formation of the universe, called the big bang theory, is based on this explanation. **Figure 20-23** illustrates the **big bang theory,** which states that approximately 15 billion years ago, the universe began with an enormous explosion.

The time-lapse photograph shown in **Figure 20-24** was taken in December 1995 by the *Hubble Space Telescope*. It shows more than 1500 galaxies at a distance of more than 10 billion light-years. These galaxies may date back to when the universe was no more than 1 billion years old. The galaxies are in various stages of development. One astronomer indicates that we may be looking back to a time when our own galaxy was forming. Studies of this nature will eventually enable astronomers to determine the approximate age of the universe.

Whether the universe expands forever or stops depends on how much matter is in the universe. All matter exerts a gravitational force. If there's enough matter, gravity will halt the expansion, and the universe will contract until everything comes to one point.

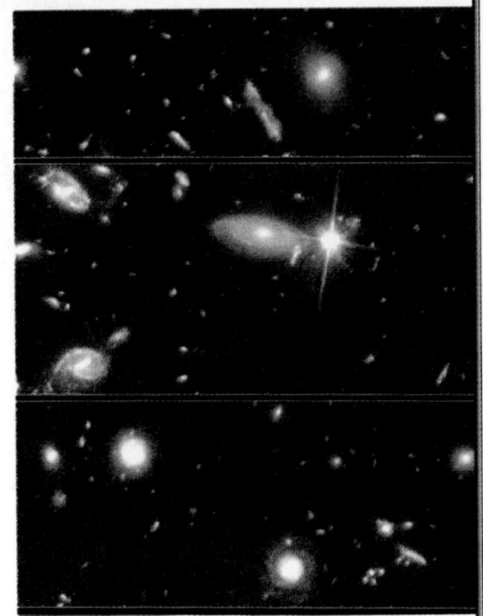

Figure 20-24 The light from these galaxies in this photo mosaic took billions of years to reach Earth.

Section Assessment

1. List the three major classifications of galaxies. What do they have in common?
2. What is the name of the galaxy that you live in? What motion do the stars in this galaxy exhibit?
3. **Think Critically:** All galaxies outside the Local Group show a red shift in their spectra. Within the Local Group, some galaxies show a red shift and some show a blue shift. What does this tell you about the galaxies in the Local Group and outside the Local Group?
4. **Skill Builder**
Predicting Astronomical distances are measured in light-years, the distance light travels in one year. It takes light from the star Betelgeuse 310 light-years to reach Earth. Do the **Chapter 20 Skill Activity** on page 981 to predict what was happening on Earth when light from distant stars began traveling toward our solar system.

Research and write a report in your Science Journal about the most recent evidence supporting or disputing the big bang theory. Describe how the big bang theory explains observations of galaxies made with spectrometers.

4 Close

Proficiency Prep

Use this quiz to check students' recall of section content.

1. **What do we call a large group of stars, gas, and dust held together by gravity?** *galaxy*
2. **What are the three main types of galaxies?** *elliptical, spiral, and irregular*
3. **Which type of galaxy is most common?** *elliptical*

Section Assessment

1. Galaxy classifications are elliptical, spiral (regular and barred), and irregular. All galaxies are large groups of stars, gas, and dust held together by gravity; they are grouped in clusters.
2. the Milky Way Galaxy; stars orbit its nucleus
3. Think Critically All galaxies within the Local Group travel through space together; however, some of them are moving toward the Milky Way, whereas others are moving away from the Milky Way. Galaxies outside the Local Group are moving away from us.

Students should include the latest information obtained by the *Hubble Space Telescope*. The red shift observed by spectrometers indicates that galaxies are moving away from us, which supports the big bang theory.

Assessment

Performance Assess students' abilities to predict by having them choose several stars from the Skill Activity and determine the exact years that light leaving the stars will reach Earth. Use **Performance Assessment in the Science Classroom,** p. 29.

CA Science Content Standards

Page 722: 4a, 4b

Page 723: 1a, 4a, 4b, 4c, 9f

Activity 20·2 Design Your Own Experiment

Recognize the Problem

Purpose

Logical-Mathematical Students will conduct an experiment that shows how distance from an object affects the object's parallax shift. L2 ELL COOP LEARN P

Process Skills

communicating, comparing and contrasting, forming operational definitions, recognizing cause and effect, separating and controlling variables, measuring in SI, using numbers, formulating models, observing and inferring, and hypothesizing

Time

one class period

Safety Precautions

Caution students to wear goggles to protect their eyes during the experiment.

Form a Hypothesis

Possible Hypotheses

Students may hypothesize that the amount of observed parallax increases as an object is moved closer.

Test Your Hypothesis

Possible Procedures

Choose three different positions on the meterstick such as 20 cm, 40 cm, and 60 cm. Mark these positions with masking tape. Attach a metric ruler to one end of the meterstick to form a T shape. Place the meterstick assembly on a table. Hold a pencil upright at one of the marked positions. Observe the pencil's apparent movement against the meterstick with first one eye closed and then the other. Repeat the process for the other marked positions.

Design Your Own Experiment

Activity 20·2

Possible Materials

- Meterstick
- Metric ruler
- Masking tape
- Pencil

Measuring Parallax

Parallax is the apparent shift in the position of an object when viewed from two locations. The nearer an object is to the observer, the greater its parallax. Do this activity to design a model and use it in an experiment that will show how distance affects the amount of observed parallax.

Recognize the Problem

How can you build a model to show the relationship between distance and parallax?

Form a Hypothesis

State a hypothesis about how a model must be built in order for it to be used in an experiment to show how distance affects the amount of observed parallax.

Goals

- **Design a model** to show how the distance from an observer to an object affects the object's parallax shift.
- **Design an experiment** that shows how distance affects the amount of observed parallax.

Safety Precautions

CAUTION: *Be sure to wear goggles to protect your eyes.*

724 CHAPTER 20 STARS AND GALAXIES

Teaching Strategies

Pair students and assign one member of each group as a recorder. The other partner should carry out the experiment. Students should then switch roles.

Troubleshooting For stability, attach the metric ruler to the end of the meterstick with tape.

Tying to Previous Knowledge

Ask students if they have ever noticed that the speedometer reading in a car appears different to a front-seat passenger than to the driver. Explain that the passenger is viewing the speedometer from an angle. Relate this to parallax.

Test Your Hypothesis

Plan

1. As a group, agree upon and write out your hypothesis statement.
2. List the steps that you need to take to build your model. Be specific, describing exactly what you will do at each step.
3. Devise a method to test how distance from an observer to an object, such as a pencil, affects the relative position of the object.
4. List the steps you will take to test your hypothesis. Be specific, describing exactly what you will do at each step.
5. Read over your plan for the model to be used in this experiment.
6. How will you determine changes in observed parallax? Remember, these changes should occur when the distance from the observer to the object is changed.
7. You should measure shifts in parallax from several different positions. How will these positions differ?
8. How will you measure distances accurately and compare relative position shift?

Do

1. Make sure your teacher approves your plan before you proceed.
2. Construct the model your team has planned.
3. Carry out the experiment as planned.
4. While conducting the experiment, write down any observations that you or other members of your group make in your Science Journal.

Analyze Your Data

1. **Compare** what happened to the object when it was viewed with one eye closed, then the other.
2. At what distance from the observer did the object appear to shift the most?

Draw Conclusions

1. **Infer** what happened to the apparent shift of the object's location as the distance from the observer was increased or decreased.
2. How might astronomers use parallax to study stars?

Expected Outcome

Answers for apparent motion of the pencil will vary. However, if students position themselves so that the meterstick is lined up with their noses, and distances of 20 cm, 40 cm, and 60 cm are used, the following results can be expected. Observed parallax is about 20 cm at the 20-cm mark, 8.5 cm at the 40-cm mark, and 4.9 cm at the 60-cm mark.

Error Analysis

Ask students how the pencil's apparent motion changed as it was placed at progressively farther distances. The pencil should appear to move less as it is placed farther away.

Analyze Your Data

1. The position of the pencil seemed to shift. In reality, nothing happened to the pencil—the movement was only apparent.
2. Answers will vary depending on distances used. The closest distance used by the group is the correct answer.

Draw Conclusions

1. As distance from the observer increased, the pencil's apparent shift decreased. As the distance from the observer decreased, the pencil's apparent shift increased.
2. Astronomers use parallax angles or shifts in the apparent position of astronomical objects to determine distances to the objects.

GO Further

Have students graph the results of the pencil's observed shifts in movement. They should use different-colored pencils to illustrate the three different distances.

Assessment

Process Have students use their thumbs at various distances from their faces to formulate a simple model that demonstrates apparent shifts of parallax for various objects in the classroom. Use **Performance Assessment in the Science Classroom**, p. 51.

CA Science Content Standards

Page 724: 1a, 9a
Page 725: 1a, 9a

FIELD GUIDE

Using the Field Guide

- Use this field guide with student pages 726–729.
- A field guide contains a key that enables the user to classify or identify an item or concept.
- Encourage students to use this field guide outside.
- In using a field guide, students will apply steps of a scientific method as they observe, investigate, and draw conclusions.
- This field guide applies nationally; local and regional field guides are usually available for more specific local use.

FIELD *ACTIVITY*

Student drawings will vary depending on the constellations chosen. Star patterns should match actual constellations. Drawings should illustrate the objects, animals, or characters that the constellations represent.

Tying to Previous Knowledge

Ask students whether they have ever seen shapes of familiar animals or objects in clouds. Tell them that locating constellations is similar to finding familiar objects represented in star patterns in the night sky.

FIELD GUIDE to Backyard Astronomy

FIELD *ACTIVITY*

Study the star maps included in this field guide. Each night for a week, about one hour after sundown, observe the stars and identify at least three constellations. Draw and label the constellations in your Science Journal. Then, using the key of constellations visible in the northern hemisphere, make drawings of the objects, animals, or characters your constellations represent.

To help them study the night sky, early astronomers developed ways to organize stars into recognizable patterns. We call these patterns constellations. Think of constellations as drawings in the sky. They represent objects, animals, or characters in stories—things that were familiar to ancient stargazers. Using this field guide, you can observe the stars year-round.

Early astronomers saw the shape of a lion in the constellation Leo.

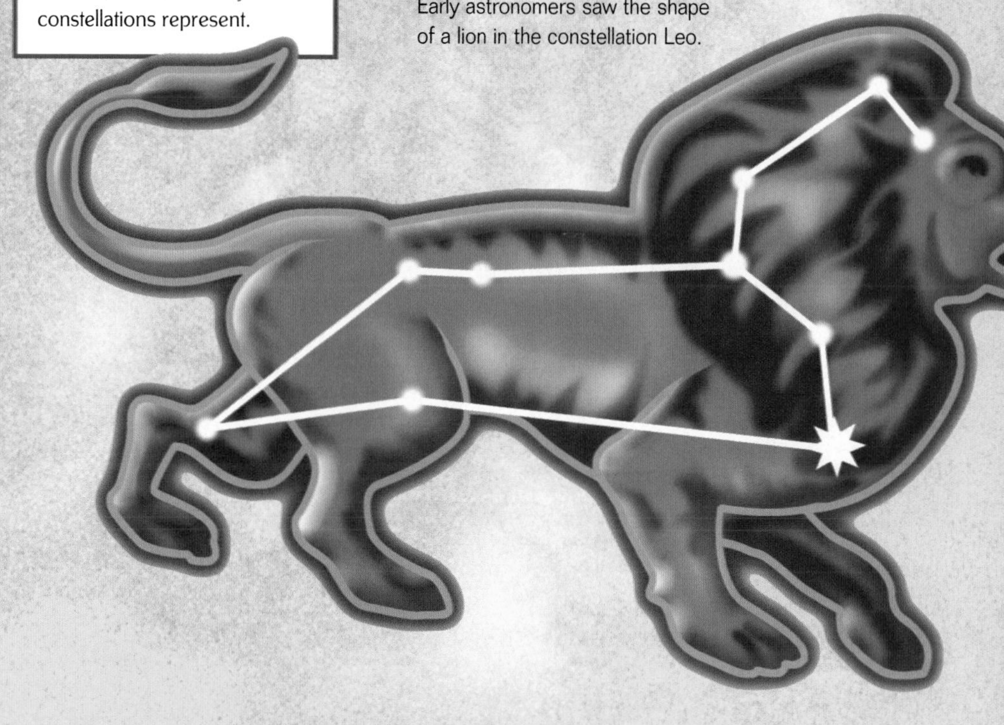

Other Field Guides to Astronomy

- Lancaster-Brown, Peter. *Skywatch.* New York: Sterling Publishing Company, Inc., 1993.
- Pasachoff, Jay M. *Peterson First Guide to Astronomy.* Boston: Houghton Mifflin Company, 1988.

Major Constellations Visible in the Northern Hemisphere

Name	Represents	Name	Represents
Andromeda	Princess	Lyra	Harp
Aquila	Eagle	Orion	Hunter
Bootes	Herdsman	Pegasus	Winged Horse
Canis Major	Big Dog	Sagittarius	Archer
Canis Minor	Little Dog	Scorpius	Scorpion
Cygnus	Swan (Northern Cross)	Taurus	Bull
Gemini	Twins	Ursa Major	Great Bear (Big Dipper)
Hercules	Hercules	Ursa Minor	Little Bear (Little Dipper)
Leo	Lion	Virgo	Virgin (Maiden)

This map shows the constellations that appear to circle the North Star, also known as Polaris. Because these constellations appear to circle Polaris, which is located almost directly over the north pole, they are called circumpolar constellations. Look toward the north to locate these constellations. To orient yourself, first locate Polaris, which is found by looking directly north, then up at an angle of roughly 35° to 45°.

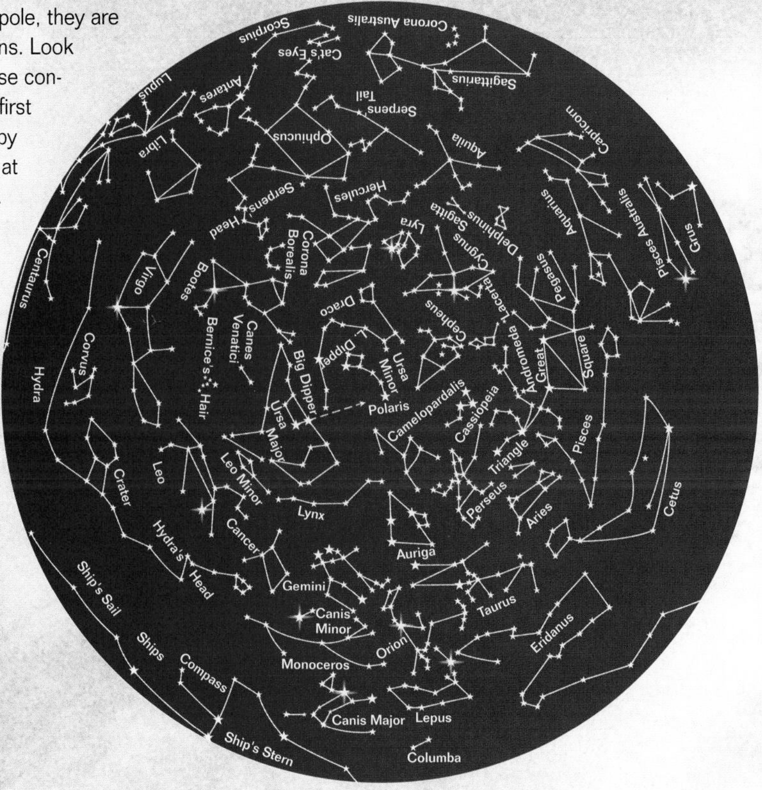

Teacher FYI

Seasonal constellations appear to rise and set each night. Different groups are visible during different seasons. Circumpolar constellations are visible year round. However, only the northern circumpolar constellations can be seen from the northern hemisphere.

Quick Demo

Obtain a globe and point out your area's exact latitude. Tell students that this figure can be used to find Polaris. For instance, if you live at a latitude of 40°N, then Polaris will be positioned 40° above your northern horizon. Polaris, in turn, can be used to locate northern circumpolar constellations.

interNET CONNECTION

Internet Addresses

____

____

____

____

For Internet tips, see Glencoe's **Using the Internet in the Science Classroom.**

CA Science Content Standards

Page 726: 1a, 4b
Page 727: 1a, 4b

FIELD GUIDE

Content Background

The celestial sphere is the imaginary dome on which the stars appear in the night sky. Each person's zenith is the imaginary point on the celestial sphere located directly above his or her head. An imaginary line drawn from the northern horizon up through the zenith then down to the southern horizon traces the celestial meridian. The celestial meridian is used to locate the constellations of each season.

VISUAL Learning

Have students locate Ursa Major in each of the four seasonal charts. Have them describe the apparent path of the constellation throughout the year. Stress that the apparent change in position is due to Earth's movement in space.

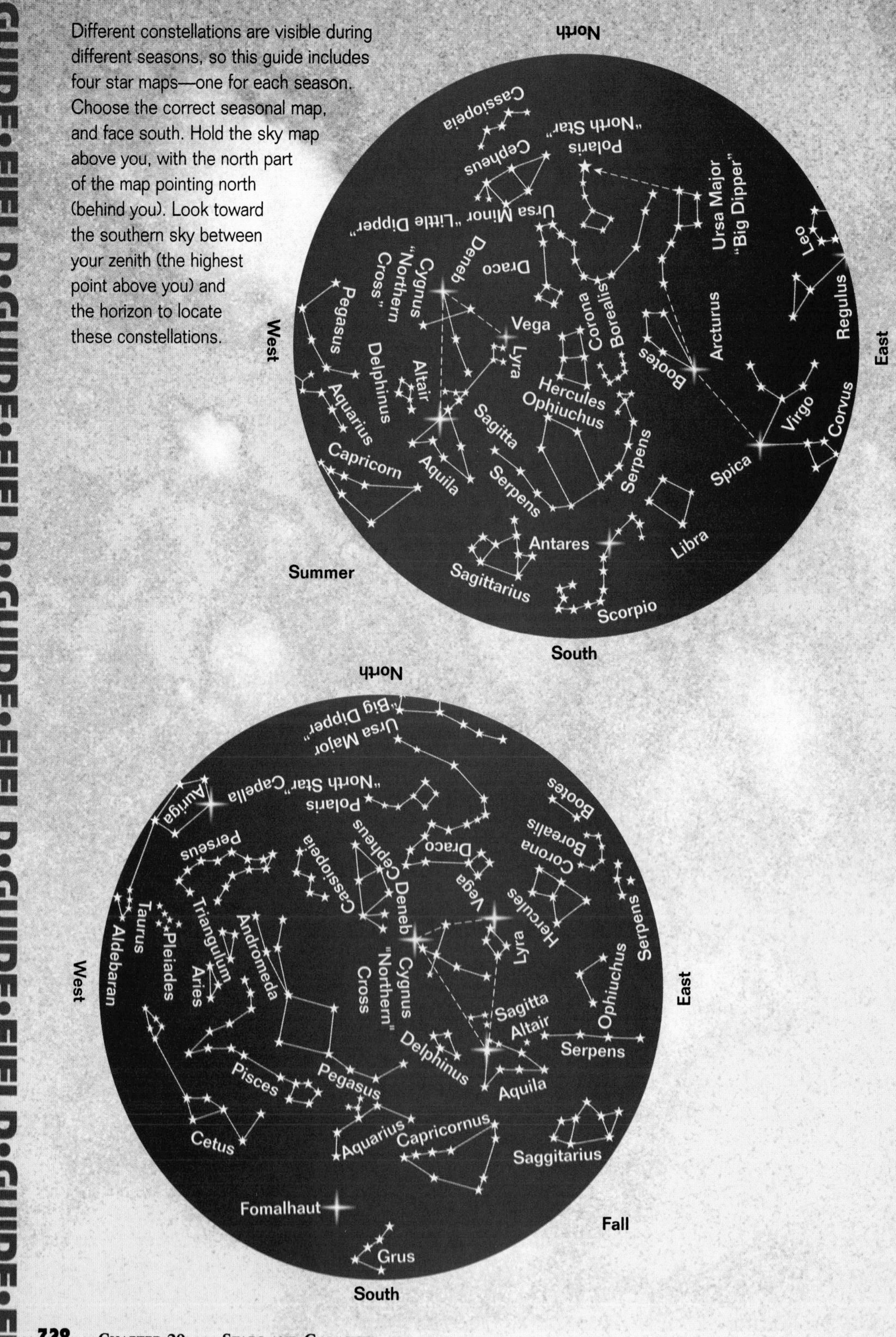

Inclusion Strategies

Learning Disabled Draw the stars of various constellations on the chalkboard. Use lines to connect the stars within each constellation. Have students draw pictures of the objects each constellation represents. They should draw their pictures on the chalkboard, around the connecting lines.

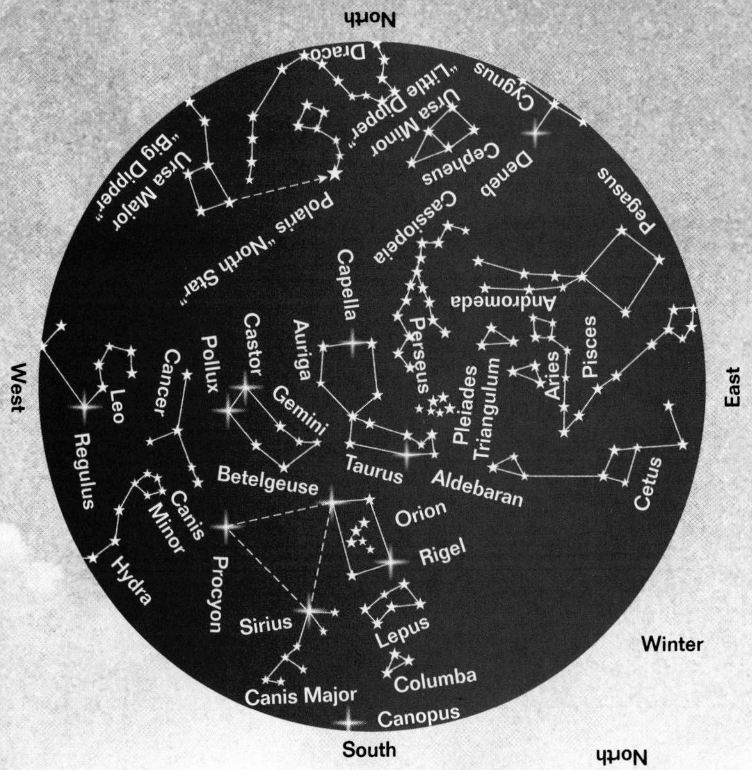

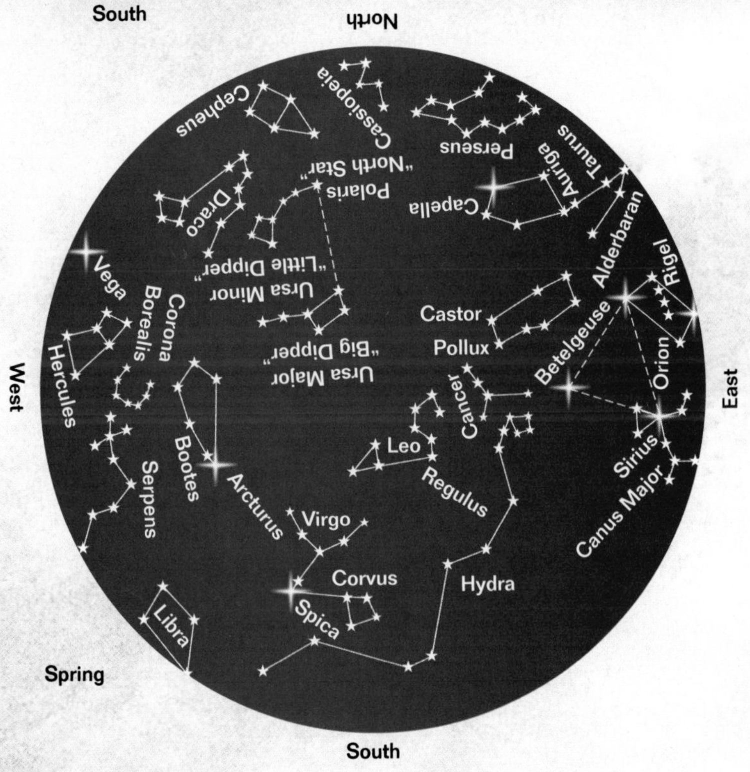

Enrichment

Obtain a circumpolar star chart showing constellations of the southern hemisphere. Have students compare and contrast the locations of circumpolar constellations in the northern and southern hemispheres.

GO Further

Have students research the brightest stars of several constellations such as Sirius A in Canis Major or Rigel in Orion. Have students make a table showing the name of each star, the constellation it is found in, its apparent magnitude, its absolute magnitude, and its distance in light-years from Earth.

Across the Curriculum

Physics Using wavelength analyses, astronomers have recently confirmed the existence of extragalactic stars—stars located outside of galaxies. Much of the research has been centered on the dark spaces that surround M86, an elliptical galaxy in Virgo. Although no planets have been discovered orbiting these stars, it is reasonable to assume that some may exist. Remind students that all the constellations visible from Earth are part of the Milky Way Galaxy. Ask them how the night sky might appear to an observer on a planet orbiting an extragalactic star. *Because the star is not part of a galaxy, few, if any, constellations would be visible. The night sky would be largely black.*

CA Science Content Standards

Page 728: 1a, 4b
Page 729: 1a, 4b

Reviewing Main Ideas can be used to preview, review, reteach, and condense chapter content.

Preview

Linguistic Have students try to answer the questions in their Science Journals. Use student answers as a source for discussion throughout the chapter.

Review

Interpersonal Have students answer the questions on separate pieces of paper and compare their answers with those of other students in the class.

Reteach

Visual-Spatial Have students look at the illustrations on these pages. Ask them to describe details that support the main ideas of the chapter found in the statement for each illustration.

OUT OF TIME?

Auditory-Musical If time does not permit teaching the entire chapter, use the information on these pages along with the chapter Audiocassettes to present the material in a condensed format.

Chapter 20 Reviewing Main Ideas

For a **preview** of this chapter, study this Reviewing Main Ideas before you read the chapter. After you have studied this chapter, you can use the Reviewing Main Ideas to **review** the chapter.

The Glencoe MindJogger, Audiocassettes, and CD-ROM provide additional opportunities for review.

Section 20-1 STARS

The magnitude of a star is a measure of the star's brightness. **Absolute magnitude** is a measure of the light emitted. **Apparent magnitude** is a measure of the amount of light received on Earth. **Parallax** is the apparent shift in the position of an object when viewed from two different positions. The closer to Earth a star is, the greater its shift in parallax. A star's temperature and composition can be determined from the star's spectrum. ***What term describes how bright a star looks from Earth?***

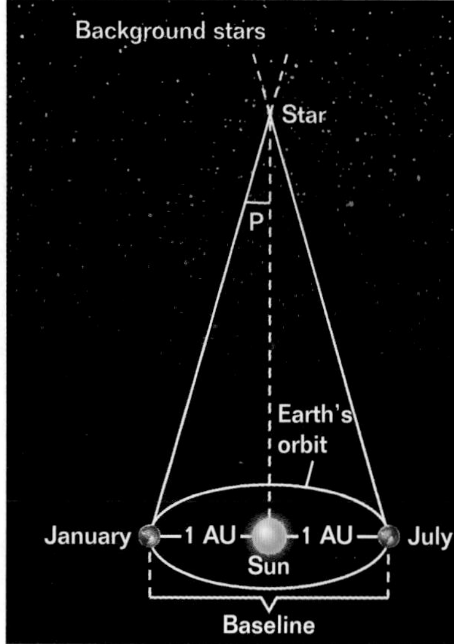

Section 20-2 THE SUN

The sun produces energy by fusing hydrogen into helium in its core. Light is given off from the photosphere, which is the lowest layer of the sun's atmosphere. **Sunspots** are areas of the sun that are cooler and less bright than surrounding areas. Sunspots, prominences, and flares are caused by the intense magnetic field of the sun, which is a main sequence star. ***Why is the sun considered an average star?***

Cultural Diversity

What's in a name? The Milky Way is the English name for the galaxy containing Earth, but it has been known by many others. Akkadians called it the Great Serpent, or the River of the Snake. In Judea, Armenia, and Syria, the galaxy was sometimes referred to as a Long Bandage. China and Japan called it Tien Ho, the Celestial River, or the Silver River. In India, the band of light was known by three names: Akash Ganga, the Bed of the Ganges; Bhagwan ki Kachahri, the Court of Go; and Swarga Duari, the Dove of Paradise. Polynesians called the cloud of lights the Long, Blue, Cloud-Eating Shark, while the Ottawa saw it as muddy water stirred up by a turtle swimming along the bottom of the sky. Ask interested students to research how other cultures may have referred to the Milky Way. L2

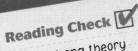

Reading Check ✓

The big bang theory is still controversial. What part of this theory is supported by evidence? What part is opinion?

Section 20-3 EVOLUTION OF STARS

When hydrogen is used up in a **main sequence** star, the star's core collapses and its temperature increases. The star becomes a **giant** or a **supergiant,** which uses helium as fuel. As the star evolves, its outer layers escape into space and the star becomes a **white dwarf.** Stars containing high amounts of mass can explode. During a supernova explosion, the outer layers of a star are blown away and the remaining core evolves into a **neutron star** or **black hole.** ***At what temperature does fusion begin inside a nebula?***

Section 20-4 GALAXIES AND THE UNIVERSE

A **galaxy** is a large group of stars, gas, and dust held together by gravity. Galaxies can be elliptical, spiral, or irregular in shape. The galaxy that our sun belongs to, the Milky Way, contains about 200 billion stars. There may be more than 100 billion galaxies in the universe. The most accepted theory about the origin of the universe is the **big bang theory.** ***What is the Local Group of galaxies?***

Answers to Questions

Section 20-1
Stars apparent magnitude

Section 20-2
The Sun Its absolute magnitude is about average, and it shines with a yellow light, which is in the middle range of visible star colors.

Section 20-3
Evolution of Stars
10 000 000 K

Section 20-4
Galaxies and the Universe
The Local Group is the galaxy cluster to which the Milky Way belongs.

GLENCOE TECHNOLOGY

CD-ROM

Glencoe Science Voyages Interactive CD-ROM

Chapter Summaries and Quizzes

Have students read the Chapter Summary then take the Chapter Quiz to determine whether they have mastered chapter content.

Assessment

Portfolio Encourage students to place in their portfolios one or two items of what they consider to be their best work. Examples include:

- MiniLab, p. 703
- Using Computers, p. 704
- Activity 20-2, pp. 724–725 P

Performance Additional performance assessments may be found in **Performance Assessment** and **Science Integration Activities.** Performance Task Assessment Lists and rubrics for evaluating these activities can be found in Glencoe's **Performance Assessment in the Science Classroom.**

Chapter 20 Assessment

Using Vocabulary

a. absolute magnitude
b. apparent magnitude
c. big bang theory
d. binary system
e. black hole
f. chromosphere
g. constellation
h. corona
i. galaxy
j. giant
k. light-year
l. main sequence
m. nebula
n. neutron star
o. parallax
p. photosphere
q. sunspot
r. supergiant
s. white dwarf

Explain the differences in the terms given below. Then explain how the terms are related.

1. absolute magnitude, apparent magnitude
2. black hole, neutron star
3. chromosphere, photosphere
4. binary system, constellation
5. light-year, parallax

Checking Concepts

Choose the word or phrase that best answers the question.

6. What do constellations form?
A) clusters
B) giants
C) black holes
D) patterns

7. What is a measure of the amount of a star's light received on Earth?
A) absolute magnitude
B) apparent magnitude
C) fusion
D) parallax

8. What increases as an object comes closer to an observer?
A) absolute magnitude
B) red shift
C) parallax
D) size

9. What begins once a nebula contracts and temperatures increase to 10 millionK?
A) main sequencing
B) a supernova
C) fusion
D) a white dwarf

10. What is about 10 km in size?
A) giant
B) white dwarf
C) black hole
D) neutron star

11. Our sun fuses hydrogen into what?
A) carbon
B) oxygen
C) iron
D) helium

12. What are loops of matter flowing from the sun?
A) sunspots
B) auroras
C) coronas
D) prominences

13. What are groups of galaxies called?
A) clusters
B) supergiants
C) giants
D) binary systems

14. Which galaxies are sometimes shaped like footballs?
A) spiral
B) elliptical
C) barred
D) irregular

15. What do scientists study to determine shifts in wavelengths of light?
A) spectrum
B) surface
C) corona
D) chromosphere

Thinking Critically

16. What is significant about the 1995 discovery by the *Hubble Space Telescope* of more than 1500 galaxies at a distance of more than 10 billion light-years?
17. How do scientists know that black holes exist if these objects don't emit any visible light?
18. Use the autumn star chart in Appendix K to determine which constellation is directly overhead at 8 P.M. on November 23 for an observer in North America.
19. How are radio waves used to detect objects in space?
20. What kinds of reactions produce the energy emitted by stars?

Using Vocabulary

1. Absolute magnitude measures light emitted by a star. Apparent magnitude measures the amount of light received on Earth from a star.
2. A black hole is an object so dense, nothing can escape its gravity field. A neutron star is the collapsed core of a supernova.
3. The photosphere is the lowest layer of the sun's atmosphere. The chromosphere lies directly above the photosphere.
4. A binary system consists of two stars orbiting each other. A constellation is a group of stars that makes a pattern in the sky.
5. A light-year is the distance light travels in one year—it is used to measure distances in space. Parallax is the apparent shift in an object's position when viewed from two different positions.

interNET CONNECTION To reinforce chapter vocabulary, use the **Study Guide for Content Mastery** booklet. Also available are activities for **Glencoe Science Voyages** on the Glencoe Science Web Site. **www.glencoe.com/sec/science/ca**

Checking Concepts

6. D
7. B
8. C
9. C
10. D
11. D
12. D
13. A
14. B
15. A

Thinking Critically

16. Astronomers are looking at galaxies that may have formed when the universe was only 1 billion years old. Studies of this nature help determine the true age of the universe.
17. Astronomers are able to use instruments to detect the X rays surrounding black holes.
18. Pegasus is almost directly overhead at this time.
19. Any object at a temperature above absolute zero emits radio waves. These waves can be gathered by radio telescopes then analyzed to determine what type of object is emitting them.
20. Stars produce energy by fusion. Hydrogen is converted into helium in main sequence stars. Helium then fuses to produce heavier elements. As nuclei are fused, mass is converted into energy.

Assessment

Developing Skills

If you need help, refer to the Skill Handbook.

21. Concept Mapping: Complete the concept map on this page that shows the evolution of a main sequence star with a mass similar to that of the sun.

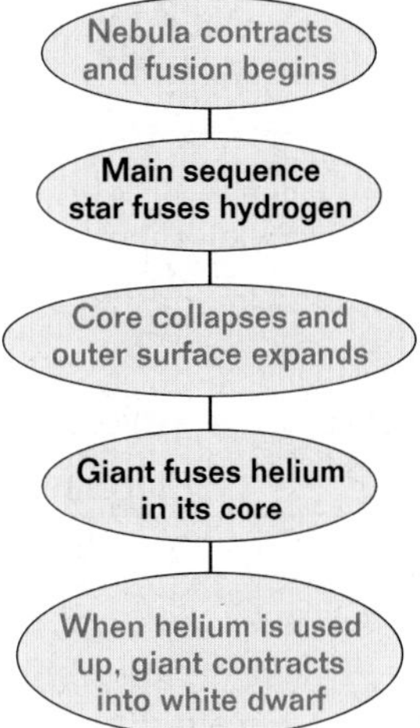

Nebula contracts and fusion begins
Main sequence star fuses hydrogen
Core collapses and outer surface expands
Giant fuses helium in its core
When helium is used up, giant contracts into white dwarf

22. Comparing and Contrasting: Compare and contrast the sun with other stars on the H-R diagram.

23. Measuring in SI: The Milky Way Galaxy is 100 000 light-years in diameter. What scale would you use if you were to construct a model of the Milky Way with a diameter of 20 cm?

24. Designing an Experiment: Design and carry out an experiment that uses sunspot locations to compare rotational periods of different latitudes of the sun.

25. Making a Model: Design and construct scale models of a spiral and a barred spiral Milky Way Galaxy. Show the approximate position of the sun in each.

Test-Taking Tip

Read the Label No matter how many times you've taken a particular test or practiced for an exam, it's always a good idea to skim through the instructions provided at the beginning of each section.

Test Practice

Use these questions to test your Science Proficiency.

1. A white dwarf star is located in the lower-left-hand corner of an H-R diagram. Which of the following statements **BEST** explains why it is positioned there?
   A) White dwarf stars have low absolute magnitudes and high surface temperatures.
   B) White dwarf stars have low absolute magnitudes and low surface temperatures.
   C) White dwarf stars have high absolute magnitudes and high surface temperatures.
   D) White dwarf stars have high absolute magnitudes and low surface temperatures.

2. Sunspots are dark areas of the sun's surface. Which of the following statements **BEST** explains why this is true?
   A) Sunspots are areas of the sun's surface that do not give off light.
   B) Sunspots appear dark because they give off more energy than surrounding areas of the sun's surface.
   C) Sunspots are hotter than surrounding areas of the sun's surface.
   D) Sunspots are cooler than surrounding areas of the sun's surface.

Assessment Resources

The **Test Practice Workbook** provides students with practice in the format, concepts, and critical-thinking skills tested in standardized exams.

Chapter Review, pp. 39–40 L2
Performance Assessment, p. 20 L2
Assessment, pp. 77–80 L2

Glencoe Technology

Chapter Review Software
Computer Test Bank
MindJogger Videoquiz

Test Practice

The Test-Taking Tip was written by The Princeton Review, the nation's leader in test preparation.

1. A
2. D

Developing Skills

21. See student page.
22. The sun is an average star in terms of mass, temperature, and its place in the evolutionary cycle. The sun differs from more massive stars in that massive stars have higher temperatures and are further along in their evolutionary cycle. Other stars such as white dwarfs are hotter than the sun but don't emit as much light.
23. 1 cm = 5000 light-years
24. Student experiments will vary. However, students should conclude that the sun rotates faster around its equator than toward its poles.
25. Student models should correspond to descriptions of spiral and barred spiral galaxies given in the student text. The sun should be positioned about two-thirds of the way outward from the nucleus of the galaxy.

Bonus Question

Observe two distant objects in opposite directions from a single viewing point. Using your knowledge of parallax, determine which object is closer. *The closer object will appear to move more when viewed through one eye, then the other.*

UNIT 6

Life's Diversity

This unit introduces students to methods by which organisms are classified. The characteristics used to classify organisms in the kingdoms Archaebacteria, Eubacteria, Protista, and Fungi are presented. Students examine plant and animal characteristics and determine how they are used to classify plants and animals into the different phyla.

Unit Overview

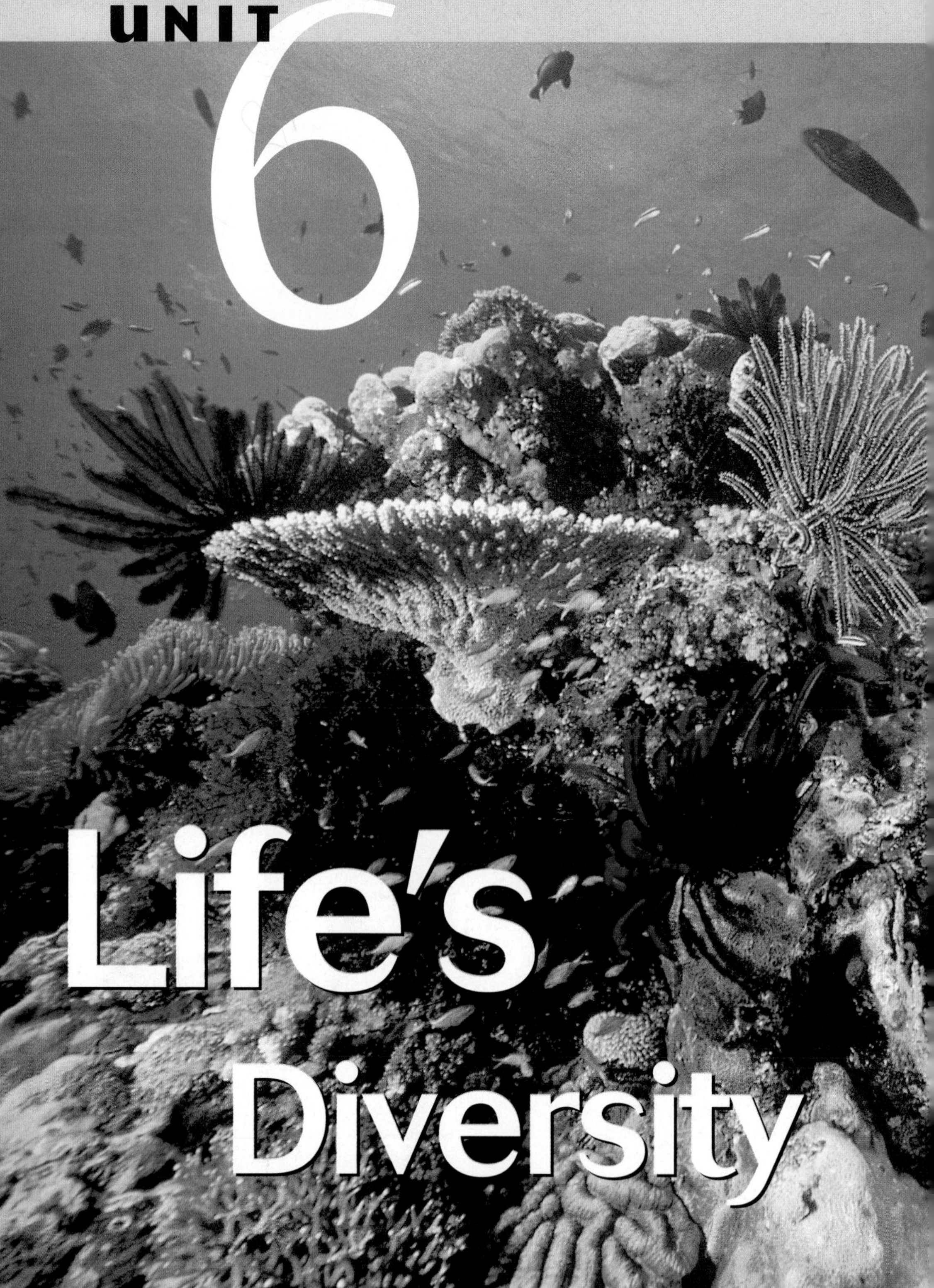

Science at Home

Fun with Fungi Have students visit a supermarket and make a list of the kinds of mushrooms that are sold in the produce section. Have them research where each species of mushroom grows and whether it is collected in the wild or grown commercially.

NATIONAL GEOGRAPHIC

What's Happening Here?

In the shallow, sunlit waters between 30 degrees north and south of the equator are the rain forests of the ocean—coral reefs. Hundreds of species of organisms live in marine communities like this one (left) in the Bismarck Sea off New Britain Island, Papua New Guinea. Coral itself is an animal, although it stays put all its life. It belongs to the same phylum as jellyfish, which float freely in the current. Why is coral considered an animal and not a plant? How is it similar to jellyfish? These are some of the questions you will answer as you learn about life's diverse forms. You will also learn about forms of life that are difficult to pigeonhole. Some thrive in the world's most hostile places, such as this Morning Glory Pool (below) in Yellowstone's Upper Geyser Basin. Here, boiling springs bring to the surface minerals that nourish algae and bacteria and tint the formations in pastel colors.

interNET CONNECTION

Explore the Glencoe Science Web Site at **www.glencoe.com/sec/science/ca** to find out more about topics found in this unit.

735

interNET CONNECTION

Internet Addresses

Explore the Glencoe Science Web Site at **www.glencoe.com/sec/science/ca** to find out more about topics found in this unit.

Introducing the Unit

What's happening here?

Have students read the text and examine the pictures. Ask them why coral might be mistaken for a plant. Ask why this might be an advantage for the coral. *Some animals would ignore it because they go after only moving prey.* Have students guess an advantage the algae and bacteria have that live in hot waters. *They do not have to compete with as many other organisms for food and space.*

Content Background

Coral and thermophiles (heat-loving bacteria) can acquire their food in unusual ways. A type of algae lines the digestive tract of some corals and photosynthesizes food. If the algae is destroyed by disease or pollution, many of the coral die. Some thermophiles live in the fissures of deep oceans where the temperature exceeds 250°C. They use hydrogen sulfide as a source of energy.

Previewing the Chapters

- Students will be somewhat familiar with some characteristics used to classify organisms. Have them look through the unit at pictures and relate the bacteria and the fungi with which they are familiar.
- Have them try to classify animals as vertebrate or invertebrate without looking at the text.

Tying to Previous Knowledge

- Have students tell what they know about bacteria, fungi, and plants.
- Have students list ways plants and animals are different.

Chapter 21 Bacteria

Section	Objectives	Activities/Features
Chapter Opener		**Explore Activity:** Observe Bacteria, p. 737
21-1 **Two Kingdoms of Bacteria** 3 Sessions 1½ Blocks	1. **Describe** the characteristics of bacterial cells. 2. **Compare** aerobic and anaerobic organisms.	**MiniLab:** Observing Bacterial Growth, p. 740 **Using Math,** p. 741 **Problem Solving:** Controlling Bacterial Growth, p. 741 **Earth Science Integration,** p. 743 **Skill Builder:** Interpreting Data, p. 743 **Using Math,** p. 743 **Activity 21-1:** Observing Cyanobacteria, p. 744
21-2 **Bacteria in Your Life** 3 Sessions 1½ Blocks	3. **Identify** some ways bacteria are helpful. 4. **Explain** the importance of nitrogen-fixing bacteria. 5. **Explain** how some bacteria cause disease.	**MiniLab:** Making Yogurt, p. 747 **Physics Integration,** p. 748 **Skill Builder:** Measuring in SI, p. 748 **Using Computers,** p. 748 **Science and Society:** Bioremediation, p. 749 **Activity 21-2:** Are there bacteria in foods?, pp. 750–751

The number of recommended single-period sessions — The number of recommended blocks
One session and one-half block are allowed for chapter review and assessment.

Activity Materials

Explore	Activities	MiniLabs
p. 737 yogurt, small dish, crystal violet, dropper, toothpick, glass slide, microscope, water, coverslip	p. 744 microscope, prepared slides of *Gloeocapsa* and *Anabaena,* micrograph photos pp. 750–751 test tubes, stoppers, test-tube rack, felt-tip marker, dropper, craft sticks, milk, buttermilk, cottage cheese, yogurt, sour cream, water, bromothymol blue	p. 740 dried beans, glass beaker, distilled water, methylene blue, dropper, microscope, microscope slides, coverslips p. 747 hot plate, milk, saucepan, oven mitts, gloves, yogurt (with live cultures), wooden spoon, thermos, refrigerator

Need Materials? Contact Science Kit at 1-800-828-7777 or at www.sciencekit.com on the Internet.
For alternate materials, see the activity on the listed page.

Standards		Reproducible Resources	Technology
National	State/Local	Test Practice Workbooks are available for use with each chapter.	English and Spanish audiocassettes are available for use with each section.
National Content Standards: UCP1, UCP2, A1, C1, C2, C3, C4, C5, E1, G3	California Science Content Standards: 5c, 6a, 9a, 9c, 9f	**Activity Worksheets,** pp. 117–118, 121 **Enrichment,** p. 60 **Laboratory Manual,** pp. 131–132 **Reinforcement,** p. 160 **Study Guide,** p. 81	**Section Focus Transparency 60** **Teaching Transparency 41** **Science Integration Transparency 21** **Glencoe Science Voyages Interactive CD-ROM**
National Content Standards: UCP2, A1, C1, C3, C4, C5, E2, F1, G1, G3	California Science Content Standards: 5c, 6a, 6b, 9a, 9b, 9c, 9f	**Activity Worksheets,** pp. 119–120, 122 **Critical Thinking/Problem Solving,** p. 21 **Enrichment,** p. 61 **Laboratory Manual,** pp. 133–134 **Multicultural Connections,** pp. 41–42 **Reinforcement,** p. 61 **Study Guide,** pp. 82–84	**Section Focus Transparency 61** **Teaching Transparency 42** **Glencoe Science Voyages Interactive Videodisc—Life** **Glencoe Science Voyages Interactive CD-ROM** **Internet Connection,** p. 746 **Internet Connection,** p. 749

Key to Teaching Strategies

The following designations will help you decide which activities are appropriate for your students.

L1 Level 1 activities should be appropriate for students with learning difficulties.

L2 Level 2 activities should be within the ability range of all students.

L3 Level 3 activities are designed for above-average students.

ELL ELL activities should be within the ability range of English Language Learners.

COOP LEARN Cooperative Learning activities are designed for small group work.

P These strategies represent student products that can be placed into a best-work portfolio.

Multiple Learning Styles logos, as described on page 55T, are used throughout to indicate strategies that address different learning styles.

Assessment Resources

Chapter Review, pp. 41–42
Assessment, pp. 81–84
Performance Assessment in the Science Classroom (PASC)
MindJogger Videoquiz
Alternate Assessment in the Science Classroom
Performance Assessment, p. 21
Chapter Review Software
Computer Test Bank

Chapter 21 Bacteria

This is a representation of key blackline masters available in the Teacher Classroom Resources. See Resource Manager boxes within the chapter for additional information.

Transparencies

Section Focus Transparencies

SECTION FOCUS TRANSPARENCY

GLUED TO THE TUBE

These giant tube worms live deep below the surface of the ocean where no sunlight reaches. Some tube worms grow several meters high. They feed on bacteria that actually live inside the tubes. There are about 10 billion bacteria in each gram of tissue within the tube worm.

1. How does the size of a tube worm compare to the size of bacteria?
2. Do you think that other organisms could tolerate having so much bacteria? Give a reason for your answer.

L2

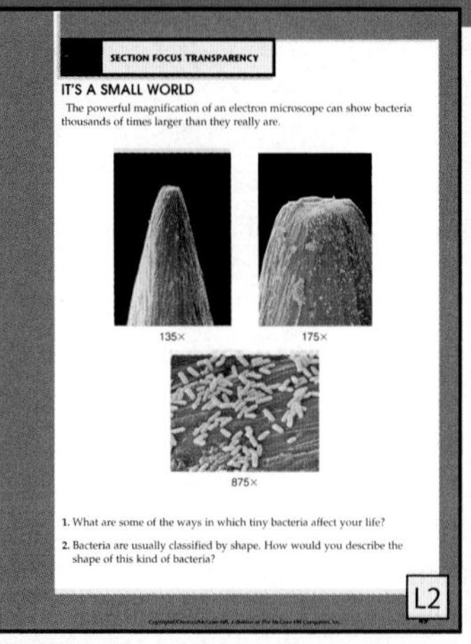

SECTION FOCUS TRANSPARENCY

IT'S A SMALL WORLD

The powerful magnification of an electron microscope can show bacteria thousands of times larger than they really are.

135×

175×

875×

1. What are some of the ways in which tiny bacteria affect your life?
2. Bacteria are usually classified by shape. How would you describe the shape of this kind of bacteria?

L2

Science Integration Transparencies

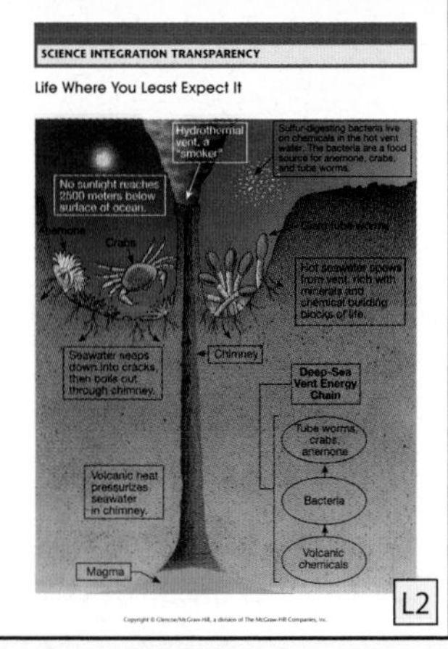

SCIENCE INTEGRATION TRANSPARENCY

Life Where You Least Expect It

L2

Teaching Transparencies

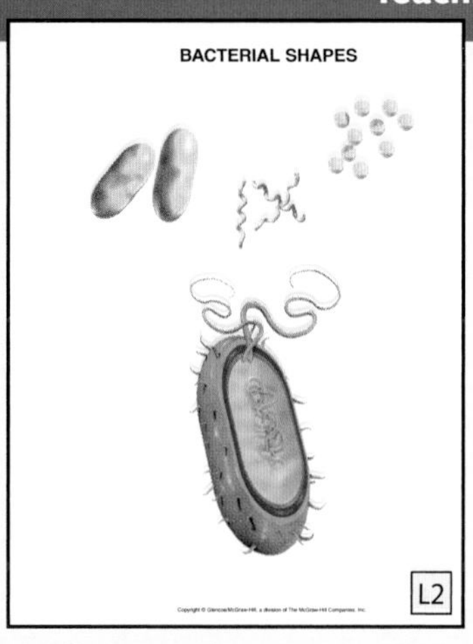

L2

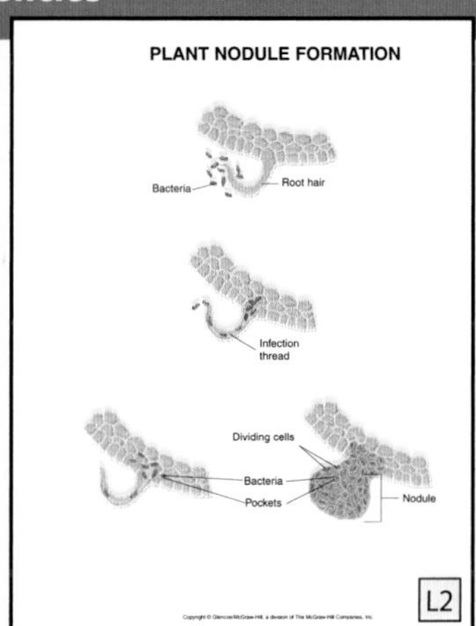

L2

Meeting Different Ability Levels

Study Guide for Content Mastery

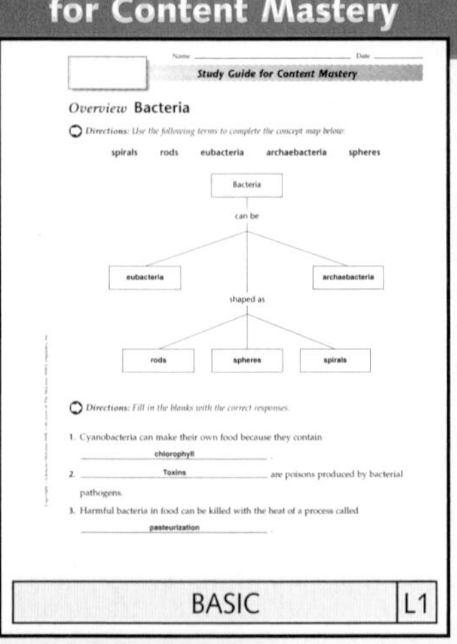

Name ______ Date ______

Study Guide for Content Mastery

Overview Bacteria

Directions: Use the following terms to complete the concept map below:

spirals rods eubacteria archaebacteria spheres

Bacteria — can be — eubacteria, archaebacteria — shaped as — rods, spheres, spirals

Directions: Fill in the blanks with the correct responses.

1. Cyanobacteria can make their own food because they contain ___chlorophyll___.
2. ___Toxins___ are poisons produced by bacterial pathogens.
3. Harmful bacteria in food can be killed with the heat of a process called ___pasteurization___.

BASIC L1

Reinforcement

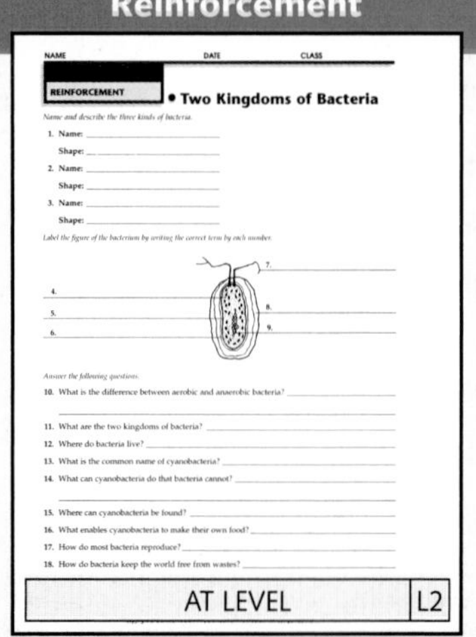

NAME ______ DATE ______ CLASS ______

REINFORCEMENT • Two Kingdoms of Bacteria

Name and describe the three kinds of bacteria.

1. Name: ______
   Shape: ______
2. Name: ______
   Shape: ______
3. Name: ______
   Shape: ______

Label the figure of the bacterium by writing the correct term by each number.

4. ______
5. ______
6. ______
7. ______
8. ______
9. ______

Answer the following questions.

10. What is the difference between aerobic and anaerobic bacteria? ______
11. What are the two kingdoms of bacteria? ______
12. Where do bacteria live? ______
13. What is the common name of cyanobacteria? ______
14. What can cyanobacteria do that bacteria cannot? ______
15. Where can cyanobacteria be found? ______
16. What enables cyanobacteria to make their own food? ______
17. How do most bacteria reproduce? ______
18. How do bacteria keep the world free from wastes? ______

AT LEVEL L2

Enrichment Worksheets

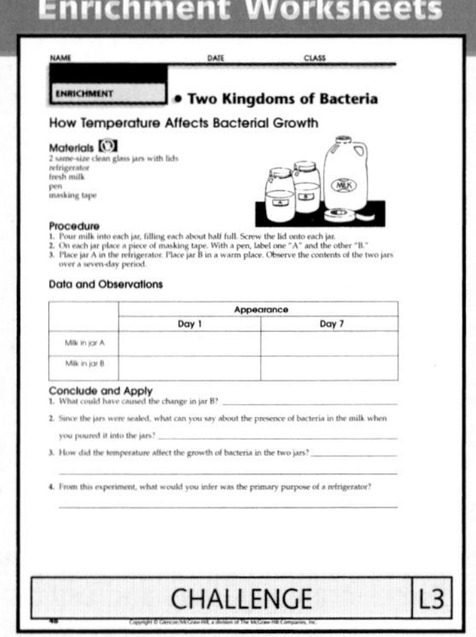

NAME ______ DATE ______ CLASS ______

ENRICHMENT • Two Kingdoms of Bacteria

How Temperature Affects Bacterial Growth

Materials

2 same-size clean glass jars with lids
refrigerator
fresh milk
pen
masking tape

Procedure

1. Pour milk into each jar, filling each about half full. Screw the lid onto each jar.
2. On each jar place a piece of masking tape. With a pen, label one "A" and the other "B."
3. Place jar A in the refrigerator. Place jar B in a warm place. Observe the contents of the two jars over a seven-day period.

Data and Observations

	Appearance	
	Day 1	Day 7
Milk in jar A		
Milk in jar B		

Conclude and Apply

1. What could have caused the change in jar B? ______
2. Since the jars were sealed, what can you say about the presence of bacteria in the milk when you poured it into the jars? ______
3. How did the temperature affect the growth of bacteria in the two jars? ______
4. From this experiment, what would you infer was the primary purpose of a refrigerator? ______

CHALLENGE L3

Resource Manager

Hands-on Activities

Activity Worksheets

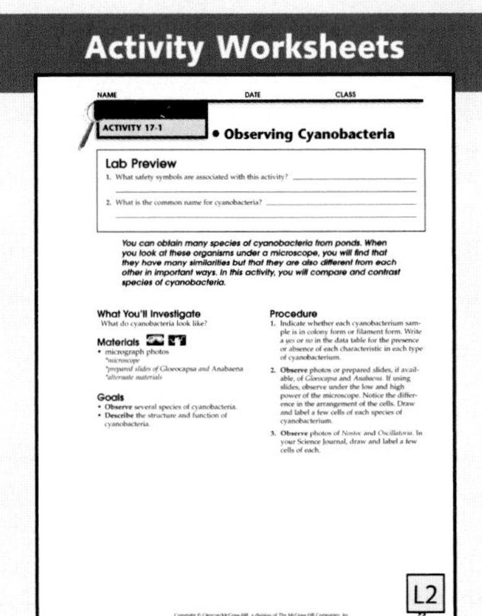

NAME DATE CLASS

ACTIVITY 17-1 • Observing Cyanobacteria

Lab Preview

1. What safety symbols are associated with this activity?
2. What is the common name for cyanobacteria?

You can obtain many species of cyanobacteria from ponds. When you look at these organisms under a microscope, you will find that they have many similarities but that they are also different from each other in important ways. In this activity, you will compare and contrast species of cyanobacteria.

What You'll Investigate

Materials

Goals

Procedure

L2

Lab Manual

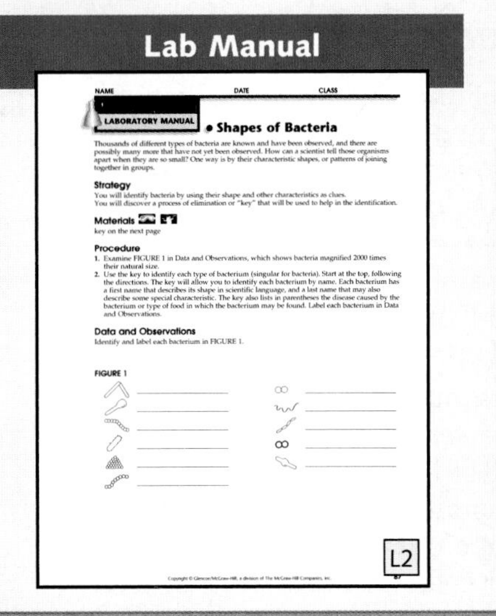

NAME DATE CLASS

LABORATORY MANUAL • Shapes of Bacteria

Strategy

Materials

Procedure

Data and Observations

FIGURE 1

L2

Accessibility

Spanish Resources

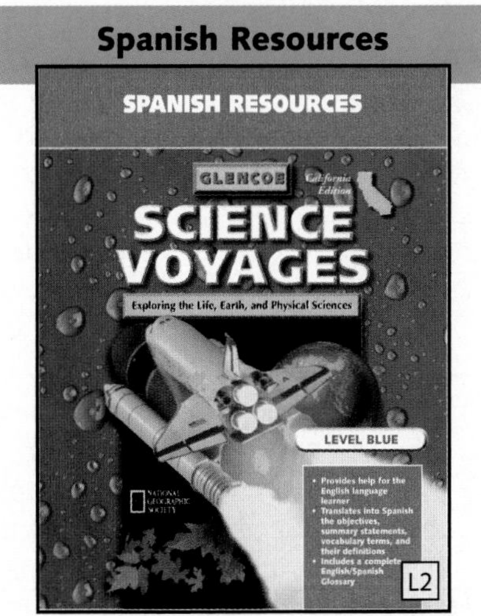

SPANISH RESOURCES

GLENCOE

SCIENCE VOYAGES

Exploring the Life, Earth, and Physical Sciences

LEVEL BLUE

L2

Assessment

Performance Assessment

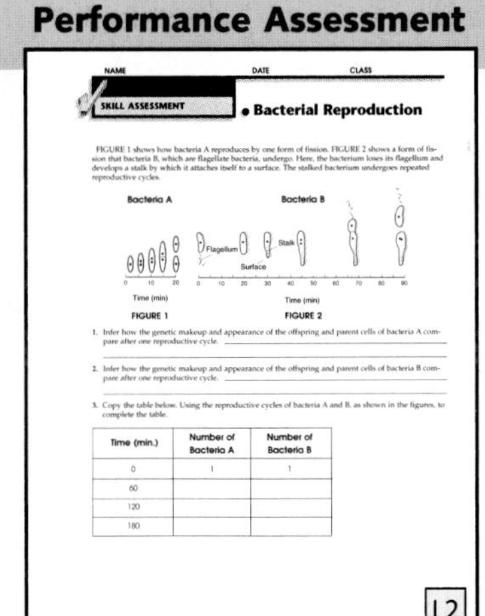

NAME DATE CLASS

SKILL ASSESSMENT • Bacterial Reproduction

Bacteria A Bacteria B

FIGURE 1 FIGURE 2

Time (min.)	Number of Bacteria A	Number of Bacteria B
0	1	1
60		
120		
180		

L2

Chapter Review

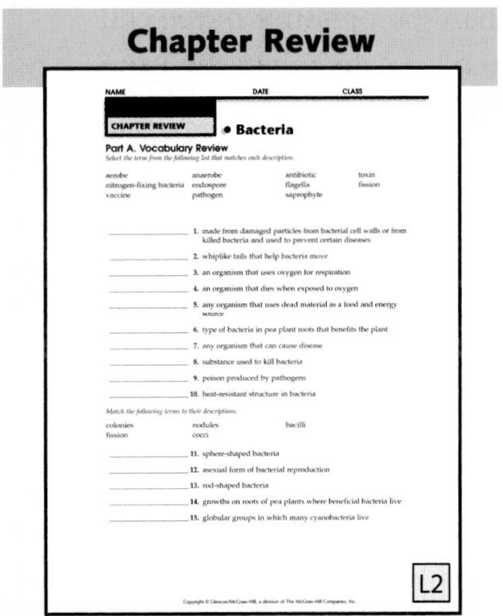

NAME DATE CLASS

CHAPTER REVIEW • Bacteria

Part A. Vocabulary Review

L2

Assessment

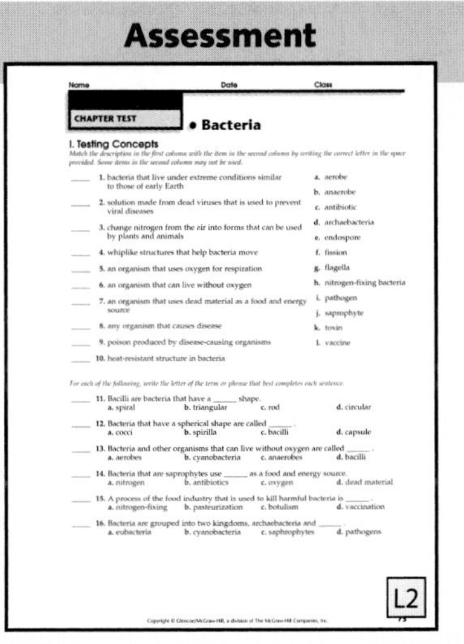

Name Date Class

CHAPTER TEST • Bacteria

I. Testing Concepts

L2

Test Practice Workbook

CALIFORNIA SCIENCE CONTENT STANDARDS PRACTICE QUESTIONS STUDENT EDITION

GLENCOE

SCIENCE VOYAGES

Exploring the Life, Earth, and Physical Sciences

LEVEL BLUE

THE PRINCETON REVIEW

L2

Extending Content

Critical Thinking/ Problem Solving

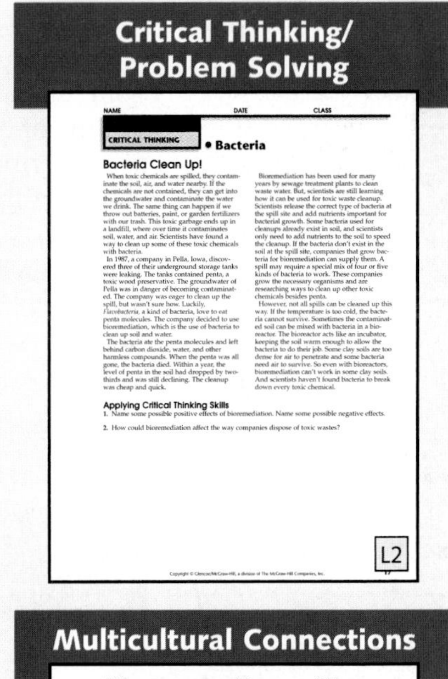

NAME DATE CLASS

CRITICAL THINKING • Bacteria

Bacteria Clean Up!

Applying Critical Thinking Skills

1. Name some possible positive effects of bioremediation. Name some possible negative effects.
2. How could bioremediation affect the way companies dispose of toxic wastes?

L2

Multicultural Connections

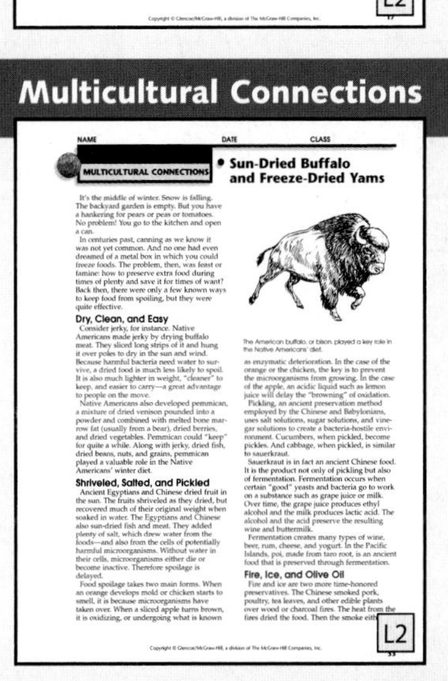

NAME DATE CLASS

MULTICULTURAL CONNECTIONS • Sun-Dried Buffalo and Freeze-Dried Yams

Dry, Clean, and Easy

Shriveled, Salted, and Pickled

Fire, Ice, and Olive Oil

L2

Helping You Prepare

What are bacteria? (Section 21-1)

Bacteria are unicellular prokaryotic organisms contained within two kingdoms. Another way of classifying organisms that some systematists now favor is to organize the diversity of life into three domains—Domain Bacteria (Kingdom Eubacteria), Domain Archaea (Kingdom Archaebacteria), and Domain Eukarya (Kingdoms Protista, Fungi, Plantae, and Animalia).

With exceptions, most bacteria—both eubacteria and archaebacteria—range between 1 μm (1 micrometer = 0.001 mm) and 5 μm in diameter. Bacteria generally have a rigid cell that maintains the shape of the organism. Bacterial cell walls prevent cells from bursting in environments where the pressure in the cell is greater than the pressure in the surrounding medium or fluid. Bacterial cells shrivel and usually die in environments where the external pressure is greater than the pressure in the cell.

Most named bacteria are members of Kingdom Eubacteria. The five major phylogenetic groups of eubacteria are based on comparisons of their ribosomal RNA. Bacteria are classified based on their diverse metabolic styles.

Bacteria have three basic shapes. Unlike the rod-shaped bacilli (singular, bacillus) and helical spirilla (singular, spirillum), cocci (singular, coccus), which are spherically shaped cells, never possess flagella.

GLENCOE TECHNOLOGY

Glencoe Science Voyages Interactive CD-ROM

Chapter Summaries

Use the Chapter Summary to introduce, teach, or review chapter material.

Cyanobacteria, formerly called blue-green algae, are bacteria that contain chlorophyll, enabling them to make their own food. These organisms probably produced most of the original free oxygen in the atmosphere about 2.5 billion years ago. They may be unicellular or colonial. Most live in freshwater, but some are colonial with fungi to form lichens.

Reproduction (Section 21-1)

All bacteria reproduce by a process of cell division known as binary fission. In binary fission, the one or more circular chromosomes of the bacterial cell are duplicated. The duplicated chromosomes attach to the cell membrane. Continued growth of the cell separates the chromosomes, and the plasma membrane eventually pinches in two as a cell wall is deposited between the daughter cells.

NATIONAL GEOGRAPHIC — **Teacher's Corner**

Products Available from Glencoe

To order the following products for use with this chapter, call Glencoe at 1-800-334-7344:

CD-ROM

NGS PictureShow: The Cell

Curriculum Kit

GeoKit: Cells and Microorganisms

Transparency Set

NGS PicturePack: The Cell

Videodisc

STV: The Cell

Products Available from National Geographic Society

To order the following products for use with this chapter, call National Geographic Society at 1-800-368-2728:

Videos

Bacteria

Discovering the Cell

Index to NATIONAL GEOGRAPHIC Magazine

"Body Beasts," by Richard Coniff, December 1998.

Uses of Bacteria (Section 21-2)

Prokaryotes have a large impact on ecology. Bacteria and fungi are the organisms primarily responsible for the decay and recycling of organic materials. Of these materials, carbon and nitrogen are essential.

Nitrogen gas can be used as a nitrogen source only by some eubacteria, including cyanobacteria. The process is called nitrogen fixation. Nitrogen is necessary for plants and animals to make proteins and amino acids. Because the nitrogen content of environments varies considerably in quantity and kinds of nitrogen-containing compounds, it is not surprising that organisms have evolved the ability to utilize more than one nitrogen source.

Harmful Bacteria (Section 21-2)

Pathogen is the name given to any organism that causes disease. An antibiotic is a chemical that is able to kill or inhibit the growth of a microorganism, usually a pathogen. Thousands of antibiotics are known, but only a few have practical uses. Many kinds of microorganisms including bacteria, protists, and fungi produce antibiotics.

The action of antibiotics is dependent on their chemical structure. Certain antibiotics affect cell wall synthesis or destroy cell membrane permeability. Others act by inhibiting protein synthesis or causing the wrong amino acid to be inserted into the growing polypeptide chain of proteins in ribosomes. Broad spectrum antibiotics act on many different kinds of organisms. Some antibiotics, such as penicillin, act only on prokaryotes. Other antibiotics like cycloheximide are active against eukaryotes but not prokaryotes. Vaccines, on the other hand, are specific to certain bacteria. This is because a vaccine is made of damaged or killed bacterial cells. The white blood cells learn to recognize this bacteria and can respond more quickly the next time that bacteria enters the body. It is important to note that antibiotics are taken *after* a pathogen enters the body, whereas a vaccine is a preventative measure.

Pasteurization (Section 21-2)

The process by which microbial populations are reduced in milk and other foods by the use of mild heat is pasteurization. Pasteurization is achieved by passing milk continuously through a heat exchanger where its temperature is raised quickly to 71°C, held there for 15 s, and then quickly cooled. The process, named for Louis Pasteur, was first used to control spoilage of wine and saved the wine industry in France. Pasteurization does not kill all the microbes present and should not be confused with sterilization, which uses high heat and pressure to kill all bacteria present. Although pasteurization was originally used to kill the organisms that cause tuberculosis, typhoid, and brucellosis, today it is used to enhance the keeping qualities of milk.

SCIENCE UPDATE

For current events or science in the news, access the Glencoe Science Web Site at **www.glencoe.com/sec/science/ca**

Teacher to Teacher

"I have students visualize the pervasiveness of bacteria by relating that if bacteria were visible and all the plants and animals were to suddenly vanish, the outlines of all of them, as well as their digestive tracts, could be seen because they are covered with bacteria."

Alton L. Biggs, Teacher
Allen Independent School District
Allen, TX

CHAPTER OVERVIEW

Section 21-1 Characteristics of bacteria are described in this section. Aerobic and anaerobic organisms are compared and contrasted.

Section 21-2 The ways that bacteria are important to humans and the environment are emphasized in this section. Examples of helpful and harmful bacteria are given.

Chapter Vocabulary

flagella	pathogen
fission	antibiotic
aerobe	vaccine
anaerobe	toxin
saprophyte	endospore
nitrogen-fixing bacteria	

Theme Connection

Systems and Interactions Bacteria have systems for maintaining homeostasis within their environments. Archaebacteria and some eubacteria have systems for living in anaerobic environments. Eubacteria interact with each other and with other species, including humans.

00:00 OUT OF TIME?

If time does not permit teaching the entire chapter, use Reviewing Main Ideas on pp. 752–753.

CHAPTER 21 Bacteria

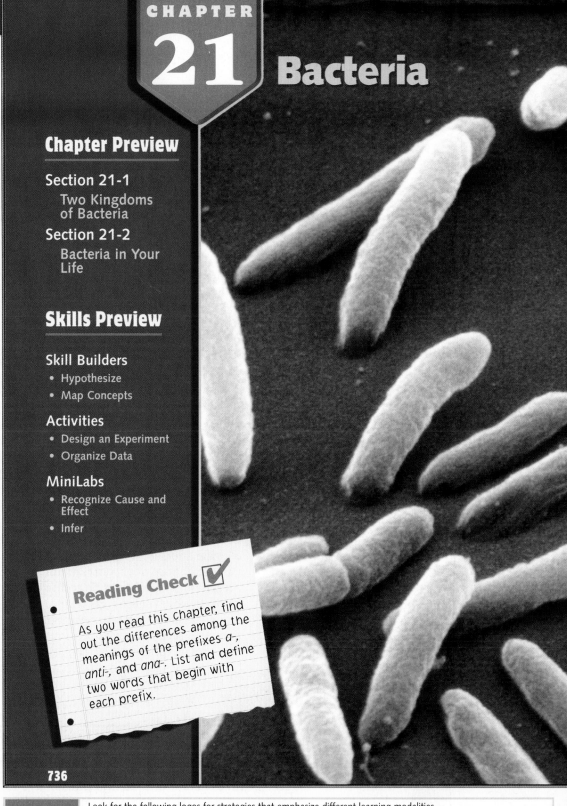

Chapter Preview

Skills Preview

Skill Builders
- Hypothesize
- Map Concepts

Activities
- Design an Experiment
- Organize Data

MiniLabs
- Recognize Cause and Effect
- Infer

Reading Check

As you read this chapter, find out the differences among the meanings of the prefixes *a-*, *anti-*, and *ana-*. List and define two words that begin with each prefix.

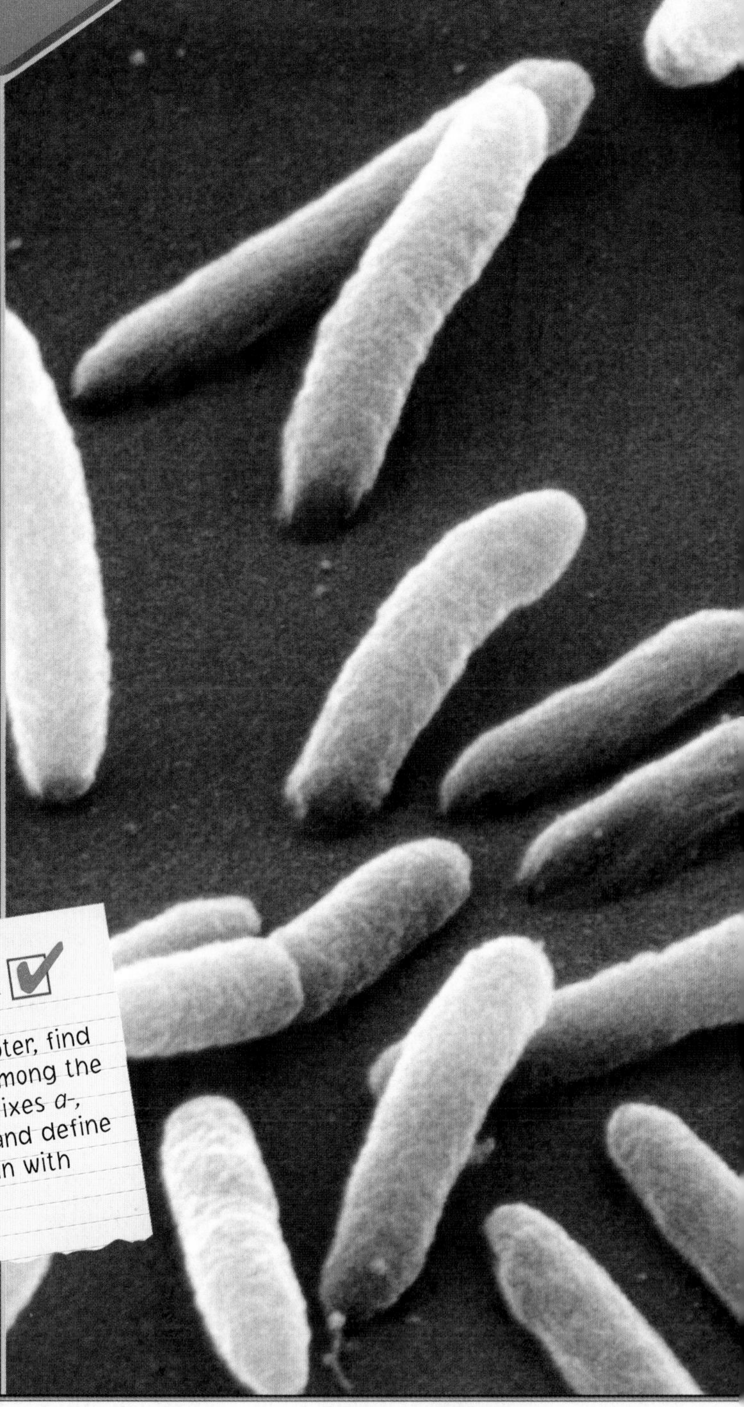

736

Multiple Learning Styles

Look for the following logos for strategies that emphasize different learning modalities.

Linguistic Using Science Words, p. 739; Science Journal, p. 751; Preview, p. 752

Logical-Mathematical MiniLab, p. 740; Skill Builder, p. 748

Visual-Spatial Quick Demo, p. 739; Reteach, pp. 742, 752; Activity, p. 747

Auditory-Musical Out of Time, p. 752

Kinesthetic Explore Activity, p. 737; Problem Solving, p. 741; Multiple Learning Styles, p. 742; Tying to Previous Knowledge, p. 746

Interpersonal Discussion, p. 739; Inclusion Strategies, p. 739; Activity, p. 742; MiniLab, p. 747; Activity, p. 750; Review, p. 752

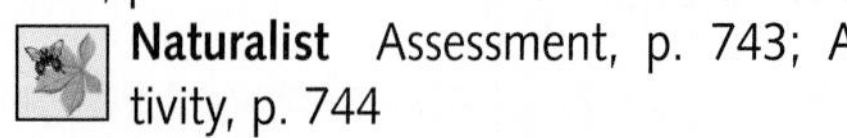

Naturalist Assessment, p. 743; Activity, p. 744

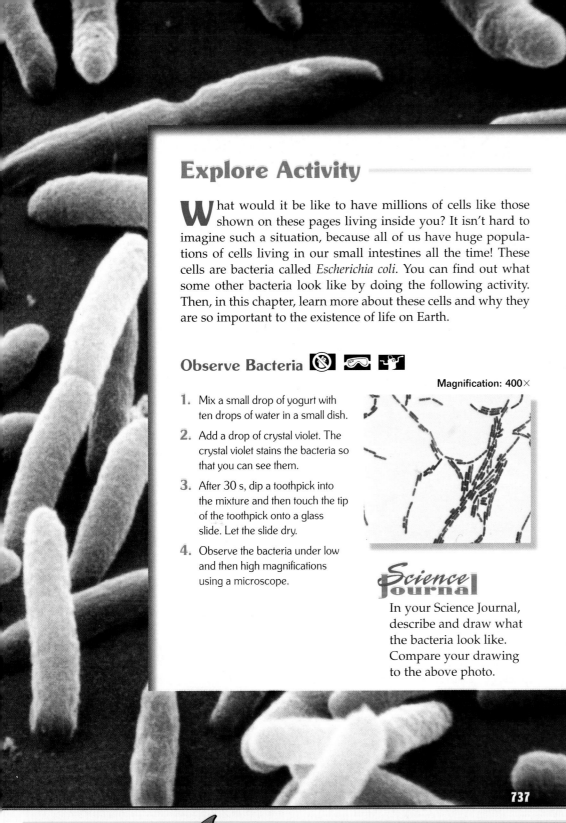

Explore Activity

What would it be like to have millions of cells like those shown on these pages living inside you? It isn't hard to imagine such a situation, because all of us have huge populations of cells living in our small intestines all the time! These cells are bacteria called *Escherichia coli.* You can find out what some other bacteria look like by doing the following activity. Then, in this chapter, learn more about these cells and why they are so important to the existence of life on Earth.

Observe Bacteria

Magnification: 400×

1. Mix a small drop of yogurt with ten drops of water in a small dish.
2. Add a drop of crystal violet. The crystal violet stains the bacteria so that you can see them.
3. After 30 s, dip a toothpick into the mixture and then touch the tip of the toothpick onto a glass slide. Let the slide dry.
4. Observe the bacteria under low and then high magnifications using a microscope.

Science Journal

In your Science Journal, describe and draw what the bacteria look like. Compare your drawing to the above photo.

Explore Activity

Purpose

Kinesthetic Use the Explore Activity to introduce bacteria. Bacteria are living organisms. Explain that students will be learning about the characteristics of these organisms. L2 ELL COOP LEARN

Preparation

Be sure to purchase fresh, plain yogurt that is made with live cultures.

Materials

yogurt, crystal violet, toothpicks, slides, microscope, small dishes, water, dropper, timer

Teaching Strategies

You will probably want to check each microscope when students have the organism focused on high power to be certain that they are looking at the bacteria.

The bacteria should be rod shaped and stained violet.

Assessment

Portfolio Have students design an experiment to determine whether yogurt bacteria are alive. They should place their experimental designs in their portfolios. Use **Performance Assessment in the Science Classroom,** p. 23. P

Assessment Planner

Portfolio
Refer to p. 753 for suggested items that students might select for their portfolios.

Performance Assessment
See p. 753 for additional Performance Assessment options.
Skill Builder, p. 748
MiniLab, pp. 740, 747
Activity 21-1, p. 744; 21-2, pp. 750–751

Content Assessment
Section Assessment, pp. 743, 748
Chapter Assessment, pp. 754–755
Proficiency Prep, pp. 743, 748

SECTION 21•1

Prepare

Refer to **What are bacteria?** and **Reproduction** on p. 736E.

Preplanning

Refer to the **Chapter Organizer** on pp. 736A–B.

1 Motivate

Bellringer

Before presenting the lesson, display **Section Focus Transparency 60** on the overhead projector. Use the accompanying **Focus Activity** worksheet. L2 ELL

Section 21-1

SECTION FOCUS TRANSPARENCY

GLUED TO THE TUBE

These giant tube worms live deep below the surface of the ocean where no sunlight reaches. Some tube worms grow several meters high. They feed on bacteria that actually live inside the tubes. There are about 10 billion bacteria in each gram of tissue within the tube worm.

1. How does the size of a tube worm compare to the size of bacteria?
2. Do you think that other organisms could tolerate having so much bacteria? Give a reason for your answer.

60

Tying to Previous Knowledge

Review the parts of a cell and the characteristics of living things with students. Point out that not all cells have the same parts.

Caption Answer

Figure 21-1 *chlorophyll*

21•1 Two Kingdoms of Bacteria

What You'll Learn

- The characteristics of bacterial cells
- The differences between aerobic and anaerobic organisms

Vocabulary

flagella **fission** **aerobe** **anaerobe**

Why It's Important

- Bacteria are found in all environments. They affect all living things.

What are bacteria?

When most people hear the word *bacteria,* they probably associate it with sore throats or other illnesses. However, very few bacteria cause illness. Most are important for other reasons. Bacteria are almost everywhere—in the air you breathe, the food you eat, the water you drink, and even at great ocean depths. A shovelful of soil contains billions of them. Millions of bacteria live on and in your body. Many are beneficial to you.

There are two types of cells—prokaryotic and eukaryotic. Bacteria are prokaryotes because they have no true nucleus. The nuclear material of a bacterial cell is made up of one or more circular chromosomes. Bacteria have cell walls and cell membranes and also contain ribosomes. Structures inside bacterial cells are not surrounded by membranes.

Types of Bacteria

Bacteria are grouped into two kingdoms—eubacteria (yoo bak TIHR ee uh) and archaebacteria (ar kee bak TIHR ee uh). Some eubacteria, such as the cyanobacteria in **Figure 21-1,** contain chlorophyll, which enables them to make their own food. They obtain their energy from the sun by photosynthesis. Most eubacteria do not make their own food. Some break down dead organisms to obtain energy. Others live as parasites and absorb nutrients from living organisms. Archaebacteria live in habitats where few organisms can live and obtain energy in other ways.

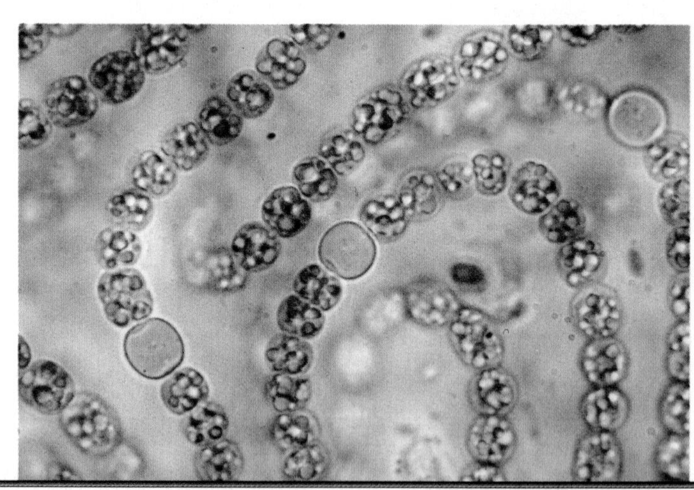

Figure 21-1 These cyanobacteria make their own food. **What do cyanobacteria contain that enables them to make food?**

Magnification: 1250×

Resource Manager

The following **Teacher Classroom Resources** can be used with Section 21-1:

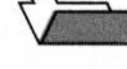 **Reproducible Masters**

Activity Worksheets, pp. 117–118, 121 L2

Enrichment, p. 60 L3

Laboratory Manual, pp. 131–132

Reinforcement, p. 60 L2

Study Guide, p. 81 L1 ELL

 **Transparencies**

Teaching Transparency 41 L2

Science Integration Transparency 21 L2

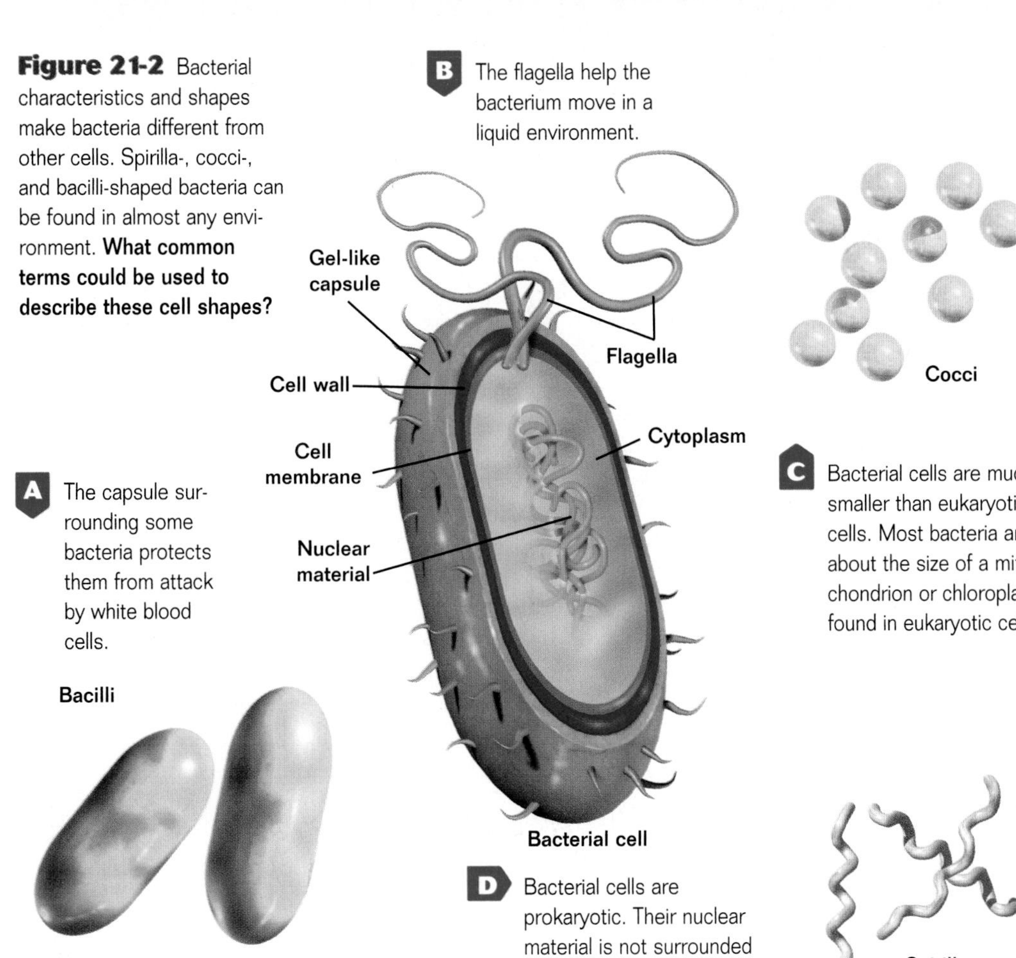
The flagella help the bacterium move in a liquid environment.
Gel-like capsule
Flagella
Cell wall
Cell membrane
Cytoplasm
Nuclear material
Cocci
Bacilli
Bacterial cell
Spirilla
The capsule surrounding some bacteria protects them from attack by white blood cells.
Bacterial cells are much smaller than eukaryotic cells. Most bacteria are about the size of a mitochondrion or chloroplast found in eukaryotic cells.
Bacterial cells are prokaryotic. Their nuclear material is not surrounded by a membrane.

Figure 21-2 Bacterial characteristics and shapes make bacteria different from other cells. Spirilla-, cocci-, and bacilli-shaped bacteria can be found in almost any environment. **What common terms could be used to describe these cell shapes?**

Bacterial Shapes

The bacteria that normally inhabit your home and body have three basic shapes—spheres, rods, and spirals. Sphere-shaped bacteria are called *cocci* (sing. *coccus*), rod-shaped bacteria are called *bacilli* (sing. *bacillus*), and spiral-shaped bacteria are called *spirilla* (sing. *spirillum*). The general characteristics of bacteria can be seen in the bacillus shown in **Figure 21-2.** It contains cytoplasm surrounded by a cell membrane and wall. Bacterial chromosomes are not located in a membrane-bound nucleus but are found in the cytoplasm. Some bacteria have a thick, gel-like capsule around the cell wall. The capsule helps the bacterium stick to surfaces. How does a capsule help a bacterium to survive?

Many bacteria float freely in the environment on air and water currents, your hands, your shoes, and even the family dog or cat. Many that live in moist conditions have whiplike tails called **flagella** to help them move.

Reading Check
What are flagella?

Inclusion Strategies

Gifted Have students research botulism. They can collect articles from magazines, newspapers, etc. They should find out as much as they can about botulin, the organism that causes botulism. As a group, they can problem solve and try to find a solution to help society cope with the disease. L3 COOP LEARN P

Across the Curriculum

Math Ask students whether they would rather have $10 every 20 minutes for 13 hours or start with one penny and have their money doubled every 20 minutes for 13 hours. *$400 by arithmetic growth or more than $5 trillion by exponential growth.* Point out that the growth rate of bacteria is like that of the penny.

2 Teach

Answer to Reading Check

whiplike tails that allow bacteria to move around in moist environments

Caption Answer

Figure 21-2 *Answers could include sphere, spiral, and rod shaped.*

Discussion

Interpersonal Have groups of students discuss the possible combinations of cocci, such as pairs (diplococci), strands (streptococci), clusters (staphylococci), etc. Explain that different species of bacteria assume all these shapes. L2 COOP LEARN

Correcting Misconceptions

Point out that prokaryotes look simple. All living cells are, in fact, complex.

Quick Demo

Visual-Spatial Demonstrate the classification of bacteria through staining by allowing students to view commercially produced slides of gram-positive and gram-negative bacteria.

Using Science Words

Linguistic Have students compare definitions of *flagella* and *flagellation.* Ask them to describe how the words are related. L2

CA Science Content Standards

Page 738: 5c, 6a
Page 739: 5c, 6a

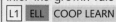

Mini Lab

Purpose

Logical-Mathematical Students will observe and infer the growth rate of bacteria.

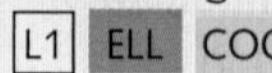

L1 ELL COOP LEARN

Materials

dried beans, distilled water, beaker, methylene blue, microscope, dropper, slides, coverslips

Teaching Strategies

- You may want to soak the beans for 24 hours prior to doing the lab. This makes it easier for students to break them apart.
- Point out that the cloudiness of the water is an indication of bacterial growth.

Safety Precautions

Tell students not to eat any of the materials and to wash their hands after handling them.

Troubleshooting Caution students not to leave beans and water in the classroom for more than five days.

Analysis

1. It usually takes three or four days.
2. bacteria
3. beans

Assessment

Process Have students hypothesize the doubling time of bacterial cells. Then have them design an experiment to test their hypothesis. Use **Performance Assessment in the Science Classroom,** p. 21.

Mini Lab

Observing Bacterial Growth

Procedure

1. Obtain two or three dried beans.
2. Break them into halves and place the halves into 10 mL of distilled water in a glass beaker.
3. Observe how many days it takes for the water to become cloudy and develop an unpleasant odor.
4. Use methylene blue to dye a drop of water from the beaker and observe it under the microscope.

Analysis

1. How long did it take for the water to become cloudy?
2. What did you observe on the slide that would make the water cloudy?
3. What do you think the bacteria were feeding on?

Eubacteria

Eubacteria is the larger of the two bacterial kingdoms. It contains so many organisms that it is hard to classify. All bacteria except archaebacteria, which you will learn about later in this chapter, are considered to be eubacteria, or "true bacteria." These organisms live in much less harsh environments than archaebacteria. As illustrated in **Figure 21-3,** eubacteria include many diverse groups, from species that live off other organisms to those that can make their own food.

Cyanobacteria

One type of eubacteria is known as cyanobacteria. Cyanobacteria are eubacteria that are producers. They make their own food using carbon dioxide, water, and energy from sunlight. Cyanobacteria contain chlorophyll and another pigment that is blue. This pigment combination gives cyanobacteria their common name, blue-green bacteria. However, some cyanobacteria are yellow, black, or red. The Red Sea gets its name from red cyanobacteria.

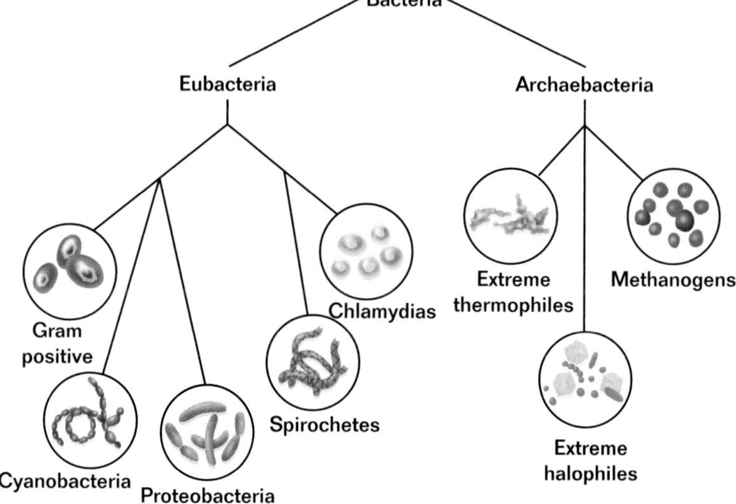

Figure 21-3 Bacteria are divided into two main groups—archaebacteria and eubacteria. **Which group contains the largest variety of organisms?**

Teacher FYI

Bacteria reproduce so quickly that there are now estimated to be five million trillion trillion of them living on Earth. If all these bacteria were gathered in one place, they would weigh as much as the United Kingdom.

Caption Answer

Figure 21-3 *eubacteria*

GLENCOE TECHNOLOGY

CD-ROM

Glencoe Science Voyages Interactive CD-ROM

Explorations

Have students do the interactive exploration *What kills germs?*

All species of cyanobacteria are one-celled organisms. However, some of these organisms live together in long chains or filaments. Look again at **Figure 21-1.** Many are covered with a gel-like substance. This adaptation enables cyanobacteria to live in globular groups called colonies. Cyanobacteria are important for food production in lakes and ponds. Since cyanobacteria make food from carbon dioxide, water, and the energy from sunlight, fish in a healthy pond can eat them and use the energy released from that food.

Have you ever seen a pond covered with smelly, green, bubbly slime? When large amounts of nutrients enter a pond, cyanobacteria and various algae increase in number and produce a matlike growth called a bloom. Available resources are quickly consumed and the cyanobacteria and various algae die. Bacteria feed on them and use up all the oxygen in the water. As a result, fish and other organisms die.

Using Math

Figure 21-4 shows a bacterium that is dividing into two cells. Measure the length of one of the new cells in millimeters. Determine the actual size of the cell by dividing the measured length by the magnification.

Problem Solving

Controlling Bacterial Growth

Bacteria may be controlled by slowing their growth, preventing their growth, or killing them. When trying to control bacteria that affect humans, it is often desirable to slow just their growth because substances that prevent bacteria from growing or that kill bacteria may harm humans. For example, bleach often is used to kill bacteria in bathrooms or on kitchen surfaces, but it is poisonous if swallowed. Antiseptic is the word used to describe substances that slow the growth of bacteria. Advertisers often claim that a substance kills bacteria, when in fact, the substance only slows the bacteria's growth. Many mouthwash advertisements, however, make this claim. How could you test several mouthwashes to see which one is the best antiseptic?

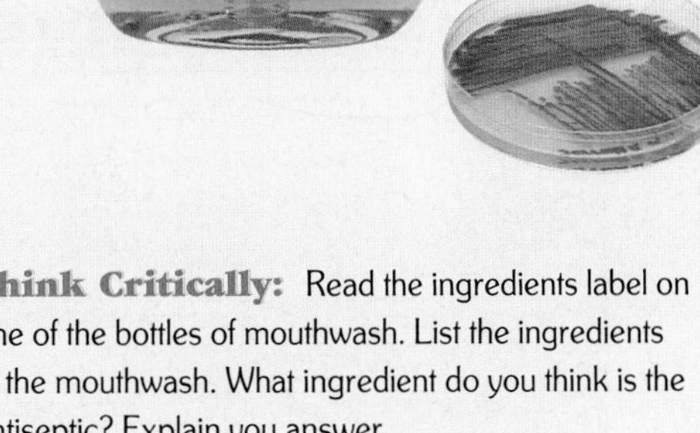

Solve the Problem

1. Choose three mouthwashes and describe an experiment that you could do to find the best antiseptic mouthwash of the three.
2. What controls would you use in your experiment?

Think Critically: Read the ingredients label on one of the bottles of mouthwash. List the ingredients in the mouthwash. What ingredient do you think is the antiseptic? Explain you answer.

Using Math

38 mm ÷ 9400 = 0.00404 mm, or slightly more than four one-thousandths of a millimeter. You also may want students to multiply the result by 1000 to find the length in micrometers. The result will be 4.04 μm.

Problem Solving

Kinesthetic Review the methods of science with students. Include hypothesis, experimentation, and controls in the review.

Solve the Problem

1. Students could place disks of paper soaked in different mouthwashes in petri dishes that have bacteria growing on them.
2. Paper disks soaked in distilled water could be used as controls.

Think Critically

Alcohol is the main active ingredient. Water, glycerin, preservatives, and dyes are also included. The dyes are solely for appearance.

Guided Reading Strategy

FlowChart A flowchart helps students logically sequence events. Students will write major stages of the sequence in large ovals and write sub-stages in smaller ovals under the larger ovals. Have students design a flowchart for a concept in this section. Sample flowchart:

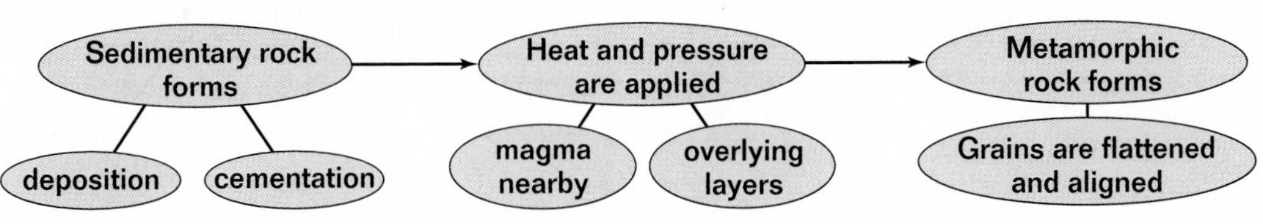

CA Science Content Standards

Page 740: 5c, 6a
Page 741: 5c, 6a, 9a, 9c, 9f

EARTH SCIENCE INTEGRATION

Black smokers were first found at volcanic vents near the Galápagos Islands. Since then, they have been found at various locations where tectonic plates collide. Archaebacteria found at these vents are the basis for an entire community based on sulfur metabolism. Scientists hypothesize that the first organisms resembled these archaebacteria.

Caption Answer

Figure 21-5 *The bacteria would have to overcome heat, high mineral content, and low oxygen levels.* Point out that these conditions are thought to be similar to those on primitive Earth.

3 Assess

Check for Understanding

Activity

Interpersonal Have students work in pairs to answer the section assessment questions to better understand the section content. L2 COOP LEARN

Reteach

Visual-Spatial To demonstrate decay, bring a piece of decomposing fruit to class. Have students observe the process over a few days or a week. L1 ELL

Extension

For students who have mastered this section, use the **Reinforcement** and **Enrichment** masters.

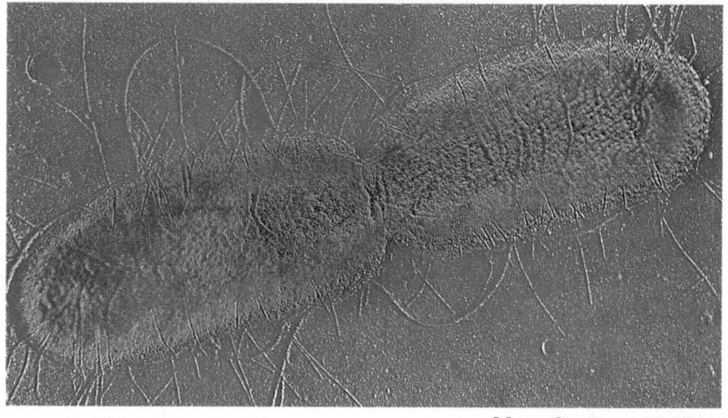

Figure 21-4 In this color-enhanced electron micrograph, a bacterium is shown undergoing fission.

Magnification: 14 400×

Reproduction

Bacteria reproduce by fission, as shown in **Figure 21-4. Fission** produces two cells with genetic material identical to that of the parent cell. It is the simplest form of asexual cell reproduction. Some bacteria exchange genetic material through a process similar to sexual reproduction. Two bacteria line up beside each other and exchange DNA through a fine tube. This results in cells with different genetic material than their parents. As a result, the bacteria may have variations that give them an advantage for surviving in changing environments.

Most bacteria live in places where there is a supply of oxygen. An organism that uses oxygen for respiration is called an **aerobe** (AY rohb). You are an aerobic organism. In contrast, some organisms, called **anaerobes** (AN uh rohbz), have variations that allow them to live without oxygen.

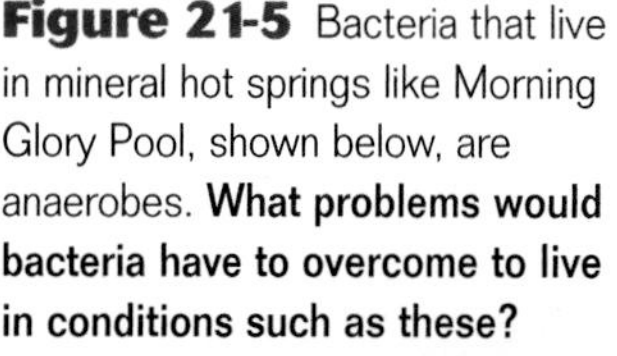

Figure 21-5 Bacteria that live in mineral hot springs like Morning Glory Pool, shown below, are anaerobes. **What problems would bacteria have to overcome to live in conditions such as these?**

Multiple Learning Styles

Kinesthetic For students who learn primarily kinesthetically, have students illustrate the binary fission of a bacterial chromosome by wrapping two pieces of yarn tied in circles around each other. Hold the circles down at one point and draw them apart.

Content Background

Binary fission is a means of reproduction in stable environments with readily available resources. When resources become limited, bacteria may reproduce via conjugation. The resulting bacteria have genetic variations that allow them to survive in the new conditions.

Archaebacteria

Kingdom Archaebacteria contains certain kinds of anaerobic bacteria, which, like eubacteria, are thought to have existed for billions of years. They are found in extreme conditions, such as the hot springs shown in **Figure 21-5,** salty lakes, muddy swamps, the intestines of cattle, and near deep ocean vents where life exists without sunlight. The conditions in which archaebacteria live today may resemble conditions found on early Earth.

Archaebacteria are divided into three groups, based on how they get energy. There are methanogens, halophiles, and thermophiles. The methanogens use carbon dioxide for energy and produce the methane gas that bubbles up out of swamps and marshes. The extreme halophiles live in salty environments such as the Great Salt Lake in Utah and the Dead Sea. Some of them require a habitat ten times saltier than seawater to grow. The last group of archaebacteria is the extreme thermophiles that survive in hot areas like the one shown in **Figure 21-6.**

Figure 21-6 Thermophiles get energy by breaking down sulfur compounds such as those escaping from the deep-sea vent found near these tube worms.

Section Assessment

1. What are the characteristics of bacteria?
2. How do aerobic and anaerobic organisms differ?
3. How do bacteria reproduce?
4. **Think Critically:** A mat of cyanobacteria is found growing on a lake with dead fish floating along the edge. What has caused these events to occur?
5. **Skill Builder**
   Interpreting Data Do the **Chapter 21 Skill Activity** on page 982 to interpret the data to determine which substance best prevents bacterial growth.

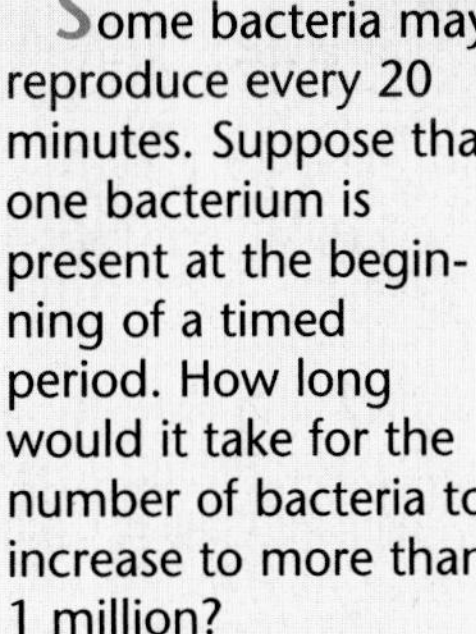

Some bacteria may reproduce every 20 minutes. Suppose that one bacterium is present at the beginning of a timed period. How long would it take for the number of bacteria to increase to more than 1 million?

4 Close

Proficiency Prep

Use this quiz to check students' recall of section content.

1. **What does the nuclear material of bacteria consist of?** *chromosomes*
2. **What process produces two cells with genetic material exactly like the parent cell?** *fission*
3. **What are organisms that can live without oxygen called?** *anaerobes*

Section Assessment

1. prokaryotic cells without membrane-bound organelles; nuclear material consists of one or more circular chromosomes; have a cell wall, cell membranes, and ribosomes
2. Aerobic organisms require oxygen to live; anaerobic organisms can live without oxygen.
3. All reproduce by fission, some also reproduce sexually.
4. Think Critically Bacteria feeding on cyanobacteria probably removed all of the oxygen from the water.

List the number present at each 20-minute interval. Each number is twice the previous number.

Answer: It would take 6 hours and 40 minutes to produce 1 048 576 bacteria.

Enrichment

Many communities provide free or low-cost compost to citizens. Check to see whether your community maintains a compost pile. You also can create a science classroom compost pile on some area of the school property. Allow students to check their compost piles and explain how bacteria work to decay the organic material in the pile.

Performance To further assess students' ability to observe cyanobacteria, set up a test where students observe slides and must identify organisms and answer questions about them. Use **Performance Assessment in the Science Classroom,** p. 49.

CA Science Content Standards

Page 742: 5c, 6a
Page 743: 5c, 6a

Activity 21•1

Purpose

Naturalist Students will observe and record the characteristics of several cyanobacteria. L2 ELL

Process Skills

observing, classifying, interpreting data, forming operational definitions

Time

50 minutes

Teaching Strategies

Troubleshooting If students have trouble seeing the jellylike layer, have them reduce the amount of light coming through the microscope's diaphragm.

Answers to Questions

1. Cyanobacteria are bluer than leaves but contain chlorophyll. Therefore, they can undergo photosynthesis.
2. Cyanobacteria are cells without visible nuclei that contain chlorophyll.
3. Cyanobacteria appear blue-green in color and may form slimy colonies in water.

Assessment

Performance Have students draw, label, and describe different cyanobacteria they observe. Use **Performance Assessment in the Science Classroom,** p. 55.

CA Science Content Standards

Page 744: 5c
Page 745: 5c

Activity 21•1 Using Scientific Methods

Observing Cyanobacteria

Materials

- Micrograph photos (see below)
  - **prepared slides of* Gloeocapsa *and* Anabaena
  - **microscope*

**Alternate Materials*

You can obtain many species of cyanobacteria from ponds. When you look at these organisms under a microscope, you will find that they have many similarities but that they are also different from each other in important ways. In this activity, you will compare and contrast species of cyanobacteria.

What You'll Investigate

What do cyanobacteria look like?

Goals

- **Observe** several species of cyanobacteria.
- **Describe** the structure and function of cyanobacteria.

Safety Precautions  

Procedure

1. **Make a data table** in your Science Journal. Indicate whether each cyanobacterium sample is in colony form or filament form. Write a *yes* or *no* for the presence or absence of each characteristic in each type of cyanobacterium.

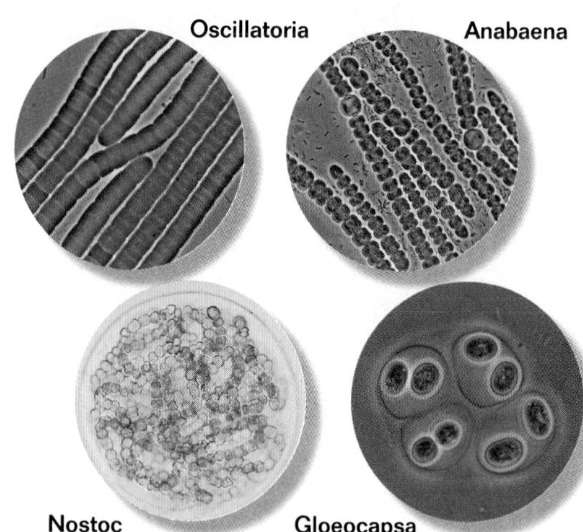

2. **Observe** photos or prepared slides, if available, of *Gloeocapsa* and *Anabaena.* If using slides, observe under the low and high power of the microscope. Notice the difference in the arrangement of the cells. In your Science Journal, draw and label a few cells of each species of cyanobacterium.
3. **Observe** photos of *Nostoc* and *Oscillatoria.* In your Science Journal, draw and label a few cells of each.

Conclude and Apply

1. How does the color of cyanobacteria compare with the color of leaves on trees? What can you infer from this?
2. How can you tell by **observing** them that cyanobacteria belong to Kingdom Eubacteria?
3. **Describe** the general appearance of cyanobacteria.

Cyanobacteria Observations

Structure	Anabaena	Gloeocapsa	Nostoc	Oscillatoria
Filament or colony	filament	colony	filament	filament
Nucleus	no	no	no	no
Chlorophyll	yes	yes	yes	yes
Gel-like layer	yes	yes	yes	yes

Science Journal

Habitat From the point of view of a frog or fish, write an essay that describes the habitat in which you would expect to find an abundance of cyanobacteria. Include what might happen if the population of cyanobacteria becomes too high.

Bacteria in Your Life 21•2

Beneficial Bacteria

Have you had any bacteria for lunch lately? Any time you eat cheese or yogurt, you eat some bacteria. Bacteria break down substances in milk to make many everyday products. Cheese-making is illustrated in **Figure 21-7.** If you have eaten sauerkraut, you ate a product made with cabbage and a bacterial culture. Vinegar is also produced by a bacterium.

Figure 21-7 Bacteria that break down proteins in milk are used in production of various kinds of cheese.

A Bacteria such as *Streptococcus lactis* added to milk cause the milk to curdle, or separate into curds (solids) and whey (liquids).

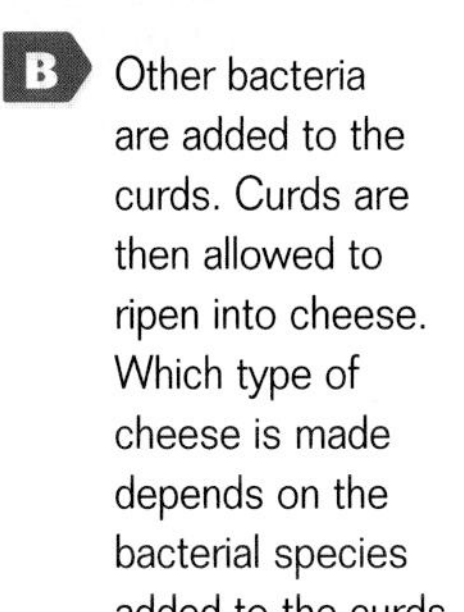

B Other bacteria are added to the curds. Curds are then allowed to ripen into cheese. Which type of cheese is made depends on the bacterial species added to the curds.

What You'll Learn

- Some ways bacteria are helpful
- The importance of nitrogen-fixing bacteria
- How some bacteria cause disease

Vocabulary

saprophyte
nitrogen-fixing bacteria
pathogen
antibiotic
vaccine
toxin
endospore

Why It's Important

- Discovering the ways bacteria affect your life can help you understand biological processes.

Uses of Bacteria

Bacteria called saprophytes (SAP ruh fitz) help maintain nature's balance. A **saprophyte** is any organism that uses dead material as a food and energy source. Saprophytes digest dead organisms and recycle nutrients so that they are available for use by other organisms. Without saprophytic bacteria, there would be layers of dead material deeper than you are tall spread over all of Earth. ☑

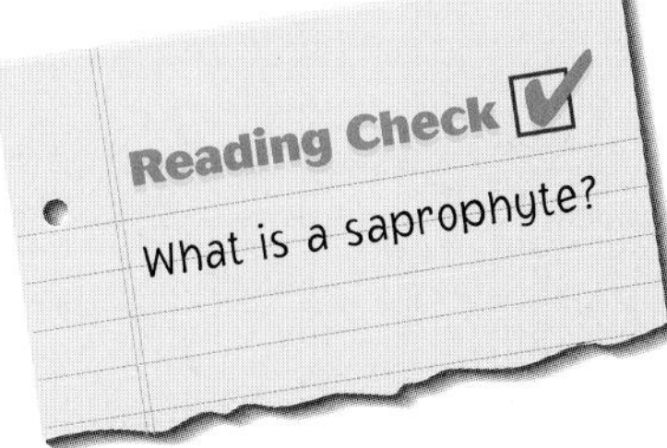
Reading Check
What is a saprophyte?

Resource Manager

The following **Teacher Classroom Resources** can be used with Section 21-2:

Reproducible Masters

Activity Worksheets, pp.119–120, 122 L2
Critical Thinking/Problem Solving, p. 21 L2
Enrichment, p. 61 L3
Home Involvement, p. 28
Laboratory Manual, pp. 133–134 L2
Multicultural Connections, pp. 41–42 L2
Reinforcement, p. 61 L2
Study Guide, pp. 82–84 L1 ELL

Transparencies

Teaching Transparency 42 L2

SECTION 21•2

Prepare

Content Background

Refer to **Uses of Bacteria, Harmful Bacteria,** and **Pasteurization** on p. 736F.

Preplanning

Refer to the **Chapter Organizer** on pp. 736A–B.

1 Motivate

Bellringer

Before presenting the lesson, display **Section Focus Transparency 61** on the overhead projector. Use the accompanying **Focus Activity** worksheet. L2 ELL

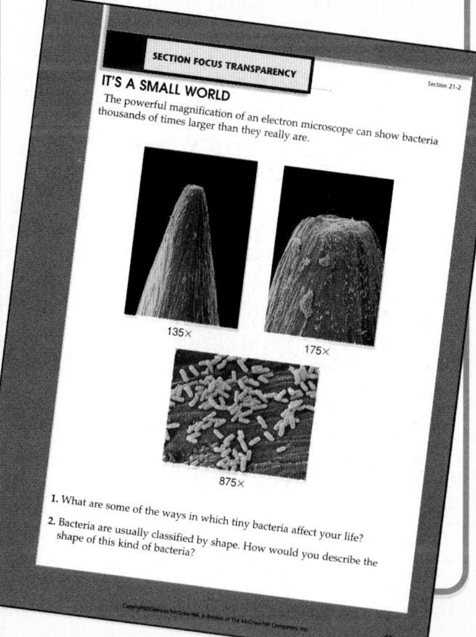

SECTION FOCUS TRANSPARENCY

Section 21-2

IT'S A SMALL WORLD

The powerful magnification of an electron microscope can show bacteria thousands of times larger than they really are.

135×

175×

875×

1. What are some of the ways in which tiny bacteria affect your life?
2. Bacteria are usually classified by shape. How would you describe the shape of this kind of bacteria?

61

Answer to Reading Check

A saprophyte is an organism that uses dead material as a food and energy source.

Tying to Previous Knowledge

Kinesthetic Have students taste cheese curds and cheeses at home. Point out that these foods were prepared using beneficial bacteria. Be sure to caution students who may have allergies to certain foods. L1 ELL

2 Teach

Discussion

- Ask students to define *germs.* Point out that many bacteria are beneficial and not pathogens.
- Discuss bacteria as an organism living in a cooperative relationship with another organism, from which both benefit. For instance, bacteria in humans supply some vitamins and are useful in the digestion of foods high in fiber.

GLENCOE TECHNOLOGY

Glencoe Science Voyages Interactive Videodisc—Life

Side 1, Lesson 3: *Decomposers: Earth's Natural Recyclers*

28262

28564

Refer to the Videodisc Teacher Guide for additional bar codes.

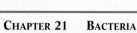

CA Science Content Standards

Page 746: 6b
Page 747: 6b

VISUALIZING Nitrogen Fixation

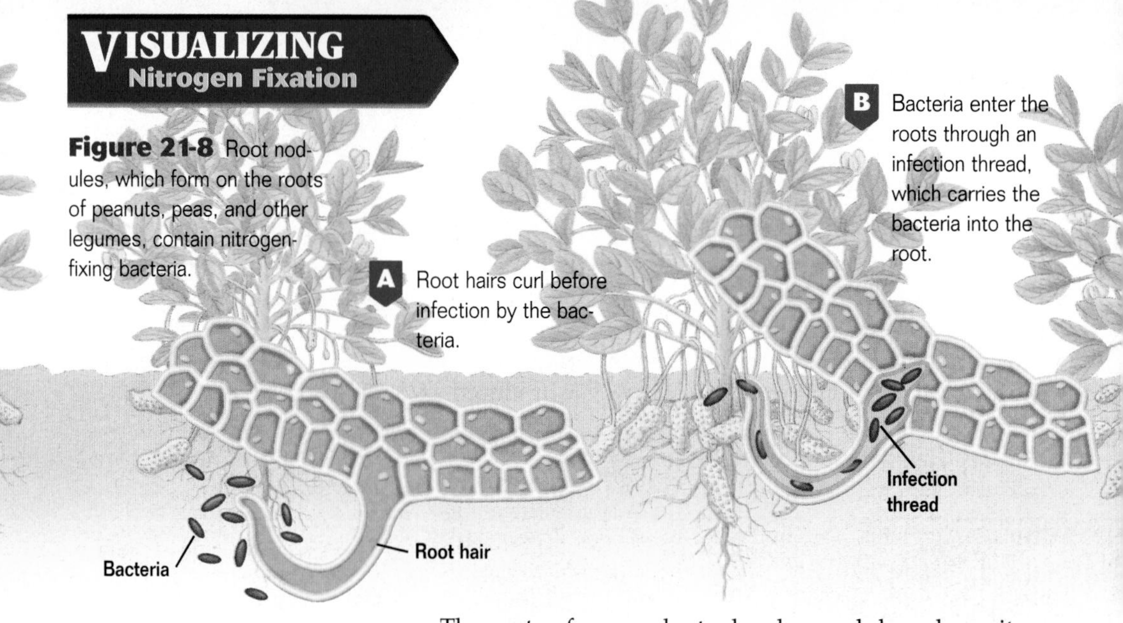

A Root hairs curl before infection by the bacteria.
B Bacteria enter the roots through an infection thread, which carries the bacteria into the root.
Bacteria
Root hair
Infection thread

Figure 21-8 Root nodules, which form on the roots of peanuts, peas, and other legumes, contain nitrogen-fixing bacteria.

The roots of some plants develop nodules when nitrogen-fixing bacteria enter them, as illustrated in **Figure 21-8.** This is especially true of legumes, a plant group that includes peas, peanuts, and clover. These **nitrogen-fixing bacteria** change nitrogen from the air into forms useful for plants and animals. Both plants and animals need nitrogen for making needed proteins and nucleic acids.

Many industries rely on bacteria. Biotechnology is putting bacteria to use in making medicines, enzymes, cleansers, adhesives, and other products. The ability of bacteria to digest oil has been extremely important in helping to clean up the extensive oil spills in Alaska, California, and Texas.

interNET CONNECTION

Visit the Glencoe Science Web Site at **www.glencoe.com/sec/science/ca** for more information about toxin-producing bacteria.

Harmful Bacteria

Some bacteria are pathogens. A **pathogen** is any organism that produces disease. If you have ever had strep throat, you have had firsthand experience with a bacterial pathogen. Other pathogenic bacteria cause anthrax in cattle, and diphtheria, tetanus, and whooping cough in humans. Bacterial diseases in humans and animals are usually treated effectively with antibiotics. An **antibiotic** is a substance produced by one organism that inhibits or kills another organism. Penicillin, a well-known antibiotic, works by preventing bacteria from making cell walls. Without cell walls, bacteria cannot survive.

Some bacterial diseases can be prevented by vaccines. A **vaccine** is made from damaged particles taken from bacterial

VISUAL Learning

Figure 21-8 Have students explain why "infection" of roots by nitrogen-fixing bacteria is beneficial for both plant and environment. *Nitrogen gas in the atmosphere is unusable for most organisms. The bacteria fix nitrogen in a form the plant can use. After the plant dies, nitrogen is available for use by other organisms.* L2

interNET CONNECTION

Internet Addresses

For Internet tips, see Glencoe's **Using the Internet in the Science Classroom.**

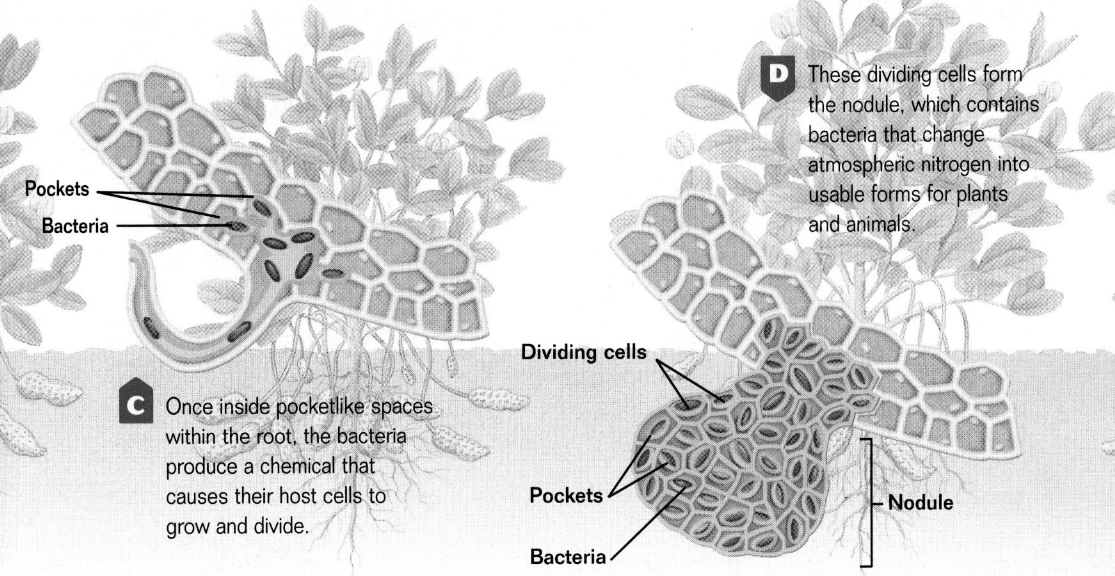

cell walls or from killed bacteria. Once injected, the white blood cells in the body learn to recognize the bacteria. If the particular bacteria then enter the body at a later time, the white blood cells immediately attack and overwhelm them. Vaccines have been produced that are effective against many bacterial diseases.

Pockets
Bacteria
C Once inside pocketlike spaces within the root, the bacteria produce a chemical that causes their host cells to grow and divide.
D These dividing cells form the nodule, which contains bacteria that change atmospheric nitrogen into usable forms for plants and animals.
Dividing cells
Pockets
Bacteria
Nodule

Some pathogens produce poisons. The poison produced by a bacterial pathogen is called a **toxin.** Botulism, a type of food poisoning, is caused by a toxin that can cause paralysis and death. The bacterium that causes botulism is *Clostridium botulinum.* Many bacteria that produce toxins are able to produce thick walls around themselves when conditions are unfavorable. This thick-walled structure is called an **endospore,** illustrated in **Figure 21-9.** Endospores can exist for hundreds of years before they begin to grow again. Botulism endospores must be exposed to heat for a long time to be destroyed. Once the endospores are in canned food, the bacteria can change back to regular cells and start producing toxins. Botulism bacteria are able to grow inside cans because they are anaerobes and do not need oxygen to live.

Making Yogurt

Procedure

1. Bring a liter of milk almost to a boil in a saucepan. **CAUTION:** *Always be careful when using a stove or hot plate. Do not eat food used in a classroom activity.*
2. Remove the pan from the burner and allow it to cool until it is lukewarm.
3. Add one or two heaping tablespoons of yogurt starter with live cultures and stir.
4. Pour the mixture into a clean thermos and put on the lid.
5. Let stand for six hours and then refrigerate overnight.

Analysis

1. What do you think was in the yogurt starter?
2. Infer why you let the milk cool before adding the starter.

Flex Your Brain

Use the Flex Your Brain activity to have students explore BACTERIA AND PLANT ROOTS.

Using an Analogy

Some antibiotics bind to fat-like molecules found in cell membranes. Just like detergents break up food and grease on dirty dishes, these antibiotics break up the fat-like molecules and destroy the cell membrane.

3 Assess

Check for Understanding

Activity

Visual-Spatial Have students make a poster that lists beneficial bacteria and their processes on one side and pathogenic bacteria and their processes on the other side. L2

Try at Home MiniLab

For additional help doing this activity at home, see the corresponding pages in the **Home Involvement** booklet.

Purpose

Interpersonal Students will infer the presence of bacteria in yogurt starter. L2 ELL COOP LEARN

Materials

milk, saucepan, yogurt starter, thermos bottle, hot plate or stove, wooden spoon, refrigerator

Teaching Strategies

Have students work cooperatively to make their yogurt.

Analysis

1. bacteria
2. Yogurt culture is alive and excess heat can kill the bacteria.

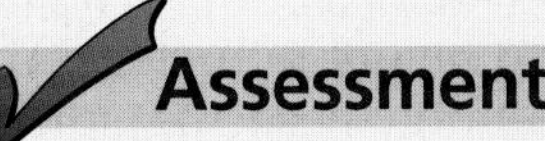

Assessment

Oral Ask students to formulate additional questions that they could test to extend the MiniLab activity. Use **Performance Assessment in the Science Classroom,** p. 19.

Content Background

Some pathogens produce exotoxins, which are proteins secreted by bacteria. Exotoxins produce symptoms even if the bacteria aren't present. Other bacteria produce endotoxins, which produce symptoms only when endotoxins are present.

Reteach

Have students list what beneficial bacteria and harmful bacteria do. L1

Extension

For students who have mastered this section, use the **Reinforcement** and **Enrichment** masters.

Caption Answer

Figure 21-9 *by exposing them to heat for a long time*

Removal of oxygen makes aerobic bacteria unable to reproduce.

4 Close

Proficiency Prep

1. **What is a drug used to kill bacteria called?** *antibiotic*
2. **What is the poison that pathogens produce called?** *toxin*

Section Assessment

1. They maintain homeostasis by recycling nutrients.
2. They change nitrogen from the atmosphere into a form that can be used by plants and animals.
3. It prevents bacteria from forming cell walls.
4. **Think Critically** The bacteria that cause botulism are anaerobes.

Using Computers

Tetanus is transmitted by objects. Other listed diseases are transmitted through the air. All listed diseases are caused by bacteria.

Figure 21-9 Bacteria sometimes form endospores when conditions become unfavorable. These structures can survive harsh winters, dry conditions, and heat. In this photo, the blue in the center of each structure is the endospore. The golden part is the cellular material. **How can botulism endospores be destroyed?**

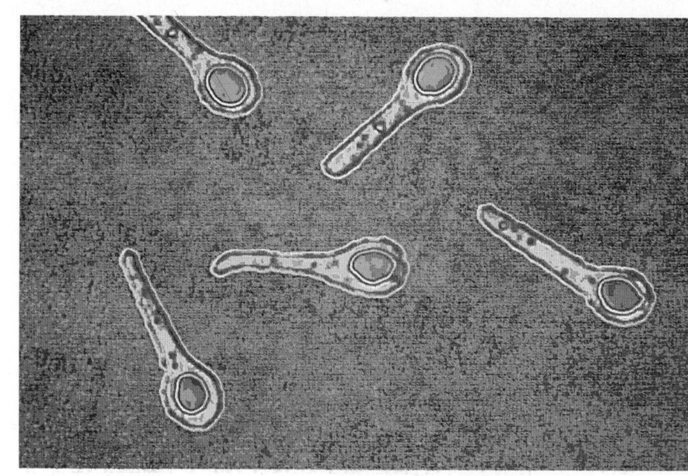

Magnification: 15 000×

Vacuum Packing
A vacuum is a space from which all gas molecules have been removed. Vacuum-packed foods have most of the air removed from around the food. How would this prevent food from spoiling?

Pasteurization

Pasteurization, a process of heating food to a temperature that kills harmful bacteria, is used in the food industry. You are probably most familiar with pasteurized milk, but some fruit juices are also pasteurized. The process is named for Louis Pasteur, who first formulated the process for the wine industry during the nineteenth century in France.

Section Assessment

1. Why are saprophytes helpful and necessary?
2. Why are nitrogen-fixing bacteria important?
3. What makes penicillin an effective antibiotic?
4. **Think Critically:** Why is botulism associated with canned foods and not fresh foods?
5. **Skill Builder**
   Measuring in SI Air may have more than 3500 bacteria per cubic meter. How many bacteria might be in your classroom? If you need help, refer to Measuring in SI in the **Skill Handbook** on page 964.

Using Computers

Spreadsheet Create a spreadsheet that includes: Disease Name, Disease Organism, Method of Transmission, and Symptoms. Enter information for the following diseases: whooping cough, tuberculosis, tetanus, diphtheria, and scarlet fever. Sort your data using Method of Transmission. If you need help, refer to page 974.

5. **Skill Builder**
Have students measure the classroom to find its length, width, and height in meters. Then have them multiply these measurements to obtain the volume in cubic meters. Multiply the volume by 3500 to obtain the number of bacteria per cubic meter.

Assessment

Performance Assess students' abilities to measure in SI units by having them calculate the same situation for a room at home. Use **Performance Assessment in the Science Classroom,** p. 29.

Science & Society

Bioremediation

Each year, tons of pollutants are released into ecosystems because of human activities. Many of these pollutants are both poisonous and long lasting. Soil, surface, and groundwater contamination results from the buildup of these harmful compounds. Traditional methods of cleaning up damaged ecosystems, such as the use of landfills and toxic-waste dumps, can be costly and ineffective as long-term solutions.

An Unusual Solution

One approach to cleaning up polluted ecosystems is bioremediation—the use of living organisms, such as bacteria, fungi, and plants, to change pollutants into harmless compounds. Some microorganisms naturally have the ability to break down harmful compounds. Scientists find and isolate these organisms, often stimulating them to clean up polluted areas. Other times, it is necessary to genetically engineer a microorganism to break down specific pollutants. Archaebacteria and eubacteria are the main organisms used in bioremediation efforts. These microorganisms break down polluting substances—even oil and gasoline—and change them into less damaging compounds, such as carbon dioxide and water. At left, technicians spray a fertilizer mix on an oil-soaked shore to promote the growth of oil-eating bacteria. Although bioremediation is not a complete cure, it is a new way to help repair damaged ecosystems.

Uses and Advantages of Bioremediation

About five to ten percent of all industrial, agricultural, and municipal wastes are being treated by bioremediation. To clean water, for example, bacteria are placed in lagoons or large containers. Then, wastewater is pumped through these sites, and the bacteria break down the pollutants in the water into harmless compounds. In another technique, pollutants are mixed into soil and broken down by microorganisms found there. An advantage of bioremediation is that it can eliminate hazardous waste where it occurs, rather than at a distant treatment site. Bioremediation has proven to be safe and effective, and it costs 60 to 90 percent less than many traditional methods.

interNET CONNECTION

Use the Glencoe Science Web Site at **www.glencoe.com/sec/science/ca** to research local waste treatment companies. Do more companies use traditional methods or bioremediation? Try to find out why a company uses a particular method.

Science & Society

Teaching Strategies

- Have students find out where the local wastewater-treatment plant is located and draw a map that displays this location in relation to water sources such as rivers or lakes.
- Take a field trip to a wastewater-treatment plant. If this is not possible, you may be able to have a person who works at a treatment plant visit the classroom.

- Many rural areas of the United States use septic systems to treat wastewater. These are not generally as efficient as municipal wastewater-treatment plants.
- Bioremediation has been demonstrated for a wide variety of organic and toxic compounds. Cleanup of oil spills by bioremediation is likely to increase in the future.

For More Information

Students can use a search engine on the Internet to get more information on bioremediation.

interNET CONNECTION

Internet Addresses

____

____

____

____

For Internet tips, see Glencoe's **Using the Internet in the Science Classroom.**

Integrating the Sciences

Earth Science Bacterial processes are useful in laboratories, sewage-treatment plants, and the food and drug industry. Bioremediation is the use of bacteria to remove harmful materials from soil or water. Some bacteria differentially take up toxins or harmful chemicals. Others convert these materials to less harmful compounds.

CA Science Content Standards

Page 748: 9f
Page 749: 3b, 6a

Activity 21

What You'll Investigate

Purpose

Interpersonal Students will determine the presence of bacteria in foods using a chemical test. L2 ELL COOP LEARN

Process Skills

observing and inferring, recognizing cause and effect, using tables, interpreting data

Procedure

Time

2 class periods

Materials

In addition to materials listed on the student page, you may substitute other dairy products.

Safety Precautions

Students should be reminded not to taste any materials, and to wash their hands thoroughly after the investigation.

Activity 21•2

Are there bacteria in foods?

Materials

- 6 test tubes
- 6 stoppers
- test-tube rack
- felt-tip marker
- 3 droppers
- 3 craft sticks
- Milk, buttermilk, cottage cheese, yogurt, sour cream, water
- bromothymol blue solution (150 mL)

You've learned that bacteria are too small to be seen without a microscope, but is there some way that you can tell if they are present in foods? Because bacteria produce carbon dioxide like other living things, a chemical test that indicates the presence of carbon dioxide can be used to tell if bacteria are growing in foods you eat.

What You'll Investigate

Is there bacteria in the food you eat?

Goals

- **Observe** color changes in test tubes containing food.
- **Determine** which foods contain the most bacteria.

Procedure

1. Use the marker to label the test tubes 1 through 6 and place them in the test tube rack.
2. Add 25 mL of bromothymol blue-indicator solution to each test tube.
3. Using a different dropper each time, add four drops of water to tube 1, four drops of milk to tube 2, and four drops of buttermilk to tube 3. Be careful not to let the drops go down the sides of the tubes.

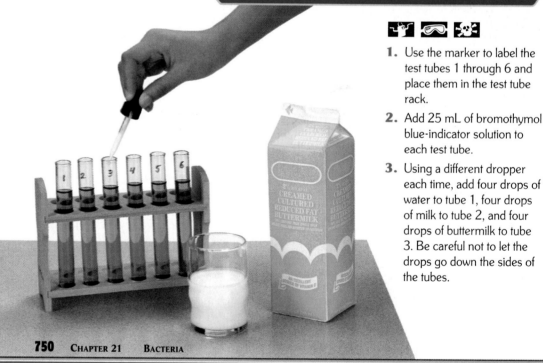

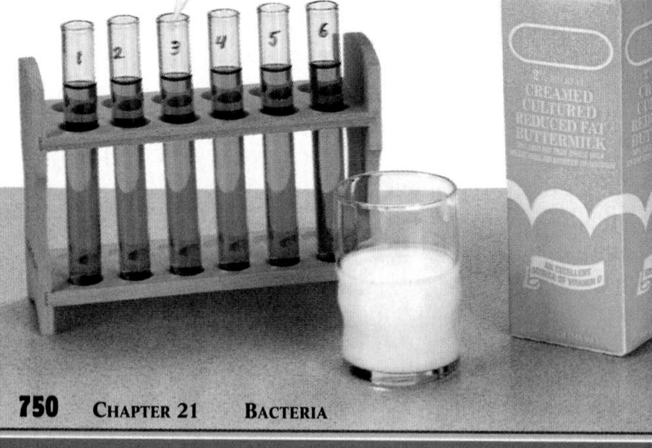

4. Using a different craft stick each time, add an amount of yogurt about the size of a green pea to tube 4, the same amount of cottage cheese to tube 5, and the same amount of sour cream to tube 6.
5. Loosely place a stopper in each tube and record the color of the contents of each tube in a data table.
6. Leave the tubes undisturbed until the end of the class period. Record the color of the contents of the tubes in the data table.
7. The next time you arrive in class, record the color of the contents of the tubes again.

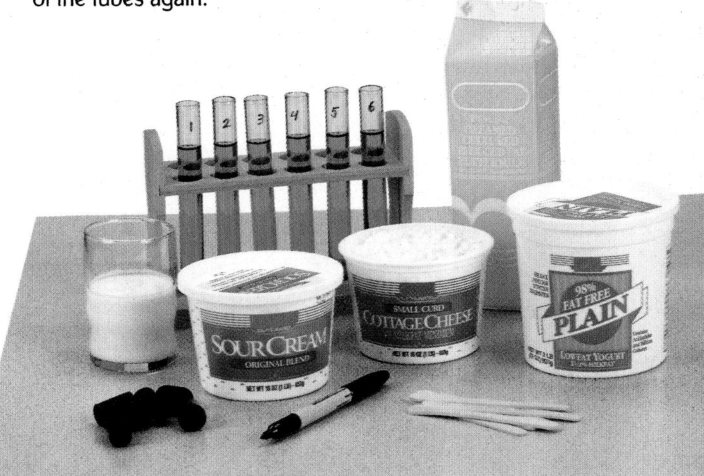

Conclude and Apply

1. Why was water added to tube 1?
2. What color does bromothymol turn if carbon dioxide is present?
3. Using strength of the color change as a guide, judge which tubes contain the most bacteria.

Data Table for Test of Bacteria in Food

Tube	Contents	Color at Start	Color at End of Class	Color One Day Later	Test + or −	Bacteria Present?
1	Water	blue	blue	blue	−	No
2	Milk	blue	green	green	+	Yes
3	Buttermilk	blue	green	green	+	Yes
4	Yogurt	blue	yellow	green	+	Yes
5	Cottage Cheese	blue	yellow	green	+	Yes
6	Sour Cream	blue	yellow	green	+	Yes

Teaching Strategies

Tying to Previous Knowledge Students may recall that bacteria cause milk to separate into curds (for example, cottage cheese) and whey. They may infer from this that cottage cheese and milk contain bacteria.

Expected Outcome

All of the dairy products should test positive, indicating that bacteria is present. The water should test negative, containing no bacteria.

Error Analysis

Have students compare their results and explain why any differences occurred.

Conclude and Apply

1. Water acted as a control so that the negative effect on bromothymol blue could be observed and compared.
2. Bromothymol turns yellow or green if carbon dioxide is present.
3. Students may have varying answers depending on the colors present in their tubes, but buttermilk and yogurt normally have the highest concentrations of bacteria present.

Students may suggest repeating the experiment with other foods.

Linguistic Students should summarize results from the lab in their Science Journal.

Assessment

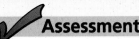

Process Have students predict what other foods or food groups might contain high concentrations of bacteria. Use **Performance Assessment in the Science Classroom,** p 55. P

CA Science Content Standards

Page 750: 6a, 9a, 9b, 9c
Page 751: 6a, 9a, 9b, 9c

Chapter 21 Reviewing Main Ideas

Reviewing Main Ideas can be used to preview, review, reteach, or condense chapter content.

Preview

Linguistic Have students try to answer the questions in their Science Journals. Use student answers as a source for discussion throughout the chapter.

Review

Interpersonal Have students answer the questions on separate pieces of paper and compare their answers with those of other students in the class.

Reteach

Visual-Spatial Have students look at the illustrations on these pages. Ask them to describe details that support the main ideas of the chapter found in the statement for each illustration.

00:00 OUT OF TIME?

Auditory-Musical If time does not permit teaching the entire chapter, use the information on these pages along with the chapter Audiocassettes to present the material in a condensed format.

Chapter 21 Reviewing Main Ideas

For a **preview** of this chapter, study this Reviewing Main Ideas before you read the chapter. After you have studied this chapter, you can use the Reviewing Main Ideas to **review** the chapter.

The Glencoe MindJogger, Audiocassettes, and CD-ROM provide additional opportunities for review.

Section 21-1 TWO KINGDOMS OF BACTERIA

Bacteria are prokaryotic cells that usually reproduce by **fission.** All bacteria contain DNA, ribosomes, and cytoplasm but lack membrane-bound organelles. Bacteria are placed into one of two kingdoms—eubacteria and archaebacteria. The eubacteria are considered to be true bacteria and contain a great variety of organisms. Archaebacteria are bacteria that exist in extreme conditions, such as deep-sea vents and hot springs. Most bacteria break down cells of other organisms to obtain food, but cyanobacteria make their own food. **Anaerobes** are bacteria that are able to live without oxygen, whereas **aerobes** need oxygen to survive. ***How do prokaryotic cells differ from eukaryotic cells?***

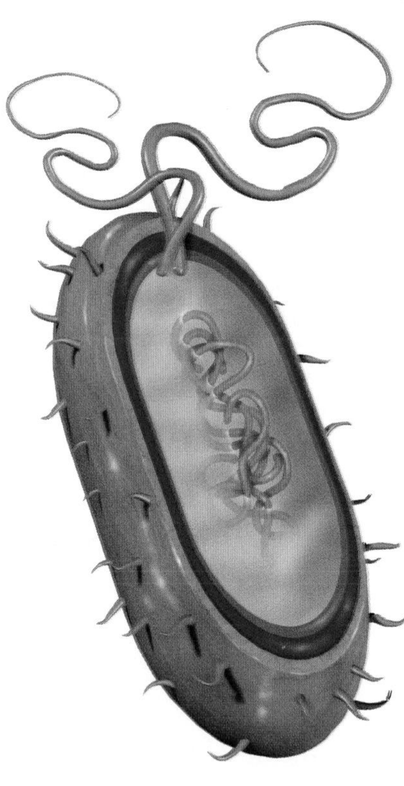

Cultural Diversity

In a Pickle Pickling—a process of food preservation that depends upon the chemical process of fermentation and the prohibition of bacterial growth in a highly acidic solution—is found in the cuisine of many cultures. Have students research different pickling processes and prepare lists of how and what products are pickled in different cultures. L1

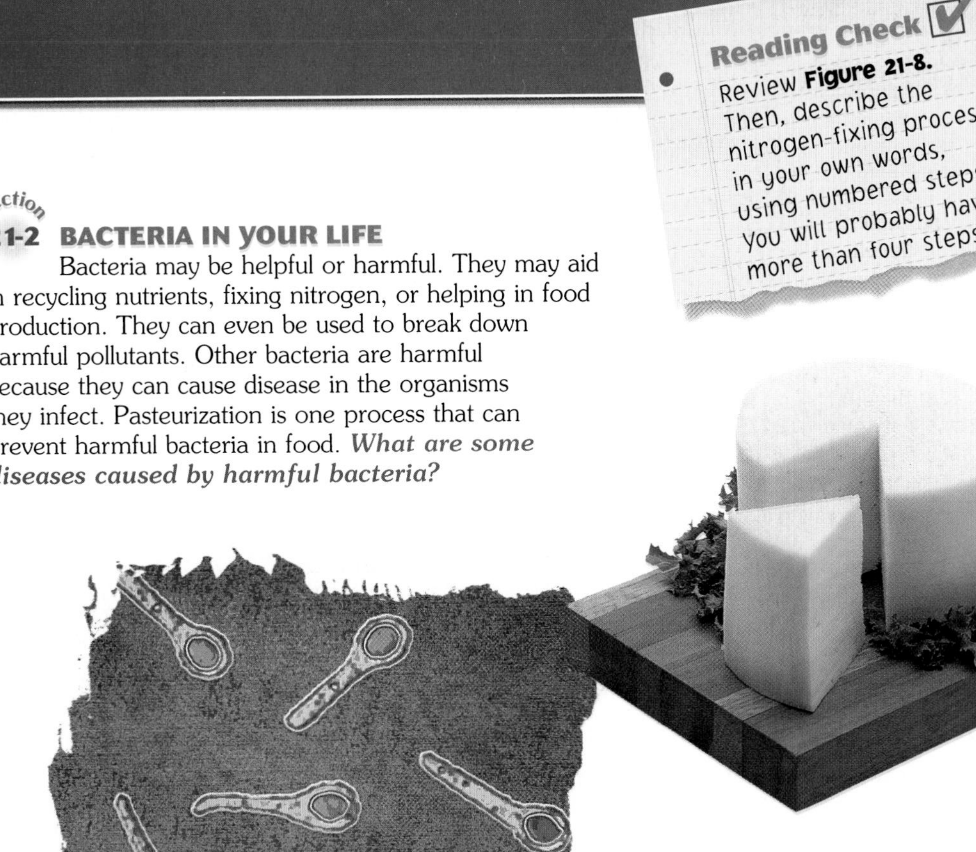

Reading Check ✓

Review **Figure 21-8.** Then, describe the nitrogen-fixing process in your own words, using numbered steps. You will probably have more than four steps.

Section 21-2 BACTERIA IN YOUR LIFE

Bacteria may be helpful or harmful. They may aid in recycling nutrients, fixing nitrogen, or helping in food production. They can even be used to break down harmful pollutants. Other bacteria are harmful because they can cause disease in the organisms they infect. Pasteurization is one process that can prevent harmful bacteria in food. ***What are some diseases caused by harmful bacteria?***

Career CONNECTION

Alice Arellano, Wastewater Operator

Alice Arellano is a wastewater control-room operator responsible for cleaning wastewater in Austin, Texas. Wastewater from peoples' homes in Austin is discharged into the Colorado River, but it first has to be treated. Treatment is a complex process that involves screening, filtering, and chemical treatment. Part of treatment involves using microorganisms, like bacteria, to break down harmful bacteria that live in the wastewater. ***How can understanding the way bacteria live help design water-treatment processes?***

Answers to Questions

Section 21-1

Two Kingdoms of Bacteria Prokaryotic cells do not have a nucleus and do not contain organelles surrounded by membranes.

Section 21-2

Bacteria in Your Life Bacteria may cause diseases such as anthrax, tetanus, and botulism.

GLENCOE TECHNOLOGY

CD-ROM

Glencoe Science Voyages Interactive CD-ROM

Chapter Summaries and Quizzes

Have students read the Chapter Summary, then take the Chapter Quiz to determine whether they have mastered chapter concepts.

Career CONNECTION

Bacteria can be chosen that are able to live in the same environment as the harmful microorganism they are to break down. Once the harmful microorganisms are eliminated, the water can be treated to kill the bacteria.

Assessment

Portfolio Encourage students to place in their portfolios one or two items of what they consider to be their best work. Examples include:

- Assessment, p. 737
- Inclusion Strategies, p. 739
- Assessment, p. 751 P

Performance Additional performance assessments may be found in **Performance Assessment** and **Science Integration Activities.** Performance Task Assessment Lists and rubrics for evaluating these activities can be found in Glencoe's **Performance Assessment in the Science Classroom.**

Using Vocabulary

1. i
2. f
3. d
4. k
5. h

interNET CONNECTION To reinforce chapter vocabulary, use the **Study Guide for Content Mastery** booklet. Also available are activities for **Glencoe Science Voyages** on the Glencoe Science Web Site. **www.glencoe.com/sec/science/ca**

Checking Concepts

6. D	11. A
7. B	12. B
8. A	13. C
9. D	14. D
10. A	15. A

Thinking Critically

16. Nitrogen would no longer be available in the form that plants could use; therefore, the plants would die unless fertilizer was added.
17. Bacteria can reproduce quickly, have means of moving, and can form endospores to survive extreme conditions.
18. Crops like beans, peas, and peanuts have bacteria that are nitrogen fixing. These crops help to increase soil fertility.
19. spheres
20. Using fresh foods and keeping them refrigerated, washing hands and all surfaces and utensils, and properly cooking foods help to prevent food poisoning.

Chapter 21 Assessment

Using Vocabulary

a. aerobe
b. anaerobe
c. antibiotic
d. endospore
e. fission
f. flagella
g. nitrogen-fixing bacteria
h. pathogen
i. saprophyte
j. toxin
k. vaccine

Each phrase below describes a science term from the list. Write the term that matches the phrase describing it.

1. organism that decomposes dead organisms
2. structure by which some organisms move
3. heat-resistant structure in bacteria
4. substance that can prevent, not cure, a disease
5. any organism that produces disease

Checking Concepts

Choose the word or phrase that best answers the question.

6. What is a way of cleaning up an ecosystem using bacteria to break down harmful compounds?
   A) landfills
   B) toxic waste dumps
   C) waste storage
   D) bioremediation
7. What do bacterial cells contain?
   A) nuclei
   B) DNA
   C) mitochondria
   D) no chromosomes
8. What do bacteria that make their own food have?
   A) chlorophyll
   B) lysosomes
   C) Golgi bodies
   D) mitochondria
9. Which of the following describes most bacteria?
   A) anaerobic
   B) pathogens
   C) many-celled
   D) beneficial
10. What is the name for rod-shaped bacteria?
    A) bacilli
    B) cocci
    C) spirilla
    D) colonies
11. What structure(s) allow(s) bacteria to stick to surfaces?
    A) capsule
    B) flagella
    C) chromosome
    D) cell wall
12. What causes blooms in ponds?
    A) archaebacteria
    B) cyanobacteria
    C) cocci
    D) viruses
13. How are nutrients and carbon dioxide returned to the environment?
    A) producers
    B) flagella
    C) saprophytes
    D) pathogens
14. Which of the following is caused by a pathogenic bacterium?
    A) an antibiotic
    B) nitrogen fixation
    C) cheese
    D) strep throat
15. Which organisms do not need oxygen to survive?
    A) anaerobes
    B) aerobes
    C) humans
    D) fish

Thinking Critically

16. What would happen if nitrogen-fixing bacteria could no longer live on the roots of plants?
17. Why are bacteria capable of surviving in all environments of the world?
18. Farmers often rotate crops such as beans, peas, and peanuts with other crops such as corn, wheat, and cotton. Why might they make such changes?
19. One organism that causes bacterial pneumonia is called pneumococcus. What is its shape?
20. What precautions can be taken to prevent food poisoning?

Developing Skills

If you need help, refer to the **Skill Handbook.**

21. Concept Mapping: Use the events chain to sequence the events following a pond bloom.

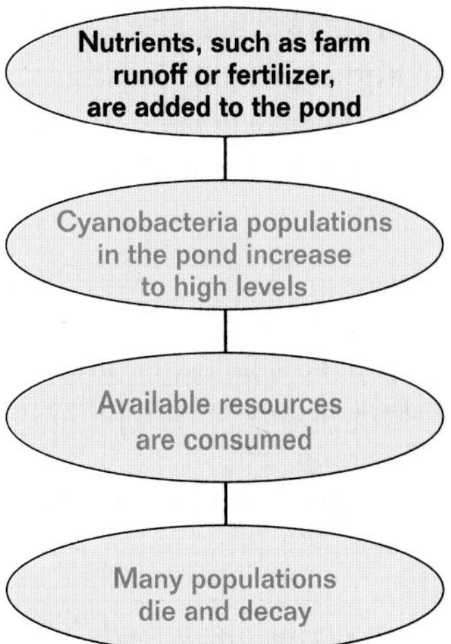

Nutrients, such as farm runoff or fertilizer, are added to the pond
Cyanobacteria populations in the pond increase to high levels
Available resources are consumed
Many populations die and decay

22. Making and Using Graphs: Graph the data from the table below. Using the graph, determine where the doubling rate would be at 20°C.

Bacterial Reproduction Rates

Temperature (°C)	Doubling Rate per Hour
20.5	2.0
30.5	3.0
36.0	2.5
39.2	1.2

23. Interpreting Data: What is the effect of temperature in question 22?

24. Design an Experiment: How could you decide if a kind of bacteria can grow anaerobically?

Test-Taking Tip

Investigate Ask what kinds of questions to expect on the test. Ask for practice tests so that you can become familiar with the test-taking materials.

Test Practice

Use these questions to test your Science Proficiency.

1. One group of bacteria are known as extremophiles, which literally means "lovers of the extreme." Which group of organisms would **BEST** fit this name?
   A) eubacteria
   B) archaebacteria
   C) cyanobacteria
   D) aerobes

2. Bioremediation has been shown to have several advantages over traditional methods of ecosystem cleanup. Which of the following is **NOT** an advantage of bioremediation?
   A) It is less time consuming.
   B) It is less costly.
   C) It is more effective.
   D) It can be done at the site of the pollution.

3. Many bacteria are considered beneficial organisms. Which of the following is **NOT** a reason they are considered beneficial?
   A) They change nitrogen in the air to a form useful for plants.
   B) They cause anthrax in cattle.
   C) They are used in food production.
   D) They are the source of some medicines.

THE PRINCETON REVIEW Test Practice

The Test-Taking Tip was written by The Princeton Review, the nation's leader in test preparation.

1. B
2. A
3. B

Developing Skills

21. See student page.
22. It would be slightly less than 2.0.
23. The most favorable temperature for growth is 30.5°C. Above that, temperature and growth rate have an inverse relationship—the growth rate decreases as the temperature increases.
24. Place the organism in an environment without oxygen and measure its growth rate.

Bonus Question

Assume that a biologist counts 50 000 bacteria in an average drop of yogurt. There are 30 drops of yogurt in a milliliter. Calculate the number of bacteria in a 250-mL serving of yogurt. *50 000 bacteria/drop × 30 drops/mL × 250 mL/serving = 375 000 000 bacteria = 375 million bacteria*

Assessment Resources

The **Test Practice Workbook** provides students with practice in the format, concepts, and critical-thinking skills tested in standardized exams.

Reproducible Masters

Assessment, pp. 81–84 L2
Chapter Review, pp. 41–42 L2
Performance Assessment, p. 21 L2

Glencoe Technology

Chapter Review Software

Computer Test Bank

MindJogger Videoquiz

Chapter 22 Protists and Fungi

Section	Objectives	Activities/Features
Chapter Opener		Explore Activity: Dissect a Mushroom, p. 757
22-1 **Kingdom Protista** 4 Sessions 2 Blocks	1. **Identify** the characteristics shared by all protists. 2. **Describe** the three groups of protists. 3. **Compare** and **contrast** the protist groups.	Earth Science Integration, p. 760 Using Math, p. 765 MiniLab: Observing Slime Molds, p. 766 Problem Solving: Puzzled About Slime, p. 767 Skill Builder: Making and Using Tables, p. 768 Using Computers, p. 768 Activity 22-1: Comparing Algae and Protozoans, p. 769
22-2 **Kingdom Fungi** 3 Sessions 1½ Blocks	4. **Identify** the characteristics shared by all fungi. 5. **Classify** fungi into groups based on their methods of reproduction. 6. **Describe** the difference between the imperfect fungi and all other fungi.	MiniLab: Interpreting Spore Prints, p. 772 Chemistry Integration, p. 773 Skill Builder: Comparing and Contrasting, p. 774 Using Math, p. 774 Science and Society: Monitoring Red Tides, p. 775 Activity 22-2: Comparing Types of Fungi, pp. 776–777

The number of recommended single-period sessions The number of recommended blocks
One session and one-half block are allowed for chapter review and assessment.

Activity Materials

Explore	Activities	MiniLabs
p. 757 edible mushroom, hand lens	p. 769 cultures of paramecium, amoeba, euglena, and spirogyra; prepared slide of slime mold; 5 coverslips; microscope; dropper; 5 microscope slides pp. 776–777 fungi cultures, cellophane tape, microscope, microscope slides, coverslips, hand lens	p. 766 live specimens of the slime mold *Physarum polycephaelum* p. 772 edible mushrooms, unlined paper

Need Materials? Contact Science Kit at 1-800-828-7777 or at www.sciencekit.com on the Internet.
For alternate materials, see the activity on the listed page.

Chapter Organizer

Standards		Reproducible Resources	Technology
National	State/Local	Test Practice Workbooks are available for use with each chapter.	English and Spanish audiocassettes are available for use with each section.
National Content Standards: UCP4, C1, C2, C3, C4, C5, D2, E2, F1	North Carolina Standard Course of Study: S2.02, S2.05, R2c, R3b, W3f, C2.1, C3.4, C3.8, M1.04	**Activity Worksheets,** pp. 123–124, 127 **Enrichment,** p. 62 **Laboratory Manual,** pp. 135–136 **Reinforcement,** p. 62 **Study Guide,** p. 86	**Section Focus Transparency 62** **Teaching Transparency 43** **The Infinite Voyage Series** **Glencoe Science Interactive Videodisc—Life** **Glencoe Science Interactive Videodisc—Earth** **Glencoe Science Voyages Interactive CD-ROM** **Internet Connection,** p. 767
National Content Standards: UCP5, A1, C1, C2, C3, C4, C5, D1, F3, G1, G3	North Carolina Standard Course of Study: S2.02, S2.05, R2a, R2b, R2c, R3b, W2d, W3f, C3.8, M1.03, M1.04	**Activity Worksheets,** pp. 125–126 **Critical Thinking/Problem Solving,** p. 22 **Enrichment,** p. 63 **Home Involvement,** p. 28 **Laboratory Manual,** pp. 137–140 **Multicultural Connections,** pp. 43–44 **Reinforcement,** p. 63 **Study Guide,** pp. 87–88	**Section Focus Transparency 63** **Teaching Transparency 44** **Science Integration Transparency 22** **Glencoe Science Interactive Videodisc—Life** **Internet Connection,** p. 775

Key to Teaching Strategies

The following designations will help you decide which activities are appropriate for your students.

L1 Level 1 activities should be appropriate for students with learning difficulties.

L2 Level 2 activities should be within the ability range of all students.

L3 Level 3 activities are designed for above-average students.

ELL ELL activities should be within the ability range of English Language Learners.

COOP LEARN Cooperative Learning activities are designed for small group work.

P These strategies represent student products that can be placed into a best-work portfolio.

Multiple Learning Styles logos, as described on page 55T, are used throughout to indicate strategies that address different learning styles.

Assessment Resources

Chapter Review, pp. 43–44
Assessment, pp. 85–88
Performance Assessment in the Science Classroom (PASC)
MindJogger Videoquiz
Alternate Assessment in the Science Classroom
Performance Assessment, p. 22
Chapter Review Software
Computer Test Bank

Chapter 22 Protists and Fungi

This is a representation of key blackline masters available in the Teacher Classroom Resources. See Resource Manager boxes within the chapter for additional information.

Section Focus Transparencies

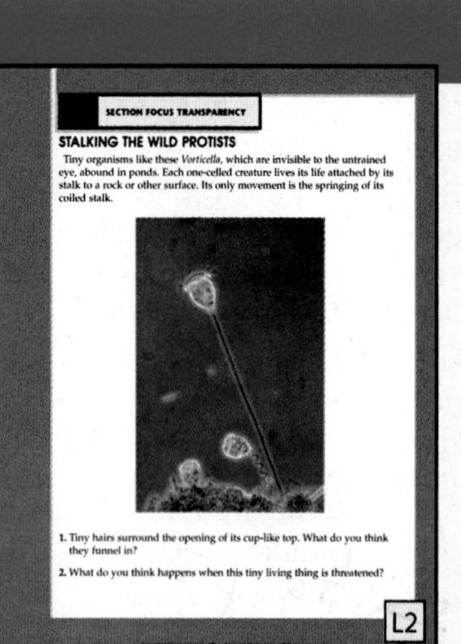
SECTION FOCUS TRANSPARENCY

STALKING THE WILD PROTISTS

Tiny organisms like these *Vorticella*, which are invisible to the untrained eye, abound in ponds. Each one-celled creature lives its life attached by its stalk to a rock or other surface. Its only movement is the springing of its coiled stalk.

1. Tiny hairs surround the opening of its cup-like top. What do you think they funnel in?
2. What do you think happens when this tiny living thing is threatened?

L2

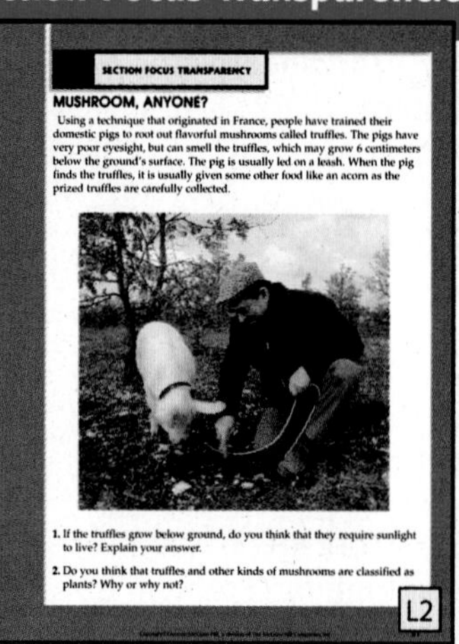
SECTION FOCUS TRANSPARENCY

MUSHROOM, ANYONE?

Using a technique that originated in France, people have trained their domestic pigs to root out flavorful mushrooms called truffles. The pigs have very poor eyesight, but can smell the truffles, which may grow 6 centimeters below the ground's surface. The pig is usually led on a leash. When the pig finds the truffles, it is usually given some other food like an acorn as the prized truffles are carefully collected.

1. If the truffles grow below ground, do you think that they require sunlight to live? Explain your answer.
2. Do you think that truffles and other kinds of mushrooms are classified as plants? Why or why not?

L2

Science Integration Transparencies

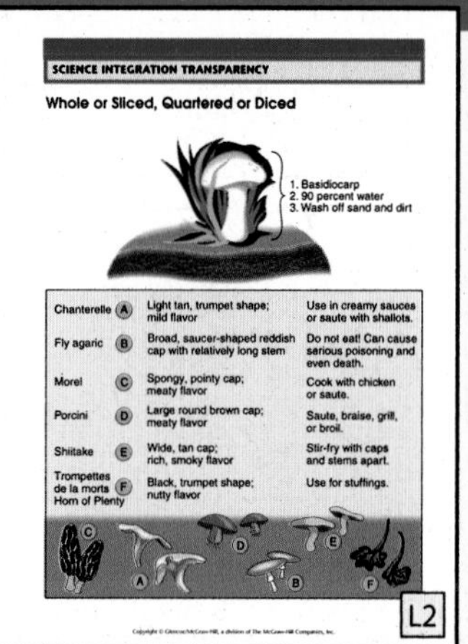
SCIENCE INTEGRATION TRANSPARENCY

Whole or Sliced, Quartered or Diced

1. Basidiocarp
2. 90 percent water
3. Wash off sand and dirt

Chanterelle	A	Light tan, trumpet shape; mild flavor	Use in creamy sauces or saute with shallots.
Fly agaric	B	Broad, saucer-shaped reddish cap with relatively long stem	Do not eat! Can cause serious poisoning and even death.
Morel	C	Spongy, pointy cap; meaty flavor	Cook with chicken or saute.
Porcini	D	Large round brown cap; meaty flavor	Saute, braise, grill, or broil.
Shiitake	E	Wide, tan cap; rich, smoky flavor	Stir-fry with caps and stems apart.
Trompettes de la morte Horn of Plenty	F	Black, trumpet shape; nutty flavor	Use for stuffings.

L2

Teaching Transparencies

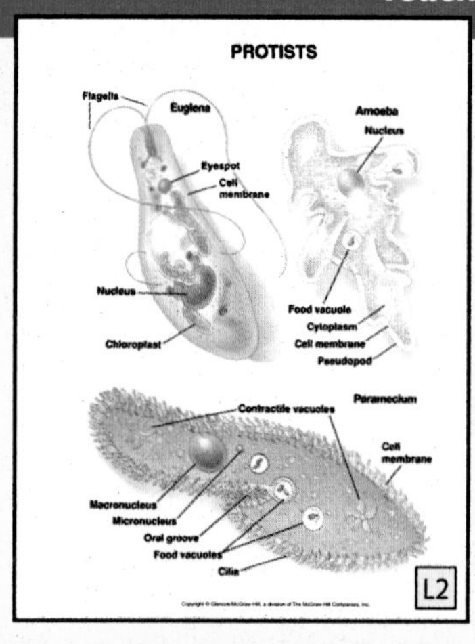

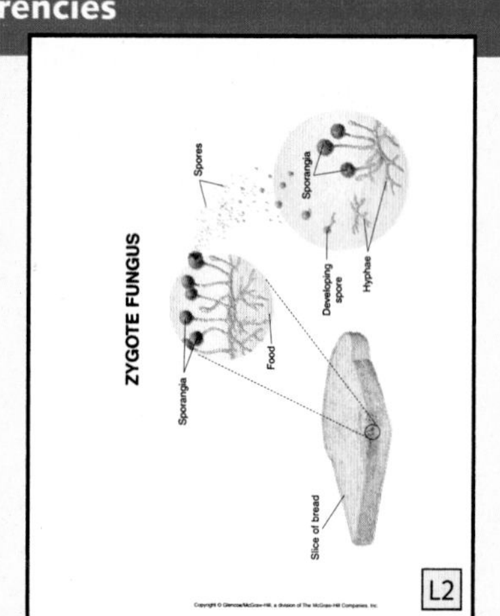

Meeting Different Ability Levels

Study Guide for Content Mastery

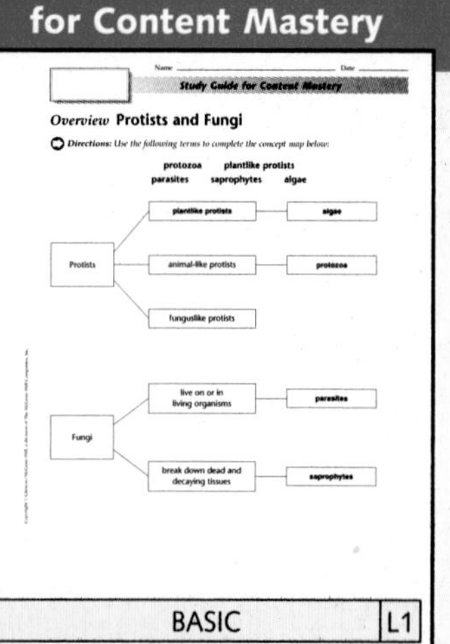
Name ______ Date ______

Study Guide for Content Mastery

Overview Protists and Fungi

Directions: Use the following terms to complete the concept map below:

protozoa, plantlike protists, parasites, saprophytes, algae

Protists → plantlike protists → algae; animal-like protists → protozoa; funguslike protists

Fungi → live on or in living organisms → parasites; break down dead and decaying tissues → saprophytes

BASIC L1

Reinforcement

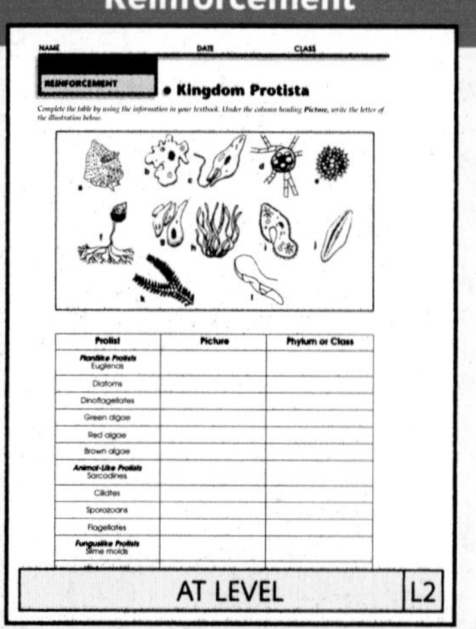
NAME DATE CLASS

REINFORCEMENT • Kingdom Protista

Complete the table by using the information in your textbook. Under the column heading Picture, write the letter of the illustration below.

Protist	Picture	Phylum or Class
Plantlike Protists Euglenas		
Diatoms		
Dinoflagellates		
Green algae		
Red algae		
Brown algae		
Animal-Like Protists Sarcodines		
Ciliates		
Sporozoans		
Flagellates		
Funguslike Protists Slime molds		

AT LEVEL L2

Enrichment Worksheets

NAME DATE CLASS

ENRICHMENT • Kingdom Protista

Protists in a Jar

Materials
grass or hay that has not been chemically treated
pond water
glass jar with top
magnifying lens

Procedure
1. Put a handful of grass or hay into the jar.
2. Fill the jar about half full with pond water.
3. Place the top on the jar, but do not screw it on. Then put the jar in a dark place for three or four days.
4. After three or four days, observe the contents of the jar. Use your magnifying lens to study the contents.

Data and Observations
1. What can you see with your magnifying lens? Describe any protists you observe. ______
2. Do any of the protists appear to be moving? ______
3. Draw the protists you observe in the space below.

Conclude and Apply
1. What structures do protists have that allow them to move from place to place? ______
2. Why might some of the protists look green? ______

CHALLENGE L3

Hands-on Activities

Activity Worksheets

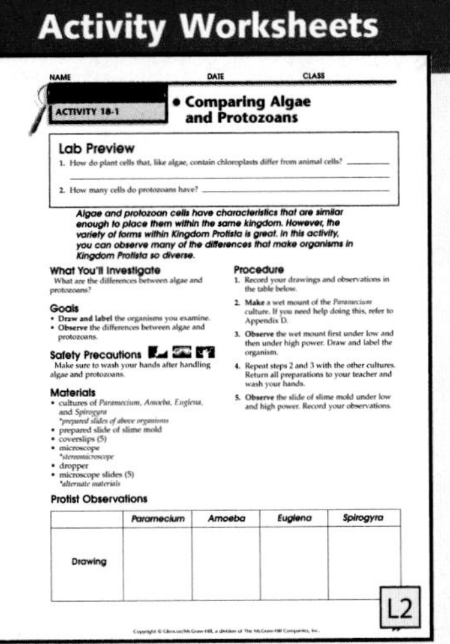
NAME DATE CLASS

ACTIVITY 18-1 ● Comparing Algae and Protozoans

Lab Preview

What You'll Investigate

Procedure

Goals

Safety Precautions

Materials

Protist Observations

	Paramecium	Amoeba	Euglena	Spirogyra
Drawing				

L2

Lab Manual

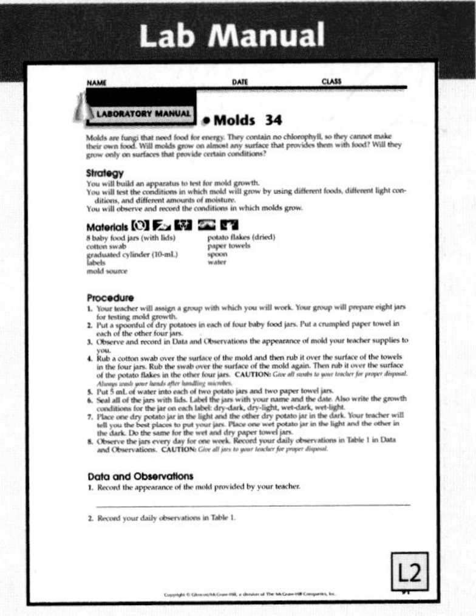
NAME DATE CLASS

LABORATORY MANUAL ● Molds 34

Strategy

Materials

Procedure

Data and Observations

L2

Accessibility

Spanish Resources

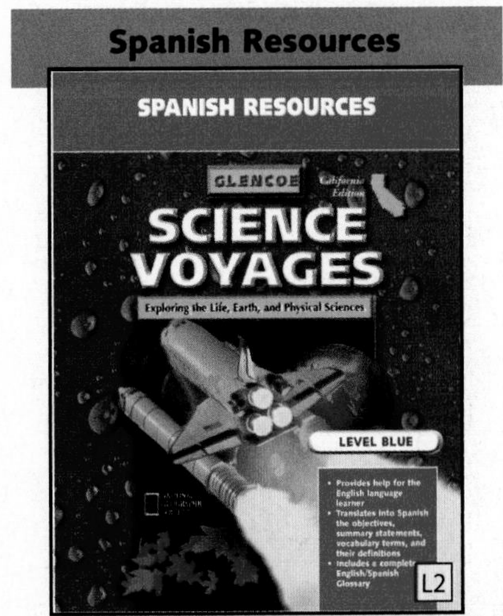
SPANISH RESOURCES

GLENCOE SCIENCE VOYAGES

Exploring the Life, Earth, and Physical Sciences

LEVEL BLUE

L2

Assessment

Performance Assessment

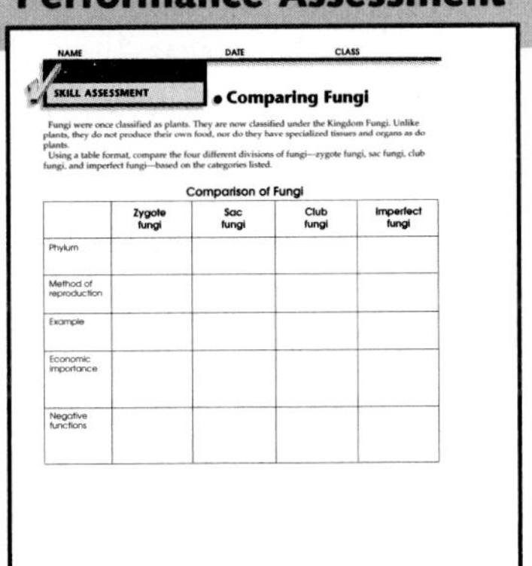
NAME DATE CLASS

SKILL ASSESSMENT ● Comparing Fungi

Comparison of Fungi

	Zygote fungi	Sac fungi	Club fungi	Imperfect fungi
Phylum				
Method of reproduction				
Example				
Economic importance				
Negative functions				

L2

Chapter Review

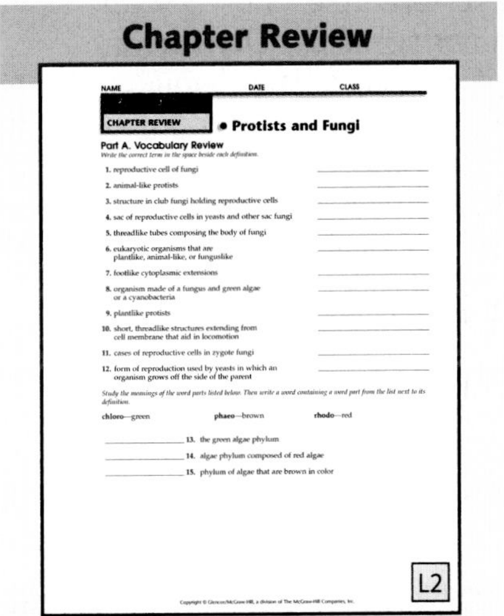
NAME DATE CLASS

CHAPTER REVIEW ● Protists and Fungi

Part A. Vocabulary Review

L2

Assessment

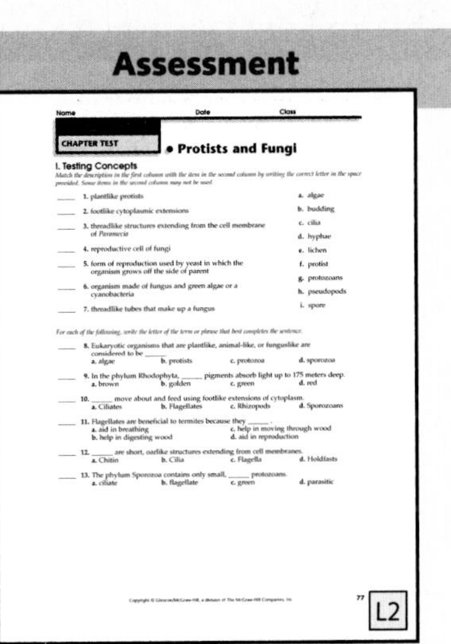
Name Date Class

CHAPTER TEST ● Protists and Fungi

I. Testing Concepts

L2

Test Practice Workbook

CALIFORNIA SCIENCE CONTENT STANDARDS PRACTICE QUESTIONS

STUDENT EDITION

GLENCOE SCIENCE VOYAGES

Exploring the Life, Earth, and Physical Sciences

LEVEL BLUE

THE PRINCETON REVIEW

L2

Extending Content

Critical Thinking/ Problem Solving

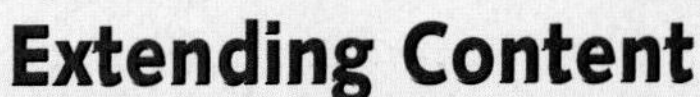

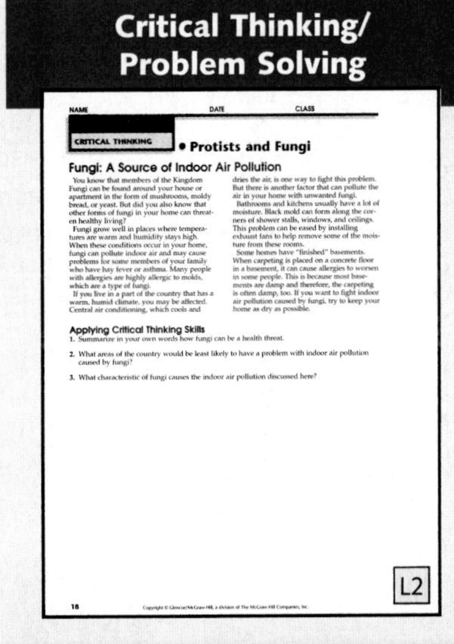
NAME DATE CLASS

CRITICAL THINKING ● Protists and Fungi

Fungi: A Source of Indoor Air Pollution

Applying Critical Thinking Skills

L2

Multicultural Connections

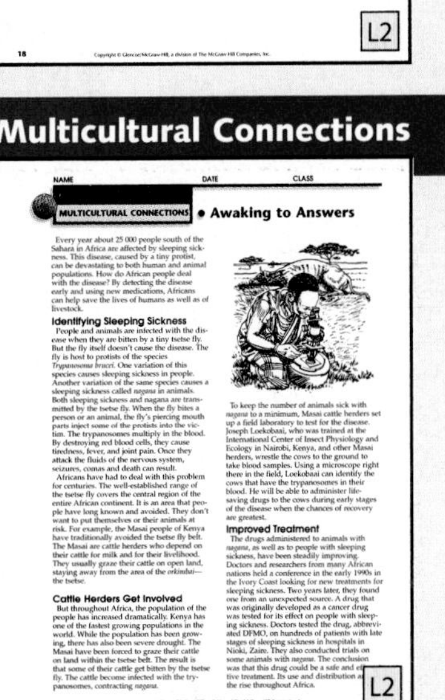
NAME DATE CLASS

MULTICULTURAL CONNECTIONS ● Awaking to Answers

Identifying Sleeping Sickness

Cattle Herders Get Involved

Improved Treatment

L2

Helping You Prepare

Evolution of Protists (Section 22-1)

Convenience is the primary reason for grouping all eukaryotes that are not animals, plants, or fungi into a single kingdom. Because the phyla of Kingdom Protista appear to have evolved independent of each other, protists pose several problems for taxonomists.

One of the major theories of evolution explains how eukaryotic cells evolved. According to this theory, chloroplasts evolved from a cyanobacterium taken up by an ancestor. Within the Kingdom Protista, protists with chloroplasts appear to have evolved differently from protists without chloroplasts.

Plantlike Protists (Section 22-1)

The chloroplasts of diatoms in the phylum Bacillariophyta most resemble those of the brown algae and dinoflagellates. Diatoms are found in both marine and freshwater habitats.

Dinoflagellates are characterized by unique chromosomes and an unusual form of mitosis that takes place within a nucleus whose nuclear membrane does not degenerate. Dinoflagellates are widespread as symbionts of corals. In this relationship, the dinoflagellates are responsible for much of the productivity of coral reefs.

The extreme diversity of the green algae in the phylum Chlorophyta is reflected by their abundance in marine, freshwater, and damp terrestrial environments, such as on tree trunks and in soil. Similar reproductive cycles, chloroplasts, and cell wall composition are all given as evidence for the assumption that green algae are the phylum from which all plants eventually evolved.

Red algae lack centrioles and flagellated cells. For this reason, most taxonomists hypothesize that these organisms descended from the most ancient eukaryotes. Red algae have complex life cycles that involve alternation of generations.

Brown algae are marine protists. Kelp, the largest of the brown algae, contribute to the productivity of the coastal marine environments. Alternation of generations with small gametophytes and large sporophytes is characteristic of this phylum.

GLENCOE TECHNOLOGY

Glencoe Science Voyages Interactive CD-Rom

Chapter Summaries

Use the Chapter Summary to introduce, teach, or review chapter material

NATIONAL GEOGRAPHIC — Teacher's Corner

Products Available from Glencoe

To order the following products for use with this chapter, call Glencoe at 1-800-334-7344:

CD-ROM

NGS PictureShow: The Cell

Transparency Set

NGS PicturePack: The Cell

Products Available from National Geographic Society

To order the following products for use with this chapter, call National Geographic Society at 1-800-368-2728:

Video

Protists: Threshold of Life

Index to National Geographic Magazine

The following articles may be used for research relating to this chapter:

"Leafcutters: Gardeners of the Ant World," by Mark W. Moffet, July 1995.

"Slime Mold: The Fungus That Walks," by Douglas B. Lee, July 1981.

"The Wild World of Compost," by Cecil E. Johnson, August 1980.

Funguslike Protists (Section 22-1)

Phylum Myxomycota contains plasmodial slime molds. These slime molds form round spore-containing capsules under unfavorable environmental conditions such as starvation. These capsules then release spores that may undergo meiosis.

Phylum Oomycota, the oomycetes, occur in water or as plant parasites. The Irish potato famine of the mid nineteenth century was caused by a member of this phylum. Oomycotes have a filamentous structure similar to that of fungi, and they exhibit alternation of generations.

Characteristics of Fungi (Section 22-2)

Fungi are characterized by their chitinous cell walls. Fungi are an important group of decomposers that absorb organic material after it is digested externally. Fungi reproduce asexually in favorable conditions, which include warm temperatures, high humidity, and a suitable food source.

Zygote Fungi (Section 22-2)

Phylum Zygomycota is made up of about 600 species of fungi, including mycorrhizae, an important group that forms mutually beneficial relationships with the roots of most species of plants. Sexual reproduction in this group occurs when appropriate mating strains grow together and produce resistant spores called zoosporangia.

Sac Fungi (Section 22-2)

Ascomycota is the largest group of fungi with more than 60 000 species. These fungi are named for the sac in which their sexual spores are produced. Some of these species form mutually beneficial relationships with cyanobacteria or algae to form lichens. Lichens are sensitive to changes in environments and are considered environmental indicators. Yeasts, important organisms in baking and brewing, are members of this phylum.

SCIENCE UPDATE

For current events or science in the news, access the Glencoe Science Web Site at **www.glencoe.com/sec/science/ca**

Imperfect Fungi (Section 22-2)

Fungal species with no known method of sexual reproduction are classified in the phylum Deuteromycota. *Penicillium* is an imperfect fungus known for its production of penicillin, but some species also are responsible for producing the colors and flavors of several types of cheese.

Club Fungi (Section 22-2)

Basidiomycota includes about 25 000 species of mushrooms, puffballs, shelf fungi, and rusts. Some species of this phylum form mycorrhizae. Others are plant parasites that cause considerable crop damage each year. Basidiomycotes are named for club-shaped structures that form the sexual spores.

Teacher to Teacher

"To introduce the topic of protists, make large bags of stretchable, knit material. Have one student step inside each bag and Velcro the end together. Instruct the students to carefully move across the floor by first extending one arm and then following it with the body. Explain to the class that an amoeba moves in this fashion."

Tonya K. Hancock
Tonya K. Hancock, Teacher
Davis Drive Middle School
Raleigh, NC

CHAPTER 22 Protists and Fungi

CHAPTER OVERVIEW

Section 22-1 Characteristics of three groups of protists are described, compared, and contrasted with each other.

Section 22-2 Fungi characteristics are identified, and fungi are classified on the basis of their method of reproduction.

Chapter Vocabulary

protist	hyphae
algae	spore
protozoans	budding
pseudopods	lichen
cilia	

Theme Connection

Systems and Interactions Evolutionary and ecological relationships of protists and fungi are discussed.

OUT OF TIME?

If time does not permit teaching the entire chapter, use Reviewing Main Ideas on pp. 778–779.

CHAPTER 22 Protists and Fungi

Chapter Preview

Skills Preview

Skill Builders
- Compare and Contrast
- Use Variables, Constants, and Controls

Activities
- Observe
- Compare

MiniLabs
- Predict
- Estimate

Reading Check

As you read this chapter, list three things you already knew about protists and fungi, and ten things you are learning about them.

756

Multiple Learning Styles

Look for the following logos for strategies that emphasize different learning modalities.

Linguistic Using Science Words, pp. 763, 764, 767; Across the Curriculum, p. 764; Science Journal, pp. 764, 775; Assessment, p. 768; Preview, p. 778

Logical-Mathematical Activity, p. 759

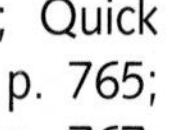

Visual-Spatial Explore Activity, p. 757; Activity, pp. 760, 769; Quick Demo, p. 763; Using an Analogy, p. 765; MiniLab, pp. 766, 772; Reteach, pp. 767, 773, 778; Activity, p. 769

Auditory-Musical Out of Time, p. 778

Kinesthetic Inclusion Strategies, p. 765; Multiple Learning Styles, p. 766

Interpersonal Activity, p. 773; Review, p. 778

Naturalist Activity, pp. 776–777

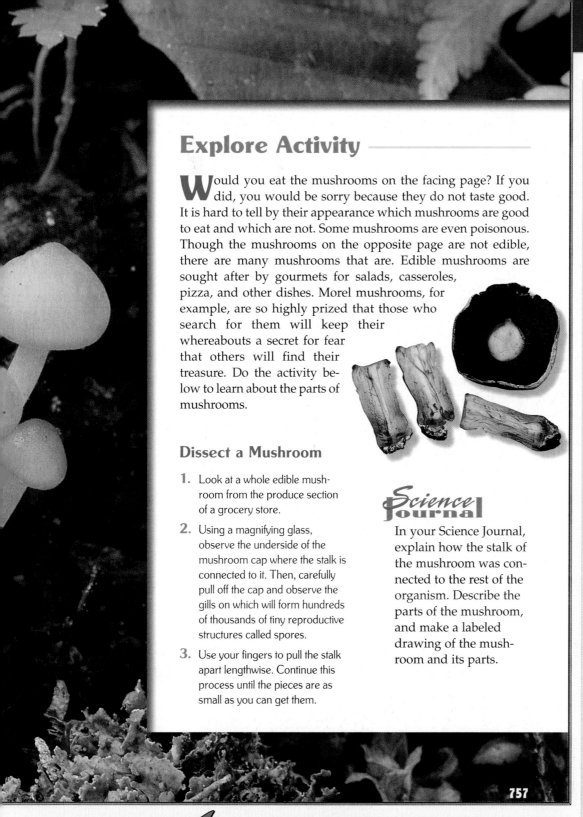

Explore Activity

Would you eat the mushrooms on the facing page? If you did, you would be sorry because they do not taste good. It is hard to tell by their appearance which mushrooms are good to eat and which are not. Some mushrooms are even poisonous. Though the mushrooms on the opposite page are not edible, there are many mushrooms that are. Edible mushrooms are sought after by gourmets for salads, casseroles, pizza, and other dishes. Morel mushrooms, for example, are so highly prized that those who search for them will keep their whereabouts a secret for fear that others will find their treasure. Do the activity below to learn about the parts of mushrooms.

Dissect a Mushroom

1. Look at a whole edible mushroom from the produce section of a grocery store.
2. Using a magnifying glass, observe the underside of the mushroom cap where the stalk is connected to it. Then, carefully pull off the cap and observe the gills on which will form hundreds of thousands of tiny reproductive structures called spores.
3. Use your fingers to pull the stalk apart lengthwise. Continue this process until the pieces are as small as you can get them.

Science Journal

In your Science Journal, explain how the stalk of the mushroom was connected to the rest of the organism. Describe the parts of the mushroom, and make a labeled drawing of the mushroom and its parts.

757

Explore Activity

Purpose

Visual-Spatial Use the Explore Activity to introduce students to fungi. Inform students that they will learn more about the kingdoms containing protists and fungi as they read the chapter. L2 ELL COOP LEARN

Preparation

Buy enough mushrooms so that each student can have one.

Materials

mushroom, magnifying lens

Teaching Strategies

- The best mushrooms to use will be those that have the membrane of the cap just separated from the stalk as opposed to those that are tightly closed.
- Encourage students to examine the mushroom gills thoroughly using a magnifying lens.
- Tell students not to eat anything used in the lab.

Descriptions will vary. Mushrooms are made up of caps, gills, stalks, and tubes that run underground.

Assessment

Oral Have students hypothesize how fungi became so widespread in the environment. *Their spores are light, numerous, and carried by air currents.* Use **Performance Assessment in the Science Classroom,** p. 21.

Assessment Planner

Portfolio
Refer to p. 779 for suggested items that students might select for their portfolios.

Performance Assessment
See p. 779 for additional Performance Assessment options.
Skill Builder, p. 774
MiniLab, pp. 766, 772
Activity 22-1, p. 769; 22-2, pp. 776–777

Content Assessment
Section Assessment, pp. 768, 774
Chapter Assessment, pp. 780–781
Proficiency Prep, pp. 768, 774

Prepare

Content Background

Refer to **Evolution of Protists, Plantlike Protists,** and **Funguslike Protists** on pp. 756E–F.

Preplanning

Refer to the **Chapter Organizer** on pp. 756A–B.

1 Motivate

Bellringer

Before presenting the lesson, display **Section Focus Transparency 62** on the overhead projector. Use the accompanying **Focus Activity** worksheet. L2 ELL

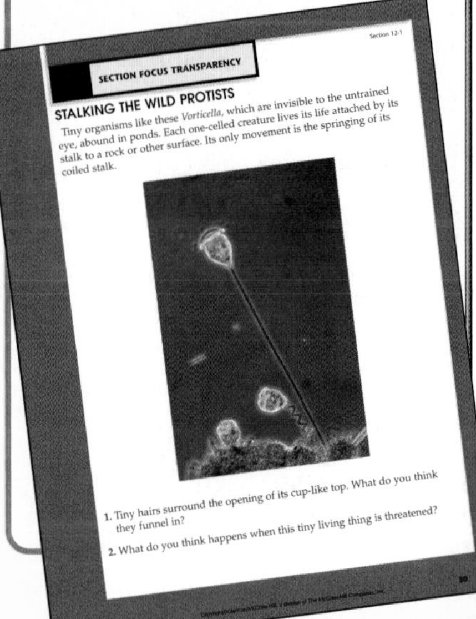

Section 12-1

SECTION FOCUS TRANSPARENCY

STALKING THE WILD PROTISTS

Tiny organisms like these *Vorticella*, which are invisible to the untrained eye, abound in ponds. Each one-celled creature lives its life attached by its stalk to a rock or other surface. Its only movement is the springing of its coiled stalk.

1. Tiny hairs surround the opening of its cup-like top. What do you think they funnel in?
2. What do you think happens when this tiny living thing is threatened?

30

Caption Answer

Figure 22-1 *Answers will vary, but students should recognize that Kingdom Protista contains many diverse organisms.*

22•1 Kingdom Protista

What You'll Learn

- The characteristics shared by all protists
- How to describe the three groups of protists
- How to compare and contrast the protist groups

Vocabulary

protist
algae
protozoans
pseudopods
cilia

Why It's Important

- Kingdom Protista shows the importance of variety in the environment.

What is a protist?

Look at the organisms in **Figure 22-1.** Do you see any similarities among them? As different as they appear, all of these organisms belong to the protist kingdom. A **protist** is a single- or many-celled organism that lives in moist or wet surroundings. All protists have a nucleus and are therefore eukaryotic. Despite these similarities, the organisms in Kingdom Protista (proh TIHS tuh) vary greatly. Some protists contain chlorophyll and make their own food, and others don't. Protists are plantlike, animal-like, and funguslike.

Evolution of Protists

Not much evidence of the evolution of protists can be found because many lack hard parts and, as a result, few fossils of these organisms have been found. However, by studying the genes of modern protists, scientists are able to trace their ancestors. Scientists hypothesize that the common ancestor of all protists was a one-celled organism with a nucleus, mitochondria, and other cellular structures. The cellular structures of this organism may have been different from those found in modern protists. Evidence suggests that protists that can't make their own food evolved differently from protists that do make their own food. Some scientists suggest that a cyanobacterium, a bacterium that contains chlorophyll, was taken up by a one-celled organism with mitochondria. As this organism changed over time, the cyanobacterium became the organism's chloroplast, the organelle where photosynthesis occurs. Plantlike protists probably developed from this kind of organism.

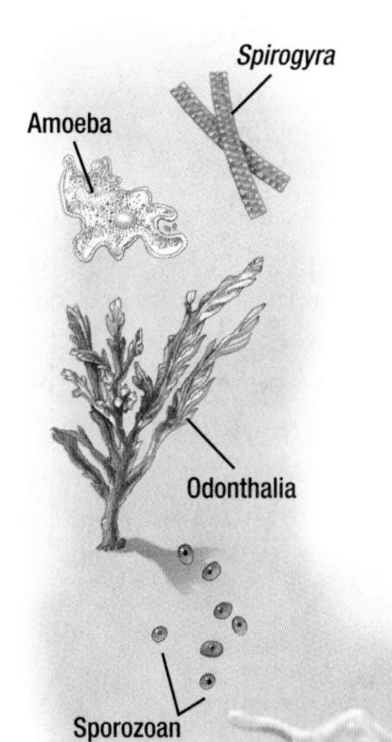

EXAMPLES OF Protists

Figure 22-1 Kingdom Protista is made up of a variety of organisms. **Using what you see in the art, write a description of a protist.**

Resource Manager

The following **Teacher Classroom Resources** can be used with Section 22-1:

 **Reproducible Masters**

Activity Worksheets, pp. 123–124, 127 L2

Enrichment, p. 62 L3

Laboratory Manual, pp. 135–136 L2

Reinforcement, p. 62 L2

Study Guide, p. 86 L1 ELL

Transparencies

Teaching Transparency 43 L2

Plantlike Protists

Plantlike protists are known as **algae** (AL jee). Some species of algae are one celled and others are many celled. All algae can make their own food because they contain the pigment chlorophyll in their chloroplasts. Even though all algae have chlorophyll, not all of them look green. Many have other pigments that cover up their chlorophyll. Species of algae are grouped into six main phyla according to their structure, pigments, and the way in which they store food.

Euglenoids

Algae that belong to the phylum Euglenophyta (yoo GLEE nuh fi tuh) have characteristics of both plants and animals. A typical euglenoid, the Euglena, is shown in **Figure 22-2.** Like plants, these one-celled algae have chloroplasts and produce carbohydrates as food. When light is not present, euglenas feed on bacteria and protists. Although euglenas have no cell walls, they do have a strong, flexible layer inside the cell membrane that helps them move and change shape. Many move by using whiplike tails called flagella. Another animal-like characteristic of euglenas is that they have an adaptation called an eyespot that responds to light.

Figure 22-2 How are Euglenas similar to both plants and animals?

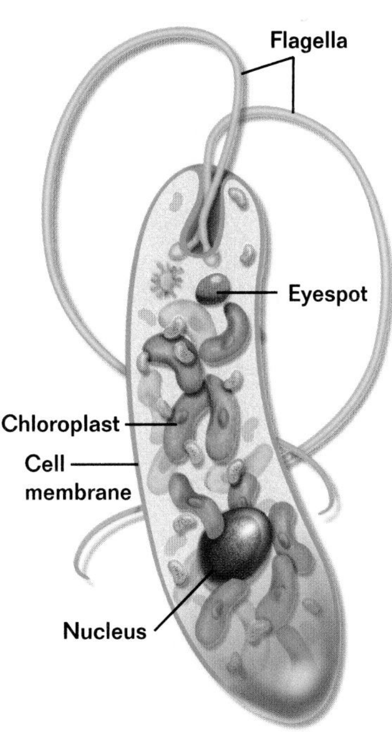

Diatoms

Diatoms, shown in **Figure 22-3,** belong to the phylum Bacillariophyta (buh sih law ree oh FI tuh) and are found in both freshwater and salt water. Diatoms are photosynthetic, which means they can make their own food. These one-celled algae store food in the form of oil. They have a golden-brown pigment that masks the green chlorophyll. For this reason, they are sometimes referred to as gold-brown algae.

Diatoms reproduce in extremely large numbers. When the organisms die, their small cell walls sink to the floor of the

Magnification: 130×

Figure 22-3 The cell wall of diatoms contain silica, the main element in glass. The body of a diatom is like a small box with a lid. Diatoms are covered with markings and pits that form patterns.

Tying to Previous Knowledge

Have students name characteristics bacteria have in common. Emphasize that organisms are classified by their similarities and differences. In this chapter, students will learn about similarities and differences among members of the Protist and Fungi Kingdoms.

2 Teach

Activity

Logical-Mathematical Divide students into cooperative groups. Provide each group with about 40 buttons to arrange in a classification system. Relate this activity to the variety of protists and the difficulty involved in classifying them. L1 ELL COOP LEARN

Teacher FYI

A pinch of diatomite contains several thousand diatom.

Caption Answer

Figure 22-2 *Euglenas have chloroplasts and produce carbohydrates for food, like plants do. Like animals, they move and respond to light.*

VISUAL Learning

Figure 22-1 Ask students to explain why the protists pictured are neither plants nor animals.

Figure 22-2 Ask students why *Euglena* needs an eyespot and flagella. *The eyespot is useful in detecting light, and the flagella propel the organism toward the light.*

Figure 22-3 Point out to students that the markings on diatoms are unique and are used by taxonomists to identify individual species.

CA Science Content Standards

Page 759: 6c

EARTH SCIENCE INTEGRATION

Diatomite, or diatomaceous earth, is a commercially valuable material composed primarily of the opaline silica cell walls of diatoms. It is mined in several deposits dated at 12 to 28 million years old. California, Nevada, Arizona, Washington, and Florida are leading producers of diatomite in the United States.

Discussion

Ask students to relate the tremendous number of diatoms in a diatomite deposit with the length of time it would take to make the deposit. Because the diatoms are microscopic, it would have taken millions of years. Ask students how the deposits could be in quarries, often high above sea level, if the deposits are made in the ocean. Mountain building can raise the deposits above sea level.

Activity

Visual-Spatial Set up a microscope and allow students to observe protists in a drop of pond water. Be sure to include both algae and protozoans. L1

Figure 22-4 Dinoflagellates usually live in the sea. Notice the groove that houses one of the two flagella that mark all members of this group.

Magnification: 3000×

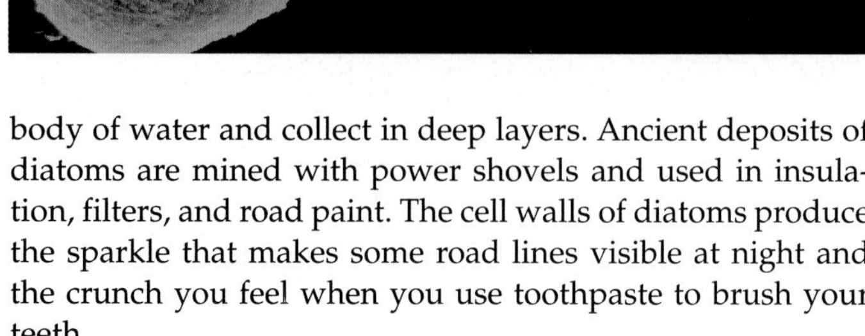

body of water and collect in deep layers. Ancient deposits of diatoms are mined with power shovels and used in insulation, filters, and road paint. The cell walls of diatoms produce the sparkle that makes some road lines visible at night and the crunch you feel when you use toothpaste to brush your teeth.

Dinoflagellates

Phylum Dinoflagellata contains species of one-celled algae called dinoflagellates that have red pigments. Because of their color, they are known as fire algae. The name *dinoflagellate* means "spinning flagellates." One of the flagella moves the cell, and the other circles the cell, causing it to spin with a motion similar to a top. Dinoflagellates, shown in **Figure 22-4,** store food in the form of starches and oils.

VISUALIZING Green Algae

Figure 22-5 There are many different shapes among the species of green algae.

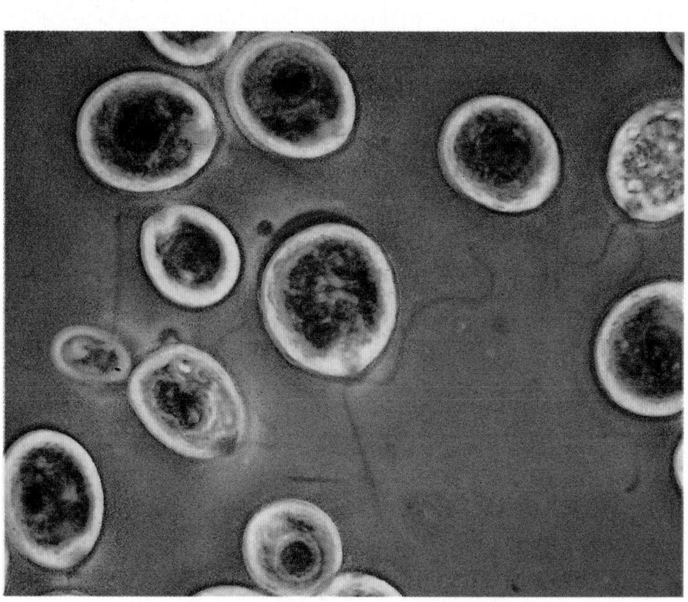

A *Chlamydomonas* is an example of a one-celled green alga. It is found in freshwater ponds and in moist soil.

Magnification: 700×

Content Background

A pellicle is the firm yet flexible outer layer of some cells. Protein fibers that overlap in the pellicles of many protists allow them to alter their shape considerably.

Almost all dinoflagellates live in salt water. They are important food sources for many saltwater organisms. Some dinoflagellates, however, do live in freshwater and are suspected to have caused health problems for humans and other organisms on the East Coast.

Green Algae

Seven thousand species of green algae form the phylum Chlorophyta (klaw RAHF uh duh), giving it the most variety of any group of protists. The presence of chlorophyll in green algae tells you that they undergo photosynthesis and produce food. They are important because nearly half of the oxygen we consume is a result of the photosynthesis of green algae.

Although most green algae live in water, others can live in many other environments, including tree trunks and other organisms. Green algae can be one-celled or many-celled. **Figure 22-5** shows different forms of green algae.

EXAMPLES OF Green Algae

- River moss
- Chlamydomonas
- Volvox
- Spirogyra
- Ulva

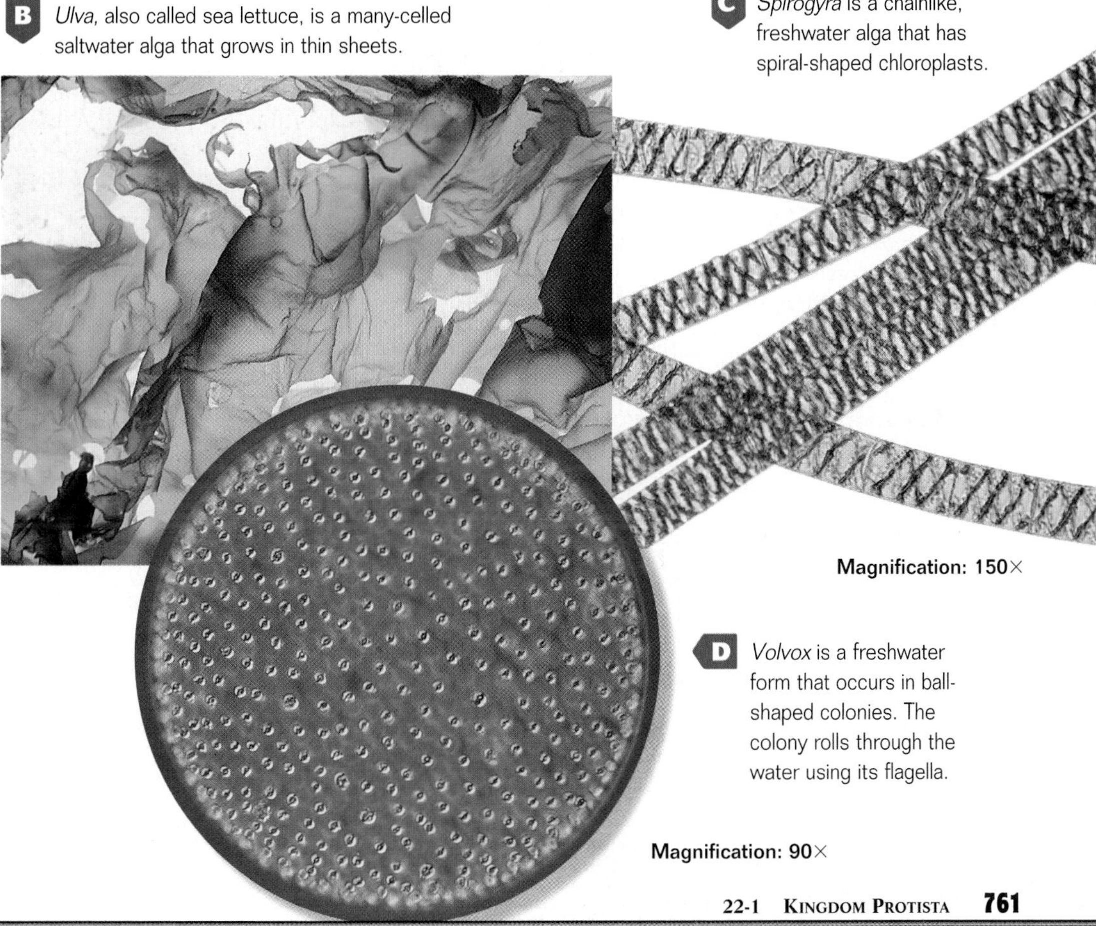

B *Ulva*, also called sea lettuce, is a many-celled saltwater alga that grows in thin sheets.

C *Spirogyra* is a chainlike, freshwater alga that has spiral-shaped chloroplasts.

Magnification: 150×

D *Volvox* is a freshwater form that occurs in ball-shaped colonies. The colony rolls through the water using its flagella.

Magnification: 90×

VISUAL Learning

Figure 22-5 Discuss the diversity of green algae with students. Point out that species similar to green algae are considered to be the ancestors of plants.

Flex Your Brain

Use the Flex Your Brain activity to have students explore ALGAE.

GLENCOE TECHNOLOGY

Videodisc

Glencoe Science Voyages Interactive Videodisc—Life

Side 2, Lesson 9 *Ecosystems: Wetlands*

45551

46775

Refer to the Videodisc Teacher Guide for additional bar codes.

The Infinite Voyage: Secrets from a Frozen World

Chapter 1 *The Southern Ocean—A Rich Marine Ecosystem* 5:30

Refer to the Videodisc Teacher Guide for bar codes and teaching strategies.

Guided Reading Strategy

Pair of Pairs This strategy encourages students to respond to a question as partners. They brainstorm together, recording their ideas on one paper. After a few minutes, they combine with another pair and share responses. Finally, the teacher asks the groups of four to share any responses. Have students use the Pair of Pairs strategy on a Think Critically question in a Section Assessment for this chapter.

Correcting Misconceptions

Point out that even though some of the brown algae, such as kelp, may grow up to 100 m long, they are not plants because they do not develop the complex organs of plants—roots, stems, and leaves.

Enrichment

Have students research the reasons that red algae can continue to photosynthesize at depths approaching 200 m. *Their red pigments are efficient at gathering the longer wavelengths of light at those depths.* L3

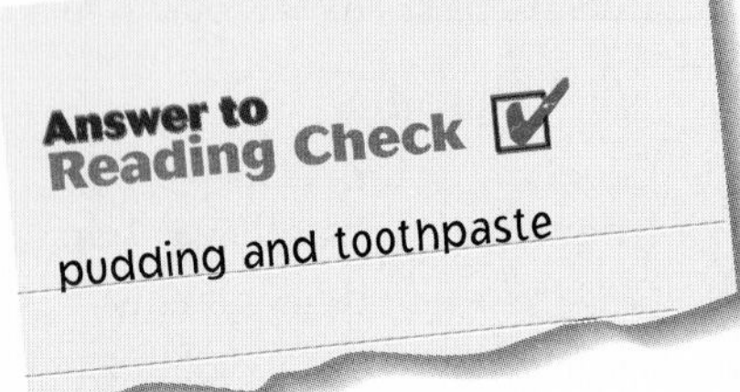
Answer to Reading Check
pudding and toothpaste

Caption Answer

Figure 22-7 *Brown algae is used in the production of certain foods, including marshmallows and ice cream.*

Content Background

Kelp have specialized structures that help them survive in their environment, much as land plants do. The most notable of these structures are gas floats found on the blades of kelp. Blades are leaf-like structures that float in the water. The blades are anchored by the holdfast. On each blade, there are gas floats, or air bladders, which cause the blade to float near the surface of the water so it can absorb sunlight for photosynthesis.

Figure 22-6 Carrageenan, a substance extracted from the red alga Irish moss, gives some puddings their smooth, creamy texture.

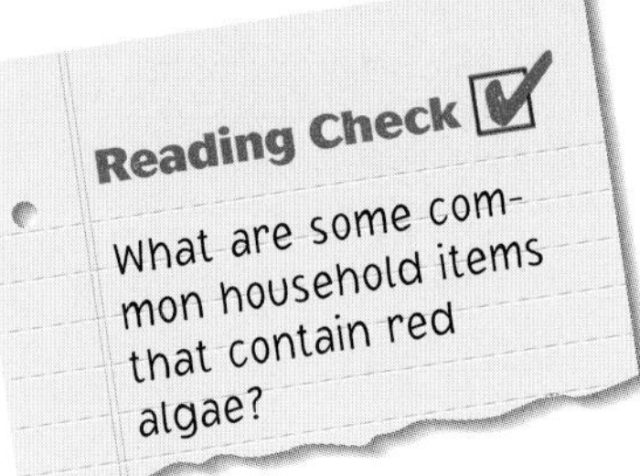
Reading Check
What are some common household items that contain red algae?

Red Algae

Red algae belong to the phylum Rhodophyta (roh DAHF uh duh). *Rhodo-* means "red" and describes the color of members of this phylum. Pudding and toothpaste are made with red algae. Carrageenan is found in red algae, such as the Irish moss shown in **Figure 22-6.** It gives toothpaste and pudding their smooth, creamy textures. Most red algae are many-celled. Some species of red algae can live up to 175 m deep in the ocean. Their red pigment allows them to absorb the limited amount of light that penetrates to those depths and enables them to produce the starch on which they live.

Figure 22-7 Giant kelp may be as much as 100 m long and can form forests like this one located off the coast of California. **What are some practical uses for brown algae?**

Brown Algae

Brown algae make up the phylum Phaeophyta (fee AHF uh duh). Members of this phylum are many-celled and vary greatly in size. They are mostly found growing in cool, saltwater environments. Kelp, shown in **Figure 22-7,** is an important food source for many fish and invertebrates. They form a dense mat of stalks and leaflike blades where small fish and other animals live. Giant kelp are the largest organisms in the protist kingdom.

People in many parts of the world eat brown algae. The thick texture of foods such as ice cream and marshmallows is produced by algin, which is found in these algae. Brown algae also are used to make fertilizer. **Table 22-1** summarizes the different phyla of plantlike protists.

Integrating the Sciences

Earth Science Have students research the distribution and makeup of plankton. Plankton are plantlike and animal-like organisms that float in the upper layers of water. They are found in salt water worldwide. Protists found in plankton include diatoms, dinoflagellates, green algae, and many protozoans. L2 P

Content Background

Of the 100 000 or so protozoans, only a few cause diseases. But, the illnesses they do cause can be severe and even fatal. Malaria, sleeping sickness, and dysentery are diseases caused by species of protozoans.

Table 22-1

The Plantlike Protists

Phylum	Example	Pigments	Other Characteristics
Euglenophyta Euglenoids		Chlorophyll	One-celled alga that moves with flagella; has eyespot to detect light.
Bacillariophyta Diatoms		Golden Brown	One-celled alga with body made of two halves. Cell walls contain silica.
Dinoflagellata Dinoflagellates		Red	One-celled alga with two flagella. Flagella cause cell to spin. Some species cause red tide.
Chlorophyta Green Algae		Chlorophyll	One- and many-celled species. Most live in water; some live out of water, in or on other organisms.
Rhodophyta Red Algae		Red	Many-celled alga; carbohydrate in red algae is used to give some foods a creamy texture.
Phaeophyta Brown Algae		Brown	Many-celled alga; most live in salt water; important food source in aquatic environments.

Animal-Like Protists

One-celled, animal-like protists are known as **protozoans.** These complex organisms live in water, soil, and in both living and dead organisms. Many types of protozoans are parasites. A parasite is an organism that lives in or on another organism. Protozoans contain special vacuoles for digesting food and getting rid of excess water. Protozoans are separated into groups—rhizopods, flagellates, ciliates, and sporozoans—by how they move. **Figure 22-8** is an example of one type of protozoan.

TRAITS OF Animal-like Protists

- One-celled
- Many are parasites
- Grouped by how they move

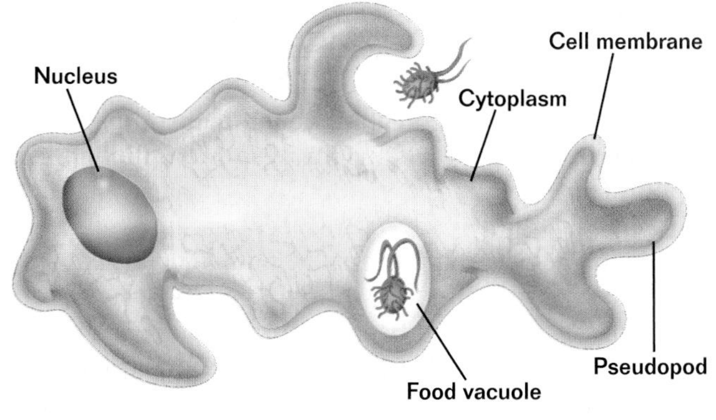

Figure 22-8 An amoeba constantly changes shape as it extends its cytoplasm to capture food and move from place to place. Many areas of the world have a species of amoeba in the water that causes the condition dysentery. Dysentery leads to a severe form of diarrhea. **Why is an amoeba classified as a protozoan?**

VISUAL Learning

Table 22-1 Have students summarize the characteristics of the plantlike protists. Ask questions based on the table and text.

Figure 22-8 Ask students to identify the two uses of pseudopods. *locomotion and food capture*

Using Science Words

Linguistic Have students determine what the prefix *pro* and the suffix *zoa* in the word *protozoan* mean. Ask them how these relate to the meaning of the word *protozoan.* L3

Quick Demo

Visual-Spatial Use model plant and animal cells to illustrate the organelles in common between algae and plants and between protozoans and animals.

Caption Answer

Figure 22-8 *Amoebas contain vacuoles for digesting food and getting rid of excess water. They move and feed using pseudopods.*

Across the Curriculum

Mathematics Have students analyze the following story by making a graph. A person who contracted malaria had the following body temperatures at the given times. When will the person have chills next?

DAY 1: 1:00 P.M.—103° (chills); 6:00 P.M.—101° (sweating); DAY 2: 1:00 A.M.—97°; 6:00 A.M.—98°; 1:00 P.M.—97°; 6:00 P.M.—99°; DAY 3: 1:00 A.M.—101° (chills); 6:00 A.M.—103°; 1:00 P.M.—103°; 6:00 P.M.—101° (sweating) *The person will next have the chills at 1:00 P.M. on Day 4.* L2 ELL P

Using Science Words

Linguistic Have students list other words that have the prefix *pseudo* or the suffix *pod* in them. Examples include *pseudonym* and *arthropod.* Ask how these relate to the word *pseudopod.*

GLENCOE TECHNOLOGY

Videodisc

Glencoe Science Voyages Interactive Videodisc—Earth

Side 2, Lesson 7 *Petroleum Formation: A Long, Slow Process*

23165

23796

23972

Refer to the Videodisc Teacher Guide for additional bar codes.

CD-ROM

Glencoe Science Voyages Interactive CD-ROM

Explorations

Have students do the interactive exploration *How can microscopic protists and fungi be characterized?*

Figure 22-9 Many saltwater rhizopods have skeletons made out of calcium carbonate, the material that makes up chalk.

A The White Cliffs of Dover in England are made almost entirely of the shells of billions of rhizopods.

B Rhizopod shells come in a variety of shapes.

Magnification: 100×

Rhizopods

The first protozoans were probably similar to members of the phylum Rhizopoda. The amoeba shown in **Figure 22-8** is a typical member of this phylum. Rhizopods move about and feed using temporary extensions of their cytoplasm called **pseudopods** (SEWD uh pahdz). The word *pseudopod* means "false foot." An amoeba extends the cytoplasm of a pseudopod on either side of a food particle such as a bacterium. Then, the pseudopod closes and the particle is trapped. A vacuole forms around the food and it is digested. Members of the phylum Rhizopoda, as shown in **Figure 22-9,** are found in freshwater and saltwater environments, and certain types are found in animals as parasites.

Figure 22-10 *Trypanosoma,* responsible for African sleeping sickness, is spread by the tsetse fly in Africa. This flagellate is the gray organism in the photo below. The red disks are blood cells. The disease causes fever, swollen glands, and extreme sleepiness.

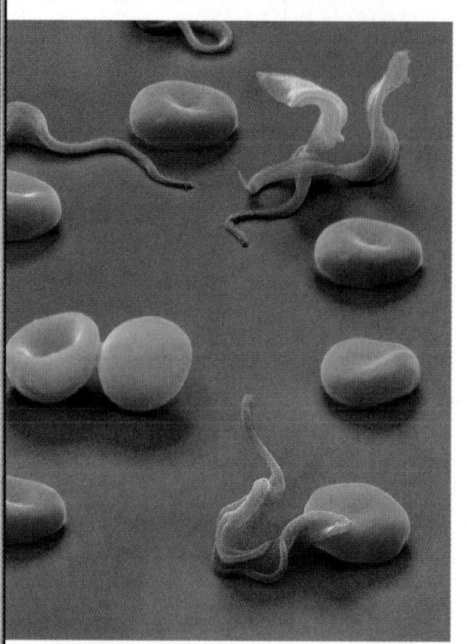

Magnification: 4000×

Flagellates

Protozoans that move using flagella are called flagellates and belong to the phylum Zoomastigina (zoe uh mas tuh JINE uh). All of the flagellates have long flagella that whip through a watery environment, moving the organism along. Many species of flagellates live in freshwater, though some are parasites.

Trypanosoma, shown in **Figure 22-10,** is a flagellate that causes African sleeping sickness in humans and other animals. Another flagellate lives in the digestive system of termites. The flagellates are beneficial to the termites because they produce enzymes that digest the wood the termites eat. Without the flagellates, the termites would not be able to digest the wood.

Across the Curriculum

Geography Have students view rhizopods called foraminifera on a prepared slide. Explain that the White Cliffs of Dover in England are primarily composed of the shells of these protozoans. Have students research the importance of Dover during World War II and write about their discovery. L2 P

Parasitic Protozoans Have students research a particular parasitic protozoan, like *Plasmodium, Trypanosoma, Giardia,* or *Trichomonas,* and write an essay about the life of a parasite from the point of view of the protozoan. L2 P

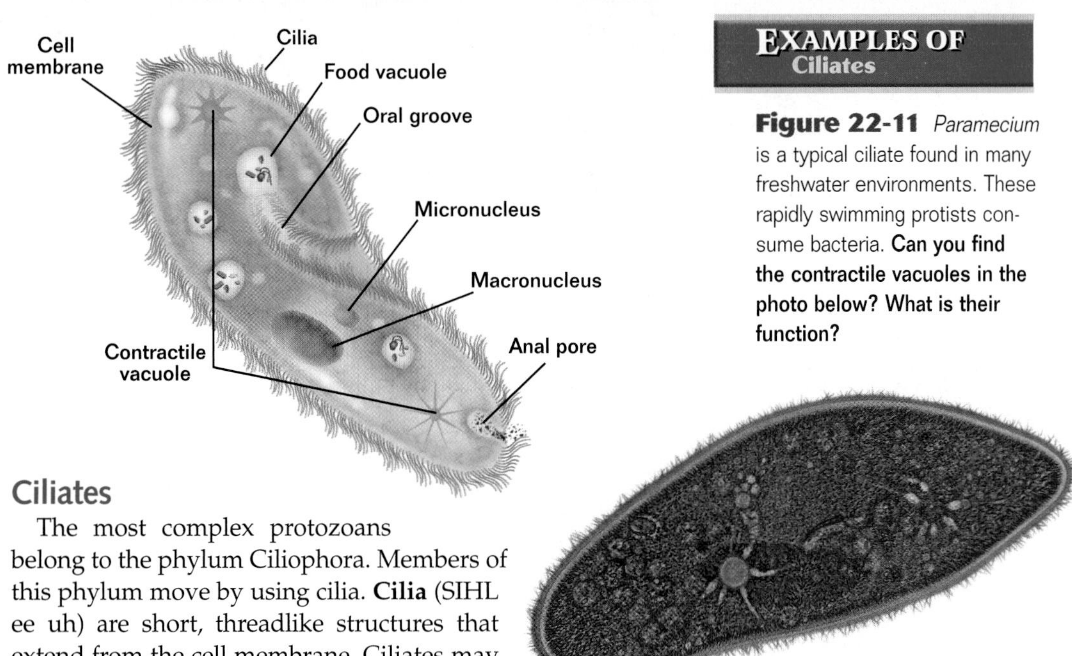

EXAMPLES OF Ciliates

Figure 22-11 *Paramecium* is a typical ciliate found in many freshwater environments. These rapidly swimming protists consume bacteria. **Can you find the contractile vacuoles in the photo below? What is their function?**

Ciliates

The most complex protozoans belong to the phylum Ciliophora. Members of this phylum move by using cilia. **Cilia** (SIHL ee uh) are short, threadlike structures that extend from the cell membrane. Ciliates may be covered with cilia or have cilia grouped in specific areas of the cell. Cilia beat in an organized way that allows the organism to move swiftly in any direction.

A typical ciliate is *Paramecium,* shown in **Figure 22-11.** In *Paramecium,* you can see another characteristic of the ciliates: each has two nuclei—a macronucleus and a micronucleus. The macronucleus controls the everyday functions of the cell. The micronucleus is used in reproduction. Paramecia usually feed on bacteria swept into the oral groove by the cilia. Once the food is inside the cell, a food vacuole forms and the food is digested. Wastes are removed through the anal pore. As the name implies, a contractile vacuole contracts and excess water is ejected from the cell.

Sporozoans

The phylum Sporozoa contains only parasitic organisms. Sporozoans have no way of moving on their own. All are parasites that live in and feed on the blood of humans and other animals, as shown in **Figure 22-12.**

Using Math

A paramecium may be about 0.1 cm long. Giant kelp, a kind of brown algae, may be as much as 100 m long—about the same length as a football field. Using these measurements, how many times larger is a giant kelp than a paramecium?

Figure 22-12 Only female *Anopheles* mosquitoes spread the sporozoan that causes malaria. Malaria is spread when an infected mosquito bites a human. This disease still causes about 1 million deaths each year worldwide.

Using Math

0.1 cm/paramecium × 1 m/100 cm × 1 giant kelp/100 m = 100 000 times larger

Using an Analogy

Visual-Spatial To help students envision what the beating of cilia is like, show them a photograph of a rowing crew. All members move together so that their oars are all in the same position at the same time. This propels the boat through the water as cilia propel a paramecium or other ciliate through its watery medium.

GLENCOE TECHNOLOGY

Videodisc

The Infinite Voyage: The Living Clock

Chapter 4 *Circadian Rhythm and the Biological Clock* 5:00

Refer to the Videodisc Teacher Guide for bar codes and teaching strategies.

Caption Answer

Figure 22-11 *Students can recognize the contractile vacuole in the picture by its shape, which resembles a starburst. The contractile vacuole gets rid of excess water.*

Inclusion Strategies

Gifted Students can make a flip book for each type of protist. On each page of the flip book, they should show one stage of the protist's movement. When the pages are placed together and flipped through, the protist should appear to move. The book will be more interesting if it has more pages showing small sections of the movement. L2 P

Learning Disabled Have students make and display three-dimensional, papier-mâché or clay models of the major protists. Include flagellates, ciliates, and rhizopods. Students should label some of the structures that allow the protists to move. L2 ELL P

CA Science Content Standards

Page 764: 6b
Page 765: 9f

MiniLab

Purpose

Visual-Spatial Students will observe the growth of slime molds and predict the best conditions for growth. L2 ELL

Materials

slime mold specimens, magnifying glass, pencil, paper

Teaching Strategies

Obtain live specimens of slime mold from a biological supply company. *Physarum polycephalum* produces good results.

Analysis

1. Drawings will vary depending on observations.
2. Lower temperatures and reduced humidity or food will result in the growth of the spore-producing form.

Assessment

Performance To assess students' understanding of slime molds, have them try to grow slime mold cultures on different surfaces with different nutrients. Use **Performance Assessment in the Science Classroom,** p. 33.

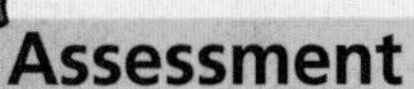

Discussion

Ask students to compare the similarities between slime molds and fungi. Both are sometimes found on decaying materials; during the spore-producing stage of the life cycle, slime molds resemble a fungus. L2

Caption Answer

Figure 22-13 *Slime molds move and behave like animal-like protists during part of their life cycle, yet like fungi, they are decomposers that reproduce with spores.*

Observing Slime Molds 

Procedure

1. Obtain live specimens of the slime mold *Physarum polycephaalum* from your teacher.
2. Observe the mold for four days.

Analysis

1. Make daily drawings and observations of the mold as it grows. Use a magnifying glass.
2. Predict the conditions under which the slime mold will change from the amoeboid form to the spore-producing form.

Funguslike Protists

Funguslike protists include several small phyla that have features of both protists and fungi. Slime molds and water molds are funguslike protists. They get energy by breaking down organic materials. Examples of slime molds are illustrated in **Figure 22-13.**

Slime Molds

Slime molds are much more attractive than their name sounds. Many are brightly colored. They form a delicate, weblike structure on the surface of their food supply. Slime molds have some protozoan characteristics. During part of their life cycle, the cells of slime molds move by means of pseudopods and behave like amoebas. Slime molds reproduce with spores the way fungi do. You will learn about reproduction in fungi in the next section.

Although most slime molds live on decaying logs or dead leaves in moist, cool, shady woods, one common slime mold is sometimes found crawling across lawns and mulch. It creeps along feeding on bacteria and decayed plants and animals. When conditions become less favorable, reproductive structures form on stalks and spores are produced.

Figure 22-13 Slime molds come in many different forms and colors ranging from brilliant yellow or orange to rich blue, violet, pink, and jet black. **How are slime molds similar to both protists and fungi?**

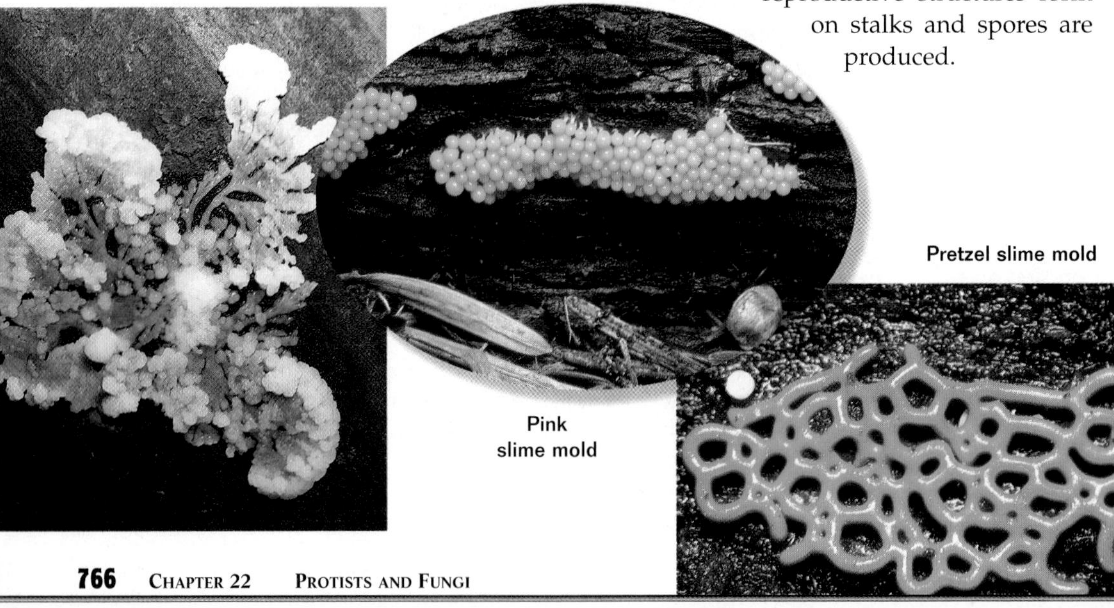

Multiple Learning Styles

Kinesthetic After having students observe the movement of a slime mold under the microscope, have them get together in a group and perform the same movements. The cytoplasm streams in one direction and then slows to a stop. Then the cytoplasm flows in the opposite direction, but not as far before stopping. In this way, the slime mold creeps across a surface. L1 ELL COOP LEARN

Water Molds and Downy Mildews

Water molds, downy mildews, and white rusts make up another phylum of funguslike protists. Most members of this large and diverse group live in water or moist places. Most water molds appear as fuzzy, white growths on decaying matter. They are called funguslike protists because they grow as a mass of threads over a plant or animal, digest it, and then absorb the organism's nutrients. Water molds have cell walls as do fungi, but their relatively simple cells are more like protozoans. Unlike fungi, they produce reproductive cells with flagella at some point in their reproductive cycles. Some water molds are parasites of plants while others feed on dead organisms. **Figure 22-14B** shows a parasitic water mold that grows on decaying fish. If you have an aquarium, you may see water molds attack a fish and cause its death.

Another important member of this phylum is a downy or powdery mildew that causes a disease on the leaves of many plants when days have been warm and nights become cooler and moist. In fact, the most well-known member of this phylum is the downy mildew, pictured in **Figure 22-14A,** that caused the Irish potato famine in the 1840s. Potatoes were

interNET CONNECTION

Visit the Glencoe Science Web Site at **www.glencoe.com/sec/science/ca** for more information about funguslike protists.

Problem Solving

Puzzled About Slime

At one time, slime molds were classified as fungi. This is because at times, when conditions are unfavorable, they dry up and look like tiny mushrooms. Now, they are classified as protists because they move like protists and have characteristics similar to protists.

Slime molds, such as the scrambled egg slime mold, can be found covering moist wood as in the photograph shown below. They may be white or bright red, yellow, or purple. If you looked at a piece of slime mold on a microscope slide, you would see that the cell nuclei move back and forth as the cytoplasm streams along. This is the method slime mold uses to creep over the wood.

Think Critically: What characteristics do slime molds share with protists? In what ways are slime molds similar to amoebas and fungi? In what ways are they different?

Scrambled egg slime mold

Internet Addresses

______

______

______

______

For Internet tips, see Glencoe's **Using the Internet in the Science Classroom.**

Problem Solving

Review with students the method by which slime molds creep across surfaces. (See the Multiple Learning Styles activity on the previous page.)

Think Critically

Slime molds are eukaryotic organisms that usually live in moist or wet surroundings. They creep across surfaces and engulf food in ways similar to amoebas. Unlike amoebas, slime molds sometimes dry up and produce spores to reproduce. Unlike fungi, slime molds sometimes engulf food and move.

3 Assess

Check for Understanding

Using Science Words

Linguistic Have students look up the words plasmodium and *Plasmodium* to be sure they understand that a plasmodium is the active body of a slime mold, but *Plasmodium* is the genus name for a protozoan that causes malaria. L2

Reteach

Visual-Spatial Have students examine photographs or illustrations of various protists and identify the life-cycle phase of each. L2

Extension

For students who have mastered this section, use the **Reinforcement** and **Enrichment** masters.

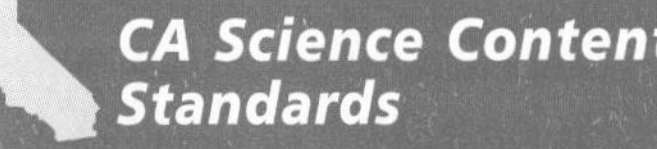

CA Science Content Standards

Page 766: 6a

4 Close

Proficiency Prep

1. **Which algae are the most numerous?** *diatoms*
2. **What are one-celled, animal-like protists?** *protozoans*

Section Assessment

1. Protists are mostly single-celled organisms that live in moist or wet surroundings. They possess membrane-bound nuclei, but do not have tissues or organs. Protists may be plantlike, animal-like, or funguslike.
2. Algae are plantlike protists with chloroplasts and cell walls. Protozoans are single-celled animal-like protists that lack cell walls and cannot produce their own food. The funguslike protists are all consumers that produce spores.
3. Plantlike protists are classified according to their structure, pigments, and the form in which they store food.
4. **Think Critically** Protists are small and do not have hard parts to be fossilized. The protists decay rapidly, leaving no trace of their existence.

Using Computers

Phylum—Rhizopoda, Zoomastigina, Ciliophora, Sporozoa; **Example Species**—*Amoeba, Trypanosoma, Paramecium, Plasmodium;* **Method of Transportation**—pseudopods, flagella, cilia, none; **Other Characteristics**—some have hard shells, many are parasites, at least two nuclei, parasitic

EXAMPLES OF Water Molds

Figure 22-14 The potato plant (A) and the fish (B) show the effects of funguslike protists.

Ireland's main crop and the primary food source for its people. When the potato crop became infected with downy mildew, potatoes rotted in the fields, leaving many people with no food. Nearly 1 million people died in the resulting famine. Many others left Ireland and emigrated to the United States. This downy mildew continues to be a problem for potato growers, even in the United States.

A The Irish potato famine in the 1840s was the result of a downy mildew.

B A parasitic water mold growing on a fish will eventually kill it. Once the fish dies, the water mold will speed the decay of the fish. In this photo, the water mold appears as string coming off the fish.

Section Assessment

1. What are the main characteristics of all protists?
2. Compare and contrast the three groups of protists.
3. How are plantlike protists classified into different phyla?
4. **Think Critically:** Why aren't there many fossils of the different groups of protists?
5. **Skill Builder**
   Making and Using Tables Do the **Chapter 22 Skill Activity** on page 983 and compare and contrast the protist groups.

Using Computers

Spreadsheet Use a spreadsheet to make a table that compares the characteristics of the four phyla of protozoans. Include phylum, example species, method of transportation, and other characteristics. If you need help, refer to page 974.

Assessment

Performance Have students write a statement in their Science Journals comparing environments of slime molds and water molds. Use **Performance Assessment in the Science Classroom,** p. 103. 

Comparing Algae and Protozoans

Algae and protozoan cells have characteristics that are similar enough to place them within the same kingdom. However, the variety of forms within Kingdom Protista is great. In this activity, you can observe many of the differences that make organisms in Kingdom Protista so diverse.

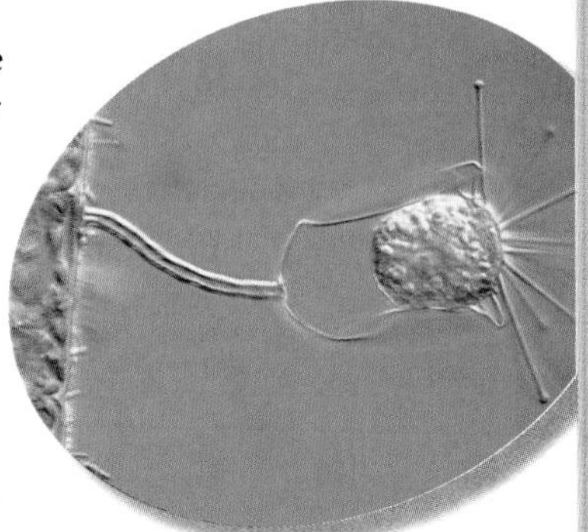

Materials

- Cultures of *Paramecium, Amoeba, Euglena,* and *Spirogyra*
  **prepared slides of above organisms*
- Prepared slide of slime mold
- Coverslips (5)
- Microscope
  **stereomicroscope*
- Dropper
- Microscope slides (5)
  **Alternate Materials*

What You'll Investigate

What are the differences between algae and protozoans?

Goals

- **Draw and label** the organisms you examine.
- **Observe** the differences between algae and protozoans.

Safety Precautions

Make sure to wash your hands after handling algae and protozoans.

Procedure

1. **Design** a data table in your Science Journal for your drawings and observations.
2. **Make** a wet mount of the *Paramecium* culture. If you need help doing this, refer to Appendix D.
3. **Observe** the wet mount first under low and then under high power. Draw and label the organism.
4. Repeat steps 2 and 3 with the other cultures. Return all preparations to your teacher and wash your hands.
5. **Observe** the slide of slime mold under low and high power. Record your observations.

Conclude and Apply

1. For each organism that could move, **label** the structure that enabled the movement.
2. Which protists make their own food? **Explain** how you know that they make their own food.
3. **Identify** those protists with animal characteristics.

Protist Observations

	Paramecium	Amoeba	Euglena	Spirogyra
Drawing	Student drawings should resemble Figure 22-11.	Student drawings should resemble Figure 22-8.	Student drawings should resemble Figure 22-2.	Student drawings should resemble Figure 22-5C.

Purpose

Visual-Spatial Students will observe the differences between algae and protozoans. L2

ELL COOP LEARN P

Process Skills

observing and inferring, defining operationally, classifying, making and using tables, comparing and contrasting

Time

50 minutes

Alternate Materials

It is best to use local materials from the same phyla, if available. If local materials are not available, prepared slides of protozoans and algae may be used. All live specimens should be obtained from a reputable supply house. No parasitic forms should be used.

Safety Precautions

Remind students to be careful when plugging the microscope into the wall outlet and when removing it. Water should be kept away from the outlet.

Teaching Strategies

Troubleshooting Maintain separate cultures for each organism. Prevent students from using the same dropper in more than one culture.

Answers to Questions

1. *Paramecium*—cilia; *Amoeba*—pseudopods; *Euglena*—flagella
2. *Spirogyra* and *Euglena* make their own food. We know they make their own food because they contain chloroplasts and, therefore, use light to photosynthesize food.
3. *Paramecium, Amoeba,* and *Euglena* are animal-like because they obtain their food from other sources and move.

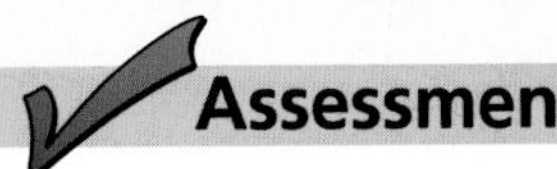

Assessment

Performance To further assess students' abilities to identify algae and protozoans, have them make and view scrapings from fish tanks, making sure they wash their hands thoroughly afterward. Use **Performance Assessment in the Science Classroom,** p. 25.

SECTION 22•2

Prepare

Content Background

Refer to **Characteristics of Fungi, Zygote Fungi, Sac Fungi, Imperfect Fungi,** and **Club Fungi** on p. 756F.

Preplanning

Refer to the **Chapter Organizer** on pp. 756A–B.

1 Motivate

Bellringer

Before presenting the lesson, display **Section Focus Transparency 63** on the overhead projector. Use the accompanying **Focus Activity** worksheet. L2 ELL

Section 12-2

SECTION FOCUS TRANSPARENCY

MUSHROOM, ANYONE?

Using a technique that originated in France, people have trained their domestic pigs to root out flavorful mushrooms called truffles. The pigs have very poor eyesight, but can smell the truffles, which may grow 6 centimeters below the ground's surface. The pig is usually led on a leash. When the pig finds the truffles, it is usually given some other food like an acorn as the prized truffles are carefully collected.

1. If the truffles grow below ground, do you think that they require sunlight to live? Explain your answer.
2. Do you think that truffles and other kinds of mushrooms are classified as plants? Why or why not?

Demonstration

Mix some yeast suspension with flour and water and put it in a warm place. Ask students to predict what will happen over the course of the day. *The dough will rise as carbon dioxide is made by the yeast.*

22•2 Kingdom Fungi

***What* You'll Learn**

- How to identify the characteristics shared by all fungi
- How to classify fungi into groups based on their methods of reproduction
- The difference between the imperfect fungi and all other fungi

Vocabulary
hyphae
spore
budding
lichen

***Why* It's Important**

- Fungi are important sources of food and medicines, and they recycle Earth's wastes.

What are fungi?

Do you think you can find members of Kingdom Fungi in a quick trip around your house or apartment? You can find fungi in your kitchen if you have mushroom soup or fresh mushrooms. Yeasts are a type of fungi used to make bread and cheese. You also may find mold, a type of fungus, growing on an old loaf of bread, or mildew, another fungus, growing on your shower curtain.

As important as fungi seem in the production of different foods, they are most important in their role as organisms that decompose or break down organic materials. Food scraps, clothing, dead plants, and animals are all made of organic material. Fungi work to decompose, or break down, all these materials and return them to the soil. The materials returned to the soil are then reused by plants. Fungi, along with bacteria, are nature's recyclers. They keep Earth from becoming buried under mountains of waste materials.

Characteristics of Fungi

Fungi were once classified as plants because, like plants, they grow anchored in soil and have cell walls. But, unlike plants, fungi do not make their own food or have the specialized tissues and organs of plants, such as leaves and roots. Most species of fungi are many-celled. The body of a fungus is usually a mass of many-celled, threadlike tubes called **hyphae** (HI fee), as illustrated in **Figure 22-15.**

Fungi don't contain chlorophyll and therefore cannot make their own food. Most fungi feed on dead or decaying tissues. Organisms that obtain food in this way are called *saprophytes.* A fungus gives off enzymes that break down food outside of

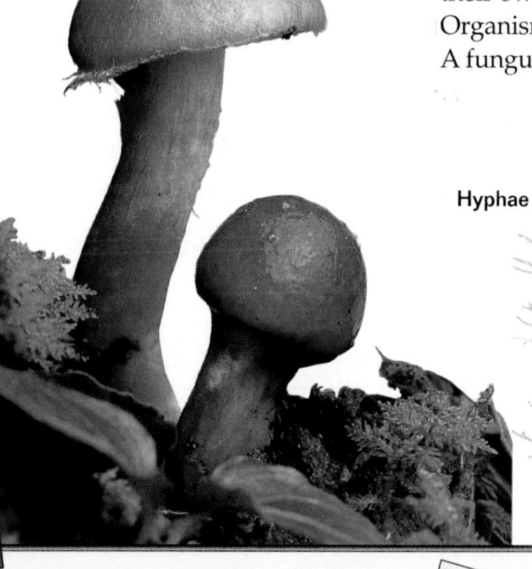

Figure 22-15 Most hyphae grow underground, though they also may form reproductive structures such as the mushrooms pictured here.

Resource Manager

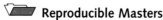

The following **Teacher Classroom Resources** can be used with Section 22-2:

Reproducible Masters
Activity Worksheets, pp. 125–126 L2
Critical Thinking/Problem Solving, p. 22 L2
Enrichment, p. 63 L3
Home Involvement, p. 28 L2
Laboratory Manual, pp. 137–140 L2
Multicultural Connections, pp. 43–44 L2
Reinforcement, p. 63 L2
Study Guide, pp. 87–88 L1 ELL

Transparencies
Teaching Transparency 44 L2
Science Integration Transparency 22 L2

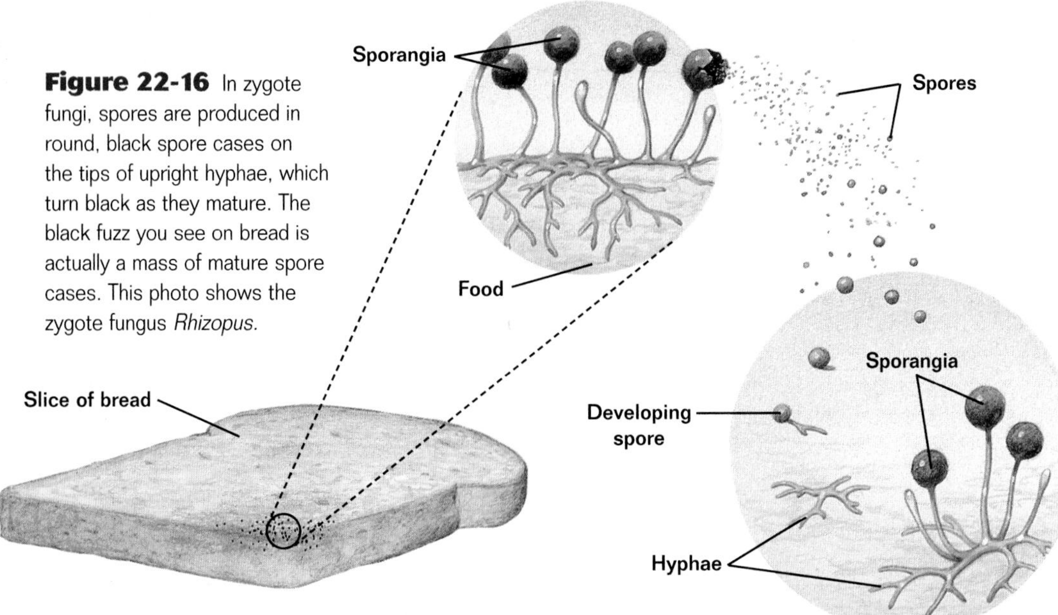

Figure 22-16 In zygote fungi, spores are produced in round, black spore cases on the tips of upright hyphae, which turn black as they mature. The black fuzz you see on bread is actually a mass of mature spore cases. This photo shows the zygote fungus *Rhizopus*.

itself. Then, the fungus cells absorb the digested food. Fungi that cause athlete's foot and ringworm are parasites. They obtain their food directly from living things.

Fungi grow best in warm, humid areas, such as tropical forests or the spaces between your toes.

A **spore** is a reproductive cell that forms new organisms without fertilization. The structures in which fungi produce spores are used to classify fungi into one of four phyla.

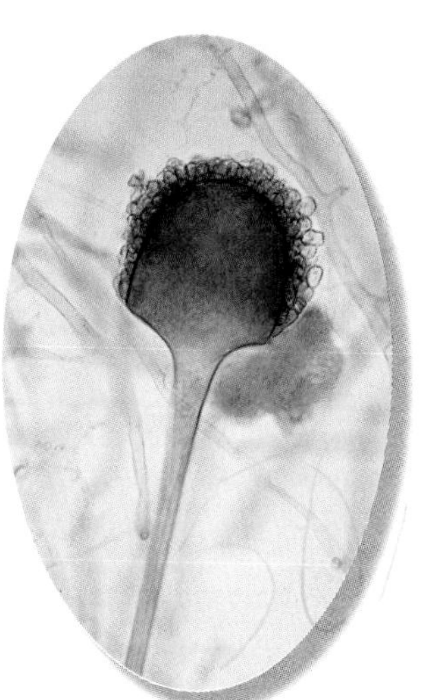

Magnification: 100×

Immature Rhizopus spore

Zygote Fungi

The fuzzy black mold that you sometimes find growing on an old loaf of bread or perhaps a piece of fruit is a type of zygote fungus. Fungi that belong to this division, the phylum Zygomycota, produce spores in round spore cases called sporangia (spuh RAN jee uh) on the tips of upright hyphae, as illustrated in **Figure 22-16.** When each sporangium splits open, hundreds of spores are released into the air. Each spore will grow into more mold if it lands where there is enough moisture, a warm temperature, and a food supply.

Sac Fungi

Yeasts, molds, morels, and truffles are all examples of sac fungi. The spores of these fungi are produced in a little saclike structure called an ascus. The phylum Ascomycota (ahs coh my COH tuh) is named for these sacs. The ascospores are released when the tip of an ascus breaks open.

2 Teach

VISUAL Learning

Figure 22-15 Invite students to explain why fungi are no longer classified as plants as they originally were. Explain that unlike plants, fungi contain no chloroplasts or cellulose cell walls.

Quick Demo

Show students some food that has mold growing on it. This is best done if the food can be kept under a plastic cover such as in a freezer storage bag. **CAUTION:** *Contact the school nurse if a student shows signs of an allergic reaction to fungi used in demonstrations during this section. It is rare, but some students may experience breathing difficulties in the presence of fungal spores.*

GLENCOE TECHNOLOGY

Videodisc

Glencoe Science Voyages Interactive Videodisc—Life

Side 1, Lesson 3 *Decomposers: Earth's Natural Recyclers*

32737

35030

Refer to the Videodisc Teacher Guide for additional bar codes.

Across the Curriculum

Mathematics The fairy ring toadstool (a type of mushroom) advances outward from the center at a rate of about 30 cm per year. One ring is estimated to be 150 years old. **How many meters in diameter is this ring?** *150 years × 30 cm/year × 2 radii = 9000 cm = 90 meters*

Content Background

Mycology is the study of fungi. Many fungi are useful commercially in baking and fermentation. Others, such as *Amanita* mushrooms, are poisonous. Caution students never to eat a mushroom that has not been identified by an expert or purchased from a grocery store.

CA Science Content Standards

Page 770: 5b
Page 771: 5b

Answer to Reading Check 

a form of asexual reproduction in which a new organism grows off the side of the parent

GLENCOE TECHNOLOGY

Videodisc

Glencoe Science Voyages Interactive Videodisc—Life

Side 2, Lesson 9 *Ecosystems: Wetlands*

46235

Refer to Videodisc Teacher Guide for additional bar codes.

Try at Home Mini Lab

For additional help doing this activity at home, see the corresponding pages in the **Home Involvement** booklet.

Purpose

 **Visual Spatial** Students will observe spores. L2 ELL

Materials

mushrooms, unlined white paper

Teaching Strategies

Caution students not to disturb the mushrooms while spore prints are being made.

Analysis

1. Sketches will vary.
2. Brown lines will be parallel or concentric rings made by falling spores.
3. Count a few spores in one area and multiply by the total area of spore production.

Try at Home Mini Lab

Interpreting Spore Prints

Procedure

1. Obtain several mushrooms from the grocery store and let them age until the undersides look brown.
2. Remove the stems and arrange the mushroom caps with the gills down on a piece of unlined white paper.
3. Let the mushroom caps sit undisturbed overnight and remove them from the paper the next day.

Analysis

1. Draw and label a sketch of the results in your Science Journal.
2. Describe the marks on the page and what made them.
3. How could you estimate the number of new mushrooms that could be produced from one mushroom cap?

Reading Check
What is budding?

Many sac fungi are well known by farmers because they destroy plant crops. Diseases caused by sac fungi are Dutch elm disease, apple scab, and ergot disease of rye.

Yeast is an economically important sac fungus. Yeasts don't always reproduce by forming spores. They also reproduce asexually by budding, as illustrated in **Figure 22-17. Budding** is a form of asexual reproduction in which a new organism grows off the side of the parent. Yeasts are used in the baking industry. As yeasts grow, they use sugar for energy and produce alcohol and carbon dioxide as waste products. The carbon dioxide causes bread to rise.

Imperfect Fungi

The so-called imperfect fungi, phylum Deuteromycota, are species of fungi in which a sexual stage has never been observed. When a sexual stage of one of these fungi is observed, the species is immediately classified as one of the other three phyla. Instead, imperfect fungi reproduce asexually, most through the use of spores. *Penicillium* is one example from this group. Penicillin, an antibiotic, is an important product of this fungus. Other examples of imperfect fungi are species that cause ringworm and athlete's foot. Because changes in classification now allow asexual fungi to be included in other phyla, *Penicillium* is sometimes considered a sac fungus.

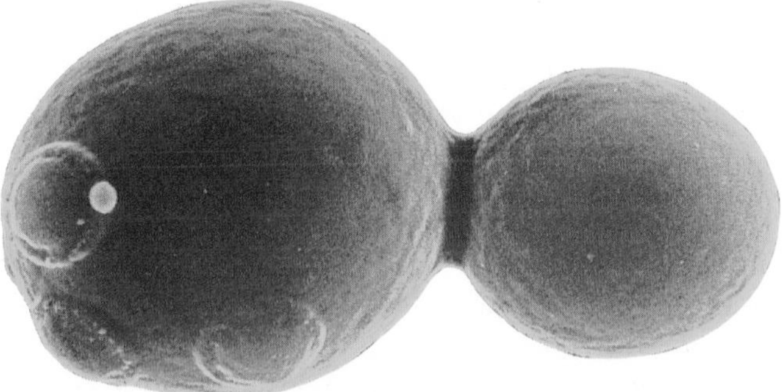
Magnification: 6100×

Figure 22-17 Yeasts can reproduce by forming buds off the side of the parents. The bud pinches off and forms an identical cell. **What are yeasts used for?**

Caption Answer

Figure 22-17 *Yeasts are used in the production of many foods.*

Assessment

Performance To further assess understanding of mushrooms and fungi in general, have students carefully tease apart a bit of the gill from under the spore cap and make a wet mount of an extremely small piece. Students should draw and describe what they see in their Science Journals. Use **Performance Assessment in the Science Classroom,** p. 55.

Figure 22-18 A mushroom is the spore-producing structure of a club fungus. The gills are thin sheets of tissue found under the mushroom cap. Spores are contained in many club-shaped structures that line the gills. **What are these club-shaped structures called?**

Club Fungi

The mushrooms shown in **Figure 22-18** are members of the phylum Basidiomycota. These fungi are commonly known as club fungi. The spores of these fungi are produced in a club-shaped structure called a basidium. The spores you observed on the gills of the mushroom in the MiniLab on the previous page were produced in the basidia.

Many of the club fungi are economically important. Rusts and smuts cause billions of dollars worth of damage to food crops each year. Cultivated mushrooms are an important food crop, but you should never eat a wild mushroom because many are poisonous.

Lichens

The colorful organisms in **Figure 22-19** are lichens. A **lichen** (LI kun) is an organism that is made of a fungus and either a green alga or a cyanobacterium. When two organisms live together, they often have a relationship in which both organisms benefit. The cells of the alga live tangled up in the threadlike strands of the fungus. The alga gets a moist, protected place to live, and the fungus gets food made by the green alga or cyanobacterium. Lichens are an important food source for many animals, including caribou and musk oxen.

CHEMISTRY INTEGRATION

pH

The measurement of how much acid or base a substance contains is its pH. Acids are measured on a pH scale that ranges from 1 to 14. Substances that have a pH lower than 7 are considered acidic. Acids become stronger as the pH decreases. The acids produced by lichens are weak, but given enough time, they can erode sedimentary rock. Look up the pH for some common acids, such as stomach acid, lemon juice, and battery acid. In your Science Journal, compare these to the pH of lichen.

Caption Answer

Figure 22-18 *basidia (singular, basidium)*

CHEMISTRY INTEGRATION

Battery acid has a pH of 1; stomach acid has a pH of 2; lemon juice has a pH of 4; the pH of acids produced by lichens is between 6.5 and 6.9. The acid produced by living things is weak. It takes many years to erode rock to produce soil.

3 Assess

Check for Understanding Activity

Interpersonal Have students work in groups to interview local physicians about the role of fungi in the health field. Students will learn that fungi can cause infection in humans, but that some fungi are also used in the production of medicine. L2 COOP LEARN

Reteach

Visual-Spatial Show students various illustrations of fungi. Ask them to identify the parts of each fungus. L2

Extension

For students who have mastered this section, use the **Reinforcement** and **Enrichment** masters.

Teacher FYI

One of the largest organisms in the world is a fungus growing under acres of forest floor in Michigan. It is estimated to weigh at least 100 tons.

CA Science Content Standards

Page 772: 6a
Page 773: 5a, 5e

4 Close

Proficiency Prep

Use this quiz to check students' recall of section content.

1. **Where are the spores of sac fungi produced?** *the ascus*
2. **What has never been observed in imperfect fungi?** *a sexual stage*

Caption Answer

Figure 22-19 *by their appearance*

Section Assessment

1. Some fungi get their food from decaying organisms, and others are parasites on living organisms.
2. Fungi cannot make their own food. Most fungi are many-celled saprophytes. They grow anchored in soil and have cell walls.
3. Lichens are an important food source for many animals, they break down rocks, and they are used to monitor pollution levels.
4. Think Critically It would be reclassified as a club fungus belonging to division Basidiomycota.

Using Math

$\frac{30\ 000}{100\ 000} \times 100\% = 30\%$

Assessment

Oral Why is it beneficial for fungi to reproduce both sexually and asexually? *Asexual reproduction allows fungi to take full and rapid advantage of a food source. Sexual reproduction provides variety for surviving in different conditions.* Use **Performance Assessment in the Science Classroom,** p. 71.

Rocks crumble as they weather. Lichens are important in the weathering process because they are able to grow on bare rock. Lichens release acids as part of their metabolism. The acids break down the rock. As bits of rock accumulate and lichens die and decay, soil is formed. This soil supports the growth of other species. Organisms, such as the lichens seen in **Figure 22-19,** that grow on bare rock are called pioneer species because they are the first organisms to appear in a barren area.

Earth scientists also use lichens to monitor pollution levels because many species of lichens quickly die when they are exposed to pollution. When the lichen species return to grow on tree trunks and buildings, it is an indication that the pollution has been cleaned up.

EXAMPLES OF Lichens

Figure 22-19 Lichens can grow upright, appear leafy, or look like a crust on bare rock. All three forms may grow near each other. **Can you think of one way that lichens might be classified?**

Crusty lichen

British soldier lichen

Leafy lichen

Section Assessment

1. How do fungi obtain food?
2. What common characteristics are shared by fungi?
3. What are some important functions of lichens?
4. **Think Critically:** If an imperfect fungus were found to produce basidia under some circumstances, how would the fungus be reclassified?
5. **Skill Builder**
   Comparing and Contrasting
   Organize information about fungi in a table. Use this information to compare and contrast the characteristics of the four divisions of fungi. Include information on lichens as a fifth division in your table. If you need help, refer to Comparing and Contrasting in the **Skill Handbook** on page 956.

Using Math

Of the 100 000 species of fungi, approximately 30 000 are sac fungi. From this information, estimate the percent of sac fungi as a part of the total fungi kingdom.

5.  **Skill Builder**

Fungi Divisions	Example	Characteristics
Zygote Fungi	Bread mold	round spore cases on upright stalks
Sac Fungi	Yeast, molds, and morels	spores grow in a protective sac
Club Fungi	Rusts and smuts	spores grow in a club-shaped structure
Imperfect Fungi	*Penicillium*	sexual stage has never been observed
Lichens	British soldier lichen	crusty, leafy, or upright; closely associated with algae or cyanobacteria

Monitoring Red Tides

What is a red tide?

Imagine a humpback whale dying and washing up on a beach. Then multiply this death by 14. Add to this grisly scene tons of dead fish littering beaches from Florida to Massachusetts. Such events actually happened in 1987. The cause was a single species of dinoflagellate, a type of microscopic algae (see inset). At times, certain kinds of dinoflagellates reproduce rapidly to form extremely dense populations, or "blooms," that turn the ocean surface red—a condition known as a red tide (see photo at left). Pigments in the dinoflagellates are responsible for the red color. It is not unusual for a red tide to stretch hundreds of kilometers along a coastline. Red tides often occur in warm, shallow parts of the ocean, or where runoff from the land adds nutrients to seawater.

Red tides can be deadly because some dinoflagellates produce poisonous substances called toxins. When a red tide occurs, the algae are so numerous that the amount of toxin in the water is concentrated enough to kill fish and marine mammals such as whales. Toxins also accumulate in the tissues of filter-feeding shellfish such as clams and mussels, making them poisonous. People who eat shellfish contaminated by a red tide can become ill and may die.

How are red tides monitored?

In the past, scientists monitored red tides by sampling seawater and shellfish for the presence of dinoflagellates. Wherever large numbers of dinoflagellates were detected, researchers would alert the public not to eat seafood from those areas. This method of monitoring red tides was not always effective, however, because only small stretches of ocean could be tested at any one time, and red tides often developed before scientists became aware of them.

More recently, satellites equipped with infrared cameras have been used to monitor red tides from space. Satellite images reveal sea-surface temperatures over huge areas of ocean and give scientists clues as to where red tides are most likely to occur. Predicting red tides before they develop can help save lives.

interNET CONNECTION

Visit the Glencoe Science Web Site at **www.glencoe.com/sec/science/ca** for more information about red tides. Determine whether there is an area or time of year in which red tides occur with noticeable frequency.

Teaching Strategies

- You may be able to find newspaper accounts of red tides, especially if you live near a coast where such phenomena occur.
- Have students research the way satellites capture images in the infrared range and the way in which the images are decoded.

- Dinoflagellates that produce red tides are a normal part of marine phytoplankton. These one-celled protists have two flagella. One flagellum is contained in a groove that runs around the equator of the organism. The other extends from the cell and is the primary means of movement.
- Red tides are produced in warmer waters of shallow marine habitats when populations of dinoflagellates increase dramatically. The dinoflagellates are filtered from water as food by shellfish, and the toxins can then be passed on to humans who consume the oysters or clams. The poison can be fatal if enough is ingested.

For More Information

National Marine Fisheries Service
1315 East-West Highway
SSMC3
Silver Springs, MD 20910

Internet Addresses

For Internet tips, see Glencoe's **Using the Internet in the Science Classroom.**

Science Journal

News Item Have students write an item that might appear on a news program to warn people about red tides. The item should contain information about the organisms that are causing the problem and health precautions to prevent poisoning.

CA Science Content Standards

Page 774: 9f

Activity 22•2

What You'll Investigate

Purpose

Naturalist Students will examine and compare fungi samples, and determine classification based on reproductive structures. L2 ELL COOP LEARN P

Process Skills

observing, classifying, interpreting data, making and using tables, comparing and contrasting

Procedure

Time

50 minutes

Materials

Bread mold, *Penicillium*, moldy foods, mushroom caps, shelf fungi, and lichens may be collected and brought in by students.

Alternate Materials

If students are unable to collect fungi samples, you can purchase many kinds of fungi from biological supply houses, or preserved slides may be used. If desired, you may grow mold by leaving bread in a warm, dark place for about a week. Fruit can be placed in a sealed plastic bag to induce the growth of mold.

Safety Precautions

- Tell students to wash their hands after handling specimens and completing the activity.
- **CAUTION:** *Some students may be allergic to fungal spores. These students may be provided with dust masks available from hardware or home supply stores. Contact the school nurse if a student shows signs of breathing difficulties. Students with asthma should obtain permission from the school nurse or their doctor before doing this activity.*

Activity 22•2

Comparing Types of Fungi

Fungi differ mainly in their reproductive structures. The diversity of these structures allows scientists to classify fungi as zygote fungi, club fungi, sac fungi, or imperfect fungi. In this activity, you will compare the reproductive structures in cultures of fungi.

Materials

- Cultures of fungi (bread mold, mushrooms, yeasts, lichens, or *Penicillium*)
- Cellophane tape
- Microscope
- Microscope slides
- Coverslips
- Magnifying lens

What You'll Investigate

How do reproductive structures of fungi compare?

Goals

- **Observe** the appearance of fungi colonies.
- **Compare** the reproductive structures of fungi cultures.
- **Draw, label, and identify** different types of fungi.

Safety Precautions

Make sure to wash your hands after handling fungi.

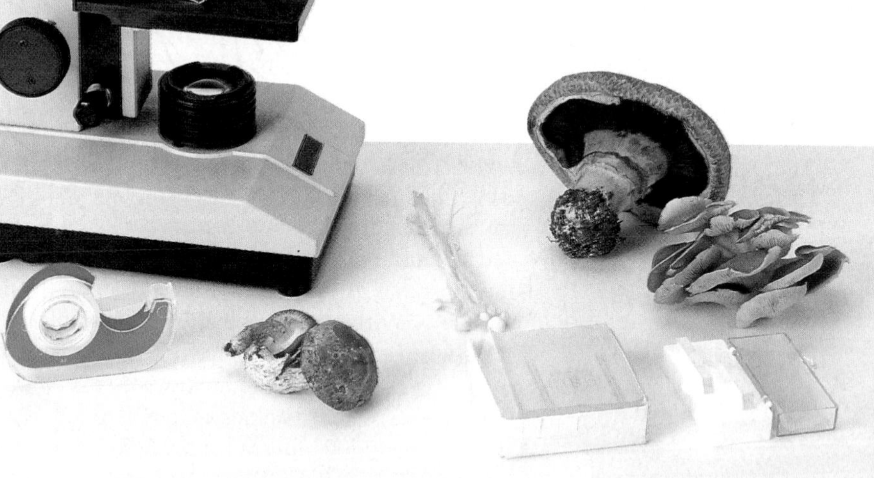

776 CHAPTER 22 PROTISTS AND FUNGI

Procedure

1. **Design** a data table like the one below in your Science Journal with columns labeled *Fungus, Colony Appearance, Reproductive Structures,* and *Fungi Division.*
2. **Compare and contrast** the cultures of fungi in drawings that you label.
3. Your teacher will demonstrate how to collect the reproductive structures of fungi with cellophane tape by gently touching the tape to your samples.
4. Place the tape, adhesive side up, on a microscope slide and cover it with a coverslip. If you need help making a wet mount, see **Appendix D.**
5. Draw and label the reproductive structures.
6. Repeat this procedure for each culture of fungus.
7. Fill in the data table you designed. One column has been done for you below.

Conclude and Apply

1. Write a description of the reproductive structures you observed. Include relative numbers, shape of cells, and size.
2. From your descriptions, explain why fungi are classified based on their reproductive structures.
3. List the four divisions of fungi, and give an example of each division.

Fungi Observations

Fungus	Colony Appearance	Reproductive Structures	Fungi Division
mushrooms	rounded stalks with clublike caps	basidia	club fungi
bread mold	fuzzy with black spots (spore cases)	sporangia	zygote fungi
Penicillium	blue-green flattened colonies growing in circles	none observed	imperfect fungi

Teaching Strategies

- Place identification labels on the specimens for students to put in their tables.
- Demonstrate how to collect fungal spores by gently touching the cellophane to the culture containing the spores.

Troubleshooting It may be necessary for you to help students focus on the spores, especially when using the higher-power objectives of the microscopes.

Expected Outcome

Students should observe sexual and asexual reproductive structures.

Error Analysis

Students may not recognize some reproductive structures. Ask students to look at photographs of these structures if they initially do not see them under the microscope.

Conclude and Apply

1. Student descriptions will be based on the cultures observed. Students should describe spores as being small, spherical objects of varying colors. The numbers will range from hundreds to thousands, depending on how many spores they collected from each specimen.
2. Many reproductive structures of the major groups of fungi are unique and distinctive.
3. The four phyla of fungi should be listed with a representative from each phylum.

GO Further

To further assess students' understanding of fungal reproductive structures, provide other samples to classify.

Assessment

Performance Have students create posters illustrating the life cycles of the various types of fungi examined in this activity. Use **Performance Assessment in the Science Classroom,** p. 73.

Reviewing Main Ideas can be used to preview, review, reteach, and condense chapter content.

Preview

Linguistic Have students try to answer the questions in their Science Journals. Use student answers as a source for discussion throughout the chapter.

Review

Interpersonal Have students answer the questions on separate pieces of paper and compare their answers with those of other students in the class.

Reteach

Visual-Spatial Have students look at the illustrations on these pages. Ask them to describe details that support the main ideas of the chapter found in the statement for each illustration.

00:00 OUT OF TIME?

Auditory-Musical If time does not permit teaching the entire chapter, use the information on these pages along with the chapter Audiocassettes to present the material in a condensed format.

Chapter 22 Reviewing Main Ideas

For a **preview** of this chapter, study this Reviewing Main Ideas before you read the chapter. After you have studied this chapter, you can use the Reviewing Main Ideas to **review** the chapter.

The Glencoe MindJogger, Audiocassettes, and CD-ROM provide additional opportunities for review.

Section

22-1 KINGDOM PROTISTA

Protists are one- or many-celled eukaryotic organisms. They are thought to have evolved from a one-celled organism with a nucleus, mitochondria, and other cellular structures. The protist kingdom has members that are plantlike, animal-like, and funguslike. Plantlike protists are classified by their structure, their pigments, and the way in which they store food. Animal-like protists are separated into groups by how they move. Funguslike protists have characteristics of both protists and fungi. ***What common names are given to each group of protists?***

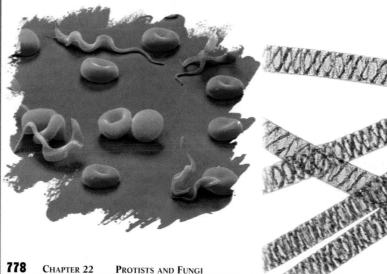

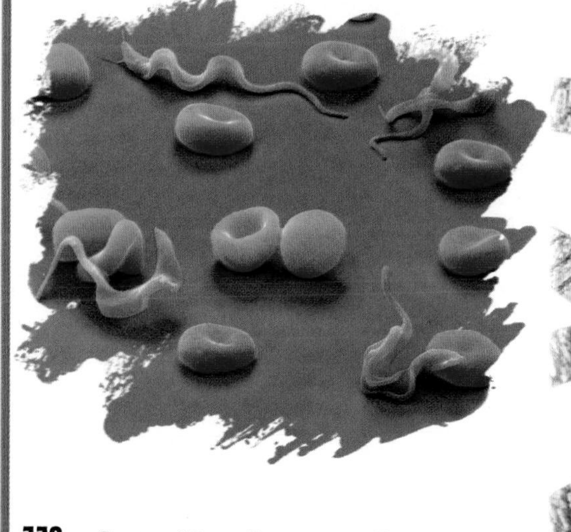

Cultural Diversity

Seaweed, Anyone? Algae grow worldwide in areas that contain enough moisture for the species of algae that grow there. Some species can survive extreme temperature or moisture conditions. Algae are used as food by people in some cultures, especially those along coastlines, and are used as animal food in others. Agar, which is extracted from red seaweed, is considered a delicacy in certain parts of Asia. When grown under controlled conditions, certain algae, such as Chlorella, are an excellent source of nutrition because they contain proteins, carbohydrates, and fats. Small "farms" that raise Chlorella have been established in several countries that rely on the algae as a food source.

Reading Check

Review "Other Characteristics" in Table 22-1. How could you break the information under this heading into at least two columns?

Section

22-2 KINGDOM FUNGI

Fungi are organisms that reproduce using **spores.** They are saprophytes, or parasites, which means they feed off other things because they cannot make their own food. One of the most important roles of fungi is to decompose organic material and return the nutrients to the soil. There are four groups of fungi: zygote fungus, sac fungus, club fungus, and imperfect fungus. Fungi are placed into one of these groups according to the structures in which they produce spores. ***Why are imperfect fungi given that name?***

Dr. Regina Benjamin, Family Practice Physician

Dr. Benjamin runs a family practice in Bayou La Batre, Alabama. She's the only doctor in town, and about 80 percent of her patients live below the poverty level. Dr. Benjamin sees a lot of skin infections caused by fungi because the environment is humid, which promotes the growth of fungus. Fungal infections can be difficult to treat. ***Why is classifying protists and fungi important for health care professionals?***

Answers to Questions

Section 22-1

Kingdom Protista Algae are plantlike protists, protozoans are animal-like protists, and funguslike protists include slime molds, water molds, and downy mildews.

Section 22-2

Kingdom Fungi Fungi are classified by the type of sexual spores they produce. Imperfect fungi have no known means of producing sexual spores.

GLENCOE TECHNOLOGY

CD-ROM

Glencoe Science Voyages Interactive CD-ROM

Chapter Summaries and Quizzes

Have students read the Chapter Summary then take the Chapter Quiz to determine whether they have mastered chapter content.

Career CONNECTION

Classification of protists and fungi are usually based on how they reproduce, obtain food, and move. Health care professionals need to know these things in order to develop effective treatments for the infections and diseases these organisms cause.

Assessment

Portfolio Encourage students to place in their portfolios one or two items of what they consider to be their best work. Examples include:

- Integrating the Sciences, p. 762
- Across the Curriculum, p. 764
- Activity 22-1, p. 769; 22-2, pp. 776–777 P

Performance Additional performance assessments may be found in the **Performance Assessment** and **Science Integration Activities.** Performance Task Assessment Lists and rubrics for evaluating these activities can be found in Glencoe's **Performance Assessment in the Science Classroom.**

Using Vocabulary

1. i
2. f
3. c
4. a
5. e

interNET CONNECTION To reinforce chapter vocabulary, use the **Study Guide for Content Mastery** booklet. Also available are activities for **Glencoe Science Voyages** on the Glencoe Science Web Site. **www.glencoe.com/sec/science/ca**

Checking Concepts

6. D
7. C
8. D
9. C
10. B
11. A
12. D
13. B
14. B
15. C

Thinking Critically

16. no warmth, low humidity, low moisture, and lots of light
17. their chloroplasts are spiral shaped
18. one-celled—one-celled; colonial—many cells arranged in a group; chains—many cells arranged in a long filament; many-celled—organism that has many different cells
19. Fungi are made of soft parts and do not usually form fossils. They live in warm, moist, humid areas that allow them to decompose rapidly. Because fungi have characteristics of plants, but also their own unique characteristics, their origin is difficult to trace.

Chapter 22 Assessment

Using Vocabulary

a. algae
b. budding
c. cilia
d. hyphae
e. lichen
f. protist
g. protozoans
h. pseudopods
i. spore

Each phrase below describes a science term from the list. Write the term that matches the phrase describing it.

1. reproductive cell of a fungus
2. eukaryotic organism that is animal-like, plantlike, or funguslike
3. threadlike structures used for movement
4. plantlike protists
5. organism made up of a fungus and an alga or a cyanobacterium

Checking Concepts

Choose the word or phrase that best answers the question.

6. Which of the following is an example of one-celled algae?
   A) paramecia
   B) lichen
   C) amoeba
   D) diatom
7. What color are members of phylum Bacillariophyta?
   A) green
   B) red
   C) golden-brown
   D) brown
8. Which of the following organisms cause red tides when found in large numbers?
   A) *Euglena*
   B) diatoms
   C) *Ulva*
   D) dinoflagellates
9. What phylum do brown algae belong to?
   A) Rhodophyta
   B) Dinoflagellata
   C) Phaeophyta
   D) Euglenophyta
10. Which of the following moves using cilia?
   A) *Amoeba*
   B) *Paramecium*
   C) *Trypanosoma*
   D) *Euglena*
11. Where would you most likely find funguslike protists?
   A) on decaying logs
   B) in bright light
   C) on dry surfaces
   D) on metal surfaces
12. Decomposition is an important role of which organisms?
   A) protozoans
   B) algae
   C) plants
   D) fungi
13. Which of the following organisms are monitors of pollution levels?
   A) club fungus
   B) lichen
   C) slime mold
   D) imperfect fungus
14. What produce the spores in mushrooms?
   A) sporangia
   B) basidia
   C) asci
   D) hyphae
15. Which of the following is an example of an imperfect fungus?
   A) mushroom
   B) yeast
   C) *Penicillium*
   D) lichen

Thinking Critically

16. What kind of environment is needed to prevent fungal growth?
17. Look at **Figure 22-5C** again. Why is *Spirogyra* a good name for this green alga?
18. Compare and contrast one-celled, colonial, chain, and many-celled algae.
19. Why do scientists find it difficult to trace the origin of fungi? Explain your answer.
20. Explain the adaptations of fungi that enable them to get food.

20. Fungi make enzymes that digest food outside the organism. Then the nutrients are absorbed by the cells.

Developing Skills

If you need help, refer to the **Skill Handbook.**

21. Observing and Inferring: Match the prefix of each alga, *Chloro-*, *Phaeo-*, and *Rhodo-*, with the correct color: brown, green, and red.

22. Concept Mapping: Complete the following concept map on a separate sheet of paper.

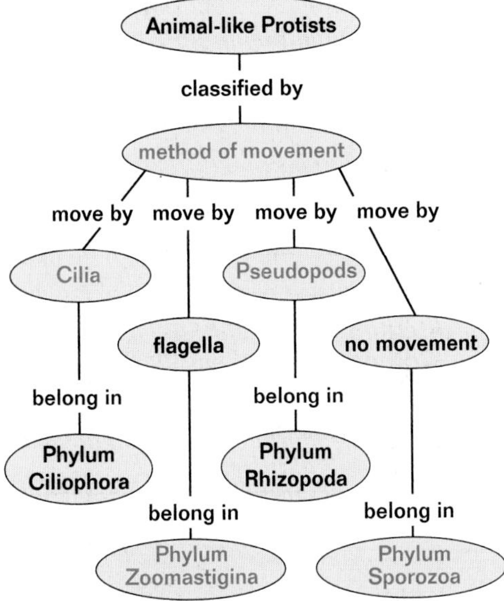

23. Comparing and Contrasting: Make a chart comparing and contrasting sac fungi, zygote fungi, club fungi, and imperfect fungi.

24. Classifying: Classify the following organisms based on their method of movement: *Euglena,* water molds, *Amoeba,* dinoflagellates, *Paramecium,* slime molds, *Trypanosoma,* and *Volvox.*

25. Design an Experiment: You find a new and unusual fungus growing in your refrigerator. Design an experiment to determine what phylum it belongs to.

THE PRINCETON REVIEW

Test-Taking Tip

Where's the Fire? Slow down! Double-check your math, and go back over reading passages. Remember that doing most of the questions and getting them right is always better than doing all the questions and getting lots of them wrong.

Test Practice

Use these questions to test your Science Proficiency.

1. Algae and plants have some characteristics in common. Which of the following **BEST** represents differences between algae and plants?
   A) Algae have cell walls, but plants do not.
   B) Plants have chlorophyll, but algae do not.
   C) Algae have cell membranes and nuclei, but plants do not.
   D) Plants have roots, stems, and leaves, but algae do not.
2. At one time, some protists were classified as animals because they moved and engulfed food. Which of the following protists are most like animals?
   A) protozoans
   B) algae
   C) slime molds and water molds
   D) zygote fungi
3. Fungi are classified according to how they produce sexual spores. Which of the following groups of fungi are **NOT** known to ever produce sexual spores?
   A) zygote fungi
   B) imperfect fungi
   C) club fungi
   D) sac fungi

Assessment Resources

The **Test Practice Workbook** provides students with practice in the format, concepts, and critical-thinking skills tested in standardized exams.

 Reproducible Masters

Chapter Review, pp. 43–44 L2

Performance Assessment, p. 22 L2

Assessment, pp. 85–88 L2

Glencoe Technology

 **Chapter Review Software**

 **Computer Test Bank**

 **MindJogger Videoquiz**

THE PRINCETON REVIEW Test Practice

The Test-Taking Tip was written by The Princeton Review, the nation's leader in test preparation.

1. D
2. A
3. B

Developing Skills

21. *chloro*—green, *phaeo*—brown, *rhodo*—red
22. See student page.
23. Charts should show that Ascomycota reproduce by budding and making spores, example—yeast; Zygomycota reproduce by producing spores in sporangia, example—bread mold; Basidiomycota reproduce by making spores in basidia, example—mushrooms. No sexual stage has been observed in imperfect fungi, they reproduce asexually by spores, example—*Penicillium.*
24. Flagella—*Euglena,* water molds, dinoflagellates, *Trypanosoma, Volvox;* pseudopods—*Amoeba,* slime molds; cilia—*Paramecium*
25. Designs will vary. Designs should include comparing the fungus to characteristics of different fungi.

Bonus Question

What are the causes and effects of a red tide? *Red tides are caused by a population explosion of dinoflagellates. Millions of these organisms cause the water to look red. Some species release a nerve toxin that can kill fish and humans.*

Chapter 23 Plants

Section	Objectives	Activities/Features
Chapter Opener		Explore Activity: Infer Which Plant Parts Are Edible, p. 783
23-1 **Characteristics of Plants** 1 Session ½ Block	1. **List** the characteristics of plants. 2. **Describe** adaptations of plants that made it possible for them to survive on land. 3. **Compare** vascular and nonvascular plants.	Using Math, p. 785 Chemistry Integration, p. 786 Problem Solving: Cause and Effect in Nature, p. 788 Skill Builder: Forming a Hypothesis, p. 789 Science Journal, p. 789
23-2 **Seedless Plants** 2 Sessions 1 Block	4. **Compare** seedless nonvascular plants with seedless vascular plants. 5. **State** the importance of nonvascular and vascular plants.	Earth Science Integration, p. 791 MiniLab: Measuring Water Absorption by a Moss, p. 791 Earth Science Integration, p. 794 Skill Builder: Concept Mapping, p. 795 Using Math, p. 795 Activity 23-1: Comparing Seedless Plants, p. 796 How It Works: Preservation in Peat Bogs, p. 797
23-3 **Seed Plants** 4½ Sessions 2 Blocks	6. **List** the characteristics of seed plants. 7. **Describe** the structures and functions of roots, stems, and leaves. 8. **Describe** the main characteristics of gymnosperms and angiosperms and their importance. 9. **Compare** monocots and dicots.	MiniLab: Observing Water Moving in a Plant, p. 799 Using Math, p. 800 Skill Builder: Classifying, p. 806 Using Computers, p. 806 Activity 23-2: Comparing Monocots and Dicots, p. 807

The number of recommended single-period sessions — The number of recommended blocks
One session and one-half block are allowed for chapter review and assessment.

Activity Materials

Explore	Activities	MiniLabs
p. 783 pencil, paper	p. 796 moss, liverwort, club moss, horsetail fern p. 807 monocot and dicot flowers, monocot and dicot seeds, scalpel, forceps, iodine solution	p. 791 *Sphagnum* moss, cheesecloth, string, scale, 500- to 750-mL container p. 799 clear container, red food coloring, whole green onion, water

Need Materials? Contact Science Kit at 1-800-828-7777 or at www.sciencekit.com on the Internet.
For alternate materials, see the activity on the listed page.

Standards		Reproducible Resources	Technology
National	State/Local	Test Practice Workbooks are available for use with each chapter.	English and Spanish audiocassettes are available for use with each section.
National Content Standards: UCP1, UCP4, UCP5, C1, C3, C4, C5, D2, E2, G1, G3	California Science Content Standards: 5a, 6a, 6b, 6c	**Enrichment,** p. 64 **Reinforcement,** p. 64 **Study Guide,** p. 90	**Section Focus Transparency 64** **Teaching Transparency 45** **Teaching Transparency 46** **National Geographic Society: STV** **Internet Connection,** p. 788
National Content Standards: UCP1, UCP5, A1, C1, C2, D1, D2, E2	California Science Content Standards: 5c, 6a, 6b, 6c, 9f	**Activity Worksheets,** pp. 129–130 **Enrichment,** p. 65 **Reinforcement,** p. 65 **Study Guide,** p. 91	**Section Focus Transparency 65** **Science Integration Transparency 23** **Glencoe Science Voyages Interactive Videodisc—Life** **Internet Connection,** p. 794
National Content Standards: UCP1, UCP5, A1, C1, C2, C4, C5, E2, F1	California Science Content Standards: 5a, 6c	**Activity Worksheets,** pp. 131–132 **Critical Thinking/Problem Solving,** p. 23 **Enrichment,** p. 66 **Laboratory Manual,** pp. 141–142 **Laboratory Manual,** pp. 143–144 **Multicultural Connections,** pp. 45–46 **Reinforcement,** p. 66 **Study Guide,** pp. 91–92	**Section Focus Transparency 66** **The Infinite Voyage Series** **Glencoe Science Voyages Interactive CD-ROM**

Key to Teaching Strategies

The following designations will help you decide which activities are appropriate for your students.

L1 Level 1 activities should be appropriate for students with learning difficulties.

L2 Level 2 activities should be within the ability range of all students.

L3 Level 3 activities are designed for above-average students.

ELL ELL activities should be within the ability range of English Language Learners.

COOP LEARN Cooperative Learning activities are designed for small group work.

P These strategies represent student products that can be placed into a best-work portfolio.

Multiple Learning Styles logos, as described on page 55T, are used throughout to indicate strategies that address different learning styles.

Assessment Resources

Chapter Review, pp. 45–46
Assessment, pp. 89–92
Performance Assessment in the Science Classroom (PASC)
MindJogger Videoquiz
Alternate Assessment in the Science Classroom
Performance Assessment, p. 23
Chapter Review Software
Computer Test Bank

Chapter 23 Plants

This is a representation of key blackline masters available in the Teacher Classroom Resources. See Resource Manager boxes within the chapter for additional information.

Transparencies

Section Focus Transparencies

SECTION FOCUS TRANSPARENCY

ALONG A ROCKY COAST

The Atlantic coast can be a rocky one. But there are living things that make their homes on the rocks. To prevent people from getting hurt, signs like this are sometimes posted.

1. Why do you think that sign is posted?
2. What could be causing this particular hazard?

L2

SECTION FOCUS TRANSPARENCY

GETTING BOGGED DOWN

In many northern bogs, large floating mats of sphagnum moss are common. For many years sphagnum moss was used for sponges in surgery. People still use sphagnum moss in gardening.

1. Why do you think sphagnum mosses were used as surgical sponges?
2. Since mosses do not have roots, how do they absorb water?

L2

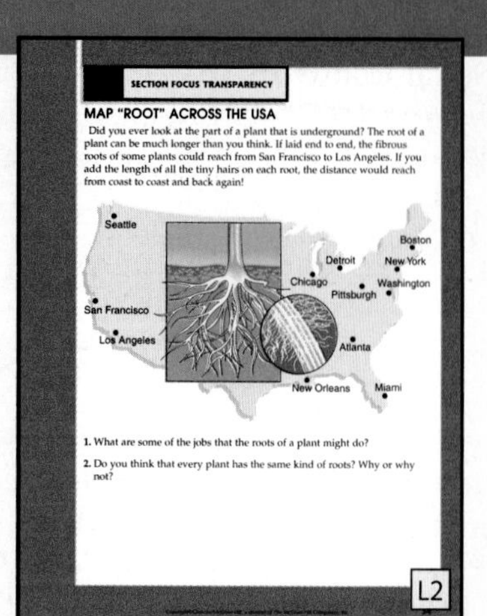

SECTION FOCUS TRANSPARENCY

MAP "ROOT" ACROSS THE USA

Did you ever look at the part of a plant that is underground? The root of a plant can be much longer than you think. If laid end to end, the fibrous roots of some plants could reach from San Francisco to Los Angeles. If you add the length of all the tiny hairs on each root, the distance would reach from coast to coast and back again!

1. What are some of the jobs that the roots of a plant might do?
2. Do you think that every plant has the same kind of roots? Why or why not?

L2

Science Integration Transparencies

SCIENCE INTEGRATION TRANSPARENCY

Fossil Plant Power

L2

Teaching Transparencies

PLANT CLASSIFICATION

L2

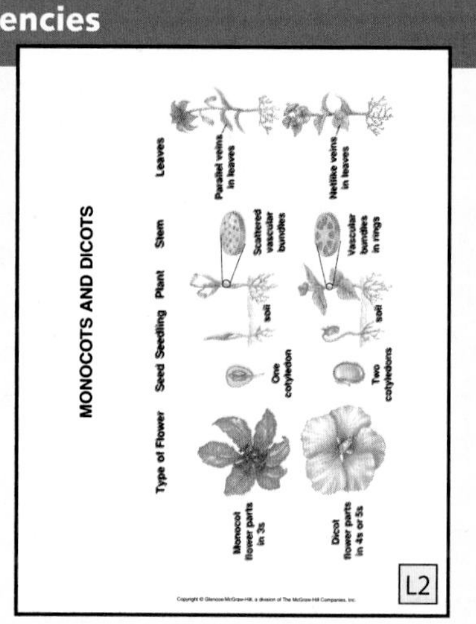

MONOCOTS AND DICOTS

L2

Meeting Different Ability Levels

Study Guide for Content Mastery

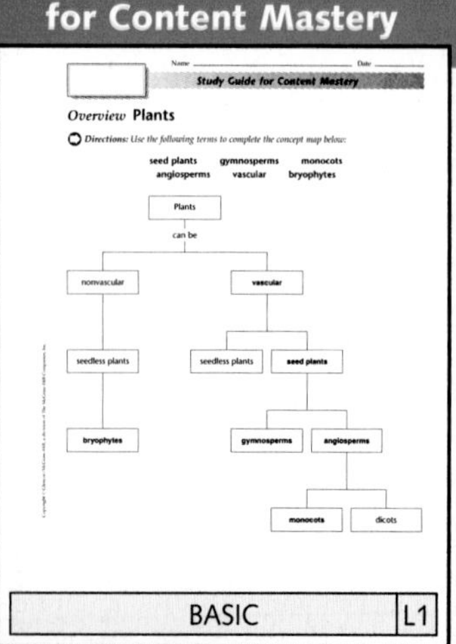

Study Guide for Content Mastery

Overview Plants

Directions: Use the following terms to complete the concept map below:

seed plants, gymnosperms, monocots, angiosperms, vascular, bryophytes

BASIC L1

Reinforcement

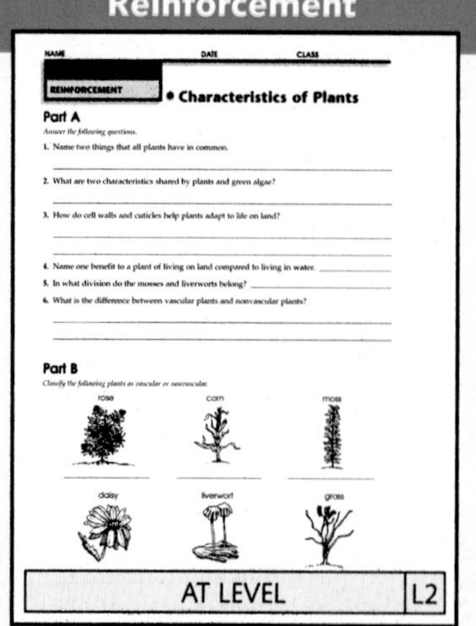

REINFORCEMENT • Characteristics of Plants

Part A

Answer the following questions.

1. Name two things that all plants have in common.
2. What are two characteristics shared by plants and green algae?
3. How do cell walls and cuticles help plants adapt to life on land?
4. Name one benefit to a plant of living on land compared to living in water.
5. In what division do the mosses and liverworts belong?
6. What is the difference between vascular plants and nonvascular plants?

Part B

Classify the following plants as vascular or nonvascular.

AT LEVEL L2

Enrichment Worksheets

ENRICHMENT • Characteristics of Plants

Sweet Celery

The following activity will show you how a vascular plant moves nutrients to all its parts.

Materials

Procedure

Data and Observations

Conclude and Apply

CHALLENGE L3

Hands-on Activities

Activity Worksheets

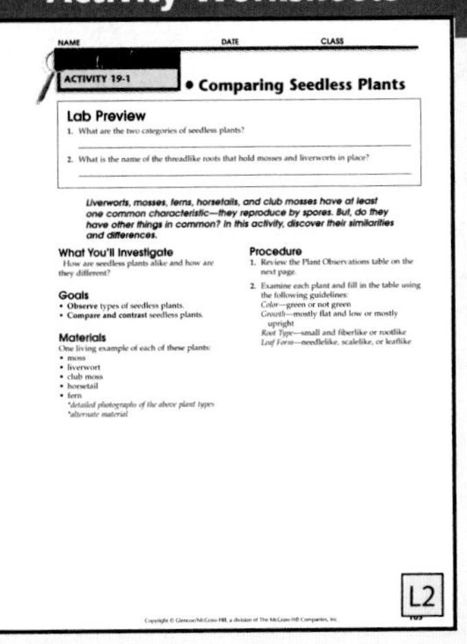

NAME DATE CLASS

ACTIVITY 19-1 • Comparing Seedless Plants

Lab Preview

1. What are the two categories of seedless plants?
2. What is the name of the threadlike roots that hold mosses and liverworts in place?

Liverworts, mosses, ferns, horsetails, and club mosses have at least one common characteristic—they reproduce by spores. But, do they have other things in common? In this activity, discover their similarities and differences.

What You'll Investigate
How are seedless plants alike and how are they different?

Goals
- Observe types of seedless plants.
- Compare and contrast seedless plants.

Materials
One living example of each of these plants:
- moss
- liverwort
- club moss
- horsetail
- fern

Procedure
1. Review the Plant Observations table on the next page.
2. Examine each plant and fill in the table using the following guidelines:
Color—green or not green
Growth—mostly flat and low or mostly upright
Root Type—small and fiberlike or rootlike
Leaf Form—needlelike, scalelike, or leaflike

L2

Lab Manual

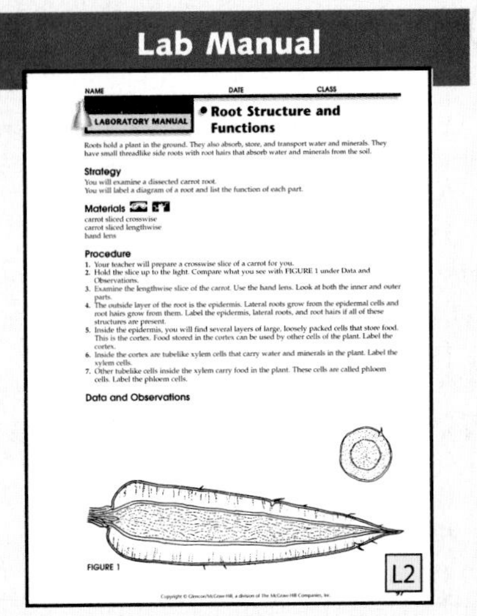

NAME DATE CLASS

LABORATORY MANUAL • Root Structure and Functions

Roots hold a plant in the ground. They also absorb, store, and transport water and minerals. They have small threadlike side roots with root hairs that absorb water and minerals from the soil.

Strategy
You will examine a dissected carrot root.
You will label a diagram of a root and list the function of each part.

Materials
carrot sliced crosswise
carrot sliced lengthwise
hand lens

Procedure
1. Your teacher will prepare a crosswise slice of a carrot for you.
2. Hold the slice up to the light. Compare what you see with FIGURE 1 under Data and Observations.
3. Examine the lengthwise slice of the carrot. Use the hand lens. Look at both the inner and outer parts.
4. The outside layer of the root is the epidermis. Lateral roots grow from the epidermal cells and root hairs grow from them. Label the epidermis, lateral roots, and root hairs if all of these structures are present.
5. Inside the epidermis, you will find several layers of large, loosely packed cells that store food. This is the cortex. Food stored in the cortex can be used by other cells of the plant. Label the cortex.
6. Inside the cortex are tubelike xylem cells that carry water and minerals in the plant. Label the xylem cells.
7. Other tubelike cells inside the xylem carry food in the plant. These cells are called phloem cells. Label the phloem cells.

Data and Observations

FIGURE 1

L2

Accessibility

Spanish Resources

SPANISH RESOURCES

GLENCOE California Edition

SCIENCE VOYAGES

Exploring the Life, Earth, and Physical Sciences

LEVEL BLUE

- Provides help for the English language learner
- Translates into Spanish the objectives, summary statements, vocabulary terms, and their definitions
- Includes a complete English/Spanish Glossary

L2

Assessment

Performance Assessment

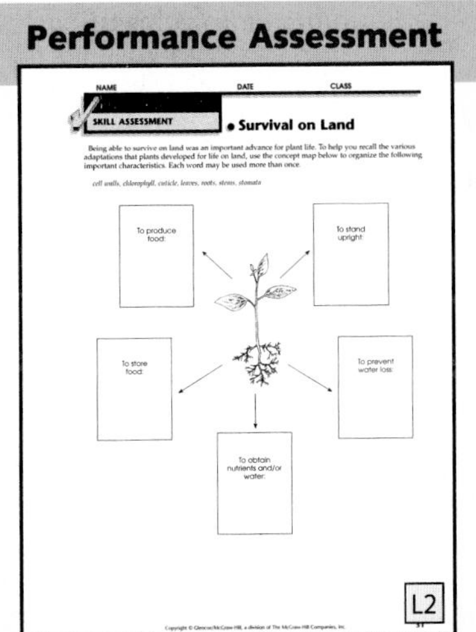

NAME DATE CLASS

SKILL ASSESSMENT • Survival on Land

Being able to survive on land was an important advance for plant life. To help you recall the various adaptations that plants developed for life on land, use the concept map below to organize the following important characteristics. Each word may be used more than once.

cell walls, chlorophyll, cuticle, leaves, roots, stems, stomata

L2

Chapter Review

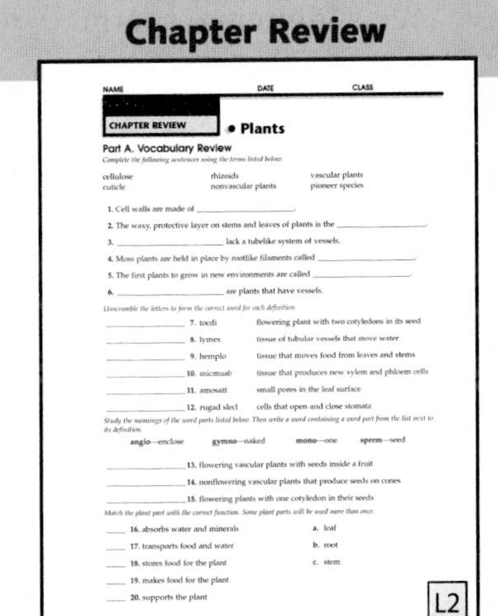

NAME DATE CLASS

CHAPTER REVIEW • Plants

Part A. Vocabulary Review

Complete the following sentences using the terms listed below.

cellulose, cuticle, rhizoids, nonvascular plants, vascular plants, pioneer species

1. Cell walls are made of ______.
2. The waxy, protective layer on stems and leaves of plants is the ______.
3. ______ lack a tubelike system of vessels.
4. Moss plants are held in place by rootlike filaments called ______.
5. The first plants to grow in new environments are called ______.
6. ______ are plants that have vessels.

Unscramble the letters to form the correct word for each definition.

7. tocdi — flowering plant with two cotyledons in its seed
8. lymex — tissue of tubular vessels that move water
9. hemplo — tissue that moves food from leaves and stems
10. miacmub — tissue that produces new xylem and phloem cells
11. amostt — small pores in the leaf surface
12. rugad slecl — cells that open and close stomata

angio—enclose, gymno—naked, mono—one, sperm—seed

13. flowering vascular plants with seeds inside a fruit
14. nonflowering vascular plants that produce seeds on cones
15. flowering plants with one cotyledon in their seeds

16. absorbs water and minerals — a. leaf
17. transports food and water — b. root
18. stores food for the plant — c. stem
19. makes food for the plant
20. supports the plant

L2

Assessment

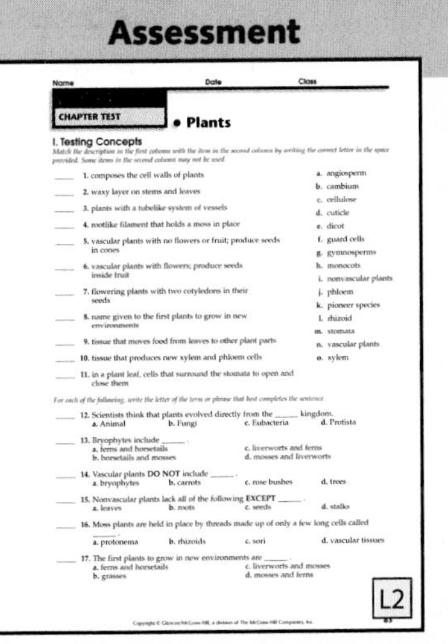

Name Date Class

CHAPTER TEST • Plants

I. Testing Concepts

1. composes the cell walls of plants
2. waxy layer on stems and leaves
3. plants with a tubelike system of vessels
4. rootlike filament that holds a moss in place
5. vascular plants with no flowers or fruit; produce seeds in cones
6. vascular plants with flowers; produce seeds inside fruit
7. flowering plants with two cotyledons in their seeds
8. name given to the first plants to grow in new environments
9. tissue that moves food from leaves to other plant parts
10. tissue that produces new xylem and phloem cells
11. in a plant leaf, cells that surround the stomata to open and close them

a. angiosperms, b. cambium, c. cellulose, d. cuticle, e. dicot, f. guard cells, g. gymnosperms, h. monocots, i. nonvascular plants, j. phloem, k. pioneer species, l. rhizoid, m. stomata, n. vascular plants, o. xylem

12. Scientists think that plants evolved directly from the ______ kingdom.
a. Animal b. Fungi c. Eubacteria d. Protista
13. Bryophytes include ______.
a. ferns and horsetails b. hornwort and mosses c. liverworts and ferns d. mosses and liverworts
14. Vascular plants DO NOT include ______.
a. bryophytes b. carrots c. rose bushes d. trees
15. Nonvascular plants lack all of the following EXCEPT ______.
a. leaves b. roots c. seeds d. stalks
16. Moss plants are held in place by threads made up of only a few long cells called ______.
a. protonema b. rhizoids c. sori d. vascular tissues
17. The first plants to grow in new environments are ______.
a. ferns and horsetails b. grasses c. liverworts and mosses d. mosses and ferns

L2

Test Practice Workbook

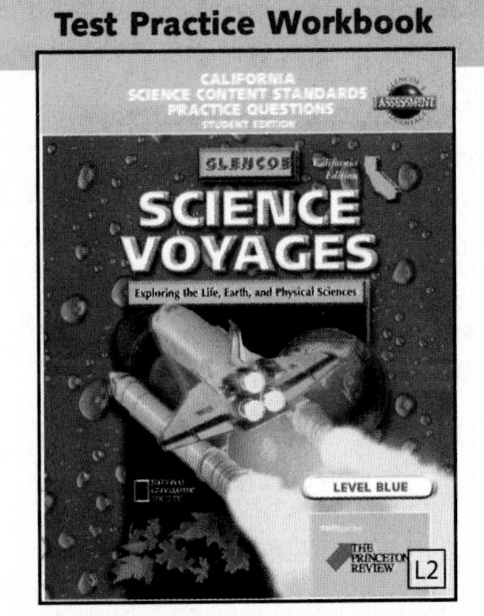

CALIFORNIA SCIENCE CONTENT STANDARDS PRACTICE QUESTIONS STUDENT EDITION

GLENCOE California Edition

SCIENCE VOYAGES

Exploring the Life, Earth, and Physical Sciences

LEVEL BLUE

THE PRINCETON REVIEW

L2

Extending Content

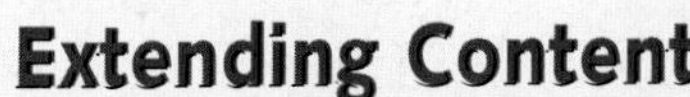

Critical Thinking/Problem Solving

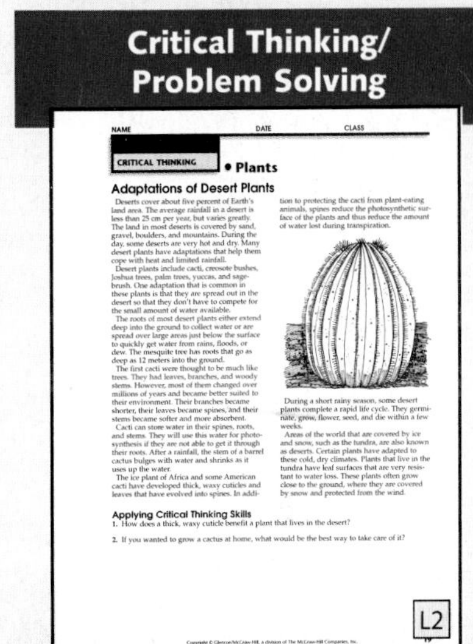

NAME DATE CLASS

CRITICAL THINKING • Plants

Adaptations of Desert Plants

Deserts cover about five percent of Earth's land area. The average rainfall in a desert is less than 25 cm per year, but varies greatly. The land in most deserts is covered by sand, gravel, boulders, and mountains. During the day, some deserts are very hot and dry. Many desert plants have adaptations that help them cope with heat and limited rainfall.

Applying Critical Thinking Skills

1. How does a thick, waxy cuticle benefit a plant that lives in the desert?
2. If you wanted to grow a cactus at home, what would be the best way to take care of it?

L2

Multicultural Connections

NAME DATE CLASS

MULTICULTURAL CONNECTIONS • Doing the Impossible

Some people commit themselves to a challenging job. Others, however, go one step further. They try to do what seems impossible!

The Impossible Forest in the Clouds

Water in the Air, Water Everywhere

To Save Nature

L2

Helping You Prepare

Characteristics of Plants
(Section 23-1)

Plants are many-celled organisms that support most life on Earth. They trap the energy of sunlight and store it as chemical energy in the food they produce. Plants exhibit great diversity in form, size, and color. They have adapted to nearly every habitat on Earth.

Origin and Evolution of Plants
(Section 23-1)

Plants are probably evolved from multicellular Chlorophyta, the green algae. Common characteristics include plant pigments, such as chlorophyll *a* and *b* and carotenoids, cell walls that consist primarily of cellulose, starch as the primary food-storage product, and similar cell division. Some plants, including mosses, liverworts, and ferns, have free-swimming sperm and require water for fertilization—another feature that occurs in green algae.

Plants have traditionally been separated into divisions, but in 1993, the International Botanical Congress made the term *phylum* an acceptable alternative. You may wish to introduce the alternate term to your students.

Classification of Plants
(Section 23-1)

Classification of plants has traditionally been based on morphological characteristics such as numbers and arrangements of leaves and structures of flowers and fruits. Recently, genetic studies have been used to make minor changes in the classification of some plants. However, derived characteristics such as vascular tissue; seed formation; and similar, easily observable characteristics are reliable features for classification.

Seedless Plants (Section 23-2)

Liverworts and hornworts are leafy with creeping gametophyte forms. Mosses have distinct leaflike and stemlike structures, but these are not homologous to the leaves and stems of vascular plants.

Seedless vascular plants include whisk ferns (Psilophyta), club mosses (Lycopoda), horsetails (Sphenophyta), and Ferns (Pterophyta). In each of these divisions, motile sperm require free water to swim to the egg.

GLENCOE TECHNOLOGY

Glencoe Science Voyages Interactive CD-ROM

Chapter Summaries

Use the Chapter Summary to introduce, teach, or review chapter material.

NATIONAL GEOGRAPHIC — Teacher's Corner

Products Available from Glencoe

To order the following products for use with this chapter, call Glencoe at 1-800-334-7344:

CD-ROMs

NGS PictureShow: Plants: What It Means to Be Green

Curriculum Kit

GeoKit: Plants

Transparency Sets

NGS PicturePack: Plants: What It Means to Be Green

VideoDisc

STV: Plants

Products Available from National Geographic Society

To order the following products for use with this chapter, call National Geographic Society at 1-800-368-2728:

Videos

Plant Classification

Vascular Tissue (Section 23-3)

The first vascular plants appeared no later than the early Silurian period, some 430 million years ago. Their dominant and nutritionally independent sporophytes and efficient solution-conducting tissues distinguish them. Most have specialized roots, stems, and leaves.

Early vascular plants had stems formed as a result of primary growth—growth from plant tips. Stems had well-marked vascular cylinders with conducting functions as they do in modern vascular plants. Secondary growth, found in all dicots and a few monocots, is an important early development. It arises by mitotic divisions of cambium tissues around the plant's periphery.

Vascular tissues are of two main types—xylem and phloem. Xylem tissue, is made of tracheids and vessel elements that carry water and dissolved minerals. Tracheids are found in all plants with vascular tissue, but vessel elements are limited almost exclusively to angiosperms. Both are long, thick, tubelike cells that have woody cell walls. Small openings called pits allow water to seep through the cell walls from tracheid to tracheid.

Unlike xylem tissue, phloem tissue is living. It is composed mostly of sieve-tube elements and companion cells. Sieve-tube elements are thin-walled cells that carry the products of photosynthesis throughout the plant. Since mature sieve-tube cells have no nuclei, companion cells help with their metabolism.

Seed Plants (Section 23-3)

The seed plants—gymnosperms and angiosperms—appeared suddenly about 65 million years ago at the beginning of the Cretaceous period. These plants dominated the land in ways no previous plants had. They developed sperm-containing pollen grains that could be transported from plants. This meant these plants could reproduce well away from water. The subsequent development of an embryo inside a protective seed coat allowed seeds to survive harsh conditions for long periods. About 200 000 of the 235 000 species of plants today are seed plants.

SCIENCE UPDATE

For current events or science in the news, access the Glencoe Science Web Site, **www.glencoe.com/sec/scince/ca**

Angiosperms (Section 23-3)

Members of the division Anthophyta, often called flowering plants or angiosperms, are the most diverse and widespread of any plant group. Diversity of angiosperms is partly due to the coevolution of their animal pollinators. Angiosperms are divided into two main groups—monocots (Monocotyledons) and dicots (Dicotyledons). Almost all of our food is produced by a few species of domesticated angiosperms. In addition, they provide medication, fiber, and other products for human use.

Teacher to Teacher

"To compare the growth rate of plants exposed to different wavelengths of light, students can grow grass seeds in greenhouses made from 2-liter plastic bottles. Cut the bottoms off the bottles and cover each with one of the colors of plastic wrap: red, blue, green, and colorless."

Janet Doughty, Teacher
H. J. MacDonald Middle School
New Bern, NC

CHAPTER 23 Plants

CHAPTER OVERVIEW

Section 23-1 Characteristics and survival adaptations of plants are described in this chapter. A brief evolutionary history of plants is given.

Section 23-2 Ecological importance and descriptions of mosses and ferns are presented. Nonvascular and vascular plants are compared.

Section 23-3 Seed plants and their organs are described and compared. Monocots and dicots are discussed and compared.

Chapter Vocabulary

cellulose
cuticle
vascular plant
nonvascular plant
rhizoid
pioneer species
xylem
phloem
cambium
stomata
guard cell
gymnosperm
angiosperm
monocot
dicot

Theme Connection

Stability and Change/Systems and Interactions The stability and change of plants over time is detailed in this chapter. Emphasis is placed on the adaptations plants have for life on land. The systems and interactions of plants also are discussed.

If time does not permit teaching the entire chapter, use Reviewing Main Ideas on pp. 806–807.

CHAPTER 23 Plants

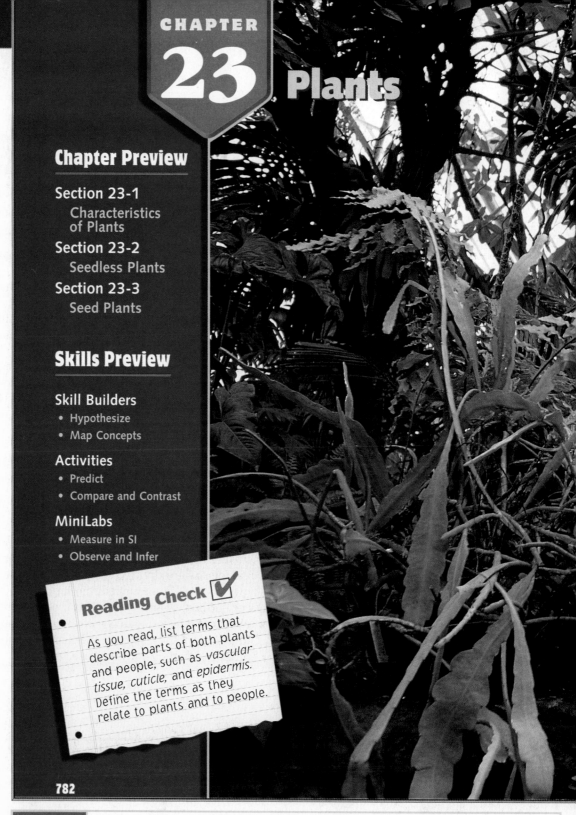

Chapter Preview

Skills Preview

Skill Builders
- Hypothesize
- Map Concepts

Activities
- Predict
- Compare and Contrast

MiniLabs
- Measure in SI
- Observe and Infer

Reading Check

As you read, list terms that describe parts of both plants and people, such as *vascular tissue, cuticle,* and *epidermis.* Define the terms as they relate to plants and to people.

782

Multiple Learning Styles

Look for the following logos for strategies that emphasize different learning modalities.

Linguistic Using Science Words, pp. 787, 794, 802; Science Journal, p. 787; Preview, p. 808

Logical-Mathematical MiniLab, p. 791; Activity, p. 796

Visual-Spatial Visual Learning, p. 785; Multiple Learning Styles, p. 786; Inclusion Strategies, p. 792; Quick Demo, p. 793; MiniLab, p. 799; Activity, p. 807

Auditory-Musical Out of Time, p. 808

Kinesthetic Visual Learning, p. 793; Making a Model, p. 794

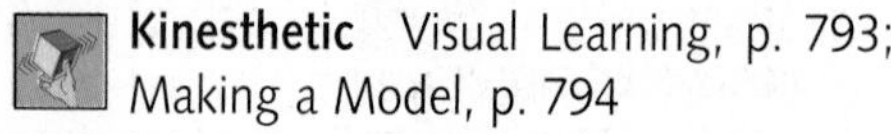

Interpersonal Reteach, p. 794; Discussion, p. 804

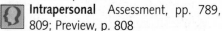

Intrapersonal Assessment, pp. 789, 809; Preview, p. 808

Naturalist Integrating the Sciences, p. 785; Inclusion Strategies, p. 792

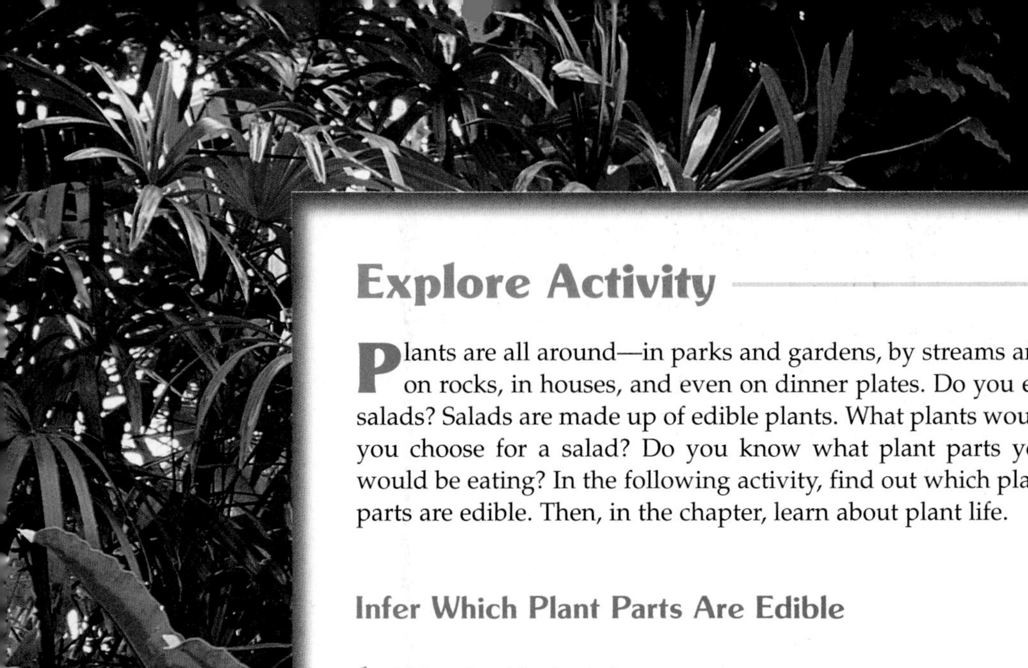

Explore Activity

Plants are all around—in parks and gardens, by streams and on rocks, in houses, and even on dinner plates. Do you eat salads? Salads are made up of edible plants. What plants would you choose for a salad? Do you know what plant parts you would be eating? In the following activity, find out which plant parts are edible. Then, in the chapter, learn about plant life.

Infer Which Plant Parts Are Edible

1. Make a list of five foods that you might eat during a typical day.
2. Decide whether the foods contain any plant parts.
3. Infer what plant parts were used to make your five foods.

Plants provide many nutrients. List the nutrients from a package of dried fruit in your Science Journal. As a class, compare the nutrients in the dried fruits each student selected.

Explore Activity

Purpose

Kinesthetic Use the Explore Activity to introduce students to plant parts. Inform students that they will be learning more about seedless plants and their parts in this chapter. L2

Preparation

You should make a master list of edible plants and the parts eaten. Add to your list others that students think of.

Materials

paper and pencil

Teaching Strategies

You may wish to offer suggestions of additional plants if students do not produce a sufficiently diverse list.

Lists will vary depending on the experiences and choices of students.

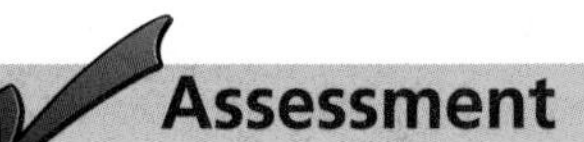

Portfolio Have students list in their portfolios additional plant parts that they eat. Use **Performance Assessment in the Science Classroom,** p. 105. P

Assessment Planner

Portfolio
Refer to p. 809 for suggested items that students might select for their portfolios.

Performance Assessment
See p. 809 for additional Performance Assessment options.
Skill Builder, pp. 789, 795
MiniLab, pp. 791, 799
Activity 23-1, p. 796; 23-2, p. 807

Content Assessment
Section Assessment, pp. 789, 795, 806
Chapter Assessment, pp. 810–811
Proficiency Prep, pp. 789, 795, 805

SECTION 23•1

Prepare

Content Background

Refer to **Characteristics of Plants, Origin and Evolution of Plants,** and **Classification of Plants** on p. 782E.

Preplanning

Refer to the **Chapter Organizer** on pp. 782A–B.

1 Motivate

Bellringer

Before presenting the lesson, display **Section Focus Transparency 64** on the overhead projector. Use the accompanying **Focus Activity** worksheet. L2 ELL

Section 13-1

SECTION FOCUS TRANSPARENCY

ALONG A ROCKY COAST

The Atlantic coast can be a rocky one. But there are living things that make their homes on the rocks. To prevent people from getting hurt, signs like this are sometimes posted.

CAUTION
DO NOT GO BEYOND THIS POINT

1. Why do you think that sign is posted?
2. What could be causing this particular hazard?

32

Tying to Previous Knowledge

Discuss the basic relationship between plants and animals. Review the concepts of producer and consumer with students.

23•1 Characteristics of Plants

What You'll Learn

- The characteristics of plants
- What plant adaptations make it possible for plants to survive on land
- Similarities and differences between vascular and nonvascular plants

Vocabulary

cellulose
cuticle
vascular plant
nonvascular plant

Why It's Important

- Plants produce food and oxygen for most organisms on Earth. Without plants, there would be no life.

What is a plant?

Do you enjoy walking along nature trails in parks like the one shown in **Figure 23-1?** Maybe you've taken off your shoes and walked barefoot on soft, cool grass. Perhaps you've climbed a tree to see what your world looks like from high in its branches. In every instance, members of the plant kingdom surrounded you.

Now look at **Figure 23-2.** These organisms, mosses and liverworts, have characteristics that identify them as plants, too. What do they have in common with grasses, trees, and ferns? What makes a plant a plant?

Characteristics of Plants

All plants are made of eukaryotic cells that have cell walls. Cell walls provide structure and protection for plant cells. Many plant cells contain the green pigment chlorophyll. Plants range in size from microscopic water ferns to giant sequoia trees that are sometimes more than 100 m in height. They have roots or rootlike structures that hold them in the ground or onto something. Plants have successfully adapted to nearly every environment on Earth. Some grow in frigid, ice-bound polar regions and others grow in hot, dry deserts. Many plants must live in or near water.

About 285 000 plant species have been discovered and identified. Scientists think many more are still to be found, mainly in tropical rain forests. If you were to make a list of all

Figure 23-1 All plants are many celled and nearly all contain chlorophyll. Grasses, trees, and ferns all are members of Kingdom Plantae.

Resource Manager

The following **Teacher Classroom Resources** can be used with Section 23-1:

 **Reproducible Masters**

Enrichment, p. 64 L3

Reinforcement, p. 64 L2

Study Guide, p. 90 L1 ELL

Content Background

Unlike multicellular algae, plants form tissues. Emphasize that although nonvascular plants do not contain organs, they do have parts analogous to leaves, roots, and stems of the vascular plants.

Figure 23-2 Plants include liverworts (A) and mosses (B).

the plants you could name, you probably would include vegetables, fruits, and field crops like wheat, rice, or corn. These plants are important food sources to humans and other consumers. Without plants, most life on Earth as we know it would not be possible.

Origin and Evolution of Plants

Where did the first plants come from? Like all life, early plants probably came from the sea, evolving from plantlike protists. What evidence is there that this is true? Both plants and green algae, a type of protist, have the same types of chlorophyll and carotenoids (KER uh tuh noydz) in their cells. Carotenoids are red, yellow, or orange pigments found in some plants and in all cyanobacteria.

Fossil Record

One way to understand the evolution of plants is to look at the fossil record. Unfortunately, plants usually decay before they form fossils. The oldest fossil plants are from the Silurian period and are about 420 million years old. Fossils of early plants are similar to the plantlike protists. Fossils of *Rhynia major*, illustrated in **Figure 23-3,** represent the earliest land plants. Scientists hypothesize that these kinds of plants evolved into some plants that exist today.

Cone-bearing plants, such as pines, probably evolved from a group of plants that grew about 350 million years ago. Fossils of these plants have been dated to the Paleozoic era, 300 million years ago. Flowering plants did not exist until the Cretaceous period, about 120 million years ago. The exact origin of flowering plants is not known.

Using Computers

Fossil evidence shows that the first land plants lived about 420 million years ago. If Earth is 4.6 billion years old, what percent of Earth's age was Earth without land plants?

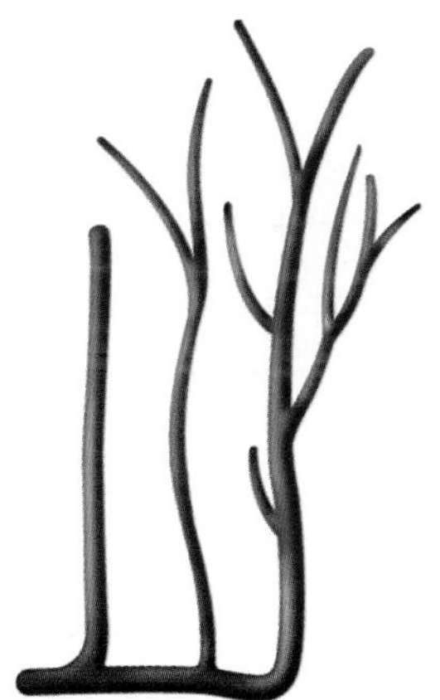

Figure 23-3 Fossils of *Rhynia major*, an extinct, small land plant, show that it had underground stems but no true roots or leaves.

2 Teach

Correcting Misconceptions

Students may think that all plants produce flowers. Explain that nonvascular plants and seedless vascular plants do not.

Activity

Ask students to brainstorm a list of features common to most plants. Allow them to propose functions for these features.

Using Math 

$$\frac{4.6 \text{ billion} - 420 \text{ million}}{4.6 \text{ billion}} \times 100\% =$$

90.87%, or about 91%

Flex Your Brain

Use the Flex Your Brain activity to have students explore PLANT CLASSIFICATION.  P

VISUAL Learning

Figure 23-2 **Which features of the organisms in the photographs suggest they are plants?** *They are green and appear to grow from soil.* **Explain how the mosses and liverworts differ from the ferns and trees in Figure 23-1.** *They are smaller and lack familiar leaves, stems, and roots.*

Integrating the Sciences

Earth Science Have students make a display of any plant fossils found within the community. Try to identify the type of plant, the type of fossil, the geologic age, and any other information for each fossil. L3

CA Science Content Standards

Page 784: 6c

CHEMISTRY INTEGRATION

Cellulose is a tough material that enables plants to stand upright. Upright plants expose more leaves to sunlight and make more food per square unit of soil surface.

Activity

Set up stations around the classroom that contain different plant parts. Have students write down the name of each plant part as they travel from station to station. L2

Enrichment

Fossils of plants are even found in Antarctica and high on mountains. These observations provide evidence of continental drift and mountain building.

Caption Answer

Figure 23-4A *Algae make food by the process of photosynthesis.*

Videodisc

STV: Plants

Unit 1: *What Is a Plant, Types of Plants* 3:40

11765-18410

Refer to the Teacher Guide for additional bar codes and teaching strategies.

CHEMISTRY INTEGRATION

Cellulose

Plant cell walls are made mostly of cellulose, an organic compound. Cellulose is made of long chains of glucose molecules, $C_6H_{12}O_6$. More than half the carbon in plants is in cellulose. Raw cotton is more than 90 percent cellulose. Infer which physical property of cellulose makes it ideal for helping plants survive on land.

Adaptations to Land

Imagine life for a one-celled green alga, a protist, floating in a shallow pool. The water in the pool surrounds and supports it. The alga can make its own food through the process of photosynthesis. Materials enter and leave the cell through the cell membrane and cell wall. The alga has everything it needs to survive.

Now, imagine a summer drought. The pool begins to dry up. Soon, the alga is on damp mud and is no longer supported by the pool's water, as shown in **Figure 23-4.** It won't starve because it still can make its own food. As long as the soil stays damp, the alga can move materials in and out through the cell membrane and cell wall. But, what will happen if the drought continues, and the soil becomes drier and drier? The alga will continue to lose water because water diffuses through the cell membrane and cell wall from where there is more water to where there is less water. Without water in its environment, the alga will dry up and die.

Protection and Support

What adaptations would make it possible for plants to survive on land? Losing water is a major problem for plants. What would help a plant conserve water? Plant cells have cell membranes, but they also have rigid cell walls outside the membrane. Cell walls contain **cellulose** (SEL yuh lohs), an organic compound made up of long chains of glucose molecules. Some woody plants, such as oaks and pines, are as much as 50 percent cellulose. Cell walls provide structure and support and help reduce water loss.

Figure 23-4 Algae must have water to survive.

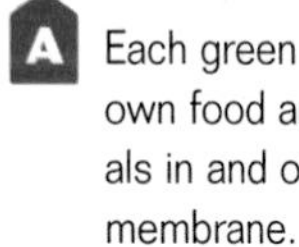

A Each green alga produces its own food and moves materials in and out through the cell membrane. **By what process do algae make food?**

B If a pond completely dries up, the algae in it will die.

Multiple Learning Styles

Visual-Spatial Ask a florist or horticulturist to use plant materials in a discussion of why plants can be both attractive and useful.

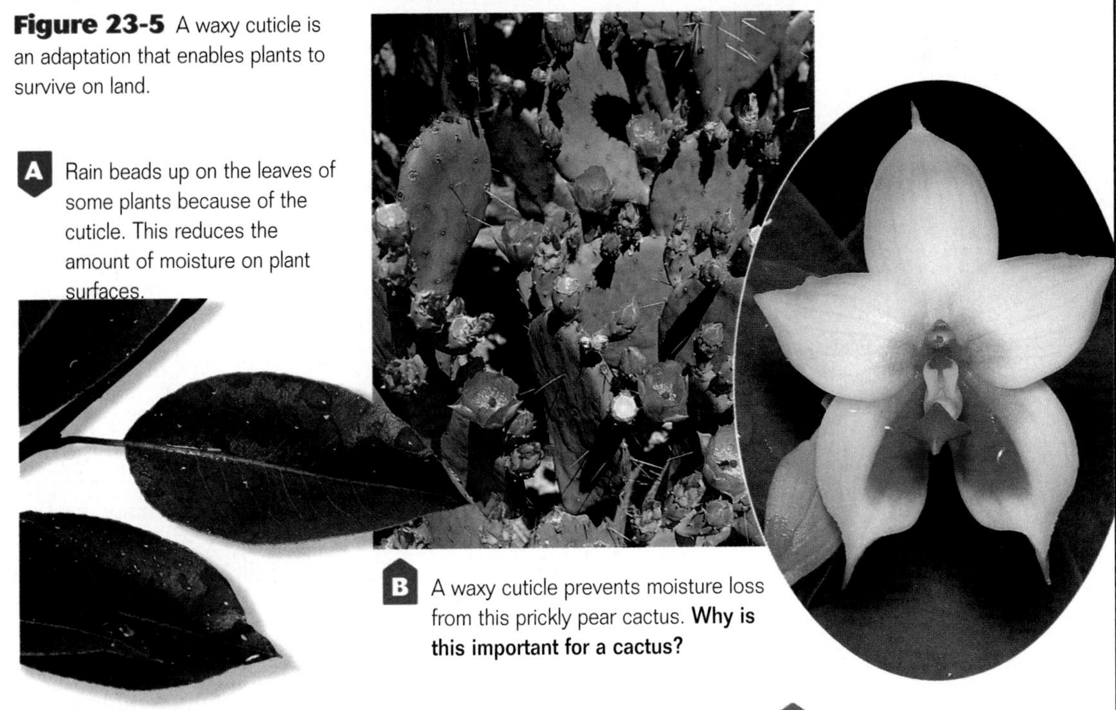

Figure 23-5 A waxy cuticle is an adaptation that enables plants to survive on land.

A Rain beads up on the leaves of some plants because of the cuticle. This reduces the amount of moisture on plant surfaces.

B A waxy cuticle prevents moisture loss from this prickly pear cactus. **Why is this important for a cactus?**

C Waxy cuticles are often found on flowers such as this orchid.

Covering the stems, leaves, and flowers of some land plants is a cuticle. The **cuticle** (KYEWT ih kul) is a waxy, protective layer secreted by the cell walls. It slows down the evaporation of water from a plant. After it rains, go outside and see how raindrops bead up on some plant surfaces, as illustrated in **Figure 23-5A.** Removing water from plant surfaces is important because too much moisture on a plant may affect cell functions. Too much surface moisture also may lead to fungal diseases. The cuticle is an adaptation that enabled plants to live on land. ☑

Reading Check
What is the protective layer secreted by cell walls?

Life on land meant that plant cells could not depend on water to support them or to move substances from one cell to the next. Support came with the evolution of stems and substances that strengthen the cell walls. Eventually, plants developed tissues that distribute materials.

Reproduction

The move to land by plants not only meant changes to reduce water loss and increase support, but it also meant a change in plant reproduction. Plants evolved from organisms that reproduced in water. They completely depended on water for reproduction and survival. Some plants still require water to reproduce, but others do not. The development of cones and flowers that produce seeds allowed these plants to survive on land.

Quick Demo

Use a spray mister to mist water onto a plant leaf that has a thick cuticle. Allow students to observe how the water beads up and runs off.

Using an Analogy

Perform the Quick Demo above using waxed paper. Ask students to explain the analogy. L2

Using Science Words

Linguistic Have students compare the meanings of the word *cuticle* as used with the skin surrounding their nails and the *cuticle* of a plant's leaf. L2

At the beginning of the class period, place a stalk of celery in a glass of water to which food coloring was added. At the end of the period and the next day, have students write their observations in their Science Journal. Cut the stalk to show the parallel vascular tubes. L2

Caption Answer

Figure 23-5B *A cuticle is important because cacti live in dry environments, and it helps to conserve moisture.*

Across the Curriculum

Physics Have students conduct activities that explain how water pressure in plants provides some rigidity and support for plants. One such activity is to run water through rubber tubing and have students notice the difference between the empty and the water-filled tubing.

CA Science Content Standards

Page 786: 3c, 5a, 6a, 6b, 6c

Page 787: 5a, 6a, 6c

23-1 Characteristics of Plants 787

*inter*NET CONNECTION

Internet Addresses

For Internet tips, see Glencoe's **Using the Internet in the Science Classroom.**

Problem Solving

Think Critically

Some plants may become extinct before they can be studied.

3 Assess

Check for Understanding

Activity

Have students prepare a bulletin board that shows examples of plant adaptations to life on land. L2

Reteach

Ask students to describe what the results for animals would have been if plants had not evolved to live on land. L1

Extension

For students who have mastered this section, use the **Reinforcement** and **Enrichment** masters.

*inter*NET CONNECTION

Visit the Glencoe Science Web Site at **www.glencoe.com/sec/science/ca** for more information about plants that are sources of medicines. In your Science Journal, list five medicines that come from plants.

Life on Land

Life on land has some advantages for plants. There is more sunlight and carbon dioxide for plants on land than in water. Plants use sunlight and carbon dioxide for the food-making process, photosynthesis. During photosynthesis, plants give off oxygen. As more and more plants adapted to life on land, the amount of oxygen in Earth's atmosphere increased. This paved the way for the evolution of organisms that depend on oxygen. In some cases, it meant that some organisms evolved together. For example, some flowering plants provided animals with food, and the animals pollinated the plant's flowers.

Classification of Plants

Today, the plant kingdom is classified into major groups called divisions, as illustrated in **Figure 23-6.** A division is the same as a phylum in other kingdoms, as listed in Appendix E of this book. A less formal way to group plants is as vascular or nonvascular plants. **Vascular plants** have tissues that make up the organ system that carries water, nutrients, and other substances throughout the plant. **Nonvascular plants** have no vascular tissue and use other ways to move water and substances.

Problem Solving

Cause and Effect in Nature

People in all cultures have used and still use plants as medicine. Some Native American cultures used willow bark to cure headaches. Heart problems were treated with foxglove in England and sea onions in Egypt. In Peru, the bark of the cinchona tree was used to treat malaria. Scientists have found that many native cures are medically sound. Willow bark contains salicylates, the main ingredient in aspirin. Foxglove, as seen in the photo to the right, is still the main source of digitalis, a drug prescribed for heart problems. Cinchona bark contains quinine, an antimalarial drug.

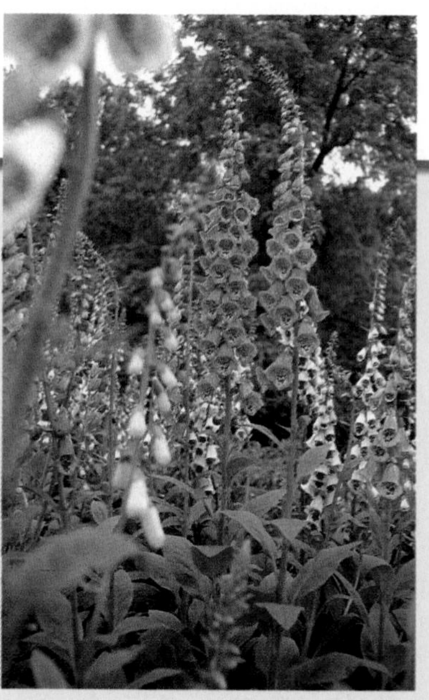

Think Critically: Predict how the destruction of the rain forests might affect research for new drugs from plants.

Caption Answer

Figure 23-6 *Some plants grow as large trees, while others remain small. Some plants have large, flat leaves. Others have leaves shaped like needles or spines. Some plants reproduce by seeds and others by spores. Some plants produce flowers, some produce cones, and others produce neither flowers nor cones.*

VISUALIZING The Plant Kingdom

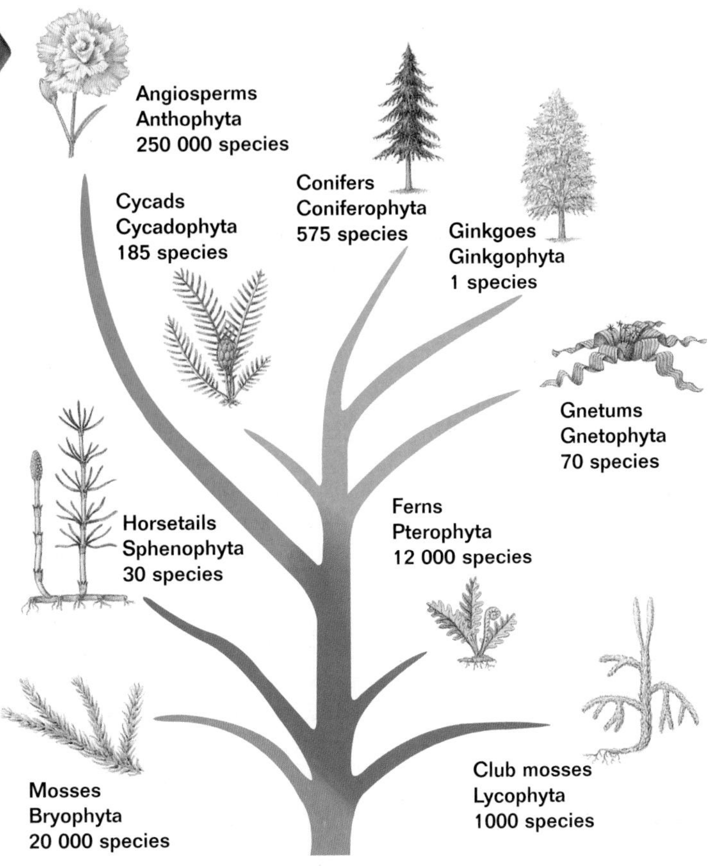

Figure 23-6 The diversity of Kingdom Plantae is represented by a branching tree, composed of different divisions. All of these plant groups are related but have differences that separate them. **What differences can you detect among the plant divisions in this illustration?**

Section Assessment

1. List the characteristics of plants.
2. Compare vascular and nonvascular plants.
3. Name three adaptations that allow plants to survive on land.
4. **Think Critically:** If you left a board lying on the grass for a few days, what would happen to the grass underneath the board? Why?
5. **Skill Builder**
   Forming a Hypothesis From what you have learned about adaptations necessary for life on land, make a hypothesis as to what types of adaptations land plants might have if they had to survive submerged in water. If you need help, refer to Forming a Hypothesis in the **Skill Handbook** on page 958.

The oldest surviving plant species is *Ginkgo biloba.* Research the history of this species, then write about it in your Science Journal.

5. **Skill Builder**
Plants submerged in water would need more chloroplasts because of less light. Also, they would need ways to get carbon dioxide from water and to keep a balance between water inside cells and outside cells.

Assessment

Performance Assess students' abilities to hypothesize about the adaptations necessary for land plants to live in water by having them devise a model for one of their suggested adaptations. Use **Performance Assessment in the Science Classroom,** p. 51.

4 Close

Proficiency Prep

Use this quiz to check students' recall of section content.

1. **What are two pigments found in many plants?** *chlorophyll, carotenoids*
2. **What are plants called that have vessels that transport materials to other cells?** *vascular plants*

Section Assessment

1. All plants are many celled and most contain chlorophyll and carotenoids. Most plants have roots or rootlike fibers that anchor them.
2. Vascular plants have tubes that carry water and food. Nonvascular plants get water and food by diffusion.
3. Plant adaptations include the cuticle, vascular tissue, and seeds.
4. Think Critically The grass would turn yellow. Light is needed to continue production of chlorophyll.

Students' reports should indicate that *Ginkgo biloba,* often called the maidenhair tree, is the only member of its division. It is native to China and has been introduced to many areas as an ornamental plant.

CA Science Content Standards

Page 788: 5a, 6a

SECTION 23•2

Prepare

Content Background

Refer to **Seedless Plants** on p. 782E.

Preplanning

Refer to the **Chapter Organizer** on pp. 782A–B.

1 Motivate

Bellringer

Before presenting the lesson, display **Section Focus Transparency 65** on the overhead projector. Use the accompanying **Focus Activity** worksheet. L2 ELL

Section 23-2

SECTION FOCUS TRANSPARENCY

GETTING BOGGED DOWN

In many northern bogs, large floating mats of sphagnum moss are common. For many years sphagnum moss was used for sponges in surgery. People still use sphagnum moss in gardening.

1. Why do you think sphagnum mosses were used as surgical sponges?
2. Since mosses do not have roots, how do they absorb water?

CA Science Content Standards

Page 791: 9f

23•2 Seedless Plants

What You'll Learn

- Characteristics of seedless nonvascular plants and seedless vascular plants
- The importance of some nonvascular and vascular plants

Vocabulary
rhizoid
pioneer species

Why It's Important

- Seedless plants are often the first to grow in damaged or disturbed environments.

Seedless Nonvascular Plants

If you were asked to name the parts of a plant, you probably would list roots, stems, leaves, and perhaps flowers. You also may know that many plants grow from seeds. But, did you know that some plants do not have all of these parts? **Figure 23-7** shows some common types of nonvascular plants.

Liverworts and Mosses (Bryophytes)

The bryophytes (BRI uh fites)—liverworts and mosses—are small, nonvascular plants that are usually just a few cells thick and only 2 cm to 5 cm in height. They have stalks that look like stems and leafy green growths. The threadlike roots of bryophytes are called **rhizoids.** Water is absorbed and distributed directly through their cell walls. Bryophytes grow in damp environments such as the forest floor, the edges of ponds and streams, and near the ocean. Bryophytes usually reproduce by spores because they do not have flowers to produce seeds.

Liverworts get their name because to some people, one type looks like a liver. It is a rootless plant that has a flattened, leaflike body. Liverworts usually have one-celled rhizoids. In the ninth century, liverworts were thought to be useful in treating diseases of the liver. The ending, *-wort,* means "herb," so the word *liverwort* means "herb for the liver." Of approximately 20 000 species of nonvascular plants, most are classified as mosses. Have you ever seen mosses growing on tree trunks, rocks, or the ground in damp or humid areas? Mosses have green, leaflike

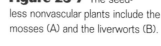

Figure 23-7 The seedless nonvascular plants include the mosses (A) and the liverworts (B).

Resource Manager

The following **Teacher Classroom Resources** can be used with Section 23-2:

Reproducible Masters

Activity Worksheets, pp. 129–130 L2
Enrichment, p. 65 L3
Reinforcement, p. 65 L2
Study Guide, p. 91

Transparencies

Science Integration Transparency 23 L2

Figure 23-8 Mosses are often among the first organisms to live in a new environment, such as this lava field. **Where do the mosses come from?**

growths in a spiral around a stalk. Their threadlike rhizoids are only a few cells in length.

The Importance of Bryophytes

Mosses and liverworts are important in the ecology of many areas. Although mosses require moist conditions to grow and reproduce, many of them can withstand long, dry periods. Often, they are among the first plants to grow in new environments, such as lava fields as shown in **Figure 23-8,** or disturbed environments, such as forests destroyed by fire.

When a volcano erupts, lava covers the land and destroys the plants living there. After the lava cools, spores of mosses and liverworts are carried by the wind to the new rocks. The spores will grow into plants if enough water is available and other growing conditions are right. Organisms that are the first to grow in new or disturbed areas like these are called **pioneer species.** As pioneer plants grow and die, decaying plant material builds up. This, along with the breakdown of rocks, begins the formation of soil. Pioneer plants change environmental conditions so that other plants can grow.

EARTH SCIENCE INTEGRATION

Soil Formation
Soil is a mixture of weathered rock and decaying organic matter (plant and animal). Infer what roles pioneer species such as lichens, mosses, and liverworts play in building soil.

MiniLab

Measuring Water Absorption by a Moss

Procedure  

1. Place a few teaspoons of *Sphagnum* moss on a piece of cheesecloth. Twist the cheesecloth to form a ball and tie it securely.
2. Weigh the ball.
3. Put 200 mL of water in a container and add the ball.
4. Predict how much water the ball will absorb.
5. Wait 15 minutes. Remove the ball and drain the excess water back into the container.

Analysis

1. Weigh the ball and measure the amount of water left in the container.
2. In your Science Journal, calculate how much water the *Sphagnum* moss absorbed.

Tying to Previous Knowledge

Point out that students may know seedless plants as club mossess used in wreaths and ferns as houseplants.

2 Teach

EARTH SCIENCE INTEGRATION

Lichens are really two organisms, a fungus and an alga, living in a mutually beneficial relationship. They secrete acids that help to break down rock. Their presence creates an environment suitable for the growth of moss and liverwort spores. Decaying lichens, mosses, and liverworts provide organic matter that mixes with rock particles creating soil for larger plants.

MiniLab

Purpose

 **Logical-Mathematical** Students will research the absorption capacity of *Sphagnum* moss.

Materials

Sphagnum moss, cheesecloth, beakers, water, graduated cylinders, balance

Teaching Strategies

- Before they begin the activity, ask students to predict how much water will be held by the moss.
- Explain that bogs help control flooding in wetlands by retaining huge amounts of water.

Analysis

1. About 100 mL will be left.
2. *Sphagnum* moss will soak up about 100 g of water.

Caption Answer

Figure 23-8 *Mosses grow from moss spores carried on air currents.*

Assessment

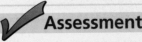

Performance Growers often mix *Sphagnum* moss with an equal part of clean sand to root plants. Have students design an experiment to test this rooting method. Use **Performance Assessment in the Science Classroom,** p. 23.

VISUAL Learning

Figure 23-9 Ask students to describe the differences and similarities between these plants and bryophytes. L2

Answer to Reading Check

Vascular tissue is composed of long, tubelike cells that carry water, minerals, and nutrients to cells.

Caption Answer

Figure 23-9 *because they have vascular tissue for support and distribution of water, minerals, and nutrients*

GLENCOE TECHNOLOGY

Videodisc

Glencoe Science Voyages Interactive Videodisc—Life

Lesson 9

Ecosystems: Wetlands

45551

Refer to Videodisc Teacher Guide for additional bar codes.

Teacher FYI

Elizabeth Britton was born in 1858 in New York City. She became one of America's foremost botanists and helped to establish the New York Botanical Garden.

Seedless Vascular Plants

The plants in **Figure 23-9** are like mosses because they are seedless plants that reproduce by spores. They are different from mosses because they have vascular tissue. The vascular tissue in the seedless vascular plants is made up of long, tubelike cells. These cells carry water, minerals, and nutrients to cells throughout the plant. Why is having cells like these an advantage to a plant? Remember that bryophytes are only a few cells thick. Each cell absorbs water directly from its environment. As a result, these plants cannot grow large. Vascular plants, on the other hand, can grow bigger and thicker because the vascular tissue distributes water and nutrients.

Reading Check

What makes up the vascular tissue in seedless vascular plants?

Types of Seedless Vascular Plants

Seedless vascular plants include the ground pines, spike mosses, horsetails, and ferns. Today, there are about 1000 species of ground pines, spike mosses, and horsetails. Ferns are more abundant, with at least 12 000 species known. Many species of seedless vascular plants are known only from fossils. They flourished during the warm, moist Paleozoic era. Fossil records show that some horsetails grew 15 m tall, unlike modern species that only grow 1 m to 2 m tall.

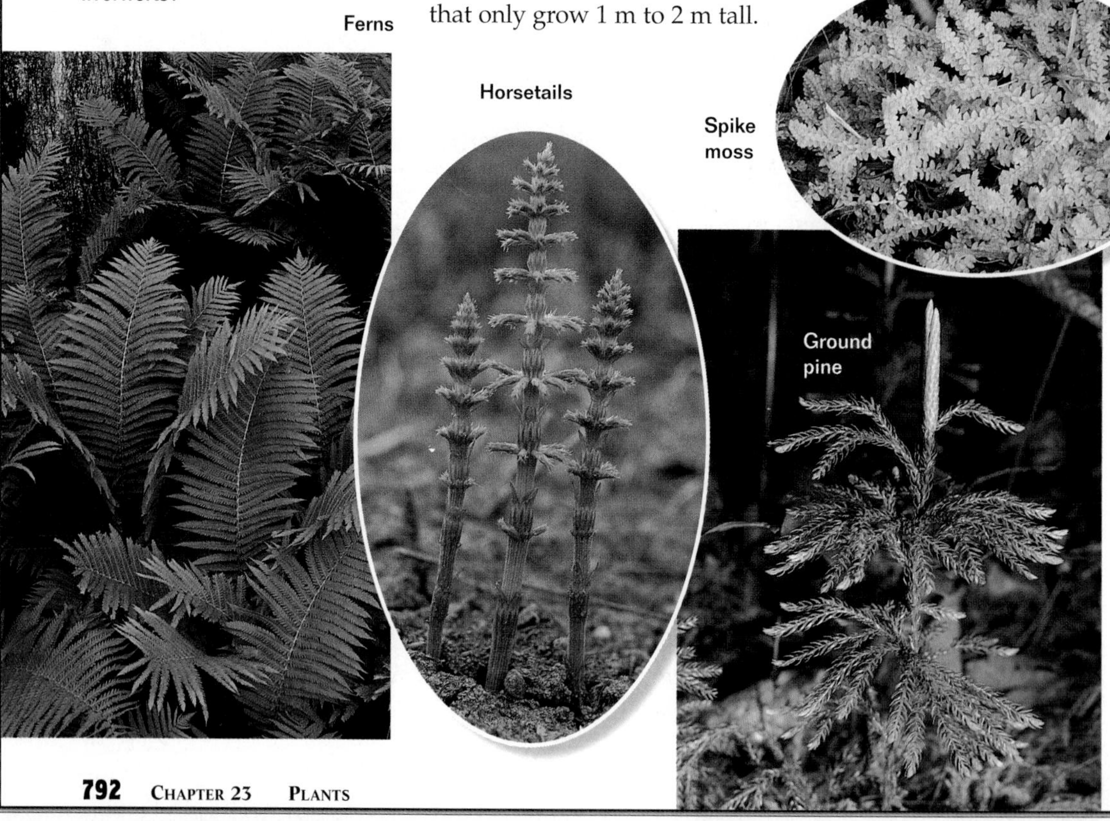

Figure 23-9 The seedless vascular plants include ground pines, spike mosses, horsetails, and ferns. **Why can these plants grow taller than mosses and liverworts?**

Inclusion Strategies

Gifted Have students read natural history books to find out why ferns have such common names as Boston fern, maidenhair fern, staghorn fern, cinnamon fern, hay-scented fern, and bracken fern. L3

Visually Impaired Prepare a sample of mosses, liverworts and ferns labeled with large print for sighted but visually impaired students to observe. Provide magnifying glasses for the students to observe these plants.

Figure 23-10 Club mosses such as ground pines (A) and spike mosses (B) produce spores at the end of stems in tiny, conelike structures. Photographers once used the dry, flammable spores of club mosses as flash powder. It burned rapidly and produced the light to take photographs.

Ground Pines and Spike Mosses

The photographs in **Figure 23-10** show ground pines and spike mosses. Both groups of plants are often called club mosses. They are seedless vascular plants with needlelike leaves. Spores are produced at the end of the stems in structures that look like tiny pine cones. Ground pines are found from arctic regions to the tropics, but never in large numbers. In some areas, they are endangered because they have been overcollected to make wreaths and other decorations.

Spike mosses resemble ground pines. One species of spike moss, the resurrection plant, is adapted to desert conditions. When water is scarce, the plant curls up and seems dead. When water becomes available, the resurrection plant unfurls its green leaves and begins making food again. The plant can repeat this process whenever necessary.

Horsetails

Horsetails have a stem structure unique among the vascular plants. Their stems are jointed and have a hollow center surrounded by a ring of vascular tissue. At each joint, leaves grow around the stem. In **Figure 23-11,** you can see these joints easily. If you pull on a horsetail stem, it will pop apart in sections. Like the club mosses, spores from horsetails are produced in a conelike structure at the tips of some stems.

Figure 23-11 The spores of horsetails are found in conelike structures on the tips of some stems.

Quick Demo

Visual-Spatial Show a variety of fern fronds. If possible, include some with sori. Note the differences in color, size, and location among fern sori.

Content Background

Ground pines are evergreen; grow in moist, wooded areas; and are generally less than 30 cm tall.

Cross sections of fern stems show a ring of xylem tissue with phloem on the inside and outside of the xylem.

Visual Learning

Kinesthetic Figure 23-11 If possible, allow students to handle the stems of horsetails. You may demonstrate how the silica in the cell walls of the plant was useful in scrubbing pots.

Discussion

How can you tell the difference between true mosses and club mosses? *True mosses produce spores in capsules on stalks. Club mosses produce spores at the ends of stems in structures that look like tiny pine cones.*

Teacher FYI

The stems of tree ferns are harvested and sold for plant supports. The dry, fibrous parts of some ferns have been used as mattress stuffing.

CA Science Content Standards

Page 793: 5c

EARTH SCIENCE INTEGRATION

Coal is composed mostly of carbon from compressed and heated simple plants from the geological past. The three kinds of coal—lignite, bituminous, and anthracite—are found in deposits distributed throughout the world.

Making a Model

Kinesthetic Have students construct a shoebox model of what they think a carboniferous swamp may have looked like. L2 ELL

3 Assess

Check for Understanding

Using Science Words

Linguistic Provide each student with a list of terms that can be used in an explanation of nonvascular plants and seedless vascular plants. Have students write paragraphs that compare and contrast these plants using the terms given. L2

Reteach

Interpersonal Give pairs of students photographs or drawings of nonvascular plants and seedless vascular plants on 3 × 5 note cards. On another set of note cards, write descriptions of the plants. Have students match descriptions with drawings. L2 COOP LEARN

Extension

For students who have mastered this section, use the **Reinforcement** and **Enrichment** masters.

Figure 23-12 Most ferns produce spores in special structures on the leaves, but the spores of the cinnamon fern are on a separate stalk.

The stems of the horsetails contain silica, a gritty substance found in sand. For centuries, horsetails have been used for polishing objects, sharpening tools, and scouring cooking utensils. Another common name for horsetails is scouring rush.

Ferns

Ferns belong to the largest group of seedless vascular plants. Ferns, like those in **Figure 23-12,** have stems, leaves, and roots. They also have characteristics of both nonvascular and vascular plants. Like the bryophytes, ferns produce spores, and they have vascular tissue like vascular plants. Today, thousands of species of ferns grow on Earth, but once there were many more. From clues left in rock layers, scientists know that during the Carboniferous period of the Paleozoic era, much of Earth was tropical. Steamy swamps covered large areas, as illustrated in **Figure 23-13.** The tallest plants were species of ferns. The ancient ferns grew as tall as 25 m—much taller than any fern species alive today. The tallest, modern tree ferns are about 3 m to 5 m in height.

interNET CONNECTION

Visit the Glencoe Science Web Site at **www.glencoe.com/sec/science/ca** for more information about which ferns are native to your state. In your Science Journal, list three of these ferns and describe their environments.

Formation of Fuel

When ferns and other plants of the Carboniferous period died, many of them became submerged in water and mud before they could decompose. This plant material built up, became compacted and compressed, and eventually turned into coal. This process took millions of years.

Today, a similar process is taking place in bogs. A bog is a poorly drained area of land that contains decaying plants. The decay process is slow because waterlogged soils do not

interNET CONNECTION

Internet Addresses

For Internet tips, see Glencoe's **Using the Internet in the Science Classroom.**

contain oxygen. The plants in bogs are mostly seedless plants like mosses and ferns. Peat, the remains of peat mosses, is mined from bogs in some countries for a low-cost fuel. Scientists hypothesize that over time, if additional layers of soil bury, compact, and compress the peat, it will become coal.

Figure 23-13 Many more species of club mosses, horsetails, and ferns grew in carboniferous swamp forests than are alive today.

Section Assessment

1. Compare and contrast the mosses and ferns.
2. What do fossil records tell us about seedless plants?
3. Under what conditions would you expect to find pioneer plants?
4. **Think Critically:** List ways seedless plants affect your life each day. (HINT: Where do electricity and heat for homes come from?)
5. **Skill Builder**
   Concept Mapping Make a concept map showing how seedless nonvascular and seedless vascular plants are related. Include these terms in the concept map: *plant kingdom, bryophytes, seedless nonvascular plants, seedless vascular plants, ferns, ground pines, horsetails, liverworts, mosses,* and *spike mosses.* If you need help, refer to Concept Mapping in the **Skill Handbook** on page 950.

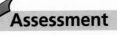

Using Computers

There are approximately 8000 species of liverworts and 9000 species of mosses. Estimate what fraction of bryophytes are mosses.

5. **Skill Builder**
   The concept map should begin with *plant kingdom.* Branching from *plant kingdom* are *nonvascular plants* and *vascular plants.* Under the former are *mosses* and *liverworts.* Under *vascular plants* are *spike mosses, ground pines, horsetails* and *ferns.*

Assessment

Portfolio Use this Skill Builder to assess students' abilities to form a concept map of the plant kingdom. Have groups of students compare individual maps and create one for the group. Use **Performance Assessment in the Science Classroom,** p. 97.

4 Close

Proficiency Prep

Use this quiz to check students' recall of section content.

1. **What are the rootlike filaments that hold moss plants in place?** *rhizoids*
2. **What are organisms that are first to grow in new areas called?** *pioneer species*

Section Assessment

1. Most mosses are smaller than ferns and lack a vascular system. Ferns are herbaceous or grow into treelike forms and have a well-developed vascular system.
2. Seedless plants dominated Earth during the carboniferous period. They were different from those found on Earth today.
3. in disturbed or new environments
4. **Think Critically** Seedless plants such as mosses and ferns formed fossil fuels. These fuels are burned to produce electricity for homes, power automobiles, and provide heat.

Using Math

8000 + 9000 = 17 000 total bryophyte species.

$\frac{9}{17}$ of bryophytes are mosses

or about 53%,

(9000 ÷ 17 000) × 100%.

CA Science Content Standards

Page 795: 6a

Activity 23•1

Purpose

Logical-Mathematical Students will observe and compare parts of seedless plants. L2 ELL P

Process Skills

observing, classifying, comparing and contrasting

Time

50 minutes

Materials

Spores and materials for growing ferns may be purchased from a biological supply house. The growth process takes several months.

Safety Precautions

Remind students not to eat any plant parts and to be careful when using microscopes.

Teaching Strategies

Soak a clay pot in water overnight. The next day, turn the pot upside down and sprinkle the spores on the bottom. Keep the inverted pot in a plastic bag to maintain high humidity. Add water as needed to keep the clay pot moist. Keep the pot in a cool location and out of direct sunlight.

Troubleshooting Sometimes mold will overtake young ferns. Contaminated cultures should be discarded. Have additional specimens ready. If spores do not grow using water only, you may add an equal volume of glycerin to the water.

Activity 23•1 Using Scientific Methods

Comparing Seedless Plants

Liverworts, mosses, ferns, horsetails, and club mosses have at least one common characteristic—they reproduce by spores. But, do they have other things in common? In this activity, discover their similarities and differences.

Materials

One living example of each of these plants:

- Moss
- Liverwort
- Club moss
- Horsetail
- Fern

**detailed photographs of the above plant types*

**Alternate Material*

What You'll Investigate

How are seedless plants alike and how are they different?

Goals

- **Observe** types of seedless plants.
- **Compare and contrast** seedless plants.

Procedure

1. Copy the Plant Observations table into your Science Journal.
2. Examine each plant and fill in the table using the following guidelines:
   Color—green or not green
   Growth—mostly flat and low or mostly upright
   Root Type—small and fiberlike or rootlike
   Leaf Form—needlelike, scalelike, or leaflike

Conclude and Apply

1. **Observe and infer** what characteristics seedless plants have in common.
2. **Hypothesize** about the differences in growth.
3. **Compare and contrast** the seedless plants.

Sample data

Plant Observations

Plant	Color	Growth	Root Type	Leaf Form
Moss	green	mostly flat and low	small and fiberlike	leaflike
Liverwort	green	mostly flat and low	small and fiberlike	leaflike
Club moss	green	mostly flat and low	small and fiberlike	scalelike or needlelike
Horsetail	green	mostly upright	rootlike	leaflike
Fern	green	mostly upright	rootlike	leaflike

Answers to Questions

1. All the seedless plants reproduce by spores, possess specialized photosynthesizing structures, and have structures that hold the plants in the ground.
2. Upright plants possess vascular tissue; flat and low-growing plants do not.
3. Mosses and liverworts are nonvascular and grow low to the ground; ground pines, horsetails, and ferns have vascular tissue and are taller.

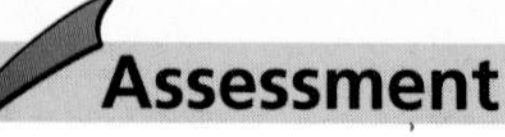

Assessment

Performance Assess students' understanding of the parts of seedless plants by having them identify the parts of living specimens and describe a function for each part. Use **Performance Assessment in the Science Classroom,** p. 71.

How it Works

Preservation in Peat Bogs

A bog is a wetland, characterized by wet, spongy, poorly drained ground. It typically contains a thin layer of living plants overlying a thick layer of partially decomposed plant material called peat. One of the major types of peat is moss peat. It is formed mostly from *Sphagnum* moss. Peat bogs are acidic, low in minerals, and lack oxygen. These conditions provide a unique environment. When some types of organisms become trapped and buried in a peat bog, they do not decay. In Europe and North America, the well-preserved bodies of humans and other animals have been found in peat bogs.

STEP BY STEP

1. Mosses and other wetland plants grow on the surface of a bog.
2. Over time, a layer of partially decayed plant matter accumulates. Eventually, this becomes a thick layer of peat.
3. A substance in the cell walls of *Sphagnum* moss reacts with, and ties up, certain nutrients. These nutrients are essential for the survival of decay-causing bacteria. Without these nutrients, the bacteria cannot live in a bog.
4. When an animal is buried in a bog, its soft tissues, such as skin and internal organs, are not destroyed by decay. But, the animal's bones are dissolved away because of the acidic environment.
5. The skin of animals buried in a peat bog undergoes a sort of tanning process. Human skin becomes leatherlike and coffee colored, as seen in the photograph below.

Think Critically

1. What kinds of information might scientists gain by studying bog-preserved ancient humans?
2. Another type of peat is fuel peat. What property of peat do you think makes it usable as a fuel?

Career CONNECTION

Archaeologists have found hundreds of preserved animals in peat bogs. An archaeologist studies ancient peoples, their remains, and their culture. Pretend you are an archaeologist. Imagine what it must be like for archaeologists to discover human remains.

How it Works

Purpose

Students learn how bogs are unique environments that provide conditions for the preservation of organic remains.

Content Background

Bogs are rich in organic compounds. A substance found in the cell walls of *Sphagnum* moss called *sphagnan* is thought to prevent bacteria from thriving in bogs.

Fossils are the remains of once-living things that are preserved in rocks, ice, tar, amber, or bogs. The best-preserved and most numerous human remains come from the Iron Age and Roman era.

Teaching Strategies

- Bring in samples of peat and *Sphagnum* mosses and have students compare and contrast them. Students should be able to state that both are plant remains.
- Discuss that both are used as mulches and soil conditioners. Sphagnum is used in floral crafts and as a soil cover in potted plants. In countries where wood is scarce, peat is used as a fuel.

Think Critically

1. the person's stature, hair, diseases, diet, age, sex, clothing, and DNA, oftentimes, the cause of death
2. It is flammable and burns slowly.

Career CONNECTION

A bachelor's degree is needed to begin work as a field archaeologist in the U.S. and to perform basic laboratory duties. Most archaeologists complete a master's degree. This requires at least one to two years of course work and a written thesis about original research. Many use this research as the basis for further study in the pursuit of a Ph.D.

CA Science Content Standards

Page 797: 6a, 6b, 6c

SECTION 23•3

Prepare

Refer to **Vascular Tissue, Seed Plants,** and **Angiosperms** on p. 782F.

Preplanning

Refer to the **Chapter Organizer** on pp. 782A–B.

1 Motivate

Bellringer

Before presenting the lesson, display **Section Focus Transparency 66** on the overhead projector. Use the accompanying **Focus Activity** worksheet. L2 ELL

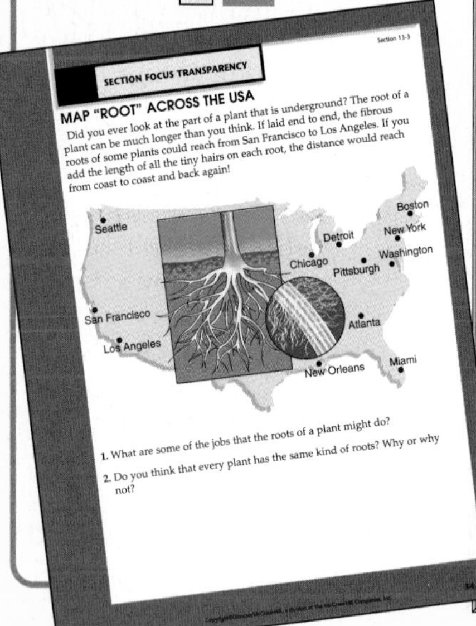
Section 13-3

SECTION FOCUS TRANSPARENCY

MAP "ROOT" ACROSS THE USA

Did you ever look at the part of a plant that is underground? The root of a plant can be much longer than you think. If laid end to end, the fibrous roots of some plants could reach from San Francisco to Los Angeles. If you add the length of all the tiny hairs on each root, the distance would reach from coast to coast and back again!

1. What are some of the jobs that the roots of a plant might do?
2. Do you think that every plant has the same kind of roots? Why or why not?

Tying to Previous Knowledge

Line up several boxes of cereal. Have students identify the plants that were used to produce the contents.

23•3 Seed Plants

***What* You'll Learn**

- The characteristics of seed plants
- The structures and functions of roots, stems, and leaves
- The main characteristics of gymnosperms and angiosperms and their importance
- Similarities and differences of monocots and dicots

Vocabulary

xylem
phloem
cambium
stomata
guard cell
gymnosperm
angiosperm
monocot
dicot

***Why* It's Important**

- Understanding seed plants will help you appreciate how much you depend on them.

What is a seed plant?

Have you ever eaten vegetables like the ones shown in **Figure 23-14?** All of these foods come from seed plants. What fruits and vegetables have you eaten today? If you had an apple, a peanut butter and jelly sandwich, or a glass of orange juice for lunch, you ate foods that came from seed plants.

Nearly all the plants you are familiar with are seed plants. Seed plants have roots, stems, leaves, and vascular tissue and produce seeds. A seed usually contains an embryo and stored food. The stored food is the source of energy for growth of the embryo into a plant. More than 250 000 species of seed plants are known in the world today. Seed plants are generally classified into two major groups: the gymnosperms and the angiosperms.

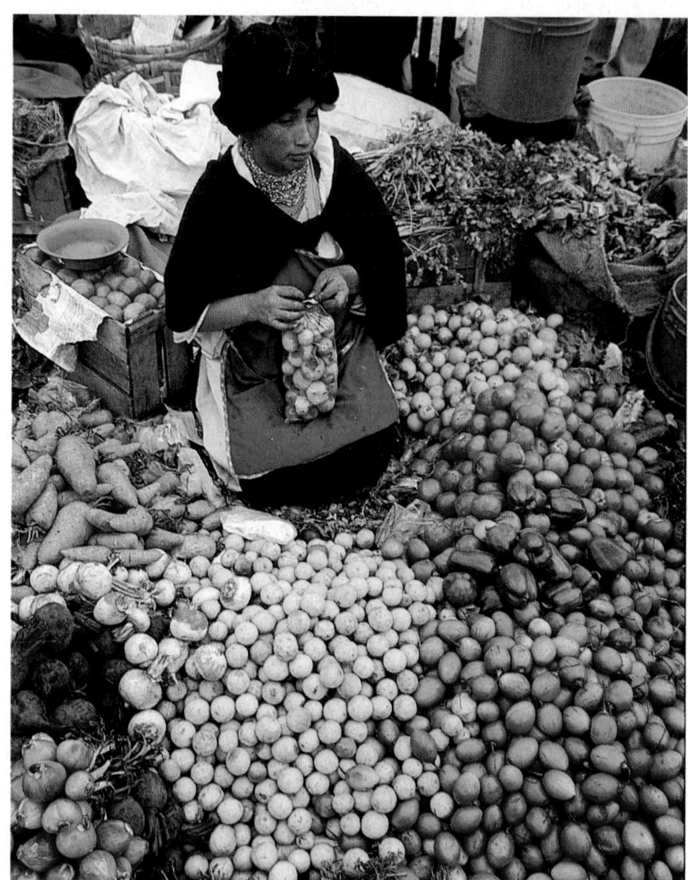

Figure 23-14 The products of plants, like these being sold at a market in Ecuador, provide food for humans. **How are plants an important part of the world's food supply?**

Resource Manager

The following **Teacher Classroom Resources** can be used with Section 23-3:

 **Reproducible Masters**

Activity Worksheets, p. 131–132 L2
Critical Thinking/Problem Solving, p. 23 L2
Enrichment, p. 66 L3
Laboratory Manual, pp. 141–142 L2
Multicultural Connections, pp. 45–46 L2
Reinforcement, p. 66 L2
Study Guide, pp. 91–92 L1 ELL

Figure 23-15 The vascular tissue of some seed plants includes xylem, phloem, and cambium. **Which of these tissues transports food throughout the plant?**

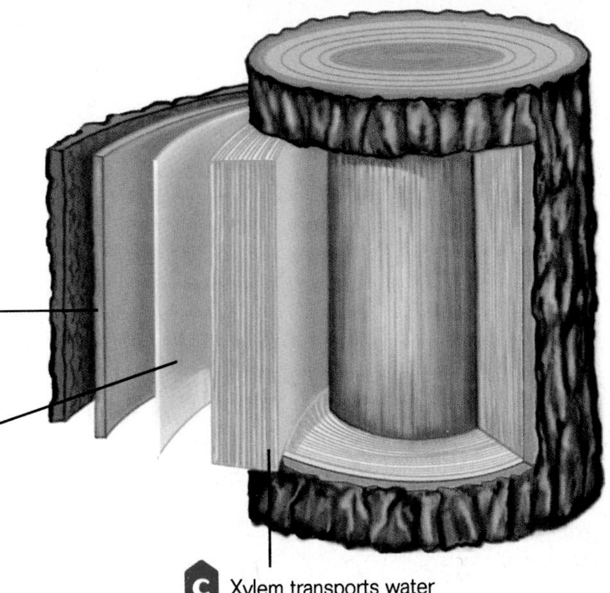

A Phloem transports dissolved sugar throughout the plant.

B Cambium produces xylem and phloem as the plant grows.

C Xylem transports water and dissolved substances throughout the plant.

Vascular Tissue

Three tissues usually make up the vascular system in a seed plant. **Xylem** (ZI lum) tissue transports water and dissolved substances from the roots throughout the plant. **Phloem** (FLOH em) tissue moves food up from where it is made to other parts of the plant where it is used or stored. In some plants, a cambium is between xylem and phloem, as shown in **Figure 23-15**. **Cambium** (KAM bee um) is a tissue that produces new xylem and phloem cells. These three tissues completely circle some stems and roots. Groups of vascular tissue called vascular bundles are found in other plants.

Stems

Did you know that the trunk of a tree is really its stem? Stems are usually above ground and support the branches, leaves, and flowers. Some stems, such as potatoes and onions, are underground. The stem allows movement of materials between leaves and roots. Some stems store food. Sugarcane has an aboveground stem that stores large quantities of food. Stems of cacti are adapted to carry on photosynthesis and make food for the rest of the plant.

MiniLab

Observing Water Moving in a Plant

Procedure

1. Into a clear container, about 10 cm tall and 4 cm in diameter, pour water to a depth of 1.5 cm. Add 15 drops of red food coloring to the water.
2. Put the root end of a whole green onion in the colored water in the container. Do not cut the onion in any way.
3. Let the onion stand overnight.
4. The next day, examine the outside of the onion. Peel off the layers of leaves and examine them.

Analysis

1. In your Science Journal, compare the appearance of the onion before and after it was in the colored water.
2. Describe the location of red color inside the onion.
3. Infer how the red color inside the onion might be related to vascular tissue.

2 Teach

MiniLab

Purpose

Visual-Spatial Students will observe how water moves through vascular tissue in plants. L2 ELL COOP LEARN

Materials

water, clear container, red food coloring, green onion, hand lens

Teaching Strategies

- Ask students to suggest how water moves into the green onion. *Water moves up into the xylem due to atmospheric pressure, diffusion, and the capillary action of water as it adheres to the inner parts of the xylem tubes.*
- Have students brainstorm methods to calculate the rate of movement of liquids in vascular tissue.

Analysis

1. Before the onion was placed in the colored water, it appeared to be white at the bottom with green leaves. The next day, the onion was pinkish and colored stripes appeared in leaves.
2. There are red, vertical stripes in the onion and its leaves.
3. The location is the xylem tubes of the vascular tissue.

Assessment

Performance Assess students' ability to recognize vascular tissue in other plants by having them identify it in carnations and carrots. Use **Performance Assessment in the Science Classroom,** p. 27.

Content Background

One theory for the rise of water in plants is called the *cohesion-tension theory.* According to this theory, water rises because of the cohesion of its molecules, its adhesion to the walls of the capillary conducting elements of xylem, and the pull created by transpiration.

Caption Answer

Figure 23-14 *Plants such as rice, corn, wheat, and oats make up the bulk of the human diet throughout the world.*

Figure 23-15 *phloem*

CA Science Content Standards

Page 799: 5a, 6c

VISUAL Learning

Figure 23-16 Use this photograph to explain to students that most plants have as much mass in the root system anchoring the plant as in the parts above ground.

Quick Demo

Give each student a piece of carrot, asparagus, and lettuce. Ask: **What part of the plant does each come from?** *carrot—root, asparagus—stem, lettuce—leaf* **What do the plants' parts have in common?** *All store food for the plant.*

Using Math

Area of a circle = πr^2

$\pi = 3.14$, $r = 15$ m

Area of soil covered = $3.14 \times 15 \text{ m} \times 15 \text{ m} = 706.5 \text{ m}^2$

Activity

Using any well-established houseplant, empty it from its pot and gently untangle the root ball. Compare the amount of roots to the aboveground portion of the plant. The amount of root growth should exceed the amount of aboveground growth. The plant can be repotted with little or no harm to it.

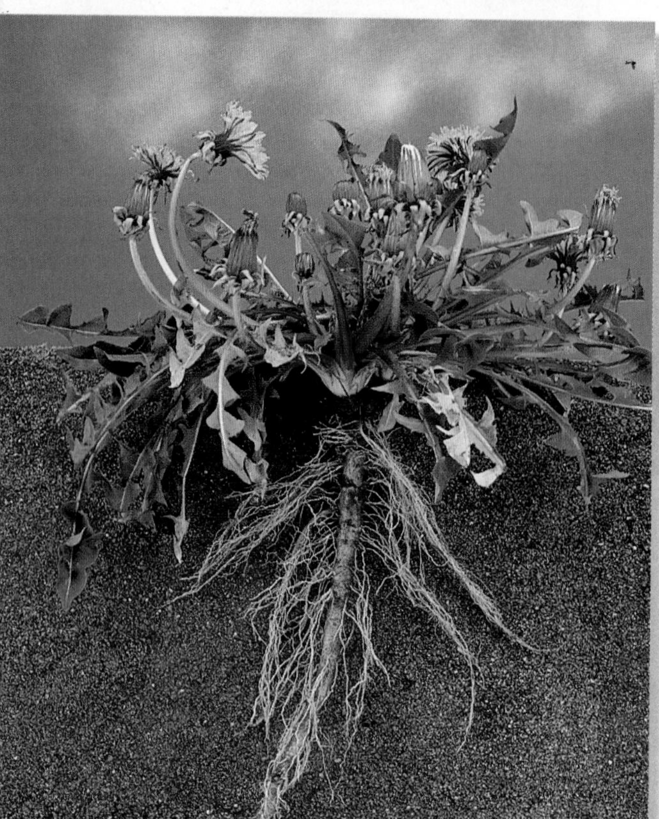

Figure 23-16 The root system of a dandelion is longer than the plant is tall. When you pull up a dandelion, you often pull off the top portion of the plant. The root quickly produces new leaves, and another dandelion grows.

Plant stems are either herbaceous (hur BAY shus) or woody. Herbaceous stems usually are soft and green, like the stems of peppers, corn, and tulips. Oak, birch, and other trees and shrubs have hard, rigid, woody stems.

Roots

Imagine a large tree growing alone on top of a hill. What is the largest part? Maybe you said the trunk or the branches. Did you consider the roots? The root systems of most plants are as large or larger than the aboveground stems and leaves, like the dandelion in **Figure 23-16.**

Roots are important to plants. Water and other substances enter a plant through its roots. Roots have vascular tissue to move water and dissolved substances from the ground up through the stems to the leaves. Roots also anchor plants. If they didn't, plants could be blown away by wind or washed away by water. Each root system must support the plant parts that are above the ground—the stem, branches, and leaves of a tree, for example. Sometimes, part or all of roots are above ground, too.

Roots may store food. When you eat carrots or beets, you eat roots that contain stored food. Root tissues also may perform special functions such as absorbing oxygen that is used in the process of respiration.

Using Computers

The roots of some cacti are shallow but grow horizontally as much as 15 m in all directions from the stem. How much soil surface area do these roots cover?

Leaves

Have you ever rested in the shade of a tree's leaves on a hot, summer day? Leaves are the organs of the plant that usually trap light and make food through the process of photosynthesis. Leaves come in many shapes, sizes, and colors.

Content Background

- The sweet potato is a fleshy root, but the white potato is a fleshy underground stem. Both are sinks, which are food-storage areas for the plant.
- Cactus spines are modified leaves that prevent water loss. The familiar stalks of celery and rhubarb are modified leaf stems that store food.

Leaf Structure

Look at the structure of a typical leaf shown in **Figure 23-17.** The epidermis is a thin layer of cells that covers and protects both the upper and lower surfaces of a leaf. A waxy cuticle that protects and reduces water loss covers the epidermis of many leaves. A feature of most leaves is stomata. **Stomata** are small pores in the leaf surfaces that allow carbon dioxide, water, and oxygen to enter and leave a leaf. The stomata are surrounded by **guard cells** that open and close the pores. The cuticle, stomata, and guard cells all are adaptations that help plants survive on land. ✓

Reading Check ✓

What is the role of stomata in a leaf?

Leaf Cells

A typical leaf is made of different layers of cells. Covering the upper and lower surfaces of a leaf is the epidermis. Just below the upper epidermis is the palisade layer. It consists of closely packed, long, narrow cells that usually contain many chloroplasts. Most of the food produced by plants is made in the palisade cells. Between the palisade layer and the lower epidermis is the spongy layer. It is a layer of loosely arranged cells separated by air spaces. In a leaf, xylem and phloem are in the spongy layer.

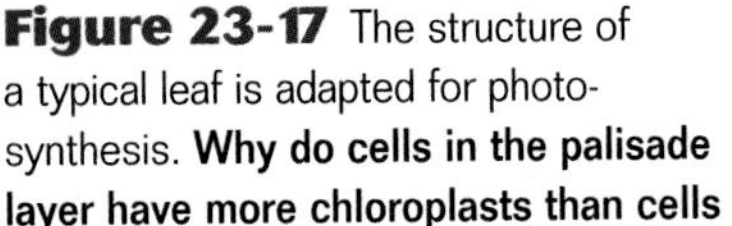

Figure 23-17 The structure of a typical leaf is adapted for photosynthesis. **Why do cells in the palisade layer have more chloroplasts than cells in the spongy layer?**

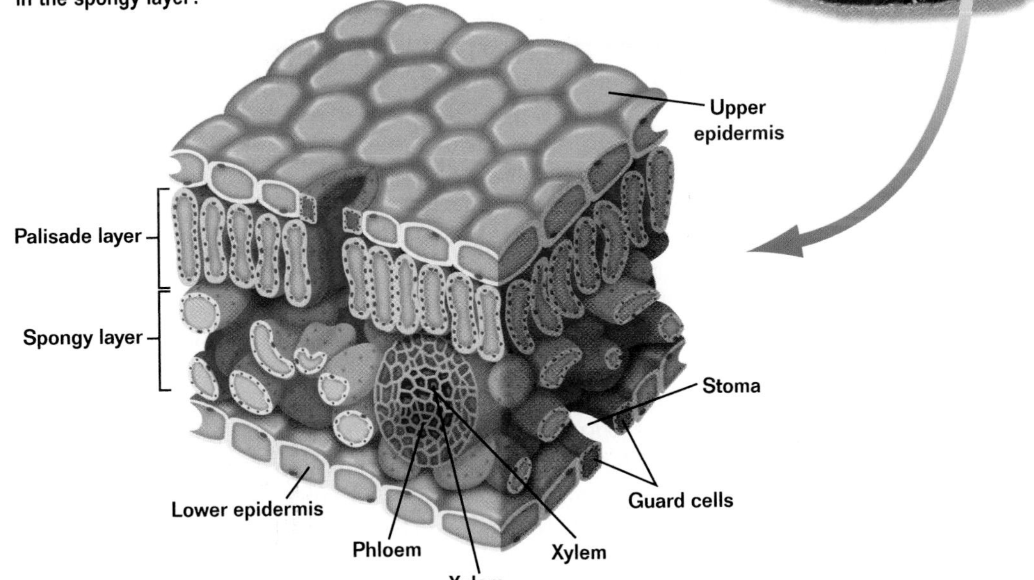

Correcting Misconceptions

Many students will believe that stomata exist to allow water to escape from plant leaves. Point out that plants generally need to conserve water. Plants must have carbon dioxide for photosynthesis. Water escapes as carbon dioxide enters.

Answer to Reading Check ✓

Stomata allow carbon dioxide to diffuse into the plant where photosynthesis takes place.

Using Science Words

Have students look in a dictionary for the meaning and derivation of botany and enter their results in their Science Journals.

Caption Answer

Figure 23-17 *Because cells in the palisade layer are usually on the side of the leaf that faces the sun. The cells in the spongy layer are shaded by the palisade layer.*

Guided Reading Strategy

Write-Draw-Discuss This strategy encourages students to actively participate in reading and lectures, assimilating content creatively. Have students write about an idea, clarifying it, then make an illustration or drawing. Ask students to share responses with the class and display several examples. Have students Write-Draw-Discuss a concept in this section.

CA Science Content Standards

Page 800: 6c

Quick Demo

Show students a pine cone, a rose, and a walnut. Ask students to explain what the plants that produce these structures have in common. *They all produce seeds.* L1

Using Science Words

Linguistic Have students look up the meanings of the Greek words *gymnos* and *spermae* from which the word *gymnosperm* is derived and explain why these organisms are given their name. L3

VISUAL Learning

Figure 23-18 There are fewer than 1000 species of gymnosperms. Of these, about 550 are conifers, including pines, firs, junipers and cedars.

Enrichment

Have students find in a dictionary the meaning of a board foot. *A board foot is a volume measure of lumber. A board measuring 12 × 12 × 1 inches is one board foot. A single giant redwood may produce as much as 480 000 board feet of lumber.*

VISUALIZING Gymnosperms

A Conifers are the largest, most diverse division of the gymnosperms. Most conifers are evergreen plants, such as this blue spruce.

B About 100 species of cycads exist today. Only one genus grows naturally in the United States. This sago palm comes from Java, an island in Indonesia.

Figure 23-18 The gymnosperms include conifers (A), cycads (B), ginkgoes (C), and gnetophytes (D).

EXAMPLES OF Gymnosperms

- Pine
- Hemlock
- Spruce
- Sago Palm
- Ginkgo
- Joint Fir

Gymnosperms

The oldest trees alive today are gymnosperms (JIHM nuh spurmz). A bristlecone pine tree in the White Mountains of eastern California is estimated to be 4900 years old. **Gymnosperms** are vascular plants that produce seeds on the surface of the female reproductive structure. The word *gymnosperm* comes from the Greek language and means "naked seed." Seeds of gymnosperms are not protected by a fruit. Gymnosperms do not produce flowers. Leaves of most gymnosperms are needlelike or scalelike. Gymnosperms are often called evergreens because most keep their leaves for more than one year.

Four divisions of plants—conifers, cycads, ginkgoes, and gnetophytes—are classified as gymnosperms. **Figure 23-18** shows examples of the four divisions. You are probably most familiar with the division Coniferophyta, the conifers. Pines, firs, spruces, redwoods, and junipers belong to this division. It contains the greatest number of gymnosperm species. All conifers produce two types of cones, the male and female reproductive structures. These are usually on the same plant. Seeds develop on the female cone.

Inclusion Strategies

Visually Impaired Bring branches from different needled conifers to class. Identify the branches then have students feel the differences in texture and smell the different aromas.

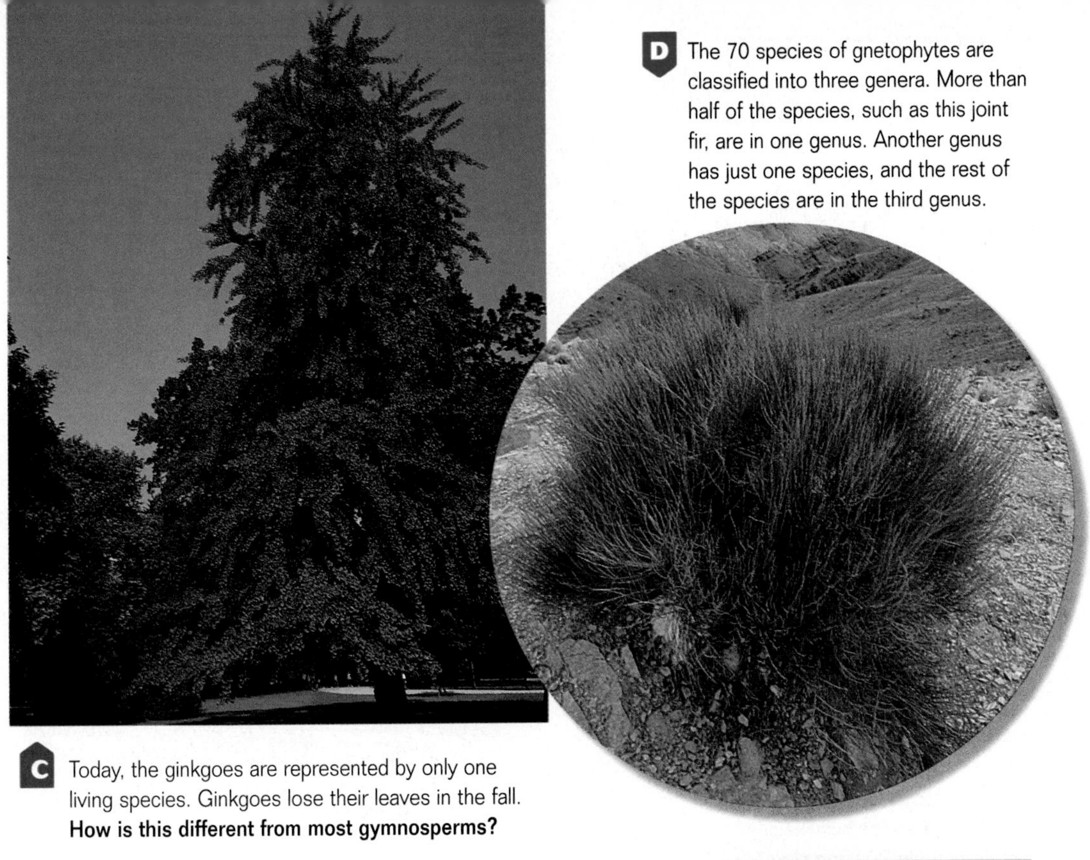

D The 70 species of gnetophytes are classified into three genera. More than half of the species, such as this joint fir, are in one genus. Another genus has just one species, and the rest of the species are in the third genus.

C Today, the ginkgoes are represented by only one living species. Ginkgoes lose their leaves in the fall. **How is this different from most gymnosperms?**

Angiosperms

When people are asked to name a plant, most people name an angiosperm (AN jee uh spurm). Angiosperms are familiar plants no matter where you live. They grow in parks, fields, forests, jungles, deserts, freshwater, salt water, cracks of sidewalks, or dangling from wires or other plants. One species of orchid even grows underground. Angiosperms make up the plant division Anthophyta. More than eighty-five percent of plant species known today belong to this division.

An **angiosperm** is a vascular plant that flowers and has a fruit that contains seeds. The fruit develops from a part or parts of one or more flowers. The flowers of angiosperms vary in size, shape, and color. Duckweed, an aquatic plant, has a flower that is only 0.1 mm long. A plant in Indonesia has a flower that is nearly 1 m in diameter and can weigh 9 kg. Nearly every color can be found in some flower, although some people would not include black. Multi-colored flowers are common. Some plants have flowers that are not easily recognized as flowers, such as those found on oak and birch trees.

Examples of Angiosperms

- **Grasses and grains**
- **Cacti**
- **Palms**
- **Garden flowers**
- **Vegetables**
- **Fruits**
- **Nuts (except pine nuts)**
- **Leafy trees (except ginkgoes)**

Caption Answers

Figure 23-18C *Most gymnosperms have needlelike or scale-like leaves that stay on the plant for more than one year.*

Figure 23-19 *A fruit grows from a flower*

Correcting Misconceptions

The common definitions for a fruit and a vegetable relate more to their culinary uses than botanical meanings. Fruits are generally served after a meal and vegetables are served in salads or with an entree. Botanically, a fruit is any plant organ that grows from part(s) of a flower(s). Therefore, tomatoes, green beans, squash, cucumbers, and peppers are fruit. Vegetables are all other edible plant structures.

Teacher FYI

Dandelions, chrysanthemums, and sunflowers belong to the family of plants called Asteraceae. What we see as a single flower is really a composite of many, individual, small flowers called florets. In fact, the family name was once Compositae.

Across the Curriculum

History Theophrastus (ca. 372–ca. 287 BCE) is known as the father of botany. His comprehensive botanical works were so complete that nearly 1800 years passed before any new discoveries were made. Have each student find the name and contributions of another pre-twentieth century botanist. Make a time line of their results.

Quick Demo

Use a variety of monocots and dicots to demonstrate the characteristics of these two groups of angiosperms.

Discussion

 **Interpersonal** Have students survey the kinds of plants they find at a supermarket. Discuss the list in class to determine if most are gymnosperms, monocots, or dicots. COOP LEARN

Teacher FYI

The grass family, Poaceae, is the largest plant family in terms of number of plants, and it is the most widely distributed. Grasses are monocots. Their flower structure is so unique that there are descriptive terms that apply to only grasses. The fibers of grass leaves are and have been used for centuries to make mats, baskets, and roof thatch.

GLENCOE TECHNOLOGY

Videodisc

The Infinite Voyage: To the Edge of the Earth

Chapter 5 *The Tropical Rain Forest* 8:00

Refer the VideodiscTeacher Guide for bar codes and teaching strategies.

CD-ROM

Glencoe Science Voyages Interactive CD-ROM

Explorations

Have students do the interactive exploration *What are the functions of the parts of a flower?*

VISUALIZING Monocots and Dicots

Figure 23-19 By observing a monocot and a dicot, their plant characteristics can be determined.

A Monocots, such as these lilies, have flower parts in multiples of three. If you had cereal for breakfast, you ate part of a monocot. Corn, rice, oats, and wheat are monocots.

B In monocots, vascular tissues are arranged as bundles scattered throughout the stem. Monocot leaves are usually more narrow than long. The vascular bundles show up as parallel veins in leaves.

Monocots and Dicots

The two classes of angiosperms are the monocots and the dicots. The terms *monocot* and *dicot* are shortened forms of the words *monocotyledon* and *dicotyledon*. The prefix *mono* means "one," and *di* means "two." A cotyledon is a seed leaf inside a seed. Therefore, **monocots** have one seed leaf inside their seeds and **dicots** have two. **Figure 23-19** compares the characteristics of monocots and dicots.

Importance of Seed Plants

Imagine that your class is having a picnic in the park. You cover the wooden picnic table with a red-checked, cotton tablecloth and pass out paper cups and plates. Your lunch includes hot dogs, potato chips, and apple cider. Perhaps you collect leaves or flowers for a science project. Later, you clean up and put leftovers in paper bags.

Now, let's imagine this scene if there were no seed plants on Earth. There would be no wooden picnic table and no

VISUAL Learning

Figure 23-20 Use this figure to compare and contrast the characteristics of monocot and dicot flowers. L2

D In dicot stems, vascular bundles occur in rings. These bundles of rings are the annual rings in woody stems. The vascular bundles are the network of veins in dicot leaves.

C Dicots, such as the hibiscus, have flower parts in multiples of four or five. Oaks, maples, and many other trees are dicots. Most vegetables and fruits are dicots, as are many garden flowers.

pulp to make paper products such as cups, plates, and bags. The hot dog came from the meat of animals that eat only plants. Bread for buns, apples for cider, and potatoes for chips all come from plants. The tablecloth is made from cotton, a plant. Without seed plants, there would be no picnic.

Uses of Gymnosperms and Angiosperms

Conifers are the most economically important gymnosperms. Most of the wood used for construction, as in **Figure 23-20,** and for paper production, comes from conifers such as pines and spruces. Resin, a waxy substance secreted by conifers, is used to make chemicals found in soap, paint, varnish, and some medicines.

Figure 23-20 The wood from conifers, such as pines, is commonly used in construction. Resin is used to make household products.

Discussion

Lead a discussion with students about why plants are important. You might ask each student to identify an important aspect of plants in general or a particular plant. L2

3 Assess

Check for Understanding

Discussion

Ask students to compare monocots and dicots by using the characteristics of each. L2

Reteach

Emphasize the important characteristics of the monocots and dicots again. Place several monocots and dicots around the room. Write a hint on an index card for each one. (Example: Notice the parallel veins in the leaves of this plant.) Have students identify them as either a monocot or a dicot by using the hints. L1

Extension

For students who have mastered this section, use the **Reinforcement** and **Enrichment** masters.

4 Close

Proficiency Prep

Use this quiz to check students' recall of section content.

1. **What plant structures have vascular tissue to move water from the soil to the leaves?** *roots*
2. **What supports the aboveground parts of the plant?** *stem*
3. **What leaf layer makes most of the food made by plants?** *palisade layer*

Multiple Learning Styles

Linguistic For one day, have students record any plant or plant-related items used or encountered in their daily routines. Compile the list of plants that students recorded.

CA Science Content Standards

Page 804: 6c
Page 805: 6c

Caption Answer

Figure 23-21 *cellulose*

Section Assessment

1. Seed plants have roots, stems, leaves, vascular tissue, and produce seeds. Their reproduction does not depend on free water.
2. Gymnosperms produce seeds on cone scales, and usually have needlelike leaves. Angiosperms produce flowers. Parts of the flower become the fruit that encloses the seeds. Angiosperms usually have broad and flat leaves.
3. It is from a dicot plant.
4. **Think Critically** If the waxy cuticle of angiosperms were not transparent, less light would reach the chloroplasts. This would reduce the rate of photosynthesis.

Using Computers

Answers will vary. For example, students may make a partial outline such as:

I. Roots
  A. Vascular tissue
    1. moves water
    2. moves minerals

Figure 23-21 Cotton is a flowering plant that yields long fibers that can be woven into a wide variety of fabrics. **What chemical compound makes up these fibers?**

The most common plants on Earth are the angiosperms. They are important to all life because they form the basis for the diets of most animals. Grains such as barley and wheat and legumes such as peas and lentils were among the first plants ever grown by humans. Angiosperms also are the source of many of the fibers used in clothing. Cotton fibers, as seen in **Figure 23-21,** grow from the outer surface of cottonseeds. The fibers of the flax plant are processed and woven into linen fabrics. The production of medicines, rubber, oils, perfumes, pesticides, and some industrial chemicals uses substances found in angiosperms.

Section Assessment

1. What are the characteristics of a seed plant?
2. Compare and contrast the characteristics of gymnosperms and angiosperms.
3. You are looking at a flower with five petals, five sepals, one pistil, and ten stamens. Is it from a monocot or dicot plant?
4. **Think Critically:** The cuticle and epidermis of leaves are transparent. If they were not transparent, what might be the result?
5. **Skill Builder**
   Classifying Conifers have needlelike or scalelike leaves. Do the **Chapter 23 Skill Activity** on page 984 to learn how to use this characteristic to classify conifers.

Using Computers

Word Processing Use a word-processing program to outline the structures and functions that are associated with roots, stems, and leaves. If you need help, refer to page 968.

Assessment

Performance Assess students' abilities to classify vegetables by structure by giving them actual vegetables to classify. Use **Performance Assessment in the Science Classroom,** p. 49. L2 ELL

Activity 23•2

Comparing Monocots and Dicots

You have read that monocots and dicots are similar because they are both groups of flowering plants. However, you also have learned that these two groups are different. Try this activity to compare and contrast monocots and dicots.

Materials

- Monocot and dicot flowers
- Monocot and dicot seeds
- Scalpel
- Forceps
- Iodine solution

What You'll Investigate

How do the characteristics of monocots and dicots compare?

Goals

- **Observe** similarities and differences between monocots and dicots.
- **Classify** plants as monocots or dicots based on flower characteristics.
- **Infer** what type of food is stored in seeds.

Procedure

1. Copy the Plant Data table in your Science Journal.
2. **Observe** the leaves on the stem of each flower. In your Science Journal, describe the monocot and the dicot leaves.
3. **Examine** the monocot and the dicot flower. For each flower, remove and count the sepals and petals. Enter these numbers on the table.
4. Inside each flower, you should see a pistil(s) and several stamens. **Count** each type and enter these numbers as "Other Observations."
5. **Examine** the two seeds. **Cut** the seeds lengthwise, **observe** each half, and **identify** the embryo and cotyledon(s).
6. Place a drop of iodine on different parts of the seed. A blue-black color indicates the presence of starch. **CAUTION:** *Iodine is poisonous. It will stain and can burn your skin.*

Conclude and Apply

1. **Compare** the numbers of sepals and petals of monocot and dicot flowers.
2. What characteristics are the same for monocot and dicot flowers?
3. Distinguish between a monocot and a dicot seed.
4. What type of food is stored in monocot and in

Plant Data

	Number of Sepals	Number of Petals	Number of Cotyledons	Other Observations
Monocot	multiple of 3	multiple of 3	1	pistil—1 stamen—multiple of 3
Dicot	multiple of 4 or 5	multiple of 4 or 5	2	pistil—1 or multiple of 4 or 5 stamen—multiple of 4 or 5

Activity 23•2

Purpose

Visual-Spatial Students will observe, compare, and contrast structures of monocots and dicots. L2 ELL COOP LEARN P

Process Skills

observing and inferring, comparing and contrasting, classifying, forming operational definitions, measuring in SI

Time

50 minutes

Safety Precautions

Caution students to be careful when using sharp instruments such as a scalpel. Students also should not ingest flower parts or seeds.

Teaching Strategies

Troubleshooting Be sure the seeds have been soaked for at least 24 hours. To clarify step 5, demonstrate how to cut the seeds in half so that students see what they are suppose to see.

Answers to Questions

1. Monocot flowers have petals and sepals in multiples of three. Dicot flowers have petals and sepals in multiples of four or five.
2. Both kinds of flowers have stigmas, styles, ovaries, filaments, anthers, pollen, petals, and sepals.
3. Dicot seeds have two cotyledons, and monocot seeds have only one cotyledon.
4. starch

Assessment

Performance Use germinated seeds to have students answer questions placed on index cards about plant parts. Use **Performance Assessment in the Science Classroom,** p. 17.

CA Science Content Standards

Page 806: 6c
Page 807: 5a, 6c

Chapter 23 Reviewing Main Ideas

Reviewing Main Ideas can be used to preview, review, reteach, and condense chapter content.

Preview

Linguistic Have students try to answer the questions in their Science Journals. Use student answers as a source for discussion throughout the chapter.

Review

Interpersonal Have students answer the questions on separate pieces of paper and compare their answers with those of other students in the class.

Reteach

Visual-Spatial Have students look at the illustrations on these pages. Ask them to describe details that support the main ideas of the chapter found in the statement for each illustration.

00:00 OUT OF TIME?

Auditory-Musical If time does not permit teaching the entire chapter, use the information on these pages along with the chapter Audiocassettes to present the material in a condensed format.

Chapter 23 Reviewing Main Ideas

For a **preview** of this chapter, study this Reviewing Main Ideas before you read the chapter. After you have studied this chapter, you can use the Reviewing Main Ideas to **review** the chapter.

The Glencoe MindJogger, Audiocassettes, and CD-ROM provide additional opportunities for review.

Section

23-1 CHARACTERISTICS OF PLANTS

Plants are made up of eukaryotic cells. They usually have some form of leaves, stems, and roots. Plants vary greatly in size and shape. Most plants are adapted to live on land. As plants evolved from aquatic to land forms, changes in structure and function occurred. The changes included how they reproduced, supported themselves, and moved substances from one part of the plant to another. The plant kingdom is classified into groups called divisions. ***What are some plant adaptations for living on land?***

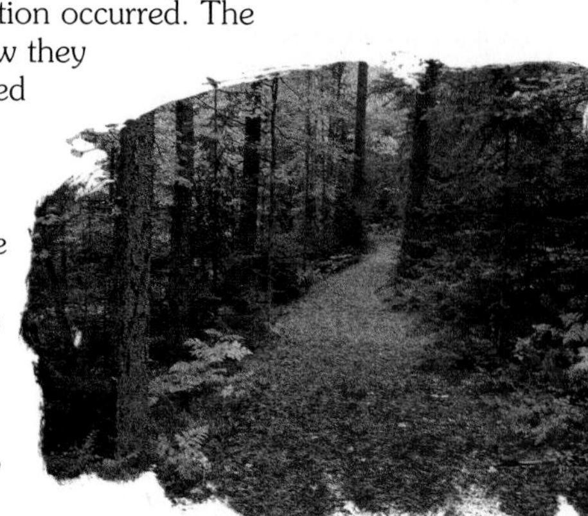

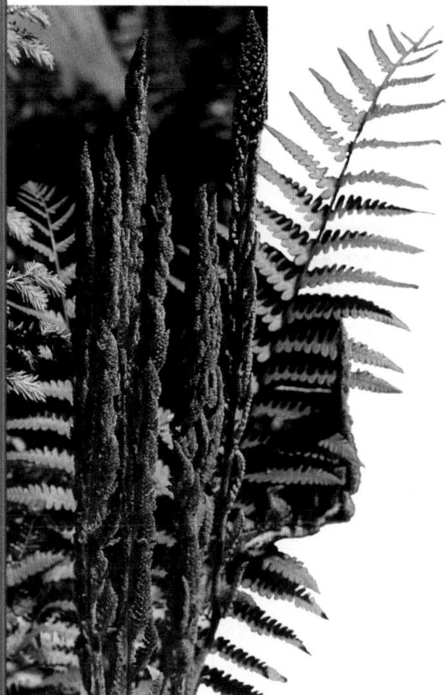

Section

23-2 SEEDLESS PLANTS

Seedless plants include **nonvascular** and **vascular** types. Bryophytes—mosses and liverworts—are seedless **nonvascular plants.** They have no true leaves, stems, roots, or vascular tissues and live in moist environments. For bryophytes, reproduction usually is by spores. Bryophytes may be considered **pioneer species** because they are some of the first plants to grow in new or disturbed environments. They change the environment so that other plant species may grow there. Club mosses, horsetails, and ferns are seedless **vascular plants.** They have vascular tissues, a pipeline that moves substances throughout the plant. Like bryophytes, these plants may reproduce by spores. When ancient forms of these plants died, they underwent a process that, over time, resulted in the formation of coal. ***How are bryophytes and ferns alike?***

Cultural Diversity

Food for Thought People from different cultures rely on different plants for food. Most cultures rely on grains indigenous to their part of the world for their main source of carbohydrates. Have students prepare posters showing different plant parts that are used for food. More familiar foods like peas, cinnamon, and tapioca may be presented as well as prickly pears and bamboo shoots.

Cultural Grains Many cultures depend on a specific grain. Discuss some examples. **What grains does the United States depend on?** *corn and wheat* Have students find out about millet, sorghum, and amaranth. Amaranth is a source of protein in South America and Africa.

Reading Check

Choose a topic in this chapter that interests you. Look it up in a reference book, an encyclopedia or on a CD. Think of a way to share what you learn.

Section 23-3 SEED PLANTS

Seed plants are what most people think of when they hear the word *plants.* These plants have adapted to survive in nearly every environment on Earth. Seed plants produce seeds and have vascular tissue, stems, roots, and leaves. Vascular tissues transport food, water, and dissolved substances in the roots, stems, and leaves. The two major groups of seed plants are gymnosperms and angiosperms. **Gymnosperms** generally have needlelike leaves and some type of cone. **Angiosperms** are plants that flower and are classified as **monocots** or **dicots.** Seed plants provide food, shelter, clothing, and many other products. ***What structures are common to all seed plants?***

Answers to Questions

Section 23-1

Characteristics of Plants Vascular tissue, cuticle, and production of seeds are three critical adaptations for life on land.

Section 23-2

Seedless Plants Bryophytes and ferns produce spores.

Section 23-3

Seed Plants Most seed plants have stems, roots, leaves, vascular tissue, and specialized structures for producing seeds without the need for free water.

GLENCOE TECHNOLOGY

CD-ROM

Glencoe Science Voyages Interactive CD-ROM

Chapter Summaries and Quizzes

Have students read the Chapter Summary, then take the Chapter Quiz to determine whether they have mastered chapter content.

Assessment

Portfolio Encourage students to place in their portfolios one or two items of what they consider to be their best work. Examples include:

- Flex Your Brain, p. 785
- Activity 23-1, p. 796
- Activity 23-2, p. 807 P

Performance Additional performance assessments may be found in the **Performance Assessment** and **Science Integration Activities.** Performance Task Assessment Lists and rubrics for evaluating these activities can be found in Glencoe's **Performance Assessment in the Science Classroom.**

Using Vocabulary

1. New xylem and phloem tissues are produced by cambium cells.
2. All angiosperms may be classified as either dicots or monocots.
3. Stomata are the openings in leaf surfaces that are surrounded by two guard cells.
4. A cuticle is a waxy, protective layer secreted by plant cells. Cellulose is the major component of plant cell walls.
5. All gymnosperms are vascular plants but not all vascular plants are gymnosperms.

interNET CONNECTION To reinforce chapter vocabulary, use the **Study Guide for Content Mastery** booklet. Also available are activities for **Glencoe Science Voyages** on the Glencoe Science Web Site. **www.glencoe.com/sec/science/ca**

Checking Concepts

6. C	11. B
7. A	12. C
8. C	13. D
9. A	14. A
10. D	15. B

Thinking Critically

16. The plant might lose so much water that it would die.
17. Something in bogs prevents decomposing bacteria from growing.
18. Succulents grow naturally in desert environments.
19. Mosses are limited to moist areas because they require free water for reproduction and because they have little or no vascular tissue for water transport.
20. Pioneer species help to break down rocks and create small pockets of soil needed by other, larger plants.

Chapter 23 Assessment

Using Vocabulary

a. angiosperm	i. nonvascular plant
b. cambium	j. phloem
c. cellulose	k. pioneer species
d. cuticle	l. rhizoid
e. dicot	m. stomata
f. guard cell	n. vascular plant
g. gymnosperm	o. xylem
h. monocot	

Explain the differences between the terms in each of the following sets.

1. xylem, phloem, cambium
2. angiosperm, dicot, monocot
3. guard cell, stomata
4. cuticle, cellulose
5. vascular plant, gymnosperm

Checking Concepts

Choose the word or phrase that best answers the question.

6. Which of the following is a seedless, vascular plant?
   A) moss C) horsetail
   B) liverwort D) pine
7. What are the small openings in the surface of a leaf surrounded by guard cells?
   A) stomata C) rhizoids
   B) cuticles D) angiosperms
8. What is the plant structure that anchors the plant?
   A) stem C) roots
   B) leaves D) guard cell
9. What kind of plants have structures that move water and other substances?
   A) vascular C) nonvascular
   B) protist D) moneran
10. What division has plants that are only a few cells thick?
   A) Anthophyta C) Pterophyta
   B) Cycadophyta D) Bryophyta
11. Where is new xylem and phloem produced?
   A) guard cells C) stomata
   B) cambium D) cuticle
12. Which of the following is **NOT** part of an angiosperm?
   A) flowers C) cones
   B) seeds D) fruit
13. In what part of a leaf does most photosynthesis happen?
   A) epidermis C) stomata
   B) cuticle D) palisade layer
14. Which of these is an advantage to life on land for plants?
   A) more direct sunlight
   B) less carbon dioxide
   C) greater space to grow
   D) less competition for food
15. What do ferns **NOT** have?
   A) fronds C) spores
   B) rhizoids D) vascular tissue

Thinking Critically

16. What might happen if a land plant's waxy cuticle were destroyed?
17. Well-preserved human remains have been found in peat bogs. Explain why this occurs.
18. Plants called succulents store large amounts of water in their leaves, stems, and roots. In what environments would you expect to find succulents growing naturally?
19. Explain why mosses are usually found on moist areas.
20. How do pioneer species change environments so that other plants may grow there?

Developing Skills

If you need help, refer to the Skill Handbook.

21. **Concept Mapping:** Complete this map for the seedless plants of the plant kingdom.

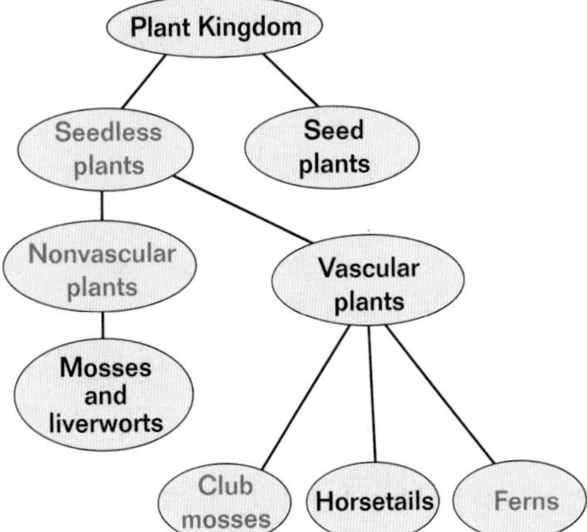

22. **Interpreting Data:** What do the data in this table tell you about where gas exchange occurs in each plant leaf?

Stomata (per mm^2)		
	Upper Surface	Lower Surface
Pine	50	71
Bean	40	281
Fir	0	228
Tomato	12	13

23. **Making and Using Graphs:** Make two circle graphs using the table in question 22.

24. **Interpreting Scientific Illustrations:** Using **Figure 23-19,** compare and contrast the *number of seed leaves, bundle arrangement in the stem, veins in leaves,* and *number of flower parts* for monocots and dicots.

Test-Taking Tip

You Are Smarter Than You Think
Nothing on the science tests that you will take this year is so difficult that you can't understand it. You can learn to master any of it. Be confident and just keep practicing your test-taking skills.

Test Practice

Use these questions to test your Science Proficiency.

1. What does the cuticle found on the surface of many plant cells help to do?
   A) increase the carbon dioxide released
   B) change the method of reproduction
   C) reduce water loss for the plant
   D) keep the surface area as small as possible
2. What is one explanation for why bryophytes grow just a few centimeters tall?
   A) They lack reproductive structures.
   B) Their rhizoids are not real roots.
   C) Many creatures trample them on the forest floor.
   D) They do not have vascular tissues.
3. What is one feature that gymnosperms and flowering plants have in common?
   A) reproduce naturally from seeds
   B) have leaves that stay on the plant for more than one year
   C) produce the same types of fruit
   D) are nonvascular plants

Test Practice

The Test-Taking Tip was written by The Princeton Review, the nation's leader in test preparation.

1. C
2. D
3. A

Developing Skills

21. See student page.
22. Gas exchange for pine and tomato leaves is nearly the same on both the upper and lower surfaces, because the number of stomata on each is about equal. Most of the gas exchange for bean leaves occurs on the lower surface. All gas exchange for fir needles happens on the lower surface.
23. The upper-surface graph should show 43° for tomatoes, 176° for pine, and 131° for bean. The lower-surface graph should show 7° for tomato, 43° for pine, 173° for bean, and 137° for fir.
24. Monocots have one seed leaf, scattered vascular bundles, parallel veins in leaves, and flower parts in multiples of three. Dicots have two seed leaves, vascular bundles in rings, a network of veins in leaves, and flower parts in multiples of four or five.

Bonus Question

Why are the petals and sepals of some flowers such as tulips brightly colored?
They are usually brightly colored to attract pollinating insects.

Assessment Resources

The **Test Practice Workbook** provides students with practice in the format, concepts, and critical-thinking skills tested in standardized exams.

Chapter Review, pp. 45–46 L2
Performance Assessment, p. 23 L2
Assessment, pp. 89–92 L2

Glencoe Technology

Chapter Review Software
Computer Test Bank
MindJogger Videoquiz

Chapter 24 Invertebrate Animals

Section	Objectives	Activities/Features
Chapter Opener		Explore Activity: Organize Animals, p. 813
24-1 What is an animal? 1 Session; ½ Block	1. **Identify** the characteristics of animals. 2. **Distinguish** between vertebrates and invertebrates. 3. **Determine** how the the body plans of animals differ.	Skill Builder: Concept Mapping, p. 816 Using Computers, p. 816
24-2 Sponges, Cnidarians, Flatworms, and Roundworms 1 Session; ½ Block	4. **Identify** the structures that make up sponges and cnidarians. 5. **Describe** how sponges and cnidarians obtain food and how they reproduce. 6. **Compare** the body plans of flatworms and roundworms.	Chemistry Integration, p. 818 MiniLab: Observing Sponge Spicules, p. 818 Skill Builder: Comparing and Contrasting, p. 822 Using Math, p. 822
24-3 Mollusks and Segmented Worms 4½ Sessions; 2 Blocks	7. **Identify** the characteristics of mollusks. 8. **Determine** the similarities and differences between an open and a closed circulatory system. 9. **Describe** the characteristics of segmented worms. 10. **Describe** the structures and digestive process of an earthworm.	Physics Integration, p. 825 Problem Solving: Leeches to the Rescue, p. 827 Skill Builder: Comparing and Contrasting, p. 828 Science Journal, p. 828 History of Science: Searching for the Giant Squid, p. 829 Activity 24-1: Garbage-Eating Worms, pp. 830–831
24-4 Arthropods and Echinoderms 3 Sessions; 1½ Blocks	11. **Identify** features used to classify arthropods. 12. **Relate** the structure of the exoskeleton to its function. 13. **Identify** the features of echinoderms.	MiniLab: Modeling Sea Stars, p. 837 Skill Builder: Observing and Inferring, p. 838 Using Math, p. 838 Activity 24-2: Observing Complete Metamorphosis, p. 839

The number of recommended single-period sessions — The number of recommended blocks
One session and one-half block are allowed for chapter review and assessment.

Activity Materials

Explore	Activities	MiniLabs
p. 813 bulletin board, index cards, markers, envelopes, colored pencils, magazines with animal pictures	pp. 830–831 red wiggler worms, 2 4-L plastic containers, 7 L soil, food scraps, eggshells, tea leaves, coffee grounds, shredded newspaper, spray bottle p. 839 large-mouthed jar, bran, dried bread, slice of apple, paper towel, cheesecloth, mealworms, rubber band	p. 818 grantia sponge, glass dish, hand lens, scissors, bleach, microscope slide, coverslip, microscope p. 837 heavy book, stopwatch

Need Materials? Contact Science Kit at 1-800-828-7777 or at www.sciencekit.com on the Internet.
For alternate materials, see the activity on the listed page.

Standards		Reproducible Resources	Technology
National	State/Local	Test Practice Workbooks are available for use with each chapter.	English and Spanish audiocassettes are available for use with each section.
National Content Standards: UCP1, UCP5, C1, C3, C4	California Science Content Standards: 6a, 6c	**Enrichment,** p. 67 **Reinforcement,** p. 67 **Study Guide,** p. 93	Section Focus Transparency 67 Teaching Transparency 47 Teaching Transparency 48
National Content Standards: UCP1, UCP5, A1, C1, C2, C3, C4, F1	California Science Content Standards: 5a, 6a	**Activity Worksheets,** p. 135 **Enrichment,** p. 68 **Multicultural Connections,** pp. 47–48 **Reinforcement,** p. 68 **Study Guide,** p. 94–95	Section Focus Transparency 68 Glencoe Science Voyages Interactive CD-ROM
National Content Standards: UCP1, UCP2, A1, C1, C3, C4, D1, E2, F1, G3	California Science Content Standards: 2e, 9a, 9b, 9c	**Activity Worksheets,** pp. 136–137 **Critical Thinking/Problem Solving** 24 **Enrichment,** p. 69 **Laboratory Manual,** pp. 145–148 **Reinforcement,** p. 39	Section Focus Transparency 69 Glencoe Science Voyages Interactive Videodisc—Life
National Content Standards: UCP1, UCP5, A1, C1, C2, C3, C4, C5, F1, G1	California Science Content Standards: 2b, 2c, 6b, 6c, 9f	**Activity Worksheets,** pp. 138–140 **Enrichment,** p. 70 **Home Involvement,** p. 37 **Laboratory Manual,** pp. 149–151 **Reinforcement,** p. 70 **Study Guide,** pp. 94–96	Section Focus Transparency 70 Science Integration Transparency 24 Internet Connection, p. 833 The Infinite Voyage Series

Key to Teaching Strategies

The following designations will help you decide which activities are appropriate for your students.

L1 Level 1 activities should be appropriate for students with learning difficulties.

L2 Level 2 activities should be within the ability range of all students.

L3 Level 3 activities are designed for above-average students.

ELL ELL activities should be within the ability range of English Language Learners.

COOP LEARN Cooperative Learning activities are designed for small group work.

P These strategies represent student products that can be placed into a best-work portfolio.

Multiple Learning Styles logos 55T are used throughout to indicate strategies that address different learning styles.

Assessment Resources

Chapter Review, pp. 47–48
Assessment, pp. 93–96
Performance Assessment in the Science Classroom (PASC)
MindJogger Videoquiz
Alternate Assessment in the Science Classroom
Performance Assessment, p. 24
Chapter Review Software
Computer Test Bank

Chapter 24 Invertebrate Animals

This is a representation of key blackline masters available in the Teacher Classroom Resources. See Resource Manager boxes within the chapter for additional information.

Section Focus Transparencies

Science Integration Transparencies

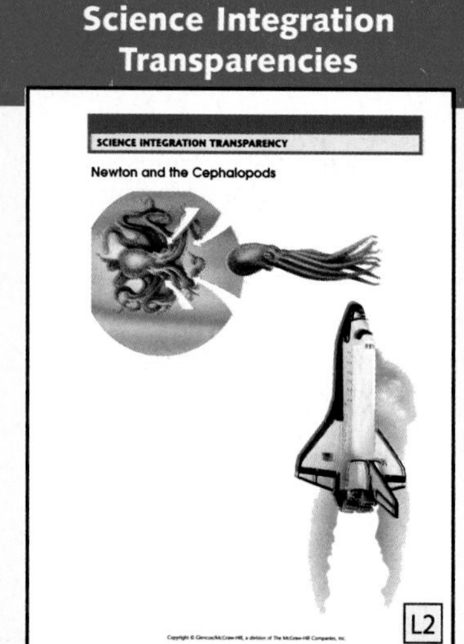

Teaching Transparencies

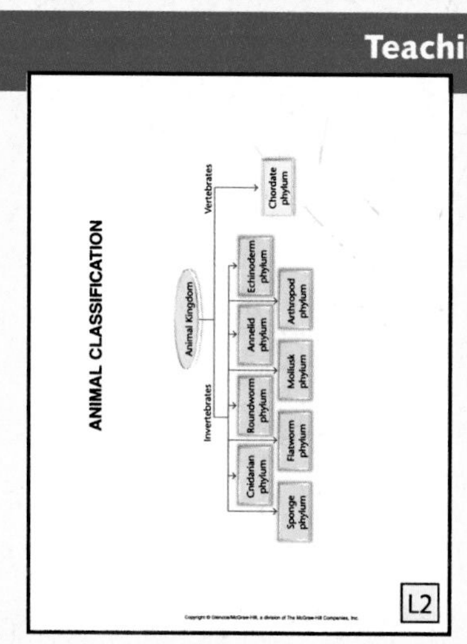

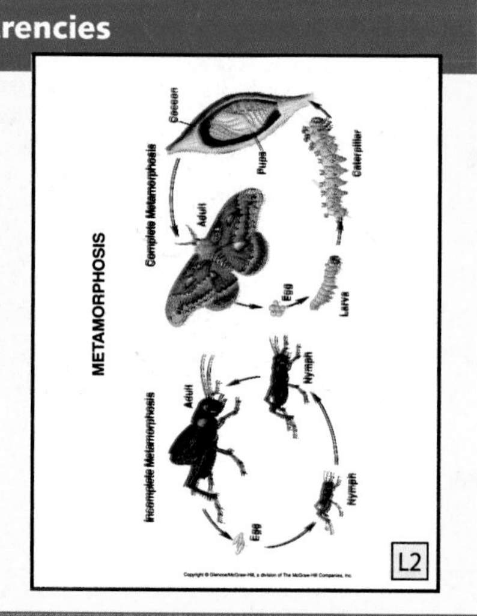

Meeting Different Ability Levels

Study Guide for Content Mastery

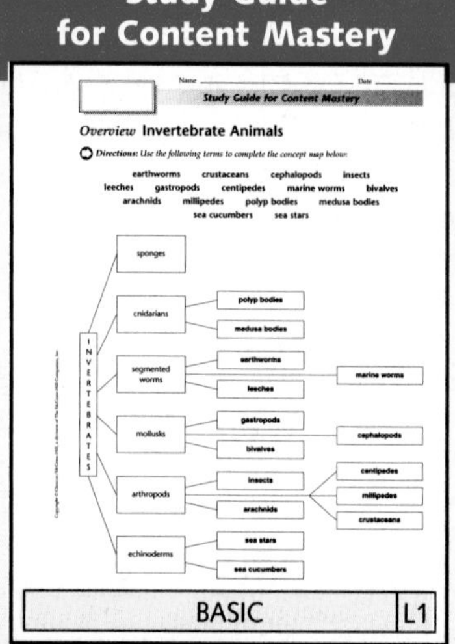

Reinforcement

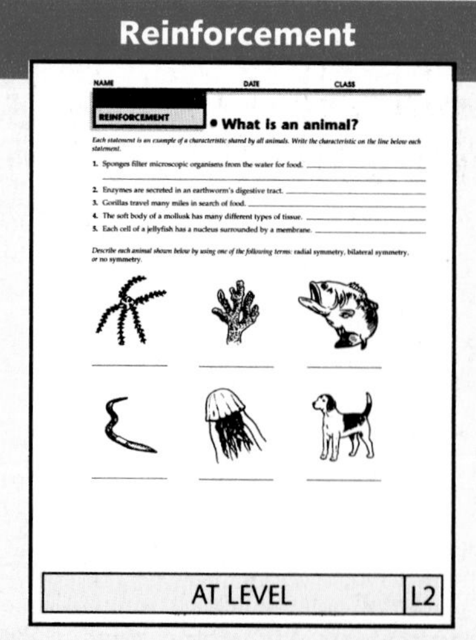

Enrichment Worksheets

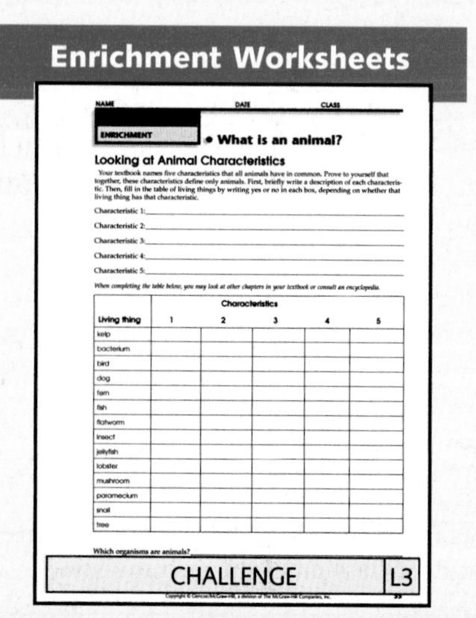

Resource Manager

Hands-on Activities

Activity Worksheets

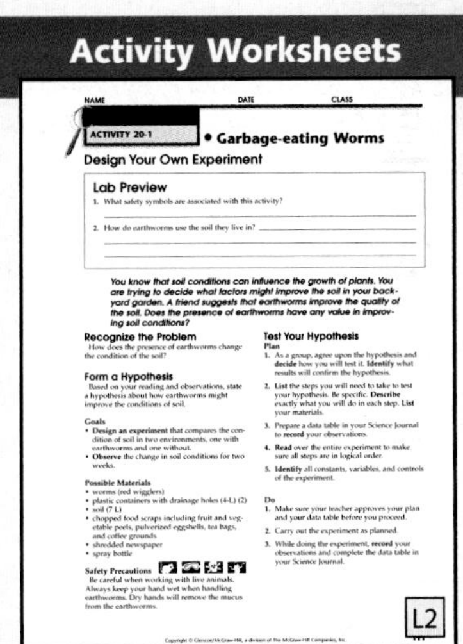

ACTIVITY 20-1 • Garbage-eating Worms

Design Your Own Experiment

Lab Preview

L2

Lab Manual

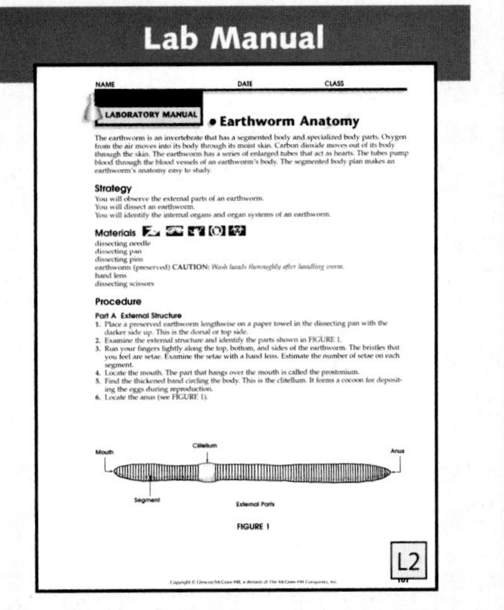

LABORATORY MANUAL • Earthworm Anatomy

Strategy

Materials

Procedure

FIGURE 1

L2

Accessibility

Spanish Resources

Assessment

Performance Assessment

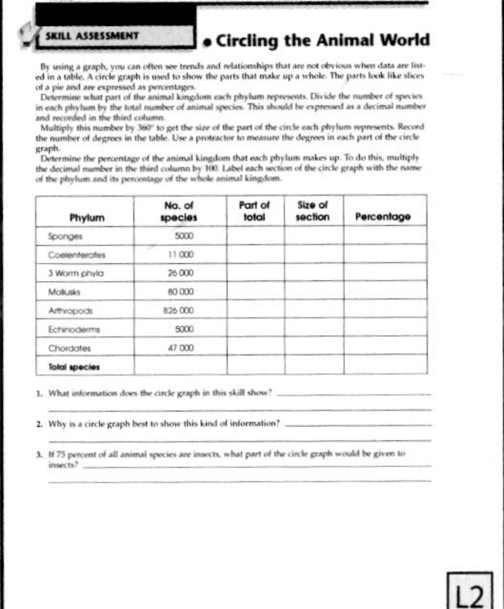

SKILL ASSESSMENT • Circling the Animal World

L2

Chapter Review

CHAPTER REVIEW • Invertebrate Animals

Part A. Vocabulary Review

Across

Down

L2

Assessment

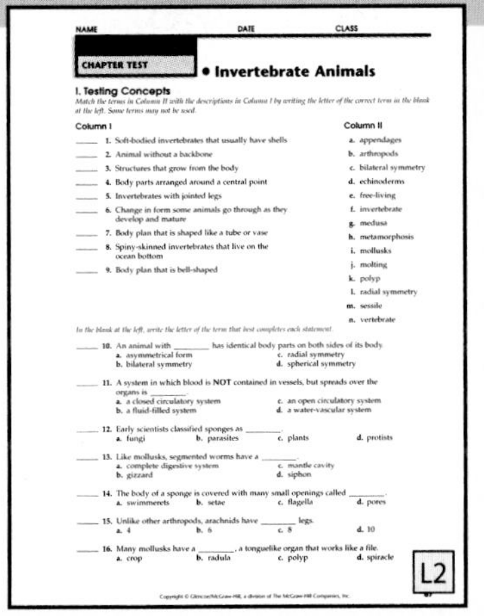

CHAPTER TEST • Invertebrate Animals

I. Testing Concepts

L2

Test Practice Workbook

Extending Content

Critical Thinking/ Problem Solving

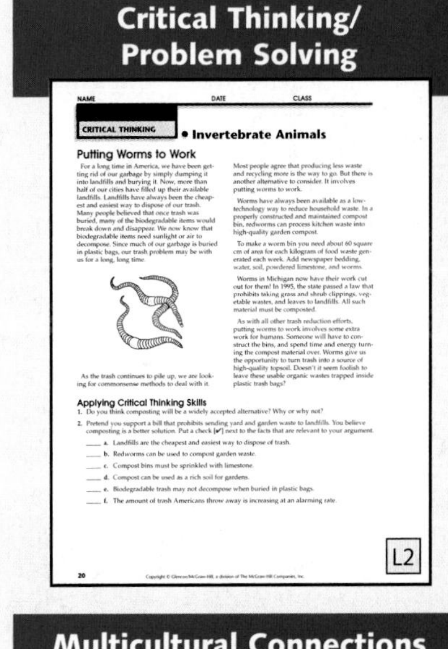

CRITICAL THINKING • Invertebrate Animals

Putting Worms to Work

Applying Critical Thinking Skills

L2

Multicultural Connections

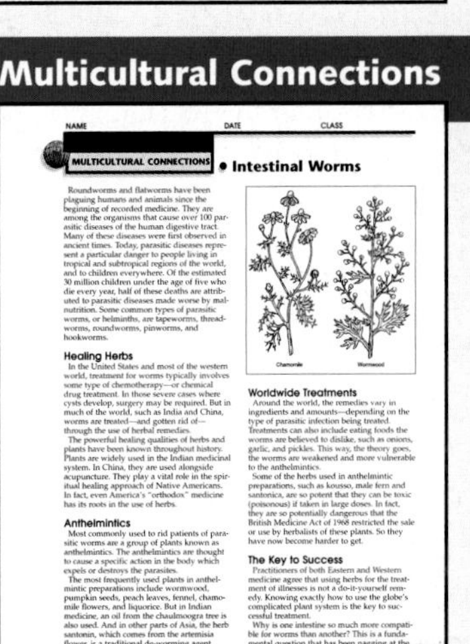

MULTICULTURAL CONNECTIONS • Intestinal Worms

Healing Herbs

Anthelmintics

Worldwide Treatments

The Key to Success

L2

Helping You Prepare

What is an animal? (Section 24-1)

Because they were protozoans, the first animals left no fossils, making it impossible to trace the origin of the animal kingdom. It is theorized that single-celled, protozoan ancestors gave rise to mulitcellular organisms. The transition from single-celled protozoan to multicellular animal most likely occurred more than once. Certain sponge cells are almost identical to a specific type of flagellated protozoa—choanoflagellate—leading some zoologists to reason that protists gave rise to modern sponges.

The three most important features that help to distinguish species from one another are symmetry, body cavities, and segmentation. An animal's symmetry often allows insight into how the organism survives in its environment. Animals with radial symmetry have body parts arranged around a central axis. Food and other sensory information usually come to these animals from all directions. These organisms often are either sessile or slow moving. An important aspect of organisms exhibiting bilateral symmetry is the concept of cephalization. Cephalization is the idea that sense organs are concentrated in the head region and focused toward the direction in which the organism is moving.

Sponges, Cnidarians, flatworms, and roundworms are for the most part masses of cells and do not have any internal cavities. Other organisms depicted in this chapter—mollusks, segmented worms, arthropods, and echinoderms—have at least one internal chamber that collects food. The digestive tract may be a one-way sac as in the sea anemone, or it may be a tube with two openings as in segmented worms.

Segmentation—the repeating of parts that contain similar organs—is a characteristic of three of the largest animal phyla: annelids (segmented worms), arthropods, and chordates (vertebrates).

GLENCOE TECHNOLOGY

Glencoe Science Voyages Interactive CD-ROM

Chapter Summaries

Use the Chapter Summary to introduce, teach, or review chapter material.

Sponges, Cnidarians, Flatworms, and Roundworms (Section 24-2)

Sponges are the least complex of all the major animal phyla. Their bodies often lack symmetry and they do not have nerve cells or sense or-

NATIONAL GEOGRAPHIC — **Teacher's Corner**

Products Available from Glencoe

To order the following products for use with this chapter, call Glencoe at 1-800-334-7344:

CD-ROMs

NGS PictureShow: Classifying Plants and Animals

NGS PictureShow: Structure of Invertebrates

Transparency Sets

NGS PicturePack: Classifying Plants and Animals

NGS PicturePack: Structure of Invertebrates

Index to National Geographic Magazine

The following articles may be used for research relating to this chapter:

"The Gift of Gardening," by William S. Ellis, May 1992.

"Deception: Formula for Survival," by Robert F. Sisson, March 1980.

"Consider the Sponge," by Michael E. Long, March 1977.

gans. Their body cells cannot even be considered to be organized into tissues.

All cnidarians are carnivorous. They capture prey using tentacles that contain stinging cells. Their bodies consist of three layers. The cells of these layers form tissues. The outer layer is the epidermis, and the inner layer is the gastrodermis. Cnidarians lack true organs. The individual cells are close enough to the surrounding liquid medium to receive oxygen and remove wastes by diffusion.

Flatworms are the simplest organisms with bilateral symmetry. The brain and nerve chords that run the length of the body are considered to be the evolutionary forerunners of a central nervous system. The middle layer of the flatworm contains muscle tissue used for locomotion. The flatworms also have complex reproductive and digestive systems. Roundworms—the phylum Nematoda—are the most widespread and abundant animals on the planet. Ninety thousand roundworms of different species can be found in a single rotting apple.

Mollusks and Segmented Worms

(Section 24-3)

Mollusks are the second largest animal phyla, with more than 100 000 identified species. Segmented worms of the phylum Annelida comprise about 9000 species and are divided into three major classes, oligochaetes (earthworms), polychaetes (marine bristleworms and tubeworms), and hirudineans (leeches).

Earthworm aeration of the soil is so beneficial that their presence in hundreds or thousands per hectare is a characteristic of a productive farm. The earthworm *Lumbricus terrestris* ingests its own weight in soil and decaying matter every 24 hours.

The skin of an earthworm is coated with mucus that keeps the skin moist so oxygen from the air can diffuse into the blood. Earthworms survive in thin films of water in slightly moist soil, but if the soil becomes flooded, they can drown.

Arthropods and Echinoderms

(Section 24-4)

Arthropods are the most diverse group of animals on Earth. More than 900 000 species have been identified. One of the fascinating aspects of many insects is the metamorphosis from egg to larva to adult.

Echinoderms, such as sea stars and sea urchins, have a number of traits that set them apart from other invertebrates. The radial symmetry of these organisms is fivefold, or pentamerous. Fossil evidence indicates that early echinoderms were bilaterally symmetrical and only later developed radial symmetry suited for a sessile, or slow moving, organism. The larvae of echinoderms are bilaterally symmetrical.

SCIENCE UPDATE

For current events or science in the news, access the Glencoe Science Web Site at **www.glencoe.com/sec/science/ca**

Teacher to Teacher

"I show students how to handle animals humanely and safely when studying the pulse of earthworms in icy, warm, and room temperature water. Place the specimen in the larger petri dish (lid) and invert the smaller dish on top. Earthworms should be kept moist and flattened slightly by the dish."

Janet Doughty

Janet Doughty, Teacher
H. J. MacDonald Middle School
New Bern, NC

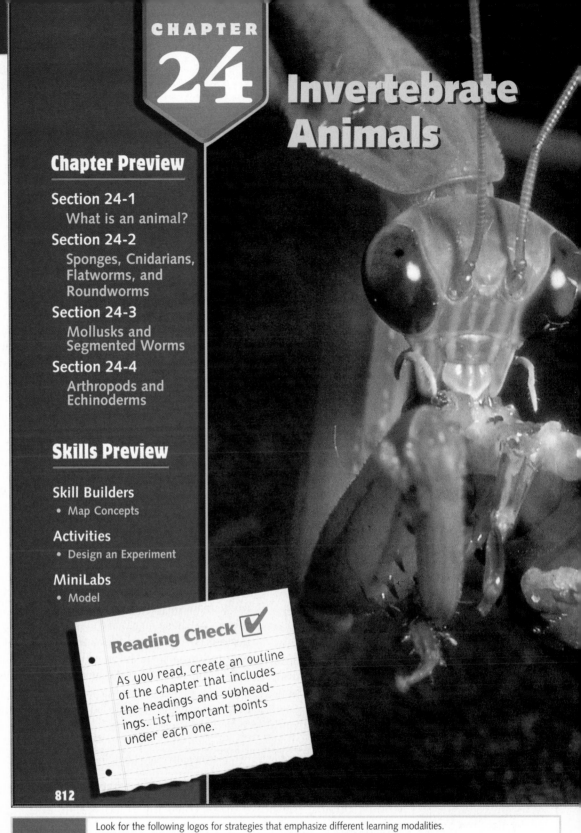

CHAPTER 24
Invertebrate Animals

CHAPTER OVERVIEW

Section 24-1 This section describes the characteristics of animals. Classification of animals and symmetry are discussed.

Section 24-2 This section describes the structure, methods of feeding, and reproduction of sponges, Cnidaria, flatworms, and roundworms.

Section 24-3 The basic body plans for mollusks and segmented worms are discussed.

Section 24-4 The features used to classify arthropods and the water vascular system of echinoderms are described.

Chapter Vocabulary

vertebrate	gills
invertebrate	radula
symmetry	open circulatory system
cnidarian	closed circulatory system
polyp	arthropod
medusa	appendage
free-living	exoskeleton
parasite	metamorphosis
mollusk	
mantle	

Theme Connection

Stability and Change The groups of animals from invertebrates show a trend toward increasing complexity.

If time does not permit teaching the entire chapter, use Reviewing Main Ideas on pp. 840–841.

CHAPTER 24

Invertebrate Animals

Chapter Preview

Skills Preview

Skill Builders
- Map Concepts

Activities
- Design an Experiment

MiniLabs
- Model

Reading Check

As you read, create an outline of the chapter that includes the headings and subheadings. List important points under each one.

812

Multiple Learning Styles

Look for the following logos for strategies that emphasize different learning modalities.

Linguistic Using Science Words, p. 821; Assessment, p. 822; Across the Curriculum, p. 825, 826; Multiple Learning Styles, p. 827; Preview, p. 840

Logical-Mathematical Across the Curriculum, p. 821

Visual-Spatial Explore Activity, p. 813; Across the Curriculum, pp. 815, 835; MiniLab, p. 818; Reteach, pp. 821, 827, 840; Activity, pp. 825, 835, 839; Quick Demo, p. 826

Auditory-Musical Out of Time, p. 840

Kinesthetic Activity, p. 819; Inclusion Strategies, pp. 819, 824; Across the Curriculum, p. 833; MiniLab, p. 836

Interpersonal Activity, pp. 815, 834; Discussion, pp. 827, 837; Review, p. 840

Naturalist Activity, pp. 830–831

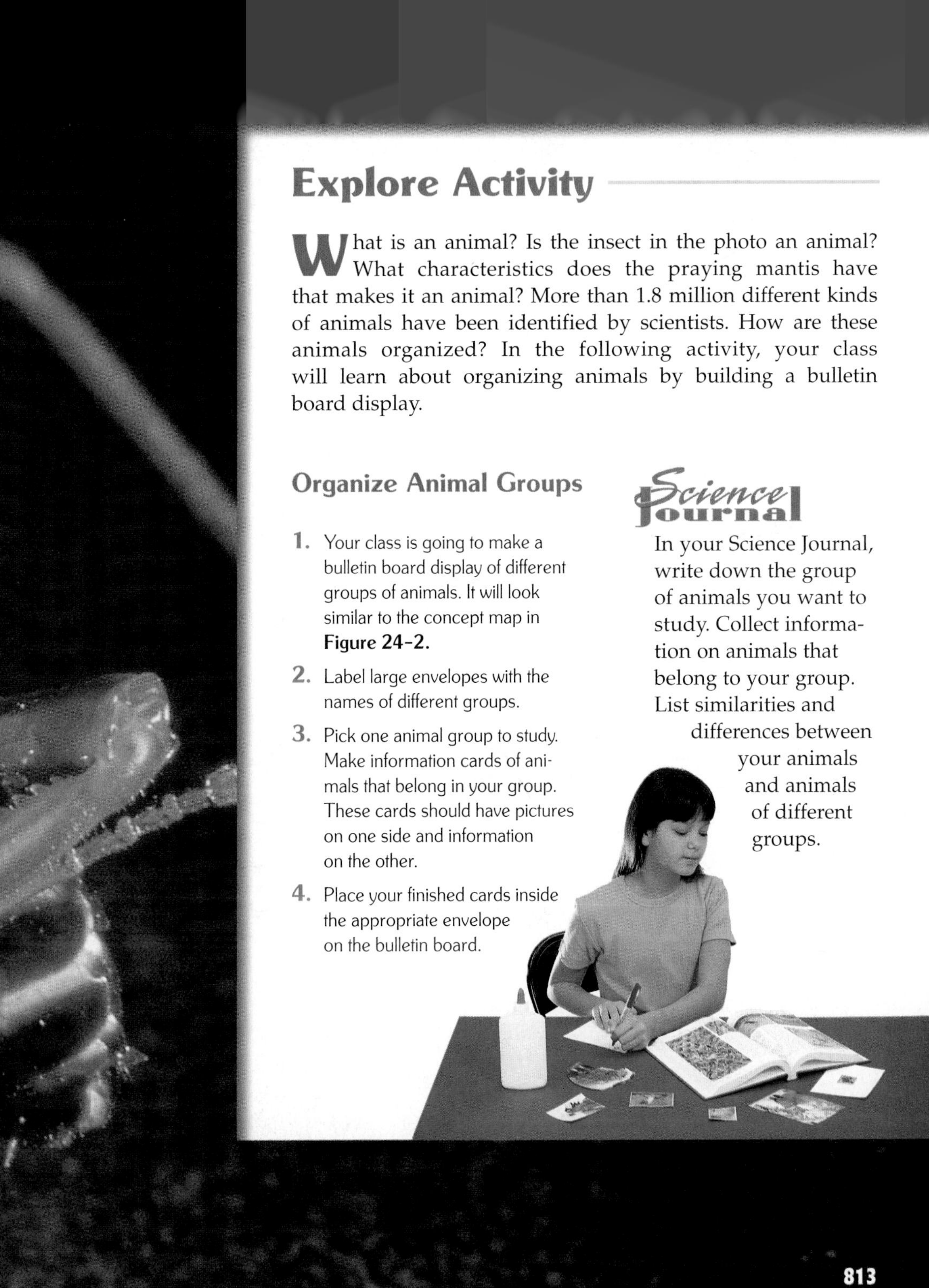

Explore Activity

What is an animal? Is the insect in the photo an animal? What characteristics does the praying mantis have that makes it an animal? More than 1.8 million different kinds of animals have been identified by scientists. How are these animals organized? In the following activity, your class will learn about organizing animals by building a bulletin board display.

Organize Animal Groups

1. Your class is going to make a bulletin board display of different groups of animals. It will look similar to the concept map in **Figure 24-2.**
2. Label large envelopes with the names of different groups.
3. Pick one animal group to study. Make information cards of animals that belong in your group. These cards should have pictures on one side and information on the other.
4. Place your finished cards inside the appropriate envelope on the bulletin board.

Science Journal

In your Science Journal, write down the group of animals you want to study. Collect information on animals that belong to your group. List similarities and differences between your animals and animals of different groups.

Assessment Planner

Portfolio
Refer to p. 841 for suggested items that students might select for their portfolios.

Performance Assessment
See p. 841 for additional Performance Assessment options.
Skill Builder, pp. 816, 828, 838
MiniLab, pp. 818, 836
Activity 24-1, pp. 830–831; 24-2, p. 839

Content Assessment
Section Assessment, pp. 816, 822, 828, 838
Content Assessment, pp. 842–843
Proficiency Prep, pp. 816, 822, 828, 838

Explore Activity

Purpose

Visual-Spatial Use the Explore Activity to introduce the characteristics that all animals share. Explain to students that they will be learning more about the characteristics of animals and how scientists classify animals into groups with similar characteristics. L2 COOP LEARN

Preparation

Clear bulletin board space for placing animal group envelopes.

Materials

20 large envelopes, 4 × 6 index cards, colored pencils, magazines with animal pictures

Teaching Strategies

Ask students what animals are the most familiar to them. They will probably suggest dogs, cats, hamsters, fish, and other pets.

Science Journal Students probably will choose, mammals, birds, and fish. Have them include the animal's means of movement and food gathering strategies so that the information can be added to their flash cards.

Assessment

Portfolio Have students make an extra flash card of their favorite animal from the groups of animals that they worked with to place in their portfolio. Use **Performance Assessment in the Science Classroom,** p. 105. P

SECTION 24•1

Prepare

Refer to **What is an animal?** on p. 812E.

Preplanning

Refer to the **Chapter Organizer** on pp. 812A–B.

1 Motivate

Bellringer

Before presenting the lesson, display **Section Focus Transparency 67** on the overhead projector. Use the accompanying **Focus Activity** worksheet. L2 ELL

SECTION FOCUS TRANSPARENCY

SHAPES IN THE SAND

Suppose you took a walk on a sandy beach. You might see some of these interesting animals in the shallow water. Starfish, brittle stars, and sea urchins all share a similar kind of body design.

1. In what large group of living things do the organisms shown belong?
2. How are the organisms shown different from you? Similar to you?

24•1 What is an animal?

What You'll Learn

- The characteristics of animals
- The difference between vertebrates and invertebrates
- How the symmetry of animals differs

Vocabulary
vertebrate
invertebrate
symmetry

Why It's Important

- All animals share common characteristics.

Animal Characteristics

Think about the animals shown in **Figure 24-1.** These animals would be described differently. They have a wide variety of body parts, as well as ways to move, get food, and protect themselves. So, what do all animals have in common? What makes an animal an animal?

1. Animals cannot make their own food. Some animals eat plants to supply their energy needs. Some animals eat other animals, and some eat both plants and animals.
2. Animals digest their food. Large food substances are broken down into smaller substances that their cells can use.
3. Most animals can move from place to place. They move to find food, shelter, and mates and to escape from predators.
4. Animals are many-celled organisms that are made of many different kinds of cells. These cells digest food, get rid of wastes, and reproduce.
5. Most animal cells have a nucleus and organelles surrounded by a membrane. This type of cell is called a eukaryotic cell.

Figure 24-1 Animals come in a variety of shapes and sizes.

A The thorny devil lizard lives in the Australian desert. It feeds on ants and survives with little water to drink.

B The largest lion's mane jellyfish was found dead on shore. It had a bell over 2 m across with tentacles that dangled over 36 m long.

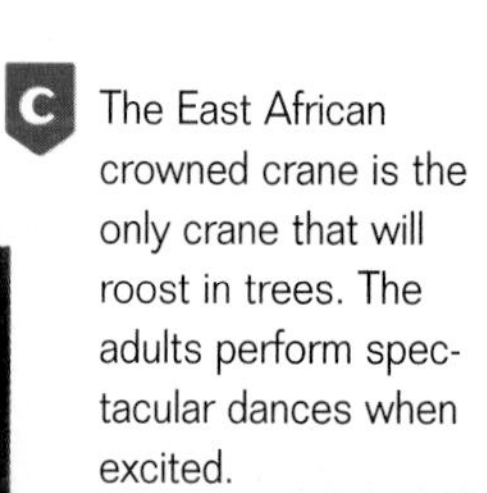

C The East African crowned crane is the only crane that will roost in trees. The adults perform spectacular dances when excited.

Tying to Previous Knowledge

Review the characteristics of animals. Make certain that students understand that animals cannot make their own food, have eukaryotic cells, and are made of many cells.

Resource Manager

The following **Teacher Classroom Resources** can be used with Section 24-1:

Reproducible Masters

Enrichment, p. 67 L3

Reinforcement, p. 67 L2

Study Guide, p. 93 L1 ELL

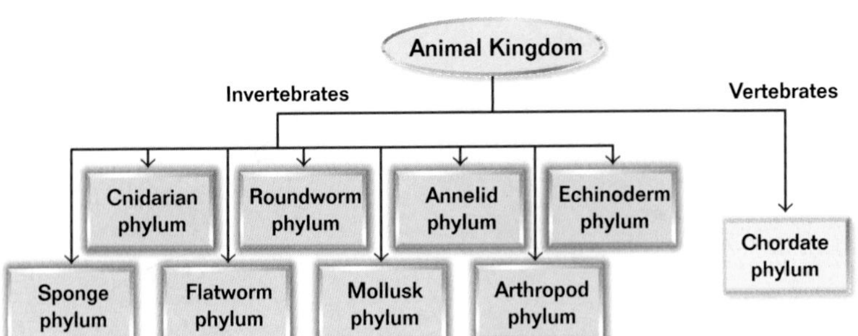

Figure 24-2 This diagram shows the relationships among different groups in the animal kingdom. Different forms of this diagram will appear at the beginning of each section in this and the following chapter. The groups that are highlighted with an orange outline are the groups that will be discussed in that particular section. For example, this section will deal with the invertebrates, which includes the sponge, cnidarian, flatworm, roundworm, mollusk, annelid, arthropod, and echinoderm phylums.

Animal Classification

Deciding whether an organism is an animal is only the first step in classifying it. Scientists place all animals into smaller, related groups. They begin by separating animals into two distinct groups—vertebrates and invertebrates. **Vertebrates** (VURT uh brayts) are animals that have a backbone. **Invertebrates** (ihn VURT uh brayts) are animals that do not have a backbone. There are far more invertebrates than vertebrates. About 97 percent of all animals are invertebrates.

Scientists classify or group the invertebrates into several different phyla (FI lah), as shown in **Figure 24-2.** The animals within each phylum share similar characteristics. These characteristics indicate that the animals within the group descended from a common ancestor. The characteristics also show a change from less complex to more complex animals as you move from phylum to phylum.

Symmetry

As you study the different groups of invertebrates, one feature becomes apparent—symmetry. **Symmetry** (SIH muh tree) refers to the arrangement of the individual parts of an object. Scientists also use body symmetry to classify animals.

Most animals have either radial or bilateral symmetry. Animals with body parts arranged in a circle around a central point have radial symmetry. These animals can locate food and gather other information from all directions. Animals with radial symmetry, such as jellyfish and sea urchins, live in water.

2 Teach

Quick Demo

Compare symmetrical and asymmetrical objects. Use rocks, chalk, and other classroom objects.

Correcting Misconceptions

Many students do not think of invertebrates as animals. Elicit student help in writing a list of familiar invertebrates on the chalkboard. This will allow you to correct misconceptions. Emphasize that the animals on the list are related by the absence of a structural characteristic—a backbone—rather than the presence of a characteristic.

Answer to Reading Check

Symmetry refers to the arrangement of the individual parts of an object.

3 Assess

Check for Understanding

Activity

Interpersonal Have students look through magazines to find pictures of animals. Then have students work in groups to identify each animal's type of body symmetry. L2 COOP LEARN

Reteach

Students can obtain instructions for folding an origami animal to reinforce the concept of symmetry. L2

Across the Curriculum

Math In mathematics, a figure has line symmetry if it can be folded with both halves aligning exactly. Have students draw figures that have line symmetry and those that do not. L2 ELL

Extension

For students who have mastered this section, use the **Reinforcement** and **Enrichment** masters.

CA Science Content Standards

Page 814: 6a, 6c

Caption Answer

Figure 24-3 *bilateral symmetry*

4 Close

Proficiency Prep

Use this quiz to check students' recall of section content.

1. **Scientists divide all animals into what two groups?** *vertebrates and invertebrates*
2. **What are two types of symmetry common to most animals?** *radial and bilateral*

Section Assessment

1. They cannot make their own food and they digest their food. Most move, are many-celled organisms made up of many different cells, and have eukaryotic cells.
2. Invertebrates lack a backbone. Vertebrates have a backbone.
3. radial, bilateral, and asymmetry; a dog is one example
4. Think Critically An animal that lives in water may be sessile, move with the water, or just move up and down in the water column. Radial symmetry allows all of these movements in water, but such an adaptation would be less useful on land.

Using Computers

Students can use examples from pictures of animals found in magazines. They should be able to identify the animal's symmetry.

A

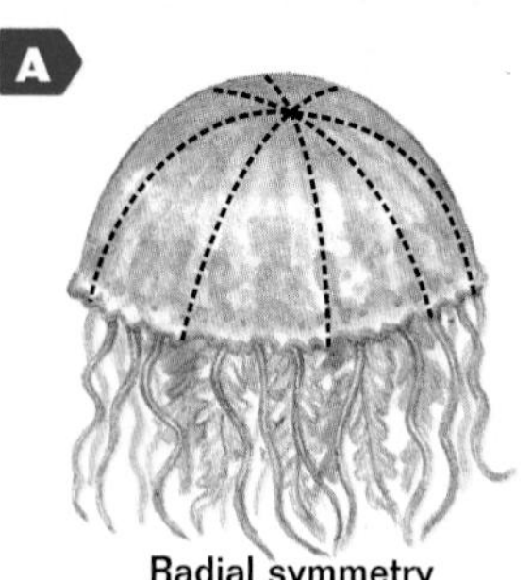

B

C

Asymmetry

Figure 24-3 Jellyfish (A) have radial symmetry, butterflies (B) have bilateral symmetry, and sponges (C) are asymmetrical. **What type of symmetry do humans exhibit?**

On the other hand, animals with bilateral symmetry have parts that are mirror images of each other. A line can be drawn down the center of their bodies to divide them into two matching parts. Grasshoppers and lobsters are bilaterally symmetrical.

Some animals have no definite shape. They are called asymmetrical. Their bodies cannot be divided into matching halves. Many sponges are asymmetrical (AY suh meh trih kul). As you learn more about invertebrates, see how their body symmetry is related to how they gather food. **Figure 24-3** shows the three ways an animal's body parts can be arranged.

Section Assessment

1. What are the characteristics of animals?
2. How are invertebrates different from vertebrates?
3. What are the types of symmetry? Name an animal that has bilateral symmetry.
4. **Think Critically** Radial symmetry is found among species that live in water. Why might radial symmetry be an adaptation uncommon among animals that live on land?
5. **Skill Builder** **Concept Mapping** Using the information in this section, make a concept map showing the steps a scientist might use to classify a new animal. If you need help, refer to Concept Mapping in the **Skill Handbook** on page 950.

Using Computers

Word Processing Create a table that you will use as you complete this chapter. Label the following columns: *animal, group,* and *body symmetry.* Create ten rows to enter animal names. If you need help, refer to page 968.

5. **Skill Builder** Students' concept maps would show first the identification of whether the animal is a vertebrate or invertebrate, then determine its symmetry, and finally compare it to other organisms.

Assessment

Performance Have students formulate additional categories for classifying animals after identifying an animal's symmetry and whether or not it has a backbone. Use **Performance Assessment in the Science Classroom,** p. 49.

Sponges, Cnidarians, Flatworms, and Roundworms

Sponges

Sponges are the simplest of animals. They bridge the gap between single-celled organisms and more complex animals. Their body structure is made of two layers of cells. Adult sponges live attached to one place. Organisms that remain attached to one place during their lifetimes are called sessile (SES ul). Because they do not move about in search of food, scientists used to classify sponges, shown in **Figure 24-4,** as plants. Once scientists found out that sponges can't make their own food, they reclassified them as animals.

Animal Kingdom
Invertebrates
Vertebrates
Cnidarian phylum
Roundworm phylum
Annelid phylum
Sponge phylum
Flatworm phylum
Mollusk phylum
Arthropod phylum

Figure 24-4 Orange finger sponges form long "fingers" from 2 cm to 20 cm in length. They are also called dead man's finger sponges.

What You'll Learn

- The structures that make up sponges and cnidarians
- How sponges and cnidarians get food and reproduce
- The body plans of flatworms and roundworms

Vocabulary

cnidarian	free-living
polyp	parasite
medusa	

Why It's Important

- Sponges, cnidarians, flatworms, and roundworms exhibit simple cell and tissue organization.

SECTION 24•2

Prepare

Refer to **Sponges, Cnidarians, Flatworms, and Roundworms** on pp. 812E–F.

Preplanning

Refer to the **Chapter Organizer** on pp. 812A–B.

1 Motivate

Bellringer

Before presenting the lesson, display **Section Focus Transparency 68** on the overhead projector. Use the accompanying **Focus Activity** worksheet. L2 ELL

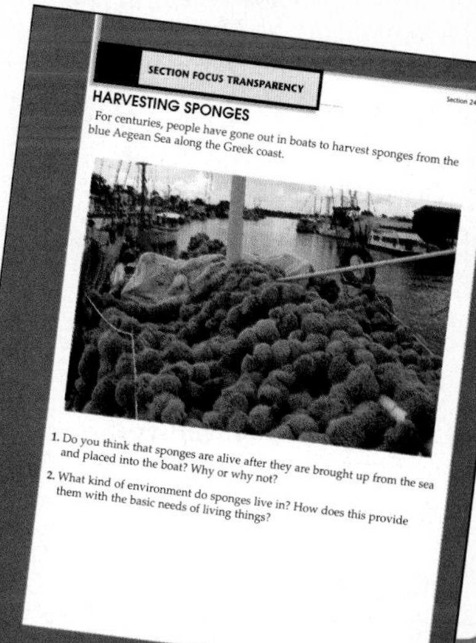
SECTION FOCUS TRANSPARENCY

Section 24-2

HARVESTING SPONGES

For centuries, people have gone out in boats to harvest sponges from the blue Aegean Sea along the Greek coast.

1. Do you think that sponges are alive after they are brought up from the sea and placed into the boat? Why or why not?
2. What kind of environment do sponges live in? How does this provide them with the basic needs of living things?

Resource Manager

The following **Teacher Classroom Resources** can be used with Section 24-2:

 **Reproducible Masters**

Activity Worksheets, p. 135 L2
Enrichment, p. 68 L3
Multicultural Connections, pp. 47–48 L2
Reinforcement, p. 68 L2

Tying to Previous Knowledge

Review cell structure, cell function, and tissue organization to help students understand differences in body structures of sponges, cnidarians, flatworms, and roundworms.

Sponges get their supply of these elements from ocean water, which contains calcium and silica.

MiniLab

Purpose

Visual-Spatial Students will observe *Grantia* sponge and determine how it is adapted to living in the water.

Materials

Grantia sponge, bleach solution, microscope slide, coverslip, microscope

Teaching Strategies

When a sponge is placed in bleach, its cells begin to break apart. The spicules do not break apart and can easily be seen under the microscope.

Safety Precautions

CAUTION: *Students should use extreme care when working with bleach and scissors.*

Analysis

1. Spicules are made of a hard substance.
2. support

Filter Feeders

Sponges live in water. They are called filter feeders because they filter food out of the water that flows through their bodies. Microscopic organisms and oxygen are carried with the water through pores into the central cavity of the sponge. The phylum that sponges belong to, Porifera, gets its name from these pores. The inner surface of the central cavity is lined with specialized cells called collar cells. Thin, whiplike structures, called flagella, extend from the collar cells and keep the water moving through the sponge. Other specialized cells digest the food, carry nutrients to all parts of the sponge, and remove wastes.

CHEMISTRY INTEGRATION

Sponge Spicules
Spicules of "glass" sponges are composed of silica. Other sponges have spicules of calcium carbonate. Where do these organisms get the silica and calcium carbonate that these spicules are made of?

Body Support and Defense

At first glance, you might think that sponges have few defenses against predators. Actually, not many animals eat sponges. The soft bodies of many sponges are supported by sharp, glasslike structures called spicules. Many other sponges have a material called spongin. Spongin can be compared to foam rubber because it makes sponges both soft and elastic. Some sponges have both spicules and spongin, which protects their soft bodies.

MiniLab

Observing Sponge Spicules

Procedure

1. Add a few drops of bleach to a microscope slide. **CAUTION:** *Do not inhale the bleach. Do not spill it on your hands, clothing, or the microscope.*
2. Put a small piece of the sponge into the bleach on the slide. Add a coverslip. Observe the cells of the sponge.

Analysis

1. Are spicules made of the same materials as the rest of the sponge? Explain.
2. What is the function of spicules?

Sponge Reproduction

Sponges are able to reproduce both sexually and asexually. Asexual reproduction occurs when a bud located on the side of the parent sponge develops into a small sponge. The small sponge breaks off, floats away, and attaches itself to a new surface. New sponges also grow when a sponge is cut or broken into pieces. The broken pieces regenerate or grow into a complete new sponge.

Most sponges that reproduce sexually produce both eggs and sperm. The sponge releases sperm into the water. Currents carry the sperm to eggs of another sponge, where fertilization occurs. The fertilized eggs grow into larvae that look different from the adult sponge. The larvae are able to swim to a different area before attaching themselves to a rock or other surface.

Assessment

Oral Tell students that the presence of freshwater sponges indicates a clean environment free of pollution. Have them suggest a reason for this. *Sponges are filter feeders and take in food from the water around them. In polluted waters, they would take in food that was polluted.* Use **Performance Assessment in the Science Classroom,** p. 17.

Content Background

Budding, regeneration, and sexual reproduction may occur simultaneously in sponges. Even though cnidarians have different body forms, they all have tentacles, two cell layers arranged into tissues, a digestive cavity, and radial symmetry.

818 Chapter 24 Invertebrate Animals

Cnidarians

Have you ever cast a fishing line into the water to catch your dinner? In a somewhat similar way, animals in the phylum Cnidaria have tentacles that are used to capture prey. Jellyfish, sea anemones, hydra, and corals belong to this phylum.

Cnidarians (NIH dar ee uns) are a phylum of hollow-bodied animals that have stinging cells. They have radial symmetry that allows them to locate food that floats by from any direction. Their bodies have two cell layers that are organized into tissues. The inner layer forms a digestive cavity where food is broken down. Their tentacles surround the mouth. Stinging cells shoot out to stun or grasp prey. The word *cnidaria* is Latin for "stinging cells." Oxygen moves into the cells from the surrounding water, and carbon dioxide waste moves out of the cells. Nerve cells work together as a nerve net throughout the whole body.

EXAMPLES OF Cnidarians

- Jellyfish
- Sea anemones
- Hydra
- Corals
- Portuguese man-of-war

Two Body Plans

Study the two cnidarians in **Figure 24-5.** They represent the two different body plans found in this animal's phylum. The vase-shaped body of the hydra is called a **polyp** (PAHL up). Although hydras are usually sessile, they can twist to capture prey. They also can somersault to a new location. Jellyfish have a free-swimming, bell-shaped body that is called a **medusa.** Jellyfish are not strong swimmers. Instead, they drift along with the ocean currents. Some cnidarians go through both the polyp and medusa stages during their life cycles. ☑

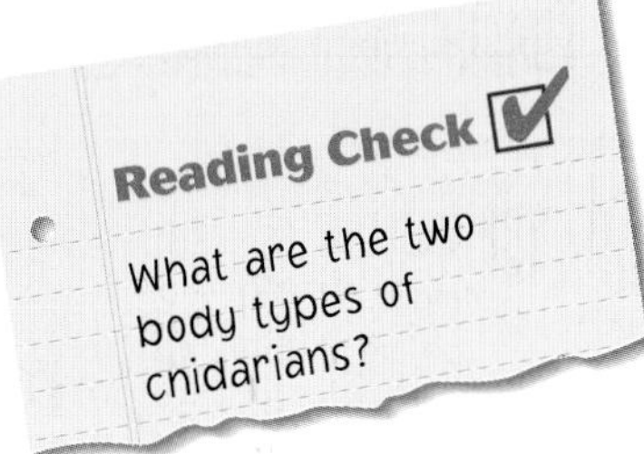

Reading Check
What are the two body types of cnidarians?

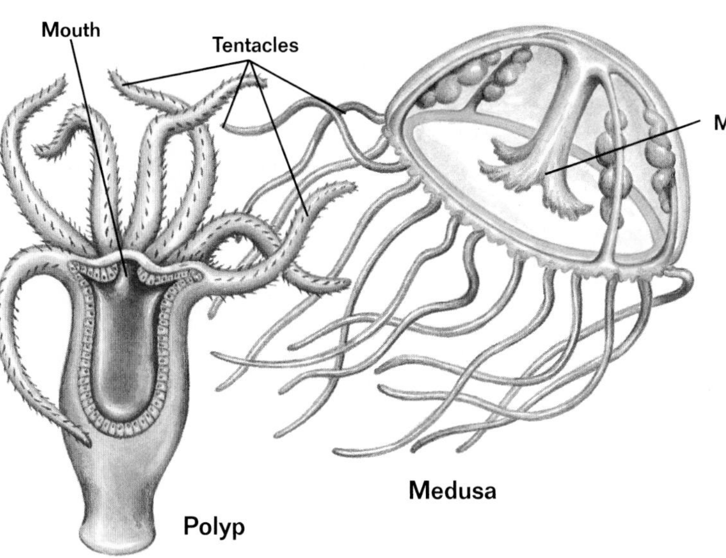

Figure 24-5 The polyp and medusa forms are the two body plans of cnidarians.

2 Teach

Flex Your Brain

Use the Flex Your Brain activity to have students explore CNIDARIANS. P

Using Science Words

Polyp is derived from the Greek word meaning "many feet." Medusa was the mythological Greek figure with writhing snakes instead of hair.

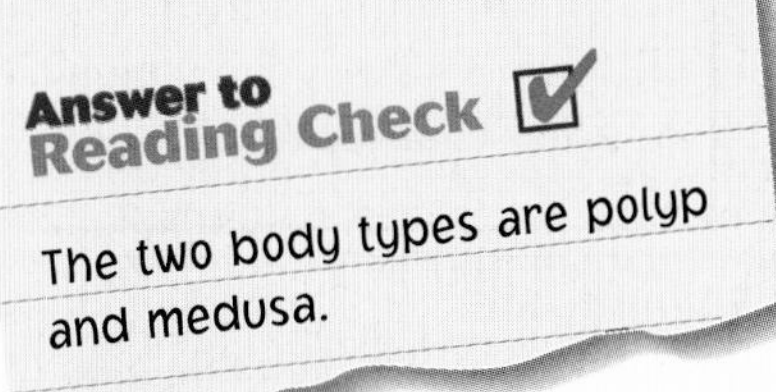

Answer to Reading Check
The two body types are polyp and medusa.

Activity

Kinesthetic Provide students with modeling clay. Have students make models of polyps and medusas. Ask them to demonstrate how these two body forms are similar. L2 ELL

Teacher FYI

The jellyfish *Chironex fleckeri,* found along sandy bottoms off the coast of Australia; may be the most venomous animal in the sea. The poison found in its stinging cells can kill a human being in three minutes.

Across the Curriculum

Language arts The hydra was named for a giant mythical water monster with nine heads. Hercules, a Greek hero, was supposed to slay the monster. But each time he cut off one head, Hydra grew two more to take its place. **How is the real hydra like the mythical one?** *A real hydra can be cut into pieces, and each piece will regenerate a new hydra.*

Inclusion Strategies

Learning Disabled Have students select one type of animal described in this chapter. Have them design and construct a detailed, three-dimensional model of the animal and use the model to demonstrate the characteristics of animals

CA Science Content Standards

Page 818: 5a, 6a

Discussion

Why would it be a reproductive advantage for a cnidarian to be able to produce both polyp and medusa forms? *The polyp form allows the organism to grow in size by budding. If conditions change and the area is no longer suitable for the organism's survival the medusa form allows the organism to move to a more suitable habitat.*

VISUAL Learning

Figure 24-7 Use this figure to initiate a discussion with students about the differences between sexual and asexual reproduction.

Enrichment

Have students research the Great Barrier Reef off the coast of Australia. L2

GLENCOE TECHNOLOGY

CD-ROM

Glencoe Science Voyages Interactive CD-ROM

Explorations

Have students do the interactive exploration *How do sponges, cnidarians, flatworms and roundworms obtain food?*

Figure 24-6 Polyps, like these hydra, reproduce by budding.

Cnidarian Reproduction

Cnidarians produce both asexually and sexually. Polyp forms of cnidarians, such as hydras, reproduce asexually by budding, as illustrated in **Figure 24-6.** The bud eventually falls off of the parent organism and develops into a new polyp. Some polyps also can reproduce sexually by releasing eggs or sperm into the water. The eggs are fertilized by sperm and develop into a new polyp. Medusa forms of cnidarians, such as jellyfish, have both an asexual and a sexual stage, which are illustrated in **Figure 24-7.** These stages alternate between generations. Medusa reproduce sexually to produce polyps, which in turn, reproduce asexually to form new medusa.

VISUALIZING Cnidarian Reproduction

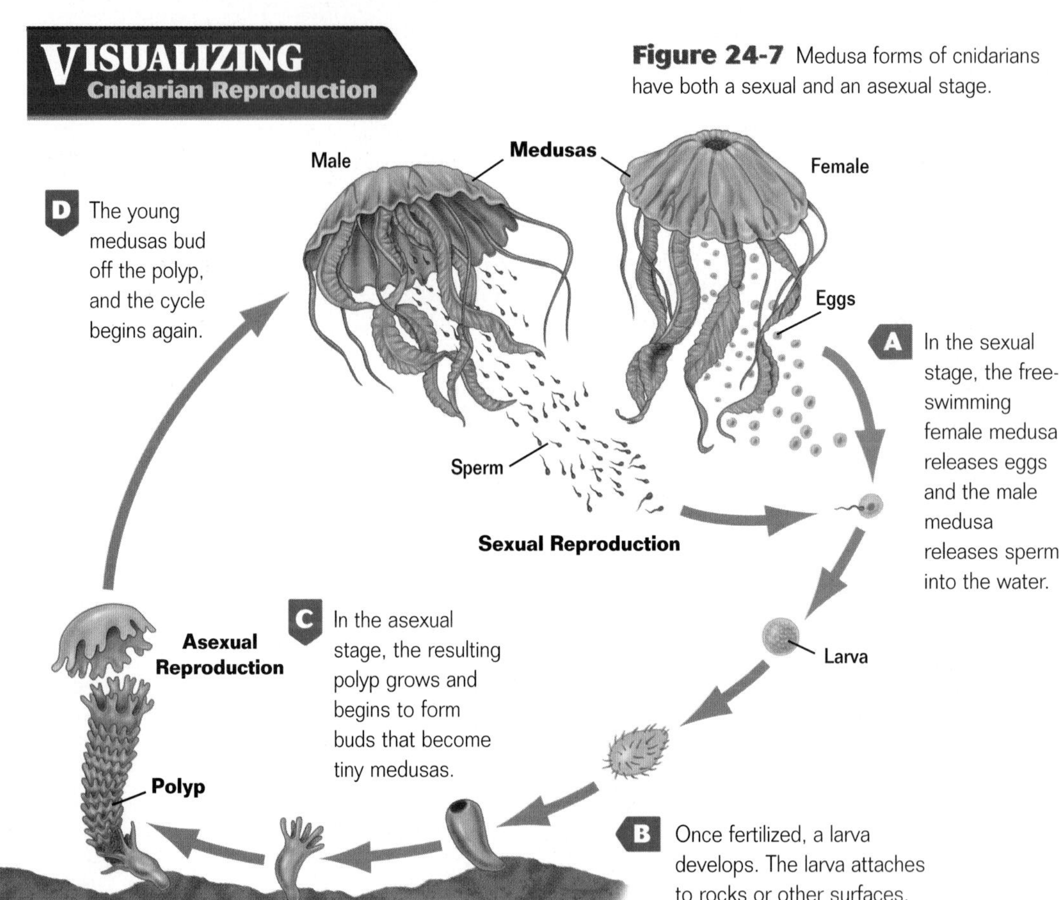
Male
Medusas
Female
Eggs
Sperm
Sexual Reproduction
Larva
Asexual Reproduction
Polyp
D The young medusas bud off the polyp, and the cycle begins again.
A In the sexual stage, the free-swimming female medusa releases eggs and the male medusa releases sperm into the water.
C In the asexual stage, the resulting polyp grows and begins to form buds that become tiny medusas.
B Once fertilized, a larva develops. The larva attaches to rocks or other surfaces.

Figure 24-7 Medusa forms of cnidarians have both a sexual and an asexual stage.

Content Background

Corals are sessile members of phylum Cnidaria and are builders of reefs throughout the world's oceans. Corals are anemonelike polyps with short tentacles. Even though corals are carnivorous, they have a symbiotic relationship with algae. Reef-building corals occur in warm, tropical waters and are not found at depths greater than about 36 m (120 ft). Reefs are built from calcium carbonate secreted from the epidermis of the coral.

Flatworms

Unlike sponges and cnidarians that wait for food to pass their way, flatworms actively search for their food. Worms are invertebrates with soft bodies and bilateral symmetry. Flatworms are members of the phylum Platyhelminthes (plat ih hel MIHN theez). They have long, flattened bodies. They also have three distinct layers of tissue organized into organs and organ systems.

Some flatworms are free-living, such as the planarian in **Figure 24-8B. Free-living** organisms don't depend on one particular organism for food or a place to live. But, most flatworms are parasites that live in or on their hosts. A **parasite** depends on its host for food and a place to live.

B Planarians have eyespots that have been known to respond to light. They also have the power to regenerate. A planarian can be cut in two, and each piece will grow into a new worm.

Tapeworms

One parasitic flatworm that lives in humans is called the tapeworm. It lacks a digestive system. To survive, it lives in the intestines of its hosts. The tapeworm absorbs nutrients directly into its body from digested material in the host's intestines. Find the hooks and suckers on the tapeworm's head in **Figure 24-8A.** The hooks and suckers attach the tapeworm to the host's intestines.

Figure 24-8 Flatworms have members that are free-living and other members that are parasites.

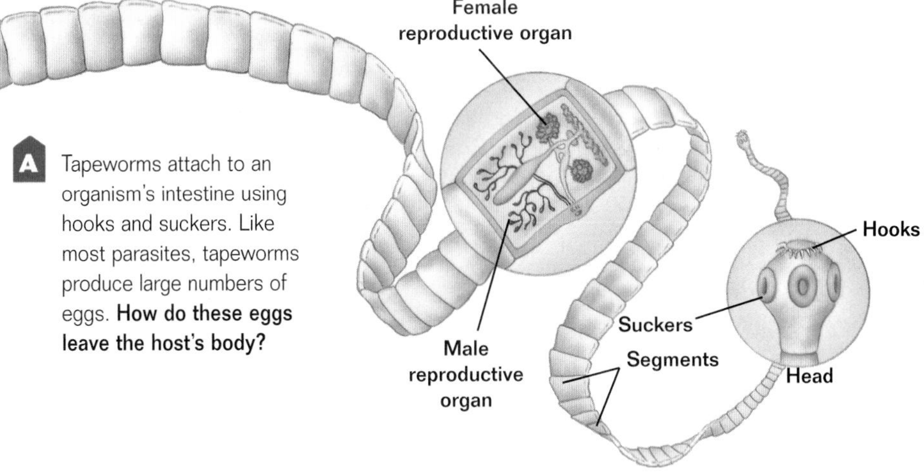

A Tapeworms attach to an organism's intestine using hooks and suckers. Like most parasites, tapeworms produce large numbers of eggs. **How do these eggs leave the host's body?**

Using Science Words

Linguistic Review the definitions of *tissue, organs,* and *organ systems.* Review bilateral symmetry. Discuss the presence or absence of tissues in organisms discussed in this section—sponges, cnidarians, flatworms, and roundworms. *Sponges do not have tissues, but cnidarians, flatworms, and roundworms do.*

Caption Answer

Figure 24-8B *The segment of the tapeworm's body that contains fertilized eggs breaks off and passes out in feces.*

3 Assess

Check for Understanding

Discussion

Review the characteristics of sponges, cnidarians, flatworms, and roundworms by asking students to volunteer in turn a fact about one of these groups. These facts could be written on the chalkboard until a complete description of each group is obtained. L2

Reteach

Visual-Spatial Have students compare and contrast polyp and medusa forms of cnidarians in their Science Journals. They should include a drawing of each with labels. L2

Extension

For students who have mastered this section, use the **Reinforcement** and **Enrichment** masters.

Across the Curriculum

Math Tapeworms as long as 9 m have been found in humans. Have students use a meterstick and measure 9 m to gain an understanding of just how long tapeworms are. L1 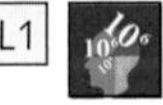

24-2 SPONGES, CNIDARIANS, FLATWORMS, AND ROUNDWORMS 821

4 Close

Proficiency Prep

Use this quiz to check students' recall of section content.

1. **What are the two body plans of cnidarians?** *medusa and polyp*
2. **What type of symmetry do flatworms and roundworms have?** *bilateral*

Section Assessment

1. Sponges filter food out of the water as it comes to them. Cnidarians actively capture prey with their tentacles that have stinging cells.
2. Worms are invertebrates with soft bodies, bilateral symmetry, and three distinct tissue layers organized into organs and organ systems.
3. Flatworms have flattened bodies with one body opening—a mouth. Roundworms' bodies have a tube within a tube and fluid in between, and two body openings—a mouth and an anus.
4. Think Critically Sponges have all the characteristics of animals. They cannot make their own food, they have eukaryotic cells, and they have many cells that have different functions, and they digest food.

Using Math

The sponge will move 15.625 mL of water in one minute.

$$\frac{22.5\text{ L}}{1\text{ day}} \times \frac{100\text{ mL}}{1\text{ L}} \times \frac{1\text{ day}}{24\text{ h}} \times \frac{1\text{ h}}{60\text{ minutes}} = \frac{15.625\text{ mL}}{\text{minute}}$$

A tapeworm grows by adding sections directly behind its head. Each body segment produces both eggs and sperm from separate male and female reproductive organs. The eggs and sperm are released into the segment. Once filled with fertilized eggs, the segment breaks off and passes out of the host's body. If another host eats a fertilized egg, the egg hatches and develops into a new worm.

Figure 24-9 Mosquitoes are the carriers of dog heartworm. Mosquitoes bite infected dogs and, in turn, infect still other dogs by biting them. The worm larva travels through the circulatory system and lodges in the heart where it interrupts normal blood flow.

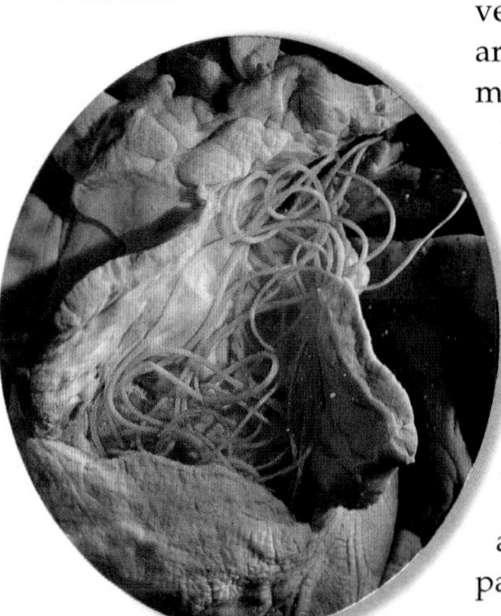

Roundworms

Dog owners regularly give their pets a medicine that prevents heartworm disease. Heartworms can kill a dog. They are just one kind of the many thousands of roundworms that make up the phylum Nematoda (nem uh TOH duh). Roundworms are the most widespread animal on Earth. Billions can live in a single acre of soil.

A roundworm's body is described as a tube within a tube, with fluid in between. The cavity separates the digestive tract from the body wall. Roundworms are also more complex than flatworms because their digestive tract is complete with two openings. Food enters through the mouth and wastes exit through an anus.

Roundworms are a diverse group. Some are decomposers. Some are predators. Some are parasites of animals and some are parasites of plants. **Figure 24-9** shows a parasitic heartworm that can infect dogs. What type of body symmetry does a roundworm have?

Section Assessment

1. How do sponges and cnidarians get food?
2. What are three common characteristics of worms?
3. Compare the body plans of flatworms and roundworms.
4. **Think Critically:** Sponges are sessile organisms. They remain attached to one place during their lifetimes. Explain why a sponge is still considered to be an animal.
5. **Skill Builder**
   Comparing and Contrasting Do the **Chapter 24 Skill Activity** on page 985 to compare and contrast types of symmetry found in different animals.

Using Math

A sponge is 1 cm in diameter and 10 cm tall. It can move 22.5 L of water through its body in a day. Calculate the volume of water it pumps through its body in one minute.

Assessment

Content Have students write poems to compare and contrast the animals studied in this section. Use the **Performance Assessment in the Science Classroom,** p. 87.

Mollusks and Segmented Worms

Mollusks

Imagine yourself walking along the beach at low tide. On the rocks by a small tide pool, you see small conelike shells. The blue-black shelled mussels are exposed along the shore, and one arm of a shy octopus can be seen inside the opening of its den. How could all of these different animals belong to the same phylum? What do they have in common?

Common Characteristics

The snail, slug, mussel, and octopus belong to the phylum Mollusca. **Mollusks** are soft-bodied invertebrates that usually have a shell. Characteristics shared by mollusks include a mantle and a large, muscular foot. The **mantle** is a thin layer of tissue covering the mollusk's soft body. It secretes the protective shell of those mollusks that have a shell. The foot is used for moving the animal or for attaching it to an object.

Between the soft body and the mantel is a space called the mantle cavity. Water-dwelling mollusks have gills in the mantle cavity. **Gills** are organs that exchange oxygen and carbon dioxide with the water. Land-dwelling mollusks have lungs to exchange gases with air. Mollusks have a complete digestive system with two openings. Many also have a scratchy, tonguelike organ called the radula. The **radula** (RAJ uh luh) acts like a file with rows of teeth to break up food into smaller pieces.

Figure 24-10

Fire Bristleworm

Octopus

Animal Kingdom
Invertebrates
Vertebrates
Cnidarian phylum
Roundworm phylum
Annelid phylum
Sponge phylum
Flatworm phylum
Mollusk phylum
Arthropod phylum

What You'll Learn

- The characteristics of mollusks
- The similarities and differences between an open and a closed circulatory system
- The characteristics of segmented worms
- The structures and digestive process of an earthworm

Vocabulary

mollusk
mantle
gills
radula
open circulatory system
closed circulatory system

Why It's Important

- Mollusks and segmented worms have specialized structures that allow them to live in their environments.

SECTION 24•3

Prepare

Refer to **Mollusks and Segmented Worms** on p. 812F.

Preplanning

Refer to the **Chapter Organizer** on pp. 812A–B.

1 Motivate

Bellringer

Before presenting the lesson, display **Section Focus Transparency 69** on the overhead projector. Use the accompanying **Focus Activity** worksheet. L2 ELL

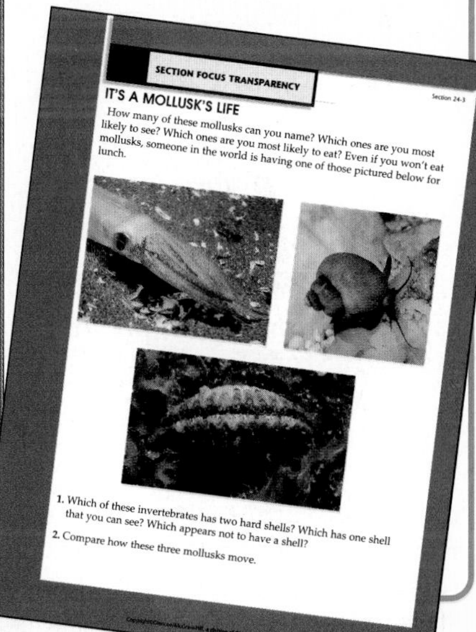

SECTION FOCUS TRANSPARENCY

Section 24-3

IT'S A MOLLUSK'S LIFE

How many of these mollusks can you name? Which ones are you most likely to see? Which ones are you most likely to eat? Even if you won't eat mollusks, someone in the world is having one of those pictured below for lunch.

1. Which of these invertebrates has two hard shells? Which has one shell that you can see? Which appears not to have a shell?
2. Compare how these three mollusks move.

Resource Manager

The following **Teacher Classroom Resources** can be used with Section 24-3:

Reproducible Masters

Activity Worksheets, pp. 136–137 L2

Critical Thinking/Problem Solving 24 L2

Enrichment, p. 69 L3

Laboratory Manual, pp. 145–148 L2

Reinforcement, p. 69 L2

CA Science Content Standards

Page 822: 9f

Tying to Previous Knowledge

Most students will be familiar with mollusks such as oysters, clams, squid, garden snails, and octopuses.

2 Teach

Content Background

Scientists have discovered mollusks living near hydrothermal vents in the ocean floor. They get their food from bacteria that live in their bodies. The bacteria use the energy in sulfide compounds to produce sugars that the mollusks use for food.

Discussion

What are some ways in which the shell of a mollusk is an adaptation? *It provides protection, helps conserve water, and enables camouflage.* L2

Teacher FYI

Wastes from cities and industry are dumped into the waters that reach the Chesapeake Bay and contribute to an excess of algae and silt. The algae and silt prevent sunlight from reaching underwater grasses, which are a key to the health of fish and crabs in the bay.

Efforts are being made today to reestablish and increase the population of oysters in the bay. Some scientists propose introducing species of oysters that are not native to the bay but may be able to survive better than native species.

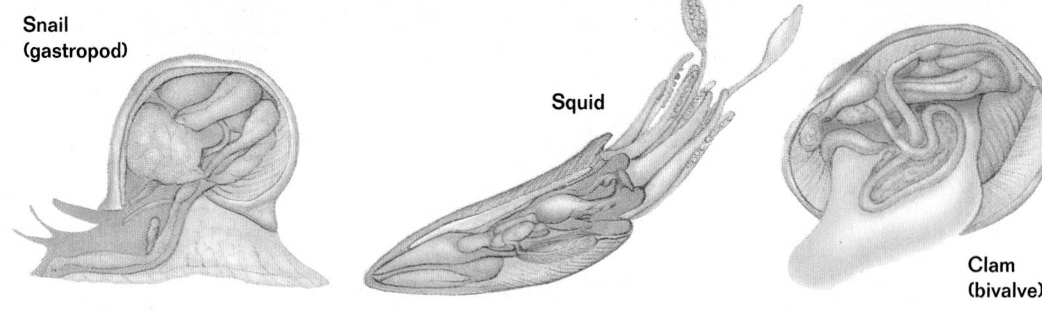

Visceral mass
Mantle
Shell
Foot

Figure 24-11 All mollusks have the same basic body plan: with a mantle, a shell, a foot, and an area called visceral mass where the body organs are located.

Some mollusks have an open circulatory system. Animals with an **open circulatory system** do not have their blood contained in vessels. Instead, the blood surrounds the organs. These organs are grouped together in a fluid-filled body cavity. **Figure 24-11** shows the basic structure of all mollusks.

Types of Mollusks

To classify mollusks, scientists first find out whether the mollusk has a shell. Then, they look at the kind of shell. They also look at the kind of foot. In this section, you will learn about three kinds of mollusks. **Figure 24-12** shows examples of two groups of mollusks—the gastropods and bivalves.

Gastropods and Bivalves

Gastropods are the largest class of mollusks. Most gastropods, such as the snails and conches, have a single shell. Slugs are also gastropods, but they don't have a shell. All move about on the large, muscular foot. A secretion of mucus allows them to glide across objects. Gastropods live in water or on land.

Bivalves are another class of mollusks. How many shells do you think bivalves have? Think of other words that start

EXAMPLES OF
Bivalves Gastropods

Figure 24-12 Although these animals look different from one another, they are all mollusks.

A Tree snails are cone-shaped gastropods ranging in size from 1 cm to 6 cm long. They feed on tiny lichens, fungi, and algae that grow on the bark, leaves, and fruit of trees.

B Scallops are marine bivalves. They swim by flapping their shells with a powerful muscle, the only part that humans eat.

Inclusion Strategies

Learning Disabled Have students make papier mâché models of all the major complex invertebrates mentioned in this section and the next section. Name cards and a list of reasons why they are important creatures in the ecosystem should be attached to each. L2 

Figure 24-13 Although the chambered nautilus's shell resembles a snail's shell, the nautilus is a cephalopod. Like the octopus and the squid, it swims using jet propulsion, as shown in **Figure 24-14.**

with *bi-*. A clam is a bivalve, or an organism with two shell halves joined by a hinge. Powerful, large muscles open and close the shells. Bivalves are water animals that are also filter feeders. Food is removed from water that is brought into and filtered through the gills.

Cephalopods

Cephalopods (SEF ah loh pawdz) are the most complex type of mollusk. Squid, octopuses, and the chambered nautilus, pictured in **Figure 24-13,** are all cephalopods. Most cephalopods have no shell but they do have a well-developed head. The "foot" is divided into tentacles with strong suckers. These animals also have a **closed circulatory system** in which blood is carried through blood vessels.

EXAMPLES OF Cephalopods

- Octopus
- Squid
- Chambered nautilus

Both the squid and octopus are adapted for quick movement in the ocean. The squid's mantle is a muscular envelope that surrounds its internal organs. Water enters the space between the mantle and the other body organs. When the mantle closes around the collar of the squid, the water is squeezed rapidly through a siphon, which is a funnel-like structure. The rapid expulsion of water from the siphon causes the squid to move in the opposite direction of the stream of water. **Figure 24-14** shows how this propulsion system works.

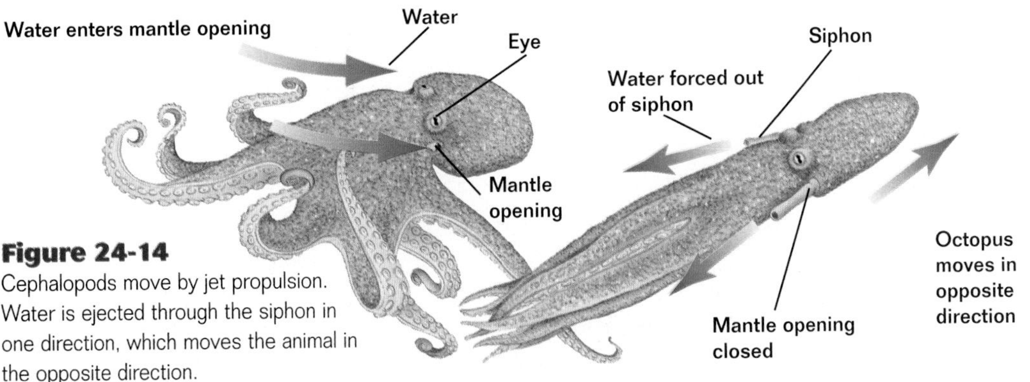

Figure 24-14
Cephalopods move by jet propulsion. Water is ejected through the siphon in one direction, which moves the animal in the opposite direction.

Activity

Visual-Spatial Collect snails from a local pond or purchase them from a pet shop. Have students observe how the snails move. Have them examine the snails' eyes with a hand lens. Have them feed lettuce to the snails and observe their feeding with the hand lens. L2 ELL COOP LEARN

Discussion

How is a squid adapted to being a predator? *It has tentacles with strong suckers for capturing prey, a well-developed nervous system, large eyes, and jet propulsion for rapid movements.* Slugs can live in places where the soil is low in calcium. Snails do not live in such places. **How does this fact related to the two different organisms?** *Snails use calcium for their shells. Slugs do not have shells.*

Newton's third law is usually stated as "reaction is always equal and opposite to action."

Using an Analogy

Relate the propulsion system used by squids to the movement that occurs when air is allowed to rapidly escape from an inflated balloon. In both cases, motion occurs in the opposite direction of the stream of air or water.

Across the Curriculum

Literature Read the poem "The Chambered Nautilus" by Oliver Wendell Holmes. Provide students with a nautilus shell to examine. Have them draw the shell and write a report in their journals about how the shell forms. L2

Integrating the Sciences

Earth Science Bivalve shells consist of intricate layers of calcium carbonate in the form of one of two minerals, calcite or aragonite. Different families of clams may use almost all calcite layers, almost all aragonite layers, or alternating layers of the two minerals in the shells. Paleontologists sometimes are able to classify bivalve fossils by their internal mineralogy and microstructure.

CA Science Content Standards

Page 825: 2e

Caption Answer

Figure 24-15 *The setae are used to hold on to the soil so that the earthworm's muscles can move the animal forward.*

GLENCOE TECHNOLOGY

Videodisc

Glencoe Science Voyages Interactive Videodisc—Life

Side 2, Lesson 9 *Ecosystems: Wetlands*

41277

Refer to Videodisc Teacher Guide for additional bar codes.

Quick Demo

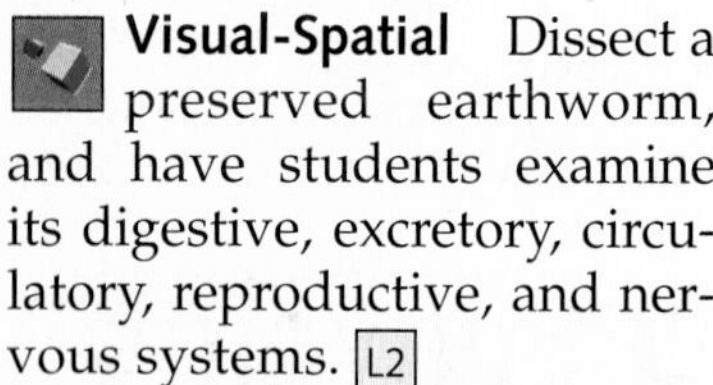

Visual-Spatial Dissect a preserved earthworm, and have students examine its digestive, excretory, circulatory, reproductive, and nervous systems. L2

Problem Solving

A leech can consume up to five times its body weight in blood. Leech saliva contains a natural anesthetic so that it can attach to a host without being noticed. Leech saliva also contains hirudin, a substance that keeps blood from clotting. Another chemical in leech saliva of interest is a vasodilator. Vasodilators enlarge blood vessel diameters.

Think Critically

The chemicals in the leeches' saliva could be reproduced and used as anticoagulation medicines. P

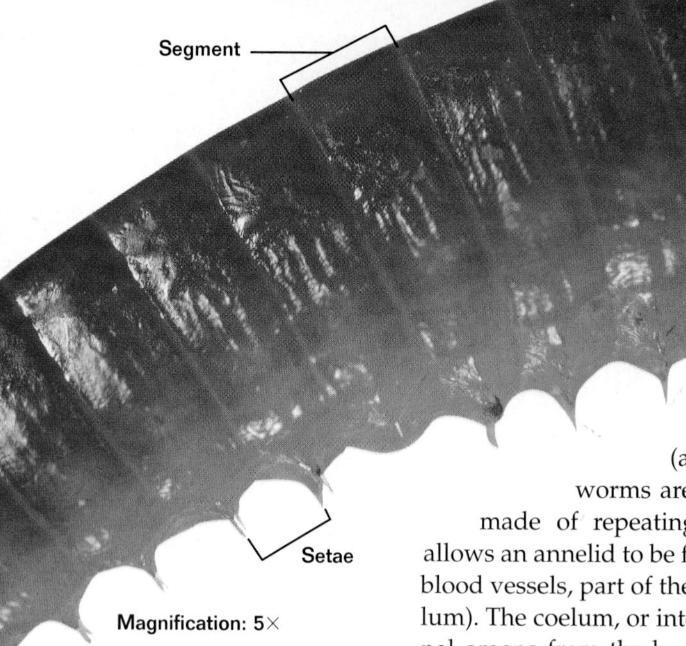

Figure 24-15 Earthworms move using bristlelike hairs called setae. **How would the setae help the earthworms move?**

Segmented Worms

What kind of animal do you think of when you hear the word *worm?* Most likely, you think of an earthworm. Earthworms belong to a group of segmented worms in the phylum Annelida (an NEL ud uh). Leeches and marine worms are also annelids. An annelid's body is made of repeating segments or rings. Segmentation allows an annelid to be flexible. Each segment has nerve cells, blood vessels, part of the digestive tract, and the coelum (SEE lum). The coelum, or internal body cavity, separates the internal organs from the body wall. Annelids also have a closed circulatory system and a complete digestive system with two body openings.

EXAMPLES OF Segmented Worms

- Earthworms
- Leeches
- Marine worms

Earthworms

Earthworms have more than 100 body segments. Setae (SEE tee), or bristlelike structures pictured in **Figure 24-15,** are found on the outside of these segments. Earthworms use the setae and two sets of muscles to move through or hold onto

Figure 24-16 Segmented worms have circulatory, respiratory, excretory, digestive, muscular, and reproductive systems.

Across the Curriculum

History Have students research and report on the uses of leeches in medicine in the 1800s and through the 1900s. *They were used for bloodletting, applied to the temples for headaches, and used to treat mental illness, gout, skin disease, and whooping cough.* L2

soil. Moving through soil is important for earthworms because they eat it. Earthworms get the energy they need to live from the bits of leaves and other living matter found in the soil. You can trace the path through an earthworm's digestive system in **Figure 24-16.** First, the soil moves to the crop, where it is stored. Behind the crop is a muscular structure called the gizzard. Here, the soil is ground. As the food passes to the intestine, it is broken down and absorbed by the blood. Undigested soil and wastes leave the worm through the anus.

What body structures are not present in the earthworm shown in **Figure 24-16?** Notice that you don't find gills or lungs. An earthworm lives in a thin film of water. It exchanges carbon dioxide and oxygen by diffusion through its skin.

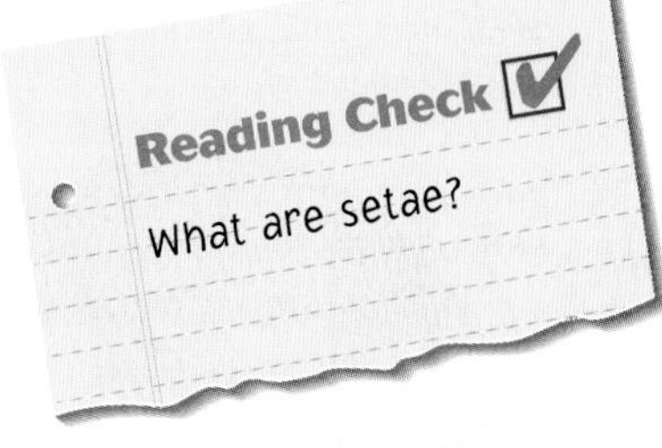
Reading Check
What are setae?

Leeches

Leeches are parasites that have a lifestyle that is different from earthworms'. These worms have flat bodies from 5 mm to 46 cm long and have sucking disks on both ends of their bodies. Leeches attach themselves to and remove blood from the body of a host. Some leeches can store as much as ten times their own weight in blood. The blood can be stored for months and released a little at a time into the digestive system. Leeches are found in freshwater, marine waters, and on land in mild and tropical regions.

Problem Solving

Leeches to the Rescue

Since ancient times, doctors have used leeches to treat a variety of diseases. Early doctors thought leeches removed the bad blood that resulted in disease. Unfortunately, so many leeches were used sometimes that patients died from blood loss. With the rise of modern medical treatments, the use of leeches was abandoned. People thought it was useless.

Now, the leech is back! Surgeons are able to reattach severed ears or fingers, but it is difficult to keep blood flowing to the reattached body part. If blood clots appear, they stop blood circulation and the cells in the ear or finger die. Medicinal leeches are the key to success. Surgeons place a leech on the reattached ear or finger. It inflicts a painless bite from a sucking disk at each end of its body. As the leech feeds on the blood, chemicals in the saliva break up clots that have already formed and prevent new clots from forming. Eventually, normal circulation is established. The leech is removed and the reattached part survives.

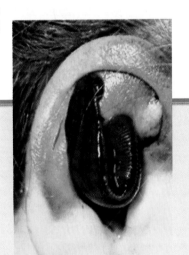

Think Critically: Blood clots are major factors in strokes and some heart and blood vessel diseases. How might research about leeches play an important role in developing treatments for these conditions?

Answer to Reading Check

Setae are bristlelike structures found on each of a worm's segments. The earthworm uses two sets of muscles attached to the setae to move through and hold on to the soil.

3 Assess

Check for Understanding

Discussion

Interpersonal Lead students in a discussion about how the body plans of the three groups of mollusks covered in this section are adapted to the different biological niches filled by each group. L2

Reteach

Visual-Spatial Have students make a chart that compares structures, environment, and way of life (free-living or parasitic) of flatworms, mollusks, and segmented worms. L1

Extension

For students who have mastered this section, use the **Reinforcement** and **Enrichment** masters.

Multiple Learning Styles

Linguistic Have students research and report on the medicinal leech *Hirudo medicinalis.* This leech produces the anticoagulant hirudin. L2

24-3 Mollusks and Segmented Worms 827

Caption Answer

Figure 24-15 *Most are marine.*

4 Close

Proficiency Prep

Use this quiz to check students' recall of section content.

1. **What is the name of the thin layer of tissue covering a mollusk's soft body?** *mantle*
2. **Describe the setae of marine worms.** *They occur in bundles along their segments.*

Section Assessment

1. gastropod, snail; bivalve, oyster; cephalopod, squid
2. An annelid's body is made up of repeating segments. Each segment has nerve cells, blood vessels, and part of the digestive tract. An internal body cavity separates internal organs from the body wall. Annelids have a closed circulatory system and a complete digestive tract with two openings.
3. Earthworms are pulled through the soil by the setae attached to each of its segments. Soil moves through the crop and then into a muscular gizzard, on to the intestine, and finally out the anus.
4. **Think Critically** It increases the flexibility of a worm and allows separate parts to move independently of each other.

Answers will vary depending on which mollusk students choose.

Figure 24-17 Polychaetes come in a variety of forms and colors. The Christmas tree (A) and feather duster (B) use their appendages to filter out food from their watery environments. **How are these organisms similar to cnidarians and sponges?**

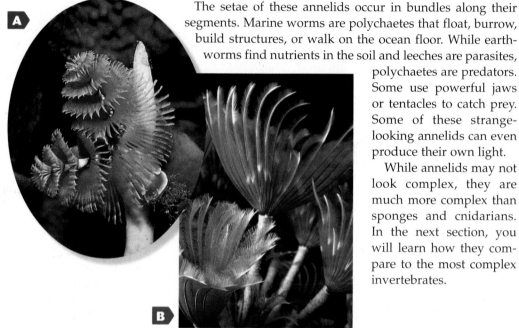

Marine Worms

Look at the animals in **Figure 24-17.** You may wonder how these feathery animals can possibly be related to the earthworm and leech. These animals belong to a third group of annelids called polychaetes (PAHL ee kitz). The word *polychaete* means "many spines." There are more species of polychaetes than of any other kind of annelid. More than 6000 known species of polychaetes have been discovered.

The setae of these annelids occur in bundles along their segments. Marine worms are polychaetes that float, burrow, build structures, or walk on the ocean floor. While earthworms find nutrients in the soil and leeches are parasites, polychaetes are predators. Some use powerful jaws or tentacles to catch prey. Some of these strange-looking annelids can even produce their own light.

While annelids may not look complex, they are much more complex than sponges and cnidarians. In the next section, you will learn how they compare to the most complex invertebrates.

Section Assessment

1. Name the three classes of mollusks and identify a member from each class.
2. What are the characteristics of segmented worms?
3. Describe how an earthworm feeds and digests its food.
4. **Think Critically:** How does an annelid's segmentation help it move?
5. **Skill Builder**
   Comparing and Contrasting Compare and contrast an open circulatory system with a closed circulatory system. If you need help, refer to Comparing and Contrasting in the **Skill Handbook** on page 956.

Science Journal

Choose a mollusk and write about it in your Science Journal. Describe its appearance, how it gets food, where it lives, and other interesting facts.

5. **Skill Builder**
   In an open circulatory system, blood is not contained in blood vessels but bathes the body's organs. In a closed circulatory system, blood is contained in blood vessels. Both systems bring nutrients to cells via the blood.

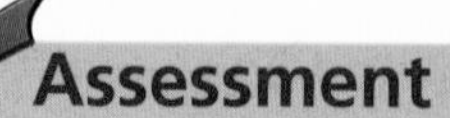

Assessment

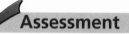

Process Compare the muscular foot of bivalves and gastropods. *Gastropod—spreads out under its body and a rippling motion moves it along; bivalve—shaped and is normally hidden inside the two shells; some bivalves move by hooking the foot into the sand and pulling themselves along.* Use **Performance Assessment in the Science Classroom,** p. 87.

NATIONAL GEOGRAPHIC

History of Science

Searching for the Giant Squid

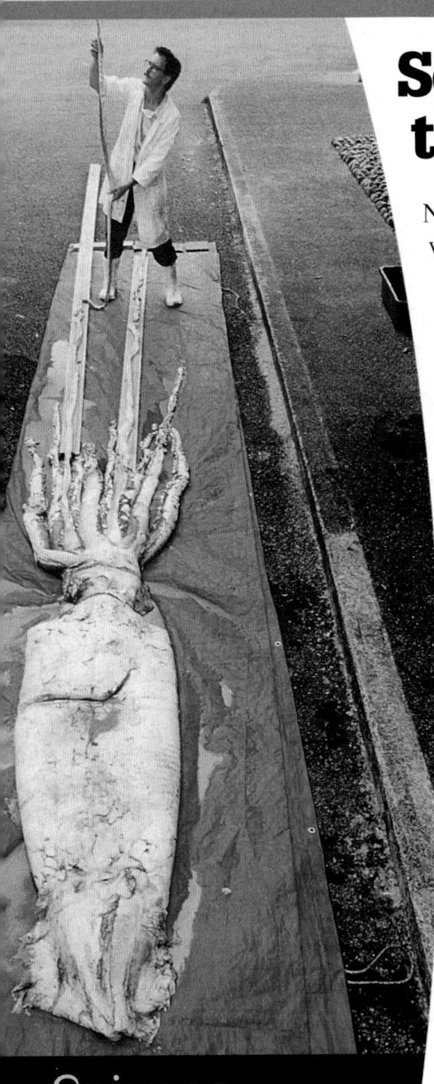

No one has ever seen a giant squid in its natural habitat, which is 300 m to 1500 m below the ocean's surface. Nor has any live, healthy giant squid been kept in an aquarium or research facility to be studied by scientists. The only live specimens of giant squid available for study have been those that washed up on beaches or were brought up in deep-sea commercial fishing nets. These squids have been sick and unsuitable for study.

Rare Find

In the late 1500s, accounts were written about several large sea creatures stranded on Norwegian shores. It was not until 1854 that scientists concluded that these creatures were giant squid. In the late 1800s, a dead giant squid caught by commercial fishers in Newfoundland became the first specimen available for study. The one-metric-ton giant squid at left was netted at a depth of 425 m in the waters off New Zealand. The creature was nearly dead when pulled on board the research vessel. The three-year-old squid measured 8 m from top to tip of tentacle and might have reached a much greater length at maturity.

The Search Goes On

The Smithsonian's Clyde Roper, one of the world's leading experts on the giant squid, has spent more than 30 years studying these remarkable animals. In 1997, Roper and his crew used the *Odyssey*, a robotic underwater vehicle, and a camera to explore the cold, black depths of Kaikoura Canyon, a deep-sea ecosystem located off New Zealand's South Island. Dr. Roper and his colleagues collected valuable information on the temperature, salt content, and depth of the ocean. On a ship at the surface, they viewed many hours of videotapes of this deep-water ecosystem—but alas, no giant squids. One day, perhaps crewed submersibles in the area will be the first to catch a glimpse of the giant squid at home.

Science JOURNAL

How big is a giant squid? Find out the length of the wall in your classroom, a school bus, and an airplane. Record the lengths in your Science Journal. Compare the lengths of these objects to an 18 m giant squid. Which is longest?

Content Background

- The largest squid ever measured was discovered at Timble Tickle in New Zealand in 1878. It was 18 m long from the tip of its torpedo-shaped body to the end of its two feeding tentacles.
- Scientists believe that one reason squid run ashore or die on the surface of the ocean is that they are deep, cold-water sea creatures. It is believed that squid will actually suffocate in warm waters for two reasons. One is that their blood doesn't carry oxygen well at higher temperatures. The other reason is that temperature seems to affect their buoyancy mechanism so that once the warm water causes them to rise to the surface, they can't sink back down into deeper water.

Teaching Strategies

- Have students write an essay on what they would experience traveling 1000 m below sea level to look for a giant squid.
- Have students research giant squid. What do scientists know about these creatures? Where do they live? What other questions are they trying to answer?

Science Journal

The average size of a giant squid is 6 m to 13 m long, with the largest squid being 18 m. Answers will vary depending on the object to which students are comparing the giant squid.

Activity 24·1 Design Your Own Experiment

Recognize the Problem

Purpose

Naturalist Students will determine whether the presence of worms affects the quality of soil. L2 ELL P

Process Skills

designing an experiment, forming a hypothesis, observing and inferring, communicating, recognizing cause and effect, separating and controlling variables, interpreting data

Time

two 45-minute periods and twice-weekly observations for two weeks

Materials

Use *Eisenia foetida* or *Lumbricus rubellus* (common names are red wigglers, brandlings, or manure worms). Purchase them from a local bait shop. The ratio of food scraps to worms is 1:2, based on weight.

Possible containers: plastic shoe box or gallon jug with top cut off. They must have at least a 10-cm depth. Drill six to ten drainage holes in the bottom.

Make sure that all food scraps are finely ground.

Safety Precautions

CAUTION: *Students should keep their hands wet and handle the worms gently. Wash hands after handling worms or soil.*

Form a Hypothesis

Possible Hypothesis

Most student hypotheses will reflect that the worms will digest the food scraps and produce healthier soil.

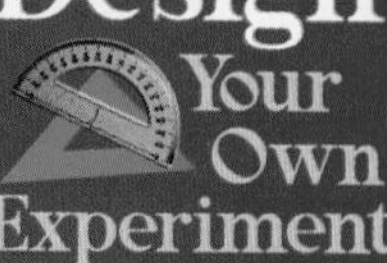

Activity 24·1

Garbage-eating Worms

You know that soil conditions can influence the growth of plants. You are trying to decide what factors might improve the soil in your backyard garden. A friend suggests that earthworms improve the quality of the soil. Does the presence of earthworms have any value in improving soil conditions?

Possible Materials

- Worms (red wigglers)
- Plastic containers with drainage holes (4 L) (2)
- Soil (7 L)
- Chopped food scraps including fruit and vegetable peels, pulverized eggshells, tea bags, and coffee grounds
- Shredded newspaper
- Spray bottle

Recognize the Problem

How does the presence of earthworms change the condition of the soil?

Form a Hypothesis

Based on your reading and observations, state a hypothesis about how earthworms might improve the conditions of soil.

Goals

- **Design an experiment** that compares the condition of soil in two environments, one with earthworms and one without.
- **Observe** the change in soil conditions for two weeks.

Safety Precautions

Be careful when working with live animals. Always keep your hands wet when handling earthworms. Dry hands will remove the mucus from the earthworms.

Test Your Hypothesis

Possible Procedures

Fill two containers of the same size with three inches of soil. Do not pack down but leave rather loose. Add worms to only one of the containers. Place a thin layer of finely chopped food scraps over the surface in each container and cover with shredded newspapers. Keep the newspaper moist. Spray with water as needed. Make observations of each container for three weeks. Make sure the ambient temperature is between 5°C and 26°C.

Test Your Hypothesis

Plan

1. As a group, agree upon the hypothesis and **decide** how you will test it. **Identify** what results will confirm the hypothesis.
2. **List** the steps you will need to take to test your hypothesis. Be specific. **Describe** exactly what you will do in each step. **List** your materials.
3. Prepare a data table in your Science Journal to **record** your observations.
4. **Read** over the entire experiment to make sure all steps are in logical order.
5. **Identify** all constants, variables, and controls of the experiment.

Do

1. Make sure your teacher approves your plan and your data table before you proceed.
2. Carry out the experiment as planned.
3. While doing the experiment, **record** your observations and complete the data table in your Science Journal.

Analyze Your Data

1. **Compare** the changes in the two sets of soil samples.
2. **Compare** your results with those of other groups.
3. What was your control in this experiment?
4. What were your variables?

Draw Conclusions

1. Did the results support your hypothesis? **Explain.**
2. **Describe** what effect you think rain would have on the soil and worms.

Teaching Strategies

Tying to Previous Knowledge
Most students know that worms aerate the soil and their excretion called casts fertilizes the soil.

Expected Outcome

Most results will show that the worms ate the food scraps and the resulting soil has a dark, rich-looking appearance.

Error Analysis

Have students compare their results and their hypotheses and explain why differences occurred.

Analyze Your Data

1. There should be less food scraps in the container with worms, and the soil should have a darker appearance.
2. Student results should be similar to those of other groups.
3. The control in this experiment was a container filled with soil, chopped food, and shredded newspapers. It was treated in the same manner as the container with worms in it.
4. The variable was the presence of worms in one container.

Draw Conclusions

1. Answers will be determined by student hypotheses.
2. Rain would compact the soil, and too much rain could drown the worms.

Assessment

Oral Have students explain the relationship between worms and soil fertility. *Worms move organic matter throughout the soil, add nitrates to the soil, and dig tunnels that allow air to go deep into the soil.* Use **Performance Assessment in the Science Classroom,** p. 17.

GO Further

Investigate the effect that worms have on the decomposition of leaves. Leaves should decompose faster in soil with worms than in soil without worms.

CA Science Content Standards
Page 830–831: 9a, 9b, 9c

Arthropods and Echinoderms

SECTION 24•4

Prepare

Refer to **Arthropods and Echinoderms** on p. 812F.

Preplanning

Refer to the **Chapter Organizer** on pp. 812A–B.

1 Motivate

Bellringer

Before presenting the lesson, display **Section Focus Transparency 70** on the overhead projector. Use the accompanying **Focus Activity** worksheet. L2 ELL

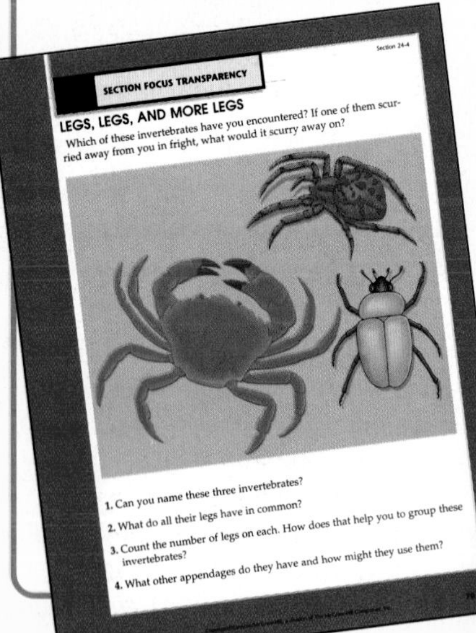

SECTION FOCUS TRANSPARENCY

LEGS, LEGS, AND MORE LEGS

Which of these invertebrates have you encountered? If one of them scurried away from you in fright, what would it scurry away on?

1. Can you name these three invertebrates?
2. What do all their legs have in common?
3. Count the number of legs on each. How does that help you to group these invertebrates?
4. What other appendages do they have and how might they use them?

Tying to Previous Knowledge

Students will be familiar with arthropods—shrimp and lobsters. All will have knowledge of insects and spiders. Use their knowledge of arthropods to identify common characteristics.

What You'll Learn

- Features used to classify arthropods
- How the structure of the exoskeleton relates to its function
- Features of echinoderms

Vocabulary
arthropod
appendage
exoskeleton
metamorphosis

Why It's Important

- Arthropods and echinoderms show great diversity and are found in many different environments.

Arthropods

By far, the largest group of animals belongs in the phylum Arthropoda. More than 900 000 species of arthropods have been discovered. The term **arthropod** comes from *arthros*, meaning "jointed," and *poda*, meaning "foot." Arthropods are animals that have jointed appendages. They are similar to annelids because they have segmented bodies. Yet, in most cases, they have fewer, more specialized segments. Instead of setae, they have different kinds of appendages. **Appendages** are the structures such as claws, legs, and even antennae that grow from the body.

Every arthropod has an **exoskeleton** that protects and supports its body. The exoskeleton also protects the arthropod from drying out. This lightweight body covering is made of a carbohydrate and a protein. As the animal grows, the exoskeleton is shed in a process called molting. The weight of the outer covering increases as the size of the animal increases. Weight and hardness of the exoskeleton produce a problem for the animal. They make it more difficult to move. The jointed appendages solve part of this problem.

Figure 24-18 shows an example of the five different types of arthropods: insects, spiders, centipedes, millipedes, and crustaceans. Find the body segments on these animals. Which arthropods appear most like the annelids?

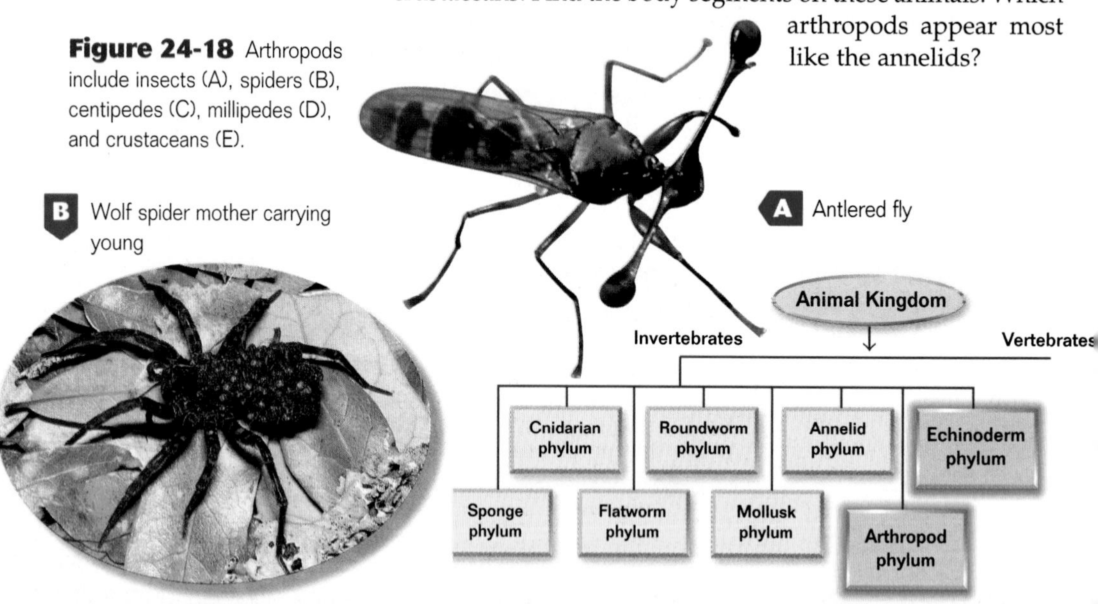

Figure 24-18 Arthropods include insects (A), spiders (B), centipedes (C), millipedes (D), and crustaceans (E).

A Antlered fly

B Wolf spider mother carrying young

Resource Manager

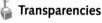

The following **Teacher Classroom Resources** can be used with Section 24-4:

Reproducible Masters

Activity Worksheets, pp. 138–140 L2
Enrichment, p. 70 L3
Home Involvement, p. 37 L2
Laboratory Manual, pp. 149–151 L2
Reinforcement, p. 70 L2
Study Guide, p. 94–96 L1 ELL

Transparencies

Science Integration Transparency 14 L2

Insects

When asked to name an insect, your answer might be some kind of flying insect, such as bee, fly, beetle, or butterfly. In fact, insects are the only invertebrates that can fly. Insects make up the largest group of invertebrates. There are more than 700 000 classified species of insects, and scientists describe more each year.

Insects have three distinct body regions, as shown in **Figure 24-18A:** the head, thorax, and abdomen. The head has well-developed sensory organs, including the eyes and antennae. The thorax has three pairs of jointed legs and, in many species, one or two pairs of wings. The wings and legs of insects are highly specialized.

The abdomen is divided into segments and has neither wings nor legs attached to it. Reproductive organs are located in this region. Insects produce many more young than can survive. For example, a single female fly can produce thousands of eggs.

Insects have an open circulatory system. Oxygen is not transported by blood in the system, but food and waste materials are. Oxygen is brought directly to tissues inside of the insect through small holes called spiracles (SPIHR ih kulz) located along the thorax and abdomen.

internet CONNECTION

Visit the Glencoe Science Web Site at **www.glencoe.com/sec/science/ca** for more information about butterflies.

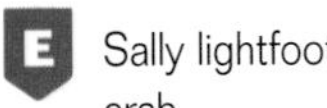

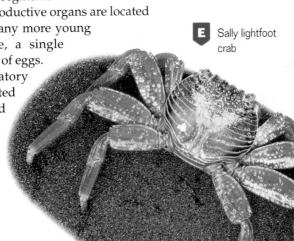

E Sally lightfoot crab

C Centipede

D Forest floor millipede

Across the Curriculum

Art Provide construction paper, modeling clay, pipe cleaners, cardboard tubes, and other materials for students to construct a model of an arachnid, centipede, millipede, crustacean, or insect. L1 ELL COOP LEARN

2 Teach

internet CONNECTION

Internet Addresses

____

____

____

____

For Internet tips, see Glencoe's **Using the Internet in the Science Classroom.**

Content Background

Most arthropods undergo four to seven molts before reaching adult size. After shedding the old exoskeleton, the body is quite soft. The animal swells by taking in extra water or air while the new exoskeleton hardens.

Using an Analogy

Compare the limitations of the arthropod exoskeleton with a person wearing a suit of armor.

Teacher FYI

Caterpillars can be collected during the summer and early fall. They may be kept in a wide-mouth glass jar with a two-piece lid. A piece of wire screen can be substituted for the lid. Feed the caterpillars a fresh supply of fresh leaves from the plant where they were collected. When they begin to pupate, place bottle caps of water in the jar.

CA Science Content Standards

Page 832: 6c
Page 833: 6b

Activity

Interpersonal Give each group a dissecting tray containing a preserved millipede, centipede, crayfish, grasshopper, and spider. Have the students list characteristics of the animals and determine how the five organisms are similar and how they are different. L2

Teacher FYI

- For three hundred years, physicians treating wounds that would not heal noticed something odd. Patients who had wounds infested with fly larvae actually healed faster than those whose wounds were clean. Today the larvae or maggots of blowflies are used in hospitals to eat at dead and decaying flesh of infected tissue. The larvae have been used on gangrenous ulcers or open sores when antibiotics have failed to cure the infection.
- Jumping spiders do not spin a web to capture prey like other spiders. Instead they are active hunters. Their legs act as mini hydraulic pistons, which propel them into precise jumps, landing on their insect prey. Their fangs inject digestive enzymes into the bodies of the insect meal as they struggle to kill the prey.

GLENCOE TECHNOLOGY

Videodisc

The Infinite Voyage: Life in the Balance

Chapter 5 *BioLatll: Classifying the Community of Insects* 6:00

Refer to the Teacher Guide for bar codes and teaching strategies.

VISUALIZING Metamorphosis

Figure 24-19

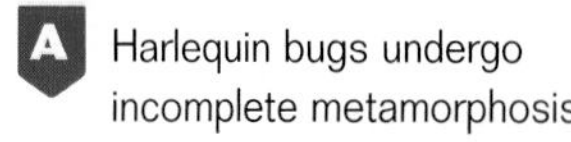

A Harlequin bugs undergo incomplete metamorphosis.

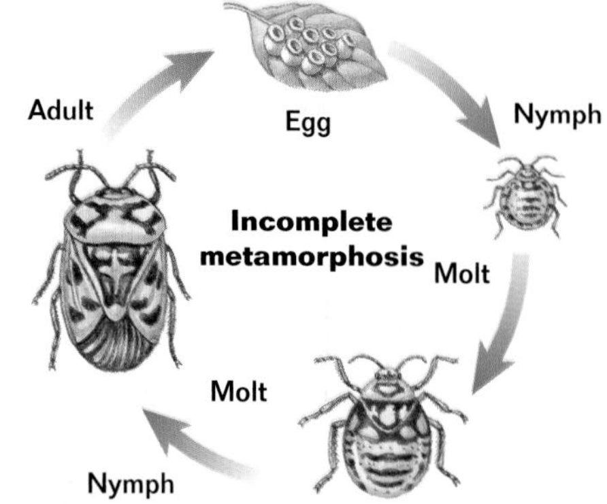

B Butterflies and moths, such as this silk moth, undergo complete metamorphosis.

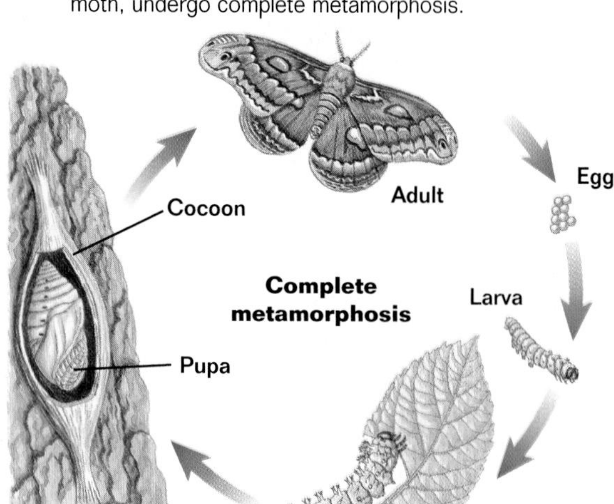

Figure 24-20 A spider's web is made from a liquid silk that the arachnid produces in its abdomen. Each kind of spider weaves its own unique style of web.

EXAMPLES OF Arachnids

- **Spiders**
- **Mites**
- **Ticks**
- **Scorpions**
- **Lice**

Metamorphosis

Identifying the young of some insects can be difficult. They don't look anything like the adult forms. This happens because many insects completely change their body form as they mature. This change in body form is called **metamorphosis** (met uh MOR fuh sus). There are two kinds of metamorphosis. Butterflies, ants, bees, and moths undergo complete metamorphosis. Complete metamorphosis has four stages: egg, larva, pupa (PYEW puh), and adult. You can trace the stages of this process in **Figure 24-19.** Notice how different the larva and pupa stages are from the adults.

Other insects go through incomplete metamorphosis, which is made up of only three stages: egg, nymph, and adult. Grasshopper nymphs look like a tiny version of the parents except they don't have wings. A nymph molts several times before reaching the adult stage. They replace their old exoskeletons as they grow larger. Grasshoppers get their wings and become adults after their final molt.

Arachnids

Spiders, ticks, mites, and scorpions are often confused with insects. They actually belong to a separate group of arthropods known as arachnids. Arachnids have two body regions. The first, called the cephalothorax (sef uh luh THOR aks), is made of the fused head and thorax regions. The abdomen is the second region. All arachnids have four pairs of legs attached to the cephalothorax.

Science Journal

Arachnids Have students choose an arachnid in this section and write about it in their Science Journals. Journal entries should reflect the characteristics of the organism, its environment, way of life, and other information.

VISUAL Learning

Figure 24-19 Have students identify the three stages of incomplete metamorphosis and the four stages of complete metamorphosis.

Figure 24-21 Millipedes (A) may have more than 100 segments in their long abdomens. Centipedes (B) may have from 15 segments to 181 segments—always an odd number.

Giant millipede

Soil centipede

Spiders are predators, but they can't chew and eat prey the way insects do. Instead, a spider uses a pair of fanglike appendages in its mouth to inject venom into the prey and paralyze it. The spider releases enzymes that turn its victim into a liquid. The spider then drinks its food. In **Figure 24-20,** a spider is weaving a web that will trap prey.

Centipedes and Millipedes

Centipedes and millipedes are long, thin, segmented arthropods that look like worms. Instead of setae, these arthropods have pairs of jointed legs. Centipedes have one pair of joined legs attached to each body segment. Millipedes have two pairs. Centipedes are predators that use poisonous venom to capture their prey. Millipedes eat plants. Besides the number of legs, how else is the centipede different from the millipede in **Figure 24-21?**

Crustaceans

The exoskeleton gets larger and heavier each time an arthropod molts. The weight of the exoskeleton can limit the size of the animal. Now, think about where you can lift the most weight—on land or in water? Water is more buoyant than air, and it provides a greater upward force on an object. Because of this buoyant property, a large, heavy exoskeleton is less limiting for arthropods that live in water. These arthropods belong to a class known as crustaceans.

Most crustaceans live in water. Examples include crabs, crayfish, lobsters, shrimp, barnacles, and water fleas. They have five pairs of jointed legs. The first pair is usually larger and thicker and is used as claws to hold food, as illustrated in **Figure 24-22.** The other four pairs are walking legs. The five pairs of appendages on the abdomen are swimmerets. These are used to help move the animals through water and for reproduction. The swimmerets also force water over the feathery gills. If a crustacean loses an appendage, it can regenerate the lost part.

EXAMPLES OF Crustaceans

- Crabs
- Crayfish
- Lobsters
- Shrimp
- Barnacles

Figure 24-22 This rock crab, found in the Atlantic Ocean, is using its claws to hold the scallop it eats.

VISUAL Learning

Figure 24-21 Point out the number of legs on each segment and the poisonous claws of the centipede. Explain that compared to centipedes, millipedes are less active and move more slowly.

Activity

Visual-Spatial Have students look under rocks and logs for isopods. Isopods are land crustaceans. There are two easily distinguishable types. When disturbed, the pill bug curls into a ball. A sow bug does not curl into a ball. Isopods can be maintained in the classroom in a jar of moist soil with a slice of potato. L2

Correcting Misconceptions

Using the word *shellfish* to refer to crustaceans is misleading. Crustaceans are not fish, nor do they have shells. They have an exoskeleton that is very different from the shells of clams and snails.

Across the Curriculum

Language Arts Have students prepare an illustrated report on the various hunting methods of spiders. Include the jumping spider, wolf spider, and trap-door spider. L2

Content Background

Phylum Echinodermata is made up of eleven classes, six of which are extinct and known only from fossils.

Echinoderms show an important evolutionary relationship to invertebrates in that they may share a common ancestor with the lower chordates.

Try at Home

Mini Lab

For additional help doing this activity at home, see the corresponding pages in the **Home Involvement** booklet.

Purpose

Kinesthetic Students will model how sea stars can open clamshells that are held closed by muscles.

Materials

heavy books, clock with a second hand

Teaching Strategies

Make sure that the books students use are not too heavy.

Analysis

1. Students should respond that the book is putting pressure on their arm muscles, causing them to tire and drop the book.
2. Sea stars put pressure on the muscles of a clam by using the suction power of their tube feet. Eventually, the muscles of the clam tire, and the shell opens.

Assessment

Performance Have students wet suction cups and press them against a variety of surfaces. Ask students if they can pick up objects with a suction cup. Compare this to tube feet. *Suction cups act like tube feet.* Use **Performance Assessment in the Science Classroom,** p. 25.

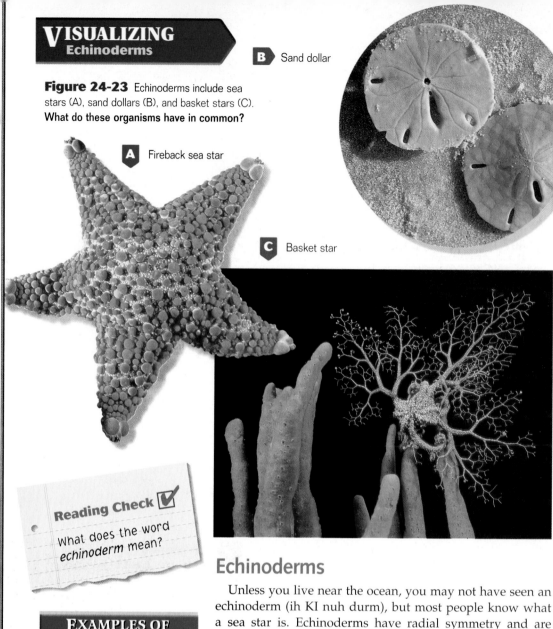

VISUALIZING Echinoderms

Figure 24-23 Echinoderms include sea stars (A), sand dollars (B), and basket stars (C). **What do these organisms have in common?**

A Fireback sea star

B Sand dollar

C Basket star

Reading Check

What does the word *echinoderm* mean?

EXAMPLES OF Echinoderms

- Sea stars
- Sea urchins
- Sand dollars
- Basket star
- Sea cucumber

Echinoderms

Unless you live near the ocean, you may not have seen an echinoderm (ih KI nuh durm), but most people know what a sea star is. Echinoderms have radial symmetry and are represented by sea stars, brittle stars, sea urchins, sand dollars, and sea cucumbers. They also don't have heads, brains, or advanced nervous systems.

The name *echinoderm* means "spiny skin." You can see from those shown in **Figure 24-23** that echinoderms have spines of various lengths that cover the outside of their bodies. Most echinoderms, such as sea stars, are supported and protected by an internal skeleton made up of calcium carbonate plates. These plates are covered by thin, spiny skin.

Caption Answer

Figure 24-23 *All have a spiny skin and a water vascular system.*

VISUAL Learning

Figure 24-23 Have students compare the body structures of these echinoderms. **Are there any similarities?** *The sea star and sand dollar have five-part symmetry.*

Water-Vascular System

Sea stars have a unique characteristic shared by all echinoderms—a water-vascular system. The water-vascular system is a network of water-filled canals. Thousands of tube feet are connected to this system. As water moves into and out of the water-vascular system, the tube feet act as suction cups and help the sea star move and eat. **Figure 24-24** shows these tube feet and how they are used to pry open a dead rock crab.

Sea stars also have a unique way of eating. Think about how you eat. You bring food to your mouth and swallow. The food then travels down to your stomach. The sea star actually pushes its stomach out of its mouth and into the opened shell of the oyster. It then digests the oyster's body while it is still inside the shell.

Like some other invertebrates, sea stars can regenerate damaged parts. Early settlers of the Chesapeake Bay area found the bay teeming with oysters. Eventually, more people moved into the area and deposited their wastes into the bay. Because some sea stars do well in polluted water, their population grew. People who harvested oysters found that the oyster population was decreasing. They decided to kill the sea stars by cutting them into pieces and

Modeling Sea Stars

Procedure

1. Hold your arm straight out, palm up.
2. Place a heavy book on your hand.
3. Have another person time how long you can hold your arm up with the book on it.

Analysis

1. Describe how your arm feels after a few minutes.
2. If the book models the sea star and your arm models the oyster, infer how a sea star successfully overcomes the oyster to obtain food.

Anus
Ray
Stomach
Mouth
Radial canal
Tube feet

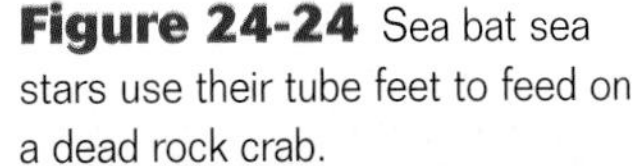
Figure 24-24 Sea bat sea stars use their tube feet to feed on a dead rock crab.

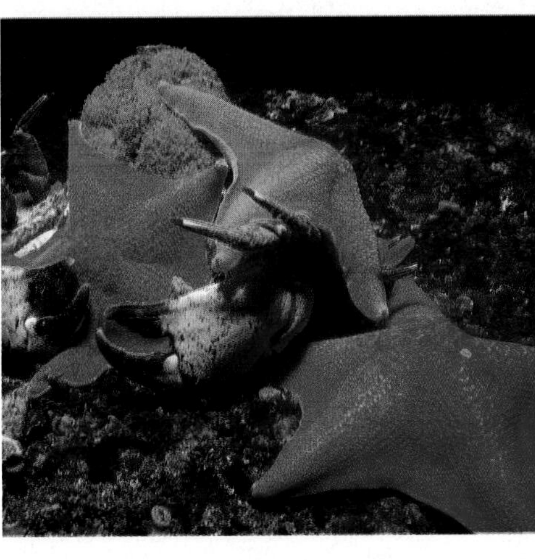

3 Assess

Check for Understanding

Discussion

Interpersonal Have students compare and contrast arthropods and echinoderms. They are both invertebrates. Arthropods have an exoskeleton of chitin and echinoderms have an internal skeleton composed of calcium carbonate. They both are organized into tissues, organs and organ systems. Arthropods have bilateral symmetry, whereas echinoderms have radial symmetry. L2

Reteach

Have students explain why arthropods molt several times during their lifetime and why echinoderms have few predators. L2

Extension

For students who have mastered this section, use the **Reinforcement** and **Enrichment** masters.

Guided Reading Strategy

Four-Corner Discussion This strategy encourages the class to debate a complex issue such as what to do about the Chesapeake Bay sea star/oyster problem. Make four signs: Strongly Agree, Agree, Disagree, Strongly Disagree. Place one sign in each corner of the room. Write on the chalkboard a statement that will elicit a reaction from students. Have the students respond on paper to the statement. After several minutes, direct them to move to the corner whose sign most closely reflects their opinions. In the corners, students share responses. Each group then selects a spokesperson to report the opinions of the group. After all groups have reported, open the floor for debate. Allow students who have changed their opinions to change corners.

CA Science Content Standards

Page 837: 2b, 2c

Using Math

52 cm average length;

$\frac{25 \text{ cm} + 30 \text{ cm} + 100 \text{ cm}}{3} = 52 \text{ cm}$

4 Close

Proficiency Prep

Use this quiz to check students' recall of section content.

1. **What does the term arthropod mean?** *jointed-foot*
2. **What are the three distinct body regions of insects?** *head, thorax, abdomen*

Section Assessment

1. jointed legs, body segments, exoskeleton
2. advantages: provides protection, supports the body; disadvantages: body outgrows exoskeleton, limits the size they can grow on land
3. spiny skin, five-part radial symmetry, a water-vascular system
4. Think Critically The sea star population would decline, as their food source would have been destroyed.

Using Math

Students can use the following equation to solve the problem.

$\frac{\text{jump (cm)}}{\text{height}} = \frac{25 \text{ cm}}{0.4 \text{ cm}}$

A person measuring 160 cm would jump 10 000 cm, or 100 m.

(25 cm × 160 cm ÷ 0.4 cm = 10 000 cm)

Using Math

Speckled sea cucumbers can grow up to 25 cm in length. The black sea cucumber can grow up to 30 cm. The sea worm sea cucumber can reach 1 m in length. Calculate the average length of these three types of sea cucumbers.

throwing them back into the bay. Within a short time, the sea star population was five times larger than before due to regeneration. The entire oyster bed was destroyed!

Sea Cucumbers

The sea cucumber in **Figure 24-25** looks nothing like the other members of the echinoderm class. They have soft bodies with a leathery covering. They have few calcium carbonate plates. Sea cucumbers have tentacles around their mouths that are used to capture food. Although they have five rows of tube feet on the sides of their bodies, they appear to be more bilaterally symmetrical than the other echinoderms. When threatened, sea cucumbers may expel their internal organs. These organs regenerate in a few weeks.

Scientists continue to study echinoderms to learn more about the process of regeneration. These animals are also important in keeping saltwater environments free of pollution. They feed on dead organisms and help recycle materials within the environment.

Figure 24-25 A sea cucumber moves along the ocean water using tube feet.

Section Assessment

1. What are three characteristics of all arthropods?
2. What are the advantages and disadvantages of an exoskeleton?
3. What characteristics set echinoderms apart from other invertebrates?
4. **Think Critically:** What might happen to the sea star population after the oyster beds are destroyed? Explain your answer.
5. **Skill Builder**
   Observing and Inferring Observe the echinoderms pictured in **Figure 24-23.** Infer why they are slow moving. If you need help, refer to Observing and Inferring in the **Skill Handbook** on page 956.

Using Math

A flea measuring 4 mm in length can jump 25 cm from a resting position. If a flea were as tall as you are, how far could it jump?

5. 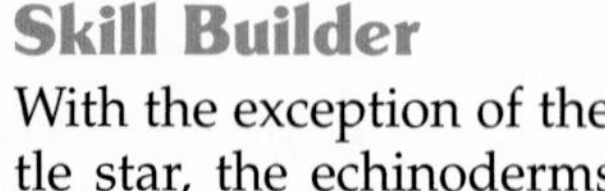
Skill Builder
With the exception of the brittle star, the echinoderms pictured have no means of movement except their tube feet. Therefore, they are not capable of rapid movement.

Assessment

Content Ask students to write in their Science Journals about how incomplete and complete metamorphosis are similar and how they are different. *Both are a series of changes. In complete metamorphosis, the young look very different from the adults.* Use **Performance Assessment in the Science Classroom,** p. 103.

Observing Complete Metamorphosis

Many insects go through the four stages of complete metamorphosis during their life cycles. Chemicals that are secreted by the body of the animal control the changes. How different do the body forms look between the stages of metamorphosis?

Materials

- Large-mouth jar or old fish bowl
- Bran or oatmeal
- Dried bread or cookie crumbs mixed with flour
- Slice of apple or carrot
- Paper towel
- Cheesecloth
- Mealworms
- Rubber band

What You'll Investigate

What do the stages of metamorphosis look like for a mealworm?

Goals

- **Observe** the stages of metamorphosis of mealworms to adult darkling beetles.
- **Compare** the physical appearance of mealworms as they go through two stages of metamorphosis.

Procedure

1. **Set up** a habitat for the mealworms by placing a 1-cm layer of bran or oatmeal on the bottom of the jar. Add a 1-cm layer of dried bread or cookie crumbs mixed with flour. Then, add another layer of bran or oatmeal.
2. **Add** a slice of apple or carrot as a source of moisture. Replace the apple or carrot daily.
3. **Place** 20 to 30 mealworms in the jar. Add a piece of crumpled paper towel.
4. **Cover** the jar with a piece of cheesecloth. Use the rubber band to secure the cloth to the jar.
5. **Observe** the mealworms daily for two to three weeks. **Record** daily observations in your Science Journal.

Conclude and Apply

1. In your Science Journal, **draw** and **describe** the mealworms' metamorphosis to adults.
2. **Identify** the stages of metamorphosis that mealworms go through to become adult darkling beetles.
3. Which of these stages did you not see during this investigation?
4. What are some of the advantages of an insect's young being different from the adult form?
5. Based on the food you placed in the habitat, **infer** where you might find mealworms or the adult darkling beetles in your house.
6. Why do you think pet stores would stock and sell mealworms?

Activity 24•2

Purpose

Visual-Spatial Students will observe the stages of the complete metamorphosis of the darkling beetle. L2 ELL COOP LEARN

Process Skills

observing, communicating, interpreting data

Time

one 45 minute period and daily observation for three to six weeks

Teaching Strategies

Mealworms are the larvae of darkling beetle, *Tenebrio molitor.* Plan on students making daily observations of the mealworms.

Troubleshooting Find a warm spot in the classroom to maintain an optimal environment for the metamorphosis of the insect. Mealworms can stay in the larval stage for up to two years depending on the environment.

Answers to Questions

1. Answers will vary.
2. egg, larva, pupa, and adult
3. egg
4. Larval forms often eat different things than the adults eat.
5. kitchen cabinets with cereal, flour, etc.
6. as food for fish, reptiles, and amphibians

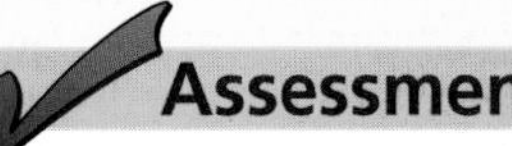

Assessment

Performance Have students observe the metamorphosis of a fruit fly and compare it with that of a mealworm. *Both are complete metamorphoses. The stages of the fruit fly are shorter than in mealworms.* Use **Performance Assessment in the Science Classroom,** p. 17.

CA Science Content Standards

Page 838: 9f

Chapter 24 Reviewing Main Ideas

Reviewing Main Ideas can be used to preview, review, reteach, and condense chapter content.

Preview

Linguistic Have students try to answer the questions in their Science Journals. Use student answers as a source for discussion throughout the chapter.

Review

Interpersonal Have students answer the questions on separate pieces of paper and compare their answers with those of other students in the class.

Reteach

Visual-Spatial Have students look at the illustrations on these pages. Ask them to describe details that support the main ideas of the chapter found in the statement for each illustration.

00:00 OUT OF TIME?

Auditory-Musical If time does not permit teaching the entire chapter, use the information on these pages along with the chapter Audiocassettes to present the material in a condensed format.

Chapter 24 Reviewing Main Ideas

For a **preview** of this chapter, study this Reviewing Main Ideas before you read the chapter. After you have studied this chapter, you can use the Reviewing Main Ideas to **review** the chapter.

The Glencoe MindJogger, Audiocassettes, and CD-ROM provide additional opportunities for review.

Section

24-1 WHAT IS AN ANIMAL?

Animals are many-celled organisms that must find and digest their own food. **Invertebrates** are animals without backbones. **Vertebrates** have backbones. Animals that have body parts arranged the same way on both sides of their bodies have bilateral **symmetry.** Animals with body parts arranged in a circle around a central point have radial symmetry. Asymetrical animals have no definite shape. ***What are five characteristics of animals?***

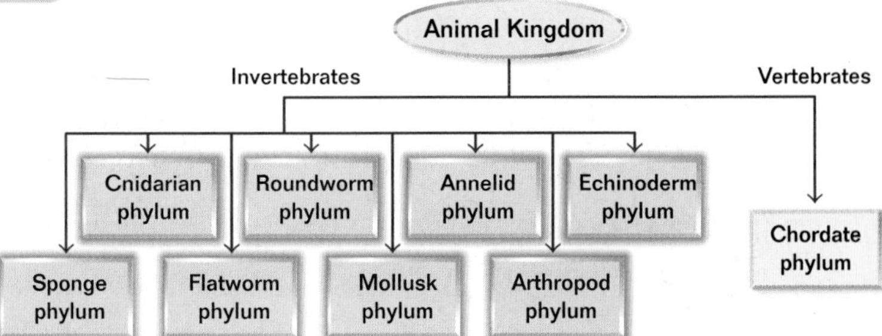

Section

24-2 SPONGES, CNIDARIANS, FLATWORMS, AND ROUNDWORMS

Sponges and cnidarians are only two layers thick. Sponge cells do not form tissues, organs, or organ systems. Sponges are sessile and obtain food and oxygen by filtering water through pores. **Cnidarian** bodies have tissues and are radially symmetrical. Most have tentacles with stinging cells that get food. Regeneration allows an organism to replace lost or damaged parts or to reproduce sexually. Flatworms and roundworms have bilateral symmetry. They have both parasitic and **free-living** members. ***Why are sponges considered the least complex of all animals?***

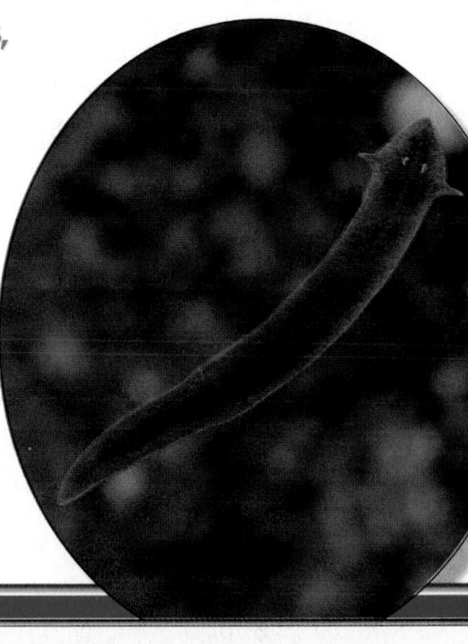

840 CHAPTER 24 INVERTEBRATE ANIMALS

Cultural Diversity

Biological Controls Zhoa Jinzao, a university vice-president in China, helped develop a technique for protecting crops from insects in the 1970s. He discovered that spiders could kill 80 to 90 percent of the harmful insects in cotton fields. Jinzao taught farmers to dig shallow pits every ten paces in their cotton field and to throw straw into the pits. Have students discuss the advantages of using spiders to control the insect population in crops.

Reading Check ✓

Choose a group of unlike objects, such as the items in your book bag or your locker. Classify these objects into groups and subgroups.

Section

24-3 MOLLUSKS AND SEGMENTED WORMS

Mollusks with one shell are gastropods. Bivalve mollusks have two shells. Cephalopods have a foot divided into tentacles and no outside shell. Except for cephalopods, mollusks have an **open circulatory system** in which the blood surrounds the organs directly. Cephalopods have a **closed circulatory system** with the blood contained in vessels. Annelids have a body cavity that separates the internal organs from the body wall. Setae help annelids move. ***How are cephalopods adapted for swimming?***

Section

24-4 ARTHROPODS AND ECHINODERMS

Arthropods are classified by the number of body segments and **appendages.** Their **exoskeletons** cover, protect, and support their bodies. Arthropods develop either by complete or incomplete **metamorphosis.** Echinoderms are spiny-skinned invertebrates most closely related to vertebrates. They move by means of a water-vascular system. ***What are some common characteristics for all arthropods?***

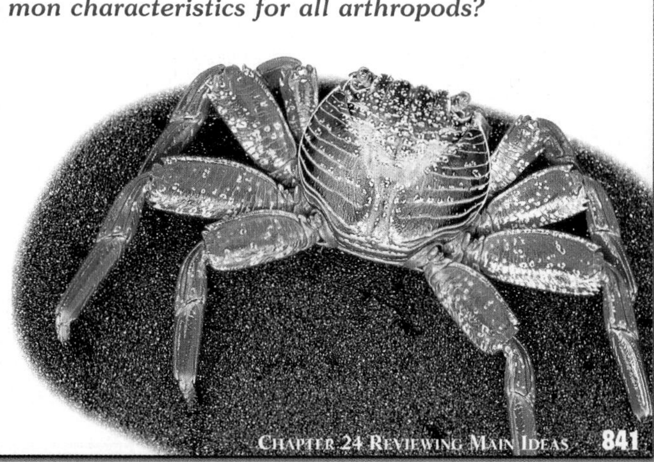

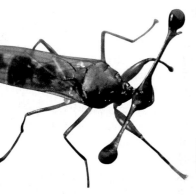

Answers to Questions

Section 24-1

What is an animal? Animals cannot make their own food. They digest their food and most can move from place to place. Animals are made of many different kinds of cells. Animal cells have a nucleus and organelles surrounded by a membrane (eukaryotic cells).

Section 24-2

Sponges, Cnidarians, Flatworms, and Roundworms Sponge bodies consist of only two cell layers. These cells are specialized but do not form tissues.

Section 24-3

Mollusks and Segmented Worms Cephalopods move by jet propulsion. Water is ejected through the funnel or siphon in one direction, which moves the animal in the opposite direction.

Section 24-4

Arthropods and Echinoderms Arthropods have exoskeletons, jointed bodies, and open circulatory systems.

GLENCOE TECHNOLOGY

CD-ROM

Glencoe Science Voyages Interactive CD-ROM

Chapter Summaries and Quizzes

Have students read the Chapter then take the Chapter Quiz to determine whether they have mastered chapter content.

Assessment

Portfolio Encourage students to place in their portfolios one or two items of what they consider to be their best work. Examples include:

- Flex your Brain, p. 819
- Problem Solving, p. 826
- Activity 24-1, pp. 830–831 P

Performance Additional performance assessments may be found in **Performance Assessment** and **Science Integration Activities.** Performance Task Assessments Lists and rubrics for evaluating these activities can be found in Glencoe's **Performance Assessment in the Science Classroom.**

Using Vocabulary

1. Medusa is bell shaped and free floating; polyp is vase shaped and usually sessile.
2. Closed-circulatory system—blood contained in vessels; open-circulatory system—blood is not contained in vessels
3. Vertebrates have backbone; invertebrates do not.
4. Mollusks have a shell for protection; arthropods have an exoskeleton for protection.
5. An exoskeleton is composed of chitin and covers an arthropod; mantle is a thin layer of tissue covering the soft body of a mollusk.

interNET CONNECTION To reinforce chapter vocabulary, use the **Study Guide for Content Mastery** booklet. Also available are activities for **Glencoe Science Voyages** on the Glencoe Science Web Site. **www.glencoe.com/sec/science/ca**

Checking Concepts

6. B	11. B
7. A	12. A
8. C	13. C
9. B	14. C
10. C	15. B

Thinking Critically

16. They reproduce by eggs and sperm; the larva of some species have flagellum that allow them to move freely.
17. Simple animals reproduce in a variety of ways so they can respond to changing conditions. This allows them to survive in poor conditions.

Chapter 24 Assessment

Using Vocabulary

a. appendage
b. arthropod
c. closed circulatory system
d. cnidarian
e. exoskeleton
f. free-living
g. gills
h. invertebrate
i. mantle
j. medusa
k. metamorphosis
l. mollusk
m. open circulatory system
n. parasite
o. polyp
p. radula
q. symmetry
r. vertebrate

Explain the differences between the terms in each of the following sets.

1. medusa, polyp
2. closed circulatory system, open circulatory system
3. vertebrate, invertebrate
4. arthropod, mollusk
5. exoskeleton, mantle

Checking Concepts

Choose the word or phrase that best answers the question.

6. Which of the following refers to animals that can be divided in half along a single line?
A) asymmetrical
B) bilaterally symmetrical
C) radially symmetrical
D) anterior

7. Which of the following do **NOT** belong to the same group?
A) fish C) jellyfish
B) hydras D) sea anemones

8. Which of the following phylums do sponges belong to?
A) Cnidaria C) Porifera
B) Nematoda D) Platyhelminthes

9. The body plans of cnidarians are polyp and which of the following?
A) larva C) ventral
B) medusa D) bud

10. Which of the following is an example of a parasite?
A) sponge C) tapeworm
B) planarian D) jellyfish

11. Which of the following covers the organs of mollusks?
A) radula C) gill
B) mantle D) foot

12. Which organism has a closed circulatory system?
A) octopus C) oyster
B) snail D) sponge

13. Which organism has two body regions?
A) insect C) arachnid
B) mollusk D) annelid

14. Which phylum has many organisms with radial symmetry?
A) annelids C) echinoderms
B) mollusks D) arthropods

15. Which of the following are sharp and cause predators to avoid eating sponges?
A) thorax C) collar cells
B) spicules D) tentacles

Thinking Critically

16. What aspect of sponge reproduction would be evidence that they are more like animals than plants?
17. What is the advantage for simple organisms to have more than one means of reproduction?
18. What are the differences between the tentacles of cnidarians and cephalopods?
19. What is the difference between budding and regeneration?
20. Centipedes and millipedes have segments. Why are they **NOT** classified as worms?

18. Cnidarians tentacles have stinging cells for stunning prey. Cephalopod tentacles have suckers for grasping prey.
19. Budding involves cells or a new individual developing on and then breaking off of the parent. Regeneration involves replacing lost parts.
20. They have jointed appendages, or legs, attached to each segment, while worms do not. Centipedes have one pair of legs per segment and millipedes have two pair of legs per section.

Developing Skills

If you need help, refer to the **Skill Handbook.**

21. **Comparing and Contrasting:** Compare and contrast the feeding habits of sponges and cnidarians.
22. **Using Variables, Constants, and Controls:** Design an experiment to test the sense of touch in planarians.
23. **Observing and Inferring:** Why are gastropods sometimes called univalves? Use examples in your answer.
24. **Classifying:** Classify the following animals into arthropod classes: *spider, grasshopper, ladybug, beetle, crab, scorpion, lobster, butterfly, tick,* and *shrimp.*
25. **Concept Mapping:** Complete the concept map of classification in the cnidarian phylum.

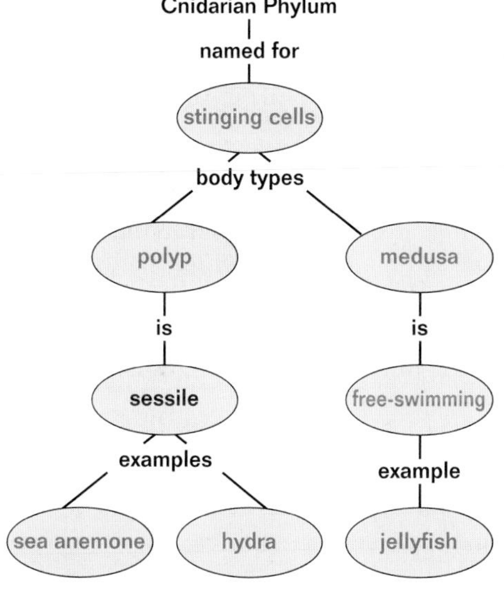

Test-Taking Tip

Words Are Easy to Learn Make a huge stack of vocabulary flash cards and study them. Use your new words in daily conversation. The great thing about learning new words is the ability to express yourself more specifically.

Test Practice

Use these questions to test your Science Proficiency.

1. Symmetry refers to the arrangement of the individual parts of an object. Which of the following organisms have radial symmetry?
   A) cnidarians
   B) sponges
   C) tapeworms
   D) mollusks
2. Echinoderms have a unique way of eating. Which of the following structures are used by echinoderms to move about and open a mollusk's shell?
   A) spicules
   B) arms
   C) spines
   D) tube feet
3. A water-vascular system is a network of water-filled canals. Which of the following phylums of invertebrates possess a water-vascular system?
   A) echinoderms
   B) arthropods
   C) mollusks
   D) cnidarians

Assessment Resources

The **Test Practice Workbook** provides students with practice in the format, concepts, and critical-thinking skills tested in standardized exams.

Reproducible Masters

Chapter Review, pp. 47–48 L2
Performance Assessment, p. 24 L2
Assessment, pp. 93–96 L2

Glencoe Technology

Chapter Review Software
Computer Test Bank
MindJogger Videoquiz

Test Practice

The Test-Taking Tip was written by The Princeton Review, the nation's leader in test preparation.

1. A
2. D
3. A

Developing Skills

21. Sponges filter microscopic plants, animals and other materials out of the water. Collar cells help move water through the sponge. Cnidarians use the stinging cells on their tentacles to paralyze an organism, and then the tentacles pull that organism into the mouth.
22. From their observations of planarians, students should be able to suggest an experiment that involves touching the planarian with natural objects and observing the movement.
23. Gastropods have only one shell, as compared to bivalves, which have two shells.
24. arachnids: spider, scorpion, tick; crustaceans: pill bug, crab, lobster; insect: grasshopper, ladybug, beetle, butterfly, flea
25. See student page.

Bonus Question

What problems do arthropods have immediately after molting? *The exoskeleton is not fully hardened right after molting. Organisms usually hide at this time, until their exoskeleton is hard enough to protect them from predators.*

Chapter 25 Vertebrate Animals

Section	Objectives	Activities/Features
Chapter Opener		Explore Activity: Model Bones, p. 845
25-1 **Fish** 1 Session ½ Block	1. **Identify** the major characteristics of chordates. 2. **Explain** the differences between ectotherms and endotherms. 3. **Describe** the characteristics that identify the three classes of fish.	Using Math, p. 847 Physics Integration, p. 848 Skill Builder: Observing and Inferring, p. 849 Using Math, p. 849
25-2 **Amphibians and Reptiles** 3 Sessions 1½ Blocks	4. **Describe** the adaptations that amphibians have for living in water and on land. 5. **Describe** frog metamorphosis. 6. **Identify** the adaptations that enable reptiles to live on land.	Skill Builder: Comparing and Contrasting, p. 854 Science Journal, p. 854 Activity 25-1: Frog Metamorphosis, p. 855
25-3 **Birds** 1 Session ½ Block	7. **Identify** the characteristics of birds. 8. **Identify** the adaptations birds have for flight.	Using Math, p. 858 Physics Integration, p. 858 MiniLab: Observing Bird Feathers, p. 859 Skill Builder: Concept Mapping, p. 860 Using Computers, p. 860 History of Science: Flight Through the Ages, p. 861
25-4 **Mammals** 4 Sessions 2 Blocks	9. **Identify** the characteristics of mammals. 10. **Explain** how mammals adapt to different environments. 11. **Distinguish** among monotremes, marsupials, and placental mammals.	MiniLab: Observing Hair, p. 863 Problem Solving: Predicting Bat Behavior, p. 864 Skill Builder: Observing and Inferring, p. 869 Using Math, p. 869 On the Internet: Bird Counts, pp. 870–871

The number of recommended single-period sessions — The number of recommended blocks
One session and one-half block are allowed for chapter review and assessment.

Activity Materials

Explore	Activities	MiniLabs
p. 845 60 index cards, tape, books	p. 855 aquarium, frog egg mass, pond water, stereoscopic microscope, watch glass, small fishnet, aquatic plants, washed gravel, boiled lettuce, large rock	p. 848 2-L plastic bottle with cap, dropper p. 859 hand lens, contour feather, down feather

Need Materials? Contact Science Kit at 1-800-828-7777 or at www.sciencekit.com on the Internet.
For alternate materials, see the activity on the listed page.

Chapter Organizer

Standards		Reproducible Resources	Technology
National	State/Local	Test Practice Workbooks are available for use with each chapter.	English and Spanish audiocassettes are available for use with each section.
National Content Standards: UCP1, UCP5, C1, C2, C3, C4, E2	California Science Content Standards: 8c, 8d, 9e, 9f	**Enrichment,** p. 71 **Reinforcement,** p. 71 **Study Guide,** p. 97	**Section Focus Transparency 71** **Teaching Transparency 49** **Teaching Transparency 50** **Glencoe Science Voyages Interactive CD-ROM** **Glencoe Science Voyages Interactive Videodisc—Life**
National Content Standards: UCP1, A1, C1, C2, C3, C5	California Science Content Standards: 9b	**Activity Worksheets,** pp. 141–142 **Enrichment,** p. 72 **Multicultural Connections,** pp. 49–50 **Reinforcement,** p. 72 **Study Guide,** p. 98	**Section Focus Transparency 72** **Internet Connection,** p. 851 **National Geographic Society: STV**
National Content Standards: UCP1, UCP5, C1, C2, C3, C5, E2	California Science Content Standards: 2b, 2d, 2e, 9b, 9f	**Activity Worksheets,** p. 143 **Critical Thinking/Problem Solving,** p. 25 **Enrichment,** p. 73 **Laboratory Manual,** pp. 155–156 **Reinforcement,** p. 73 **Study Guide,** p. 99	**Section Focus Transparency 73** **Internet Connection,** p. 861
National Content Standards: UCP1, UCP5, C1, C2, C3, C4, C5	California Science Content Standards: 9a, 9b, 9e, 9f	**Activity Worksheets,** p. 144 **Enrichment,** p. 74 **Laboratory Manual,** pp. 153–154 **Reinforcement,** p. 74 **Study Guide,** pp. 99–100	**Section Focus Transparency 74** **Science Integration Transparency 25** **Internet Connection,** p. 865 **Glencoe Science Voyages Interactive Videodisc—Life**

Key to Teaching Strategies

The following designations will help you decide which activities are appropriate for your students.

L1 Level 1 activities should be appropriate for students with learning difficulties.

L2 Level 2 activities should be within the ability range of all students.

L3 Level 3 activities are designed for above-average students.

ELL ELL activities should be within the ability range of English Language Learners.

COOP LEARN Cooperative Learning activities are designed for small group work.

P These strategies represent student products that can be placed into a best-work portfolio.

Multiple Learning Styles logos, as described on page 55T, are used throughout to indicate strategies that address different learning styles.

Assessment Resources

Chapter Review, pp. 49–50
Assessment, pp. 97–100
Performance Assessment in the Science Classroom (PASC)
MindJogger Videoquiz
Alternate Assessment in the Science Classroom
Performance Assessment, p. 25
Chapter Review Software
Computer Test Bank

Chapter 25 Vertebrate Animals

This is a representation of key blackline masters available in the Teacher Classroom Resources. See Resource Manager boxes within the chapter for additional information.

Transparencies

Section Focus Transparencies

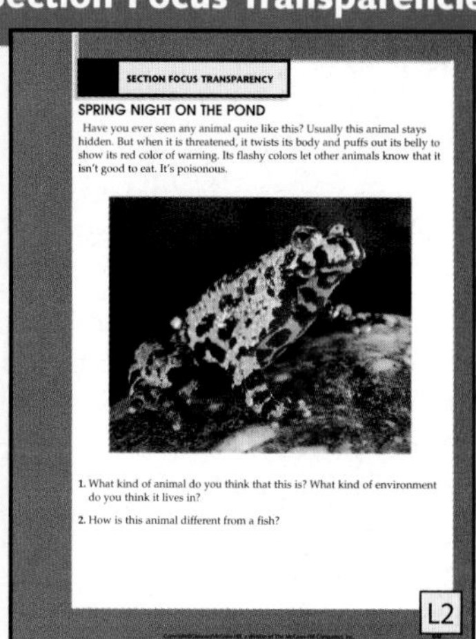

Science Integration Transparencies

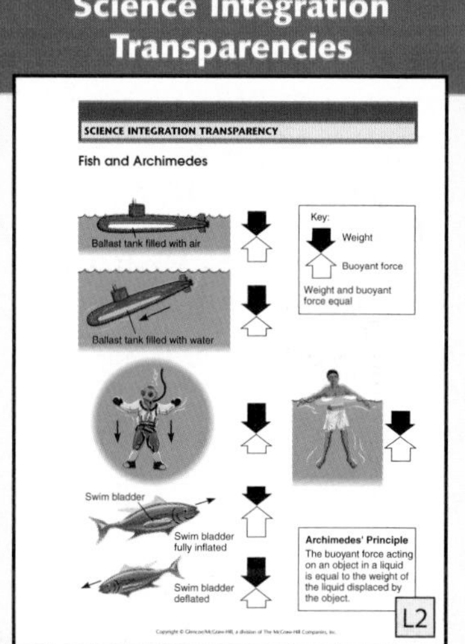

Teaching Transparencies

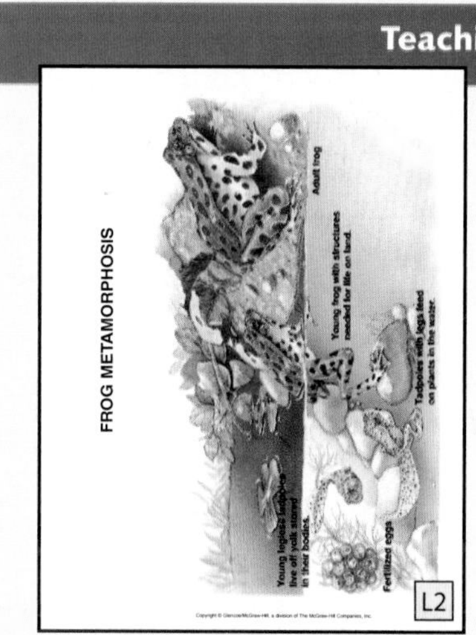

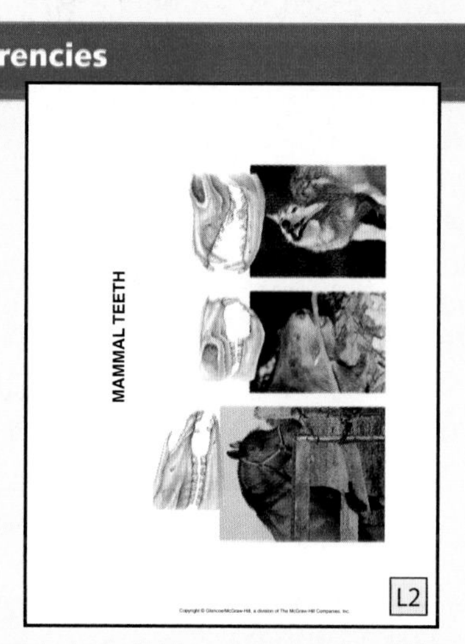

Meeting Different Ability Levels

Study Guide for Content Mastery

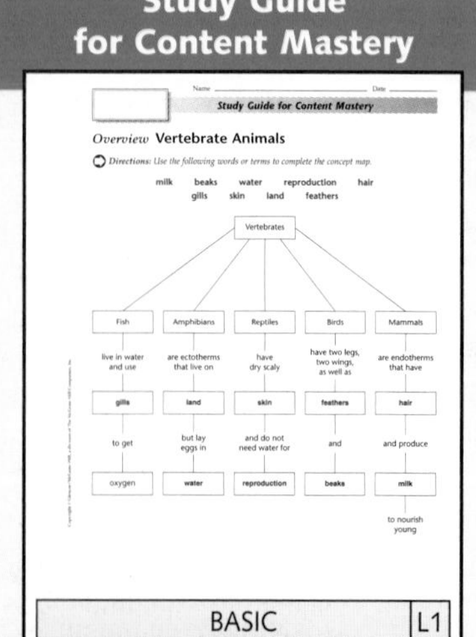

Reinforcement

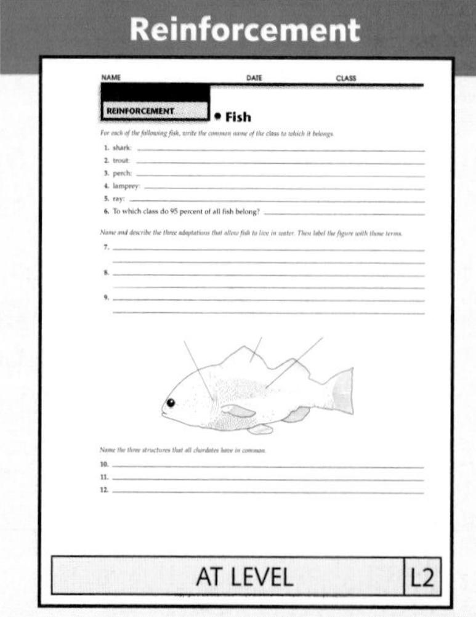

Enrichment Worksheets

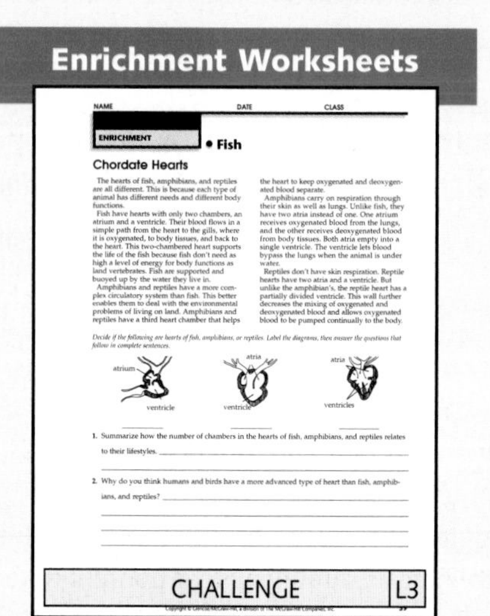

Resource Manager

Hands-on Activities

Activity Worksheets

ACTIVITY 21-1 • Frog Metamorphosis

Lab Preview

Frogs and other amphibians use external fertilization to reproduce. Female frogs lay hundreds of jellylike eggs in water. Male frogs then fertilize these eggs. Once larvae hatch, the process of metamorphosis begins. Over a period of time, young tadpoles develop into adult frogs.

What You'll Investigate

Goals

Materials

Procedure

L2

Lab Manual

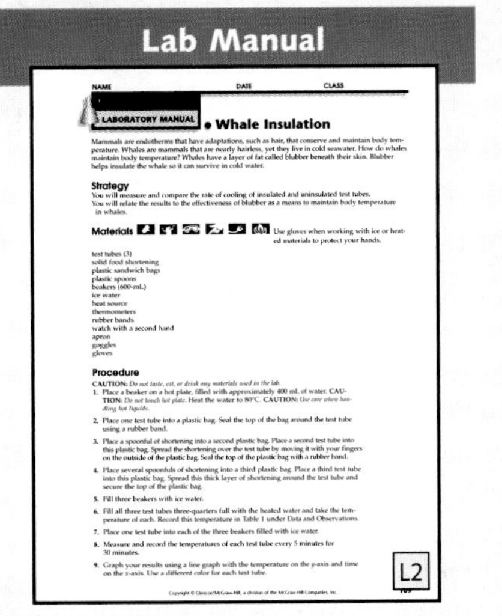
LABORATORY MANUAL • Whale Insulation

Strategy

Materials

Procedure

L2

Accessibility

Spanish Resources

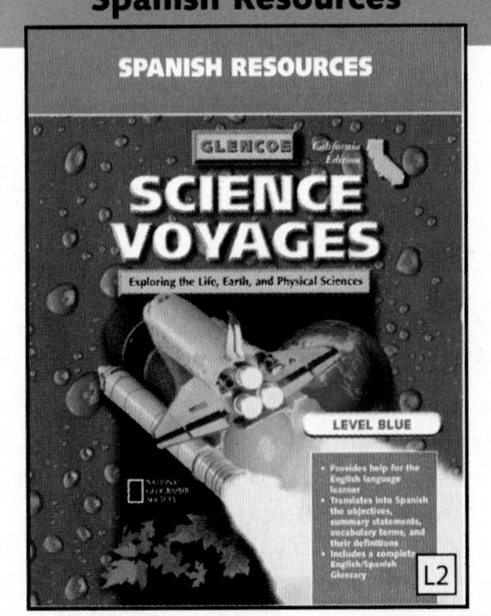
SPANISH RESOURCES

GLENCOE SCIENCE VOYAGES

Exploring the Life, Earth, and Physical Sciences

LEVEL BLUE

L2

Assessment

Performance Assessment

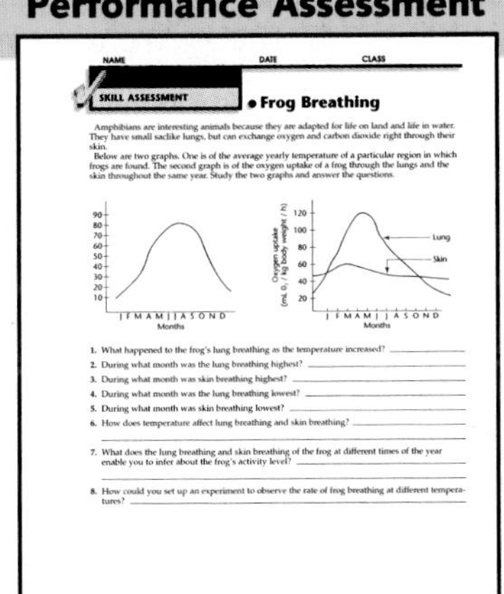
SKILL ASSESSMENT • Frog Breathing

L2

Chapter Review

CHAPTER REVIEW • Vertebrate Animals

Part A. Vocabulary Review

L2

Assessment

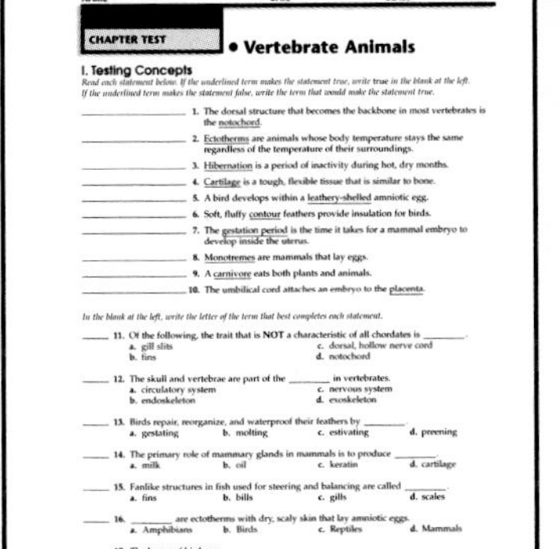
CHAPTER TEST • Vertebrate Animals

I. Testing Concepts

L2

Test Practice Workbook

CALIFORNIA SCIENCE CONTENT STANDARDS PRACTICE QUESTIONS

GLENCOE SCIENCE VOYAGES

Exploring the Life, Earth, and Physical Sciences

LEVEL BLUE

THE PRINCETON REVIEW

L2

Extending Content

Critical Thinking/ Problem Solving

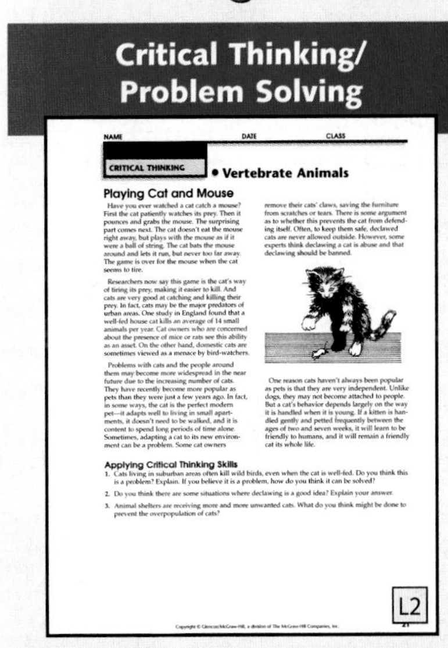
CRITICAL THINKING • Vertebrate Animals

Playing Cat and Mouse

Applying Critical Thinking Skills

L2

Multicultural Connections

MULTICULTURAL CONNECTIONS • Whose beach is it anyway?

Day of Decision

People Power, Turtle Power

L2

Chapter 25 Vertebrate Animals

Helping You Prepare

What is a vertebrate? (Section 25-1)

When studying the structure of an animal, it is important to distinguish between traits that are of common origin—homology—and indicate a common ancestry in descent and features that are of similar function but of unlike origin—analogy. The bones in the wings of bats and birds are homologous, as they are a modification of forelimb bones of land vertebrates. The wings of insects, even though similar in function, are analogous as they are most likely derived from extensions of the body wall.

All the organ systems represent homologies in vertebrates. Much of the evidence comes from comparative studies of embryonic development. For example, fish have a two-chambered heart and gills for the exchange of oxygen and carbon dioxide. In the gills, the blood in the capillaries has lost nearly all its pressure, which seriously reduces the efficiency of the entire circulatory system. Amphibians have a three-chambered heart with two atria that separate systemic and pulmonary circulation. Even with only one ventricle, studies have shown that there is little mixing of oxygenated and deoxygenated blood. Reptiles have an incomplete four-chambered heart. The atria are completely separated, but the septum of the right and left ventricles is incomplete. Birds and mammals have four-chambered hearts that completely separate blood into systemic and pulmonary circulation.

GLENCOE TECHNOLOGY

Glencoe Science Voyages Interactive CD-ROM

Chapter Summaries

Use the Chapter Summary to introduce, teach, or review chapter material.

Characteristics of Fish (Section 25-1)

Some fish are considered warm-blooded, but are not truly endotherms. Bluefin tuna are able to maintain a body temperature as much as 25°F higher than that of the surrounding water. Blood is heated in the swimming muscles that run down the center of the body and are well insulated. Blood vessels carrying cold blood from the gills to the body have contact with blood vessels carrying warm blood from the body to the gills. Cold blood coming from the gills is warmed before reaching the inside of the body and blood from the body is cooled on its way to the gills. Thus, the fish retain precious body heat while swimming in cold water.

NATIONAL GEOGRAPHIC — **Teacher's Corner**

Products Available from Glencoe

To order the following products for use with this chapter, call Glencoe at 1-800-334-7344:

CD-ROMs

Mammals: A Multimedia Encyclopedia

NGS PictueShow: Classifying Plants and Animals

NGS PictureShow: Structure of Vertebrates 1

NGS PictureShow: Structure of Vertebrates 2

Curriculum Kit

GeoKit: Fish, Reptiles, and Amphibians

Transparency Sets

NGS PicturePack: Classifying Plants and Animals

NGS PicturePack: Structure of Vertebrates 1

NGS PicturePack: Structure of Vertebrates 2

Videodisc

STV: Animals

Products Available from National Geographic Society

To order the following products for use with this chapter, call National Geographic Society at 1-800-368-2728:

Book

National Geographic Book of Mammals

Video

Reptiles and Amphibians

Bony Fish (Section 25-1)

An important adaptation in most bony fish is the swim bladder—an air sac that helps control the depth at which the fish swims. The swim bladder in a fish allows it to adjust its density so it can rise or sink.

The swim bladder adjusts the density of a fish by an exchange of gases with the blood. When the swim bladder inflates, the fish becomes more buoyant and rises in the water. When the swim bladder deflates, the fish becomes less buoyant and sinks until the density of the fish is equal to the density of the surrounding liquid.

Amphibians (Section 25-2)

Amphibians are sensitive to changes in their environment. Because they live on land and reproduce in water, they are directly affected by chemical changes in their environment, including those resulting from soil erosion and water pollution. Amphibians also absorb gases through their skin, making them susceptible to air pollutants as well.

Reptiles (Section 25-2)

Reptiles vary greatly in size, shape, and color. Giant pythons, 10 m in length, can swallow deer whole. Some sea turtles have a mass of almost one metric ton and can swim faster than you can run. Three-horned lizards have movable eye sockets and tongues as long as their bodies. Reptiles live on every continent except Antarctica and in all the oceans except those in polar regions.

Birds (Section 25-3)

In 1861, in a limestone quarry in Bavaria, Germany, one of the world's best-known fossils was found. The skeleton suggested that it was a small, bipedal, insect-eating dinosaur. Upon further study, the unmistakable imprint of wings and feathers was discovered. Feathers are one of the defining characteristics of all birds. The animal was given the name *Archaeopteryx lithographica.* Unlike modern birds, *Archaeopteryx* had teeth, a long tail, free-floating ribs, and wings with claws attached to movable fingers. Except for wings, these are all characteristics of small dinosaurs. It is considered one of the intermediary species linking reptiles and birds.

Body Systems in Mammals (Section 25-4)

The digestive system of mammals varies according to the kind of food the animals eat. Carnivores have short digestive systems compared to those of herbivores because meat is more easily digested than plant material. Herbivores need long digestive systems to help break down the carbohydrate called cellulose found in plants.

SCIENCE UPDATE

For current events or science in the news, access the Glencoe Science Web Site at **www.glencoe.com/sec/science/ca**

Teacher to Teacher

"To introduce and reinforce the characteristics of vertebrates, borrow animals from a pet store. Get at least one example from each of the five phyla of vertebrates. Have students list characteristics for each animal group. Instruct students how to handle animals humanely and safely."

Maureen E. Allen

Maureen Allen, Science Resource Specialist
Brywood Elementary School
Irvine, CA

CHAPTER 25 Vertebrate Animals

Chapter Overview

Section 25-1 This section describes the major characteristics of chordates and fish.

Section 25-2 This section examines amphibian adaptations for their dual life on land and water and characteristics that set reptiles apart from amphibians.

Section 25-3 This section describes how the internal and external features of birds are adaptations for flight.

Section 25-4 This section examines the features used to classify mammals and their different reproductive strategies.

Chapter Vocabulary

chordate
endoskeleton
ectotherm
endotherm
fish
fin
cartilage
amphibian
hibernation
estivation
reptile
bird
contour feather
down feather
mammal
monotreme
marsupial
placental mammal
herbivore
carnivore
omnivore

Theme Connection

Stability and Change Adaptations that fish, amphibians, reptiles, birds, and mammals have to their environments result in the species becoming stable in its environment.

OUT OF TIME?

If time does not permit teaching the entire chapter, use Reviewing Main Ideas on pages 872–873.

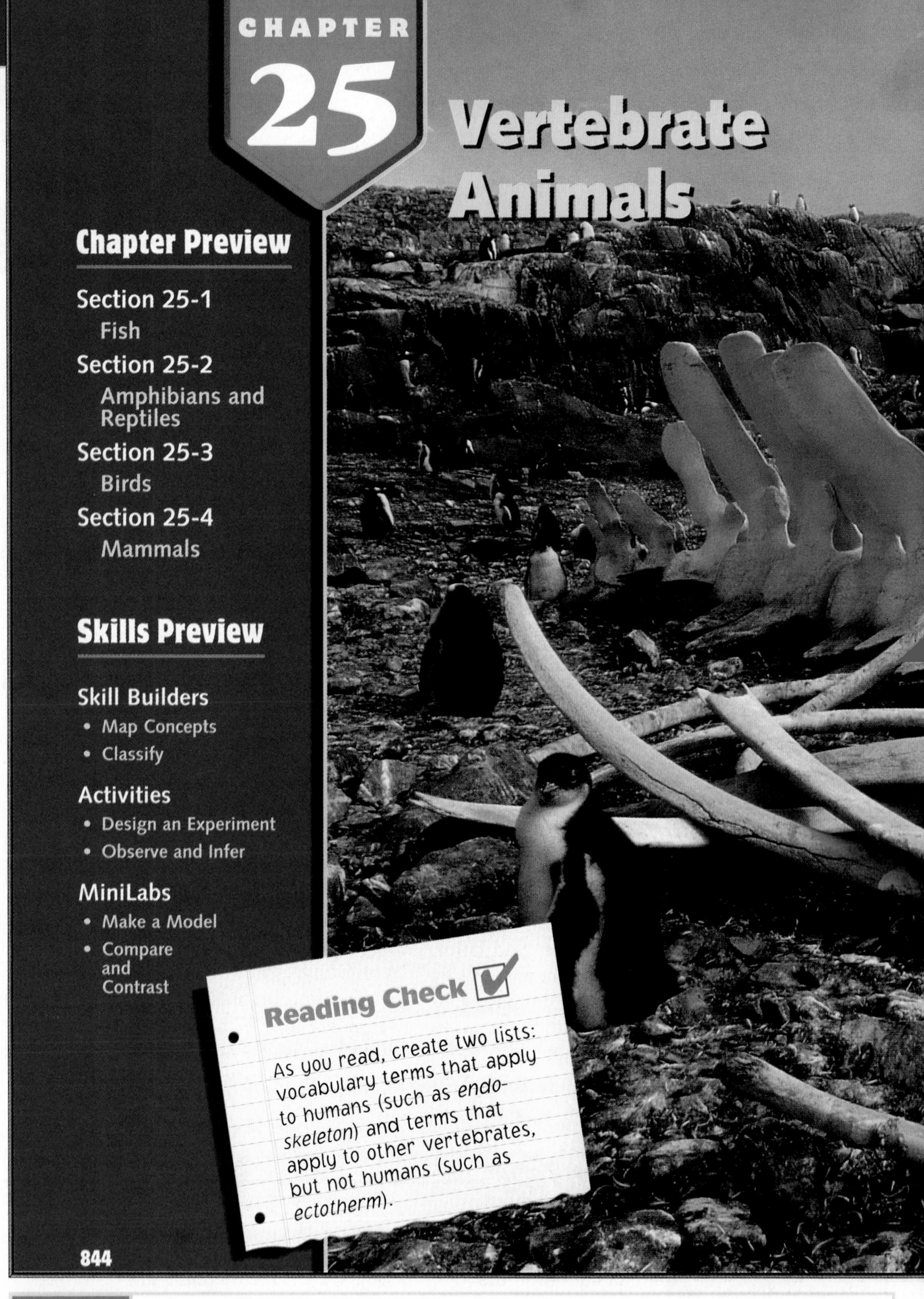

CHAPTER 25
Vertebrate Animals
Chapter Preview
Section 25-1 Fish
Section 25-2 Amphibians and Reptiles
Section 25-3 Birds
Section 25-4 Mammals
Skills Preview
Skill Builders
• Map Concepts
• Classify
Activities
• Design an Experiment
• Observe and Infer
MiniLabs
• Make a Model
• Compare and Contrast
Reading Check
As you read, create two lists: vocabulary terms that apply to humans (such as *endoskeleton*) and terms that apply to other vertebrates, but not humans (such as *ectotherm*).
844

Multiple Learning Styles

Look for the following logos for strategies that emphasize different learning modalities.

Linguistic Using Science Words, p. 851; Across the Curriculum, p. 866; Enrichment, p. 866; Preview, p. 872

Visual-Spatial Activity, pp. 848, 855, 864, 868; Quick Demo, p. 852; Assessment, p. 854; Science Journal, p. 857; Visual Learning, p. 857; MiniLab, pp. 859, 863; Multiple Learning Styles, p. 863; Reteach, p. 872

Auditory-Musical Out of Time, p. 872

Kinesthetic Inclusion Strategies, p. 847; Assessment, p. 860

Interpersonal Explore Activity, p. 845; Inclusion Strategies, p. 857; Activity, p. 857; Reteach, p. 868; Review, p. 872

Naturalist Reteach, p. 853; Activity, pp. 871–872

Explore Activity

You have something in common with the whale remains on the opposite page. This common feature protects some of the organs inside your body. It supports and gives your body shape. It also works with your muscles to help move your body. This common feature is your skeleton. Most internal skeletons are made of bone. Bones are many shapes and sizes. They must be strong enough to carry your weight yet light enough for you to move. To learn more about the structure of bones, complete the following Explore Activity.

Model Bones

1. Think about the different shapes of your bones. What shape is your shoulder blade? Your hip bone? Your neck? Your ribs?
2. Use five index cards to make bone models. Fold and bend the cards into different shapes. Use tape to hold the shapes if necessary.
3. Stack books on top of each card to find out which shape supports the most weight.

In your Science Journal, draw a picture of each bone model. Infer which shape would make the strongest bone. Write a paragraph comparing the strengths of each bone model.

Assessment Planner

Porfolio
Refer to p. 873 for suggested items that students might select for their portfolios.

Performance Assessment
See p. 873 for additional Performance Assessment options.
Skill Builder, pp. 849, 854, 860
MiniLab, pp. 859, 863
Activity 25-1, p. 855; 25-2, pp. 870–871

Content Assessment
Section Assessment, pp. 849, 854, 860, 869
Chapter Assessment, pp. 874–875
Proficiency Prep, pp. 849, 854, 860, 869

Explore Activity

Purpose

Interpersonal Use the Explore Activity to have students formulate models showing what shapes of structures are the strongest. L2 ELL COOP LEARN

Materials

4 × 6 note cards, tape, small books

Teaching Strategies

- Students may roll index cards into tubes or fold them into squares or triangles.
- Encourage students to make at least three different models that they can test. Have students in the group take turns actually building the model, sketching the model that was built, and recording data about the strength of the models on a chart or graph.

Be sure inferences and sketches are clearly matched to the paragraphs. Students should justify all inferences.

Assessment

Process Have students work in pairs to create the tallest tower they can from a single sheet of notebook paper. Allow them to use scissors and tape in the tower's construction. Have students relate their results to the results of the Explore Activity. Use **Performance Assessment in the Science Classroom,** p. 97.

SECTION 25•1

Prepare

Refer to **What is a vertebrate?, Characteristics of Fish,** and **Bony Fish** on pp. 844E–F.

Preplanning

Refer to the **Chapter Organizer** on pp. 844A–B.

1 Motivate

Bellringer

Before presenting the lesson, display **Section Focus Transparency 71** on the overhead projector. Use the accompanying **Focus Activity** worksheet. L2 ELL

Section 15-1

SECTION FOCUS TRANSPARENCY

GOING FOR A RIDE

In the past, many kinds of fish were important to Pacific Islanders. People not only ate fish, but also used fish scales to smooth their wooden canoes. Some scientists think that the people of Tahiti sailed 3000 miles of the Pacific Ocean to settle the islands of Hawaii. Their fast outrigger canoes transported them through waters that were home to many flying fish and hungry sharks.

1. How are fish different from animals like octopus or squid that might live in the ocean?
2. What kind of structures do fish have that make them well adapted for life in the ocean?
3. The skeletons of bony fish and sharks have a major difference. Do you know what it is?

Tying to Previous Knowledge

Ask students to describe what vertebrae are and have them infer what animals known as vertebrates are. Ask them to name as many kinds of vertebrates as possible. L2

25•1 Fish

What You'll Learn

- The major characteristics of chordates
- The difference between ectotherms and endotherms
- The characteristics of the three classes of fish

Vocabulary

chordate
endoskeleton
ectotherm
endotherm
fish
fin
cartilage

Why It's Important

- Fish have many adaptations for living in water.

What is a vertebrate?

Suppose you took a survey in which you asked your classmates to list their pets. Probably dogs, cats, birds, snakes, and fish appear on the list. A large percentage of the animals listed, along with yourself, would belong to a group called vertebrates. Vertebrates are animals with backbones. They are the most complex of three animal groups that belong to the Chordate phylum, as illustrated in **Figure 25-1.** All **chordates** have a notochord, which is a rod of stiffened tissue. Chordates also have a hollow nerve cord in their backs and gill slits. In most vertebrates, a backbone made of vertebra replaces the notochord as the animal develops.

Whereas most invertebrates have exoskeletons, vertebrates have an internal system of bones called an **endoskeleton.** *Endo-* means "within." The vertebrae, skull, and other bones of the endoskeleton support and protect the animal's internal organs. The skeleton also provides a place where muscles are attached.

Vertebrates have two different ways of dealing with internal body temperature. Most vertebrates are ectotherms. **Ectotherms** are vertebrates whose body temperature changes with the temperature of their surroundings. **Endotherms** are animals with a constant body temperature. The body temperature of an endotherm usually remains the same no matter what the temperature of its surrounding environment.

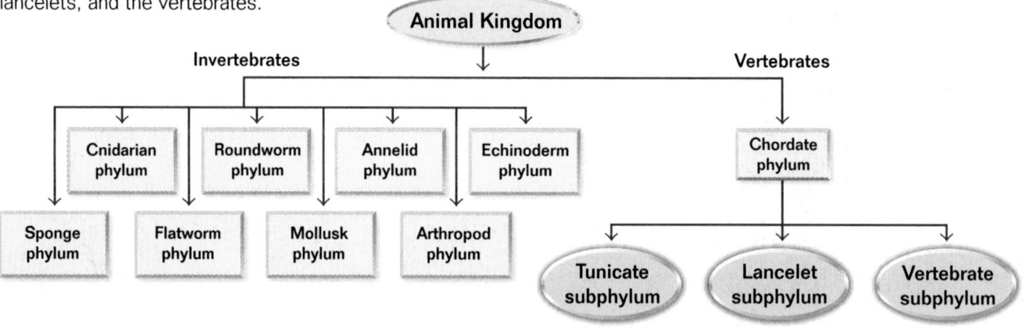

Figure 25-1 This concept map showing the different groups of animals will appear at the beginning of each section. The groups that are highlighted with a red outline are the groups to be discussed. This diagram shows that the Chordate phylum is made up of three groups: the tunicates, the lancelets, and the vertebrates.

Resource Manager

The following **Teacher Classroom Resources** can be used with Section 25-1:

 **Reproducible Masters**

Enrichment, p. 71 L3

Reinforcement, p. 71 L2

Study Guide, p. 97 L1 ELL

Animal Kingdom
Invertebrates | Vertebrates
Chordate phylum
Tunicate subphylum | Lancelet subphylum | Vertebrate subphylum
Jawless fish class | Cartilaginous fish class | Bony fish class | Other classes of vertebrates

Figure 25-2 Fish make up three classes of vertebrates. The hagfish (A) is an example of a jawless fish. The trout (B) is a bony fish. The stingray (C) is an example of a cartilaginous fish.

Traits of Fish

Because nearly three-quarters of Earth is covered with water, it is not surprising that the largest group of vertebrates lives in water. **Figure 25-2** illustrates how fish relate to other vertebrates. Fish can be found in warm desert pools and the subfreezing Arctic ocean. They swim in shallow streams and far down in the ocean depths.

Fish are ectotherms that live in water and use gills to get oxygen. Gills are fleshy filaments that are filled with tiny blood vessels. The heart of the fish pumps blood to the gills. As blood passes through the gills, it picks up oxygen from water that is passing over the gills. Carbon dioxide is released from the blood into the water.

Most fish have fins. **Fins** are fanlike structures used for steering, balancing, and moving. Usually, they are paired. Those on the top and bottom stabilize the fish. Those on the side steer and move the fish. Scales are another common characteristic of fish although not all fish have scales. Scales are hard, thin, overlapping plates that cover the skin. These protective plates are made of a bony material.

Using Math

Make a circle graph of the number of fish species currently classified. There are 70 species of jawless fish, 820 species of cartilaginous fish, and 23 500 species of bony fish. What percent of this graph is accounted for by cartilaginous fish?

2 Teach

GLENCOE TECHNOLOGY

CD-ROM

Glencoe Science Voyages Interactive CD-ROM

Explorations

Have students do the interactive exploration *How are fish adapted to their environments?*

Flex Your Brain

Use the Flex Your Brain activity to have students explore CHORDATES. P

Using Math

1.1 percent of the circle graph (or 4°) represents cartilaginous fish; 98.7 percent (or 355°) represents bony fish; 0.18 percent (or 0.6°) represents jawless fish.

Inclusion Strategies

Learning Disabled Have students make a mobile of the different types of fish mentioned in this chapter (jawless, cartilaginous, and bony). Beneath each type, have them write the information that they find most interesting about it. L2

PHYSICS INTEGRATION

To adjust to changes in water pressure, scuba divers use devices called buoyancy compensators that work similarly to a fish or submarine.

GLENCOE TECHNOLOGY

Videodisc

Glencoe Science Voyages Interactive Videodisc—Life

Side 2, Lesson 5 *Structural Adaptations in Animals*

4103

Refer to Videodisc Teacher Guide for additional bar codes.

3 Assess

Check for Understanding Activity

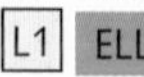

Visual-Spatial Have students examine X-ray photographs of a vertebrate to observe an endoskeleton. L1 ELL

Reteach

Have students explain how their own lungs can act like a fish's swim bladder. L2

Extension

For students who have mastered this section, use the **Reinforcement** and **Enrichment** masters.

Caption Answer

Figure 25-3 *fins, gills, swim bladder*

Types of Fish

Scientists group fish into three distinct classes. They are bony fish, jawless fish, and cartilaginous fish. Bony fish have skeletons made of bone, while cartilaginous fish and jawless fish both have endoskeletons made of cartilage. **Cartilage** (KART uh lihj) is a tough, flexible tissue that is similar to bone but is not as hard. Your ears and the tip of your nose are made of cartilage.

Bony Fish

About 95 percent of all fish belong to the class known as bony fish. The body structure of a typical bony fish, a tuna, is shown in **Figure 25-3.** These fish have skeletons made of bone. Their scales are covered with slimy mucus that allows the water to easily flow over the fishes' bodies as they swim in water. The majority of bony fish use external fertilization to reproduce. Females release large numbers of eggs into the water. Males release sperm as they swim over the eggs.

An important adaptation in most bony fish is the swim bladder. This air sac helps control the depth at which the fish swim. Transfer of gases between the swim bladder and the blood, mostly oxygen in deep-water fish and nitrogen in shallow-water fish, changes the inflation of the swim bladder. As the swim bladder fills with gases, the fish becomes more buoyant and rises in the water. When the bladder deflates, the fish becomes less buoyant and sinks lower in the water.

EXAMPLES OF Bony Fish

- Trout
- Cod
- Salmon
- Catfish
- Tuna
- Sea horse

PHYSICS INTEGRATION

Regulating Buoyancy
Unlike fish that regulate the gas content of their fish bladders, submarines pump water into and out of special chambers to regulate the vertical forces that cause the submarine to sink or rise.

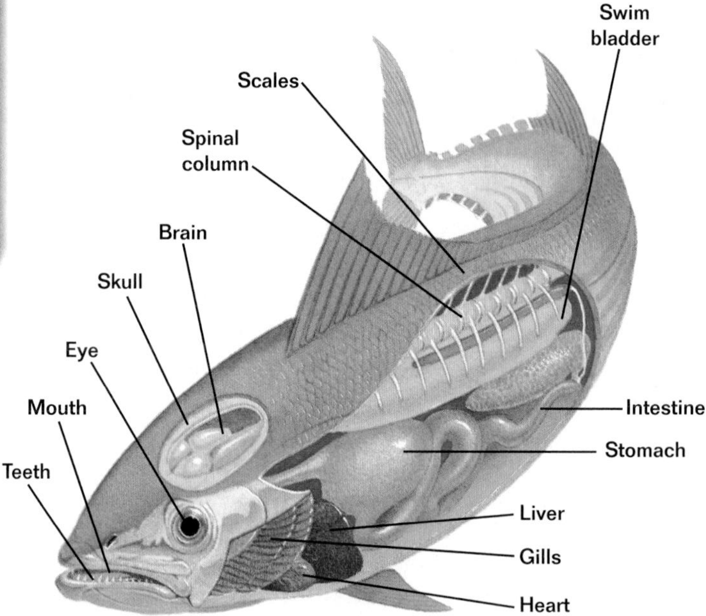

Figure 25-3 Although there are many different kinds of bony fish, they all share basic structures. **What are two unique fish structures?**

Guided Reading Strategy

Quickwrites This strategy, sometimes called freewrites, lets students use spontaneous writing to discover what they already know. Have students write a list of ideas about a topic, then share these ideas with the class. Next, have students write their ideas in a paragraph without worrying about punctuation, spelling, and grammar. Have students use a Quickwrite to share ideas during or after a learning experience in this chapter.

Figure 25-4 This sea lamprey (A) with its sucker disk mouth belongs to the class of jawless fish. Sharks (B) belong to the cartilaginous class and are efficient at finding and killing food.

Jawless and Cartilaginous Fish

Few fish belong to the class known as jawless fish. Jawless fish have long, scaleless, tubelike bodies and an endoskeleton made of cartilage. They have round mouths but no jaws, as seen in **Figure 25-4A.** Their mouths act like suckers with sharp toothlike parts. Once a lamprey attaches itself to another larger fish, it uses the toothlike parts to scrape through the host's skin. It then feeds on the blood of the larger fish.

Sharks, skates, and rays are cartilaginous fish. Cartilaginous fish have skeletons made of cartilage just like the jawless fish. However, cartilaginous fish, such as the shark in **Figure 25-4B,** have movable jaws and scales. Their scales feel rough like sandpaper. Most cartilaginous fish are predators.

Section Assessment

1. What are three characteristics of chordates?
2. Name the three classes of fish. What materials make up their skeletons?
3. Compare and contrast ectotherms and endotherms.
4. **Think Critically:** Female fish lay thousands of eggs. Why aren't lakes overcrowded with fish?
5. **Skill Builder**
Observing and Inferring Fish without swim bladders, such as sharks, must move constantly, or they sink. They need more energy to maintain this constant movement. What can you infer about the amount of food sharks must eat when compared to another fish of similar size that have swim bladders? If you need help, refer to Observing and Inferring in the **Skill Handbook** on page 956.

Using Math

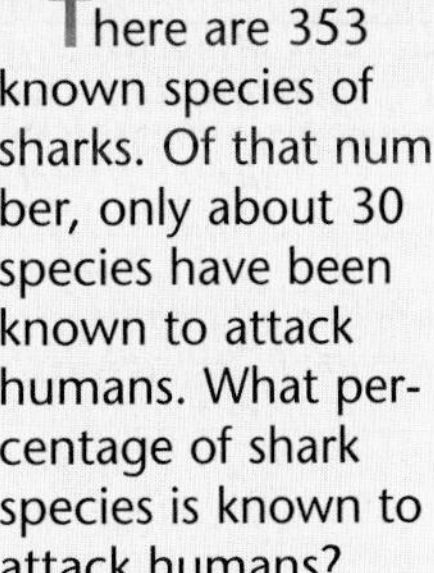

There are 353 known species of sharks. Of that number, only about 30 species have been known to attack humans. What percentage of shark species is known to attack humans?

4 Close

Proficiency Prep

Use this quiz to check students' recall of section content.

1. **What is the term used to describe an animal with a constant body temperature?** *endotherm*
2. **What material makes up the endoskeletons of jawless fish?** *cartilage*

Section Assessment

1. a notochord, a dorsal hollow nerve cord, and gill slits
2. bony fish—bone; jawless and cartilaginous fish—cartilage
3. The body temperatures of ectotherms change with their surroundings. The body temperatures of endotherms stay the same.
4. Think Critically Many eggs are not fertilized; some eggs and young fish are eaten.
5. **Skill Builder**
Sharks need more energy, and food provides this energy. Sharks have to eat a greater amount of food than fish of a similar size that have swim bladders.

Using Math

$\frac{27 \text{ species}}{250 \text{ species}} \times 100\% = 11\%$

Assessment

Process Have students make a table comparing the characteristics of the three classes of fish. Use **Performance Assessment in the Science Classroom,** p. 37.

CA Science Content Standards

Page 848: 8c, 8d, 9e
Page 849: 9f

SECTION 25•2

Prepare

Refer to **Amphibians** and **Reptiles** on p. 844F.

Preplanning

Refer to the **Chapter Organizer** on pp. 844A–B.

1 Motivate

Bellringer

Before presenting the lesson, display **Section Focus Transparency 72** on the overhead projector. Use the accompanying **Focus Activity** worksheet. L2 ELL

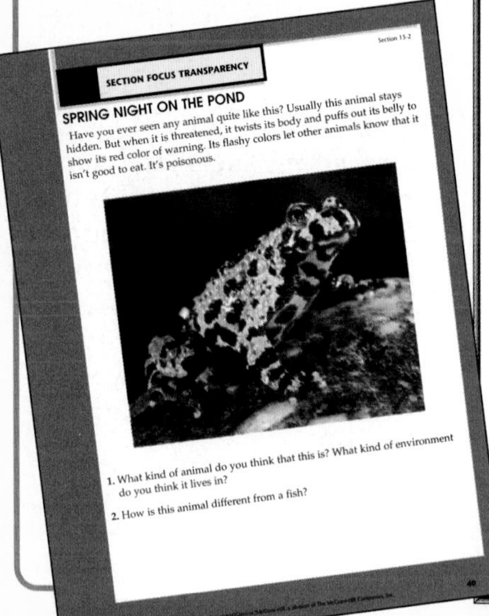

SECTION FOCUS TRANSPARENCY

Section 25-2

SPRING NIGHT ON THE POND

Have you ever seen any animal quite like this? Usually this animal stays hidden. But when it is threatened, it twists its body and puffs out its belly to show its red color of warning. Its flashy colors let other animals know that it isn't good to eat. It's poisonous.

1. What kind of animal do you think that this is? What kind of environment do you think it lives in?
2. How is this animal different from a fish?

Tying to Previous Knowledge

Ask students to list adaptations a fish would need to survive on land.

25•2 Amphibians and Reptiles

What You'll Learn

- How amphibians have adapted to live in water and on land
- What happens during frog metamorphosis
- The adaptations that allow reptiles to live on land

Vocabulary
amphibian
estivation
hibernation
reptile

Why It's Important

- Amphibians are adapted to living in both water and on land while reptiles live only on land.

Amphibians

Have you ever heard of a person leading a double life? Amphibians are animals that lead double lives. In fact, the term *amphibian* comes from the Greek word *amphibios*, which means "double life." **Amphibians** are vertebrates that spend part of their lives in water and part on land. They are also ectotherms, which means that their internal body temperatures changes with their environment. Frogs, toads, and salamanders such as the barred tiger salamander pictured in **Figure 25-5** are the most common kinds of amphibians.

Amphibian Adaptations

Living on land is different from living in water. Air temperature changes more quickly and more often than water temperature. Also, air doesn't support body weight as well as water. Certain adaptations help amphibians survive both in water and on land.

Amphibians have behavioral adaptations that allow them to cope with swings in the air temperature of their particular environment. During cold winter months, they are inactive. They bury themselves in mud or leaves until the temperature warms up. In winter, this period of inactivity and lower metabolic needs

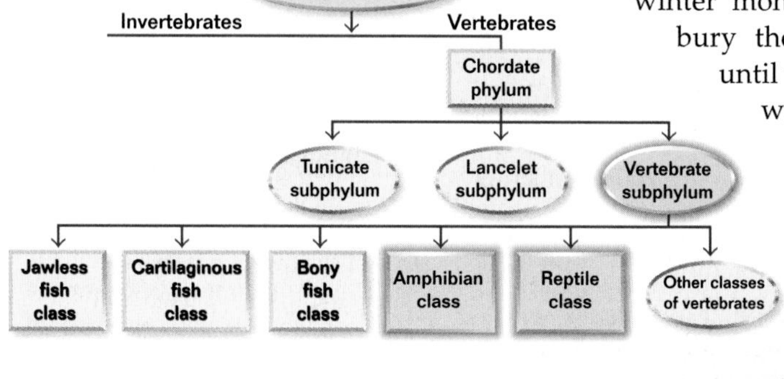

Figure 25-5 This barred tiger salamander has legs that extend straight out from the body.

Resource Manager

The following **Teacher Classroom Resources** can be used with Section 25-2:

 **Reproducible Masters**

Activity Worksheets, pp. 141–142 L2
Enrichment, p. 72 L3
Multicultural Connections, pp. 49–50 L2
Reinforcement, p. 72 L2
Study Guide, p. 98

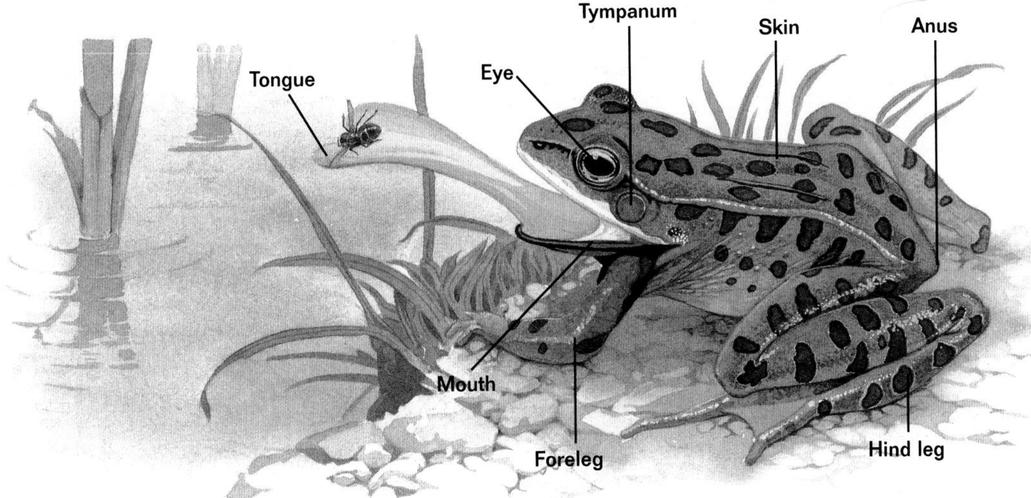

Figure 25-6 A frog's body is adapted for life in the water and on land. **What adaptations can you see in this illustration?**

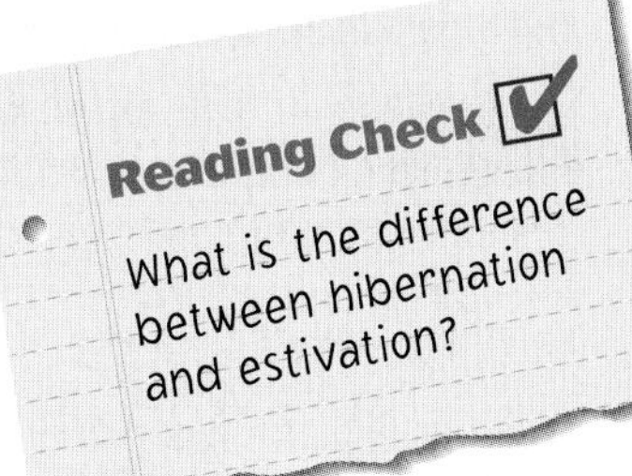

is called **hibernation.** Metabolic needs refer to the chemical activities in an organism that enable it to live, grow, and reproduce. Amphibians that live in hot, drier environments are inactive and hide in the ground where it is likely to be cooler and more humid. This kind of inactivity during hot, dry summer months is called **estivation.**

Amphibians have a strong endoskeleton made of bones. The skeleton helps to support the bodies of amphibians while on land. Adult frogs and toads have short, broad bodies, with four legs and no neck or tail. The strong hind legs are used for swimming and jumping.

Another adaptation increases amphibians' chances of survival on land. Instead of using gills to obtain oxygen from water, lungs become the primary method of obtaining oxygen from air. To increase the oxygen supply, amphibians exchange oxygen and carbon dioxide through their moist, scaleless skin or the lining of their mouths.

Moving to land provides an increased food supply for adult amphibians. Land habitats offer a variety of insects as food for these organisms. **Figure 25-6** shows some adaptations used to catch prey. The tympanic membranes, or eardrums, vibrate in response to sound and are used for hearing. Large eyes provide excellent vision. The long sticky tongue extends quickly to capture the insect and bring it into the waiting mouth.

interNET CONNECTION

Visit the Glencoe Science Web Site at **www.glencoe.com/sec/science/ca** for more information about amphibians.

2 Teach

Answer to Reading Check

Hibernation is a period of inactivity and lower metabolic needs during the winter. Estivation is inactivity during the hot, dry summer months.

interNET CONNECTION

Internet Addresses

For Internet tips, see Glencoe's **Using the Internet in the Science Classroom.**

Using Science Words

Linguistic Hibernation comes from the Latin word *hibernare,* which means "to pass the winter." Estivation is derived from the Latin word *aestas,* meaning "summer." Ask students what other animals spend either their winter or summer months in an inactive state. Answers may include more examples of hibernation, such as bears and groundhogs than estivation

VISUAL Learning

Figure 25-6 **Why must amphibians keep their skin moist?** *Amphibians have small lungs; most gas exchange is done through the skin, which must be moist for this to occur.*

Caption Answer

Figure 25-6 *Answers will vary, but could include that the frog has webbed feet, strong legs and a long, sticky tongue.*

Teacher FYI

Because of their unique lifecycle, amphibians are considered to be biological indicators. Biological indicators are species whose overall health reflects the health of their particular ecosystem as well.

Videodisc

STV: Rainforest

Unit 5 *Nocturnal Life, Frogs, Eggs, and Snakes* 3:33

24503-30894

Refer to the Teacher Guide for additional bar codes and teaching strategies.

Quick Demo

Visual-Spatial Place a live frog at the front of the classroom in an aquarium. Have students observe the frog to determine its adaptations. From student responses, make a table on the chalkboard that lists the adaptations that a frog has for living on the land and in the water. Students can copy this table into their Science Journals.

Discussion

Why do frogs and toads seem to suddenly appear after a rain? *They come out to hunt for food when the air is moist.*

Correcting Misconceptions

Many people think snakes sting with their tongues. Actually, snakes use their tongues to detect chemicals in the air.

Amphibian Metamorphosis

Although young animals such as kittens and calves are almost miniature duplicates of their parents, young amphibians look nothing like their parents. Metamorphosis is a series of body changes that occur during the life cycle of an amphibian. Most amphibians go through a two-stage metamorphosis as illustrated in **Figure 25-7.** The larval stage lives in water, and the adult lives on land.

Most amphibians mate in water. Here, the eggs hatch, and the young larval forms live. The larvae have no legs and breathe through gills. You can see that as the larval form of frogs, called tadpoles, go through metamorphosis, they change form. The young tadpoles develop body structures needed for life on land, including legs and lungs. The rate at which metamorphosis occurs depends on the species, the water temperature, and the amount of available food. The less available food is and the cooler the water temperatures are, the longer it takes for metamorphosis to occur.

VISUALIZING Frog Metamorphosis

Figure 25-7 Frogs undergo a two-stage metamorphosis from the larval stage that lives in water to the adult stage that lives on land.

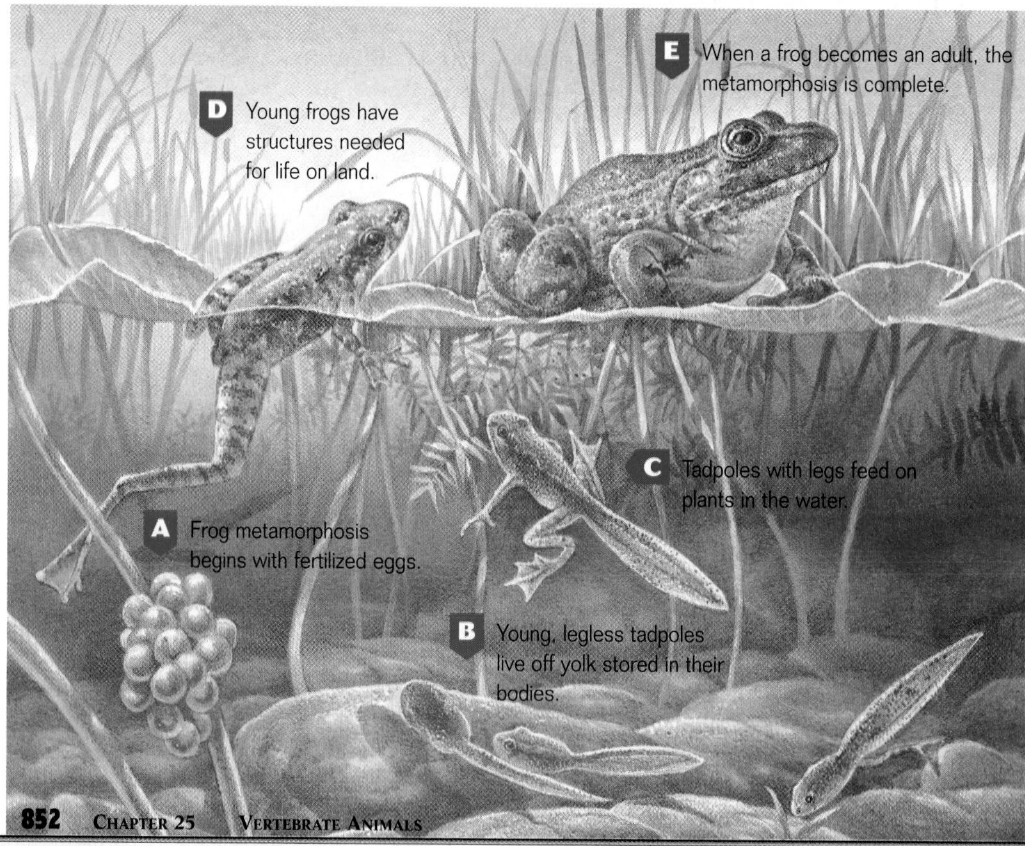
E When a frog becomes an adult, the metamorphosis is complete.
D Young frogs have structures needed for life on land.
C Tadpoles with legs feed on plants in the water.
A Frog metamorphosis begins with fertilized eggs.
B Young, legless tadpoles live off yolk stored in their bodies.
852 CHAPTER 25 VERTEBRATE ANIMALS

VISUAL Learning

Figure 25-7 **How could having two different forms in the life cycle help the species to survive?** *Answers may include that one form may be better adapted at escaping predators than another form.*

Content Background

Biologists divide amphibians into three orders: Urodela, the salamanders; Anura, the frogs and toads; and Apoda, the wormlike caecilians. There are about 250 species of salamanders in the world. Most are found in North America.

Figure 25-8 The green tree viper snake (A), the collared lizard (B), the spotted turtle (C), and the American alligator (D) are all reptiles.

Reptiles

The snake, lizard, turtle, and crocodile in **Figure 25-8** are all reptiles. A **reptile** is an ectothermic vertebrate with dry, scaly skin. Reptiles are vertebrates that do not depend on water for reproduction. Several adaptations allow reptiles to live on land.

Types of Reptiles

Reptiles vary greatly in size, shape, and color. Turtles are covered with a hard shell. They withdraw into the shell for protection. They eat insects, worms, fish, and plants. Alligators and crocodiles are feared predators that live in and near water. These large reptiles live in tropical climates.

Lizards and snakes are the largest group of reptiles. Lizards have movable eyelids, external ears, and legs with clawed toes. Snakes don't have eyelids, ears, or legs. Instead of hearing sounds, they feel vibrations in the ground. Snakes are also sensitive to chemicals in the air. They use their tongue to "smell" these chemicals.

Teacher FYI

Rattlesnakes inject their prey with poison and then let them go. They then follow the scent of their own poison to find the prey and eat them at their leisure.

Some snakes prey on other poisonous snakes. These snakes do not die from ingesting the different types of venom. Researchers studying the Australian tiger snake found that the snake produces an antivenin that neutralizes not only its own venom but also a wide variety of other snake venoms.

3 Assess

Check for Understanding

Discussion

Why are reptiles likely to be less affected by acid rain and ozone depletion than amphibians are? *Reptiles breathe only with lungs; for amphibians, respiration occurs also through the skin, so they absorb poisonous gases and chemicals along with oxygen. Reptiles have eggs with a hard shell; amphibians lay their eggs in the water.*

Reteach

Naturalist Prepare a quiz game of descriptions of lizards, turtles, alligators, crocodiles, snakes, frogs, toads, and salamanders. Let students classify the animals as amphibians or reptiles and name a characteristic of each. L2 COOP LEARN

Integrating the Sciences

Chemistry Snake venom contains poisonous proteins and toxins. The venom of poisonous snakes is produced and stored in specialized glands within the snake's head. Hemotoxins and neurotoxins attack red blood cells and the nervous system.

Across the Curriculum

Language Arts, Math Many people are wary of reptiles. Have students write questions about reptiles to find out how people feel about these animals. They can give the survey to their classmates. Have students graph the results and share them with the class. L3 COOP LEARN

Extension

For students who have mastered this section, use the **Reinforcement** and **Enrichment** masters.

4 Close

Proficiency Prep

Use this quiz to check students' recall of section content.

1. **How do reptiles breathe?** *with lungs*
2. **What is the term used to describe animals that are inactive during the summer?** *estivation*

Section Assessment

1. Water—moist and smooth skin, larvae have gills and live exclusively in the water; land—lungs, strong skeleton, legs
2. jellylike egg, larva, breathes with gills and adult with lungs
3. Internal fertilization; leathery shell surrounds egg or live births; thick, dry waterproof skin; scales prevent water loss and injury; lungs.
4. Think Critically Predators think they are poisonous snakes and leave them alone.

Amphibians breathe through their skin, so they must keep their skin wet to survive.

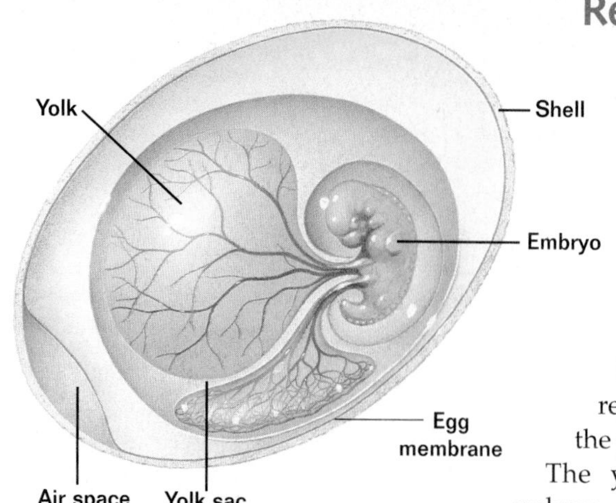

Figure 25-9 The amniotic egg is one of the adaptations reptiles have for living on land. Young reptiles hatch from their eggs fully developed.

Reptile Adaptations

Two major adaptations are involved when reptiles reproduce. Internal fertilization is much more efficient than external fertilization. With internal fertilization, sperm are deposited directly into the female's body. Sperm don't have to make their way through water to get to the eggs. Once fertilized, reptile eggs have another advantage over amphibian eggs. **Figure 25-9** shows the internal structure of a reptile's egg. The embryo develops within the protective environment of the amniotic egg. The yolk supplies food for the developing embryo. A leathery shell provides more protection than the jelly-covered frog's egg. When hatched, the young reptiles are fully developed. With some snakes, the young even develop and mature within the female's body. Then, the young snakes are born alive.

Another adaptation for life on land includes a thick, dry, waterproof skin. This skin is covered with scales and prevents dehydration and injury. All reptiles breathe with lungs. Even sea snakes and sea turtles must come to the surface to breathe.

Section Assessment

1. List the adaptations amphibians have for living in water and on land.
2. Sequence the steps of frog metamorphosis.
3. List the adaptations reptiles have for living on land.
4. **Think Critically:** Some harmless snakes have the same red, yellow, and black colors as the poisonous coral snake. How is this coloring an advantage for a nonpoisonous snake?
5. **Skill Builder**
   Comparing and Contrasting Compare and contrast the types of eggs amphibians and reptiles have. If you need help, refer to Comparing and Contrasting in the **Skill Handbook** on page 956.

In your Science Journal, explain why it is important for amphibians to live in moist or wet environments.

5. **Skill Builder**
Amphibians must return to the water to lay their jelly-covered eggs, which are fertilized externally. Reptile eggs have a leathery shell, are fertilized internally, and are laid on land.

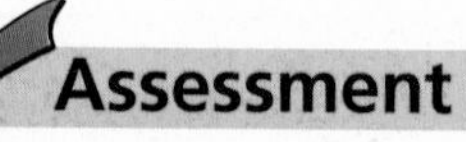

Assessment

Performance Assess students' understanding of metamorphosis by having them prepare a poster that compares frog metamorphosis with insect metamorphosis. Use **Performance Assessment in the Science Classroom,** p. 73.

Frog Metamorphosis

Frogs and other amphibians use external fertilization to reproduce. Female frogs lay hundreds of jellylike eggs in water. Male frogs then fertilize these eggs. Once larvae hatch, the process of metamorphosis begins. Over a period of time, young tadpoles develop into adult frogs.

What You'll Investigate

What changes occur as a tadpole goes through metamorphosis?

Goals

- **Observe** how body structures change as a tadpole develops into an adult frog.
- **Determine** how long metamorphosis takes to be completed.

Materials

- Aquarium or jar (4 L)
- Frog egg mass
- Lake or pond water
- Stereoscopic microscope
- Watch glass
- Small fishnet
- Aquatic plants
- Washed gravel
- Lettuce (previously boiled)
- Large rock

Procedure

1. **Copy** the data table in your Science Journal.
2. As a class, use the aquarium, pond water, gravel, rock, and plants to prepare a water habitat for the frog eggs.
3. **Place** the egg mass in the water of the aquarium. Use the fishnet to separate a few eggs from the mass. **Place** these eggs in the watch glass. The eggs should have the dark side up. **CAUTION:** *Handle the eggs with care.*
4. **Observe** the eggs. **Record** your observations in the data table.
5. **Observe** the eggs twice a week. **Record** any changes that occur.
6. Continue observing the tadpoles twice a week after they hatch. **Identify** the mouth, eyes, gill cover, gills, nostrils, fin on the back, hind legs, and front legs. **Observe** how tadpoles eat boiled lettuce that has been cooled.

Conclude and Apply

1. How long does it take for the eggs to hatch and the tadpoles to develop legs?
2. Which pair of legs appears first?
3. **Explain** why the jellylike coating around the eggs is important.
4. **Compare** the eyes of young tadpoles with the eyes of older tadpoles.
5. **Calculate** how long it takes for a tadpole to change into a frog.

Sample Data

Frog Metamorphosis

Date	Observations
	Observations will vary according
	to the kind of frog eggs used. Students
	should note fishlike appearance of
	tadpoles, disappearance of the tail,
	and development of legs.

2. the hind legs
3. It protects the eggs and keeps them from drying out.
4. The eyes of young are on each side of the head, as in fish. In older ones, they are nearer the tops of the head.
5. approximately two to four months, depending on the species

Assessment

Oral Have students sequence the events that occur as a frog develops from a frog egg into an adult frog. Use **Performance Assessment in the Science Classroom,** p. 71.

Activity 25•1

Purpose

Visual-Spatial Students will observe tadpole metamorphosis and use observations to study the life cycle of a frog. L2 ELL COOP LEARN P

Process Skills

observing and inferring, classifying, sequencing, forming operational definitions

Time

30 minutes on the first day, ten minutes of observations per day thereafter

Alternate Materials

Tap water aged for 48 hours can be used instead of pond water.

Safety Precautions

Caution students to use extreme care when working with live animals.

Teaching Strategies

Troubleshooting The eggs must be handled carefully if they are to hatch. Make sure the temperature of the water remains at 20°C.

- Field-collected eggs can be shipped from supply houses in January, February, and March. Peeper and toad eggs develop rapidly.
- Boil the lettuce leaves for ten minutes, then cool them.

Answers to Questions

1. Answers will vary from eight to 20 days. Legs develop in approximately four weeks, depending on the species.

CA Science Content Standards

Page 855: 9b

SECTION 25•3

Prepare

Refer to **Birds** on p. 844F.

Preplanning

Refer to the **Chapter Organizer** on pp. 844A–B.

1 Motivate

Bellringer

Before presenting the lesson, display **Section Focus Transparency 73** on the overhead projector. Use the accompanying **Focus Activity** worksheet. L2 ELL

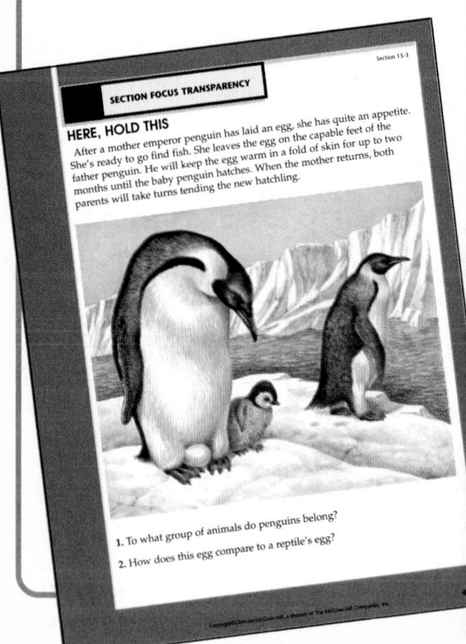

Section 25-3

SECTION FOCUS TRANSPARENCY

HERE, HOLD THIS

After a mother emperor penguin has laid an egg, she has quite an appetite. She's ready to go find fish. She leaves the egg on the capable feet of the father penguin. He will keep the egg warm in a fold of skin for up to two months until the baby penguin hatches. When the mother returns, both parents will take turns tending the new hatchling.

1. To what group of animals do penguins belong?
2. How does this egg compare to a reptile's egg?

Tying to Previous Knowledge

Have students compare reptile characteristics from the previous section with the characteristics they know of birds. They should be able to list some common characteristics, such as different skin coverings.

25•3 Birds

What You'll Learn

- The characteristics of birds
- How birds have adapted in order to fly

Vocabulary
bird
contour feather
down feather

Why It's Important

- Many birds demonstrate structural and behavioral adaptations for flight.

Characteristics of Birds

Have you ever heard the term *pecking order?* Originally, it meant the ranking order of all the birds within a flock. High-ranking birds peck at lower-ranking birds to keep them away from food. This action is an example of a behavioral characteristic. Now, let's look at some physical characteristics of birds.

Despite the wide variety of birds, they all share some common characteristics. **Birds** are vertebrates with two legs, two wings, and bills, or beaks. They lay hard-shelled eggs, have feathers, and are endotherms. Recall that endothermic vertebrates keep a constant body temperature no matter what the temperature of the environment. Birds are the only animals that have feathers. The hard-shelled eggs protect the developing birds. Birds often sit on these eggs to keep them warm until they hatch. You learned that endotherms maintain a constant body temperature. A bird's body temperature is about 40°C. Your body temperature is about 37°C. Bird watchers can tell where a bird lives and what it eats by looking at the type of wing, beak, and feet it has. **Figure 25-10** illustrates some of the more than 8600 species of birds.

Animal Kingdom
Invertebrates
Vertebrates
Chordate phylum
Tunicate subphylum
Lancelet subphylum
Vertebrate subphylum
Jawless fish class
Bony fish class
Reptile class
Mammal class
Cartilaginous fish class
Amphibian class
Bird class

Figure 25-10 Birds are classified into orders based on the characteristic beaks, feet, feathers, and other physical features.

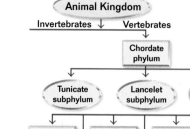

A Flightless land birds, such as ostriches, have their wings reduced in size and strong feet with fused toes for running.

B King penguins use their wings as paddles to propel themselves through water.

Resource Manager

The following **Teacher Classroom Resources** can be used with Section 25-3:

Reproducible Masters

Activity Worksheets, p. 143 L2

Critical Thinking/Problem Solving, p. 25 L2

Enrichment, p. 73 L3

Laboratory Manual, pp. 155–156 L2

Reinforcement, p. 73 L2

Study Guide, p. 99

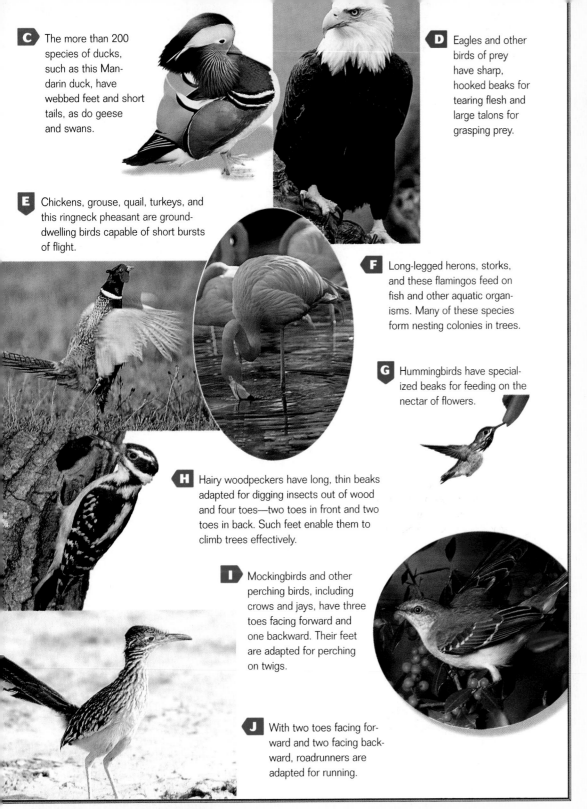

C The more than 200 species of ducks, such as this Mandarin duck, have webbed feet and short tails, as do geese and swans.

D Eagles and other birds of prey have sharp, hooked beaks for tearing flesh and large talons for grasping prey.

E Chickens, grouse, quail, turkeys, and this ringneck pheasant are ground-dwelling birds capable of short bursts of flight.

F Long-legged herons, storks, and these flamingos feed on fish and other aquatic organisms. Many of these species form nesting colonies in trees.

G Hummingbirds have specialized beaks for feeding on the nectar of flowers.

H Hairy woodpeckers have long, thin beaks adapted for digging insects out of wood and four toes—two toes in front and two toes in back. Such feet enable them to climb trees effectively.

I Mockingbirds and other perching birds, including crows and jays, have three toes facing forward and one backward. Their feet are adapted for perching on twigs.

J With two toes facing forward and two facing backward, roadrunners are adapted for running.

Inclusion Strategies

Learning Disabled Have students form small groups and develop a bird-feeding plan for your area. Have students determine which species to feed. Students should list the locations and kinds of food these birds will need. Bird species will vary with geographic location. Feeders may be used, or students might plant particular plant species that attract specific birds. L2

Bird Diary Ask students to draw or take pictures of different birds found around the school or their home. They should identify the birds and start a bird diary in their Science Journals. Have them note the time of day that they saw the bird, its location, and any interesting observations. L2

2 Teach

VISUAL Learning

Figure 25-10B What adaptations do penguins have for swimming in a cold climate? *Penguins are insulated with feathers and a layer of fat. They have webbed feet and their wings are modified flippers for swimming underwater.*

Activity

Interpersonal Divide the class into pairs. Have one student keep time and count while the other holds his or her arms straight out and flaps them up and down. See how many times a person can flap in one minute and how long it takes for the person to tire. Explain that just as our leg muscles are well developed for walking, the chest muscles of most birds are well developed for flying. L2 ELL COOP LEARN

Teacher FYI

Some birds and mammals have developed unique mutualistic relationships.

- Honey guide birds lead badgers to beehives. The badgers feed on honey and the bird gets the leftovers.
- Ostriches and gazelles feed near each other. They watch for predators and can alert each other to an approaching predator. Their visual abilities differ, so each benefits from the other specie's watchfulness.

Using Math

Student answers will vary. Students can use either a line graph or a bar graph to show their results.

PHYSICS INTEGRATION

Lift and streamlining enable birds and airplanes to fly. Drag is a rearward force on a body (airplane or bird) moving through a fluid (air).

Using an Analogy

Birds and mammals are endotherms. Students can think of an endotherm as a furnace that burns fuel to produce energy. In the case of animals the process of respiration and oxidation of food is analogous to the burning of fuel in a furnace. Further proof to support the analogy can be demonstrated by having students breathe out onto their hands and observe that their breath is warm. L2

Answer to Reading Check

(See page 859.) Contour feathers are the long feathers of the tail and wings and are used in flight. Down feathers are small and fluffy and are used to trap air to help keep the bird warm.

Using Math

Count the number of different birds you observe outside during a certain time each day for three days. Graph your data.

Adaptations for Flight

Most body adaptations for birds are designed to enable them to fly. Their bodies are streamlined. Their skeletons are light, yet strong. If you could look inside the bone of a bird, you would see that it is hollow. Flying requires that they have a rigid body. Fused vertebrae provide the needed rigidity, strength, and stability. Birds need a good supply of oxygen to fly. Efficient hearts and lungs aid in respiration. The lungs are connected to air sacs that can be found throughout the body. Air sacs make a bird lighter for flight and help bring more oxygen to the blood. Large, powerful flight muscles in the wings are attached to the breastbone or sternum. Birds beat their wings to attain both thrust and lift. Slow motion pictures show that birds beat their wings both up and down as well as forward and back.

PHYSICS INTEGRATION

A bird's wing provides lift without constant beating. Like the airplane wing in **Figure 25-11,** a bird's wing is curved on top. It is flat or slightly curved on the bottom. A wing with this shape is important. As air moves across the wings, it has a greater distance to move across the top of the wing than along the bottom. The longer path taken by the air moving over the upper surface reduces the air pressure there. As a result, greater pressure is felt on the lower surface of the wing. The difference in air pressure results in lift.

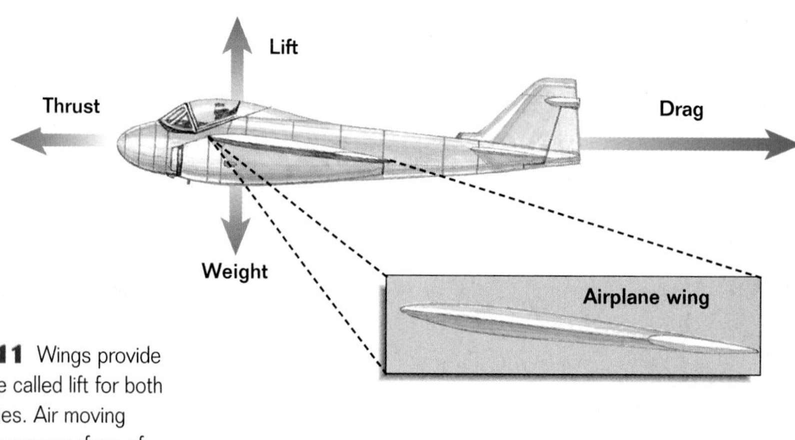

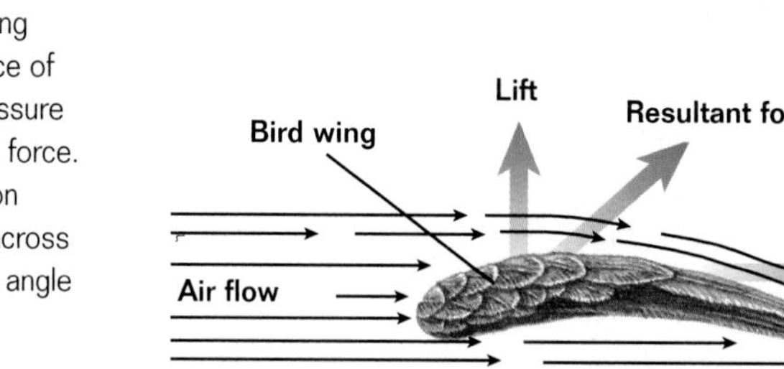

Figure 25-11 Wings provide the upward force called lift for both birds and airplanes. Air moving over the curved upper surface of the wing reduces the air pressure there, resulting in an upward force. The amount of lift depends on wing area, the speed of air across the wing, and the shape and angle of the wing.

Using Science Words

Explain that birds belong to the class Aves. *Aves* is the Latin word for birds, and it is the root of bird-related words such as *avian* and *aviary*.

Integrating the Sciences

Earth Science The evolution of birds is more difficult to trace in the fossil record than the evolution of many other animals. Ask students to apply what they know about fossils and birds and infer why birds are scarce in the fossil record. *Their bones are lightweight and small so they do not become fossilized as easily as many other kinds of land animals.* L2

Figure 25-12 Adult birds such as this great gray owl have an insulating layer of down feathers under their contour feathers. The owlets, like other young birds, are completely covered with down.

The Function of Feathers

Every body part of a bird is designed with flight in mind. Each feather is designed for flight. A bird's body is covered with two types of feathers, contour feathers and down feathers. Strong, lightweight **contour feathers** give birds their coloring and streamlined shape. Surface contour feathers overlap each other. This means that the bird can move more easily through the air or water. Feather colors and pattern are important because they identify a bird's species and sex. They also serve as protection that helps blend some birds into their surroundings. Contour feathers are also used to fly. It is these long feathers on the wings and tail that help the bird to steer and keep from spinning out of control.

Have you ever noticed that the hair on your arm stands up on a cold day? This response is your body's way to trap and keep warm air next to your skin. Birds have a similar response. This response helps birds maintain a constant body temperature. The birds in **Figure 25-12** have down feathers that trap and keep warm air next to their bodies. Soft, fluffy **down feathers** provide an insulating layer next to the skin of adult birds and cover the bodies of young birds. ☑

Mini Lab

Observing Bird Feathers

Procedure

1. Use a hand lens to examine a contour feather.
2. Hold the shaft end while carefully bending the opposite end. Observe what happens when you release the bent end.
3. Examine a down feather with a hand lens.
4. Hold each feather separately. Blow on them. Note any differences in the way each reacts to the stream of air.

Analysis

1. What happens when you release the bent end of the contour feather?
2. Which of the two feathers would you find on a bird's wing?
3. Which type of feather would you find in a pillow? Why?

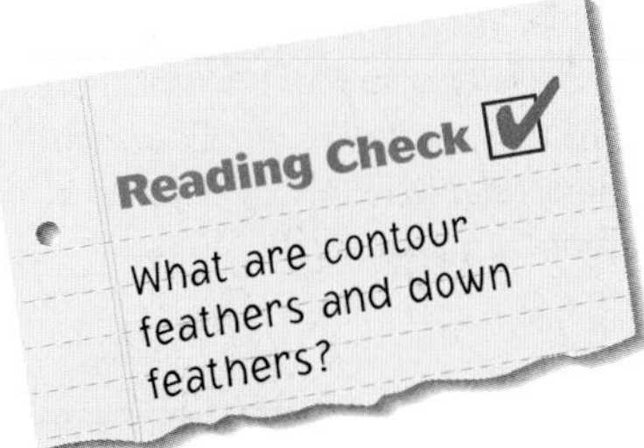

Reading Check
What are contour feathers and down feathers?

Mini Lab

Purpose

Visual-Spatial Students will observe the structure of a contour feather and a down feather. L2 ELL COOP LEARN

Materials

contour feather, down feather, hand lens

Feathers can be obtained from a biological supply company.

Teaching Strategies

Troubleshooting Some students may be allergic to feathers. Feathers can be kept in clear plastic bags and observed.

Analysis

1. It goes back to its previous position without breaking.
2. contour
3. Down feathers can trap air and would make for a fluffy pillow.

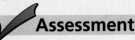

Assessment

Content Have students explain how the structure of a contour feather is adapted for flight. Use **Performance Assessment in the Science Classroom,** p. 71.

3 Assess

Check for Understanding

Enrichment

About 80 species of birds have become extinct since the 1600s. Have students research and report on the moa, the dodo, the great auk, the Labrador duck, the heath hen, and the passenger pigeon. L2

Science Journal

Down Jackets Have students explain why down feathers are used to make warm coats for humans. Ask them to examine some synthetic materials used in making warm coats and compare them with down feathers. L3

CA Science Content Standards

Page 858: 2b, 2d, 2e
Page 859: 9b

Reteach

Have students describe how the area near your school can be made into a more favorable habitat for birds. L2

Extension

For students who have mastered this section, use the **Reinforcement** and **Enrichment** masters.

4 Close

Proficiency Prep

Use this quiz to check students' recall of section content.

1. **What feathers are used for flight?** *contour*
2. **What is the process of a bird's rubbing oil over its feathers?** *preening*
3. **What are the soft, fluffy feathers that cover the bodies of young birds?** *down*

Section Assessment

1. endotherms, feathers, lay eggs with a hard shell, incubate eggs
2. The hollow bones in a bird's skeleton make the bird lighter, as do inflated air sacs.
3. Think Critically Reptiles are ectotherms and rely on warm weather for egg development. Birds are endotherms and incubate their eggs.

Using Computers

Student spreadsheets should show that the different birds beat their wings 600 times, 690 times, 8100 times, and 21 000 times, respectively.

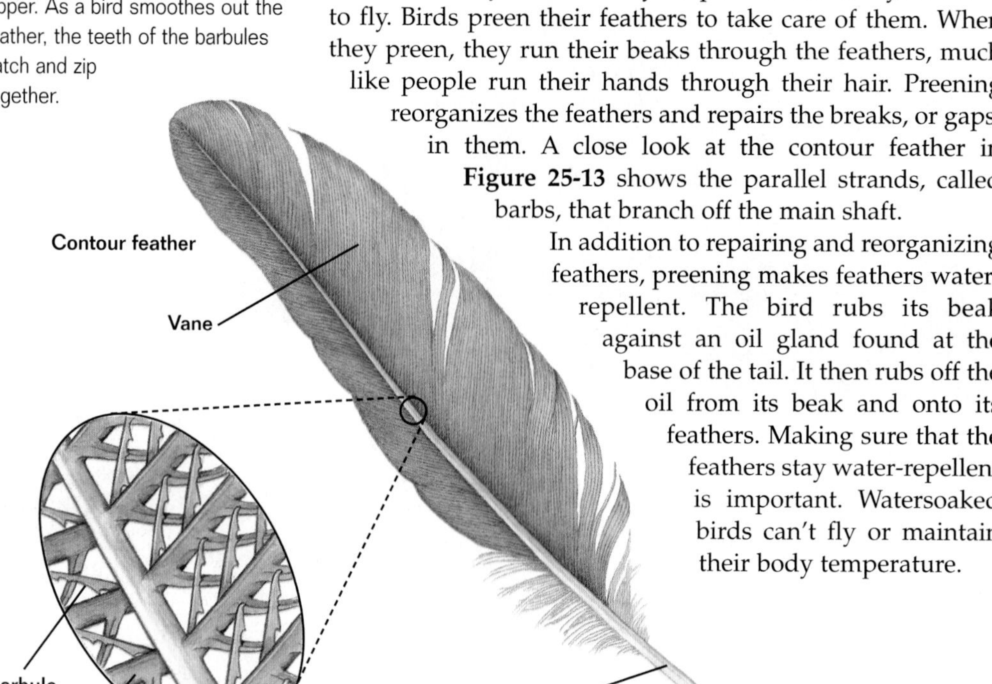

Figure 25-13 Each barb in a contour feather has many smaller barbules that act like the teeth of a zipper. As a bird smoothes out the feather, the teeth of the barbules catch and zip together.

Care of Feathers

Feathers may be strong but they need to be kept in good condition. Only then can they keep birds warm, dry, and able to fly. Birds preen their feathers to take care of them. When they preen, they run their beaks through the feathers, much like people run their hands through their hair. Preening reorganizes the feathers and repairs the breaks, or gaps, in them. A close look at the contour feather in **Figure 25-13** shows the parallel strands, called barbs, that branch off the main shaft.

In addition to repairing and reorganizing feathers, preening makes feathers water-repellent. The bird rubs its beak against an oil gland found at the base of the tail. It then rubs off the oil from its beak and onto its feathers. Making sure that the feathers stay water-repellent is important. Watersoaked birds can't fly or maintain their body temperature.

Section Assessment

1. List four characteristics shared by all birds.
2. Explain how a bird's skeleton is adapted for flight.
3. **Think Critically:** Explain why birds can reproduce in the arctic but reptiles cannot.
4. **Skill Builder**
   Concept Mapping Make a network tree concept map that details the characteristics of birds. Use the following terms in your map: *birds, adaptations for flight, air sacs, beaks, eggs, feathers, hollow bones,* and *wing.* If you need help, refer to Concept Mapping in the **Skill Handbook** on page 950.

Using Computers

Spreadsheet Every 10 s a crow beats its wings 20 times, a robin 23 times, a chickadee 270 times, and a hummingbird 700 times. Using a spreadsheet, find out how many times the wings of each bird beat during a five-minute flight? If you need help, see page 974.

4. **Skill Builder**
   Concept maps should show a simple network tree beginning with birds, then adaptations for flight, which include hollow bones, feathers, and air sacs. Eggs, beaks, and wings should be on a level with adaptations for flight.

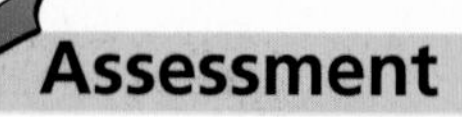

Assessment

Performance Assess students' abilities to compare and contrast by having them examine beaks and feet of birds indigenous to your area. Have students make a model of a hypothetical bird's feet, and have them describe the bird's lifestyle. Use **Performance Assessment in the Science Classroom,** p. 51.

860 CHAPTER 25 VERTEBRATE ANIMALS

History of Science

Flight Through the Ages

For thousands of years, people watched birds soar through the sky and yearned to experience the freedom of flight. The Maori people of what is now New Zealand made kites shaped like birds. The ancient Chinese loved kites, too (inset), and made them in all shapes and sizes.

In the early sixteenth century, artist and inventor Leonardo da Vinci made notes and diagrams about birds and flying machines. He reasoned that a bird's wings must work according to certain laws of physics and math and that therefore people should be able to build a device that could imitate the action of a bird in flight.

Da Vinci's drawings of flying machines inspired the invention of the ornithopter, or flapping-wing machine. People continued to experiment with these odd-looking devices—made out of willow, silk, and feathers—but never managed to get more than a few feet off the ground.

In the early 1800s, English scientist Sir George Cayley carried out his own studies of birds and bird flight. He concluded that it was impossible for people to fly using artificial flapping wings. Eventually, Cayley designed the first successful fixed-wing glider that could carry a person—a milestone that inspired Wilbur and Orville Wright.

Only after the Wright brothers solved a number of problems with gliding aircraft and built several gliders themselves did they focus on building an engine-powered aircraft. The Wright brothers identified the successful features of other aircraft and then added their own ideas about lift, the action of air currents, and the shape of wings. On December 17, 1903, Orville and Wilbur Wright made the world's first powered, sustained, and controlled flights in an airplane, the longest of which was 260 m. That momentous day set the stage for the evolution of many different kinds of engine-powered craft, from biplanes to supersonic jets and space shuttles.

Science JOURNAL

Think of how a bird flies. In your Science Journal, record the similarities and differences between airplane flight and the flight of birds.

25-3 BIRDS 861

Content Background

- The Maori culture depicted the god Rehua as a bird and thought it to be the ancestor of all kites. Kite flying was considered a ritual in the Maori culture as well as in China and Japan.
- In the late 1800s, Otto Lilienthal studied the lifting power of surfaces and the best form of wing curvature and movement of center pressure with a variety of wing angles—an important part of the stability of aircraft.

Teaching Strategies

- Have students work to develop their own kites. Test the designs to see how they fly or have them design their own gliders or paper airplanes.
- Research the different types of airplanes. Trace their history from biplanes to supersonic jets.
- Research the laws of flight such as stability, air, and wing lift.

For Additional Information

Visit the Glencoe Science Web Site at **www/ glencoe.com/sec/science/ca** for more information about the history of flight.

Science Journal

Airplanes are designed to use an airfoil similar to those of flying birds. Lift and streamlining enable both birds and airplanes to fly. The wing area and shape determine the amount of lifting force the wing produces. Lift increases with the speed of the plane or bird. Airplanes extend flaps and slats during both takeoff and landing in order to increase air lift at low speeds. Birds increase their lift when flying slowly by flapping their wings vigorously, by extending a feather as a slat, and by spreading wing feathers and tail.

CA Science Content Standards

Page 860: 9f

Page 861: 2b, 2e

SECTION 25•4

Prepare

Content Background

Refer to **Body Systems in Mammals** on p. 844F.

Preplanning

Refer to the **Chapter Organizer** on pp. 844A–B.

1 Motivate

Bellringer

Before presenting the lesson, display **Section Focus Transparency 74** on the overhead projector. Use the accompanying **Focus Activity** worksheet. L2 ELL

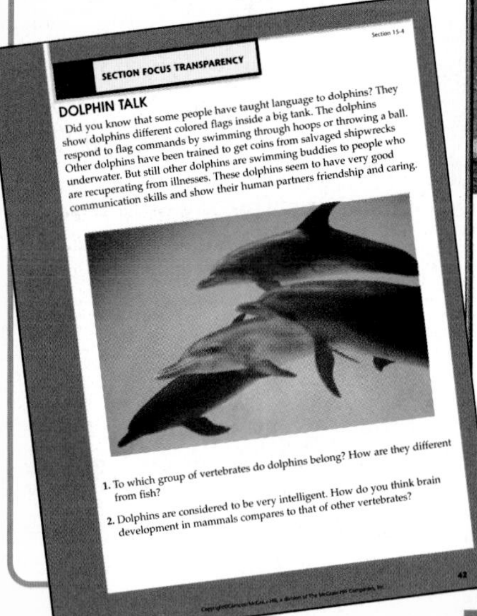

Section 15-4

SECTION FOCUS TRANSPARENCY

DOLPHIN TALK

Did you know that some people have taught language to dolphins? They show dolphins different colored flags inside a big tank. The dolphins respond to flag commands by swimming through hoops or throwing a ball. Other dolphins have been trained to get coins from salvaged shipwrecks underwater. But still other dolphins are swimming buddies to people who are recuperating from illnesses. These dolphins seem to have very good communication skills and show their human partners friendship and caring.

1. To which group of vertebrates do dolphins belong? How are they different from fish?
2. Dolphins are considered to be very intelligent. How do you think brain development in mammals compares to that of other vertebrates?

42

Tying to Previous Knowledge

Birds and mammals are endotherms and have four limbs for movement.

25•4 Mammals

What You'll Learn

- The characteristics of mammals
- How mammals adapt to different environments
- The difference among monotremes, marsupials, and placental mammals

Vocabulary

mammal
monotreme
marsupial
placental mammal
herbivore
carnivore
omnivore

Why It's Important

- Mammals—which include humans—all share many structural characteristics.

Characteristics of Mammals

How many different kinds of mammals can you name? Cats, dogs, bats, dolphins, horses, and people are all mammals. They live on land and in water, in cold and in hot climates. They burrow through the ground or fly through the air. Mammals have many characteristics that they share with other vertebrates. For example, they all have an internal skeleton with a backbone. But what characteristics make mammals unique?

Mammals are endotherms that have hair and produce milk to nourish their young. Being endothermic is not unique. Birds also are endotherms. However, mammals are unique because their skin is covered with hair or fur. Hair is mostly made of a protein called keratin. Some mammals, such as bears, are covered with thick fur. Others, like humans, have patches of hair. Still others, like the whale pictured in **Figure 25-14,** are almost hairless. Hair insulates the mammal's body from both cold and heat. It also protects the animal from wind and rain. Wool, spines, quills, and certain horns are made of keratin. What function do you think quills and spines serve?

Mammary Glands

Mammals put a great deal of time and energy into the care of their young. This begins at birth. Female mammals have mammary glands that form in the skin. During pregnancy, they increase in size. After birth, milk is produced and released in these glands. For the first weeks or months, the milk provides all of the nutrition that the young mammal needs.

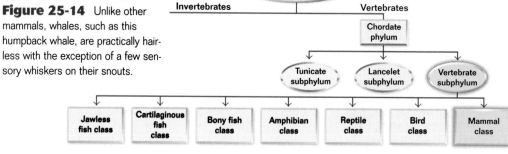

Figure 25-14 Unlike other mammals, whales, such as this humpback whale, are practically hairless with the exception of a few sensory whiskers on their snouts.

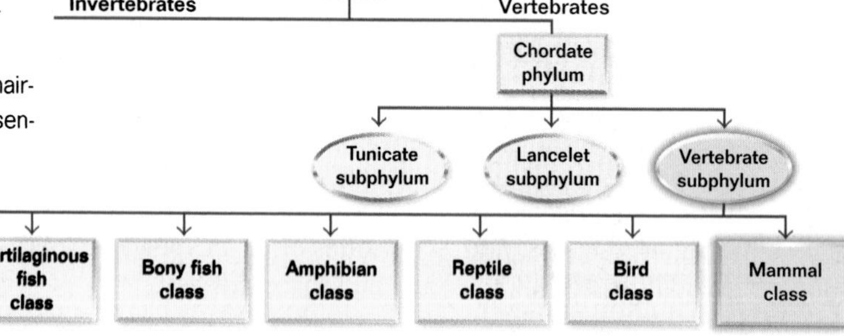

Resource Manager

The following **Teacher Classroom Resources** can be used with Section 25-4:

Reproducible Masters

Activity Worksheets, p. 144 L2

Enrichment, p. 74 L3

Laboratory Manual, pp. 153–154 L2

Reinforcement, p. 74 L2

Study Guide, pp. 99–100 L1 ELL

Transparencies

Science Integration Transparency 25 L2

Body Systems

Think of all the different activities that mammals do. They run, swim, climb, hop, fly, and so on. They live active lives. Their body systems must be able to support all of these activities. Well-developed lungs made of millions of microscopic sacs called alveoli allow the exchanges of carbon dioxide and oxygen.

Mammals also have a more complex nervous system than other animals. The brain, spinal cord, and nerves allow these animals to utilize their senses and to gather information from their surrounding environment. They quickly sense and react to changes in their environment. Mammals are able to learn and remember more than other animals. The large brain plays an important part in this ability. In fact, the brain of a mammal is usually larger than the brain of other animals of the same size. Another factor in a mammal's ability to learn is the time spent by its parents to care for and teach it as it matures.

All mammals reproduce sexually and have internal fertilization. Most mammals give birth to live young after a period of development inside an organ called a uterus. While some mammals are nearly helpless when born, others must be able to stand and move quickly after birth. Why do you think a young deer must be able to run soon after it is born?

Mammal Classification

Once an egg is fertilized, the developing mammal is called an embryo. Mammals can be divided into three groups based on how their embryos develop.

Monotremes

Look at the animal in **Figure 25-15.** The duck-billed platypus looks like someone took parts from several different animals and put them together as a practical joke.

Observing Hair

Procedure

1. Brush or comb your hair to remove a few loose hairs.
2. Take two hairs from your brush that look like they still have the root attached.
3. Make a wet mount slide of the two hairs, being sure to include the root.
4. Focus on the hairs with the low-power objective. Draw what you see.
5. Switch to the high-power objective and focus on the hairs. Draw what you see.

Analysis

1. Describe the characteristics of hair and root.
2. Infer how hair keeps an organism warm.

Figure 25-15 A duck-billed platypus is a mammal, yet it lays eggs. **Why is it classified as a mammal?**

2 Teach

Purpose

Visual-Spatial Students will observe the characteristics of hair.

Materials

slides, droppers, and microscopes

Teaching Strategies

- Be sure students obtain hairs with the root still attached.
- You will have to help the students focus on the hairs on high power.

Analysis

1. The inside of the hair is made of parallel layers of material, while the outside is covered with overlapping layers of cells.
2. It provides insulation.

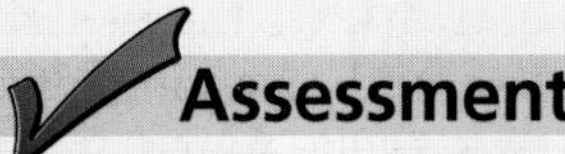

Assessment

Performance Have students examine cat, dog, and horsehair and compare each type with human hair. *Cat and dog hair is shorter, usually tapered, and may show several different color patterns. Horsehair is extremely coarse.* Use **Performance Assessment in the Science Classroom,** p. 25. P

Caption Answer

Figure 25-15 *It has hair and mammary glands and is an endotherm.*

Multiple Learning Styles

Visual-Spatial Have students make or find a wall map of the world. On the map, they can place drawings and magazine pictures of some of the mammals that live in the different areas of the world. Students can visit a local zoo to take pictures of animals to add to the map. L3

Across the Curriculum

Language Arts Ask students to make a list of expressions that draw an analogy between the behavior of a mammal and the behavior of a person. Some examples include slow as a snail, quiet as a mouse, busy as a beaver, sly as a fox, and slothful. L2

CA Science Content Standards

Page 863: 9b

Content Background

Monotreme eggs are flexible and leathery like reptile eggs. Platypuses often curl up around their eggs. It uses its bill to dig burrows in stream banks and to scoop up worms and other invertebrates from the bottoms of streams. The platypus reaches a length of about 46 cm and has thick, brown fur, a broad, flat tail, and webbed feet. The hind legs have sharp spines connected to poison glands used in defense.

Activity

Visual-Spatial Have students examine the small voles, rats, and mice that can be found in owl pellets. Students should examine carefully any skulls found in the pellets. They should also look at the skulls found in their classmates' pellets. The teeth can be used to identify small rodents. L2 ELL COOP LEARN

Problem Solving

Discuss with students that different types of sensory cells in the bat's brain interpret echoes to determine the location and some physical properties of the objects, creating a spatial map that governs the bat's behavior.

Think Critically

Bats locate an object from reflected sound waves. They would have difficulty in a place that absorbs sound waves rather than reflects them. If a bat's mouth and nose are covered, it is unable to emit sounds for echolocation and it would not be able to locate objects. P

But, in fact, the duck-billed platypus belongs to the smallest group of mammals called monotremes. **Monotremes** lay eggs with tough leathery shells. The female incubates the eggs for about ten days. Mammary glands that produce the milk of monotremes lack nipples. When the young hatch, they nurse by licking up the milk that seeps through the skin surrounding the glands. The duck-billed platypus and two species of spiny anteaters are the only surviving members of this group.

Figure 25-16 Marsupials carry their developing young in a pouch on the outside of their bodies. Opossums are the only marsupials found in North America.

Marsupials

Can you think of an animal that carries its young in a pouch? Mammals that do this are called marsupials. **Marsupials** are pouched mammals that give birth to immature offspring. Their embryos develop for only a few weeks within the uterus. When the young are born, they are naked, blind, and not fully formed. Using their sense of smell, the young crawl into the pouch and attach themselves to a nipple. Here they complete their development. Most marsupials live in Australia, Tasmania, and New Guinea. Kangaroos, koalas, Tasmanian devils, and wallabies are marsupials. The opossum in **Figure 25-16** is a marsupial that lives in North America.

Problem Solving

Predicting Bat Behavior

Bats are acrobats of the night. They can fly around obstacles and can find insects to eat in complete darkness. Have you ever wondered how they do this? Some bats emit, or send out, extremely high-pitched sounds through the mouth and nose when hunting for food. These sounds are usually too high pitched for humans to hear. Bats also make noises that people hear, from whining sounds to loud twitters and squeaks. Bats can catch fast-flying insects or darting fish and at the same time avoid branches, wires, and other obstacles in a process called echolocation. The sound waves they send out travel in front of them, and this helps them locate objects.

The diagram illustrates what happens when a sound wave emitted by a bat comes in contact with an object.

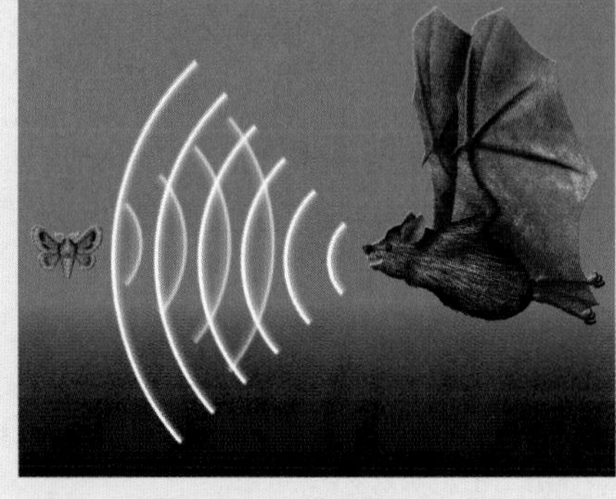

Think Critically: How does a bat locate an object in the dark? Explain what might happen to bats if they were allowed to search for food in a soundproof room, where walls absorb most of the sound. Infer what would happen if a bat's mouth and nose are covered.

Integrating the Sciences

Earth Science Mammals diversified during the Cenozoic era. Monotremes and marsupials developed in Australia and South America; placental mammals dominated North America. When North America and South America joined, placental mammals spread south. Australia remained geographically separate; it has the most diverse population of monotremes and marsupials in the world.

Placental Mammals

By far, the largest number of mammals belongs to the third group known as placental mammals. The most important characteristic of **placental mammals** is that their embryos develop in the uterus of the female. This time of development, from fertilization to birth, is the gestation period. Gestation periods vary greatly among placental mammals. Imagine waiting almost two years for the young elephant in **Figure 25-17** to be born! Placental mammals are named for the placenta, a saclike organ developed by the growing embryo that is attached to the uterus. The placenta absorbs oxygen and food from the mother's blood. An umbilical cord, **Figure 25-18,** attaches the embryo to the placenta. Several blood vessels in the umbilical cord act as a transportation system. Food and oxygen are transported from the placenta to the embryo. Waste products are taken away.

Figure 25-17 Gestation periods vary among mammals. While an elephant carries its young for 624 days, a golden hamster's gestation period is about 16 days.

*inter***NET** CONNECTION

Visit the Glencoe Science Web Site at **www.glencoe.com/sec/science/ca** for more information about small mammals.

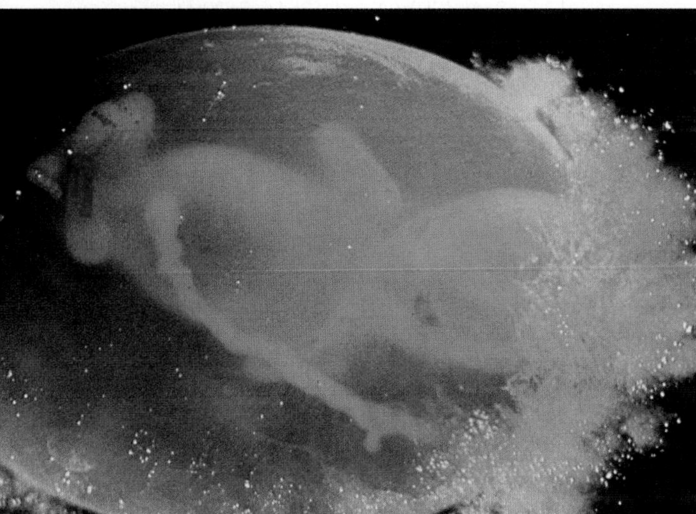

Figure 25-18 A placental mammal's embryo, such as this human embryo, develops in the uterus of a female. The umbilical cord allows the embryo to receive food and oxygen from the mother.

Discussion

What advantages do developing young marsupials have compared with the developing young of monotremes? *The developing young of marsupials are protected in their mother's pouch. The young of monotremes are left alone while the parents leave to find food, making the young more vulnerable to predators.* **Why are mammals important to people today?** *Answers will vary but could include that we get meat, milk, hides, and fur from them. They are a critical part of the food web.*

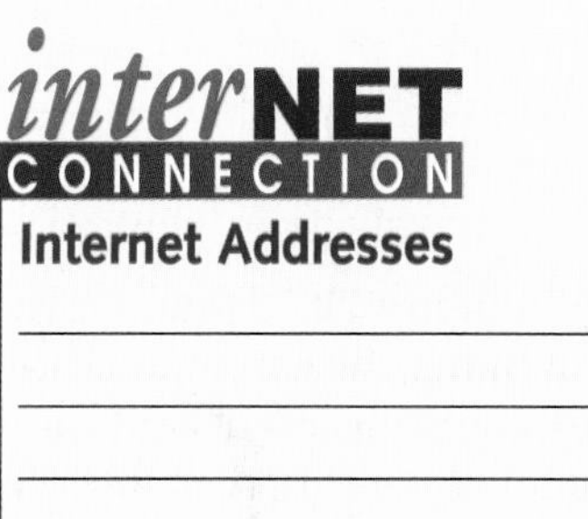

*inter***NET** CONNECTION

Internet Addresses

For Internet tips, see Glencoe's **Using the Internet in the Science Classroom.**

GLENCOE TECHNOLOGY

Videodisc

Glencoe Science Voyages Interactive Videodisc—Life

Side 2, Lesson 5 *Structural Adaptations in Animals*

4827

Refer to Videodisc Teacher Guide for additional bar codes.

Content Background

The large mammalian brain, especially the region called the cerebrum, and the ability to maintain a constant internal temperature allowed mammals to develop the potential for quick responses and movement. This advantage ismade possible by evolutionary advances of their limbs and nervous systems. The combination of all these evolutionary advances has made mammals highly successful in all habitats.

Content Background

Black bears mate in May or June. The fertile egg does not start active development until about October. During the summer months the female bear continues to feed in preparation for winter hibernation. Cubs are born in January after only about three months of development. At birth, cubs are blind and weigh about eight ounces. At one year of age they weigh 30–70 pounds.

Enrichment

Linguistic Have students research and report on gestation periods and the average number of offspring born to different species. Ask students to evaluate the data by comparing the size or activity of these organisms with the length of gestation. Some gestation periods are:

opossum	12 days
hamster	16 days
mouse	20 days
rabbit	31 days
dog	61 days
cat	63 days
guinea pig	68 days
cow	281 days
horse	336 days
camel	406 days
giraffe	442 days
whale	450 days
elephant	650 days

L3

You have learned the basic characteristics that distinguish mammals—vertebrae, hair or fur, mammary glands that produce milk, type of teeth, and the ability of young to learn. In addition, each kind of animal has certain adaptations that enable it to live successfully within its environment. Some of the 4000 species of mammals are shown in **Figure 25-19.**

Figure 25-19 In addition to monotremes (A) and marsupials (B), many of the major orders of placental mammals are shown here.

A **Monotremata** (mahn uh tru MAH tah): Monotremes, such as this duck-billed platypus, are the only egg-laying mammals.

B **Marsupiala** (mar sew pee AH luh): Pouched mammals include kangaroos, shown here, and opossums.

C **Insectivora** (ihn sek tih VOR ah): Burrowing woodland moles have poor eyesight but an excellent sense of touch to catch insects.

D **Edentata** (ee duhn TAH tuh): Armadillos, shown here, anteaters, and tree sloths are toothless or have few teeth with which to eat insects.

E **Chiroptera** (cher OP ter uh): Bats are the only true flying mammals. Their front limbs are designed for flight. They use echolocation, a process that uses sound and echoes, to navigate while flying.

F **Carnivora** (kar NIH vor uh): The household cat and dog are meat-eaters that have canine teeth used to capture prey. This red fox is also a carnivore.

G **Cetacea** (sih TAY shuh): Marine mammals, including dolphins, spend their entire lives in the ocean.

Across the Curriculum

Literature Have students go to the library and find a book that has one or more mammals either as characters or as important aspects of the story. For example, *Incident at Hawk's Hill* by Allan W. Eckert tells the story of a six-year-old boy who survives two months in the wild living with a female badger. L2

866 CHAPTER 25 VERTEBRATE ANIMALS

H **Proboscidea** (proh boh SIH dee uh): Elephants are the largest land mammals. They have an elongated nose that forms a trunk.

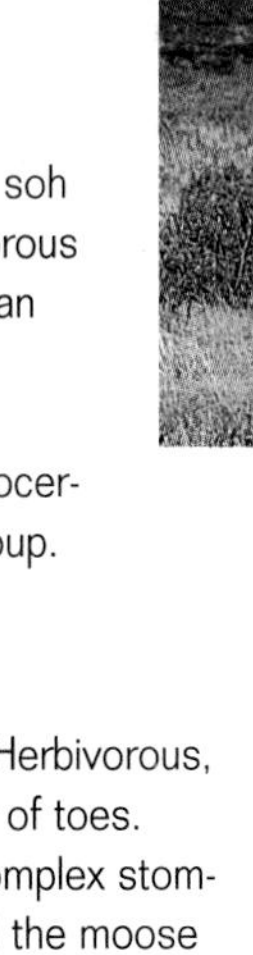

I **Perissodactyla** (per ih soh DAHK tih luh): Herbivorous hoofed mammals with an odd number of toes. Horses, zebras, tapirs (shown here), and rhinoceroses belong to this group.

J **Artiodactyla** (ar tee oh DAHK tih luh): Herbivorous, hoofed mammals have an even number of toes. They also have large, flat molars and complex stomachs. Cows, camels, deer, giraffes, and the moose (shown here) belong to this group.

K **Rodentia** (roh DEN cha): The largest order, these gnawing mammals have two pairs of chisel-shaped teeth that never stop growing. These teeth wear down through use. This golden mouse, along with squirrels, beavers, porcupines, and gophers are in this group.

L **Lagomorpha** (lah gah MOR fuh): Lagomorphs include herbivorous rabbits, hares, and pikas. This Eastern cottontail rabbit has long hind legs that are adapted for jumping and running. It also has two pairs of upper incisors.

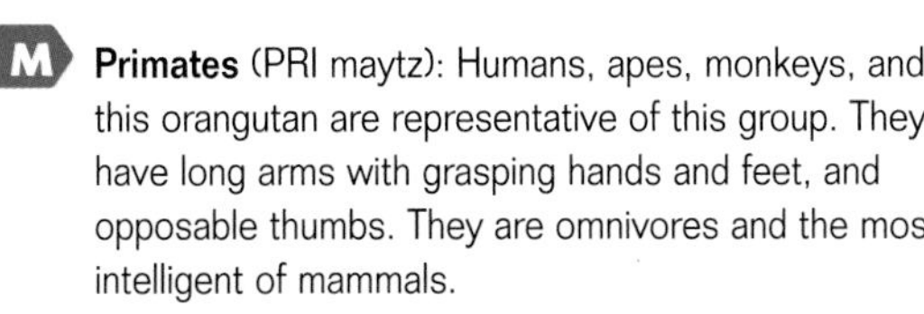

M **Primates** (PRI maytz): Humans, apes, monkeys, and this orangutan are representative of this group. They have long arms with grasping hands and feet, and opposable thumbs. They are omnivores and the most intelligent of mammals.

Content Background

Armadillos are the only members of the order Edentata that live in the United States. The armadillo's most distinguishing feature is a hardened skin, which is arranged in a pattern of either six or nine bands around its body. The tough band acts like armor to protect the armadillo from predators.

Teacher FYI

Polar bears of the class Carnivora are well adapted for living in the Arctic. Like all mammals, they are endotherms but still need special adaptations to survive in the frozen world of the Arctic. Their skin is black and acts as a solar collector. A polar bear's fur is made of clear, hollow hairs that have rough inner surfaces. Light is refracted (bent) by the rough inner surface of the hair giving the polar bears their white color.

Visual Learning

Figure 25-19 Have students look at the photographs and captions on these two pages. **Which is the only order of mammals capable of sustained flight?** *Chiroptera* **Which order of mammals spends their entire lives in the water?** *Cetacea* **Which order contains the largest land mammals?** *Proboscidea* **Which order consists of hoofed mammals with an even number of toes?** *Artiodactyla* **Which order has some members with pairs of chisel-shaped teeth that never stop growing?** *Rodentia*

Answer to Reading Check

Herbivores eat only plants, carnivores eat only meat, and omnivores eat plants and meat.

Correcting Misconceptions

Camels do not store water in their humps. The humps contain fat, an energy-conserving adaptation that enables them to survive in the desert where food and water are scarce.

Caption Answer

Figure 25-20 *Horses are herbivores, hyenas are carnivores, and humans are omnivores.*

3 Assess

Check for Understanding Activity

Visual-Spatial Have students draw a mammal and label its parts, indicating the specialized adaptations that make it a mammal and help it to survive. They should include information about how the mammal reproduces, what kind of skin and teeth it has, how it moves, how its lungs and heart function, and so on. L2

Reteach

Interpersonal Have students group the following characteristics under the headings *Mammals, Birds,* and *Both Mammals and Birds:* the most fully developed brains, endothermic, hollow bones, hair, feathers, shelled eggs, nurse their young, give birth to live young, extended parental care, outer ears, keen sense of smell, phylum Chordata, class Aves. L2

Figure 25-20 Mammals have teeth specialized for the food they eat. **How would you classify a horse (A), a hyena (B), and a human (C)? Herbivore? Carnivore? Omnivore?**

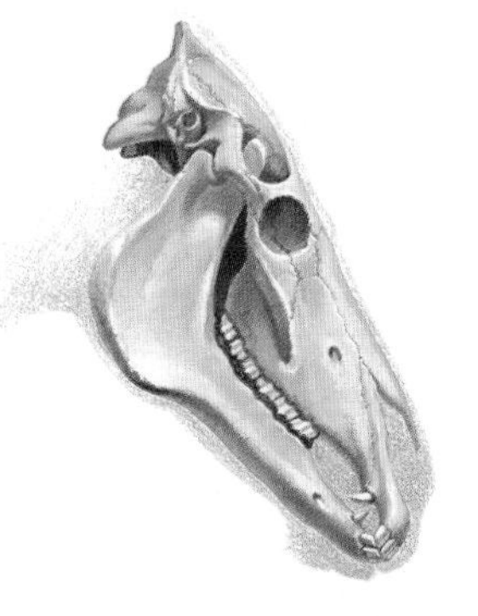

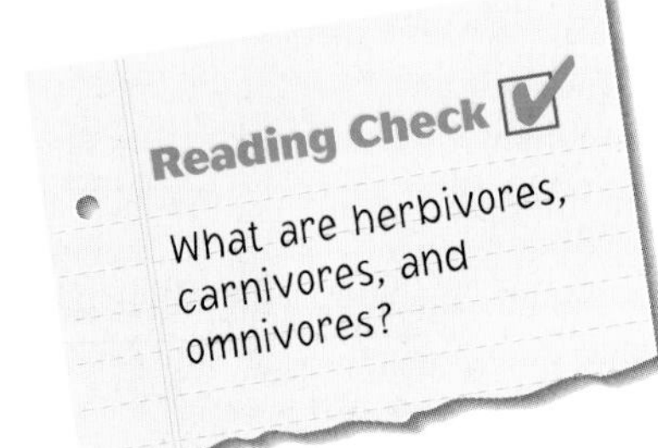

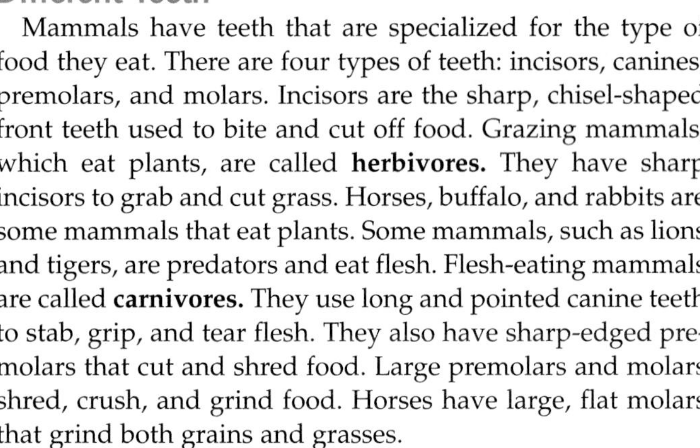

Different Teeth

Mammals have teeth that are specialized for the type of food they eat. There are four types of teeth: incisors, canines, premolars, and molars. Incisors are the sharp, chisel-shaped front teeth used to bite and cut off food. Grazing mammals, which eat plants, are called **herbivores.** They have sharp incisors to grab and cut grass. Horses, buffalo, and rabbits are some mammals that eat plants. Some mammals, such as lions and tigers, are predators and eat flesh. Flesh-eating mammals are called **carnivores.** They use long and pointed canine teeth to stab, grip, and tear flesh. They also have sharp-edged premolars that cut and shred food. Large premolars and molars shred, crush, and grind food. Horses have large, flat molars that grind both grains and grasses.

Some mammals eat both plants and animals. These mammals are called **omnivores.** Humans are capable of being omnivores. They have all four types of teeth. You usually can tell whether a mammal eats plants, other animals, or both from the kind of teeth it has. Look at **Figure 25-20.**

Reading Check What are herbivores, carnivores, and omnivores?

868 CHAPTER 25 VERTEBRATE ANIMALS

Mammals Today

Mammals are important in maintaining a balance in the environment. Large carnivores, such as lions, help control populations of grazing animals. Bats help pollinate flowers, and some pick up plant seeds in their fur and distribute them. But mammals are in trouble today. As millions of acres of wildlife habitat are developed for housing and recreational areas, many mammals are left without food, shelter, and space to survive. The Bengal tiger pictured in **Figure 25-21** lives in India and is considered an endangered species.

Figure 25-21 Illegal poaching and decreasing habitat help account for the extreme decline in the Bengal tiger population in nature. In the early 1900s, there were around 100 000 tigers, but that has declined by roughly 95 percent this century.

Section Assessment

1. Describe five characteristics of all mammals and explain how these characteristics allow mammals to survive in different environments.
2. Compare and contrast herbivores with omnivores.
3. **Think Critically:** Compare reproduction in placental mammals with that of monotremes and marsupials.
4. **Skill Builder**
   Observing and Inferring Mammals have many adaptations to their environments. Do the **Chapter 25 Skill Activity** on page 986 to observe tracks to infer how mammals' feet are adapted.

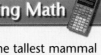

Using Math

The tallest mammal is the giraffe, which stands at 5.6 m tall. Calculate your height in meters and determine how many of you it would take to be as tall as a giraffe.

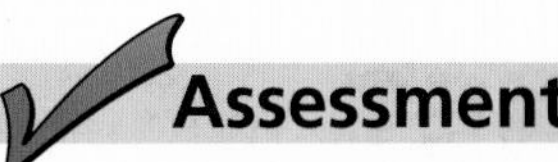

Assessment

Performance Assess students' abilities to classify another selection of mammals from Figure 25-19. Use **Performance Assessment in the Science Classroom,** p. 49.

Extension

For students who have mastered this section, use the **Reinforcement** and **Enrichment** masters.

4 Close

Proficiency Prep

Use this quiz to check students' recall of section content.

1. **What kinds of animals eat plants?** *herbivores*
2. **What is the organ inside the female in which placental mammals develop?** *uterus*
3. **What attaches the embryo to the placenta?** *the umbilical cord*

Section Assessment

1. All mammal characteristics allow them to adapt to most environments. Characteristics include: endothermic, have hair, have mammary glands that produce milk to feed their young, have teeth, have well-developed lungs, have a large brain, reproduce sexually.
2. Herbivores eat only plants; omnivores eat plants and animals.
3. Think Critically Placental mammals are more developed at birth and have a better chance of surviving.

Using Math

5.6 m (height in meters of student) = number of students needed to equal height of giraffe

CA Science Content Standards

Page 869: 9f

Recognize the Problem

Naturalist Students will research information about bird watching and about the local bird populations. Students will then design a procedure to scientifically observe birds. After students have collected and analyzed their data, they will post their results to the Glencoe Science Web Site to share with other students around the country. Students can compare their findings with the results from other students to draw various conclusions on bird behavior, population, and environment.

Form a Hypothesis

Internet Students will gather data from the Internet sites that can be accessed through the Glencoe Science Web Site at **www.glencoe.com/sec/science/ca.** Students can post their findings on the site and get information from other schools around the country.

Non-Internet Sources Many communities have nature centers that have information about local birds.

Time Required

from one week to one month

Preparation

Internet Access the Glencoe Science Web Site at **www.glencoe.com/sec/science/ca** to run through the steps that the students will follow.

Non-Internet Sources Bring to class field guides and other books about local birds.

Activity 25•2

Bird Counts

Birds can be found almost everywhere. No single place is best. You can see them in many different habitats—in a city park or an open field, along the riverbank, or at the shore. Many bird-watchers make their observations in the early morning when birds are most active. While bird-watching, care must be taken not to scare the birds with movement or noise.

It's simple to get started bird-watching. You can attract birds to your yard at home or at school by filling a bird feeder with seeds that birds like most. Then, sit back and observe the birds while they enjoy your hospitality.

Recognize the Problem

What type of bird is present in your neighborhood in the largest number?

Form a Hypothesis

Think about the types of birds that you observe around your neighborhood. What types of food do they eat? Do all birds come to a bird feeder? Make a hypothesis about the type of bird that you think you will see most often at your bird feeder.

Goals

- **Observe** the types of birds in your neighborhood.
- **Research** how to attract birds to a bird feeder.
- **Build** a bird feeder.
- **Identify** the types of birds observed.
- **Graph** your results in order to communicate them with other students.

Data Source

Go to the Glencoe Science Web Site at **www.glencoe.com/sec/science/ca** for more information about how to build a bird feeder, hints on bird watching, and data from other students.

interNET CONNECTION

Internet Addresses

____

____

____

____

For Internet tips, see Glencoe's **Using the Internet in the Science Classroom.**

Test Your Hypothesis

Plan

1. **Research** general information about how to attract and identify birds. Determine where you will make your observations.
2. **Search** reference materials to find out how to build a bird feeder. Do all birds eat the same types of seeds?
3. What variables can you control in this activity? How long will you make your observations? Does the season or the weather conditions affect your observations?
4. What will you do to **identify** the birds that you do not recognize?

Do

1. Make sure your teacher approves your plan before you start.
2. **Record** your data in your Science Journal each time you **observe** your bird feeder.

Analyze Your Data

1. **Describe** the location where you made your observations and the time of year.
2. **Calculate** the total number of each type of bird by adding the numbers you recorded each day.
3. **Graph** your data. Will your results be best displayed in a line, circle, or bar graph?
4. **Post** your data on the Glencoe Science Web Site.

Draw Conclusions

1. What type of bird was present in your neighborhood in the largest number?
2. Did all of your classmates' data agree with yours? Why or why not?
3. **Compare and contrast** your observations with the observations posted by other students on the Glencoe Science Web Site. **Map** the data you collect from the Web site to **recognize** patterns in bird populations.
4. Many birds include an enormous number of insects in their diet. **Infer** the need for humans to maintain a healthy environment for birds.

Test Your Hypothesis

Teaching Strategies

- Have field guides available for students in the class where they can look up information about birds they've seen.
- Have a discussion about binoculars. Describe how they can be helpful and what the numbers tell you.
- Remind students that birds also like water. A bird bath with two inches of clean water placed in the shade will attract birds.
- Obtain a checklist of the birds that can be spotted in your state. Pass out the list to the students so they can start checking off birds from the list.

Have students use a tape recorder to make an audio collection of bird calls. Have students practice identifying the birds just by the sounds that they make.

References

Birding (Nature Company Guide), Time-Life, 1995.

The Birder's Handbook: A Field Guide to the Natural History of North American Birds, Paul Ehrlich, Fireside, 1988.

Assessment

Portfolio Have students design an identification guide based solely on their observations. In the guide, students should include the identifying marks they saw, the habitats where they found the bird, and any other unique characteristic they noticed about their bird during observations.

CA Science Content Standards

Page 870–871: 9a, 9b, 9e

Chapter 25 Reviewing Main Ideas

Reviewing Main Ideas can be used to preview, review, reteach, and condense chapter content.

Preview

Linguistic Have students try to answer the questions in their Science Journals. Use student answers as a source for discussion throughout the chapter.

Review

Interpersonal Have students answer the questions on separate pieces of paper and compare their answers with those of other students in the class.

Reteach

Visual-Spatial Have students look at the illustrations on these pages. Ask them to describe details that support the main ideas of the chapter found in the statement for each illustration.

00:00 OUT OF TIME?

Auditory-Musical If time does not permit teaching the entire chapter, use the information on these pages along with the chapter Audiocassettes to present the material in a condensed format.

Chapter 25 Reviewing Main Ideas

For a **preview** of this chapter, study this Reviewing Main Ideas before you read the chapter. After you have studied this chapter, you can use the Reviewing Main Ideas to **review** the chapter.

The Glencoe MindJogger, Audiocassettes, and CD-ROM provide additional opportunities for review.

Section

25-1 VERTEBRATES AND FISH

All animals in the Chordate Phylum have a notochord, dorsal hollow nerve cord, and gill slits. The body temperature of an **ectotherm** changes with its environment. **Endothermic** animals maintain body temperature. **Fish** are ectotherms that have scales and **fins.** Classes of fish include jawless fish, cartilaginous fish, and bony fish. ***Why can't jawless fish be predators?***

Section

25-2 AMPHIBIANS AND REPTILES

Amphibians are vertebrates that spend part of their lives in water and part on land. Most frogs, toads, and salamanders are amphibians that go through metamorphosis from a water-living larva to a land-living adult. **Reptiles** are ectothermic land animals that have dry, scaly skin. Turtles, crocodiles, alligators, snakes, and lizards are reptiles. Reptiles lay eggs with a leathery skin. ***Why does the reptile's egg provide better protection for the embryo than a frog's egg?***

Collared lizard

Barred tiger salamander

872 CHAPTER 25 VERTEBRATE ANIMALS

Cultural Diversity

Earliest Bird Sankar Chatterjee is best known for his discovery of *Protoavis,* a 225-million-year-old fossil that may turn out to be the earliest known bird. The fossil was discovered in the 1980s in the Dockum fossil beds of West Texas. According to Chatterjee, *Protoavis* predates *Archaeopteryx,* which was thought to be the first bird, by approximately 75 million years. Chatterjee's work examines bird fossils from all over the world and relates them to the evolution of birds. One of his most controversial theories involves an evolutionary link between birds and dinosaurs.

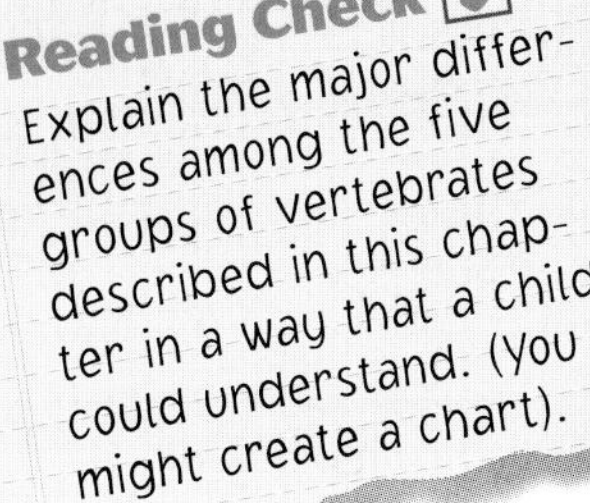

Reading Check
Explain the major differences among the five groups of vertebrates described in this chapter in a way that a child could understand. (You might create a chart).

Hummingbird

Section

25-3 BIRDS

Birds are endotherms that are covered with feathers and lay eggs. Their front legs are modified into wings. Adaptations birds have for flight include wings, feathers, and a light, strong skeleton. Birds lay eggs enclosed in hard shells. Most birds keep their eggs warm until they hatch. ***How do down feathers keep a bird warm?***

Mandarin duck

Flamingo

Bat

25-4 MAMMALS

Mammals are endotherms with hair. Female mammals have mammary glands that produce milk. There are three groups of mammals. **Monotremes** are mammals that lay eggs. **Marsupials** are mammals that have pouches for the development of their embryos. **Placental mammals** have offspring that develop within the female's uterus. ***What are some adaptations of mammals that allow them to be endothermic?***

Red fox

Answers to Questions

Section 25-1

Vertebrates and Fish Jawless fish such as the lamprey have round mouths but no jaws. Its mouth acts like a sucker with sharp, toothlike parts; these are used to scrape through the larger fish's skin, where it feeds on its blood.

Section 25-2

Amphibians and Reptiles Amphibians must return to the water to lay their jellylike eggs. Reptile eggs have a leathery shell and are laid on land.

Section 25-3

Birds Down feathers of a bird trap and keep warm air next to its skin.

Section 25-4

Mammals Oxygen-rich and oxygen-poor blood do not mix.

GLENCOE TECHNOLOGY

CD-ROM

Glencoe Science Voyages Interactive CD-ROM

Chapter Summaries and Quizzes

Have students read the Chapter Summary then take the Chapter Quiz to determine whether they have mastered the chapter content.

Assessment

Portfolio Encourage students to place in their portfolios one or two items of what they consider to be their best work. Examples include:

- Flex Your Brain, p. 847
- Activity 25-1, p. 855
- Problem Solving, p. 864 P

Performance Additional performance assessments may be found in **Performance Assessment** and **Science Integration Activities.** Performance Task Assessments Lists and rubrics for evaluating these activities can be found in Glencoe's **Performance Assessment in the Science Classroom.**

Using Vocabulary

1. ectotherm that lives in water and uses gills to get oxygen; trout and shark
2. ectotherm that spends part of its life in water and part on land; frog and salamander
3. ectotherm with dry, scaly skin and do not depend on water for reproduction; lizard and snake
4. endotherm with two legs, two wings, bills, feathers, and lays eggs; duck and ostrich
5. endotherm that has hair and produces milk to nourish its young; whale and monkey

interNET CONNECTION To reinforce chapter vocabulary, use the **Study Guide for Content Mastery** booklet. Also available are activities for **Glencoe Science Voyages** on the Glencoe Science Web Site. **www.glencoe.com/sec/science/ca**

Checking Concepts

6. D	11. C
7. D	12. A
8. C	13. C
9. C	14. A
10. C	15. B

Thinking Critically

16. Accept all logical answers with appropriate support. Answers may include the fact that their skin absorbs all gases and chemicals in the area, including the poisonous ones.
17. internal fertilization for reproduction; amniotic egg; thick, dry, waterproof skin
18. Hair traps air in land animals. Whales live in water and are insulated with large amounts of fat.
19. They most likely have long, pointed canine teeth to stab, grip, and tear flesh. Also, their premolars would be sharp to cut and shred flesh.
20. The amniotic egg with its leathery shell provides a developing embryo with protection from drying out and from being eaten. Reptile eggs can be laid anywhere on land, thus freeing reptiles from a reliance on water for reproduction.

Developing Skills

21. Fish lay a large number of unprotected eggs that are externally fertilized. Reptiles, birds, and mammals all have internal fertilization. Reptiles lay eggs with a leathery shell, and birds lay eggs with a hard shell. Most mammals give birth to live young after a period of development inside the uterus.
22. See student page.

Chapter 25 Assessment

Using Vocabulary

a. amphibian
b. bird
c. carnivore
d. cartilage
e. chordate
f. contour feather
g. down feather
h. ectotherm
i. endoskeleton
j. endotherm
k. estivation
l. fin
m. fish
n. herbivore
o. hibernation
p. mammal
q. marsupial
r. monotreme
s. omnivore
t. placental mammal
u. reptile

Define the following Vocabulary terms and give two examples of each.

1. fish
2. amphibian
3. reptile
4. bird
5. mammal

Checking Concepts

Choose the word or phrase that best answers the question.

6. Which of the following animals have fins, scales, and gills?
   A) amphibians C) reptiles
   B) crocodiles D) fish
7. Which of the following stuctures is used for steering and balancing?
   A) cartilage C) bone
   B) endoskeleton D) fin
8. Which of the following is **NOT** an example of a bony fish?
   A) trout C) shark
   B) bass D) goldfish
9. Which of the following has a swim bladder?
   A) shark C) trout
   B) lamprey D) skate
10. Which of the following is **NOT** an adaptation that helps a bird fly?
    A) hollow bones C) hard-shelled eggs
    B) fused vertebrae D) feathers
11. Which of the following does **NOT** have scales?
    A) birds C) frogs
    B) snakes D) fish
12. Which of the following are vertebrates with lungs and moist skin?
    A) amphibians C) reptiles
    B) fish D) lizards
13. Which of the following are mammals that lay eggs?
    A) carnivores C) monotremes
    B) marsupials D) placental mammals
14. Which of the following have mammary glands but no nipples?
    A) marsupials C) monotremes
    B) placental mammals D) omnivores
15. Which of the following animals eat only plant materials?
    A) carnivores C) omnivores
    B) herbivores D) endotherms

Thinking Critically

16. Why do you think there are fewer species of amphibians on Earth than any other type of vertebrate?
17. What important adaptation allows a reptile to live on land while an amphibian must return to water to live out part of its life cycle?
18. Give two reasons why whales have little hair.
19. You observe a mammal catching and eating a rabbit. What kind of teeth does this animal probably have? Tell how it uses its teeth.

20. Explain how the development of the amniotic egg led to the early success of reptiles.

Developing Skills

If you need help, refer to the **Skill Handbook.**

21. **Comparing and Contrasting:** Compare and contrast the eggs of fish, reptiles, birds, and mammals. How well does each egg type protect the developing embryo?
22. **Concept Mapping:** Complete the concept map describing groups of mammals.

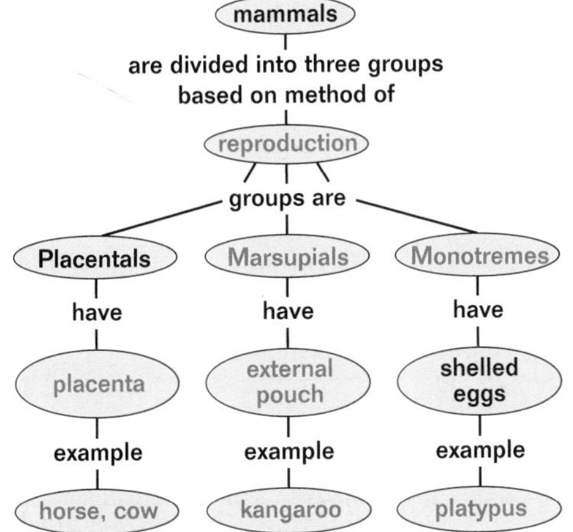

23. **Designing an Experiment:** Design an experiment to find out the effect of water temperature on frog egg development.
24. **Observing and Inferring:** How could you use the feet of a bird to identify it?
25. **Comparing and Contrasting:** Compare and contrast the teeth of herbivores, carnivores, and omnivores. How is each tooth type adapted to the animal's diet?

Test-Taking Tip

Let Bygones Be Bygones Once you have read a question, consider the answers and choose one. Then, put that question behind you. Don't try to keep the question in the back of your mind, thinking that maybe a better answer will come to you as the test continues.

Test Practice

Use these questions to test your Science Proficiency.

1. Vertebrates make up a large percentage of animals. Which of the following statements is true of all vertebrates?
   A) Vertebrates are animals without backbones.
   B) All vertebrates have a notochord.
   C) Only fish have gill slits.
   D) Dorsal hollow nerve cords always develop into a spinal cord with a brain at the front end.
2. Placental mammals, along with monotremes and marsupials, are the orders that make up mammals. Which of the following animals is an example of a placental mammal?
   A) elephant
   B) koala
   C) duck-billed platypus
   D) turtle
3. Which of the following terms describes inactivity during the summer?
   A) estivation
   B) hibernation
   C) metamorphosis
   D) preening

THE PRINCETON REVIEW **Test Practice**

The Test-Taking Tip was written by The Princeton Review, the nation's leader in test preparation.

1. B
2. A
3. A

23. Students should design an experiment with a control that has a set temperature and groups with higher and lower temperatures as the independent variables. The dependent variable for each should be how the egg develops.
24. The blood vessels carrying blood to the bird's feet and the blood vessels carrying blood from the feet back to the heart are intermingled. As the warm blood from the body comes in contact with cold blood from the feet, blood from the body cools and blood heading back to the body warms. This way the bird's body heat is conserved.
25. Herbivores have large incisors for cutting off blades of grass. Carnivores have small incisors and large canine teeth to grip and tear food. Omnivores have canines and incisors to feed on plants and animals.

Bonus Question

In what ways are birds and mammals similar? *Birds and mammals are endotherms; provide extended periods of care for their young; live in and adapt to nearly any environment found on Earth.*

Assessment Resources

The **Test Practice Workbook** provides students with practice in the format, concepts, and critical-thinking skills tested in standardized exams.

 Reproducible Masters

Chapter Review, pp. 49–50 L2

Performance Assessment, p. 25 L2

Assessment, pp. 97–100 L2

Glencoe Technology

UNIT 7

You and the Environment

In this unit, students will learn about the impact humans have on Earth's land, air, and water. They will begin by learning about the human population explosion. Conservation of land and other resources is described. The unit concludes with a discussion of the causes and effects of pollution.

Unit Overview

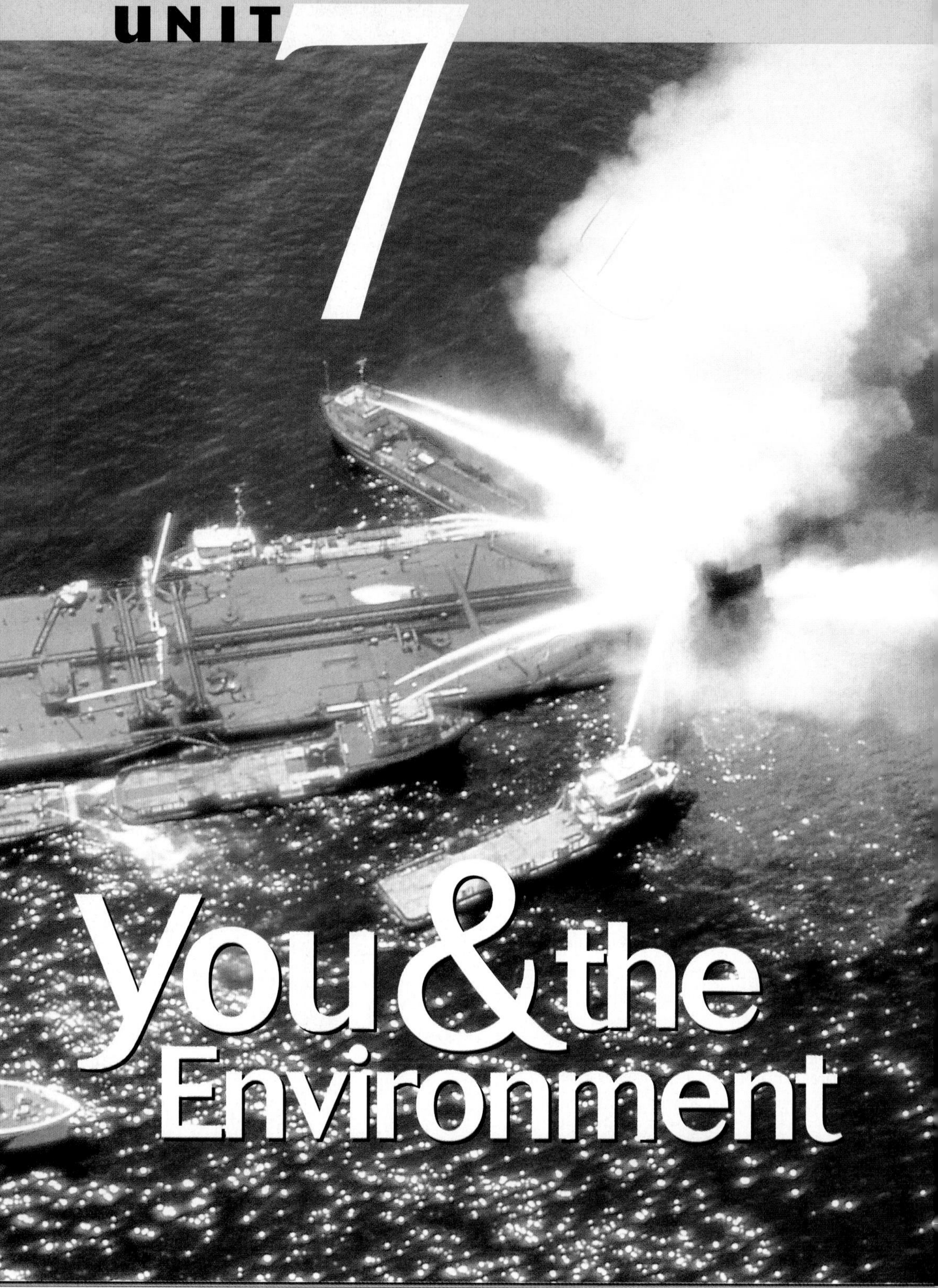

Science at Home

Population and Resources Have students research what percentage of the world's population is represented by industrialized countries. Have them find out what percentage of the world's resources are used by these countries.

NATIONAL GEOGRAPHIC

What's Happening Here?

The ocean is Earth's last frontier. Only recently have explorers searched its remotest depths to reveal some of its special secrets. In places, the water is so deep that if Mount Everest were to rise from the ocean floor, its peak would still be 2000 meters from the surface. With so much water, can't the ocean wash away whatever is dumped into it? Not any longer. Each year in the United States, thousands of oil spills are reported. When the tanker *Megaborg* exploded in the Gulf of Mexico in 1990 (left), it dumped 4.6 million gallons and threatened wetlands bordering Galveston Bay. Some environmental problems are not accidental—people discarding trash in the wrong place, for instance. The rings of a six-pack holder will cut short the life of this young Western Gull (below). As the human population grows, the wear and tear on our planet is showing. How serious are the consequences, and how can we help? These are some of the questions addressed in this unit.

interNET CONNECTION

Explore the Glencoe Science Web Site at **www.glencoe.com/sec/science/ca** to find out more about topics found in this unit.

877

interNET CONNECTION

Internet Addresses

Explore the Glencoe Science Web Site at **www.glencoe.com/sec/science/ca** to find out more about topics found in this unit.

Introducing the Unit

What's happening here?

Have students read the text and look at the pictures. Ask what they think happens to marine life when oil spills occur. Ask what other types of trash might be hazardous to wildlife.

Content Background

Oil from an oil spill can damage feathers, clog gills, kill embryos when the oil seeps into eggs, and poison animals when they ingest contaminated food and water. Even the process of cleaning feathers damages them. Fish or birds can get tangled in plastic six-pack can holders. The animal dies slowly because as it grows, the holder does not stretch. Fish line can tangle the legs and beaks of waterbirds. Bottle caps, pop tops, and polystyrene cups cause internal injuries when eaten by animals. Deer cut their tongues on half-open cans. Small animals get trapped in empty bottles and starve to death.

Previewing the Chapters

Have students identify photographs in the chapters that indicate an impact on the land, air, and water due to human activities. Have students identify these human activities.

Tying to Previous Knowledge

Have students list actions they have seen that cause pollution or waste resources.

Chapter 26 Our Impact on Land

Section	Objectives	Activities/Features
Chapter Opener		**Explore Activity:** Draw a Population Growth Model, p. 879
26-1 **Population Impact on the Environment** 2 Sessions 1 Block	1. **Interpret** data from a graph that shows human population growth. 2. **List** reasons for Earth's rapid increase in human population. 3. **List** several ways each person in an industrialized nation affects the environment.	**Life Science Integration,** p. 881 **Using Math,** p. 882 **Skill Builder:** Making and Using Graphs, p. 883 **Using Math,** p. 883 **Activity 26-1:** A Crowded Encounter, pp. 884–885
26-2 **Using Land** 2 Sessions 1 Block	4. **List** ways that we use land. 5. **Discuss** environmental problems created because of land use. 6. **List** things you can do to help protect the environment.	**MiniLab:** Classify Your Trash for One Day, p. 889 **Problem Solving:** The Effects of Trash Disposal, p. 891 **MiniLab:** Modeling Runoff, p. 892 **Using Math,** p. 894 **Skill Builder:** Communicating, p. 894 **Using Computers,** p. 894
26-3 **Recycling** 4½ Sessions 2 Blocks	7. **List** the advantages of recycling. 8. **List** the advantages and disadvantages of mandatory recycling.	**Skill Builder:** Making and Using Tables, p. 897 **Science Journal,** p. 897 **Activity 26-2:** A Model Landfill, p. 898 **Science and Society Feature:** Using Plants to Reduce Pollution, p. 899 **Field Guide to Waste Management,** pp. 900–903

The number of recommended single-period sessions — The number of recommended blocks
One session and one-half block are allowed for chapter review and assessment.

Activity Materials

Explore	Activities	MiniLabs
p. 879 ruler, paper, pencil	pp. 884–885 small objects such as dried beans, popcorn, or paper clips; 250-mL beaker; clock or watch p. 898 2 2-L bottles, soil, thermometer, plastic wrap, graph paper, rubber band, trash	p. 889 paper, pencil p. 892 2 buckets, water

Need Materials? Contact Science Kit at 1-800-828-7777 or at www.sciencekit.com on the Internet.
For alternate materials, see the activity on the listed page.

Standards		Reproducible Resources	Technology
National	**State/Local**	Test Practice Workbooks are available for use with each chapter.	English and Spanish audiocassettes are available for use with each section.
National Content Standards: UCP2, A1, C4, F2, F5	California Science Content Standards: 9a, 9e, 9f	**Activity Worksheets,** pp. 145–146 **Enrichment,** p. 75 **Laboratory Manual,** pp. 157–160 **Reinforcement,** p. 75 **Study Guide,** p. 101	**Section Focus Transparency 75** **Teaching Transparency 51** **The Infinite Voyage Series**
National Content Standards: UCP5, A1, B1, C4, D1, F2, F5	California Science Content Standards: 5b, 6a, 7a, 9a, 9b, 9f	**Activity Worksheets,** p. 149 **Critical Thinking/Problem Solving,** p. 26 **Enrichment,** p. 76 **Multicultural Connections,** pp. 51–52 **Reinforcement,** p. 76	**Section Focus Transparency 76** **The Infinite Voyage Series** **Glencoe Science Voyages Interactive Videodisc—Earth**
National Content Standards: UCP5, A1, F1, F2, F5	California Science Content Standards: 5b, 5c, 7c, 9e	**Activity Worksheets,** p. 150 **Activity Worksheets,** pp. 147–148 **Enrichment,** p. 77 **Laboratory Manual,** pp. 161–162 **Reinforcement,** p. 77 **Study Guide,** pp. 102–104	**Section Focus Transparency 77** **Teaching Transparency 52** **Science Integration Transparency 26** **Glencoe Science Voyages Interactive CD-ROM** **Internet Connection,** p. 897 **Internet Connection,** p. 899 **Internet Connection,** p. 901

Key to Teaching Strategies

The following designations will help you decide which activities are appropriate for your students.

L1 Level 1 activities should be appropriate for students with learning difficulties.

L2 Level 2 activities should be within the ability range of all students.

L3 Level 3 activities are designed for above-average students.

ELL ELL activities should be within the ability range of English Language Learners.

COOP LEARN Cooperative Learning activities are designed for small group work.

P These strategies represent student products that can be placed into a best-work portfolio.

Multiple Learning Styles logos, as described on page 55T, are used throughout to indicate strategies that address different learning styles.

Assessment Resources

Chapter Review, pp. 51–52
Assessment, pp. 101–104
Performance Assessment in the Science Classroom (PASC)
MindJogger Videoquiz
Alternate Assessment in the Science Classroom
Performance Assessment, p. 26
Chapter Review Software
Computer Test Bank

Chapter 26 Our Impact on Land

This is a representation of key blackline masters available in the Teacher Classroom Resources. See Resource Manager boxes within the chapter for additional information.

Transparencies

Section Focus Transparencies

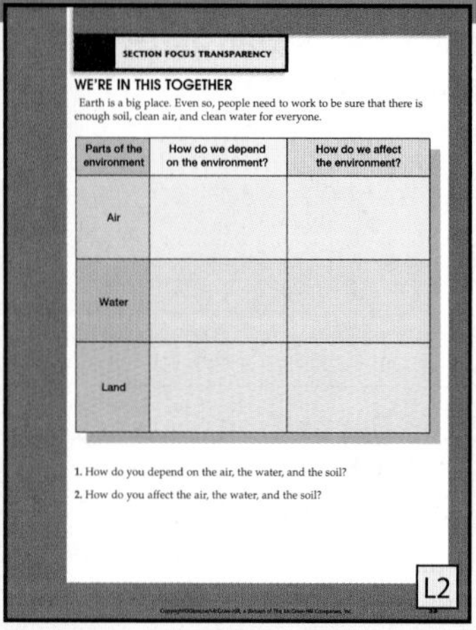

SECTION FOCUS TRANSPARENCY

WE'RE IN THIS TOGETHER

Earth is a big place. Even so, people need to work to be sure that there is enough soil, clean air, and clean water for everyone.

Parts of the environment	How do we depend on the environment?	How do we affect the environment?
Air		
Water		
Land		

1. How do you depend on the air, the water, and the soil?
2. How do you affect the air, the water, and the soil?

L2

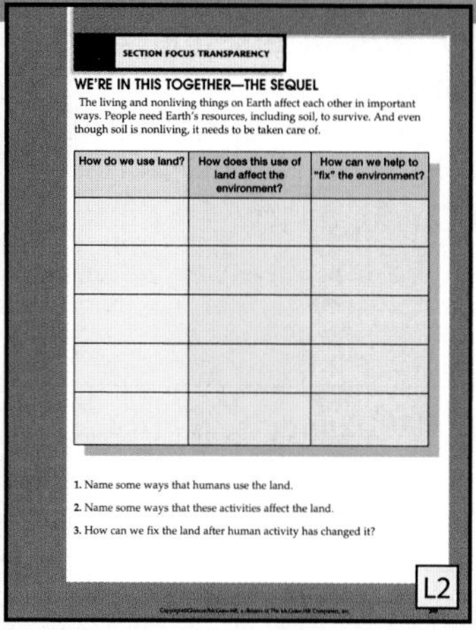

SECTION FOCUS TRANSPARENCY

WE'RE IN THIS TOGETHER—THE SEQUEL

The living and nonliving things on Earth affect each other in important ways. People need Earth's resources, including soil, to survive. And even though soil is nonliving, it needs to be taken care of.

How do we use land?	How does this use of land affect the environment?	How can we help to "fix" the environment?

1. Name some ways that humans use the land.
2. Name some ways that these activities affect the land.
3. How can we fix the land after human activity has changed it?

L2

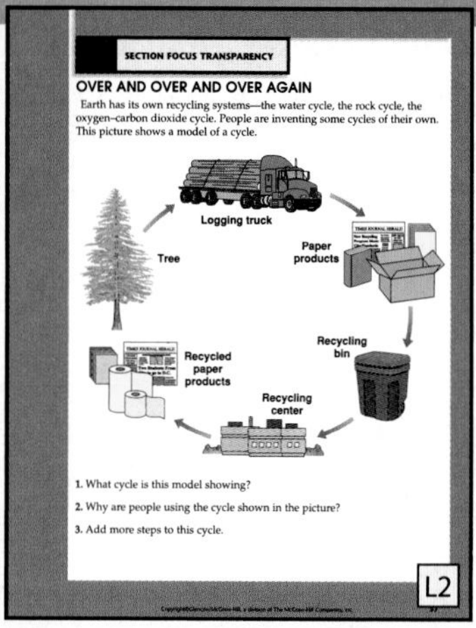

SECTION FOCUS TRANSPARENCY

OVER AND OVER AND OVER AGAIN

Earth has its own recycling systems—the water cycle, the rock cycle, the oxygen–carbon dioxide cycle. People are inventing some cycles of their own. This picture shows a model of a cycle.

Logging truck
Tree
Paper products
Recycling bin
Recycling center
Recycled paper products

1. What cycle is this model showing?
2. Why are people using the cycle shown in the picture?
3. Add more steps to this cycle.

L2

Science Integration Transparencies

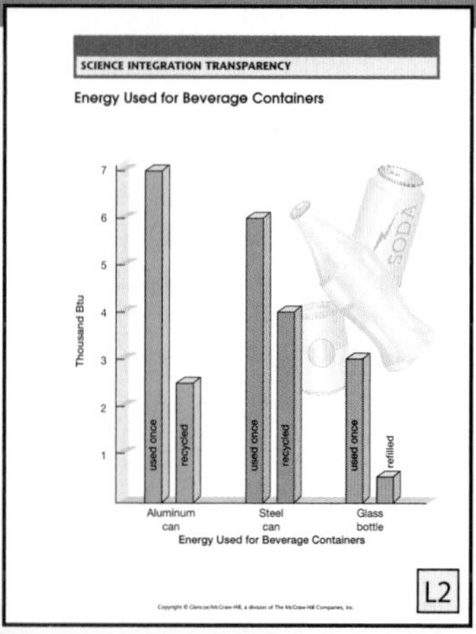

SCIENCE INTEGRATION TRANSPARENCY

Energy Used for Beverage Containers

Thousand Btu
1
2
3
4
5
6
7
used once
recycled
used once
recycled
used once
refilled
Aluminum can
Steel can
Glass bottle
Energy Used for Beverage Containers

L2

Teaching Transparencies

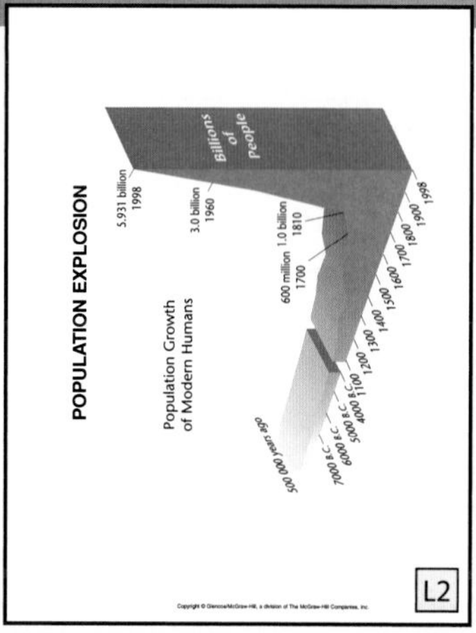

POPULATION EXPLOSION

Population Growth of Modern Humans

Billions of People
5.931 billion 1998
3.0 billion 1960
1.0 billion 1810
600 million 1700

L2

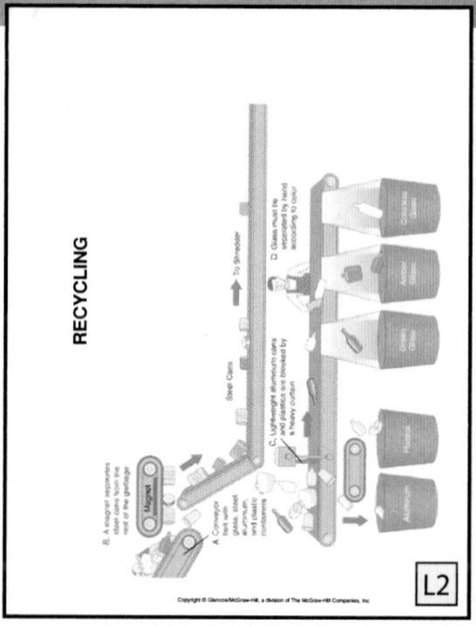

RECYCLING

L2

Meeting Different Ability Levels

Study Guide for Content Mastery

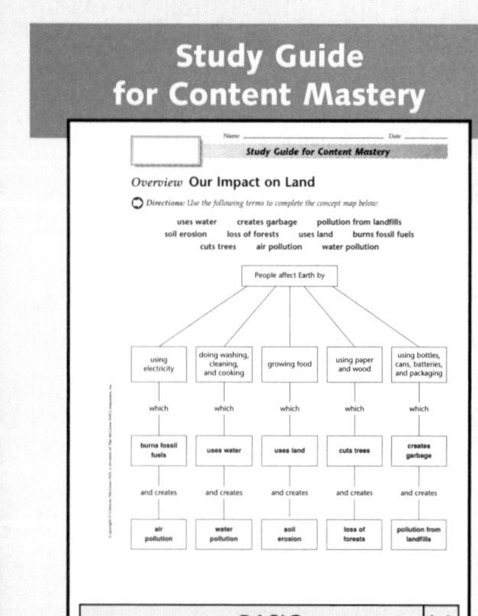
Study Guide for Content Mastery

Overview Our Impact on Land

Directions: Use the following terms to complete the concept map below:

uses water, creates garbage, pollution from landfills, soil erosion, loss of forests, uses land, burns fossil fuels, cuts trees, air pollution, water pollution

People affect Earth by

using electricity	doing washing, cleaning, and cooking	growing food	using paper and wood	using bottles, cans, batteries, and packaging
which	which	which	which	which
burns fossil fuels	uses water	uses land	cuts trees	creates garbage
and creates	and creates	and creates	and creates	and creates
air pollution	water pollution	soil erosion	loss of forests	pollution from landfills

BASIC L1

Reinforcement

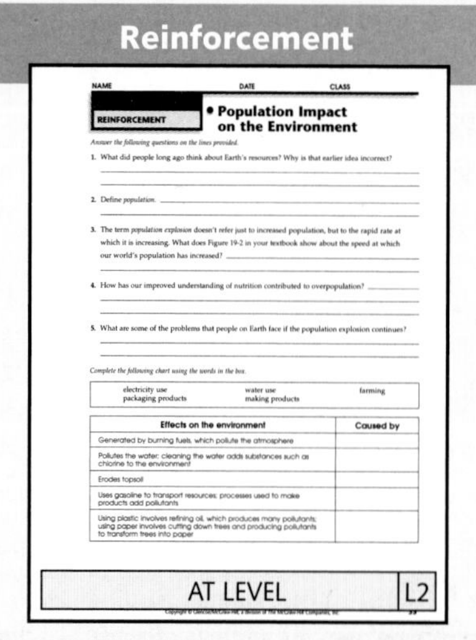
NAME DATE CLASS

REINFORCEMENT

Population Impact on the Environment

Answer the following questions on the lines provided.

1. What did people long ago think about Earth's resources? Why is that earlier idea incorrect?
2. Define *population.*
3. The term *population explosion* doesn't refer just to increased population, but to the rapid rate at which it is increasing. What does Figure 19-2 in your textbook show about the speed at which our world's population has increased?
4. How has our improved understanding of nutrition contributed to overpopulation?
5. What are some of the problems that people on Earth face if the population explosion continues?

Complete the following chart using the words in the box.

electricity use, packaging products, water use, making products, farming

Effects on the environment	Caused by
Generated by burning fuels, which pollute the atmosphere	
Pollutes the water; cleaning the water adds substances such as chlorine to the environment	
Erodes topsoil	
Uses gasoline to transport resources; processes used to make products add pollutants	
Using plastic involves refining oil, which produces many pollutants; using paper involves cutting down trees and producing pollutants to transform trees into paper	

AT LEVEL L2

Enrichment Worksheets

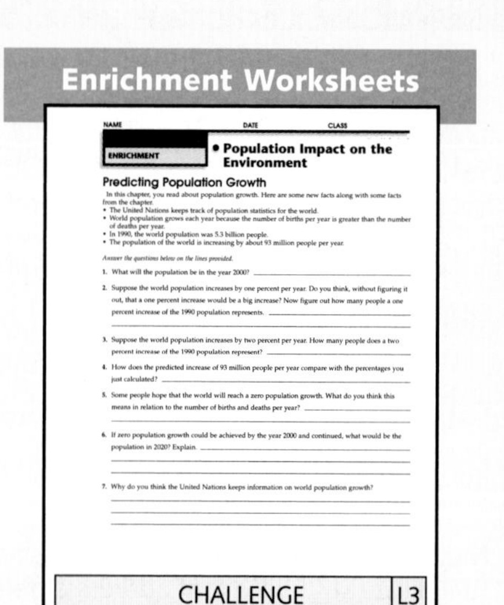
NAME DATE CLASS

ENRICHMENT

Population Impact on the Environment

Predicting Population Growth

In this chapter, you read about population growth. Here are some new facts along with some facts from the chapter.

- The United Nations keeps track of population statistics for the world.
- World population grows each year because the number of births per year is greater than the number of deaths per year.
- In 1990, the world population was 5.3 billion people.
- The population of the world is increasing by about 93 million people per year.

Answer the questions below on the lines provided.

1. What will the population be in the year 2000?
2. Suppose the world population increases by one percent per year. Do you think, without figuring it out, that a one percent increase would be a big increase? Now figure out how many people a one percent increase of the 1990 population represents.
3. Suppose the world population increases by two percent per year. How many people does a two percent increase of the 1990 population represent?
4. How does the predicted increase of 93 million people per year compare with the percentages you just calculated?
5. Some people hope that the world will reach a zero population growth. What do you think this means in relation to the number of births and deaths per year?
6. If zero population growth could be achieved by the year 2000 and continued, what would be the population in 2020? Explain.
7. Why do you think the United Nations keeps information on world population growth?

CHALLENGE L3

Hands-on Activities

Activity Worksheets

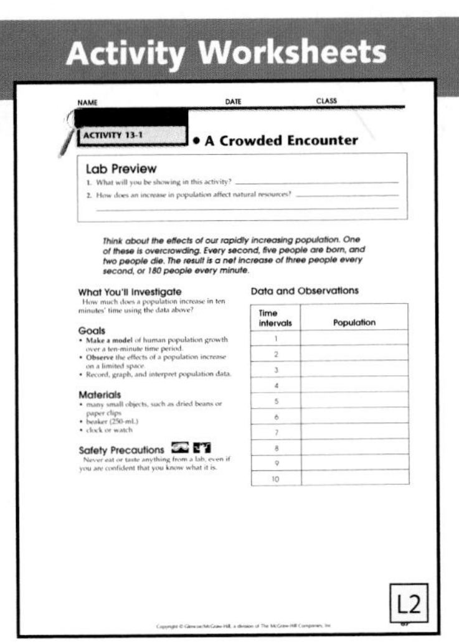
NAME DATE CLASS

ACTIVITY 13-1 • A Crowded Encounter

Lab Preview

Think about the effects of our rapidly increasing population. One of these is overcrowding. Every second, five people are born, and two people die. The result is a net increase of three people every second, or 180 people every minute.

What You'll Investigate

Data and Observations

Time intervals	Population
1	
2	
3	
4	
5	
6	
7	
8	
9	
10	

Goals

Materials

Safety Precautions

L2

Lab Manual

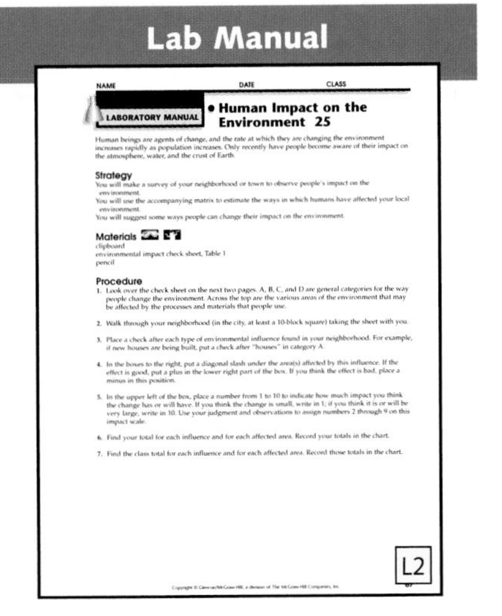
NAME DATE CLASS

LABORATORY MANUAL • Human Impact on the Environment 25

Strategy

Materials

Procedure

L2

Accessibility

Spanish Resources

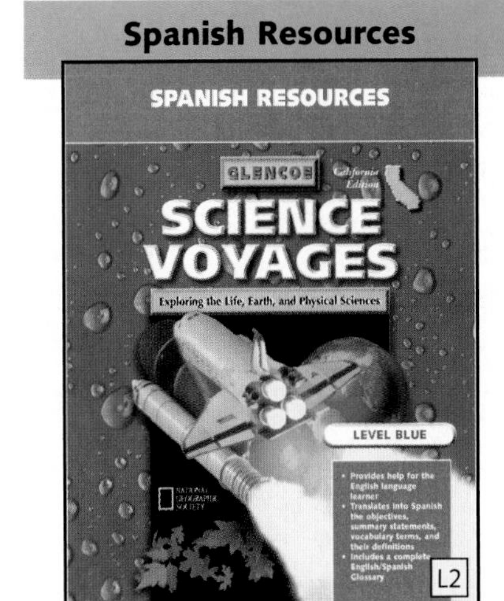
SPANISH RESOURCES

GLENCOE SCIENCE VOYAGES

Exploring the Life, Earth, and Physical Sciences

LEVEL BLUE

L2

Assessment

Performance Assessment

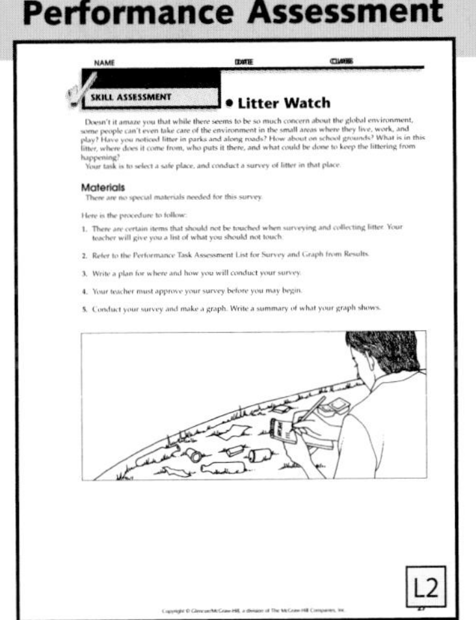
NAME DATE CLASS

SKILL ASSESSMENT • Litter Watch

Materials

L2

Chapter Review

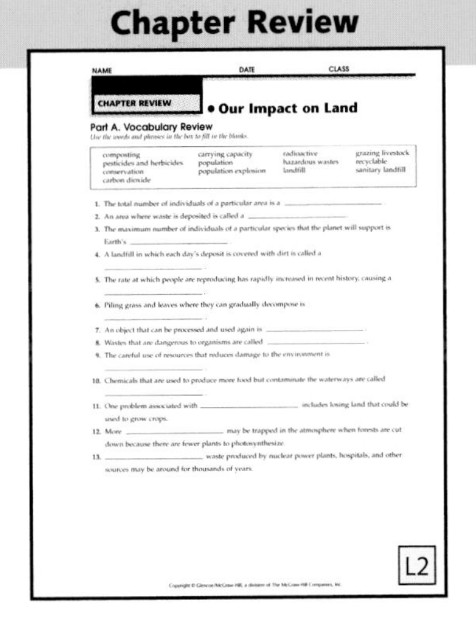
NAME DATE CLASS

CHAPTER REVIEW • Our Impact on Land

Part A. Vocabulary Review

L2

Assessment

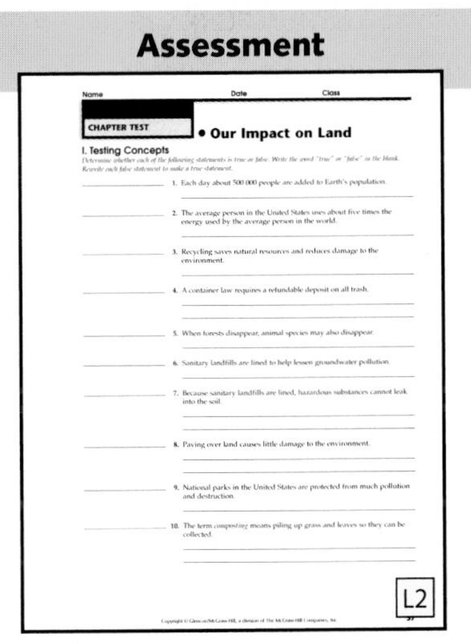
Name Date Class

CHAPTER TEST • Our Impact on Land

I. Testing Concepts

L2

Test Practice Workbook

CALIFORNIA SCIENCE CONTENT STANDARDS PRACTICE QUESTIONS

GLENCOE SCIENCE VOYAGES

Exploring the Life, Earth, and Physical Sciences

LEVEL BLUE

L2

Extending Content

Critical Thinking/ Problem Solving

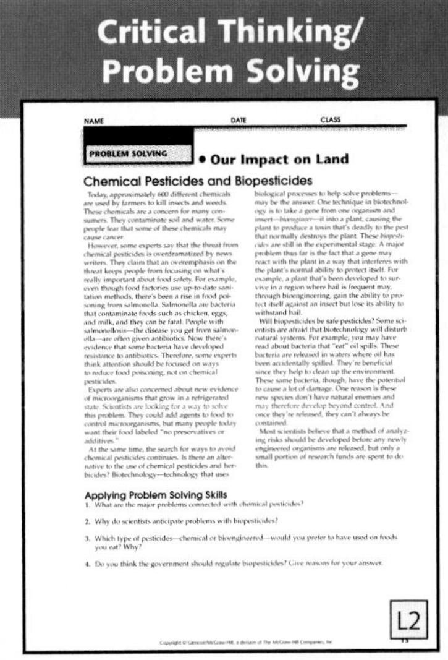
NAME DATE CLASS

PROBLEM SOLVING • Our Impact on Land

Chemical Pesticides and Biopesticides

Applying Problem Solving Skills

L2

Multicultural Connections

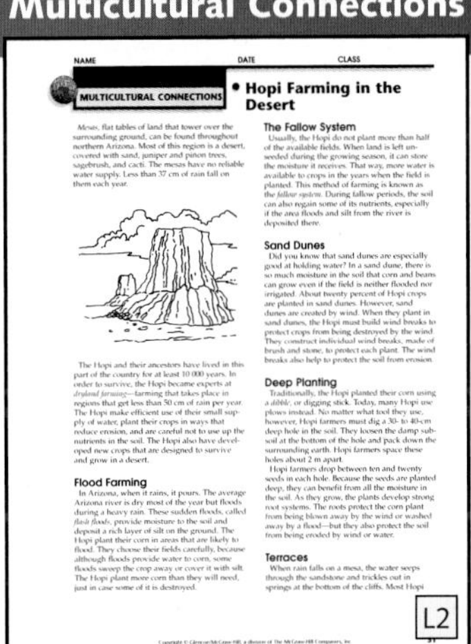
NAME DATE CLASS

MULTICULTURAL CONNECTIONS • Hopi Farming in the Desert

The Fallow System

Sand Dunes

Deep Planting

Flood Farming

Terraces

L2

Helping You Prepare

Human Population (Section 26-1)

Ninety percent of the world's population increase is expected in developing countries. In western industrial nations, the birthrate is relatively constant, but better diet and disease controls extend the life span.

How People Affect the Environment (Section 26-1)

There are few parts of the environment that are not in some way affected by human activities. People move soil, change the vegetation, add chemicals, and remove minerals. People use water, divert water, and pollute water. People pollute air. People raise some plants and animals for food, hunt animals, use insecticides and herbicides, and change the habitat of organisms. Humans are the only species on Earth with so many effects on the environment. With this much power, it is important to responsibly plan for the quality of the planet.

Land Usage (Section 26-2)

In the contiguous 48 states, close to half of the land area in most cities is used for roads, highways, and parking lots. This equals two percent of the total land surface, or an area the size of the state of Georgia.

GLENCOE TECHNOLOGY

Glencoe Science Voyages Interactive CD-ROM

Chapter Summaries

Use the Chapter Summary to introduce, teach, or review chapter material.

Each year due to population growth, the world's farmers have to feed 95 million more people with trillions fewer kilograms of topsoil. There is less topsoil because the land is severely eroded due to home construction, road construction, and farming practices.

Phytoremediation (Section 26-2)

Phytoremediation can be used to clean up both contaminated soil and water. Contaminants that can be removed include metals, pesticides, solvents, explosives, petroleum and some other hydrocarbons, and even leachates from landfills. In all cases of phytoremediation, the roots are involved in removing the contaminants.

NATIONAL GEOGRAPHIC — **Teacher's Corner**

Products Available from Glencoe

To order the following products for use with this chapter, call Glencoe at 1-800-334-7344:

Videodisc

GTV: Planetary Manager

Products Available from National Geographic Society

To order the following products for use with this chapter, call National Geographic Society at 1-800-368-2728:

Videos

Healing the Earth

The Living Earth

Recycling: It's Everybody's Job

Recycling: The Endless Cycle

Index to National Geographic Magazine

The following articles may be used for research relating to this chapter:

"Feeding the Planet," by T.R. Reid, October 1998.

"Population," by Joel L. Swerdlow, October 1998.

"Women and Population," by Erla Zwingle, October 1998.

There are several methods of phytoremediation. A few of these methods include breaking down (degrading) organic pollutants, filtering metal contaminants from water, trapping metal contaminates from soil, and capturing and volatilizing water contaminants. The process of breaking down pollutants is called phytodegradation, filtering contaminants from water is rhizofiltration, trapping contaminates in soil is phytoextraction, and capturing and volatilizing water contaminates is phytovolatilization.

Usually, phytoremediation is used only at sites with low contaminant concentrations and where the contaminants are in shallow areas where plant roots can reach. In the case of groundwater pollution, the water can be treated by pumping it out of the ground and using it to irrigate trees.

Conserving Resources (Section 26-2)

Resources include energy sources, as well as groundwater, surface water, air, biological diversity, soil, forests, and many other things. Human activities threaten many of these resources. The management of these resources depends directly on the economy of a region and the value the population places on these resources.

Waste deposited in sanitary landfills or open dumps is sometimes called urban ore because it contains many materials that could be recycled and used again to provide energy or useful products.

Precycling is one way to conserve resources. Precycling means to reduce waste before one even buys an item. For example, shoppers precycle by buying food in bulk, reducing the amount of packaging they consume. Precycling also means buying products in environmentally friendly packages. People also can precycle by purchasing products packaged in materials made from recycled products.

SCIENCE UPDATE

For current events or science in the news, access the Glencoe Science Web Site at **www.glencoe.com/sec/science/ca**

Recyclable Objects (Section 26-3)

People in the United States annually produce enough garbage to completely fill five million large truck trailers. That would be a fleet stretching end-to-end, twice around the world at the equator. Many items in this garbage could be recycled.

Recyclable materials can be used in many ways. Some plastics are melted down and spun into polyester fiber that is used to make sleeping bags, insulation, and fishing line. Also, plastics can be made into rot-resistant materials for picnic tables, waterfront decks, boat hulls, and bath tubs. Old tires can be shredded and used for fuel, new rubber, plastic products, and as substitutes for concrete and asphalt in road pavement.

Teacher to Teacher

"I have students record key information about each chapter in their Science Journals, leaving the left side (about 1/4 of the page) blank. For homework, they create possible test questions from the information. They also create questions after demonstrations and experiments. Students use these questions to prepare for tests."

Patricia M. Horton, Mentor Teacher
Summit Intermediate School
Etiwanda, CA

CHAPTER 26 Our Impact on Land

CHAPTER OVERVIEW

Section 26-1 This section describes the human population explosion and discusses ways people affect the environment.

Section 26-2 Concepts presented in this section include how people use land, the environmental problems that result from these activities, and ways people can help protect the environment.

Section 26-3 The advantages of recycling are introduced. Both mandatory and voluntary recycling are described.

Chapter Vocabulary

carrying capacity
population
population explosion
landfill
hazardous waste
conservation
composting
recyclable

Theme Connection

Systems and Interactions Many different human activities affect the environment. With an increase in human population, these effects become more pronounced.

00:00 OUT OF TIME?

If time does not permit teaching the entire chapter, use Reviewing Main Ideas on pages 904–905.

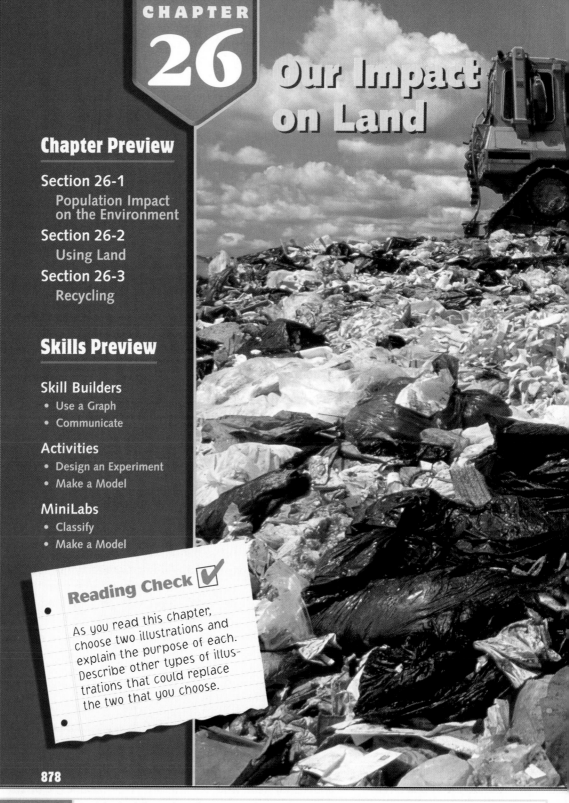

CHAPTER 26 Our Impact on Land

Chapter Preview

Skills Preview

Skill Builders

- Use a Graph
- Communicate

Activities

- Design an Experiment
- Make a Model

MiniLabs

- Classify
- Make a Model

Reading Check

As you read this chapter, choose two illustrations and explain the purpose of each. Describe other types of illustrations that could replace the two that you choose.

878

Multiple Learning Styles

Look for the following logos for strategies that emphasize different learning modalities.

Linguistic Reteach, p. 882; Preview, p. 904

Logical-Mathematical Explore Activity, p. 879; Activity, p. 884

Visual-Spatial Inclusion Strategies, p. 881; Assessment, p. 883; Using an Analogy, p. 888; Science Journal, p. 892; Multiple Learning Styles, p. 896; Activity, p. 898; Reteach, p. 904

Auditory-Musical Out of Time?, p. 904

Kinesthetic MiniLab, 456

Interpersonal MiniLab, p. 889; Inclusion Strategies, p. 889; Discussion, p. 893; Reteach, p. 893; Activity, p. 896; Review, p. 904

Naturalist Making a Model, p. 887

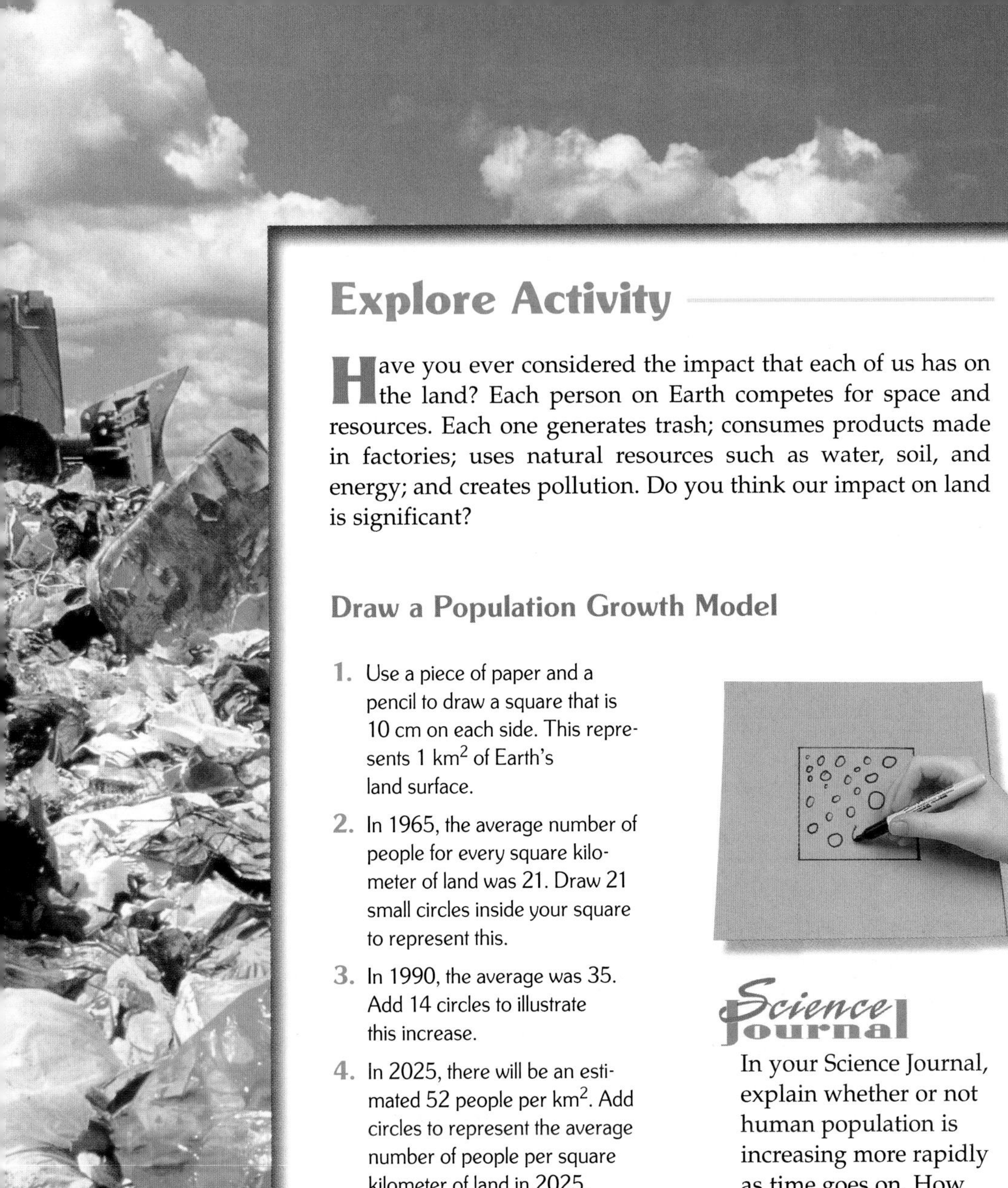

Explore Activity

Have you ever considered the impact that each of us has on the land? Each person on Earth competes for space and resources. Each one generates trash; consumes products made in factories; uses natural resources such as water, soil, and energy; and creates pollution. Do you think our impact on land is significant?

Draw a Population Growth Model

1. Use a piece of paper and a pencil to draw a square that is 10 cm on each side. This represents 1 km^2 of Earth's land surface.
2. In 1965, the average number of people for every square kilometer of land was 21. Draw 21 small circles inside your square to represent this.
3. In 1990, the average was 35. Add 14 circles to illustrate this increase.
4. In 2025, there will be an estimated 52 people per km^2. Add circles to represent the average number of people per square kilometer of land in 2025.
5. Prepare a bar graph that shows population density for each year discussed above.

Science Journal

In your Science Journal, explain whether or not human population is increasing more rapidly as time goes on. How do you think population growth affects the environment?

Assessment Planner

Portfolio

Refer to p. 905 for suggested items that students might select for their portfolios.

Performance Assessment

See p. 905 for additional Performance Assessment options.
Skill Builder, pp. 883, 894, 897
MiniLab, pp. 889, 892
Activity 26-1, pp. 884-885, 26-2, p. 898

Content Assessment

Section Assessment, pp. 883, 894, 897
Chapter Assessment, pp. 906–907
Proficiency Prep, pp. 883, 893

Explore Activity

Purpose

Logical-Mathematical Use the Explore Activity to introduce students to human population growth. L2 ELL COOP LEARN

Preparation

You may want to discuss scale drawings with the students before they perform this activity. The scale of their drawing in this activity is 1:10 000.

Materials

metric ruler, pencil, one piece of paper

Teaching Strategies

Students should be reminded that the information they are using is the world average. Students may need to be reminded that population density is the number of people living in a region divided by the area of that region.

Science Journal Students should explain that population is increasing more rapidly. They may infer that the environment will be damaged as more and more demands are placed upon it.

Assessment

Performance Draw an additional square representing the 1990 average population density in the United States and compare it with the world average used in the Explore Activity. The 1990 United States population density was 25 people per square kilometer. Hypothesize about how the United States population density might differ from the world average in 2025. Use **Performance Assessment in the Science Classroom,** p. 21.

SECTION 26•1

Prepare

Content Background

Refer to **Human Population** and **How People Affect the Environment** on p. 878E.

Preplanning

Refer to the **Chapter Organizer** on pp. 878A–B.

1 Motivate

Bellringer

Before presenting the lesson, display **Section Focus Transparency 75** on the overhead projector. Use the accompanying **Focus Activity** worksheet. L2 ELL

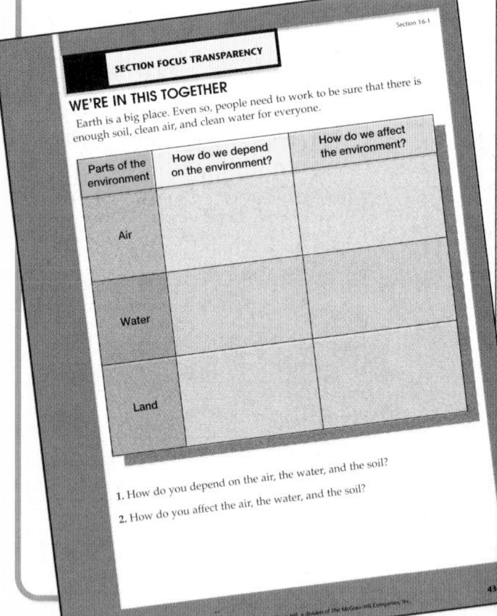

Section 26-1

SECTION FOCUS TRANSPARENCY

WE'RE IN THIS TOGETHER

Earth is a big place. Even so, people need to work to be sure that there is enough soil, clean air, and clean water for everyone.

Parts of the environment	How do we depend on the environment?	How do we affect the environment?
Air		
Water		
Land		

1. How do you depend on the air, the water, and the soil?
2. How do you affect the air, the water, and the soil?

Tying to Previous Knowledge

Students know about the diversity of life on Earth. Ask them how human population growth will affect the availability of land and water for other organisms.

26•1 Population Impact on the Environment

What You'll Learn

- How to interpret data from a graph that shows human population growth
- Reasons for Earth's rapid increase in human population
- Several ways each person in an industrialized nation affects the environment

Vocabulary

carrying capacity
population
population explosion

Why It's Important

- Humans directly impact the environment. The more humans there are, the greater the impact.

The Human Population Explosion

At one time, people thought of Earth as a world with unlimited resources. They thought the planet could provide them with whatever materials they needed. Earth seemed to have an endless supply of metals, fossil fuels, and rich soils. Today, we know this isn't true. Earth has a carrying capacity. The **carrying capacity** is the maximum number of individuals of a particular species that the planet will support. Thus, Earth's resources are limited. Unless we treat those resources with care, they will disappear.

Many years ago, few people lived on Earth. Fewer resources were used and less waste was produced than today. But, in the last 200 years, the number of people on Earth has increased at an extremely rapid rate. The increase in the world population has changed the way we must view our world and how we care for it for future generations, like the babies in **Figure 26-1.**

Figure 26-1 The human population is growing at an increasingly rapid rate. **Why does Earth have a carrying capacity?**

Resource Manager

The following **Teacher Classroom Resources** can be used with Section 26-1:

 **Reproducible Masters**

Activity Worksheets, pp. 145–146 L2

Enrichment, p. 75 L3

Home Involvement, p. 4 L2

Laboratory Manual, pp. 157–160 L2

Reinforcement, p. 75 L2

Study Guide, p. 101 L1 ELL

 **Transparencies**

Teaching Transparency 51 L2

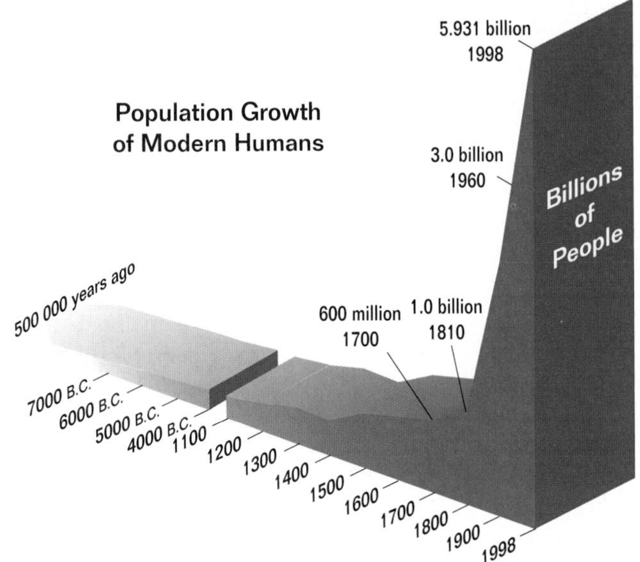

Figure 26-2 The human species, *Homo sapiens,* may have appeared about 500 000 years ago. Our population numbers remained relatively steady until about 200 years ago. **Why have we experienced such a sharp increase in growth rate since about 1800?**

Human Population

A **population** is the total number of individuals of a particular species in a particular area. The area can be small or large. For example, we can talk about the human population of one particular community, such as Los Angeles, or about the human population of the entire planet.

Have you ever wondered how many people live on Earth? The global population in 1998 was 5.9 billion. Each day, the number of humans increases by approximately 215 000. Earth is now experiencing a **population explosion.** The word *explosion* is used because the rate at which the population is growing has increased rapidly in recent history.

Our Increasing Population

Look at **Figure 26-2.** You can see that it took hundreds of thousands of years for Earth's population to reach 1 billion people. After that, the population increased much faster. Population has increased so rapidly in recent years because the death rate has been slowed by modern medicine, and we have better sanitation and better nutrition. This means that more people are living longer. Also, the number of births has increased because more people survive to the age at which they can have children.

The population explosion has seriously affected the environment. Scientists predict even greater changes as more people use Earth's limited resources. The population is predicted to be about 11 billion by 2100—nearly twice what it is now.

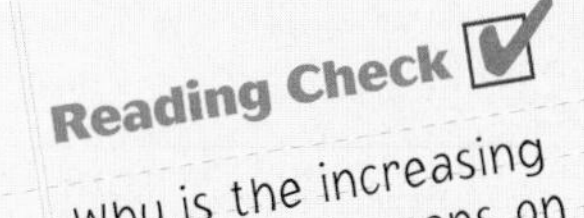

Why is the increasing number of humans on Earth called a population explosion?

Carrying Capacity

One of the things that affects carrying capacity is food. When a region does not have enough food, animals either migrate or starve. Infer what other factors determine the carrying capacity of a particular region for a species.

2 Teach

Caption Answer

Figure 26-1 *Potential food production, natural resources, and living space are all limited. Serious environmental hazards could result from overpopulation.*

Figure 26-2 *Death rate has slowed down because of better medicines, sanitation, and nutrition; and birthrate has increased because more people have reached the age at which they can have children.*

Answer to Reading Check

The rate of population growth has increased rapidly (explosively) over the past 200 years.

fresh, unpolluted water; space to live

Correcting Misconceptions

Students will likely believe that the rapidly increasing human population in developing countries poses the most serious threat to the environment. Inform them that each person living in a developed nation like the United States uses more resources and creates more wastes than others in developing nations around the world.

Inclusion Strategies

Gifted Have students make population charts or graphs that compare the populations of Europe, Asia, Africa, North America, and South America. L3

Integrating the Sciences

Life Science In nature, individuals within any population compete for resources. When population density is low, resources are abundant, and population increases. As the population approaches the carrying capacity, resources limit the population. Only the stronger and better-adapted individuals can survive to reproduce.

CA Science Content Standards

Page 881: 9e

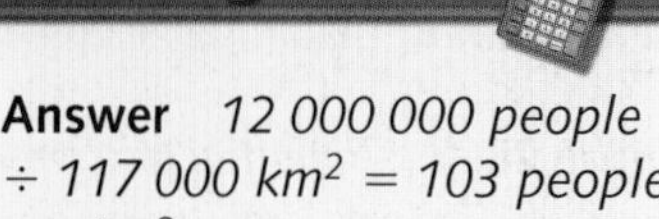

Answer *12 000 000 people ÷ 117 000 km² = 103 people per km²*

Caption Answer

Figure 26-3 *fossil fuels, water, mineral resources, trees*

GLENCOE TECHNOLOGY

Videodisc

The Infinite Voyage: Life in the Balance

Chapter 6 *Southern California's Chaparral: Extinction by Development* 9:00

Refer to the Teacher Guide for bar codes and teaching strategies.

3 Assess

Check for Understanding

Discussion

Ask students, "How does my being on Earth change Earth? What can I do to create a positive balance between people and the environment?"

Reteach

Linguistic Have students keep a diary for one day of all activities they perform that significantly affect the environment. L1

Extension

For students who have mastered this section, use the **Reinforcement** and **Enrichment** masters.

CA Science Content Standards

Page 882: 9e, 9f

Page 883: 9e

Using Math

The population density of a region is the average number of people per unit of area. Find the population density of Pennsylvania, which has a population of about 12 million people and an area of about 117 000 km².

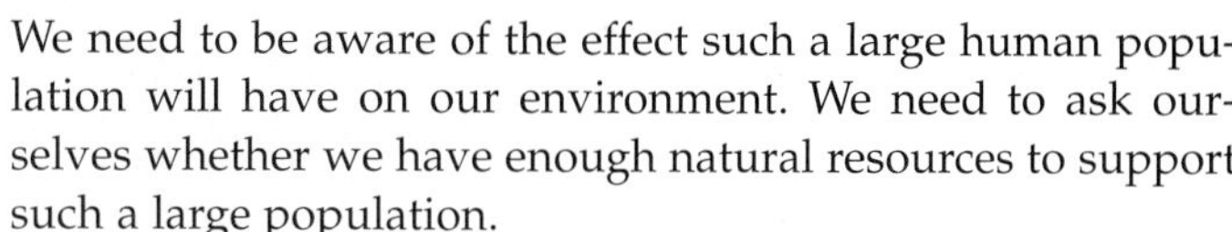

We need to be aware of the effect such a large human population will have on our environment. We need to ask ourselves whether we have enough natural resources to support such a large population.

How People Affect the Environment

By the time you're 75 years old, you will have produced enough garbage to equal the mass of six African elephants (43 000 kg). You will have consumed enough water to fill 100 000 bathtubs (26 million L). If you live in the United States, you will have used five times as much energy as an average person living elsewhere in the world.

Our Daily Activities

In your daily activities, you use electricity, some of which is generated by the burning of fuels. The environment changes when fuels are mined and again, later, when they are burned. The water that you use must be made as clean as possible before being returned to the environment. You eat food, which takes land to grow. Much of the food you eat is grown using chemical substances, such as pesticides and herbicides, to kill insects and weeds. These chemicals can get into water supplies and threaten the health of living things if they become too concentrated. How else do you and other people affect the environment?

Many of the products you buy are packaged in plastic and paper. Plastic is made from oil. The process of refining oil produces pollutants. Producing paper requires cutting down trees, using gasoline to transport them to a paper mill, and producing pollutants in the process of transforming the trees into paper. **Figure 26-3** shows some items that may require these activities to produce them.

We change the land when we remove resources from it, and we further impact the environment when we shape those resources into usable products. Then, once we've produced and consumed products, we must dispose of them. Look at **Figure 26-4.** Unnecessary packaging is only one of the problems associated with waste disposal.

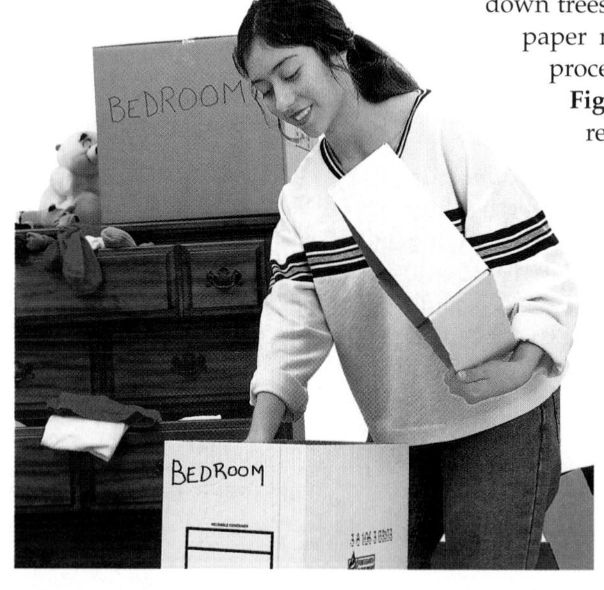

Figure 26-3 Every day, you use many of Earth's resources. **What resources were consumed to produce the items shown in this photograph?**

Content Background

At a 1994 conference, a researcher stated that Earth is headed for a mass extinction within 50 to 100 years. According to another researcher, there is currently a loss of 300 species each day. The biggest causes for these extinctions are pollution and habitat destruction.

The Future

As the population continues to grow, more demands will be made on the environment. Traffic-choked highways, overflowing garbage dumps, shrinking forests, and vanishing wildlife are common. What can we do? People are the problem, but we also are the solution. As you learn more about how we affect the environment, you'll discover what you can do to help make the future world one that everyone can live in and enjoy. An important step that we can take is to think carefully about our use of natural resources. If everyone learns to conserve resources, we can make a positive impact on the environment.

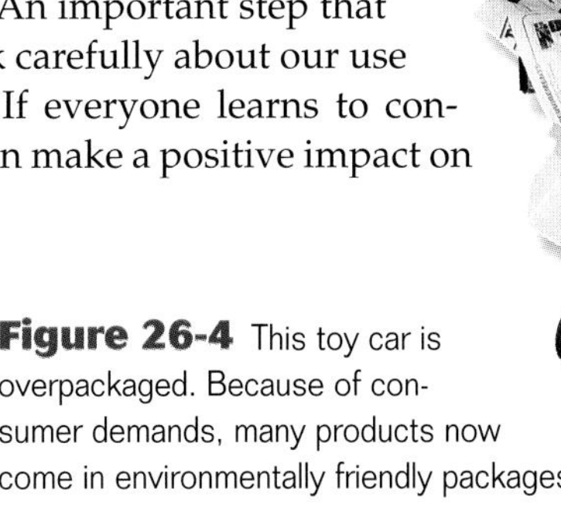

Figure 26-4 This toy car is overpackaged. Because of consumer demands, many products now come in environmentally friendly packages.

Section Assessment

1. Using **Figure 26-2**, estimate how many years it took for the *Homo sapiens* population to reach 1 billion. How long did it take to triple to 3 billion?
2. Why is human population increasing so rapidly?
3. **Think Critically:** In nonindustrial nations, individuals have less negative impact on the environment than citizens in industrialized nations. In your Science Journal, explain why you think this is so.
4. **Skill Builder**
   Making and Using Graphs Use **Figure 26-2** to answer the questions below. If you need help, refer to Making and Using Graphs in the **Skill Handbook** on page 953.
   a. Early humanlike ancestors existed more than 4 million years ago. Why does the graph indicate that it should extend back only 500 000 years?
   b. How would the slope of the graph change if, in the near future, the growth rate were cut in half?

Using Math

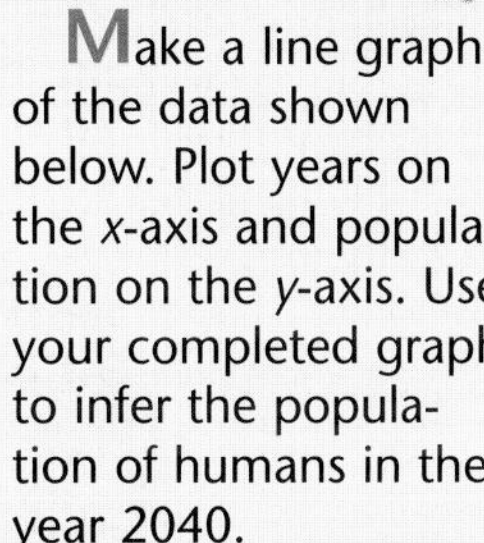

Make a line graph of the data shown below. Plot years on the *x*-axis and population on the *y*-axis. Use your completed graph to infer the population of humans in the year 2040.

Human Population in Billions

1998	2010	2025
5.931	6.849	7.923

4 Close

Proficiency Prep

Use this quiz to check students' recall of section content.

1. **What is the total number of individuals of a particular species in a particular area?** *population*
2. **What is the rapid increase in the number of humans on Earth?** *population explosion*
3. **How much more energy does an average person in the United States use than an average person living elsewhere?** *five times as much*

Section Assessment

1. It took almost 500 000 years for the *Homo sapiens* population to reach 1 billion. It took only 150 years (1810–1960) to triple.
2. The death rate has been slowed by modern medicine, better sanitation, and better nutrition. Births have increased because more people have reached the age where they can have children.
3. Think Critically People living in nonindustrialized nations use less water, energy, and food and generate less garbage.
4. **Skill Builder**
   a. The graph represents the population growth of modern humans, *Homo sapiens*.
   b. The slope would decrease by half of its current slope. The population would continue to increase, but at a slower rate.

Assessment

Performance Assess students' abilities to make and use graphs by having them determine when human population reached 2 billion. That occurred around 1912. Use **Performance Assessment in the Science Classroom,** p. 41.

Using Math

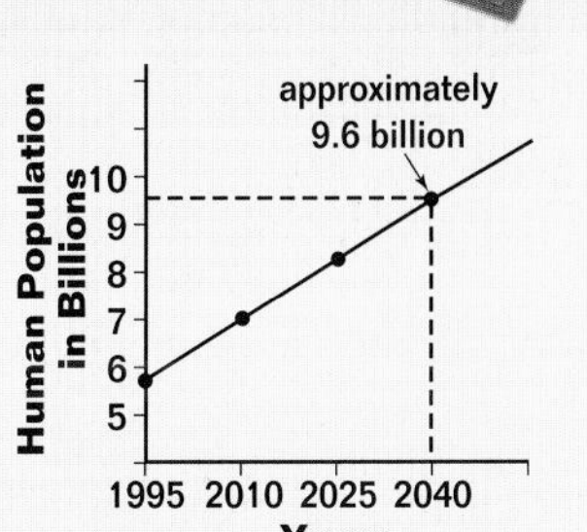

Activity 26-1

What You'll Investigate

Purpose

Logical-Mathematical Students will model population increase in ten minutes. L2 COOP LEARN

Process Skills

making models, using numbers, communicating, forming a hypothesis, designing an experiment, interpreting data, making and using tables, making and using graphs

Procedure

Time

40 minutes

Materials

Have 360 small items such as dried beans for each team to use. A 1-pound (484-g) bag of black-eyed peas contains approximately 2100 beans.

Safety Precautions

Remind students not to eat or taste materials used in the lab.

Teaching Strategies

- Have students count out 36 objects for each minute before they begin timing.
- Have students refer to **Figure 26-2** to help them make their graph.

A Crowded Encounter

Think about the effects of our rapidly increasing human population. One of these is overcrowding. Every second, five people are born, and two people die. The result is a net increase of three people every second, or 180 people every minute.

Materials

- Many small objects, such as dried beans, popcorn, or paper clips
- Beaker (250 mL)
- Clock or watch

What You'll Investigate

Goals

- **Make a model** of human population growth over a ten-minute time period.
- **Observe** the effects of a population increase on a limited space.
- Record, graph, and interpret population data.

Safety Precautions

Never eat or taste anything from a lab, even if you are confident that you know what it is.

Time	Population
1 minute	180
2 minutes	360
3 minutes	540
4 minutes	720
5 minutes	900
6 minutes	1080
7 minutes	1260
8 minutes	1440
9 minutes	1620
10 minutes	1800

Procedure

1. Use the empty beaker to represent the space left on Earth that is unoccupied by humans at the moment you begin.
2. Let each of your small objects represent five people.
3. **Design** a table with two columns. One column will show the time (1 to 10 minutes), and the other column will show the population at the designated time.
4. **Begin timing** your first minute. At the end of one minute, place the appropriate number of small items in your beaker. **Record** the data in your table. Continue for each minute of time.
5. After completing your table, **make a graph** that shows the time in minutes on the horizontal axis and the population on the vertical axis.

Conclude and Apply

1. At the end of ten minutes, what is the net increase in human population?
2. **Compare and contrast** the graph you just made with the graph shown in **Figure 26-2.** How do you account for the differences?
3. Today, approximately 5.9 billion people inhabit Earth. That number will double in about 40 years. Assuming the rate remains unchanged, **predict** what the population will be 80 years from now.
4. Suggest ways in which the net increase in human population affects Earth's limited resources.

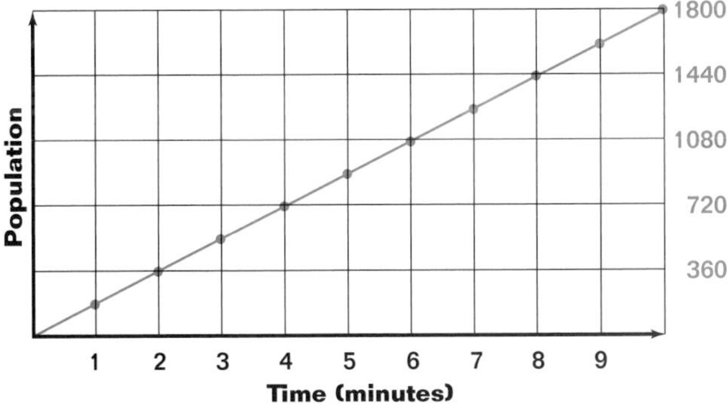

Expected Outcome

Students will see that over time, the beaker becomes crowded with objects.

Error Analysis

Have students compare their results with what they expected would happen before they made the model.

Conclude and Apply

1. based on the sample data, 1800 people
2. Both graphs show human population growth. **Figure 26-2** is flatter where it begins than the graph in this lab because the rate of increase today is much greater than in the early years of human population growth. Another difference is that **Figure 26-2** shows population growth over thousands of years, while the graph in this activity shows growth over minutes of time. Therefore, exponential growth is not evident in the graph in this activity.
3. In 40 years, the population will be $5.9 + 5.9 = 11.8$ billion; in 80 years, it will be $11.8 + 11.8 = 23.6$ billion.
4. People use more fossil fuels and mineral resources. Land use increases resulting in habitat destruction and increased soil erosion. Air and water pollution may increase.

Assessment

Performance To further assess students' understanding of population growth, have them graph ten years of growth in the United States. In 1990, the estimated population of the United States was 251 million. The population increases by about 2.2 million people each year. Use **Performance Assessment in the Science Classroom,** p. 39. P

GO Further

Tell students that if you gathered all humans on Earth into one place, they would take up only a small portion of Earth's surface. Then ask them to explain why human population growth is a problem. Students should realize that although people's bodies do not take up much space, croplands, buildings, factories, mines, roads, and other things used by people occupy much of the land.

CA Science Content Standards

Page 884: 9a, 9e
Page 885: 9a

SECTION 26•2

Prepare

Refer to **Land Usage, Phytoremediation,** and **Conserving Resources** on pp. 878E–F.

Preplanning

Refer to the **Chapter Organizer** on pp. 878A–B.

1 Motivate

Bellringer

Before presenting the lesson, display **Section Focus Transparency 76** on the overhead projector. Use the accompanying **Focus Activity** worksheet. L2 ELL

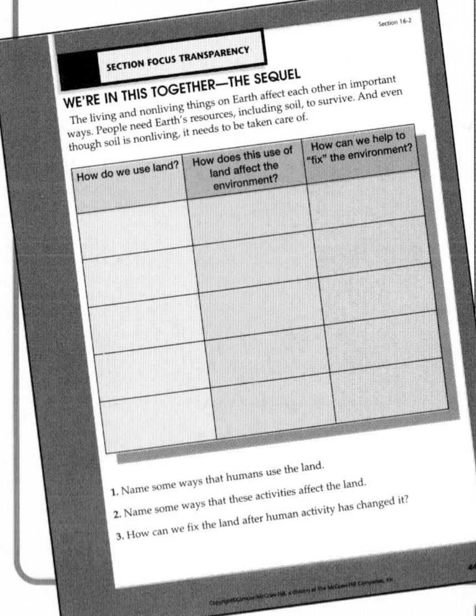

SECTION FOCUS TRANSPARENCY

Section 26-2

WE'RE IN THIS TOGETHER—THE SEQUEL

The living and nonliving things on Earth affect each other in important ways. People need Earth's resources, including soil, to survive. And even though soil is nonliving, it needs to be taken care of.

How do we use land?	How does this use of land affect the environment?	How can we help to "fix" the environment?

1. Name some ways that humans use the land.
2. Name some ways that these activities affect the land.
3. How can we fix the land after human activity has changed it?

26•2 Using Land

What You'll Learn

- Ways that we use land
- Environmental problems created because of land use
- Things you can do to help protect the environment

Vocabulary
landfill
hazardous waste
conservation
composting

Why It's Important

- Land is a resource that we need to use responsibly.

Land Usage

You may not think of land as a natural resource. Yet, it is as important to people as oil, clean air, and clean water. Through agriculture, logging, garbage disposal, and urban development, we use land—and sometimes abuse it.

Farming

Earth's total land area is 149 million km^2. We use about 16 million km^2 as farmland. Even so, about 20 percent of the people living in the world are hungry. Millions starve and die each year. To fight this problem, some farmers work to increase the productivity of croplands by using higher-yield seeds and chemical fertilizers. Herbicides and pesticides also are used to reduce weeds, insects, and other pests that can damage crops.

Other farmers rely on organic farming techniques to lessen the environmental impact of chemicals on the land and to increase yield. **Figure 26-5** shows an organic farm in China that has been farmed for many centuries.

Figure 26-5 Organic farming techniques can rebuild topsoil rather than deplete it. Organic farmers use natural fertilizers, crop rotation, and biological pest controls to help their crops thrive.

Resource Manager

The following **Teacher Classroom Resources** can be used with Section 26-2:

 **Reproducible Masters**

Activity Worksheets, p. 149 L2

Critical Thinking/Problem Solving, p. 26 L2

Enrichment, p. 76 L3

Multicultural Connections, pp. 51–52 L2

Reinforcement, p. 76 L2

Figure 26-6 Farmers reduce erosion with contour plowing, as shown on this farm in Washington State. Erosion is reduced because the path of plowing follows the shape of the land. **How can contour plowing control the direction that water flows in a farm field?**

Whenever vegetation is removed from an area, such as on construction sites, mining sites, or tilled farmland, the soil can erode easily. With plants gone, nothing prevents the soil from being carried away by running water and wind. Several centimeters of topsoil may be lost in one year. In some places, it can take more than 1000 years for new topsoil to develop and replace eroded topsoil. Some farmers practice no-till farming, which reduces erosion because land is not loosened by plowing. **Figure 26-6** shows another way farmers work to reduce erosion.

Grazing Livestock

Land also is used for grazing livestock. Animals such as cattle eat vegetation and then often are used as food for humans. In the United States, the majority of land used for grazing is unsuitable for crops. However, about 20 percent of the total cropland in our country is used to grow feed for livestock, such as the corn shown in **Figure 26-7.**

A square kilometer of vegetable crops can feed many more people than a square kilometer used to raise livestock. Some people argue that a more efficient use of the land would be to grow crops directly for human consumption, rather than for livestock. For many, however, meat and dairy products are an important part of their diet. They also argue that livestock have ecological benefits that justify livestock production.

Figure 26-7 Corn, as shown on this farm in Lancaster, Pennsylvania, is used for human food, for livestock feed, and for industrial products such as ceramics, textiles, ethanol, and paint. About half the corn grain raised in the United States is fed to livestock.

Tying to Previous Knowledge

Students likely have seen open fields and forested areas disappear as new homes, shopping malls, and highways are built. In this section, they will learn other ways that land use impacts the environment.

2 Teach

Caption Answer

Figure 26-6 *water follows along the plowed rows instead of flowing straight downhill.*

Making a Model

Naturalist To model the way organic farmers use natural fertilizers, have students design and build a school compost pile. Be certain that it meets all local health regulations. Use the compost to construct flower beds on school property. L2

ELL COOP LEARN

Flex Your Brain

Use the Flex Your Brain activity to have students explore DEFORESTATION.

GLENCOE TECHNOLOGY

Videodisc

The Infinite Voyage: Life in the Balance

Chapter 3 *Rondonia: Home of a Dying Rain Forest* 4:00

Refer to the Teacher Guide for bar codes and teaching strategies.

Guided Reading Strategy

Cause-and-Effect Chart This strategy is used to focus on cause-and-effect reasoning. In the center, students will write the topic that they are trying to understand. To the left of center, write the apparent causes of the topic. On the right side, write the apparent effects of the topic. Have students design a Cause-and-Effect Chart for a concept in this section.

Sample Chart:

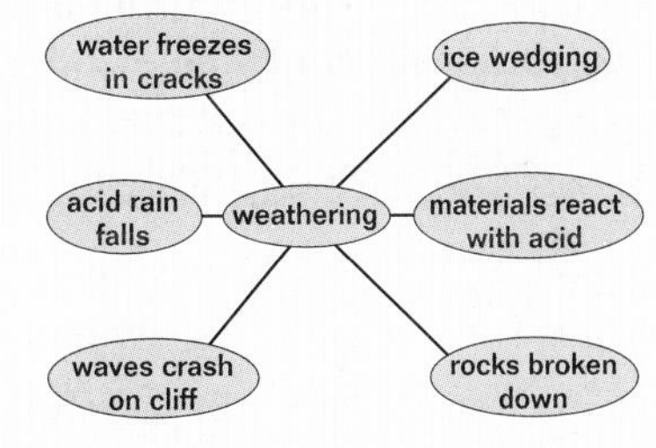

CA Science Content Standards

Page 886: 9b

Answer to Reading Check

Plants remove carbon dioxide from the air during photosynthesis. Carbon dioxide and water are transformed to a simple sugar and oxygen.

Discussion

What are two ways organisms living outside the tropics suffer when rain forests are cut down? *There is a reduction of oxygen and an addition of carbon dioxide in the atmosphere. Organisms need oxygen to breathe. Carbon dioxide contributes to the greenhouse effect. Habitat is lost, and biodiversity declines as a result.*

Teacher FYI

About five percent of the landfill space in the United States is filled with soiled disposable diapers. The EPA estimates that three million metric tons of feces and urine end up in landfills rather than in sewage treatment plants because people don't wash diapers before they throw them away. These soiled diapers can result in the spread of diseases.

Using an Analogy

Visual-Spatial Have students locate the world's rain forests on a globe. In order to do this, they may first need to use a world atlas. Also, have them locate South America and Massachusetts on the globe. Emphasize that each year in South America, an area of rain forest the size of Massachusetts is estimated to be destroyed. L2

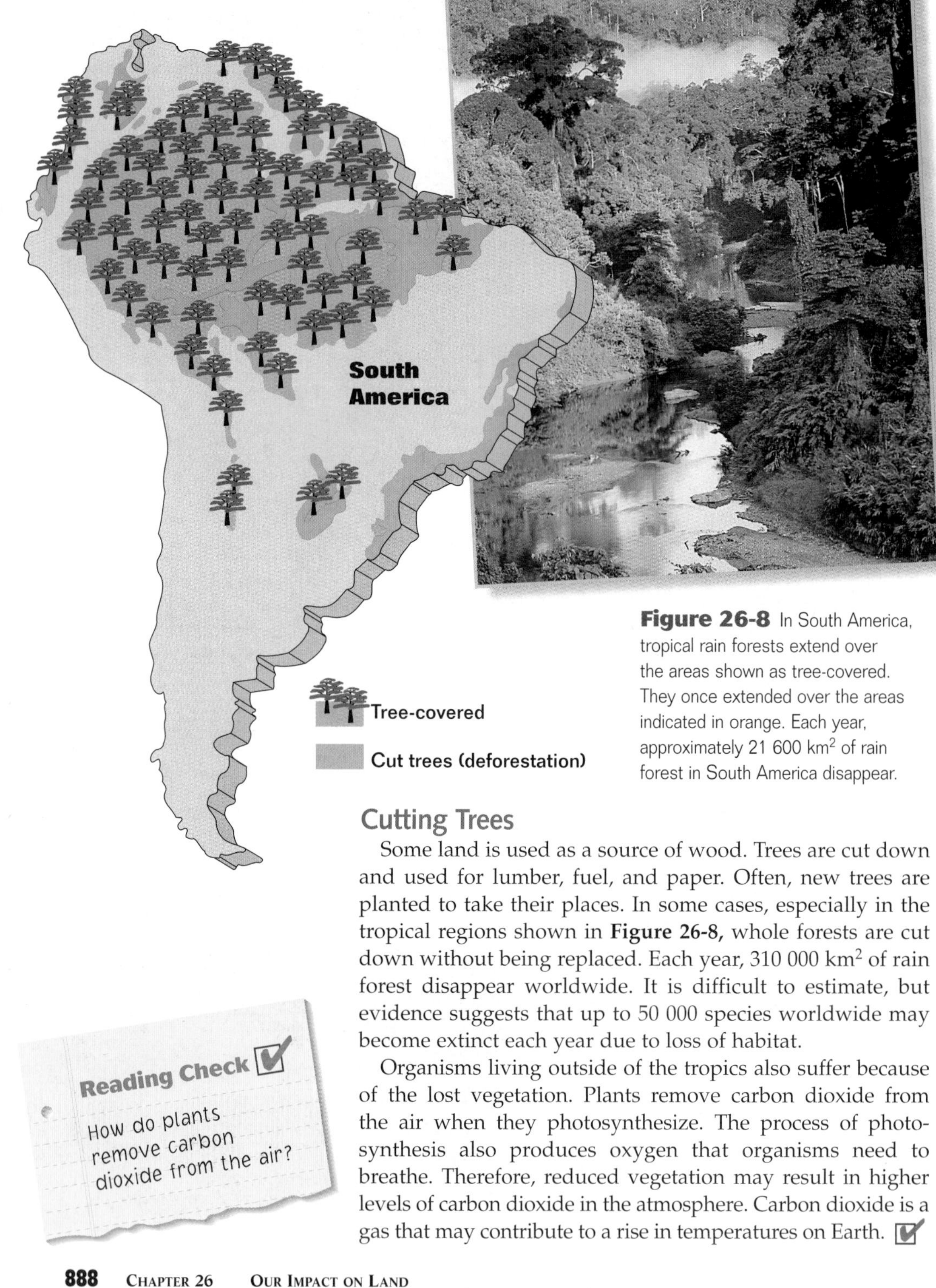

Figure 26-8 In South America, tropical rain forests extend over the areas shown as tree-covered. They once extended over the areas indicated in orange. Each year, approximately 21 600 km^2 of rain forest in South America disappear.

Cutting Trees

Some land is used as a source of wood. Trees are cut down and used for lumber, fuel, and paper. Often, new trees are planted to take their places. In some cases, especially in the tropical regions shown in **Figure 26-8,** whole forests are cut down without being replaced. Each year, 310 000 km^2 of rain forest disappear worldwide. It is difficult to estimate, but evidence suggests that up to 50 000 species worldwide may become extinct each year due to loss of habitat.

Reading Check

How do plants remove carbon dioxide from the air?

Organisms living outside of the tropics also suffer because of the lost vegetation. Plants remove carbon dioxide from the air when they photosynthesize. The process of photosynthesis also produces oxygen that organisms need to breathe. Therefore, reduced vegetation may result in higher levels of carbon dioxide in the atmosphere. Carbon dioxide is a gas that may contribute to a rise in temperatures on Earth.

Enrichment

Have students research the status of local landfills. Students should find out how long local landfills can continue to operate. They should discover if any are in danger of closing because of limited space. L3

Landfills

Land also is used when we dispose of the products we consume. About 60 percent of our garbage goes into landfills. A **landfill** is an area where waste is deposited. In a *sanitary landfill,* such as the one illustrated in **Figure 26-9,** each day's deposit is covered with dirt. The dirt prevents the deposit from blowing away and reduces the odor produced by the decaying waste. Sanitary landfills also are designed to prevent liquid wastes from draining into the soil and groundwater below. A sanitary landfill is lined with plastic, concrete, or clay-rich soils that trap the liquid waste.

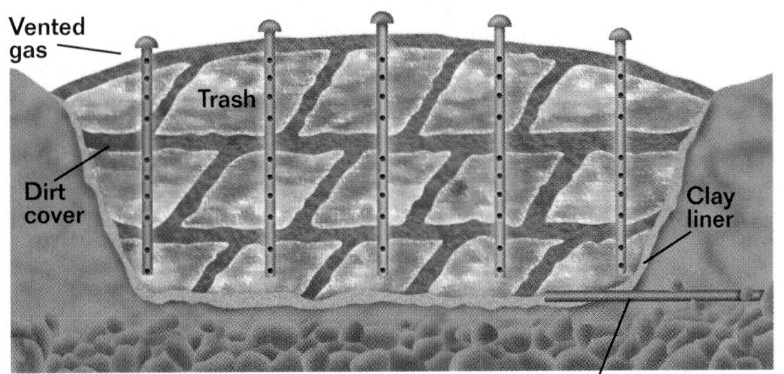

Figure 26-9 The vast majority of our garbage is deposited in landfills. **What are some problems associated with landfill disposal?**

Sanitary landfills greatly reduce the chance that pollutants will leak into the surrounding soil and groundwater. However, some may still find their way into the environment.

Another problem is that we're filling up our landfills and running out of acceptable areas to build new ones. Many materials placed into landfills decompose slowly.

Hazardous Wastes

Some of the wastes we put into landfills are dangerous to organisms. Poisonous, cancer-causing, or radioactive wastes are called **hazardous wastes.** Hazardous wastes are put into landfills by everyone—industries and individuals alike. We contribute to this problem when we throw away insect sprays, batteries, drain cleaners, bleaches, medicines, and paints.

It may seem that when we throw something in the garbage can, even if it's hazardous, it's gone and we don't need to be concerned with it anymore. Unfortunately, our garbage does not disappear. It can remain in a landfill for hundreds of years. In the case of radioactive waste, it

Classifying Your Trash for One Day

Procedure

1. Prepare a table for yourself with the following column headings: *Paper, Plastic, Glass, Metal, Food Waste.*
2. During the day, record everything you throw out in the appropriate column.
3. At the end of the day, determine the number of trash items in each column.

Analysis

1. Rank each column by number from the least trash items (number 5) to the most trash items (number 1).
2. Compare your rankings with those of others in your household.
3. Compare your daily activities with others to account for differences in the tables.
4. What activities can you change to decrease the amount of trash you produce?

Try at Home MiniLab

For additional help doing this activity at home, see the corresponding pages in the **Home Involvement** booklet.

Purpose

Interpersonal Students will discover what types of items they routinely discard and will consider ways to reduce their daily trash. COOP LEARN P

Materials

clipboards or notebooks, paper, pencil

Teaching Strategies

Ask students to bring in their results to the class and to implement any trash-reducing strategies that they may suggest.

Analysis

1. Answers will vary.
2. Answers will vary, but some differences likely will be noted between household members.
3. Answers will vary. Some activities will be similar for all students, but activities unique to individuals or groups of students should be noticeable.
4. Buying materials with less packaging and reusing certain items such as paper will reduce the trash generated.

Performance Have students calculate the percentage of their wastes that are recyclable. Use **Performance Assessment in the Science Classroom,** p. 29.

Caption Answer

Figure 26-9 *Answers will vary, but students should mention that acceptable landfill space is scarce, some materials placed into landfills decompose slowly, and some hazardous wastes can leak into surrounding soil and groundwater.*

Inclusion Strategies

Hearing Impaired Have hearing impaired students work with several classmates to tabulate cumulative results for the Mini-Lab for the whole class. Suggested changes in individual activities and trash disposal habits then can be generalized for the class as a whole. L2 COOP LEARN

CA Science Content Standards

Page 888: 6a
Page 889: 9f

may remain harmful for thousands of years, creating problems for many future generations. Fortunately, industries and individuals are becoming more aware of the problems associated with landfills and are disposing of their wastes in a more responsible manner. You can help by disposing of hazardous wastes you generate at home at special hazardous waste-collection sites. Contact your local government to find out about dates, times, and locations of collections in your area. You can learn more about disposing wastes in the **Field Guide to Waste Management** at the end of this chapter.

Phytoremediation

Earlier, you learned that hazardous substances sometimes contaminate soil. These contaminants may come from nearby industries, residential areas, or landfills. Water contaminated from such a source can filter into the ground and leave behind the toxic substances within soil. Did you know that plants are sometimes used to help fix this problem? Methods of phytoremediation (*phyto* means "plant"; *remediation* means "to fix, or remedy a problem") are being studied to help decontaminate soil.

Extracting Metals

Certain varieties of plants can help remove metals from soil. When soil becomes too concentrated with metallic elements, human health may be at risk. Plant roots can absorb certain metals such as copper, nickel, and zinc. **Figure 26-10** shows how metals are absorbed from the soil and taken into plant tissue. Plants that become concentrated with metals from soil must eventually be harvested and either composted to obtain and recycle the metals or incinerated. If incineration is used to dispose of the plants, the ash residue must be handled carefully and disposed of at a hazardous waste site.

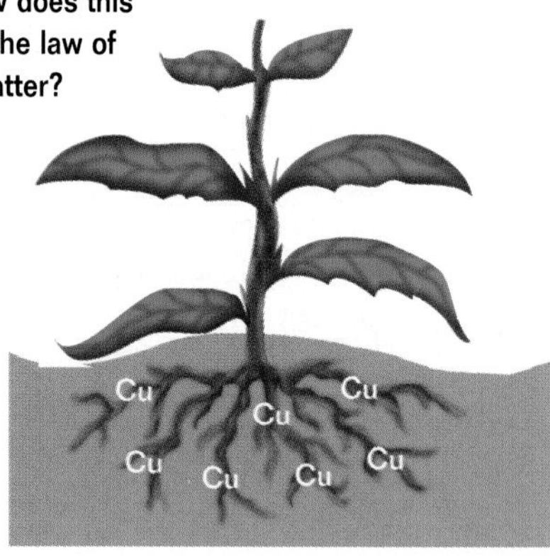

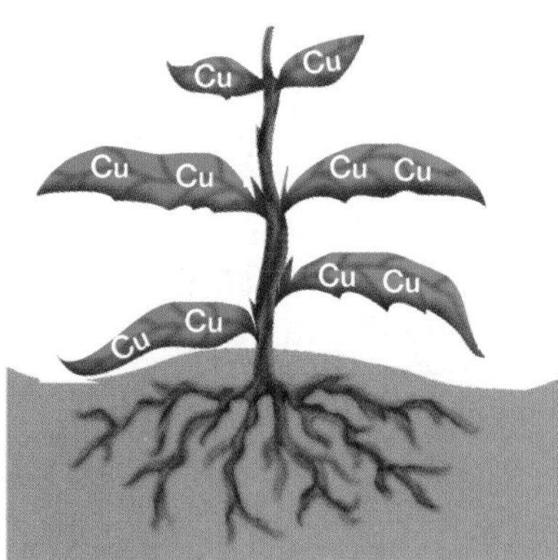

Figure 26-10 Metals such as copper can be removed from soil and incorporated into the tissues of plants. **How does this process illustrate the law of conservation of matter?**

Caption Answer

Figure 26-10 *The copper is not destroyed. It is just transferred from soil to plant tissues.*

Content Background

When plants used in phytoremediation are incinerated, the volume of ash is only about ten percent of the volume of the soil that was contaminated. Therefore, much less hazardous waste landfill space is required for disposal of these plant residues than would be necessary if all the soil had to be placed into this type of landfill.

Discussion

Why do you suppose many people don't like the idea of landfills being created near their homes? *Wastes may leak into soil and groundwater. The odor may ruin their property's value.*

Using Science Words

Have students hypothesize the meaning of the following words: *phytohormone, phytology,* and *phytoplankton.* Have them check their definitions with a dictionary.

GLENCOE TECHNOLOGY

Videodisc

Glencoe Science Voyages Interactive Videodisc—Earth

Side 2, Lesson 6 *Pollution Detectives*

9974

Refer to Videodisc Teacher Guide for additional bar codes.

Breaking Down Organic Contaminants

Organic contaminants are hazardous wastes that contain carbon, hydrogen, and other elements such as oxygen, nitrogen, or chlorine. Some common examples of hazardous wastes are gasoline, oil, and solvents. Enzymes are chemical substances that can speed chemical reactions. Some enzymes that can break down organic pollutants are found in plant tissue. Similar to metals extraction, this type of cleanup occurs at the root of the plant. The enzyme is released by the root and causes the organic pollutant in the soil to break down into harmless substances, some of which are useful to the plant and promote its growth.

Human-Built Structures

Concrete and asphalt are quickly replacing grass and woodlands in our communities. The impact on the environment, particularly in urban and suburban areas, is easy to observe. Asphalt and concrete absorb solar radiation. The atmosphere is then heated by conduction and convection, which causes the air temperature to rise. You may have observed this if you've ever traveled from a rural area to the city and noticed a rise in temperature.

Problem Solving

The Effects of Trash Disposal

In the early days of the United States, the population was sparse and few people considered the impact of their actions on the environment. They threw their trash into rivers, buried it, or burned it. Today, we must consider the consequences of our methods of trash disposal. The graph at right shows how we deposit our waste.

Think Critically: More than half of the states in our country are running out of landfill space. New landfills will have to be made, but most people have a NIMBY attitude. NIMBY means "Not In My BackYard." People don't want to live near a landfill. What percent of our trash presently goes into landfills? If we reduce the amount of trash in landfills, what alternatives do we have for disposal? How could these alternatives influence the environment? List the pros and cons for each alternative you think of in your Science Journal.

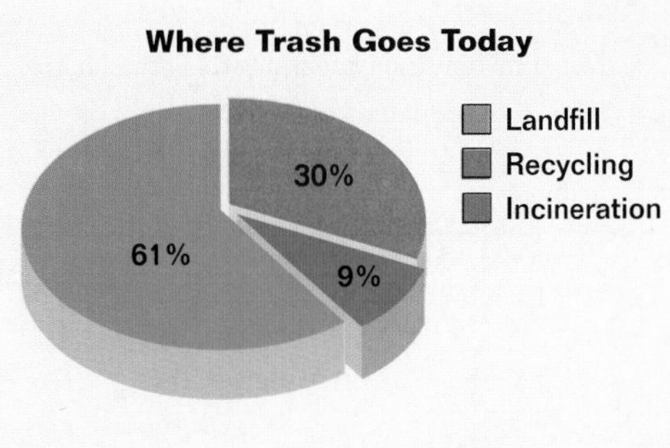

Across the Curriculum

History The following is a quote from Chief Seattle of the Native American Suquamish people. His words were in response to President Franklin Pierce's offer to buy land from the Suquamish people in 1854. Chief Seattle expressed the difference in the way his people viewed the land and the way people of European descent viewed it. "He treats his mother, the earth, and his brother, the sky, as things to be bought, plundered, sold like sheep or bright beads. His appetite will devour the earth and leave behind only a desert..." Ask students to respond in their journals to Chief Seattle's words. Students should relate Seattle's thoughts to their own view of how present-day Americans view Earth. L2

CHEMISTRY INTEGRATION

Enzymes are biological catalysts. Enzymes act by combining with specific substances to form intermediate compounds (complexes) that then may break down into final reaction products. Rates of normally slow reactions are accelerated because the intermediate compounds form and break down comparatively rapidly.

Problem Solving

Between 1960 and 1985, landfill use rose rapidly. It remained high until 1988, then it started to decline. The use of incinerators peaked in 1960, dipped to its lowest point in 1985, and then began rising again. Recycling rose slowly from 1960 to 1990. Since that time, it has risen more rapidly.

Think Critically

About 61 percent goes into landfills. Alternatives for disposal include incineration, composting, and recycling. Incineration can introduce harmful pollutants into the atmosphere but significantly reduces waste volume, and the energy released can be used to generate electricity. Composting and recycling are more environmentally safe but only can be used for certain types of waste.

CA Science Content Standards

Page 890: 7a
Page 891: 6a

26-2 USING LAND 891

MiniLab

Purpose

Kinesthetic Students will observe runoff over a paved surface and over an unpaved surface and compare the results. L2 ELL COOP LEARN

Materials

two buckets of water for every four or five students

Teaching Strategies

- Explain to students that the amount of runoff will influence the potential of streams to flood in urban areas.
- Have students perform this activity during fall or spring, when the ground is not frozen.

Troubleshooting Fill buckets only one-half to two-thirds full to avoid spillage while transporting the water outside.

Analysis

1. Most of the water should flow along the surface of pavement rapidly; some could flow through cracks in pavement. Much of the water should soak into the ground in grassy areas.
2. Water flows rapidly over pavement because it is mostly impermeable. Grassy areas are more permeable, which allows water to soak in.

Assessment

Oral To further assess students' understanding of runoff, ask them how large cities could be designed to reduce runoff into nearby streams and sewer systems. Use **Performance Assessment in the Science Classroom,** p. 71.

Figure 26-11 Some cities are working to preserve green space within city limits, such as this area in Portland, Oregon. **How does more green space in the city improve the environment?**

Modeling Runoff

Procedure

1. Divide into groups of four or five.
2. Obtain two buckets of water for each group from your teacher.
3. With your teacher present, carefully take your buckets outside.
4. Find a paved area and a grassy area on your school grounds.
5. Pour one bucket of water on the paved area and observe how the water flows on the pavement.
6. Repeat step 5 for the grassy area.

Analysis

1. Describe how the water flowed over each area.
2. Infer what properties of the pavement and the grassy area control how the water flows over each.

Paving over the land prevents water from easily soaking into the soil. Instead, it runs off into sewers or streams. During heavy rainstorms in paved areas, sewer pipes can overflow or become clogged with debris. This causes increased runoff of rainwater directly into streams, and increases the risk of flooding in urban and suburban areas.

A stream's discharge increases when more water enters its channel. Stream discharge is the volume of water flowing past a point per unit of time. For example, the Mississippi River discharges an average of about 19 000 m^3 of water into the Gulf of Mexico every second. This is a large volume of moving water, but the Mississippi is a major river. Many thousands more cubic meters flow per second when the Mississippi is flooding. If discharge increases too rapidly, as happens in urban areas from time to time, a stream can flow over its banks and flood a populated area. This happened to the Mississippi and Missouri Rivers and their tributaries during the summer of 1993.

Increased runoff also influences groundwater. Some of the water that does not soak into the soil evaporates. This reduces the amount of water in groundwater aquifers. Many communities rely on groundwater for drinking water. But covering more and more land with roads, sidewalks, and parking lots prevents the water from reaching aquifers.

Some cities are actively preserving more space that cannot be paved over. This type of activity, shown in **Figure 26-11,** beautifies the urban environment, increases the area into which water can soak, and provides more space for recreation.

Science Journal

Population Explosion Have students determine some of the problems they think will occur as the human population continues to increase. Have them discuss some possible solutions in a report or on a chart, graph, or map in their Science Journals. L2

Page 892: 9a
Page 893: 5b

Natural Preserves

Not all land on Earth is being utilized to produce usable materials or for storing waste. Look at **Figure 26-12.** Some land remains mostly uninhabited by people. National forest lands, grasslands, and parks in the United States are protected from many of the problems that you've read about in this section. In many countries throughout the world, land is set aside as natural preserves. As the world population continues to rise, the strain on our environment is likely to increase. Preserving some land in its natural state should continue to benefit future generations.

Conserving Resources

In the United States and other industrialized countries, people have a throwaway lifestyle. When we are done with something, we throw it away. This means more products must be produced to replace what we've thrown away, more land is used, and landfills overflow. You can help by conserving resources. **Conservation** is the careful use of resources to reduce damage to the environment.

Reduce, Reuse, Recycle

The United States makes up only five percent of the world's human population, yet it consumes 25 percent of the world's natural resources. Each of us can reduce our consumption of materials in simple ways, such as using both sides of notebook paper or carrying lunch to school in a nondisposable container. Ways to conserve resources include reducing our use of materials and reusing and recycling materials. Reusing an item means finding another use for it instead of throwing it away. You can reuse old clothes by giving them to someone else or by cutting them into rags. The rags can be used in place of paper towels for cleaning jobs around your home.

Figure 26-12 Many countries set aside land as natural preserves. **How do these natural preserves benefit humans and other living things?**

3 Assess

Check for Understanding

Discussion

Interpersonal Review with students the various ways that humans have changed Earth over the past century. Have students suggest ways to better balance our need to use land with our need for a quality environment. L2 COOP LEARN

Reteach

Interpersonal Have students list at least five different items that one or more members of the group discarded today. Have them describe at least two ways each of these items could have been reused. An example is that a piece of notebook paper, used on only one side, can still be used for sketching or writing. The paper also can be used to cover the bottom of a bird cage. L1 COOP LEARN

Extension

For students who have mastered this section, use the **Reinforcement** and **Enrichment** masters.

4 Close

Proficiency Prep

Use this quiz to check students' recall of section content.

1. **What is about 20 percent of all cropland used for?** *producing food for livestock*
2. **What gas is removed from the atmosphere by plants?** *carbon dioxide*
3. **What is the process of using plants to remove metals from contaminated soil?** *phytoremediation*

Caption Answer

Figure 26-11 *by providing habitat for many plants and animals and by reducing runoff*

Figure 26-12 *by preserving large tracts of natural land for wildlife habitat and by preserving naturally beautiful regions for future generations to enjoy*

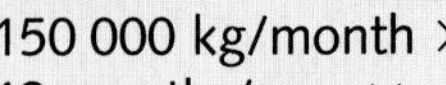

Using Math

150 000 kg/month ×
12 months/year ×
17 trees/1000 kg =
30 600 trees/year

Section Assessment

1. farming, grazing livestock, source of wood, landfills, mines, structures, natural preserves
2. agriculture: soil erosion, pesticide and herbicide pollution; mining: loss of vegetation, polluted runoff into streams, lakes and aquifers, loss of natural habitats; trash disposal: leakage into soil and water, landfills take up a lot of space
3. Phytoremediation can be used to remove metals from contaminated soil or water and to break down certain organic contaminants.
4. Think Critically Answers will vary. For example, an old tire could be reused as a tire swing or as part of an obstacle course.

Using Computers

Letters should address the issues that concern people: a landfill's odor, unsightliness, and the danger of substances leaking into soil and groundwater.

Using Math

Assume 17 fewer trees are cut down when 1000 kg of paper are recycled. Calculate the number of trees conserved per year if 150 000 kg of paper are recycled each month.

Reusing plastic and paper bags is another way to reduce waste. Some grocery stores even pay a few cents when you return and reuse paper grocery bags.

Outdoors, there are things you can do, too. If you cut grass or rake leaves, you can compost these items instead of putting them into the trash. **Composting** means piling yard wastes where they can gradually decompose. The decomposed matter can be used as fertilizer in gardens or flower beds. Some cities no longer pick up yard waste to take to landfills. In these places, composting is common. If everyone in the United States composted, it would reduce the trash put into landfills by 20 percent.

The Population Outlook

The human population explosion already has had devastating effects on the environment and the organisms that inhabit Earth. It's unlikely that the population will begin to decline in the near future. To compensate, we must use our resources wisely. Conserving resources by reducing, reusing, and recycling is an important way that you can make a difference.

Section Assessment

1. In your Science Journal, list six ways that people use land.
2. Discuss environmental problems that are sometimes created by agriculture, mining, and trash disposal.
3. How can phytoremediation positively impact the environment?
4. **Think Critically:** Choose one of the following items, and list three ways it can be reused: an empty milk carton, vegetable scraps, used notebook paper, or an old automobile tire. Be sure your uses are environmentally friendly.
5. **Skill Builder**
   Communicating Do the **Chapter 26 Skill Activity** on page 987 to find out ways in which an environmental problem can be communicated.

Using Computers

Word Processing
Suppose that a new landfill is needed in your community. Where do you think it should be located? Now, suppose that you want to convince people that you've selected the best place for the landfill. Use your word-processing skills to write a letter to the editor of the local newspaper, listing reasons in favor of your choice. If you need help, refer to page 968.

Assessment

Oral Use this Skill Builder to assess students' communication skills. Ask students to explain how people can help correct many of the environmental problems that they help create. Use **Performance Assessment in the Science Classroom,** p. 71.

VISUAL Learning

Figure 26-13 Have students create their own sketches illustrating what must happen before the recyclable items get to the recycling plant.

CA Science Content Standards

Page 894: 5b
Page 895: 5b

Recycling

26•3

Recyclable Objects

Did you know that any object is **recyclable** if it can be processed and then used again? Look at **Figure 26-13.** Glass and aluminum are two of the many things that can be recycled.

Paper makes up about 40 percent of the mass of our trash. If it is recycled, landfill space and trees are conserved. Also, the production of recycled paper takes 58 percent less water and generates 74 percent fewer air pollutants than the production of brand-new paper made from trees.

How much energy do you think is saved when you recycle one aluminum can? Answer: enough energy to keep a TV running for about three hours. Twenty aluminum cans can be recycled with the energy that is needed to produce a single brand-new can from aluminum ore.

What You'll Learn

- The advantages of recycling
- The advantages and disadvantages of required recycling

Vocabulary
recyclable

Why It's Important

- Recycling helps conserve resources and reduces solid waste.

VISUALIZING Recycling

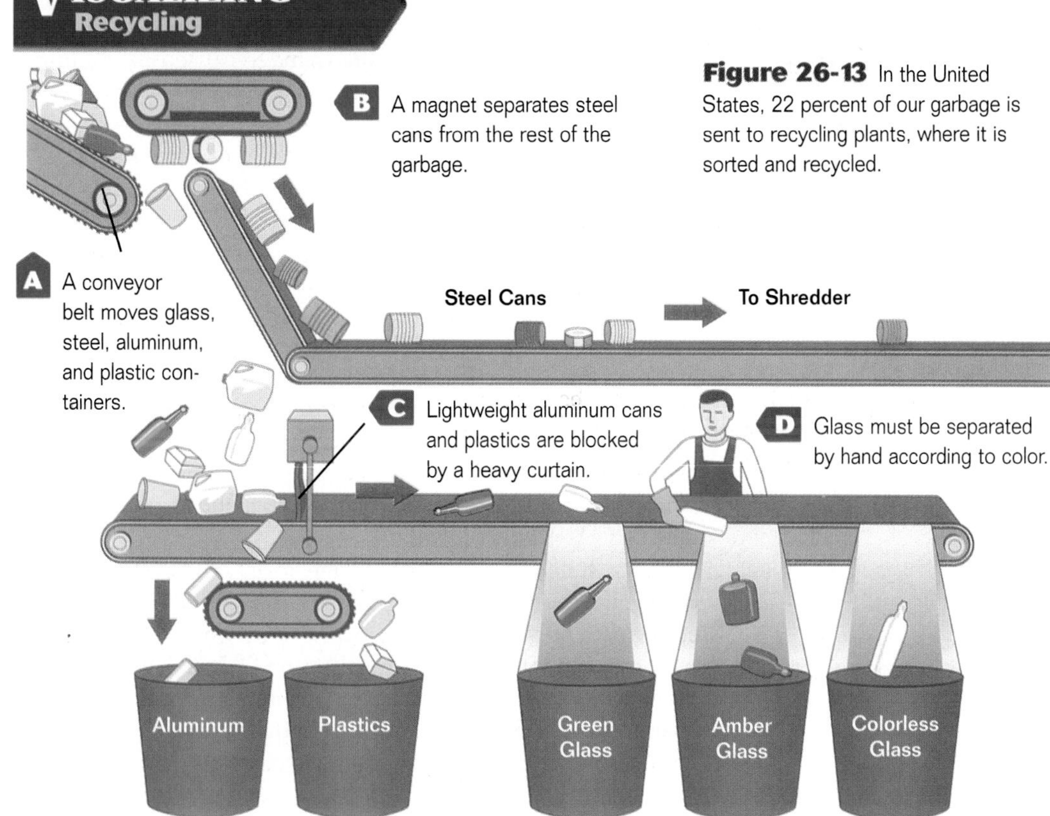

Figure 26-13 In the United States, 22 percent of our garbage is sent to recycling plants, where it is sorted and recycled.

Resource Manager

The following **Teacher Classroom Resources** can be used with Section 26-3:

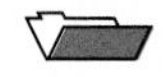 **Reproducible Masters**

Enrichment, p. 77 L3
Reinforcement, p. 77 L2
Study Guide, pp. 102–104 L1 ELL
Activity Worksheets, pp. 147–148, 150 L2
Laboratory Manual, pp. 161–162 L2

 **Transparencies**

Teaching Transparency 52 L2
Science Integration Transparency 26 L2

SECTION 26•3

Prepare

Refer to **Recyclable Objects,** p. 878F.

Preplanning

Refer to the **Chapter Organizer** on pp. 878A–B.

1 Motivate

Bellringer

Before presenting the lesson, display **Section Focus Transparency 77** on the overhead projector. Use the accompanying **Focus Activity** worksheet. L2 ELL

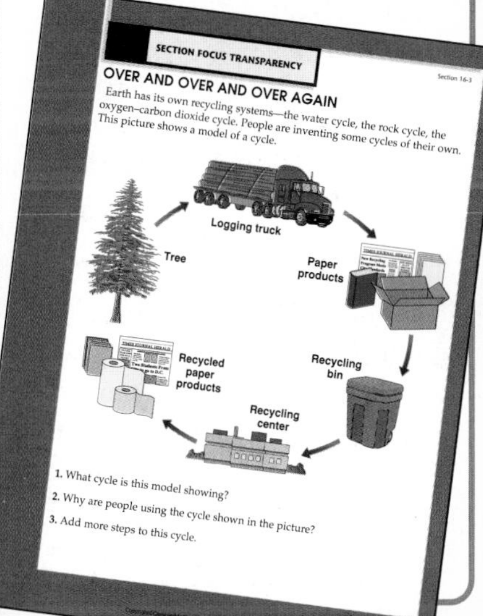

Tying to Previous Knowledge

Students already know the meaning of the term *recycle.* In this section, students will learn the many ways that the environment is helped when people recycle. They will learn about the advantages and disadvantages of mandatory recycling.

2 Teach

Activity

Interpersonal Have students set up a trash recycling center at school. Students can maintain areas for collecting glass, metals, and paper. L2 ELL COOP LEARN

GLENCOE TECHNOLOGY

CD-ROM

Glencoe Science Voyages Interactive CD-ROM

Explorations

Have students do the interactive exploration *How much landfill space can be saved in a year by recycling?*

3 Assess

Check for Understanding

Discussion

Why don't people recycle more? *Some people aren't in the habit; many areas don't have recycling centers, or the centers only recycle certain items; there aren't markets for some items.*

Reteach

Have students respond to the following problem: "Suppose your friend starts making bracelets from metal scraps. You help her by starting a recycling center for metal scraps. You clean, sort, and sell metal scraps at a profit to your jeweler friend. Predict what will happen if no one buys her bracelets." *She will quit buying metal scraps, and the recycling business will end.*

Extension

For students who have mastered this section, use the **Reinforcement** and **Enrichment** masters.

Figure 26-14 Recycling saves landfill space, energy, and natural resources. Many community volunteers adopt sections of a highway. They pick up trash and recycle the salvageable part.

Everyone agrees that recycling is good for the environment. It saves landfill space, energy, and natural resources. Recycling also helps reduce the damage caused by mining, cutting trees, and manufacturing. Did you know that if you recycle, you will reduce the trash you generate in your lifetime by 60 percent? If you don't recycle, you'll generate trash equal to at least 600 times your mass. No one argues that recycling is not a good thing. The question is should recycling be required?

Required Recycling

Many things are thrown away because some people aren't in the habit of recycling. In the United States, much less garbage is recycled than in countries with mandatory recycling, such as Japan and Germany. Mandatory recycling means that people are required to recycle. This creates new jobs in reuse industries, such as the production of items from recycled plastics.

Many states already have some form of recycling laws. People in these states comply with the laws because they benefit directly in some way. For example, in some places people who recycle pay lower trash-collection fees. In other places, garbage is not collected if it contains items that should have been recycled. **Figure 26-14** shows typical containers used to help people organize their recyclable objects.

Multiple Learning Styles

Visual-Spatial Organize a field trip to a recycling plant. Have students bring a camera to take pictures of the process. Use the pictures to make a poster showing the process. Have students explain what is taking place under each picture. L2 COOP LEARN

Content Background

Recycling aluminum uses one twentieth of the energy that is required for extracting new aluminum from bauxite. Other metals that are recycled include platinum, gold, silver, copper, lead, and iron.

896 CHAPTER 26 OUR IMPACT ON LAND

In some states, a refundable deposit is made on all beverage containers. This means paying extra money at the store for a drink. You get your money back if you return the container to the store for recycling. Some people suggest that if we had a national container law, we could save enough energy to light up a large city for four years. ☑

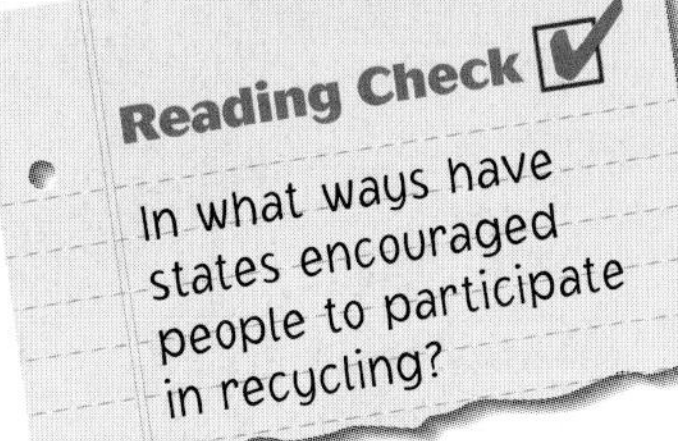

Reading Check
In what ways have states encouraged people to participate in recycling?

Voluntary Recycling

Today, many people already recycle voluntarily because their cities provide curbside collection or convenient drop-off facilities. In this case, people have the freedom to decide whether or not to recycle, without government intervention.

Some people argue that the cost of recycling outweighs the benefits. Recycling requires money to pay for workers, trucks, and buildings. Also, some workers, such as miners and manufacturers who make brand-new containers, might lose their jobs.

Another problem is what to do with all of the recyclable items. Recycling businesses must make a profit, or they can't exist. The only way to make a profit in recycling is to sell the recycled material, so there must be a market for the material. Whether voluntary or mandatory, recycling conserves resources. In addition to saving landfill space, recycling also protects our environment by minimizing our need to extract raw materials from Earth.

interNET CONNECTION

Visit the Glencoe Science Web Site at **www.glencoe.com/sec/science/ca** to learn more about conservation. Make a list of conservation tips for individuals.

Section Assessment

1. List at least four advantages of recycling.
2. What are the advantages and disadvantages of mandatory recycling?
3. **Think Critically:** Spend a day at home keeping track of what you throw away and what you recycle. Record these items in your Science Journal. Did you throw away anything that could have been recycled?
4. **Skill Builder**
   Making and Using Tables As you will see in the **Field Guide to Waste Management** at the end of this chapter, plastics must be carefully sorted before they can be reprocessed into new usable items. Do the Activity in the field guide to find out how to organize your recyclable plastic items. If you need help, refer to Making and Using Tables in the **Skill Handbook** on page 952.

In your Science Journal, write a letter to your local chamber of commerce suggesting ways to encourage businesses to recycle.

Answer to Reading Check

Those who recycle pay a lower trash-collection fee. Garbage isn't collected if it contains items that should have been recycled. A refundable deposit is made on all beverage containers

4 Close

Quick Demo

Use a magnet to demonstrate how steel and aluminum cans are separated from one another.

Section Assessment

1. saves landfill space, energy, and resources; reduces damage from mining, logging, and manufacturing
2. Advantages are: more people will recycle, jobs are created, much energy is saved, resources are conserved, less landfill space is required, the environment is protected because there is less mining activity.
   Disadvantages are: voluntary recycling is working well in some areas, and people have the choice to participate or not, so that choice would be gone; cost outweighs the benefits; some jobs are lost; there is no market for some of the materials.
3. **Think Critically** Answers will vary.

Science Journal

Students may include in their letters that recycling containers and pick-up services should be made convenient to businesses. P

interNET CONNECTION

Internet Addresses

For Internet tips, see Glencoe's **Using the Internet in the Science Classroom.**

CA Science Content Standards

Page 896: 5b
Page 897: 5b

Activity 26•2

Purpose

Visual-Spatial Students will observe the rate of decomposition of various materials in a model landfill. L2 ELL COOP LEARN

Process Skills

communicating, recognizing cause and effect, making models, making and using tables, observing and inferring, comparing and contrasting, interpreting data

Time

30 minutes set up; two to three minutes each day for two weeks to read thermometers, 30 minutes at the end of two weeks

Safety Precautions

- Caution students to be careful when cutting the tops off of the bottles.
- Do not use meat, fish, or dairy scraps.
- Caution students to wash their hands after handling garbage.

Teaching Strategies

- Have members of each group predict what they think will happen to the sizes of the operating model landfills and to their internal temperatures before they start.
- Have student groups place their second landfill model in a refrigerator. These models will be used for comparison in Question 2.
- Set up a control landfill model of soil and water only, to provide comparative temperature data to that of the operating landfills.

Answers to Questions

1. Since microorganism activity is most rapid in warm, moist environments, decomposition rates would be significantly lower under dry conditions.
2. Rates of decomposition tend to be slower at lower temperatures.
3. The items are composed of different materials. Those that are more biodegradable, usually those composed of paper or soft organic materials, tend to decompose faster.
4. Plastics decompose very slowly, therefore, they take up landfill space for longer periods of time.

A Model Landfill

When garbage is put into landfills, it is covered under other trash and soil and isn't exposed to sunlight and other things that help decomposition. When examined by a researcher, one landfill was found to contain grass clippings that were still green and bread that had not molded.

Materials

- Bottles (2L) (2)
- Soil
- Thermometer
- Plastic wrap
- Graph paper
- Rubber band
- Trash (including fruit and vegetable scraps, a plastic item, a metal item, a foam cup, and notebook paper or newsprint)

What You'll Investigate

At what rates do different materials decompose in a landfill?

Goals

- **Make a model** of a sanitary landfill.
- **Compare and contrast** the decomposition of different materials in a landfill.

Safety Precautions

CAUTION: *Be especially careful not to expose your skin or eyes to garbage items.*

Procedure

1. **Cut** off the tops of two 2-L bottles.
2. **Add** soil to each bottle until it is half filled.
3. On graph paper, **trace** the outline of all the garbage items that you will place into each bottle. **Label** each outline and keep the tracings.
4. **Place** the items, one at a time, in each bottle. Completely **cover** each item with soil.
5. **Add** water to your landfill until the soil is slightly moist. **Place** a thermometer in each bottle and seal the bottle with the plastic wrap and a rubber band. **Store** one bottle in a cold place and put the other on a shelf.
6. **Check** the temperature of your landfill on the shelf each day for two weeks. **Record** the temperatures in a data table that you design.
7. After two weeks, **remove** all of the items from the soil in both bottles. Trace the outlines of each on a new sheet of graph paper. **Compare** the sizes of the items with their original sizes.
8. **Wash** your hands thoroughly after cleaning up your lab space. Be sure to dispose of each item properly as instructed by your teacher.

Conclude and Apply

1. Most decomposition in a landfill is due to the activity of microorganisms. The organisms can live only under certain temperature and moisture conditions. **Explain** how the decomposition rates would have differed if the soil had been completely dry.
2. **Compare** your results with the results from the bottle that was stored at a cold temperature. **Explain** the differences you observe.
3. Why do some items decompose more rapidly than others?
4. What problems are created in landfills by plastics?

Assessment

Performance Design an experiment to find out how the depth a material is buried in a landfill affects its rate of decomposition. Use **Performance Assessment in the Science Classroom,** p. 23.

Using Plants to Reduce Pollution

Pollution-Absorbing Plants

Plants are helping clean up hazardous chemicals in soil and water. By taking in pollutants through their roots, some plants can make hazardous substances less harmful to humans and other organisms. These helpful plants include poplar trees, mustard (left), and fescue grass (below).

Fescue to the Rescue

High concentrations of the metal selenium (suh LEE nee uhm) are harmful to the environment. In central California, soil became contaminated when irrigation water containing selenium flowed through fields. Farmers in the area planted fescue grass and Indian mustard to absorb selenium from the contaminated irrigation water. Researchers have found that mustard and fescue are able to convert selenium metal into a gas that is eventually given off by the plants. Scientists suggest that the gas is many times less harmful to the environment than concentrated levels of selenium in soils.

Advantages of Using Plants

Using plants to control or eliminate certain types of pollution is becoming increasingly popular. Cost is one reason. It is often less expensive to use plants than other methods of reducing pollutants. Plants clean up contaminated soil or water on the site, so there is no expense of digging up soil or removing water. Plants also can make an area more attractive. Finally, few, if any, people object to using plants to reverse the negative effects of pollution.

interNET CONNECTION

To find information about the Environmental Protection Agency's Citizen's Guide to Phytoremediation, visit the Glencoe Science Web Site at **www.glencoe.com/sec/science/ca.**

Teaching Strategies

- Have students contact local environmental consulting firms and ask them about possible uses of phytoremediation in your region. A scientist from one of these firms may be willing to visit your classroom.
- Have students brainstorm to list limitations of the phytoremediation technique. For example, plant roots may not penetrate to sufficient depth, or appropriate plants may not be able to survive at some polluted sites.

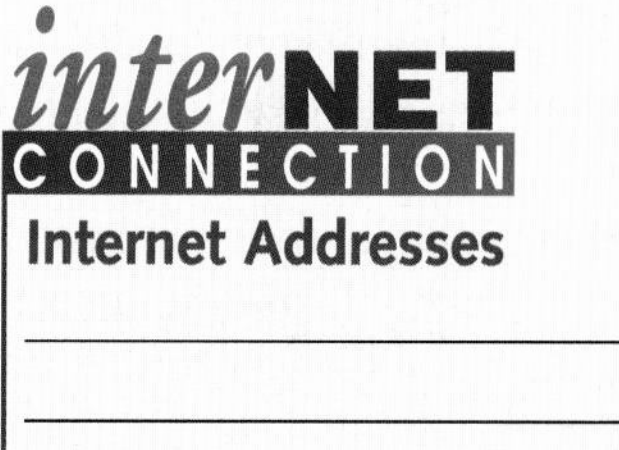

Internet Addresses

___

___

___

___

For Internet tips, see Glencoe's **Using the Internet in the Science Classroom.**

For More Information

National Center for Environmental Publications and Information (NCEPI)
P.O. Box 42419
Cincinnati, Ohio 45242

Content Background

In addition to agricultural applications, phytoremediation can be used to reduce the concentrations of a wide variety of industrial pollutants, including toxic metals and organic compounds. However, the technique is best suited to lower levels of contamination at shallow depth; hence it often is used to extract pollutants left behind by other cleanup methods.

CA Science Content Standards

Page 899: 5c

FIELD GUIDE

Using the Field Guide

Use the field guide with student pages 889-899.

- A field guide enables the user to classify or identify an item or concept.
- In using a field guide, students will apply steps of a scientific method as they observe, investigate, and draw conclusions.
- This field guide applies nationally; local and regional field guides are usually available for more specific local use.
- Encourage students to use the field guide outside.

FIELD *ACTIVITY*

Numbers are placed on plastic products by recyclers to indicate the type of plastic resin used in their manufacture. The sorting of plastic products for recycling is based on this number system. It does not necessarily mean that they are recyclable.

The Plastics Code System is presented in **Table 26-1.** The code includes seven different sorting divisions. Code 7 includes all types not covered by codes 1–6. Code 7 comprises the smallest amount of recycled plastics.

The percentage of containers each code comprises and what those containers can be recycled into are listed.

Tying to Previous Knowledge

Help students recall that many of the items they use each day are made of recyclable plastics. Have students bring in empty, plastic soft-drink bottles and show the recycling code that is imprinted on each bottle.

FIELD GUIDE *to Waste Management*

FIELD *ACTIVITY*

The type of plastic contained in a recyclable item is indicated by a coded number placed on the item. Arrange collection centers at your school for plastic to be recycled. Name your collection activity and advertise it with posters. Operate the collection of recyclable plastics for one week. Use the Plastics Code System Table in this field guide to organize the plastic products by code number so they can be recycled. Arrange to have your plastics taken to a recycling center. Make a bar graph that shows how many pieces of each type of plastic you collected. In your Science Journal, list examples of products that can be made from the collected plastics.

Managing waste properly can reduce the use of resources and prevent pollution. People can do three things to cut down on waste production and reduce harm to the environment. They can follow the three Rs of waste management: reduce, reuse, and recycle. For example, a 450-g family-size box of cereal uses a lot less cardboard than 18 single-serving boxes that each contain 25 g of cereal. Finding another function for used items such as wrapping gifts with old magazines or newspapers greatly reduces waste. And, you can use many products every day that are recyclable. You can also help complete the cycle by purchasing items that are made from recycled materials.

Household Hazardous Wastes

- Household Hazardous Wastes (HHWs) are products containing chemicals that can cause injury or are harmful if used, stored, or disposed of improperly. Some of these products include household and car batteries, bleach and household cleaners, paint, paint thinner, old motor oil, old gasoline, herbicides and pesticides.
- These chemicals pose a threat to people (especially children, firefighters, and refuse workers) and to our environment.
- HHWs have caution words, skull and crossbones, or special handling directions.
- Some communities provide information to help people dispose of HHWs properly.
- Follow these steps to reduce HHWs:
  1. Whenever possible, buy nontoxic alternatives to hazardous products.
  2. If you buy a hazardous product, buy only what you need to do the job.
  3. Before you put leftover products on the shelf, try to find someone who can use them.

Teacher FYI

When separating plastics into groups according to code number, they often must be further separated because of color. The color of plastic can limit how recycled plastic can be used.

*inter*NET CONNECTION

Internet Addresses

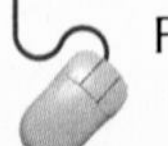

For Internet tips, see Glencoe's **Using the Internet in the Science Classroom.**

Plastics

- Plastics are among the most difficult products to recycle. Most plastics are composed of complex molecules that tend not to break down easily.
- Many different types of plastics exist, and they often cannot be recycled together.
- **Table 26-1** below lists the codes used to identify specific types of plastics used in products. This helps people sort common plastic items for proper recycling.
- Plastic beverage containers are recycled into insulation, carpet yarn, strapping, and packing material.

Table 26-1

The Plastics Code System

Code	Material	% of Containers	Reclaimed For
1 PET	Polyethylene terephthalate	7	Carpet, food packaging, fiberfill, fibers, and auto parts
2 HDPE	High-density polyethylene	31	Drainage pipes, drums, traffic cones, plastic lumber, and combs
3 V	Vinyl chloride	5	Pipes, hoses, mud flaps, and tile
4 LDPE	Low-density polyethylene	33	Mixed with HDPE to produce cases, recycling bins, and garbage bags
5 PP	Polypropylene	9	Household and janitorial products
6 PS	Polystyrene	11	Insulation and food trays
7 Other	All others and mixed	4	Storage containers, lumber, and animal-pen floors

Content Background

Code 2 plastic, also known as HDPE (high density polyethylene) is the most useful kind for recycling. Among other things, it is used to make translucent, white, milk jugs. Because of its neutral color, it can be changed into other colors during recycling.

During recycling, bales of HDPE are broken and ground into small flakes about 1 cm in diameter. The small flakes are washed and floated in a solution to remove heavy impurities. The clean, plastic pieces are then dried by hot air and packaged to be used for the production of plastic pipes, traffic cones, plastic lumbers, combs, trash cans, and bottles for holding materials other than food.

VISUAL Learning

Examine the box of recyclable plastic items shown on this page. Name some products that you think were contained in the plastic containers shown. Make a list of the products named that you use in your home.

Using Science Words

The first six code numbers of plastic are also referred to by what type of plastic they contain. Some of the terms used to describe the different recyclable plastics are common. For example, plastic code 6 is also called PS (polystyrene). This type of plastic may be familiar to students. It is commonly used in cups, food trays, and other packaging.

Content Background

PET (polyethylene terephthalate), also known as plastic code #1, can be very useful in recycling. Carpet companies use recycled PET in the manufacture of polyester carpets. Carpets are often made from up to 100 percent of this recycled material.

CA Science Content Standards

Page 900: 9e

Content Background

Glass that is received from households and businesses must be processed before being reused as raw material for new glass products. First, the recyclable glass is loaded onto a conveyor and passed under a magnet to remove any iron material. Second, the glass is hand picked to remove foreign material such as ceramics or other impurities. Third, the glass is crushed into small pellets known as cullet. Finally, the cullet is passed under a metal detector to remove any leftover metallic material, and the cleaned cullet is stored or shipped to glass manufacturers.

Teacher FYI

Recyclable precious metals are obtained from numerous sources. Examples include jewelry and watchbands; electronic parts such as circuit boards, chips, wires, and switches; dental caps, crowns and fillings; paints; and photographic and X-ray film.

Activity

Interview your principal about the types of glass and metals that are recycled at your school. Present your findings to the class as a short oral report.

Glass

- Glass is often separated by color into green, brown, or colorless types before recycling.
- Most glass bottles are recyclable, but some glassware is not because it is too thin. For example, broken or burned-out lightbulbs cannot be recycled.
- New products made from recycled glass include beverage containers.

Metals

- A variety of metals are recyclable, such as aluminum beverage cans and steel used in a variety of canned goods.
- Aluminum is processed to make lawn chairs, siding, cookware, or new beverage cans.
- Even precious metals such as silver, gold, and platinum used in laboratories or in jewelry, for example, are recyclable.

Inclusion Strategies

Learning Disabled Have students visit several restaurants near their homes or their school. Have them meet with the restaurant manager or staff and determine what glass or metallic materials are used. Have students collect samples of the recyclable products used by the restaurants and determine how they should be separated for recycling.

Paper

- Plain white paper, newspaper, magazines, and telephone books are common paper goods that can be recycled. New products made from these items include newsprint, cardboard, egg cartons, and building materials.
- Not all glossy and colored papers are recyclable at all recycling centers.

- As for any recycled material, you should check with your neighborhood recycling center for specific instructions about properly sorting your paper goods.

Yard Waste

- Grass clippings, leaves, sticks, and other yard wastes can be placed in bags and taken to your local recycling center. Some communities provide for the collection of yard wastes from your home after you gather them together.
- Another approach is to practice your own mulching. Rake your leaves and then place them on a garden plot to compost over the winter. This will enrich the soil in your garden when you're ready to plant in the spring.
- Some communities shred sticks and leaves to make mulch. Whatever the approach, recycling yard waste reduces the amount of material we send to landfills.

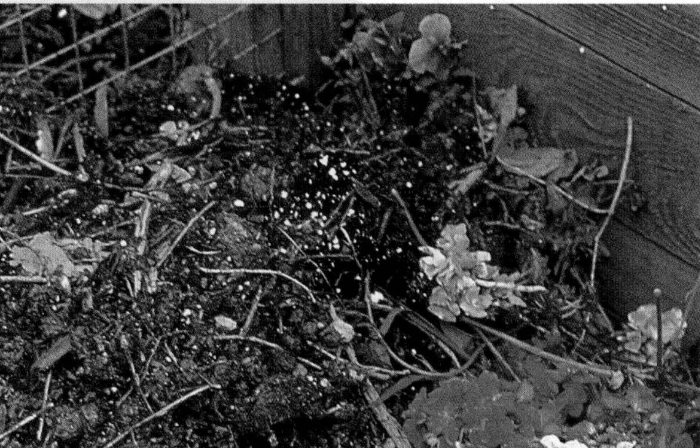

Activity

During the fall or spring, organize a lawn and garden cleanup on your school grounds. Collect leaves, twigs, and other debris from flowerbeds and grass. Arrange to have your school's yard waste collected properly for recycling.

Correcting Misconceptions

Grass clippings are the largest contributor to yard waste. For many years, people believed that it was necessary to catch grass clippings in order to have a healthy, lush green lawn. With the current crises many cities are facing with overflowing landfills and restrictions on the dumping of yard waste, mowers are now becoming equipped with mulching attachments which help recycle grass clippings into mulch.

Content Background

The quality of recyclable paper varies substantially. For example, some inks and adhesives used on paper products are difficult, and therefore costly, to remove during the processing of paper into new paper goods. Proper sorting of high-quality paper such as white office paper increases the percentage of paper that is recycled.

CA Science Content Standards

Page 903: 5b, 7c

Reviewing Main Ideas can be used to preview, review, reteach, and condense chapter content.

Preview

Linguistic Have students try to answer the questions in their Science Journals. Use student answers as a source for discussion throughout the chapter.

Review

Interpersonal Have students answer the questions on separate pieces of paper and compare their answers with those of other students in the class. COOP LEARN

Reteach

Visual-Spatial Have students look at the illustrations on these pages. Ask them to describe details that support the main ideas of the chapter found in the statement for each illustration.

OUT OF TIME?

Auditory-Musical If time does not permit teaching the entire chapter, use the information on these pages along with the chapter Audiocassettes to present the material in a condensed format.

Chapter 26 Reviewing Main Ideas

For a **preview** of this chapter, study this Reviewing Main Ideas before you read the chapter. After you have studied this chapter, you can use the Reviewing Main Ideas to **review** the chapter.

The Glencoe MindJogger, Audiocassettes, and CD-ROM provide additional opportunities for review.

Section 26-1 POPULATION IMPACT ON THE ENVIRONMENT

The rapid increase in human **population** in recent years is due to an increase in the birthrate, advances in medicine, better sanitation, and better nutrition. ***How does an increase in the number of humans affect Earth's carrying capacity for other organisms?***

SOUTH ATLANTIC OCEAN
INDIAN OCEAN
500 000 years ago
7000 B.C.
6000 B.C.
5000 B.C.
4000 B.C.
1100
1200
1300
1400
1500
1600
1700
1800
1900
1998
600 million 1700
1.0 billion 1810
3.0 billion 1960
5.931 billion 1998
Billions of People

Cultural Diversity

Healing the Land More than 223 million acres of the world's grasslands have become barren, arid, and unable to support life. Overgrazing by cattle and sheep is the major cause of destruction of grasslands, but leaving pasture unused can also be destructive. Allan Savory worked as a wildlife biologist and tracker in Zimbabwe for 40 years before moving to New Mexico and beginning his program of holistic land management. Savory has established a Center for Holistic Resource Management that works with ranchers from many western states, including Texas, Colorado, and California. The center promotes an understanding of the total environment and attempts to preserve a most precious natural resource, Earth itself. Have students use a map or globe to locate the places mentioned in this feature.

Reading Check

List at least two facts and two opinions related to population growth or related to recycling.

Section

26-2 USING LAND

Land is used for farming, grazing livestock, lumber, and mining coal and mineral ores. We also build structures and **landfills** on land. Land becomes polluted by **hazardous wastes** thrown away by industries and individuals. Fertilizers and pesticides pollute groundwater and soil. ***What happens to soil quality and atmospheric carbon dioxide when trees are cut down?***

Section

26-3 RECYCLING

Recycling, reducing, and reusing materials are important ways we can conserve natural resources. Recycling saves energy and much-needed space in landfills. Some parts of the world have mandatory recycling, while other parts have voluntary programs. ***Why do some people oppose having mandatory recycling programs?***

Answers to Questions

Section 26-1

Population Impact on the Environment The greater the number of humans, the greater the amount of land needed for homes, roads, landfills, etc. The result is loss of habitat for other organisms. Earth's carrying capacity for other organisms decreases.

Section 26-2

Using Land When trees are alive, their leaves and small branches fall to the ground and become humus. Their roots grow through soil, breaking apart and mixing soil particles. Trees also take carbon dioxide out of air and release oxygen. When trees are cut down, soil becomes less fertile and more compact, erosion increases, and more carbon dioxide remains in the atmosphere.

Section 26-3

Recycling They feel that recycling should be a choice not a mandate. Some people feel that the cost of recycling outweighs the benefits. Also, miners and manufacturers who make brand-new containers might lose their jobs because of recycling.

Assessment

Portfolio Encourage students to place in their portfolios one or two items of what they consider to be their best work. Examples include:

- Assessment, p. 885
- MiniLab, p. 889
- Science Journal, p. 897 P

Performance Additional performance assessments may be found in **Performance Assessment** and **Science Integration Activities.** Performance Task Assessment Lists and rubrics for evaluating these activities can be found in Glencoe's **Performance Assessment in the Science Classroom.**

GLENCOE TECHNOLOGY

CD-ROM

Glencoe Science Voyages Interactive CD-ROM

Chapter Summaries and Quizzes

Have students read the Chapter Summary then take the Chapter Quiz to determine whether they have mastered chapter content.

Using Vocabulary

1. f
2. c
3. e
4. h
5. a

interNET CONNECTION To reinforce chapter vocabulary, use the **Study Guide for Content Mastery** booklet. Also available are activities for **Glencoe Science Voyages** on the Glencoe Science Web Site. **www.glencoe.com/sec/science/ca**

Checking Concepts

6. B
7. D
8. C
9. D
10. B
11. D
12. C
13. C
14. D
15. D

Thinking Critically

16. With less packaging, there is less need for space for disposal of solid wastes in landfills.
17. Oxygen is constantly being added to Earth's atmosphere via photosynthesis. It's renewable.
18. Often, farmers can't afford machinery, improved strains of seeds, pesticides, or fertilizers. Insects often destroy crops. Lack of fertilizers causes soil nutrients to become depleted.
19. Fewer trees are available to produce oxygen and remove CO_2 from the air. Other vegetation is probably dying, too. The decrease in plants causes an increase in soil erosion. Species of plants and animals that depend on the forest habitat may become extinct if they are unable to adapt to the changes produced by the dying trees.

Chapter 26 Assessment

Using Vocabulary

a. carrying capacity
b. composting
c. conservation
d. hazardous waste
e. landfill
f. population
g. population explosion
h. recyclable

Which vocabulary word describes the phrase or process given below?

1. total number of individuals of a particular species in an area
2. careful use of resources
3. area lined with plastic, concrete, or clay where garbage is dumped
4. items that can be processed and used again
5. maximum number of individuals of a particular type that the planet will support

Checking Concepts

Choose the word or phrase that best answers the question.

6. Where is most of the trash in the United States disposed of?
A) recycling centers
B) landfills
C) hazardous waste sites
D) old mine shafts

7. Between 1960 and 1998, world population increased by how many billions of people?
A) 5.9 C) 1.0
B) 3.2 D) 2.9

8. What percent of Earth's resources does the United States use?
A) 5 C) 25
B) 10 D) 50

9. About what percent of U.S. cropland is used to grow feed for livestock?
A) 100 C) 50
B) 1 D) 20

10. What do we call an object that can be processed in some way so that it can be used again?
A) trash C) disposable
B) recyclable D) hazardous

11. What is about 40 percent of the mass of our trash made up of?
A) glass C) yard waste
B) aluminum D) paper

12. In which type of facility do humans cover trash with soil?
A) recycling center C) sanitary landfill
B) surface mine D) coal mine

13. By what order of magnitude are people starving each year?
A) the hundreds C) the millions
B) the thousands D) the billions

14. Organisms living outside the tropics suffer when rain forests are cut down. This is because fewer trees are available to produce which?
A) carbon dioxide C) water
B) methane D) oxygen

15. Which of the following is an example of a hazardous waste?
A) piece of glass C) steel can
B) plastic jug D) can of paint

Thinking Critically

16. How would reducing the packaging of consumer products impact our disposal of solid wastes?

17. Renewable resources are those resources that can be replenished by nature in the foreseeable future. Nonrenewable resources cannot be replenished. Which kind of resource is oxygen? Explain.

20. Answers will vary but might include providing collection bins in a convenient place or actually going door to door to collect the cans. If the interest were community-wide, people might be given a monetary incentive to recycle.

18. Although land is farmable in many developing countries, hunger is a major problem in many of these places. Give some reasons why this might be so.
19. Forests in Germany are dying due to acid rain. What effects might this loss of trees have on the environment?
20. Describe how you could encourage your neighbors to recycle their aluminum cans.

Developing Skills

If you need help, refer to the Skill Handbook.

21. **Making and Using Graphs:** In a population of snails, each snail produces two offspring each month. Each offspring also produces two offspring. Using the graph below, determine how many new snails would be produced during the fifth month if the initial population were only two snails.
22. **Interpreting Scientific Illustrations:** Why does the curve of the line graph below change its slope over time? Suppose half of the snails died after six months. Draw a new graph to illustrate the effect.

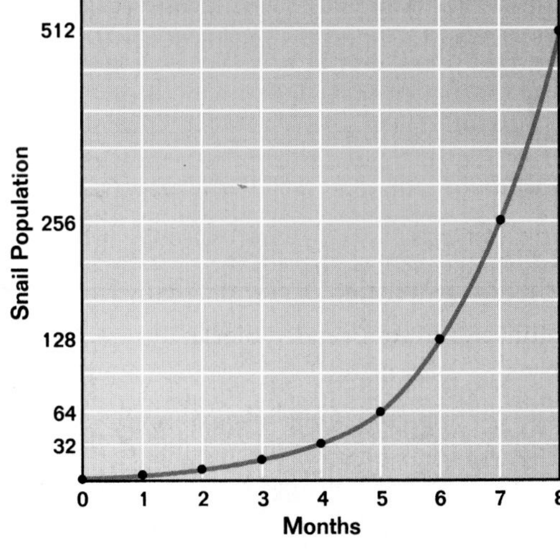

Test-Taking Tip

Don't Be Afraid to Ask for Help Ask for advice on things you don't understand. If you're practicing for a test and find yourself stuck, unable to understand why you got a question wrong, or unable to do it in the first place, ask for help.

Test Practice

Use these questions to test your Science Proficiency.

1. In some areas of the world, when rain forests are destroyed for lumber, a few fast-growing species of trees are planted in their place. Why is this a problem?
   A) The trees won't grow as quickly as the original rain forest trees.
   B) The tree farm won't produce oxygen.
   C) The roots of the new trees won't hold the soil.
   D) The biodiversity is decreased.
2. In 1946, there were 2.4 billion people on Earth. In 1998, there were 5.9 billion people. By how much did world population increase in 52 years?
   A) 226 percent
   B) 41 percent
   C) 146 percent
   D) 69 percent
3. Which of the following must be true for a recycling center to be profitable?
   A) The center must recycle glass.
   B) Mandatory recycling is enforced.
   C) Glossy and colored paper are recycled.
   D) There is a market for the recycled items.

Test Practice

The Test-Taking Tip was written by The Princeton Review, the nation's leader in test preparation.

1. D
2. C
3. D

Developing Skills

21. During the fifth month, 64 new snails would be added to the population. 126 total snails would be present if no snails died during the five-month period.
22. The growth rate is exponential. Each offspring contributes to the population growth, not just the original pair of snails. If half of the population died after six months, the population would drop. The growth would then begin doubling from there.

Bonus Question

Why is recycling paper good for the environment? *Probably the biggest advantage of recycling paper is that it saves trees. Recycling paper also saves landfill space, energy, and water.*

Assessment Resources

The **Test Practice Workbook** provides students with practice in the format, concepts, and critical-thinking skills tested in standardized exams.

Reproducible Masters

Chapter Review, pp. 51–52 L2
Performance Assessment, p. 26 L2
Assessment, pp. 101–104 L2

Glencoe Technology

Chapter Review Software
Computer Test Bank
MindJogger Videoquiz

Chapter 27 Our Impact on Air and Water

Section	Objectives	Activities/Features
Chapter Opener		Explore Activity: Observe Your Air, p. 909
27-1 **Air Pollution** 4½ Sessions 2 Blocks	1. **Identify** different sources of air pollutants. 2. **Describe** how air pollution affects people and the environment. 3. **Explain** how air pollution can be reduced.	MiniLab: Identifying Acid Rain, p. 912 Using Math, p. 913 Using Math, p. 915 Skill Builder: Making and Using Graphs, p. 916 Science Journal, p. 916 How It Works: Bee Probes, p. 917 Activity 27-1: What's in the air?, pp. 918–919
27-2 **Water Pollution** 3 Sessions 1½ Blocks	4. **List** types of water pollutants and their sources. 5. **Describe** ways that international agreements and U.S. laws are designed to reduce water pollution. 6. **Relate** ways you can help reduce water pollution.	Problem Solving: Interpreting Pollution Sources, p. 922 Life Science Integration, p. 923 Life Science Integration, p. 924 MiniLab: Observing Water Hardness, p. 925 Skill Builder: Interpreting Data, p. 926 Using Computers, p. 926 Activity 27-2: Water Use, p. 927

The number of recommended single-period sessions — The number of recommended blocks
One session and one-half block are allowed for chapter review and assessment.

Activity Materials

Explore	Activities	MiniLabs
p. 909 cloth, hand lens or microscope	pp. 918–919 plain gelatin, hot plate, pan, marker, refrigerator, 4 plastic lids, hand lens, water p. 927 home water meter	p. 912 plastic container, pH paper p. 925 baby food jars, tap water, pond water, stream water, liquid soap

Need Materials? Contact Science Kit at 1-800-828-7777 or at www.sciencekit.com on the Internet.
For alternate materials, see the activity on the listed page.

Chapter Organizer

Standards		Reproducible Resources	Technology
National	State/Local	Test Practice Workbooks are available for use with each chapter.	English and Spanish audiocassettes are available for use with each section.
National Content Standards: UCP2, A1, A2, D1, F1, F2, F3, F5	California Science Content Standards: 5e, 9a, 9c, 9e, 9f	**Activity Worksheets,** pp. 151–152, 155 **Enrichment,** p. 78 **Multicultural Connections,** pp. 53–54 **Reinforcement,** p. 78 **Study Guide,** pp. 105	**Section Focus Transparency 78** **Teaching Transparency 53** **Teaching Transparency 54** **Science Integration Transparency 27** **Internet Connection,** p. 911 **The Infinite Voyage Series** **Internet Connection,** p. 916
National Content Standards: A1, C3, C4, F2, F3, F5, G2	California Science Content Standards: 5a, 5b, 9a, 9e, 9f	**Activity Worksheets,** p.153–154, 156 **Critical Thinking/Problem Solving,** p. 27 **Enrichment,** p. 79 **Home Involvement,** p. 28 **Reinforcement,** p. 79 **Study Guide,** pp. 106–108	**Section Focus Transparency 79** **Glencoe Science Voyages Interactive CD-ROM**

Key to Teaching Strategies

The following designations will help you decide which activities are appropriate for your students.

L1 Level 1 activities should be appropriate for students with learning difficulties.

L2 Level 2 activities should be within the ability range of all students.

L3 Level 3 activities are designed for above-average students.

ELL ELL activities should be within the ability range of English Language Learners.

COOP LEARN Cooperative Learning activities are designed for small group work.

P These strategies represent student products that can be placed into a best-work portfolio.

Multiple Learning Styles logos, as described on page 55T, are used throughout to indicate strategies that address different learning styles.

Assessment Resources

Chapter Review, pp. 53–54
Assessment, pp. 105–108
Performance Assessment in the Science Classroom (PASC)
MindJogger Videoquiz
Alternate Assessment in the Science Classroom
Performance Assessment, p. 27
Chapter Review Software
Computer Test Bank

Chapter 27 Our Impact on Air and Water

This is a representation of key blackline masters available in the Teacher Classroom Resources. See Resource Manager boxes within the chapter for additional information.

Section Focus Transparencies

SECTION FOCUS TRANSPARENCY

SMOGGY, SMOGGY VIEW

This photograph shows what might be a beautiful view—but wait. Something is wrong with this view. What's going on here? Take a close look and see if you can tell.

1. What problem can you see in this photograph?
2. What natural things do you think are causing the problem?
3. What human activities do you think are causing the problem?

L2

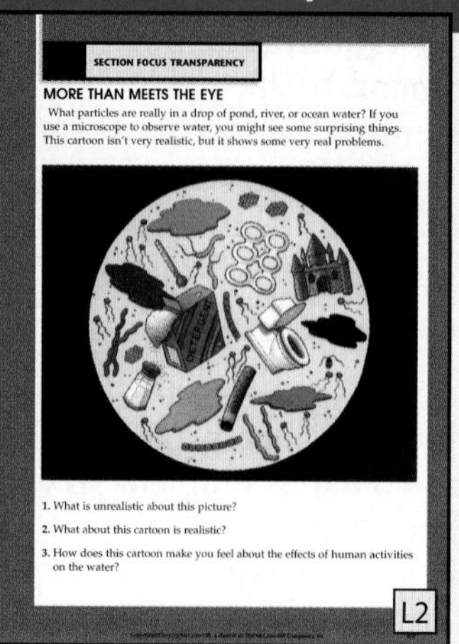

SECTION FOCUS TRANSPARENCY

MORE THAN MEETS THE EYE

What particles are really in a drop of pond, river, or ocean water? If you use a microscope to observe water, you might see some surprising things. This cartoon isn't very realistic, but it shows some very real problems.

1. What is unrealistic about this picture?
2. What about this cartoon is realistic?
3. How does this cartoon make you feel about the effects of human activities on the water?

L2

Science Integration Transparencies

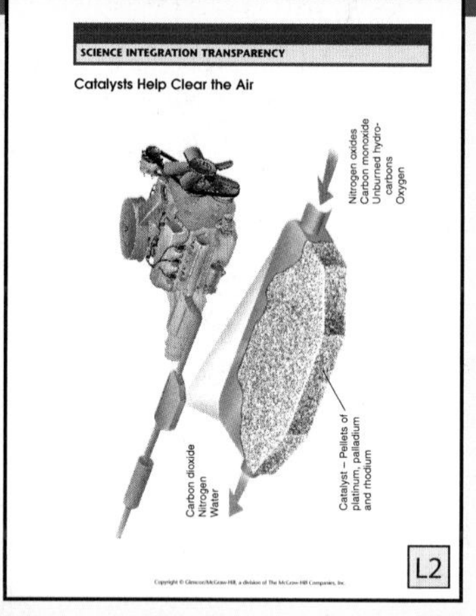

SCIENCE INTEGRATION TRANSPARENCY

Catalysts Help Clear the Air

L2

Teaching Transparencies

L2

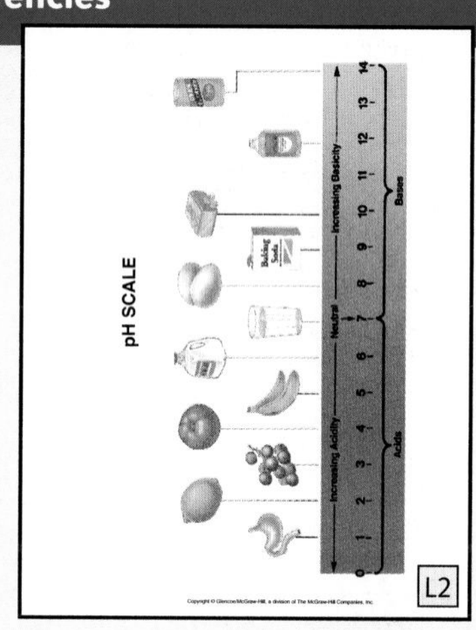

L2

Meeting Different Ability Levels

Study Guide for Content Mastery

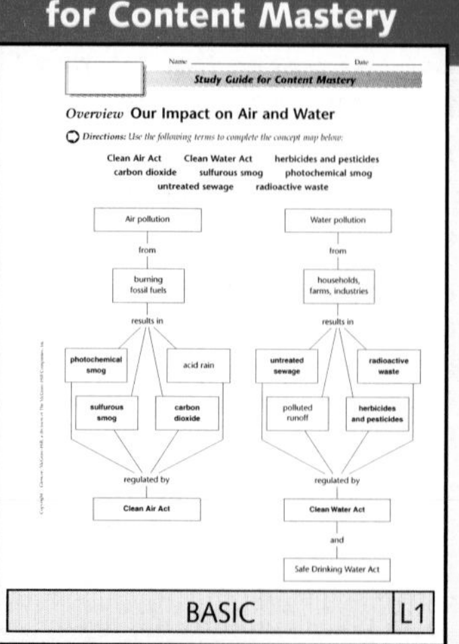

Name Date

Study Guide for Content Mastery

Overview Our Impact on Air and Water

Directions: Use the following terms to complete the concept map below:

Clean Air Act, Clean Water Act, herbicides and pesticides, carbon dioxide, sulfurous smog, photochemical smog, untreated sewage, radioactive waste

BASIC L1

Reinforcement

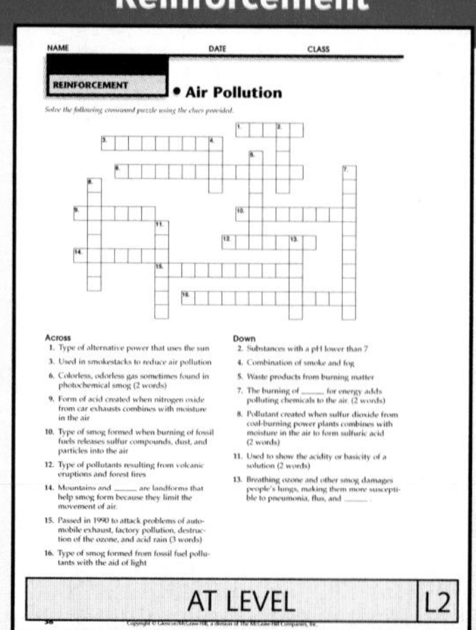

NAME DATE CLASS

REINFORCEMENT • Air Pollution

Solve the following crossword puzzle using the clues provided.

Across

1. Type of alternative power that uses the sun
3. Used in smokestacks to reduce air pollution
6. Colorless, odorless gas sometimes found in photochemical smog (2 words)
9. Form of acid created when nitrogen oxide from car exhausts combines with moisture in the air
10. Type of smog formed when burning of fossil fuels releases sulfur compounds, dust, and particles into the air
12. Type of pollutants resulting from volcanic eruptions and forest fires
14. Mountains and ____ are landforms that help smog form because they limit the movement of air.
15. Passed in 1990 to attack problems of automobile exhaust, factory pollution, destruction of the ozone, and acid rain (3 words)
16. Type of smog formed from fossil fuel pollutants with the aid of light

Down

2. Substances with a pH lower than 7
4. Combination of smoke and fog
5. Waste products from burning matter
7. The burning of ____ for energy adds polluting chemicals to the air. (2 words)
8. Pollutant created when sulfur dioxide from coal-burning power plants combines with moisture in the air to form sulfuric acid (2 words)
11. Used to show the acidity or basicity of a solution (2 words)
13. Breathing ozone and other smog damages people's lungs, making them more susceptible to pneumonia, flu, and ____

AT LEVEL L2

Enrichment Worksheets

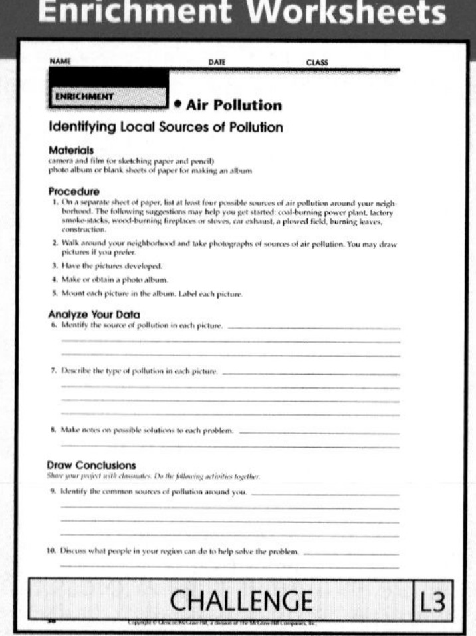

NAME DATE CLASS

ENRICHMENT • Air Pollution

Identifying Local Sources of Pollution

Materials

camera and film (or sketching paper and pencil)
photo album or blank sheets of paper for making an album

Procedure

1. On a separate sheet of paper, list at least four possible sources of air pollution around your neighborhood. The following suggestions may help you get started: coal-burning power plant, factory smokestacks, wood-burning fireplaces or stoves, car exhaust, a plowed field, burning leaves, construction.
2. Walk around your neighborhood and take photographs of sources of air pollution. You may draw pictures if you prefer.
3. Have the pictures developed.
4. Make or obtain a photo album.
5. Mount each picture in the album. Label each picture.

Analyze Your Data

6. Identify the source of pollution in each picture.
7. Describe the type of pollution in each picture.
8. Make notes on possible solutions to each problem.

Draw Conclusions

Share your project with classmates. Do the following activities together.

9. Identify the common sources of pollution around you.
10. Discuss what people in your region can do to help solve the problem.

CHALLENGE L3

Hands-on Activities

Activity Worksheets

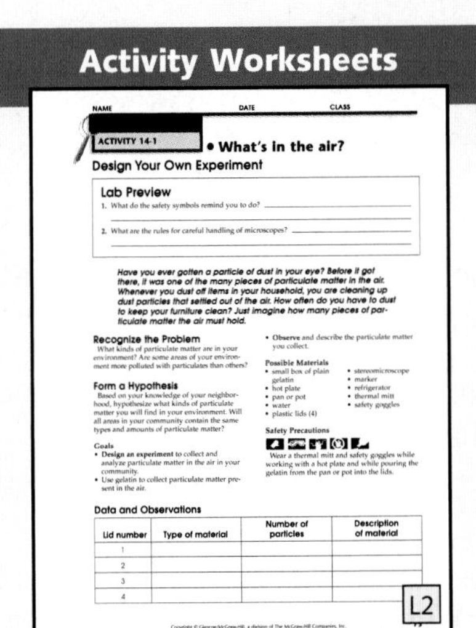
ACTIVITY 14-1 • What's in the air?

Design Your Own Experiment

Lab Preview

Recognize the Problem

Form a Hypothesis

Data and Observations

L2

Lab Manual

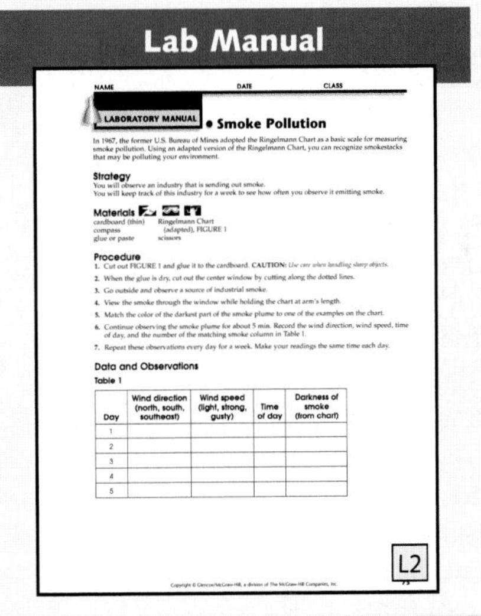
LABORATORY MANUAL • Smoke Pollution

Strategy

Materials

Procedure

Data and Observations

L2

Accessibility

Spanish Resources

SPANISH RESOURCES
GLENCOE
SCIENCE VOYAGES
Exploring the Life, Earth, and Physical Sciences
LEVEL BLUE
L2

Assessment

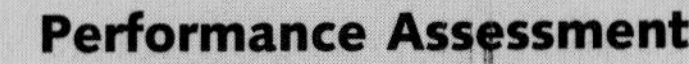
Performance Assessment

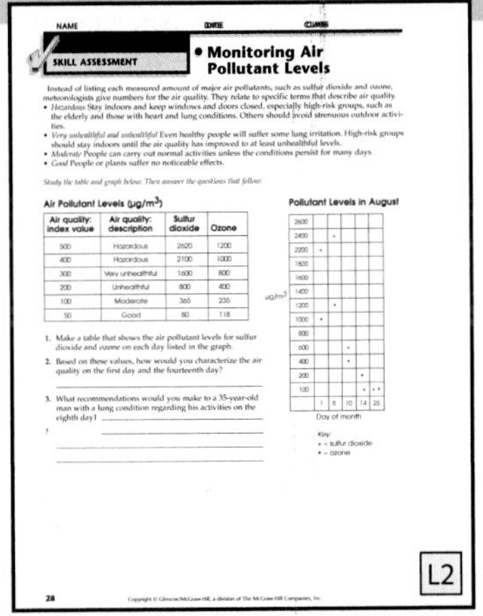
SKILL ASSESSMENT • Monitoring Air Pollutant Levels

L2

Chapter Review

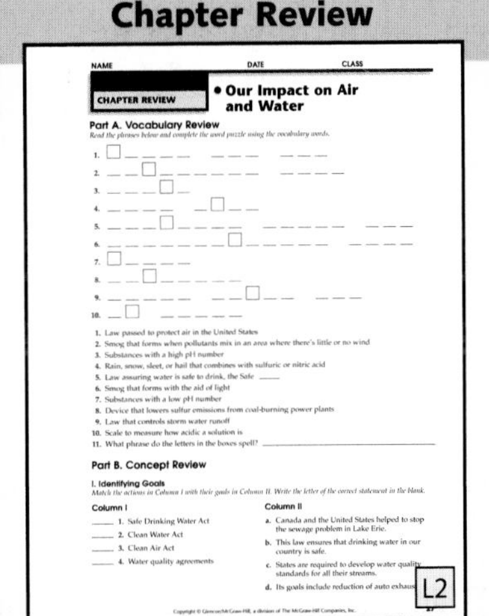
CHAPTER REVIEW • Our Impact on Air and Water

Part A. Vocabulary Review

Part B. Concept Review

L2

Assessment

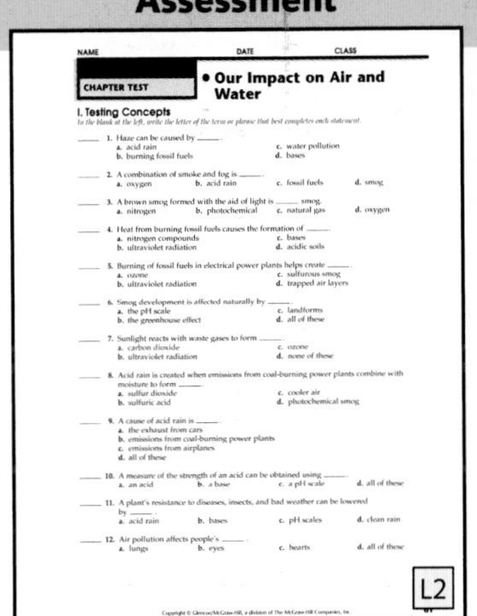
CHAPTER TEST • Our Impact on Air and Water

I. Testing Concepts

L2

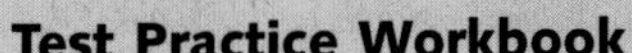
Test Practice Workbook

Extending Content

Critical Thinking/ Problem Solving

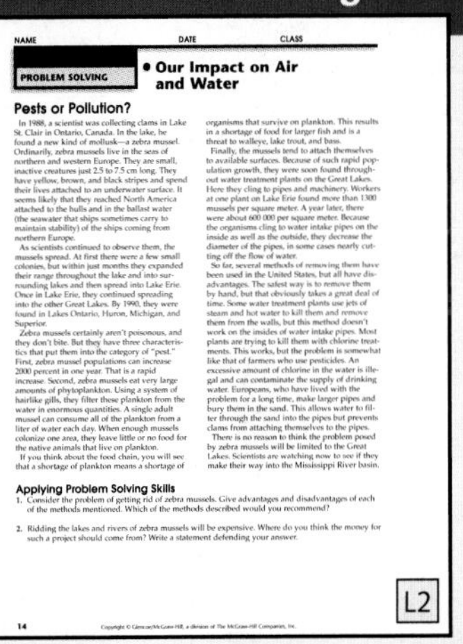
PROBLEM SOLVING • Our Impact on Air and Water

Pests or Pollution?

Applying Problem Solving Skills

L2

Multicultural Connections

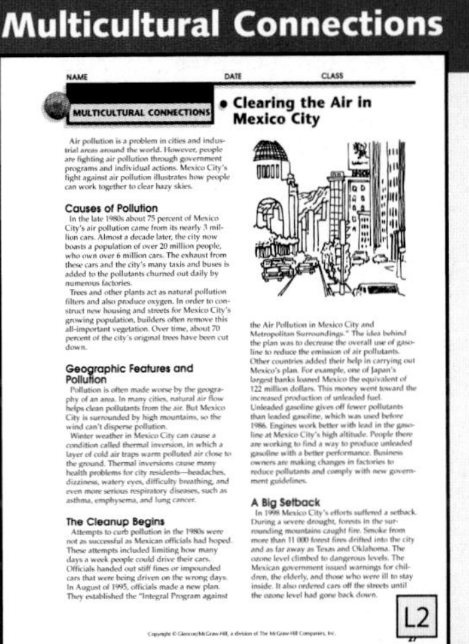
MULTICULTURAL CONNECTIONS • Clearing the Air in Mexico City

Causes of Pollution

Geographic Features and Pollution

The Cleanup Begins

A Big Setback

L2

Helping You Prepare

What causes air pollution?
(Section 27-1)

Common indoor pollutants include copying-machine fluids, cleaning fluids, cigarette smoke, paint, and items that contain formaldehyde. Another indoor pollutant is radon-222, a radioactive gas produced by the radioactive decay of uranium-238.

In urban areas, carbon monoxide, nitrogen oxides, hydrocarbons, and particulate matter are the primary outdoor air pollutants.

The carbon dioxide content in Earth's atmosphere has increased tremendously since the 1850s. Much of this increase has been attributed to the burning of fossil fuels.

Smog (Section 27-1)

Pyrite, also called fool's gold, is a common component of coal beds. When coal containing this mineral is burned, sulfur dioxide is produced. This contributes to sulfurous smog.

Acid Rain (Section 27-1)

If soil has a low pH, acid rain falling onto it will be damaging. But, if acid rain falls onto soil that has a high pH, the acid is neutralized. Soils in the midwestern states have a high pH. However, northeastern states and eastern Canada are acidic. When acid rain falls in these areas, it is harmful to plants and fish.

Water with a pH of 5 or less is considered unlikely to be able to support most forms of life. Around the world each year, acid rain causes billions of dollars in economic damage.

GLENCOE TECHNOLOGY

Glencoe Science Voyages Interactive CD-ROM

Chapter Summaries

Use the Chapter Summary to introduce, teach, or review chapter material.

How Air Pollution Affects Our Health (Section 27-1)

When we breathe, air travels down nasal passages, past the vocal cords and larynx, and into the trachea. From there, it passes through the bronchi and into the lungs. The first line of defense against air pollutants is the hair and mucus that line the nasal passages. Hairs filter the air, and mucus traps the particles. Sneezing is the body's way of getting rid of particles that are trapped in these passages. If particles travel into the trachea, cilia (tiny hairlike structures) are irritated. We react to this irritation by coughing. This forces the dust to rise back up to the mouth.

NATIONAL GEOGRAPHIC — **Teacher's Corner**

Products Available from Glencoe

To order the following products for use with this chapter, call Glencoe at 1-800-334-7344:

Curriculum Kit

GeoKit: Pollution

Poster

Pollution

Videodisc

GTV: Planetary Manager

Products Available from National Geographic Society

To order the following products for use with this chapter, call National Geograpic Society at 1-800-368-2728:

Videos

The Living Earth

Pollution: World at Risk

"Recycling," by Noel Grove, July 1994

Reducing Air Pollution
(Section 27-1)

Despite the Clean Air Act, more than 150 million people in the United States live in metropolitan areas where ozone and/or carbon monoxide levels exceed federal health standards.

In U.S. cities where smog is a serious problem, systems have been installed to warn people when pollution reaches unsafe levels.

Technology exists that enables pollution to be traced to its source when the pollutant is present in as little as one part per trillion parts of air.

Causes and Effects of Water Pollution (Section 27-2)

Substantial amounts of pesticides have percolated into groundwater in at least 34 states. More than 100 million people in the United States rely on underground wells for their drinking water.

Some of the toxins in Lake Erie originate from as far away as Central America. The toxins are carried there by wind.

Reducing Water Pollution
(Section 27-2)

In the United States, 40 percent of water sources do not presently meet basic water-quality standards. The Clean Water Act requires states to identify these water sources and to establish Total Daily Maximum Loads or TDMLs for pollutants. States must prioritize cleanup based on the severity of the pollution problem and the intended use of a water source. For the cleanup to be successful, it is essential that all possible pollution sources be identified.

SCIENCE UPDATE

For current events or science in the news, access the Glencoe Science Web Site at **www.glencoe.com/sec/science/ca**

Bioremediation (Section 27-2)

The purpose of bioremediation is to clean up pollution problems more rapidly than nature can. Bioremediation has been used in municipal and industrial waste-treatment systems where hydrocarbon wastes are degraded by bacterial action. Besides bacteria, fungi and plants also are used successfully in some kinds of bioremediation.

Biostimulation is bioremediation using indigenous bacterial species only. Bioaugmentation is the addition of microorganisms that are known to be degraders of specific contaminants.

How can you help? (Section 27-2)

Nonpoint source pollution has been identified as the nation's largest water-quality problem. Students can take an active role in helping the community identify and correct runoff problems. Students can participate in water-quality monitoring, water conservation, beach and river cleanups, and recycling projects.

Teacher to Teacher

"I often visit the art class to watch how the art teacher teaches students to draw trees, plants, humans, animals, landscapes, etc. I use what I have learned in creating diagrams and illustrations in class. You can improve your science teaching from watching other disciplines."

Leonard G. Rodríguez

Leonard G. Rodríguez, Assistant Principal
First Avenue Middle School
Pasadena, CA

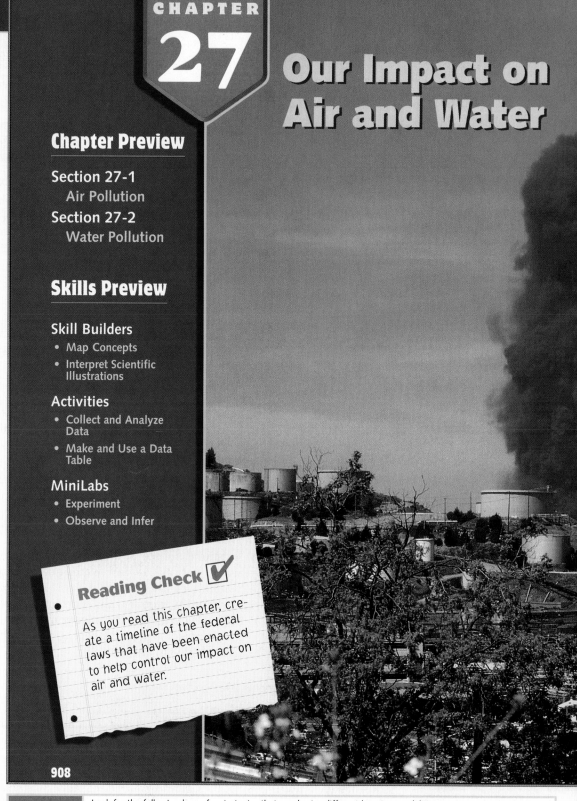

CHAPTER 27
Our Impact on Air and water

CHAPTER OVERVIEW

Section 27-1 This section examines the causes of smog and acid rain and describes how air pollution affects human health. Ways of reducing air pollution also are presented.

Section 27-2 Some of the causes and effects of water pollution are discussed. A few ways to reduce water pollution are explored.

Chapter Vocabulary

photochemical smog
sulfurous smog
acid rain
pH scale
acid
base
Clean Air Act
scrubber
Safe Drinking Water Act
Clean Water Act

Theme Connection

Systems and Interactions Human activities affect and are affected by pollution of Earth's air and water systems. Interactions among humans and these systems are the focus of the chapter.

00:00 OUT OF TIME?

If time does not permit teaching the entire chapter, use Reviewing Main Ideas on pp. 928–929.

CHAPTER 27

Our Impact on Air and Water

Chapter Preview

Skills Preview

Skill Builders
- Map Concepts
- Interpret Scientific Illustrations

Activities
- Collect and Analyze Data
- Make and Use a Data Table

MiniLabs
- Experiment
- Observe and Infer

Reading Check

As you read this chapter, create a timeline of the federal laws that have been enacted to help control our impact on air and water.

908

Multiple Learning Styles

Look for the following logos for strategies that emphasize different learning modalities.

Linguistic Using Science Words, p. 911; Multiple Learning Styles, pp. 912, 923; Science Journal, pp. 912, 914, 922; Enrichment, p. 921; Preview, p. 928

Logical-Mathematical Activity, pp. 918–919

Visual-Spatial Explore Activity, p. 909; Quick Demo, p. 911; Inclusion Strategies, p. 915; Activity, p. 924; Reteach, p. 928

Auditory-Musical Out of Time, p. 928

Kinesthetic Making a Model, p. 913; MiniLab, p. 925

Interpersonal MiniLab, p. 912; Activity, p. 913; Discussion, p. 915; Reteach, pp. 915, 924; Review, p. 928

Intrapersonal Activity, p. 927

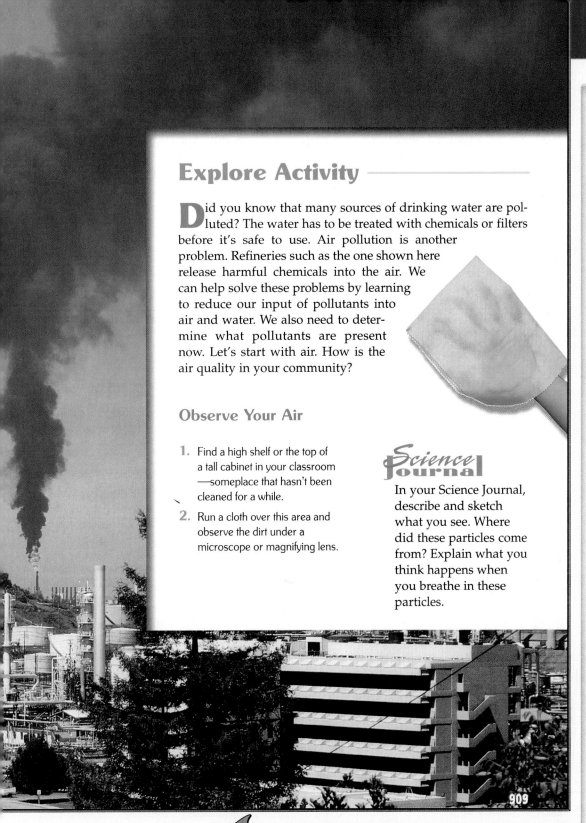

Explore Activity

Did you know that many sources of drinking water are polluted? The water has to be treated with chemicals or filters before it's safe to use. Air pollution is another problem. Refineries such as the one shown here release harmful chemicals into the air. We can help solve these problems by learning to reduce our input of pollutants into air and water. We also need to determine what pollutants are present now. Let's start with air. How is the air quality in your community?

Observe Your Air

1. Find a high shelf or the top of a tall cabinet in your classroom —someplace that hasn't been cleaned for a while.
2. Run a cloth over this area and observe the dirt under a microscope or magnifying lens.

Science Journal

In your Science Journal, describe and sketch what you see. Where did these particles come from? Explain what you think happens when you breathe in these particles.

909

Explore Activity

Purpose

Visual-Spatial Use the Explore Activity to introduce students to air pollution. Inform students that they will be learning more about pollution of Earth's atmosphere and hydrosphere as they read the chapter.

Preparation

Before doing this activity obtain a stereomicroscope and have students bring in clean, cloth rags.

Materials

clean, cloth rags; a dusty shelf; stereomicroscope

Teaching Strategies

You may want to have students discuss how materials are carried by wind.

Safety Precautions Students with dust allergies should wear a mask while dust samples are being collected.

Students should explain that they are carried in the air. They go into the students' lungs when they breathe.

Assessment

Performance Have students compare and contrast the different particles that they examined under the stereomicroscope. Use **Performance Assessment in the Science Classroom,** p. 27.

Assessment

Portfolio

Refer to p. 929 for suggested items that students might select for their portfolios.

Performance Assessment

See p. 929 for additional Performance Assessment options.
Skill Builder, p. 916
MiniLab, pp. 912, 925
Activity, 27-1, pp. 918–919; 27-2, p. 927

Content Assessment

Section Assessment, pp. 916, 926
Chapter Assessment, pp. 930–931
Proficiency Prep, pp. 916, 926

SECTION 27•1

Prepare

Refer to **What causes air pollution?, Smog, Acid Rain, How Air Pollution Affects Our Health,** and **Reducing Air Pollution** on pp. 908E–F.

Preplanning

Refer to the **Chapter Organizer** on p. 908A–B.

1 Motivate

Bellringer

Before presenting the lesson, display **Section Focus Transparency 78** on the overhead projector. Use the accompanying **Focus Activity** worksheet. L2 ELL

SECTION FOCUS TRANSPARENCY

SMOGGY, SMOGGY VIEW

This photograph shows what might be a beautiful view—but wait. Something is wrong with this view. What's going on here? Take a close look and see if you can tell.

1. What problem can you see in this photograph?
2. What natural things do you think are causing the problem?
3. What human activities do you think are causing the problem?

Tying to Previous Knowledge

Assure students that they will be adding to their existing knowledge about chemical reactions and air pollution.

27•1 Air Pollution

What You'll Learn

- The different sources of air pollutants
- How air pollution affects people and the environment
- How air pollution can be reduced

Vocabulary
photochemical smog
sulfurous smog
acid rain
pH scale
acid
base
Clean Air Act
scrubber

Why It's Important

- Air pollution can affect your health and the health of others.

What causes air pollution?

Have you ever noticed that the air looks hazy on some days? Do you know what causes this haziness? Some industries generate dust and chemicals. Other human activities add pollutants to the air, too. Look at **Figure 27-1.** Cars, buses, trucks, trains, and planes all burn fossil fuels for energy. Their exhaust—the waste products from burning the fossil fuels—adds polluting chemicals to the air. Other sources include smoke from burning trash and dust from plowed fields, construction sites, and mines.

Natural sources also add pollutants to the air. Volcanic eruptions, forest fires, and grass fires all emit dust and chemicals into the air. Volcanic eruptions even cause temporary changes in climate by blocking out sunlight when ash erupts.

Smog

Figure 27-2 shows the major sources of air pollution. Around cities, polluted air is called *smog,* a word made by combining the words *smoke* and *fog.* Two types of smog are common—photochemical smog and sulfurous smog.

Photochemical Smog

In areas such as Los Angeles, Denver, and New York City, a hazy, brown blanket of smog is created when sunlight reacts with pollutants in the air. This brown smog is called **photochemical smog** because it forms with the aid of light. The pollutants get into the air when fossil fuels are burned. Coal, natural gas, and gasoline are burned by factories, airplanes, and cars. Burning fossil fuels causes nitrogen and oxygen to combine chemically to form nitrogen compounds. These compounds react in the presence of sunlight and produce other substances. One of the substances produced is ozone. Ozone in the stratosphere protects us

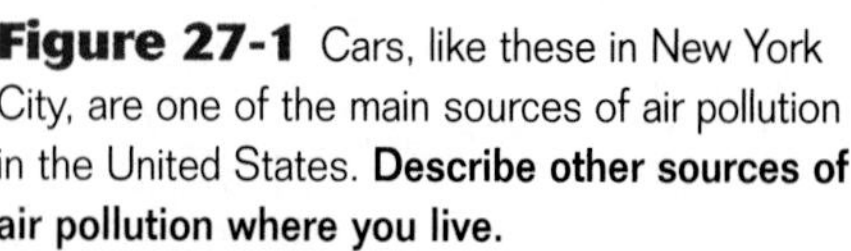
Figure 27-1 Cars, like these in New York City, are one of the main sources of air pollution in the United States. **Describe other sources of air pollution where you live.**

Resource Manager

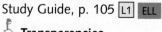

The following **Teacher Classroom Resources** can be used with Section 27-1:

 **Reproducible Masters**

Activity Worksheets, pp. 151–152, 155 L2
Enrichment, p. 78 L3
Multicultural Connections, pp. 53–54 L2
Reinforcement, p. 78 L2
Study Guide, p. 105 L1 ELL

Transparencies

Teaching Transparency 53, 54 L2
Science Integration Transparency 27 L2

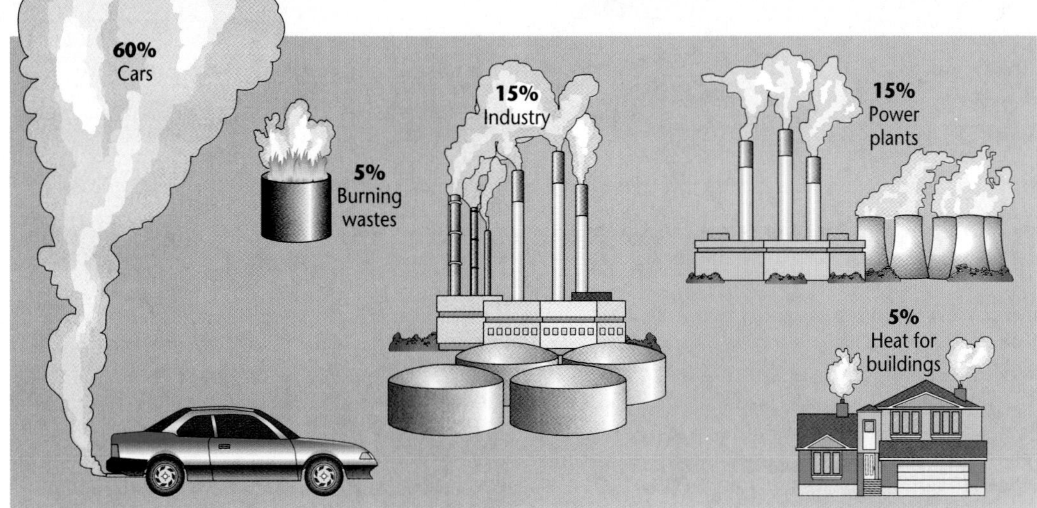

Figure 27-2 There are five major sources of human-created smog. **Which three sources combined produce 90 percent of human-created smog?**

from the sun's ultraviolet radiation. But ozone that forms in smog near Earth's surface causes health problems.

Sulfurous Smog

A second type of smog is called **sulfurous smog.** It's created when coal is burned in electrical power plants and home furnaces. The burning releases sulfur compounds, dust, and smoke particles into the air. Sulfurous smog forms when these substances collect in an area where there's little or no wind. A blanket of gray smog may hang over a city for several days and be hazardous to breathe.

Nature and Smog

Nature plays an important role in creating smog. Sunlight helps form photochemical smog. Sulfurous smog forms when weather systems are calm and the air is not being moved around. Normally, warmer air is near Earth's surface. But, sometimes warm air overlies cool air, trapping cool air mixed with pollutants near the ground. Eventually, the weather changes and cleaner air is blown in, dispersing the pollutants in the air.

Landforms also enhance smog development. For example, air with smog can be blocked by surrounding mountains. This prevents smog from being dispersed by winds. Dense, dirty air tends to collect in valleys in this way.

Smog isn't the only air pollution problem we have. Chlorofluorocarbons (CFCs) from air conditioners and refrigerators are thought to be destroying the ozone layer in the stratosphere. Some scientists suggest that carbon dioxide released from burning coal, oil, natural gas, and forests could contribute to increasing temperatures on Earth.

Visit the Glencoe Science Web Site at **www.glencoe.com/sec/science/ca** for more information about smog.

Caption Answers

Figure 27-1 *Answers will vary but should include burning trash, burning fossil fuels, volcanic eruptions, industrial pollutants, forest fires, and dust from construction sites.*

Figure 27-2 *cars, industry, and power plants*

Internet Addresses

For Internet tips, see Glencoe's **Using the Internet in the Science Classroom.**

2 Teach

Using Science Words

Linguistic Have students research why certain chemicals that destroy ozone molecules are called chlorofluorocarbons. L2

Quick Demo

Visual-Spatial Coal, oil, natural gas, and trees contain hydrocarbons. To demonstrate what happens when hydrocarbons burn, secure a candle to the bottom half of a petri dish. Pour just enough phenol red into the dish to cover the bottom. Pour the same amount into the other half of the petri dish. Place both containers on top of a sheet of white paper. Light the candle and invert a tall, narrow jar over the candle. Have students observe the color change in the dish containing the candle. Explain that as the candle burns, carbon dioxide is released into the air. The phenol red is used to detect the carbon dioxide. As the carbon dioxide dissolves in the phenol red, the pH is reduced and the phenol red turns yellow.

GLENCOE TECHNOLOGY

Videodisc

The Infinite Voyage: Crisis in the Atmosphere

Chapter 2 *Studying Man-Made Carbon Dioxide* 1:00

Refer to the Teacher Guide for bar codes and teaching strategies.

CA Science Content Standards

Page 911: 5e

MiniLab

Purpose

Interpersonal Students will determine whether their community has acid rain. L2 ELL COOP LEARN

Materials

pH paper, glass or plastic containers

Teaching Strategies

Have students collect their samples at about the same time or at least from the same source of precipitation.

Analysis

1. Students' samples should have reasonably similar pH levels. The acidity of the precipitation will depend on your geographic location and the prevailing wind direction.
2. Answers will vary.

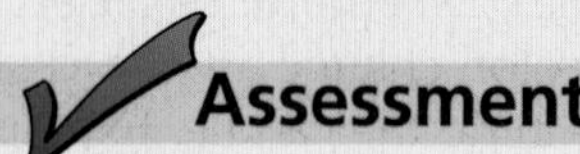

Performance To further assess students' understanding of acid rain, have them collect and test water samples from the same location over a period of time. Have them determine whether the pH varies from day to day. Use **Performance Assessment in the Science Classroom,** p. 25.

Discussion

How do cars contribute to the acid rain problem? *Nitrogen oxide from car exhaust combines with moisture in air to form nitric acid.* **If the pH of a substance is 4, is this substance an acid or a base?** *an acid*

Identifying Acid Rain

Procedure

1. The next time it rains or snows, use a glass or plastic container to collect a sample of the precipitation.
2. Use pH paper to determine the acidity level of your sample. If you have collected snow, melt it before measuring its pH.
3. Record the indicated pH of your sample and compare it with the results of other classmates who have followed the same procedure.

Analysis

1. What is the average pH of the samples obtained from this precipitation?
2. Compare and contrast the pH of your samples with those of the substances shown on the pH scale in **Figure 27-4.**

Figure 27-3 These trees are dying because acids in the soil have lowered the trees' resistance to diseases, insects, and bad weather. Acid rain also increases the acidity of streams, rivers, and lakes, killing fish. Acid rain even damages the surfaces of buildings and cars.

Acid Rain

Another major pollution problem is acid rain. Acid rain is created when sulfur dioxide from coal-burning power plants combines with moisture in the air to form sulfuric acid. It also is created when nitrogen oxides from car exhausts combine with moisture in the air to form nitric acid. The acidic moisture falls to Earth as rain or snow. We call this **acid rain.** Acid rain can poison organisms, as shown by the dying trees in **Figure 27-3.**

To understand what is meant by an acid, we use the **pH scale,** shown in **Figure 27-4.** Substances with a pH lower than seven are **acids.** The lower the number, the greater the acidity. Substances with a pH above seven are **bases.** Acid rain is sometimes as acidic as lemon juice.

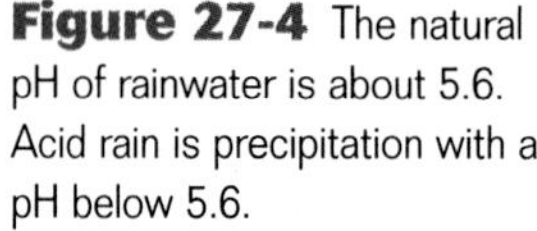

Figure 27-4 The natural pH of rainwater is about 5.6. Acid rain is precipitation with a pH below 5.6.

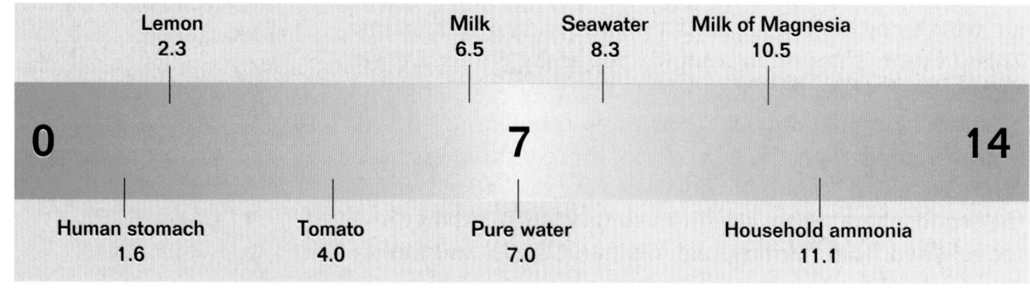

Multiple Learning Styles

Linguistic Have students brainstorm to compose a list of antipollution logos to promote conservation and recycling. They also can construct posters or banners that use the logos. L2

Acid Rain Have students write one or two paragraphs to describe the effects of acid rain. *Acid rain removes essential nutrients from soil. It lowers a plant's resistance to diseases, insects, and bad weather. Acid rain can kill organisms living in lakes. Finally, it damages the surfaces of buildings and other structures.* L2

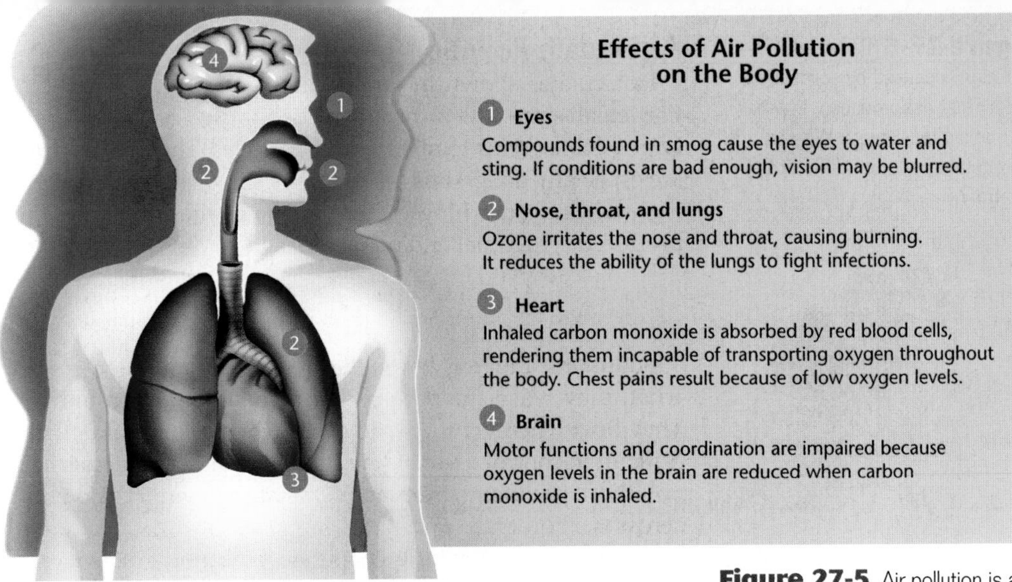

Effects of Air Pollution on the Body
1 Eyes
Compounds found in smog cause the eyes to water and sting. If conditions are bad enough, vision may be blurred.
2 Nose, throat, and lungs
Ozone irritates the nose and throat, causing burning. It reduces the ability of the lungs to fight infections.
3 Heart
Inhaled carbon monoxide is absorbed by red blood cells, rendering them incapable of transporting oxygen throughout the body. Chest pains result because of low oxygen levels.
4 Brain
Motor functions and coordination are impaired because oxygen levels in the brain are reduced when carbon monoxide is inhaled.
1
2
2
2
3
4

Figure 27-5 Air pollution is a health hazard. Compounds in the air can affect your body.

How Air Pollution Affects Your Health

Suppose you're an athlete in a large city and you're training for a big, upcoming competition. You have to get up at 4:30 A.M. to exercise. Later in the day, the smog levels will be so high that it won't be safe for you to do strenuous exercise. In southern California, in Denver, and in other areas, athletes adjust their training schedules to avoid exposure to ozone and other smog. Schools schedule football games for Saturday afternoons when smog levels are low. Parents are warned to keep their children indoors when smog exceeds certain levels. **Figure 27-5** shows how breathing dirty air, especially taking deep breaths of it, can cause health problems.

Health Disorders

How hazardous is dirty air? Approximately 250 000 people in the United States suffer from pollution-related breathing disorders. About 60 000 deaths each year in the United States are blamed on air pollution. Ozone damages lung tissue, making people more susceptible to diseases such as pneumonia and asthma. Less severe symptoms of breathing ozone include burning eyes, dry throat, and headache. ☑

Carbon monoxide also contributes to air pollution. A colorless, odorless gas, carbon monoxide makes people ill, even in small concentrations.

What do you suppose happens when you inhale the humid air from acid rain? Acid is deposited deep inside your lungs. This causes irritation, reduces your ability to fight respiratory infections, interferes with oxygen absorption, and puts stress on your heart.

Using Math

The pH scale is a logarithmic scale. This means that there is a tenfold difference for each pH unit. For example, pH 4 is ten times more acidic than pH 5 and 100 times more acidic than pH 6. Calculate how much more acidic pH 1 is than pH 4.

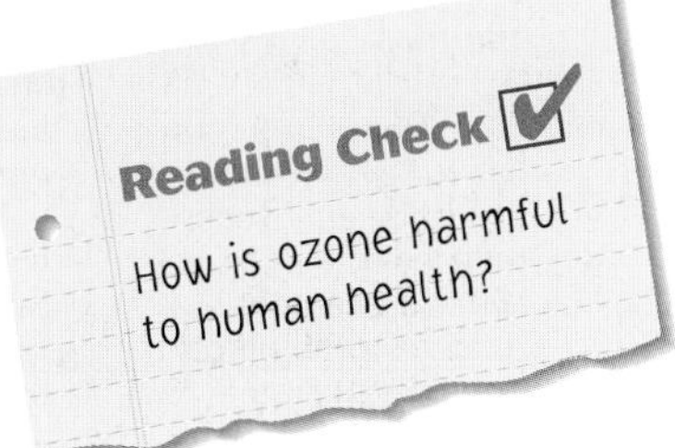

Reading Check
How is ozone harmful to human health?

Using Math

$4 - 1 = 3$ pH units,
$10^3 = 1000$ times more acidic

Teacher FYI

Lakes that have become acidic as a result of acid rain can be treated by adding limestone.

Activity

Interpersonal Have students produce a newspaper that deals with environmental problems. Distribute it throughout the school or community.

Making a Model

Kinesthetic Have pairs of students simulate acid rain by adding a few drops of lemon juice to a sample of tap water. Have them use pH ion paper and a pH color chart to determine the pH of the lemon water. Then, instruct them to slowly add just enough baking soda or ammonia to neutralize the acid. L2

ELL COOP LEARN

Answer to Reading Check

Burning eyes, dry throat, and headache may result. In severe cases, it damages lung tissue, making people more susceptible to diseases like pneumonia and asthma.

Across the Curriculum

Health Have students research to find sources of indoor air pollution. Have them study the health effects of asbestos, formaldehyde, radon, cigarette smoke, and other substances found in buildings. L2 P

Content Background

The Environmental Protection Agency has found that toxic chemicals found inside most American homes are more likely to cause some type of cancer than outdoor air pollutants.

CA Science Content Standards

Page 913: 5e, 9f

Caption Answer

Figure 27-6 *Wind carries the pollutants across borders between states and countries.*

GLENCOE TECHNOLOGY

 **Videodisc**

The Infinite Voyage: Crisis in the Atmosphere

Chapter 5 *Chlorofluorocarbons and Their Effect on the Ozone Layer* 4:00

Chapter 10

Los Angeles Smog and Air Quality Plan 6:30

Refer to the Teacher Guide for bar codes and teaching strategies.

Environmental Awareness Have students identify and explain in their Science Journals the tradeoffs involved when a person changes his or her lifestyle in order to conserve Earth's resources. *For example, walking instead of driving to the store will save energy but will take more time and effort.* L2

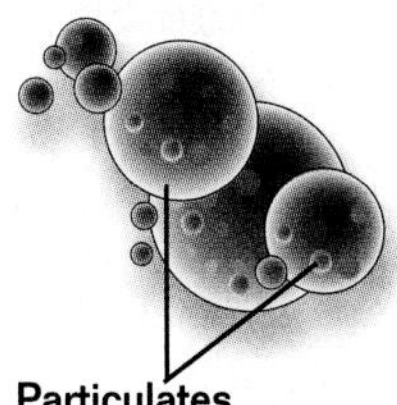

Figure 27-6 Particulate pollution is caused by solids in the air that are produced, in part, by burning fossil fuels. **Why is particulate pollution difficult to control?**

Particulate Pollution

Particulates shown in **Figure 27-6,** can also harm people. Particulates are fine airborne solids that range in size from large visible grains to microscopic particles. The fine particles are especially dangerous because they disrupt normal breathing and can cause lung disease. Some of these particles are produced when coal and oil are burned.

Reducing Air Pollution

Pollutants moving through the atmosphere don't stop when they reach the borders between states and countries. They float wherever the wind carries them. This makes them difficult to control. Even if one state or country reduces its air pollution, pollutants from another state or country can blow across the border.

When states and nations cooperate, pollution problems can be reduced. Diplomats from around the world have met on several occasions since 1990 to try to eliminate some kinds of air pollution. Of particular concern are chlorofluorocarbons and carbon dioxide.

Air Pollution in the United States

The Congress of the United States has passed several laws to protect the air. The 1990 **Clean Air Act** attacked the problems of smog, chlorofluorocarbons, particulates, and acid rain by regulating car manufacturers, coal technologies, and other industries. In **Table 27-1,** you can read about some of these regulations.

Table 27-1

Clean Air Regulations

Urban Air Pollution	Acid Rain	Airborne Toxins	Ozone-Depleting Chemicals
By 1996, all new cars had to have their nitrogen oxide emissions reduced by 60 percent and hydrocarbons reduced by 35 percent from 1990 levels.	In 1990, nitrogen oxide emissions had to be reduced by several million tons immediately. Sulfur dioxide emissions must be reduced by 14 million tons from 1990 levels by the year 2000.	Beginning in 1995, industries had to limit the emission of 200 compounds that cause cancer and birth defects.	In 1990, industries were required to immediately phase out ozone-depleting chemicals.

Integrating the Sciences

Life Science Invite a physician to talk to your class about health problems associated with air pollution. Ask the physician to discuss ways to reduce exposure to air pollution.

The good news is that since the passage of the Clean Air Act, the quality of the air in some regions of the United States has improved. The bad news is that one of four U.S. citizens still breathes unhealthy air.

It is the role of the federal Environmental Protection Agency to monitor progress toward the goals of the Clean Air Act. However, consumers must pay increased prices and taxes and change their habits in order to really help protect the environment. The Clean Air Act can work only if we all cooperate. You can conserve energy and reduce trash in several ways. When you do these things, you also are reducing air pollution. We all must do our share to clean up the air.

Reducing Emissions

The main source of the nitric acid in acid rain is car exhaust. Better emission-control devices on cars will help reduce acid rain. So will car pooling and public transportation because they reduce the number of trips and, therefore, the amount of fuel used.

Coal-burning power plants can help reduce air pollutants, too. Some coal has a lot of sulfur in it. When the coal is burned, the sulfur combines with moisture in the air to form sulfuric acid. Power plants can wash coal to remove some sulfur before the coal is burned. Burning cleaner coal produces less sulfur in the smoke. Power plants also can run the smoke through a scrubber. A **scrubber** lets the gases in the smoke dissolve in water, as they would in nature, until the smoke's pH increases to a safe level. **Figure 27-7** illustrates how an electrostatic separator removes particulates.

Using Math

Suppose a car travels 18 000 miles per year. How many gallons of gas must it burn in one year if it gets 20 miles per gallon? 30 miles per gallon? If a car emits 20 pounds of carbon dioxide for each gallon of gas burned, how much more carbon dioxide is emitted by a 20-mile-per-gallon car than a 30-mile-per-gallon car in one year? Convert your answer from pounds to kilograms.

D The smoke, now stripped of its pollutants, is released through the smokestack.

C The smoke with its positively charged particles of pollution moves past negatively charged plates. The positively charged particles are attracted by and held to the negatively charged plates.

B The plates give the particles of pollution a positive electric charge.

A A fan blows the polluted smoke past electrically charged plates.

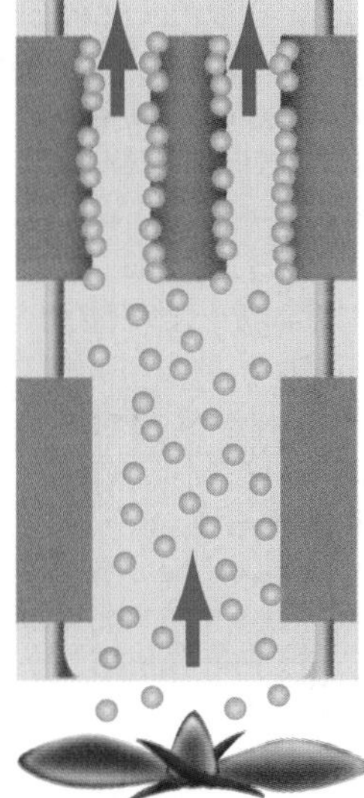

Figure 27-7
Smokestack scrubbers and electrostatic separators remove the pollutants from industrial smoke.

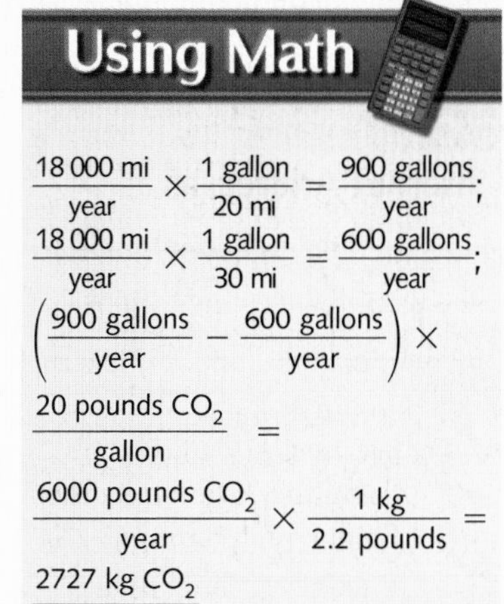

Using Math

$$\frac{18\,000\text{ mi}}{\text{year}} \times \frac{1\text{ gallon}}{20\text{ mi}} = \frac{900\text{ gallons}}{\text{year}};$$

$$\frac{18\,000\text{ mi}}{\text{year}} \times \frac{1\text{ gallon}}{30\text{ mi}} = \frac{600\text{ gallons}}{\text{year}};$$

$$\left(\frac{900\text{ gallons}}{\text{year}} - \frac{600\text{ gallons}}{\text{year}}\right) \times \frac{20\text{ pounds }CO_2}{\text{gallon}} =$$

$$\frac{6000\text{ pounds }CO_2}{\text{year}} \times \frac{1\text{ kg}}{2.2\text{ pounds}} = \frac{2727\text{ kg }CO_2}{\text{year}}$$

3 ASSESS

Check for Understanding

Discussion

Interpersonal Ask students who they think should be responsible for protecting Earth's resources for future generations.

Reteach

Interpersonal Have student partners review what they know about conserving resources, recycling, and air pollution. Have the partners make lists of at least 15 things they can do to help reduce air pollution. Have a class contest to see which student pair can list the most items. L2 COOP LEARN

Extension

For students who have mastered this section, use the **Reinforcement** and **Enrichment** masters.

Inclusion Strategies

Gifted Have students identify sources of local air pollution. Then, have them refer to maps showing the locations of the sources and local wind patterns. Have students predict where pollutants from the sources would be most concentrated. L3

CA Science Content Standards

Page 915: 9f

Figure 27-8 This geyser in Yellowstone Geyser Basin, Wyoming, indicates that a magma chamber, a potential source of geothermal power, exists in this area.

Visit the Glencoe Science Web Site at **www.glencoe.com/sec/science/ca** for more information about solar cars and solar cookers. How does a solar car work? How do solar cookers concentrate solar energy?

Alternative Sources of Power

Another thing humans could do to reduce air pollution is to switch to other power sources such as solar, wind, nuclear, and geothermal power. **Figure 27-8** shows a geyser that indicates a possible source of geothermal power. However, these alternative sources have disadvantages, too. And, even if everyone agreed to make changes, it would take years for some areas to change. This is because many people, especially in the midwestern states, depend on coal-burning power plants for home heating and electricity. Changing the kind of power used would be costly.

The 1990 Clean Air Act requires great reductions in auto exhaust and sulfur dioxide emissions. This will cost billions of dollars. Thousands of people have lost jobs in mining, factories, and in coal-burning power plants. However, new jobs are created as humans discover alternative sources of power.

Section Assessment

1. In what ways does air pollution affect the health of people?
2. How can changes in human activities reduce air pollution?
3. **Think Critically:** The Clean Air Act of 1970 required that coal-burning power plants use tall smokestacks so that air pollutants would be ejected high into the sky, where high-altitude winds would disperse them. Power plants in the midwestern states complied with that law, and people in eastern Canada began complaining about acid rain. Explain the connection.
4.  **Skill Builder**
Making and Using Graphs Make a bar graph of **Figure 27-2** that shows sources of smog on the *x*-axis and percent contribution of smog on the *y*-axis. How much more smog is created by cars than industries? If you need help, refer to Making and Using Graphs in the **Skill Handbook** on page 953.

In your Science Journal, create a crossword puzzle using at least 12 important terms found in this section.

interNET CONNECTION

Internet Addresses

For Internet tips, see Glencoe's **Using the Internet in the Science Classroom.**

4 CLOSE

Proficiency Prep

Use this quiz to check students' recall of section content.

1. **What is smog?** *polluted air around cities*
2. **What is a substance with a pH lower than 7?** *acid*

Section Assessment

1. Air pollution increases susceptibility to pneumonia, influenza, and asthma; it also causes burning eyes, dry throats, stress on hearts, and sometimes deaths.
2. by reducing fossil fuel consumption and emissions of other harmful chemicals
3. Think Critically Sulfur dioxide mixes with water vapor in the air to form sulfuric acid. Clouds drift northeast and drop acid rain onto Canada.

Puzzles will vary, but words must be spelled correctly. Students should provide Across and Down clues. P

4. **Skill Builder** Student bar graphs should show that cars contribute 60 percent of human-created smog; industry, 15 percent; power plants, 15 percent; heating buildings, 5 percent; and burning wastes, 5 percent. Cars contribute four times more smog than industries. The *y*-axis of students' bar graphs should be drawn to scale.

Assessment

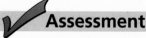

Oral Ask students why it often is better to display data in a bar graph than to simply list the data. Use **Performance Assessment in the Science Classroom,** p. 39.

Bee Probes

Honeybee colonies have been used for centuries to provide honey and pollinate flowers, fruit trees, and other crops. But now, scientists have found a new use for the busy insect. Honeybee colonies are used globally to indicate the presence of hazardous materials in the environment. Millions of established colonies provide constant monitoring. Because honeybees can live under many different environmental conditions, small colonies can be introduced almost anywhere hazardous substances are suspected.

Scientists at the University of Montana have designed electronic beehives (left) that provide useful information about the environment. Electronic hives record the behavior of every bee, including how often it flies, the pollen it gathers, and how the bees control the environment in the hives. Pollutants brought into the hives by the bees are detected using electronic instruments attached to the hives.

1. Bees leave the hives and pick up water, nectar, pollen, and airborne water particles.
2. When bees return to the hives, they fan their wings to control the air temperature in the hives.
3. Pollutants in the environment that were picked up by the bees are released into the air of the hives as the bees fan their wings.
4. Pollutants released by the bees are measured using chemical probes attached to the hives.
5. The chemical data are analyzed to determine what pollutants were brought into the hives from the local environment.

Career CONNECTION

Behavioral biologists usually have a bachelor's degree in biology or zoology. They enjoy observing animals for long periods of time. Write a letter to a local zoo or animal park. Ask biologists who work there to send you information about their careers and their education.

Think Critically

1. Why are bees useful animals for detecting pollution?
2. What are common causes of pollution in your area?
3. Research how a miner's canary was used to warn about hazardous substances. How is this similar to how honeybee colonies are being used?
4. Think about other environmentally sensitive organisms. In your Science Journal, write how you think other organisms could be used to protect the environment.

NATIONAL GEOGRAPHIC How it Works

Purpose

Students are introduced to how scientists use honeybees to collect and measure environmental pollution.

Content Background

Honeybees are social animals that live in hives. When they leave the hive, bees pick up materials in the air, including pollutants. When they return to the hives, they fan their wings to regulate the air temperature in the hives. This fanning releases pollutants picked up from the local environment, which can then be analyzed chemically to identify and quantify the pollutants.

VISUAL Learning

Have students look at the photograph of the beehive and guess how many bees can live in the hive. An average hive usually contains 40 000 to 50 000 bees.

Teaching Strategies

Have students research beehives and then design their own hive. Students should write a brief paragraph describing their design. Students should include where a pollutant-collecting device should be placed in the hive.

Think Critically

1. Bees are mobile and can be monitored.
2. Answers will vary and may include vehicles, individuals, and industries.
3. Canaries were brought into underground mines. When a canary died, miners were evacuated. Bees detect pollution in smaller quantities and provide an earlier warning system; the canary warned of more imminent danger.
4. Answers will vary.

Invite a behavioral biologist or zoologist to visit the class. Have students prepare questions for the visiting scientist about how organisms might indicate environmental problems.

CA Science Content Standards

Page 916: 9e

Activity 27•1 Design Your Own Experiment

Recognize the Problem

Purpose

Logical-Mathematical Design and carry out an experiment to collect particulate matter that is carried by air. L2 ELL COOP LEARN

Process Skills

designing an experiment, communicating, forming a hypothesis, observing and inferring, making and using tables, making and using graphs, classifying, interpreting data

Time

15 to 20 minutes to plan the experiment, 25 to 30 minutes to prepare gelatin lids, 40 minutes one week later to analyze the data and draw conclusions

Materials

Place lids with gelatin in a refrigerator to solidify before having students place them into the environment.

Alternate Materials

If gelatin is not available, petroleum jelly can be rubbed onto lids, petri dishes, or microscope slides.

Safety Precautions

Caution students to use thermal mitts and safety goggles while working with the hot plate and hot gelatin.

CA Science Content Standards

Page 918: 9a
Page 919: 9a, 9b, 9c, 9e, 9g

Design Your Own Experiment

Activity 27•1

What's in the air?

Have you ever gotten a particle of dust in your eye? Before it got there, it was one of the many pieces of particulate matter in the air. Whenever you dust off items in your household, you are cleaning up dust particles that settled out of the air. How often do you have to dust to keep your furniture clean? Just imagine how many pieces of particulate matter the air must hold.

Possible Materials

- Small box of plain gelatin
- Hot plate
- Pan or pot
- Water
- Marker
- Refrigerator
- Plastic lids (4)
- Microscope
  *Hand lens

**Alternate materials*

Recognize the Problem

What kinds of particulate matter are in your environment? Are some areas of your environment more polluted with particulates than others?

Form a Hypothesis

Based on your knowledge of your neighborhood, hypothesize what kinds of particulate matter you will find in your environment. Will all areas in your community contain the same types and amounts of particulate matter?

Goals

- **Design an experiment** to collect and analyze particulate matter in the air in your community.
- **Use** gelatin to collect particulate matter present in the air.
- **Observe** and describe the particulate matter you collect.

Safety Precautions

Wear a thermal mitt, safety goggles, and an apron while working with a hot plate and while pouring the gelatin from the pan or pot into the lids. Don't eat anything in the lab.

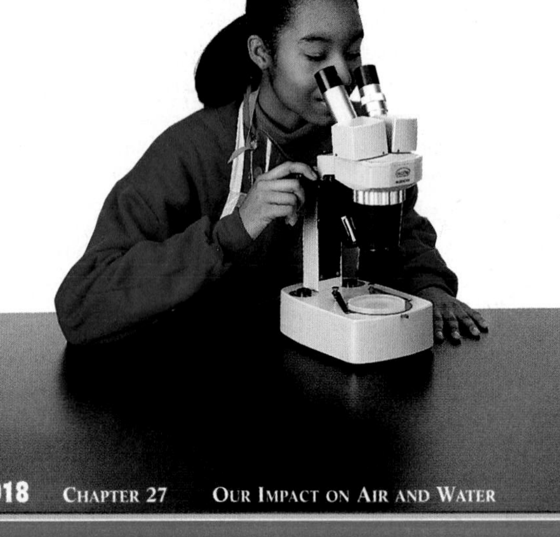

Form A Hypothesis

Possible Hypotheses

Students might hypothesize that they will find soot, dust particles, and pieces of plants and insects. They may will think that different areas of the community will contain different types and amounts of particulate matter.

Test Your Hypothesis

Possible Procedures

Empty a box of plain gelatin into a pot. Stir in the appropriate amount of water. Heat the mixture on a hot plate. Pour the mixture onto plastic lids. Place the lids into a refrigerator overnight. The next day, place the lids at various outside locations. Check the lids daily and record observations in the data table. At the end of one week, examine the lids with a stereomicroscope.

Test Your Hypothesis

Plan

1. As a group, agree upon and **write** out your hypothesis.
2. As a group, **list** the steps you need to take to test your hypothesis. Be specific, describing exactly what you will do at each step.
3. **List** your materials.
4. **Design** a data table in your Science Journal so that it is ready to use as your group collects data.
5. **Mix** the gelatin according to the directions on the box. Carefully pour a thin layer of gelatin into each lid. Use this to collect air particulate matter.
6. **Decide** where you will place each plastic lid in order to collect particulate matter in the air.
7. **Read** over your entire experiment to make sure that all steps are in a logical order.
8. **Identify** any constants, variables, and controls of the experiment.

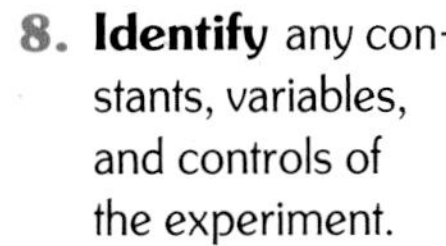

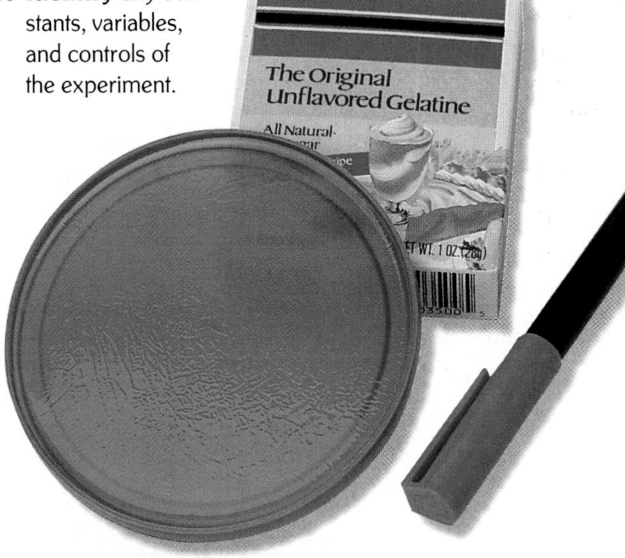

Do

1. Make sure your teacher approves your plan before you proceed.
2. Carry out the experiment as planned.
3. While the experiment is going on, write down any observations that you make and complete the data table in your Science Journal.

Analyze Your Data

1. **Describe** the types of materials you collected in each lid.
2. **Graph** your results using a bar graph. Place the number of particulates on the *y*-axis and the test-site location on the *x*-axis.

Draw Conclusions

1. Which test-site location yielded the most particulates? **Infer** why this is so.
2. Which of the particulates can you relate directly to the activities of humans?

Teaching Strategies

Most of the materials collected will be dust and soot. Have students study maps that show the locations of nearby industries and weather maps that show local wind patterns. See if they can establish a correlation.

Troubleshooting The lids with gelatin can be prepared in advance to save time.

Expected Outcome

Students will observe that particulate matter has stuck to the gelatin.

Error Analysis

Have students compare their results and their hypotheses and explain why any differences occurred.

Analyze Your Data

1. Materials will vary, but dust particles, soot, paint chips, plant seeds, pieces of leaves and twigs, and small insects might be found.
2. Graphs will vary.

Draw Conclusions

1. Some lids were placed closer to the source of the material (the factory, the tree, etc.). Another factor is the direction of the wind.
2. The soot, some of the dust, and paint chips are probably created by human activities.

Assessment

Performance Have students classify the various types of particulate matter that they collected. Use **Performance Assessment in the Science Classroom,** p. 49.

Sample Data Table

Lid number	Lid location	Number of particles	Types of particles
1	next to tree	15	plant fragments, insects
2	school parking lot	14	soot, dust
3	near factory	18	mostly soot
4	grassy field	20	dust, insects plant fragments

GO Further

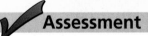

Ask students: **Do you think any of the materials you collected might be harmful to humans? Explain your answers.** *Answers will vary according to the types of materials that are collected. Soot, dust, and pollen cause respiratory problems.* **How does your body filter solid particles from the air you breathe?** *The hairs and mucus in the nose filter particulate matter.*

SECTION 27•2

Prepare

Content Background

Refer to **Causes and Effects of Water Pollution, Reducing Water Pollution, Bioremediation,** and **How can you help?** on p. 908F.

Preplanning

Refer to the **Chapter Organizer** on pp. 908A–B.

1 Motivate

Bellringer

Before presenting the lesson, display **Section Focus Transparency 79** on the overhead projector. Use the accompanying **Focus Activity** worksheet. L2 ELL

Section 17-1

SECTION FOCUS TRANSPARENCY

SMOGGY, SMOGGY VIEW

This photograph shows what might be a beautiful view—but wait. Something is wrong with this view. What's going on here? Take a close look and see if you can tell.

1. What problem can you see in this photograph?
2. What natural things do you think are causing the problem?
3. What human activities do you think are causing the problem?

46

Tying to Previous Knowledge

Ask students if they have been warned not to swim at a beach or fish in a lake or river because of polluted water.

27•2 Water Pollution

What You'll Learn

- Types of water pollutants and their sources
- Ways that international agreements and U.S. laws are designed to reduce water pollution
- Ways that you can help reduce water pollution

Vocabulary

Safe Drinking Water Act
Clean Water Act

Why It's Important

- Many human activities cause water pollution. There are ways you can help reduce the problem.

Causes and Effects of Water Pollution

Suppose you were hiking along a stream or lake and became thirsty. Do you think it would be safe to drink the water? In most cases, it wouldn't. Many streams and lakes in the United States are polluted, such as the one shown in **Figure 27-9.** Even streams that look clear and sparkling may not be safe for drinking.

Pollutants from humans or other organisms can get into the oceans, streams, groundwater, and lakes. Sometimes pollutants travel from one source of water to another, such as when a contaminated stream flows into a lake. There is strong reason to believe that some of these pollutants cause birth defects and health problems such as cancer, dysentery, and liver damage in humans and other animals.

Pollution Sources

How do you think pollutants get into the water? Bacteria and viruses get into the water because some cities illegally dump untreated sewage directly into the water supply. Underground septic tanks can leak, too. Radioactive materials can get into the water from leaks at nuclear power plants and radioactive waste disposal sites.

Pesticides, herbicides, and fertilizers from farms and lawns are picked up by rainwater and carried into streams. Some people dump motor oil into sewers after

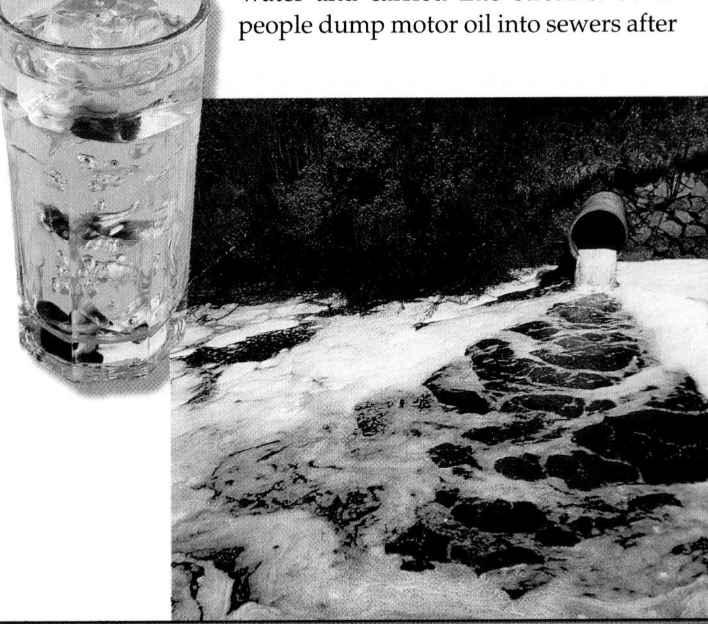

Figure 27-9 Your drinking water comes from nearby streams, lakes, or groundwater. Before we can use water for daily activities, we must purify it. After we use it, we must clean it again before we return it to the environment. **What are some sources of water pollution?**

Resource Manager

The following **Teacher Classroom Resources** can be used with Section 27-2:

 **Reproducible Masters**

Activity Worksheets, pp. 153–154, 156 L2

Critical Thinking/Problem Solving, p. 27 L2

Enrichment, p. 79 L3

Home Involvement, p. 28 L2

Reinforcement, p. 79 L2

Study Guide, pp. 106–108 L1 ELL

Figure 27-10 The water hyacinth plant removes many pollutants from water. Water hyacinths can be used at wastewater-treatment facilities (shown at left) to clean water before it flows back into streams and aquifers.

they've changed the oil in their cars. Water running through mines also carries pollutants to streams and underground aquifers. Some factories illegally dump industrial chemicals directly into water. Waste from landfills and hazardous waste facilities leaks into the surrounding soil and groundwater.

Most water pollution is caused by legal, everyday activities. If left untreated, water would remain polluted after we flush our toilets, wash our hands, brush our teeth, and water our lawns. Nitrogen and phosphorus from household detergents, soaps, and other cleaning agents must be removed before water is returned to a source, such as a stream or reservoir. Water also is polluted when oil and gasoline run off of pavement, down storm sewers, and into streams. These pollutants must be removed at water-treatment facilities like those in **Figures 27-10** and **27-11.**

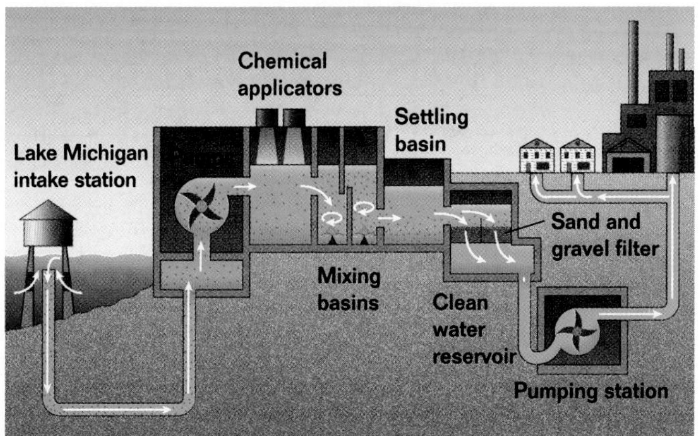

Figure 27-11 This water-purification plant in Chicago provides drinking water for millions of people. Water taken from Lake Michigan is pumped into a tank where alum, chlorine, lime, and other compounds are added to kill microorganisms. The water is thoroughly mixed, and the large particles of matter settle out. Some smaller particles are filtered by sand and gravel. Clean water is then pumped to consumers.

2 Teach

Enrichment

Linguistic Have students find out the source of their local water supply. Have them investigate who determines whether or not the supply is pure, how often the supply is tested, and how the wastewater is treated. P

Teacher FYI

The Great Lakes contain 95 percent of the fresh surface water in the United States and 20 percent of the world's fresh surface water.

Discussion

What causes most water pollution? *everyday activities like flushing toilets, washing hands, brushing teeth, watering lawns, and water running off of pavement* **How can runoff from a coal mine pollute groundwater with sulfuric acid?** *The sulfur in the coal mixes with the water, producing sulfuric acid. This acidic water travels through pores in the soil and into the groundwater.*

Flex Your Brain

Use the Flex Your Brain activity to have students explore WATER POLLUTION.

Caption Answer

Figure 27-9 *Answers may include pesticides, herbicides, mine runoff, industrial chemicals, and raw sewage.*

Guided Reading Strategy

Jigsaw In this collaborative learning technique, individuals become experts on a portion of a text and share their expertise with a small group, called their home group. Everyone shares responsibility for learning the assigned reading. Assign each person in each home group an expert number (1 through 5, for example). Have students gather into the expert groups that correspond to the number they were assigned. Have them read, discuss, and master chapter concepts and determine how best to teach them to their home groups. Have students return to their home groups and share the content they learned in their expert groups. Have students use the Jigsaw strategy with the student text for this section.

CA Science Content Standards

Page 920: 5a
Page 921: 5a

Problem Solving

More than half of the nation's 2000 watersheds are facing water-quality problems due to nonpoint source pollution. You can find out about the overall health of your watershed by accessing the EPA's Surf Your Watershed Web Site.

Think Critically

The likely source is sewage from city 3. Not enough information is given to tell if the pollution is coming from a point source like untreated wastes piped into the river or from a nonpoint source like runoff from an overflowing septic tank.

Correcting Misconceptions

Many students think that if a particular pollutant is no longer added to a lake, it will eventually disappear. This is not true with some pollutants. A group of chemicals called polychlorinated biphenyls (PCBs) were banned in the United States in 1979. However, they remain in high concentrations at the bottom of many lakes, where they have become trapped in the mud and have been passed through food chains.

Reducing Water Pollution

Several countries have worked together to reduce water pollution. Let's look at one example. Lake Erie is on the border between the United States and Canada. In the 1960s, Lake Erie was so polluted by phosphorus from sewage, soaps, and fertilizers that it was turning into a green, soupy mess. Large areas of the lake bottom no longer had oxygen and, therefore, no life.

International Cooperation

In the 1970s, the United States and Canada made two water quality agreements. The two countries spent $15 billion to stop the sewage problem. Today, the green slime is gone and the fish are back. However, more than 300 human-made chemicals can still be found in Lake Erie, and some of them are hazardous. The United States and Canada are studying ways to get them out of the lake.

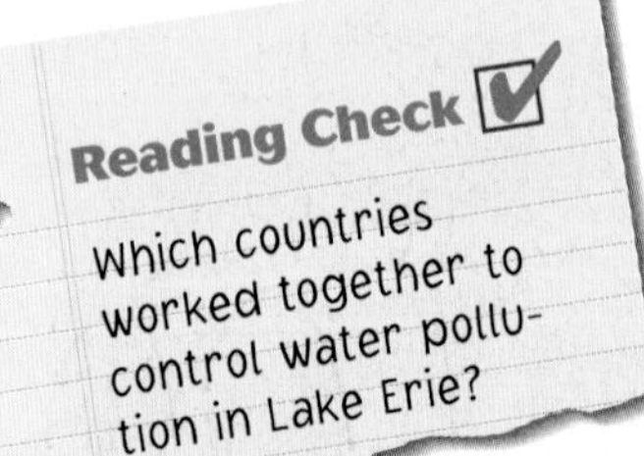

Reading Check
Which countries worked together to control water pollution in Lake Erie?

Problem Solving

Interpreting Pollution Sources

Water pollution comes in a variety of forms: heavy metals like lead and manganese from mines, bacteria from septic tanks, herbicides and pesticides from agriculture, thermal pollution from factories, acids from power plants and automobiles, sediments from construction sites, and so on.

In analyzing a possible source of water pollution in a river, chemists look for two types: point source and nonpoint source. Point sources occur where factories and cities pipe their untreated wastes directly into lakes and rivers. Nonpoint sources are runoff from farms, cities, mines, and construction sites. Analyze the map below and the chart of pollution test results to answer the Think Critically questions below.

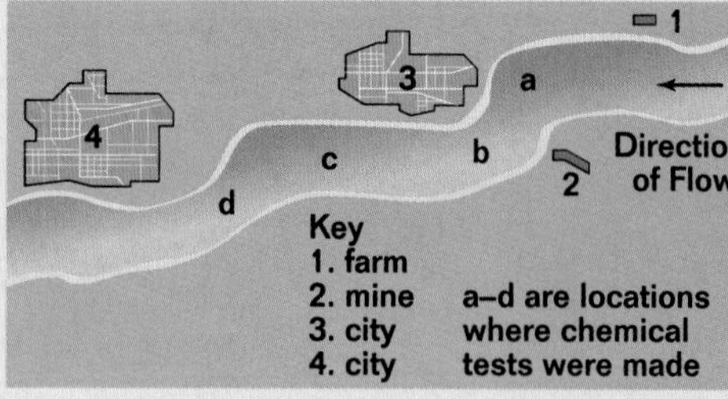

a–d are locations where chemical tests were made

Think Critically: What is the likely source of the nitrates and bacteria found at sites c and d that weren't present at sites a and b? Is there enough information to tell if this is a case of point-source or nonpoint-source pollution? Explain.

Pollution Test Results

Test Site	Chemicals Present in Water
a	nitrates commonly found in fertilizers
b	lead and nitrates commonly found in fertilizers
c	nitrates and bacteria commonly found in sewage, lead, nitrates commonly found in fertilizers
d	nitrates and bacteria commonly found in sewage, lead, nitrates commonly found in fertilizers

Across the Curriculum

Civics Have students find out how a bill becomes a law in Congress. Have them outline the steps involved in their Science Journals, and prepare a poster that illustrates the process. L2 P

Report on Planet Earth Have each student write a story from the point of view of someone who comes to Earth from another planet to find smog, polluted water, and litter. Students also could write from the point of view of someone who lived 100 years ago but who is seeing today's world. L2

The U.S. Congress also has reduced water pollution by passing several laws, including the 1996 Safe Drinking Water Act amendments and the 1987 Clean Water Act.

The 1996 **Safe Drinking Water Act** amendments aim to strengthen health standards for drinking water and to protect rivers, lakes, and streams that are sources of drinking water. These amendments also provide the public with a right to know about contaminants that could be in their tap water.

Figure 27-12 Sewage, industrial wastes, and solid wastes pollute many rivers and lakes. However, these sources of pollution can be controlled and the water made safe for recreational purposes. **How does the 1987 Clean Water Act encourage communities to clean up their water?**

Clean Water Act

The 1987 **Clean Water Act** gives money to states for building sewage and wastewater-treatment facilities. The money is also for controlling runoff from streets, mines, and farms. Runoff caused up to half of the water pollution in the United States before 1987. This act also requires states to develop quality standards for all their streams.

The U.S. Environmental Protection Agency (EPA) makes sure that cities comply with both the Safe Drinking Water Act and the Clean Water Act. Most cities and states are working hard to clean up their water. Look at **Figure 27-12.** Many streams that once were heavily polluted by sewage and industrial wastes are now safe for recreation.

However, much remains to be done. For example, the EPA recently discovered that 30 percent of the nation's rivers, 42 percent of its lakes, and 32 percent of its estuaries are still polluted from farm runoff and municipal sewage overflows from cities. An estimated 40 percent of the country's freshwater supply is still not usable because of pollution. Since 1972, the U.S. government has spent more than 260 billion dollars on sewage system improvements. However, more than 1000 cities still have substandard water-treatment facilities.

LIFE SCIENCE INTEGRATION

Amphibian Decline
All over the world, the amphibian population is declining. Scientists do not know for sure what is causing the decline, but some suspect it is caused by pollution. What are amphibians? What types of pollution might affect amphibians?

Caption Answer

Figure 27-12 *The act gives money to states for building sewage and wastewater-treatment facilities, and for controlling runoff.*

LIFE SCIENCE INTEGRATION

Amphibians are animals that usually spend their juvenile life in water and their adult life on land or water. Examples include toads, frogs, and salamanders. They are susceptible to water pollution, soil pollution, and air pollution.

GLENCOE TECHNOLOGY

 **CD-ROM**

Glencoe Science Voyages Interactive CD-ROM

Explorations

Have students do the interactive exploration *How can we save water?*

 **Videodisc**

Glencoe Science Voyages Interactive Videodisc—Earth

Side 2, Lesson 6 *Pollution Detectives*

14858

Refer to Videodisc Teacher Guide for additional bar codes.

Multiple Learning Styles

Linguistic Some people in Congress have proposed that the federal standards in the Clean Water Act of 1987 be made voluntary instead of mandatory because they create financial strain on some communities. Ask students how they feel about this proposal. Encourage students to write to their congressional representatives to express their personal views on this subject. L2

CA Science Content Standards

Page 923: 9f

LIFE SCIENCE INTEGRATION

Most bioremediation techniques are designed to degrade petroleum compounds in oxygenated environments, but other organic contaminants are degraded more easily in an anaerobic environment. Much research presently is being done to develop methods to degrade contaminants in the absence of oxygen.

Using an Analogy

Relate adding nitrogen and phosphorus to water to improve bacterial growth to fertilizing grass and trees to promote growth. All organisms need nutrients for optimal growth.

VISUAL Learning

Figure 27-13 The groundwater is oxygenated by forcing air into the injection well with a compressor or by injecting hydrogen peroxide into the aquifer.

3 Assess

Check for Understanding Activity

Visual-Spatial Have students search newspapers and magazines for articles about water pollution. Have students relate the articles they find to section content. L2

Bioremediation

LIFE SCIENCE INTEGRATION

Bioremediation (*bio* = "life"; *remediation* = "the act of remedying, or fixing a problem") uses organisms to consume or make a hazardous substance harmless. Examples of resources cleaned by bioremediation include soil, sediment, groundwater, and surface water. Some hazardous substances that are removed by bioremediation include oil, gasoline, and other organic pollutants.

Microorganisms

Did you know that bacteria are organisms that are helpful in cleaning up the environment? Although these organisms are so small you would need a microscope to see them, they often are able to consume or make some toxic wastes harmless. Bacteria already may be present in a contaminated site or may be brought in from the outside. For these microorganisms to be successful, they must be kept healthy enough to consume waste in a reasonable amount of time.

One way that water is treated to remove pollutants like oil and gasoline is to inject it with oxygen. The oxygen creates a healthy environment for some types of bacteria. Nutrients such as nitrogen and phosphorus also are necessary for the bacteria. These nutrients may be in the contaminated site already or pumped in if the site does not contain enough of them. Contaminated groundwater is first pumped to the surface using extraction wells, then pretreated with concentrated bacteria to remove some of the waste. The groundwater is then injected back underground and oxygenated. The oxygen

Figure 27-13 Bioremediation can help clean water right at the location of a contaminated site.

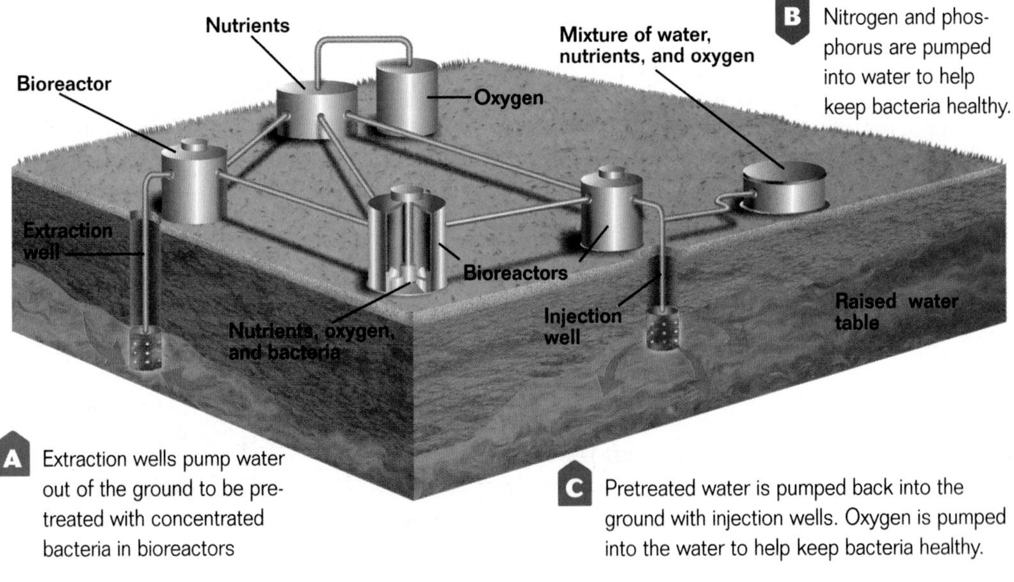

B Nitrogen and phosphorus are pumped into water to help keep bacteria healthy.

A Extraction wells pump water out of the ground to be pretreated with concentrated bacteria in bioreactors

C Pretreated water is pumped back into the ground with injection wells. Oxygen is pumped into the water to help keep bacteria healthy.

Reteach

Interpersonal Have student pairs make posters depicting sources of and solutions to various kinds of water pollution. Hang the posters throughout the school building. L1 ELL COOP LEARN P

Content Background

Bioventing and biofiltration are two types of bioremediation being researched. In bioventing, air is forced through soil mixed with fungus. In biofiltration, bacteria or fungi are fixed to tiny particles of material. Then, contaminated air is allowed to flow through the material.

CA Science Content Standards

Page 924: 5a, 5b
Page 925: 9a

stimulates bacteria to consume or break down the remaining waste. **Figure 27-13** shows the basic components of *in situ* bioremediation, which means that the decontamination can take place right at the field site.

Observing Water Hardness

Procedure

1. When minerals such as calcium carbonate, magnesium carbonate, or sulfates are dissolved in water, the water is said to be *hard*. This is a type of natural pollution that occurs in some areas.
2. Use small containers such as baby food jars to collect samples of water from the tap, a nearby pond or well, and a local stream.
3. Add one drop of liquid soap to each jar.
4. Cap each container tightly and shake it rapidly.
5. Observe how many soapsuds are produced in each container.

Analysis

1. Which of your water samples had the hardest water? (Hint: The container with the most suds contains the softest water.)
2. Infer what problems might be caused by having a hard water supply in your home or community.

How can you help?

As you have discovered in this chapter, humans often are the cause of our environmental problems. But, we also are the solution. What can you do to help?

Dispose of Wastes Safely

When you dispose of household chemicals such as paint and motor oil, don't pour them down the drain or onto the ground. Also, don't put them out to be picked up with your other trash.

Hazardous wastes poured directly onto the ground move through the soil and eventually reach the groundwater below. When you pour them down the drain, they flow through the sewer, through the wastewater-treatment plant, and into wherever the wastewater is drained, usually a stream. This is how rivers become polluted. If you put hazardous wastes out with the trash, they end up in landfills, where they may leak out.

What should you do with these wastes? First, read the label on the container for instructions on disposal. Don't throw the container into the trash if the label specifies a different method of disposal. Recycle if you can. Many cities have recycling facilities for metal, glass, and plastic containers. Store chemical wastes so that they can't leak. If you live in a city, call the sewage office, water office, or garbage disposal service and ask them how to safely dispose of these wastes in your area.

We all must do our part to help conserve water and reduce water pollution. Consider some changes you can make in your life that will make a difference.

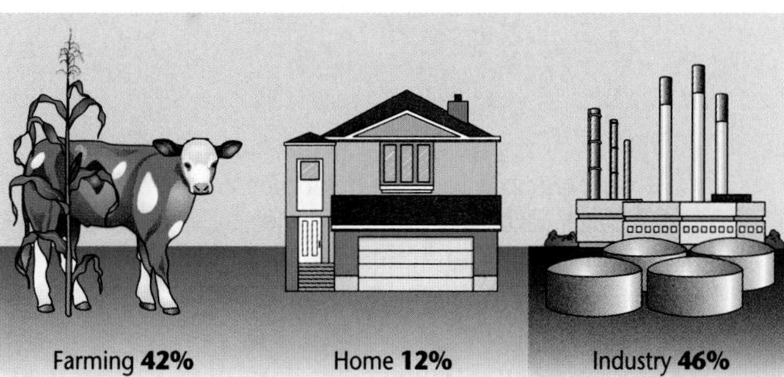

Figure 27-14 The industries that produce the products you use each day consume nearly half of the fresh water used in the United States.

Try at Home **MiniLab**

For additional help doing this activity at home, see the corresponding pages in the **Home Involvement** booklet.

Purpose

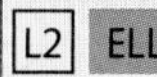
Kinesthetic Students will determine whether local water supplies have hard water. L2 ELL

Materials

small containers with caps, liquid soap, water samples, glass marking pen

Teaching Strategies

Tell students that household water softeners make water soft by replacing magnesium and calcium in the water with sodium.

Troubleshooting

- The temperature of each sample, the amount of each sample, the amount of liquid soap added, and the amount and force of the shaking all must be constant.
- Remind students to label the contents of each container.

Analysis

1. The hardest water will be the sample producing the least amount of suds when the sample and liquid soap are combined and shaken.
2. Minerals build up inside teakettles, dishwashing machines, hot-water tanks, hot-water heating systems, and industrial boilers, blocking water passages.

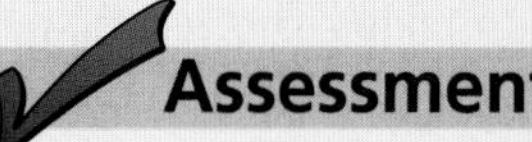

Assessment

Performance Have students evaporate the water from their samples and observe and draw the minerals that are left behind. Use **Performance Assessment in the Science Classroom,** p. 25.

Extension

For students who have mastered this section, use the **Reinforcement** and **Enrichment** masters.

4 Close

Proficiency Prep

Use this quiz to check students' recall of section content.

1. **What 1987 legislation gives money to states for building sewage and wastewater-treatment facilities?** *Clean Water Act*
2. **What government agency makes sure that cities comply with the Safe Drinking Water Act and the Clean Water Act?** *Environmental Protection Agency*

Section Assessment

1. properly dispose of hazardous wastes or recycle them, conserve energy, and conserve water
2. Point-source pollution occurs when untreated wastes are piped directly into lakes and rivers. Nonpoint sources are runoff from farms, cities, mines, and construction sites.
3. oil, gasoline, and other organic pollutants
4. **Think Critically** They include bacteria and viruses from the cattle feces, pesticides and herbicides from the sugarcane fields, industrial wastes, and wastes from the burning of fossil fuels.

Using Computers

The list of ways might include taking shorter showers, turning off the water when brushing teeth, using the dishwasher and washing machines only for full loads, putting a bottle of water in the toilet tank, watering the lawn only when necessary, fixing leaky faucets, recycling, and conserving energy.

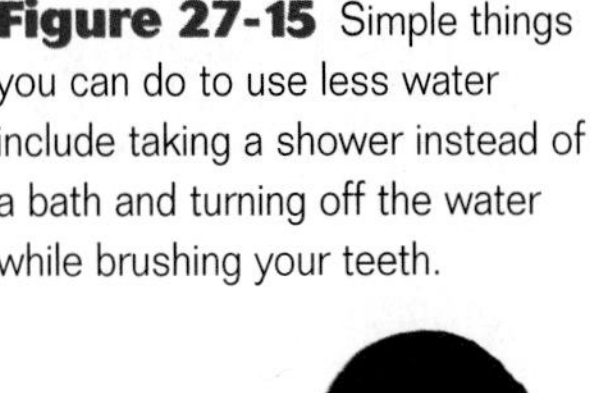

Figure 27-15 Simple things you can do to use less water include taking a shower instead of a bath and turning off the water while brushing your teeth.

Conserve Energy and Water

Another way you can reduce water pollution is to conserve energy. Decreasing the use of fuels reduces the amount of acid rain that will fall into forests and streams. Decreasing your power usage will help reduce the input of hazardous materials into the environment.

Another way you can help is to conserve water. Look at **Figure 27-14.** How much water do you use every day? You use water every time you flush a toilet, take a bath, clean your clothes, wash dishes, wash a car, or use a hose or lawn sprinkler. Typical U.S. citizens, like the one shown in **Figure 27-15,** use from 380 L to 950 L of water every day.

All of this water must be purified before it reaches your home. It takes a lot of energy to treat water and pump it to your home. Remember, when you use energy, you add to the pollution problem.

Section Assessment

1. What are three things you can do to help reduce water pollution?
2. What is the difference between point-source and nonpoint-source pollution?
3. What hazardous substances can be removed from water using bioremediation?
4. **Think Critically:** Southern Florida is home to millions of people, dairy farms, and sugarcane fields. It is also the location of Everglades National Park—a shallow river system with highly polluted waters. What kinds of pollutants do you think are in the Everglades? How do you think they got there?
5. **Skill Builder**
   Interpreting Data Have you ever wondered how scientists determine the sources of water pollution in a lake or a river? Do the **Chapter 27 Skill Activity** on page 988 to see an example of how this is done.

Using Computers

Word Processing Design a pamphlet to inform people how they can reduce the amount of water they use. Be creative and include graphics in your pamphlet. Use word-processing utilities to check your spelling and grammar. If you need help, refer to page 968.

Assessment

Oral Assess students' abilities to interpret data by having them explain how chemical analysis of groundwater from wells could be used to locate sources of groundwater pollution. Use **Performance Assessment in the Science Classroom,** p. 71.

Water Use

Materials

- Home water meter

How much water goes down the drain at your house? Did you know that up to 75 percent of the water used in homes is used in the bathroom? Flushing the toilet accounts for 50 percent of that water. The rest is for bathing, showering, washing hands, and brushing teeth. By learning to read a water meter, you can find out how much water your family uses.

What You'll Investigate

How much water does your family use?

Goals

- **Calculate** your family's water usage.
- **Infer** how your family can conserve water.

Background

There are several different types of water meters. Meter A has six dials. As water moves through the meter, the pointers on the dials rotate. To read a meter like A, find the dial in A with the lowest denomination, which in this case is 10. Record the last number that the pointer on that dial has passed. Continue this process for each dial in the meter. Meter A therefore shows 28 853 gallons. Meter B is read like a digital watch. It indicates 1959.9 cubic feet. Meter C is similar to meter B but indicates water use in cubic meters. If you have a meter that is different from these, contact your area's water department for help on reading your meter.

A

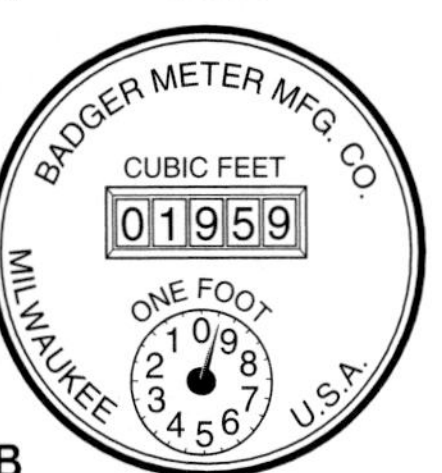

B

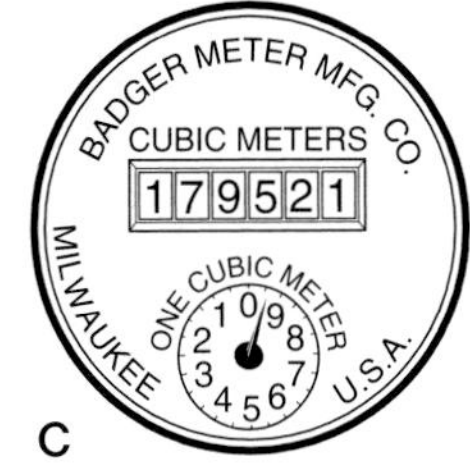

C

Procedure

1. **Design** a data table and **record** your home water meter reading at the same time of the day for eight days.
2. **Subtract** the previous day's reading to determine the amount of water used each day.
3. **Record** how much water is used in your home each day. Also, record the activities in your home that use water each day.
4. **Plot your data** on a graph like the one shown below. Label the vertical axis with the units used by your meter.

Conclude and Apply

1. **Calculate** the average amount of water each person in your family used during the week by dividing the total amount of water used by the number of persons.
2. **Infer** how the time of year might affect the rate at which your family uses water.
3. What are some things your family could do to conserve water?

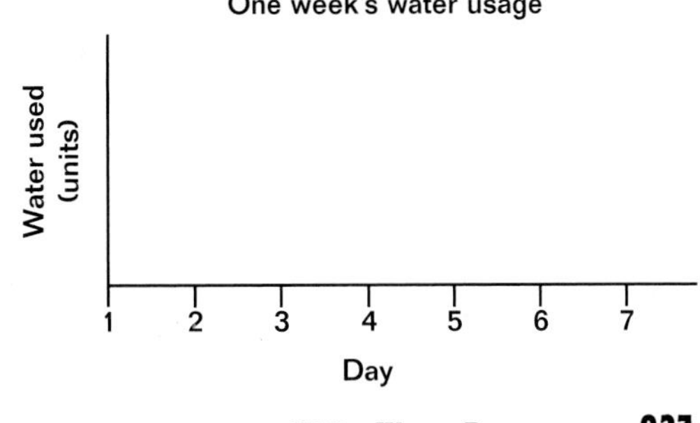

Activity 27•2

Purpose

Intrapersonal Students will calculate home water usage. L2 ELL

Process Skills

using numbers, making and using tables, making and using graphs, observing and inferring, interpreting data, comparing and contrasting

Time

ten minutes each day for eight days at home to do steps 1–3, 30 minutes for graphing and answering questions in class on the ninth day

Teaching Strategies

- If your community uses only water from wells, you may supply hypothetical meter readings for the eight days so students can complete the activity.
- After students have collected their data, make a list on the chalkboard or overhead projector showing the range of water use from highest to lowest for the class. This should be done without identifying which family is which. This will allow students to see how the rate of water usage in their home compares with the usage by other families.

Troubleshooting Be sure students understand the differences among the water meters and can identify which type is used in their homes. Make sure students understand the units in which water useage is measured.

Assessment

Performance To further assess students' understanding of water usage, have them take water-meter readings for eight more days, this time while the family conserves water. Have students compare their results with the results when water was not being conserved. Use **Performance Assessment in the Science Classroom,** p. 25.

Answers to Questions

1. Answers will vary.
2. It might be affected because lawn watering and car washing are seasonal activities.
3. Answers may include fixing leaky faucets, taking shorter showers, and not letting water run while brushing teeth.

CA Science Content Standards

Page 926: 5b
Page 927: 9a, 9e, 9f

Chapter 27 Reviewing Main Ideas

Reviewing Main Ideas can be used to preview, review, reteach, and condense chapter content.

Preview

Linguistic Have students try to answer the questions in their Science Journals. Use student answers as a source for discussion throughout the chapter.

Review

Interpersonal Have students answer the questions on separate pieces of paper and compare their answers with those of other students in the class.

Reteach

Visual-Spatial Have students look at the illustrations on these pages. Ask them to describe details that support the main ideas of the chapter found in the statement for each illustration.

00:00 OUT OF TIME?

Auditory-Musical If time does not permit teaching the entire chapter, use the information on these pages along with the chapter Audiocassettes to present the material in a condensed format.

Chapter 27 Reviewing Main Ideas

For a **preview** of this chapter, study this Reviewing Main Ideas before you read the chapter. After you have studied this chapter, you can use the Reviewing Main Ideas to **review** the chapter.

The Glencoe MindJogger, Audiocassettes, and CD-ROM provide additional opportunities for review.

Section

27-1 CAUSES OF AIR POLLUTION

Many human activities impact our air and water. **Smog, acid rain,** and water pollution are consequences of our activities. When fossil fuels are burned, polluting chemicals are added to the air. Construction dust and smoke from burning fuels pollute the air. Nature also contributes to air pollution. Air pollutants don't have boundaries. They float between states and countries. National and international cooperation is necessary to reduce the problem. The purpose of the **Clean Air Act** is to reduce problem chemicals in the air. ***Which national agency has the job ofmonitoring progress toward the goals of the Clean Air Act?***

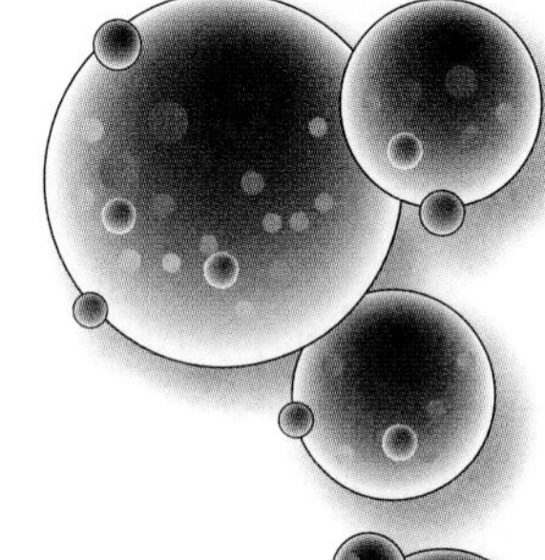

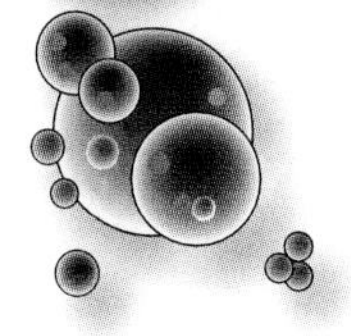

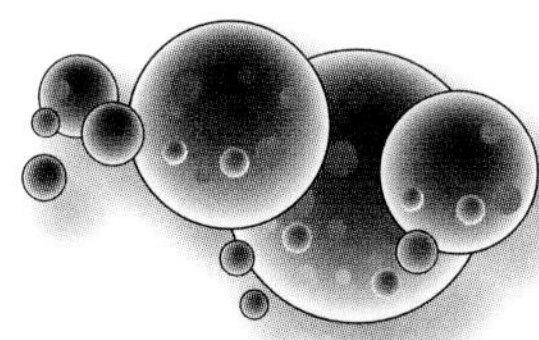

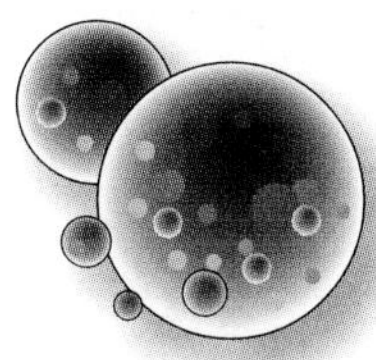

Cultural Diversity

Polluted Water The Vistula River, the largest river in Poland, is so polluted that its waters cannot even be used by industries; it would corrode the machinery. Much of its pollution is blamed on thousands of outdated European factories that pump pollutants into the air and water. Cost estimates for cleaning up the river have ranged from $100 million to $15 billion. Sweden has contributed $60 million to help clean it up because this river contributes about 40 percent of the total nitrogen runoff into the Baltic Sea. The United States also has contributed money for environmental aid to Poland. **Why must all countries work together to control pollution?** *Pollution doesn't stop at political boundaries.*

Reading Check

Explain how the topics of air and water pollution might be approached differently in a health textbook than in a science book.

Section 27-2 WATER POLLUTION

Water pollution has many sources. A few of these sources include underground septic tanks that leak; runoff of pesticides, herbicides, and fertilizers from lawns and farms; and even water flushed down toilets. National and international cooperation is necessary if water pollution is to be reduced. In the United States, the **Safe Drinking Water Act** and the **Clean Water Act** set up standards for sewage and wastewater-treatment facilities and for runoff from roadways and farms. Most waterways are cleaner now than before these acts were voted on by Congress. But, many of the nation's streams, rivers, and lakes are still polluted. ***How can oil dripping from a car eventually pollute a stream?***

Career CONNECTION

Craig Cox, Hydrogeologist

As a hydrogeologist, Craig Cox works with companies to help prevent groundwater contamination. Unused chemicals can soak into the ground, just like water can, contaminating the water table. Craig examines how industries dispose of dangerous materials to ensure they don't drain into the water table, contaminating drinking water. ***What would a hydrogeologist look for to determine the danger of groundwater being contaminated by a chemical spill?***

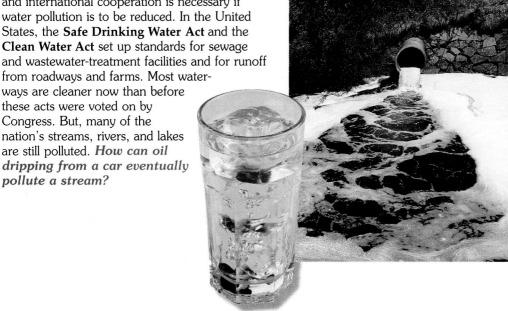

Answers to Questions

Section 27-1

Causes of Air Pollution the Environmental Protection Agency

Section 27-2

Water Pollution Oil can drip into the soil and be carried in the groundwater to a stream, or it can drip onto pavement and eventually wash into a storm sewer that leads to a stream.

GLENCOE TECHNOLOGY

CD-ROM

Glencoe Science Voyages Interactive CD-ROM

Chapter Summaries and Quizzes

Have students read the Chapter Summary then take the Chapter Quiz to determine whether they have mastered chapter content.

Career CONNECTION

how close the spill is to an aquifer; how easily and how rapidly dangerous chemicals could migrate into an aquifer

Assessment

Portfolio Encourage students to place in their portfolios one or two items of what they consider to be their best work. Examples include:

- Across the Curriculum, pp. 913, 922
- Science Journal, p. 916
- Enrichment, p. 921
- Reteach, p. 924 P

Performance Additional performance assessments may be found in **Performance Assessment** and **Science Integration Activities.** Performance Task Assessment Lists and rubrics for evaluating these activities can be found in Glencoe's **Performance Assessment in the Science Classroom.**

Using Vocabulary

1. g
2. b
3. d
4. i
5. a

interNET CONNECTION To reinforce chapter vocabulary, use the **Study Guide for Content Mastery** booklet. Also available are activities for **Glencoe Science Voyages** on the Glencoe Science Web Site. **www.glencoe.com/sec/science/ca**

Checking Concepts

6. D	**11.** B
7. B	**12.** A
8. B	**13.** C
9. B	**14.** C
10. B	**15.** A

Thinking Critically

16. Cities could broadcast health alerts that would take effect when the amount of pollutants in the air surpasses a certain level. At these times, factories that contribute to the pollution could be closed and people with respiratory problems would be advised to stay indoors.

17. Most industries provide products that improve the quality of life. However, many by-products of industrial processes pollute Earth's air, water, and soil.

18. Plants such as water hyacinths remove many pollutants from water.

Chapter 27 Assessment

Using Vocabulary

a. acid
b. acid rain
c. base
d. Clean Air Act
e. Clean Water Act
f. pH scale
g. photochemical smog
h. Safe Drinking Water Act
i. scrubber
j. sulfurous smog

Using the list above, replace the underlined words with the correct Vocabulary words.

1. Smog that forms with the aid of light contains ozone near Earth's surface.
2. Acidic rain, snow, sleet, or hail is created when sulfur dioxide combines with moisture in the air.
3. A law passed to protect air in the United States regulates car manufacturers.
4. A device that lowers sulfur emissions from coal-burning power plants increases the pH of smoke.
5. A substance with a low pH number can be toxic to organisms.

Checking Concepts

Choose the word or phrase that best answers the question.

6. What causes more smog pollution than any other source?
   A) power plants
   B) burning wastes
   C) industries
   D) cars
7. What forms when chemicals react with sunlight?
   A) pH
   B) photochemical smog
   C) sulfurous smog
   D) acid rain
8. What are substances with a low pH known as?
   A) neutral
   B) acidic
   C) dense
   D) basic
9. What combines with moisture in the air to form acid rain?
   A) ozone
   B) sulfur dioxide
   C) lead
   D) oxygen
10. The industries that produce the products you use each day consume how much of the freshwater used in the United States?
    A) one-tenth
    B) one-half
    C) one-third
    D) two-thirds
11. Which law was enacted to reduce the level of car emissions?
    A) Clean Water Act
    B) Clean Air Act
    C) Safe Drinking Water Act
    D) Hazardous Waste Act
12. What is the pH of acid rain?
    A) less than 5.6
    B) between 5.6 and 7.0
    C) greater than 7.0
    D) greater than 9.5
13. What kind of pollution are airborne solids that range in size from large grains to microscopic?
    A) pH
    B) ozone
    C) particulate
    D) photo
14. What causes most water pollution?
    A) illegal dumping
    B) industrial chemicals
    C) everyday water use in the home
    D) wastewater-treatment facilities
15. Which act gives money to local governments to treat wastewater?
    A) Clean Water Act
    B) Clean Air Act
    C) Safe Drinking Water Act
    D) Hazardous Waste Act

Thinking Critically

16. How might cities with smog problems lessen the dangers to people who live and work in the cities?
17. How are industries both helpful and harmful to humans?

19. The heat could kill organisms and cause excessive evaporation of water. Evaporation can cause substances in the water to become concentrated, which could cause organisms to become sick and perhaps die.

20. Desert dwellers must pump groundwater or pipe in surface water. The water then must be stored in covered containers to reduce evaporation. Conservation also would be important in such communities.

18. How do plants help reduce water pollution?
19. Thermal pollution occurs when heated water is dumped into a nearby body of water. What effects does this type of pollution have on organisms living in the water?
20. What steps might a community in a desert area take to cope with water-supply problems?

Developing Skills

If you need help, refer to the **Skill Handbook.**

21. **Hypothesizing:** Earth's surface is nearly 75 percent water. Yet, much of this water is not available for many uses. Explain.
22. **Recognizing Cause and Effect:** What effect will an increase in the human population have on the need for freshwater?
23. **Concept Mapping:** Complete a concept map of the water cycle. Indicate how humans interrupt the cycle. Use the following phrases: *evaporation occurs, purified, drinking water, atmospheric water, wastewater, precipitation falls,* and *groundwater or surface water.*

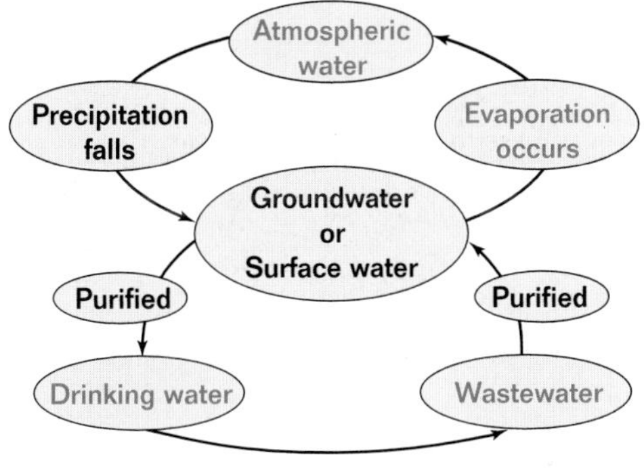

Test-Taking Tip

Use as Much Time as You Can You will not get extra points for finishing early. Work slowly and carefully on any test and make sure you don't make careless errors because you are hurrying to finish.

Test Practice

Use these questions to test your Science Proficiency.

1. Both acid rain and photochemical smog can be reduced by limiting emissions of a certain chemical from the exhaust of cars. Which chemical is it?
   A) sulfur C) carbon
   B) ozone D) nitrogen oxide
2. Determine approximately how much more acidic lemon juice is than milk. Use **Figure 27-4** and the information in Using Math in Section 27-1 to help you answer this question.
   A) 100 C) 1000
   B) 10 000 D) 100 000
3. All of the following events happen when you inhale acid rain. Which event is the **LAST** in the series of events?
   A) Stress is put on your heart.
   B) Acid is deposited deep inside your lungs.
   C) Your lungs become irritated.
   D) Oxygen absorption by the lungs is difficult.

Test Practice

The Test-Taking Tip was written by The Princeton Review, the nation's leader in test preparation.

1. D
2. B
3. A

Developing Skills

21. Much of the water at Earth's surface is salt water, which must be processed before being used in most instances.
22. An increase in the human population will increase the demand for freshwater.
23. See student page.

Bonus Question

List natural sources of air pollution. *volcanic eruptions, forest fires, and grass fires*

Assessment Resources

The **Test Practice Workbook** provides students with practice in the format, concepts, and critical-thinking skills tested in standardized exams.

Reproducible Masters

Chapter Review, pp. 53–54 L2
Performance Assessment, p. 27 L2
Assessment, pp. 105–108 L2

Glencoe Technology

Chapter Review Software
Computer Test Bank
MindJogger Videoquiz

Appendices

Appendix A

Safety in the Science Classroom

1. Always obtain your teacher's permission to begin an investigation.
2. Study the procedure. If you have questions, ask your teacher. Be sure you understand any safety symbols shown on the page.
3. Use the safety equipment provided for you. Goggles and a safety apron should be worn during an investigation.
4. Always slant test tubes away from yourself and others when heating them.
5. Never eat or drink in the lab, and never use lab glassware as food or drink containers. Never inhale chemicals. Do not taste any substances or draw any material into a tube with your mouth.
6. If you spill any chemical, wash it off immediately with water. Report the spill immediately to your teacher.
7. Know the location and proper use of the fire extinguisher, safety shower, fire blanket, first aid kit, and fire alarm.
8. Keep all materials away from open flames. Tie back long hair and loose clothing.
9. If a fire should break out in the classroom, or if your clothing should catch fire, smother it with the fire blanket or a coat, or get under a safety shower. NEVER RUN.
10. Report any accident or injury, no matter how small, to your teacher.

Follow these procedures as you clean up your work area.

1. Turn off the water and gas. Disconnect electrical devices.
2. Return all materials to their proper places.
3. Dispose of chemicals and other materials as directed by your teacher. Place broken glass and solid substances in the proper containers. Never discard materials in the sink.
4. Clean your work area.
5. Wash your hands thoroughly after working in the laboratory.

Table A-1

First Aid

Injury	Safe Response
Burns	Apply cold water. Call your teacher immediately.
Cuts and bruises	Stop any bleeding by applying direct pressure. Cover cuts with a clean dressing. Apply cold compresses to bruises. Call your teacher immediately.
Fainting	Leave the person lying down. Loosen any tight clothing and keep crowds away. Call your teacher immediately.
Foreign matter in eye	Flush with plenty of water. Use eyewash bottle or fountain.
Poisoning	Note the suspected poisoning agent and call your teacher immediately.
Any spills on skin	Flush with large amounts of water or use safety shower. Call your teacher immediately.

Appendix B

SI/Metric to English Conversions

	When you want to convert:	To:	Multiply by:
Length	inches	centimeters	2.54
	centimeters	inches	0.39
	feet	meters	0.30
	meters	feet	3.28
	yards	meters	0.91
	meters	yards	1.09
	miles	kilometers	1.61
	kilometers	miles	0.62
Mass and Weight*	ounces	grams	28.35
	grams	ounces	0.04
	pounds	kilograms	0.45
	kilograms	pounds	2.2
	tons (short)	tonnes (metric tons)	0.91
	tonnes (metric tons)	tons (short)	1.10
	pounds	newtons	4.45
	newtons	pounds	0.23
Volume	cubic inches	cubic centimeters	16.39
	cubic centimeters	cubic inches	0.06
	cubic feet	cubic meters	0.03
	cubic meters	cubic feet	35.30
	liters	quarts	1.06
	liters	gallons	0.26
	gallons	liters	3.78
Area	square inches	square centimeters	6.45
	square centimeters	square inches	0.16
	square feet	square meters	0.09
	square meters	square feet	10.76
	square miles	square kilometers	2.59
	square kilometers	square miles	0.39
	hectares	acres	2.47
	acres	hectares	0.40
Temperature	Fahrenheit	5/9 (°F − 32) =	Celsius
	Celsius	9/5 (°C) + 32 =	Fahrenheit

*Weight as measured in standard Earth gravity

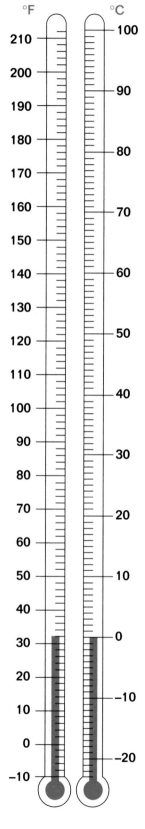

Appendix C

SI Units of Measurement

Table C-1

SI Base Units					
Measurement	**Unit**	**Symbol**	**Measurement**	**Unit**	**Symbol**
length	meter	m	temperature	kelvin	K
mass	kilogram	kg	amount of substance	mole	mol
time	second	s			

Table C-2

Units Derived from SI Base Units		
Measurement	**Unit**	**Symbol**
energy	joule	J
force	newton	N
frequency	hertz	Hz
potential difference	volt	V
power	watt	W
pressure	pascal	Pa

Table C-3

Common SI Prefixes					
Prefix	**Symbol**	**Multiplier**	**Prefix**	**Symbol**	**Multiplier**
	Greater than 1			Less than 1	
mega-	M	1 000 000	*deci-*	d	0.1
kilo-	k	1 000	*centi-*	c	0.01
hecto-	h	100	*milli-*	m	0.001
deca-	da	10	*micro-*	μ	0.000 001

Appendix D

Care and Use of a Microscope

Care of a Microscope

1. Always carry the microscope holding the arm with one hand and supporting the base with the other hand.
2. Don't touch the lenses with your fingers.
3. Never lower the coarse adjustment knob when looking through the eyepiece lens.
4. Always focus first with the low-power objective.
5. Don't use the coarse adjustment knob when the high-power objective is in place.
6. Store the microscope covered.

Using a Microscope

1. Place the microscope on a flat surface that is clear of objects. The arm should be toward you.
2. Look through the eyepiece. Adjust the diaphragm so that light comes through the opening in the stage.
3. Place a slide on the stage so that the specimen is in the field of view. Hold it firmly in place by using the stage clips.
4. Always focus first with the coarse adjustment and the low-power objective lens. Once the object is in focus on low power, turn the nosepiece until the high-power objective is in place. Use ONLY the fine adjustment to focus with the high-power objective lens.

Making a Wet-Mount Slide

1. Carefully place the item you want to look at in the center of a clean, glass slide. Make sure the sample is thin enough for light to pass through.
2. Use a dropper to place one or two drops of water on the sample.
3. Hold a clean coverslip by the edges and place it at one edge of the drop of water. Slowly lower the coverslip onto the drop of water until it lies flat.
4. If you have too much water or a lot of air bubbles, touch the edge of a paper towel to the edge of the coverslip to draw off extra water and force out air.

Appendix E

Diversity of Life: Classification of Living Organisms

Scientists use a six-kingdom system of classification of organisms. In this system, there are two kingdoms of organisms, Kingdoms Archaebacteria and Eubacteria, which contain organisms that do not have a nucleus and lack membrane-bound structures in the cytoplasm of their cells. The members of the other four kingdoms have cells which contain a nucleus and structures in the cytoplasm that are surrounded by membranes. These kingdoms are Kingdom Protista, Kingdom Fungi, the Kingdom Plantae, and the Kingdom Animalia.

Kingdom Archaebacteria

One-celled prokaryotes; absorb food from surroundings or make their own food by chemosynthesis; found in extremely harsh environments including salt ponds, hot springs, swamps, and deep-sea hydrothermal vents.

Kingdom Eubacteria

Cyanobacteria one-celled prokaryotes; make their own food; contain chlorophyll; some species form colonies; most are blue-green

Bacteria one-celled prokaryotes; most absorb food from their surroundings; some are photosynthetic; many are parasites; round, spiral, or rod-shaped

Kingdom Protista

Phylum Euglenophyta one-celled; can photosynthesize or take in food; most have one flagellum; euglenoids

Phylum Bacillariophyta one-celled; make their own food through photosynthesis; have unique double shells made of silica; diatoms

Phylum Dinoflagellata one-celled; make their own food through photosynthesis; contain red pigments; have two flagella; dinoflagellates

Phylum Chlorophyta one-celled, many-celled, or colonies; contain chlorophyll; make their own food; live on land, in fresh water, or salt water; green algae

Phylum Rhodophyta most are many-celled; photosynthetic; contain red pigments; most live in deep saltwater environments; red algae

Phylum Phaeophyta most are many-celled; photosynthetic; contain brown pigments; most live in saltwater environments; brown algae

Phylum Foraminifera many-celled; take in food; primarily marine; shells constructed of calcium carbonate, or made from grains of sand; forams

Phylum Myxomycota
Slime Mold
Magnification: 5×

Phylum Chlorophyta
Desmids Magnification: 50×

Appendix E

Phylum Rhizopoda one-celled; take in food; move by means of pseudopods; free-living or parasitic; amoebas

Phylum Zoomastigina one-celled; take in food; have one or more flagella; free-living or parasitic; zoomastigotes

Phylum Ciliophora one-celled; take in food; have large numbers of cilia; ciliates

Phylum Sporozoa one-celled; take in food; no means of movement; parasites in animals; sporozoans

Phylum Myxomycota and Acrasiomycota: one- or many-celled; absorb food; change form during life cycle; cellular and plasmodial slime molds

Phylum Oomycota many-celled; live in fresh or salt water; are either parasites or decomposers; water molds, rusts and downy mildews

Kingdom Fungi

Phylum Zygomycota many-celled; absorb food; spores are produced in sporangia; zygote fungi; bread mold

Phylum Ascomycota one- and many-celled; absorb food; spores produced in asci; sac fungi; yeast

Phylum Basidiomycota many-celled; absorb food; spores produced in basidia; club fungi; mushrooms

Phylum Deuteromycota: members with unknown reproductive structures; imperfect fungi; penicillin

Lichens organisms formed by symbiotic relationship between an ascomycote or a basidiomycote and green alga or cyanobacterium

Kingdom Plantae

Non-seed Plants

Division Bryophyta nonvascular plants; reproduce by spores produced in capsules; many-celled; green; grow in moist land environments; mosses and liverworts

Division Lycophyta many-celled vascular plants; spores produced in conelike structures; live on land; are photosynthetic; club mosses

Division Sphenophyta vascular plants; ribbed and jointed stems; scalelike leaves; spores produced in conelike structures; horsetails

Division Pterophyta vascular plants; leaves called fronds; spores produced in clusters of sporangia called sori; live on land or in water; ferns

Division Bryophyta
Liverwort

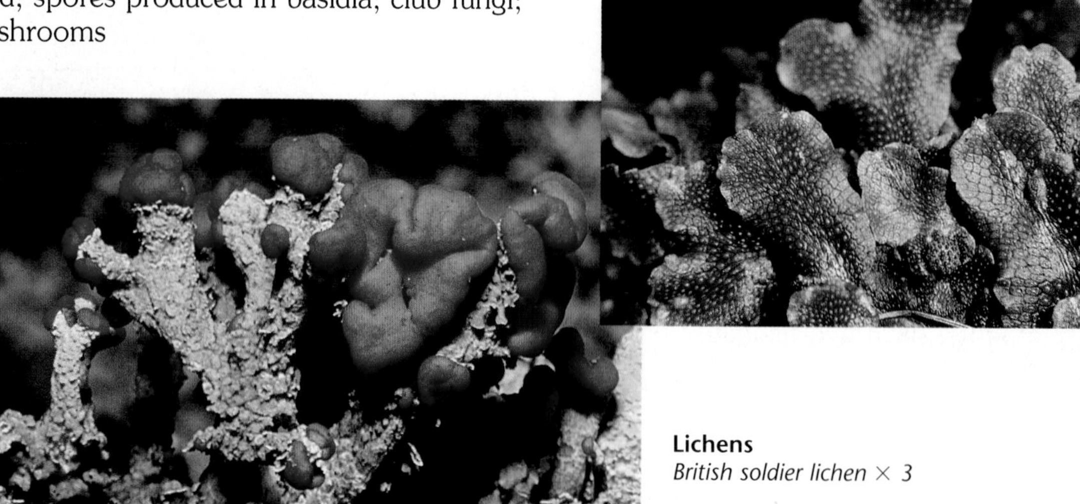

Lichens
British soldier lichen × 3

Appendix E

Seed Plants

Division Ginkgophyta: deciduous gymnosperms; only one living species; fan-shaped leaves with branching veins; reproduces with seeds; ginkgos

Division Cycadophyta: palmlike gymnosperms; large featherlike leaves; produce seeds in cones; cycads

Division Coniferophyta: deciduous or evergreen gymnosperms; trees or shrubs; needlelike or scalelike leaves; seeds produced in cones; conifers

Division Gnetophyta: shrubs or woody vines; seeds produced in cones; division contains only three genera; gnetum

Division Anthophyta: dominant group of plants; ovules protected in an ovary; sperm carried to ovules by pollen tube; produce flowers and seeds in fruits; flowering plants

Kingdom Animalia

Phylum Porifera: aquatic organisms that lack true tissues and organs; they are asymmetrical and sessile; sponges

Phylum Cnidaria: radially symmetrical organisms; have a digestive cavity with one opening; most have tentacles armed with stinging cells; live in aquatic environments singly or in colonies; includes jellyfish, corals, hydra, and sea anemones

Phylum Platyhelminthes: bilaterally symmetrical worms; have flattened bodies; digestive system has one opening; parasitic and free-living species; flatworms

Phylum Cnidaria
Jellyfish

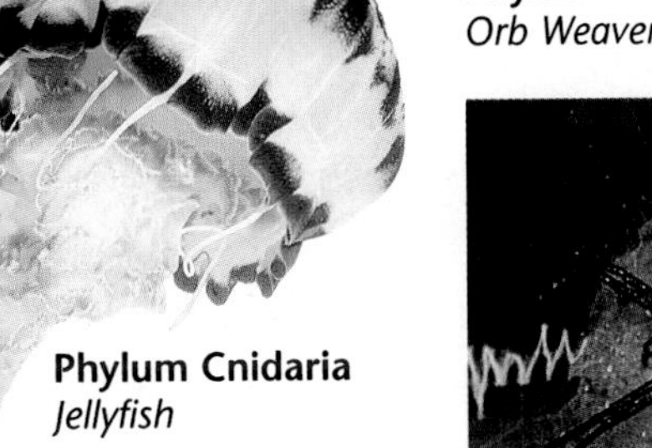

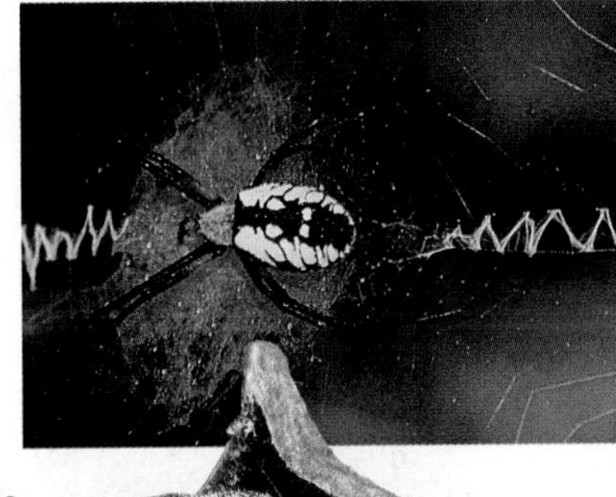

Phylum Arthopoda
Orb Weaver Spider

Phylum Arthropoda
Hermit Crab

Phylum Mollusca
Florida Fighting Conch

Division Coniferophyta
Pine cone

Division Anthophyta
Strawberry Blossoms

Division Anthophyta
Strawberries

Phylum Annelida
Sabellid Worms
Feather Duster

Appendix E

Phylum Nematoda: round, bilaterally symmetrical body; digestive system with two openings; many parasitic forms but mostly free-living roundworms

Phylum Mollusca: soft-bodied animals, many with a hard shell; a mantle covers the soft body; aquatic and terrestrial species; includes clams, snails, squid, and octopuses

Phylum Annelida: bilaterally symmetrical worms; have round, segmented bodies; terrestrial and aquatic species; includes earthworms, leeches, and marine polychaetes

Phylum Arthropoda: largest phylum of organisms; have segmented bodies; pairs of jointed appendages; have hard exoskeletons; terrestrial and aquatic species; includes insects, crustaceans, spiders, and horseshoe crabs

Phylum Echinodermata: marine organisms; have spiny or leathery skin; water-vascular system with tube feet; radial symmetry; includes sea stars, sand dollars, and sea urchins

Phylum Chordata: organisms with internal skeletons; specialized body systems; paired appendages; all at some time have a notochord, dorsal nerve cord, gill slits, and a tail; include fish, amphibians, reptiles, birds, and mammals

Phylum Arthropoda
Giant Swallowtail Butterfly

Phylum Echinodermata
Blood Sea Star and Red Sea Urchin

Phylum Chordata
Eastern Box Turtle

Phylum Chordata
Lemon Butterfly fish

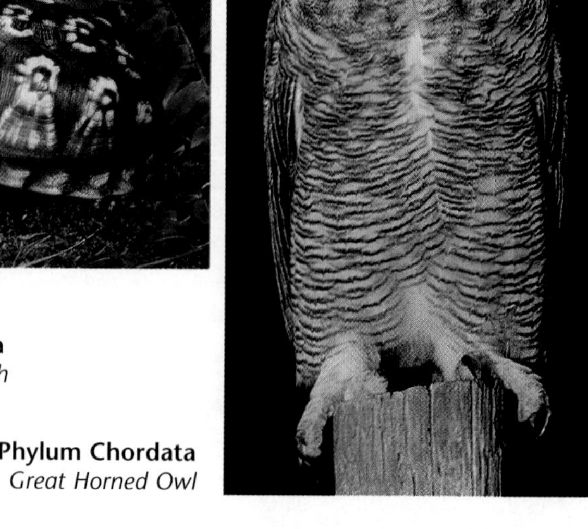

Phylum Chordata
Great Horned Owl

Appendix F

Minerals

Mineral (formula)	Color	Streak	Hardness	Breakage pattern	Uses and other properties
graphite (C)	black to gray	black to gray	1–1.5	basal cleavage (scales)	pencil lead, lubricants for locks, rods to control some small nuclear reactions, battery poles
galena (PbS)	gray	gray to black	2.5	cubic cleavage perfect	source of lead, used in pipes, shields for X rays, fishing equipment sinkers
hematite (Fe_2O_3)	black or reddish brown	reddish brown	5.5–6.5	irregular fracture	source of iron; converted to "pig" iron, made into steel
magnetite (Fe_3O_4)	black	black	6	conchoidal fracture	source of iron, naturally magnetic, called lodestone
pyrite (FeS_2)	light, brassy, yellow	greenish black	6–6.5	uneven fracture	source of iron, "fool's gold"
talc ($Mg_3Si_4O_{10}(OH)_2$)	white greenish	white	1	cleavage in one direction	used for talcum powder, sculptures, paper, and tabletops
gypsum ($CaSO_4 \cdot 2H_2O$)	colorless, gray, white brown	white	2	basal cleavage	used in plaster of paris and dry wall for building construction
sphalerite (ZnS)	brown, reddish brown, greenish	light to dark brown	3.5–4	cleavage in six directions	main ore of zinc; used in paints, dyes and medicine
muscovite ($KAl_3Si_3O_{10}(OH)_2$)	white, light gray, yellow, rose, green	colorless	2–2.5	basal cleavage	occurs in large flexible plates; used as an insulator in electrical equipment, lubricant
biotite ($K(Mg, Fe)_3(AlSi_3O_{10})(OH)_2$)	black to dark brown	colorless	2.5–3	basal cleavage	occurs in large flexible plates
halite (NaCl)	colorless, red, white, blue	colorless	2.5	cubic cleavage	salt; soluble in water; a preservative

Appendix F

Minerals

Mineral (formula)	Color	Streak	Hardness	Breakage pattern	Uses and other properties
calcite ($CaCO_3$)	colorless, white, pale blue	colorless, white	3	cleavage in three directions	fizzes when HCl is added; used in cements and other building materials
dolomite ($CaMg(CO_3)_2$)	colorless, white, pink green, gray black	white	3.5–4	cleavage in three directions	concrete and cement; used as an ornamental building stone
fluorite (CaF_2)	colorless, white, blue green, red yellow, purple	colorless	4	cleavage in four directions	used in the manufacture of optical equipment; glows under ultraviolet light
hornblende ($(CaNa)_{2\text{-}3}(Mg,Al,Fe)_5(Al,Si)_2Si_6O_{22}(OH)_2$)	green to black	gray to white	5–6	cleavage in two directions	will transmit light on thin edges; 6-sided cross section
feldspar ($KAlSi_3O_8$) ($NaAlSi_3O_8$) ($CaAl_2Si_2O_8$)	colorless, white to gray, green	colorless	6	two cleavage planes meet at ~90° angle	used in the manufacture of ceramics
augite ($(Ca, Na)(Mg, Fe, Al)(Al, Si)_2O_6$)	black	colorless	6	cleavage in two directions	square or 8-sided cross section
olivine ($(Mg, Fe)_2SiO_4$)	olive, green	none	6.5–7	conchoidal fracture	gemstones, refractory sand
quartz (SiO_2)	colorless, various colors	none	7	conchoidal fracture	used in glass manufacture, electronic equipment, radios, computers, watches, gemstones

Appendix G

Rocks

Rock Type	Rock Name	Characteristics
Igneous (intrusive)	Granite	Large mineral grains of quartz, feldspar, hornblende, and mica. Usually light in color.
	Diorite	Large mineral grains of feldspar, hornblende, mica. Less quartz than granite. Intermediate in color.
	Gabbro	Large mineral grains of feldspar, hornblende, augite, olivine, and mica. No quartz. Dark in color.
Igneous (extrusive)	Rhyolite	Small mineral grains of quartz, feldspar, hornblende, and mica or no visible grains. Light in color.
	Andesite	Small mineral grains of feldspar, hornblende, mica or no visible grains. Less quartz than rhyolite. Intermediate in color.
	Basalt	Small mineral grains of feldspar, hornblende, augite, olivine, mica or no visible grains. No quartz. Dark in color.
	Obsidian	Glassy texture. No visible grains. Volcanic glass. Fracture looks like broken glass.
	Pumice	Frothy texture. Floats. Usually light in color.
Sedimentary (detrital)	Conglomerate	Coarse-grained. Gravel or pebble-sized grains.
	Sandstone	Sand-sized grains 1/16 to 2 mm in size.
	Siltstone	Grains are smaller than sand but larger than clay.
	Shale	Smallest grains. Usually dark in color.
Sedimentary (chemical or biochemical)	Limestone	Major mineral is calcite. Usually forms in oceans, lakes, rivers, and caves. Often contains fossils.
	Coal	Occurs in swampy. low-lying areas. Compacted layers of organic material, mainly plant remains.
Sedimentary (chemical)	Rock Salt	Commonly forms by the evaporation of seawater.
Metamorphic (foliated)	Gneiss	Well-developed banding because of alternating layers of different minerals, usually of different colors. Common parent rock is granite.
	Schist	Well-defined parallel arrangement of flat, sheet-like minerals, mainly micas. Common parent rocks are shale, phyllite.
	Phyllite	Shiny or silky appearance. May look wrinkled. Common parent rocks are shale, slate.
	Slate	Harder, denser, and shinier than shale. Common parent rock is shale.
Metamorphic (non-foliated)	Marble	Interlocking calcite or dolomite crystals. Common parent rock is limestone.
	Soapstone	Composed mainly of the mineral talc. Soft with a greasy feel.
	Quartzite	Hard and well cemented with interlocking quartz crystals. Common parent rock is sandstone.

Appendix H

Topographic Map Symbols

Primary highway, hard surface
Secondary highway, hard surface
Light-duty road, hard or Improved surface
Unimproved road
Railroad: single track and multiple track
Railroads in juxtaposition

Buildings

Schools, church, and cemetery — cem

Buildings (barn, warehouse, etc)
Wells other than water (labeled as to type) — o oil o gas
Tanks: oil, water, etc. (labeled only if water) — water
Located or landmark object; windmill
Open pit, mine, or quarry; prospect

Marsh (swamp)

Wooded marsh

Woods or brushwood

Vineyard
Land subject to controlled inundation

Submerged marsh

Mangrove

Orchard

Scrub

Urban area

Spot elevation — ×7369
Water elevation — 670

Index contour
Supplementary contour
Intermediate contour

Depression contours

Boundaries: National
State
County, parish, municipal
Civil township, precinct, town, barrio
Incorporated city, village, town, hamlet
Reservation, National or State
Small park, cemetery, airport, etc.
Land grant
Township or range line, United States land survey
Township or range line, approximate location

Perennial streams
Elevated aqueduct
Water well and spring
Small rapids

Large rapids

Intermittent lake

Intermittent streams
Aqueduct tunnel

Glacier
Small falls

Large falls

Dry lake bed

Appendix I

Weather Map Symbols

Sample Plotted Report at Each Station

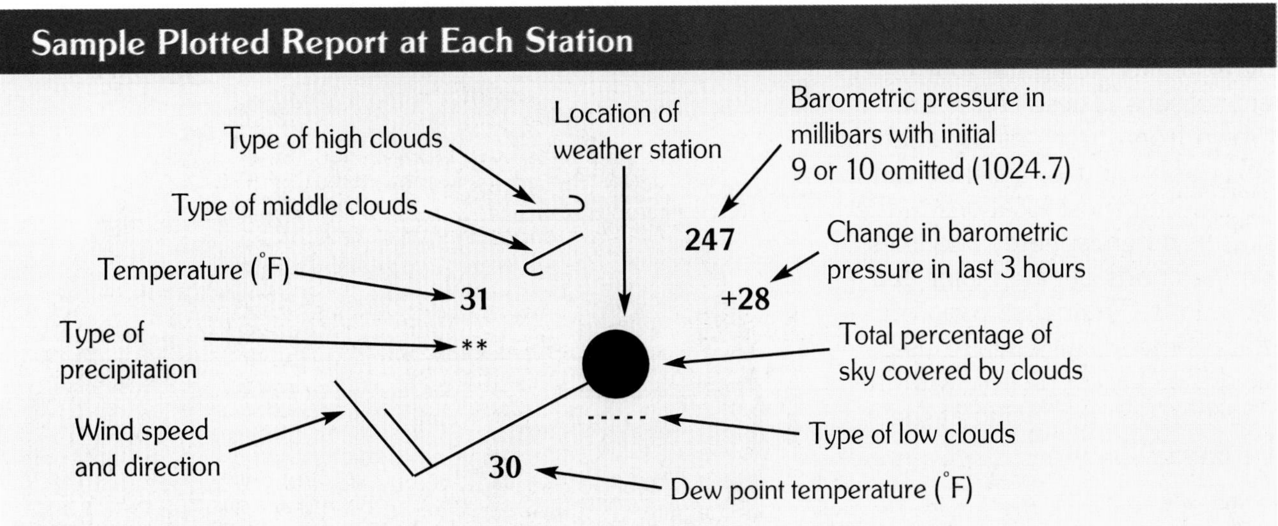

Sample Plotted Report at Each Station

Precipitation	Wind Speed and direction	Sky coverage	Some types of high clouds
Fog	0 knots; calm	No cover	Scattered cirrus
Snow	1-2 knots	1/10 or less	Dense cirrus in patches
Rain	3-7 knots	2/10 to 3/10	Veil of cirrus covering entire sky
Thunder-storm	8-12 knots	4/10	Cirrus not covering entire sky
Drizzle	23-17 knots	1/2	
Showers	17-22 knots	6/10	
	23-27 knots	7/10	
	48-52 knots	Overcast with openings	
	1 knot = 1.852 km/h	Complete overcast	

Some types of middle clouds	Some types of low clouds	Fronts and pressure systems	
Thin altostratus layer	Cumulus of fair weather	(H) or High	Center of high-or
Thick altostratus layer	Stratocumulus	(L) or Low	low-pressure system
Thin altostratus in patches	Fractocumulus of bad weather		Cold front
Thin altostratus in bands	Stratus of fair weather		Warm Front
			Occluded front
			Stationary front

Appendix J

Star Charts

Shown here are star charts for viewing stars in the northern hemisphere during the four different seasons. These charts are drawn from the night sky at about 35° north latitude, but they can be used for most locations in the northern hemisphere. The lines on the charts outline major constellations. The dense band of stars is the Milky Way. To use, hold the chart vertically, with the direction you are facing at the bottom of the map.

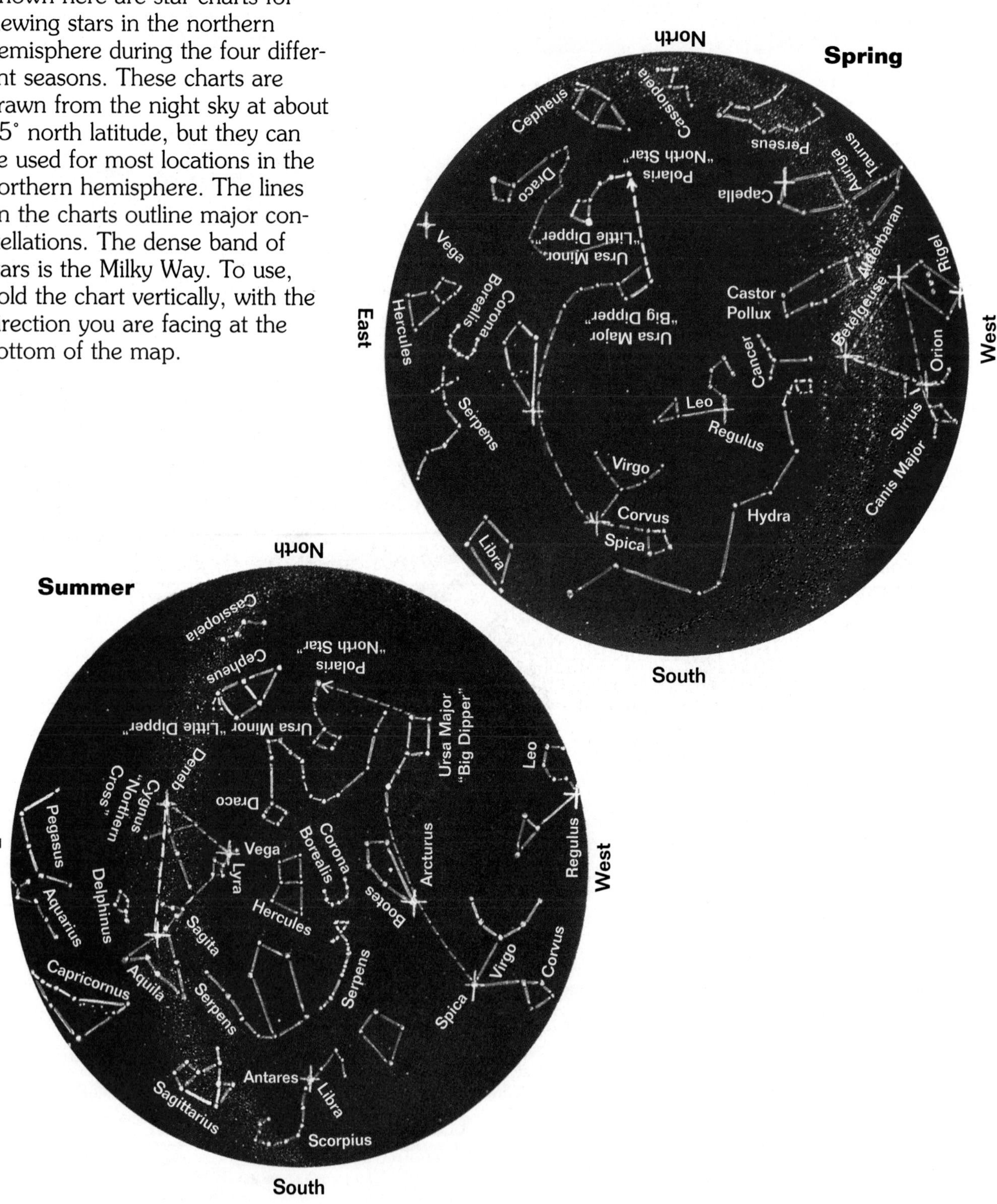

Appendix J

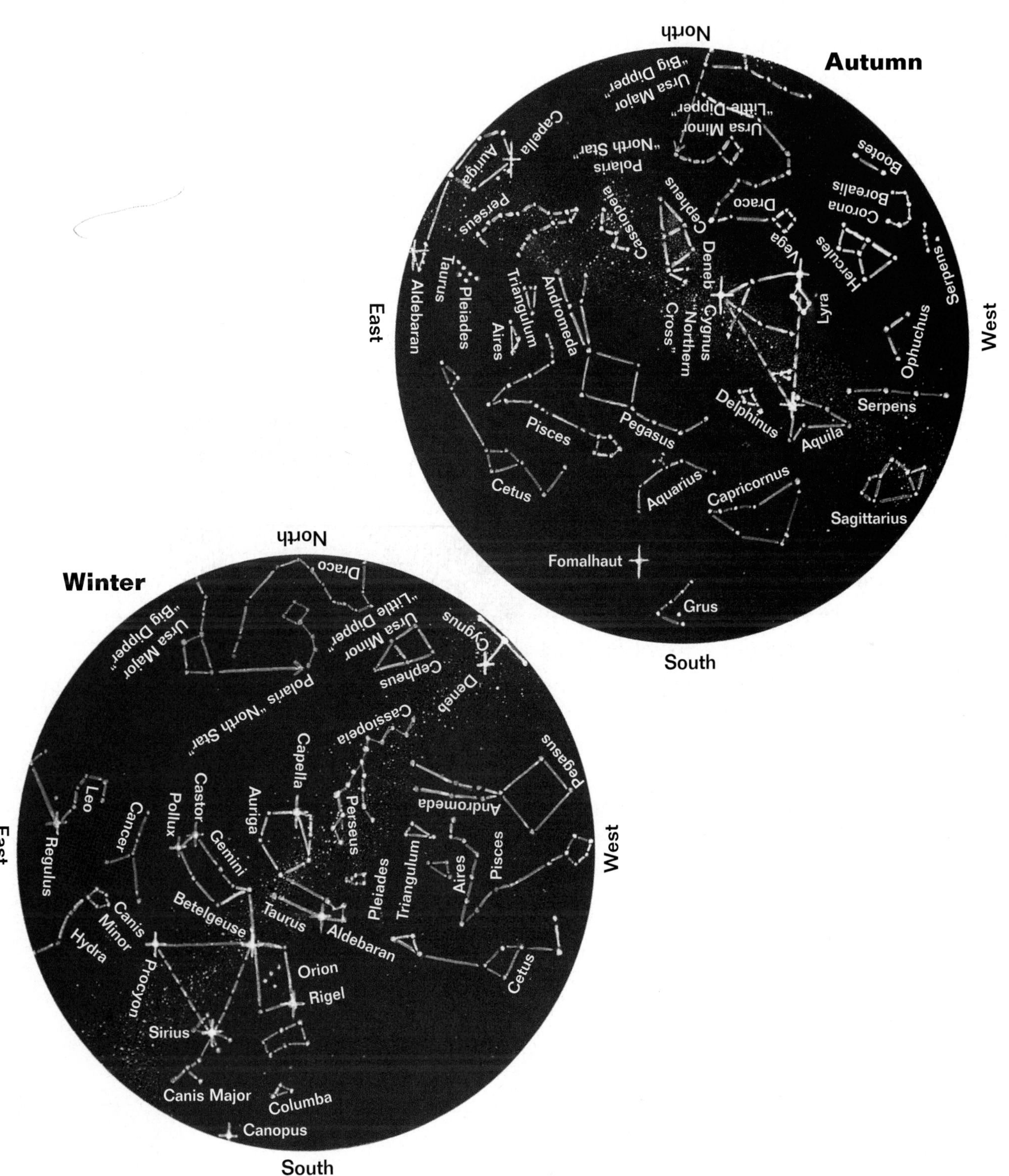

Autumn
North
Ursa Major "Big Dipper"
Ursa Minor "Little Dipper"
Polaris "North Star"
Capella
Auriga
Perseus
Cassiopeia
Cepheus
Draco
Bootes
Corona Borealis
Hercules
Vega
Serpens
Lyra
Deneb
Cygnus "Northern Cross"
Ophuchus
East
Taurus
Aldebaran
Pleiades
Triangulum
Aires
Andromeda
West
Delphinus
Serpens
Aquila
Pegasus
Pisces
Cetus
Aquarius
Capricornus
Sagittarius
Fomalhaut
Grus
South
Winter
North
Draco
Ursa Major "Big Dipper"
Ursa Minor "Little Dipper"
Cygnus
Polaris "North Star"
Cepheus
Deneb
Cassiopeia
Pegasus
Capella
Castor
Leo
Pollux
Cancer
Auriga
Perseus
Andromeda
East
Regulus
Gemini
Pleiades
Triangulum
Aires
Pisces
West
Canis Minor
Betelgeuse
Taurus
Aldebaran
Hydra
Procyon
Orion
Rigel
Cetus
Sirius
Canis Major
Columba
Canopus
South

Skill Handbook

Table of Contents

Organizing Information

Communicating

The communication of ideas is an important part of our everyday lives. Whether reading a book, writing a letter, or watching a television program, people everywhere are expressing opinions and sharing information with one another. Writing in your Science Journal allows you to express your opinions and demonstrate your knowledge of the information presented on a subject. When writing, keep in mind the purpose of the assignment and the audience with which you are communicating.

Examples Science Journal assignments vary greatly. They may ask you to take a viewpoint other than your own; perhaps you will be a scientist, a TV reporter, or a committee member of a local environmental group. Maybe you will be expressing your opinions to a member of Congress, a doctor, or to the editor of your local newspaper, as shown in **Figure 1.** Sometimes, Science Journal writing may allow you to summarize information in the form of an outline, a letter, or in a paragraph.

Figure 1 A Science Journal entry

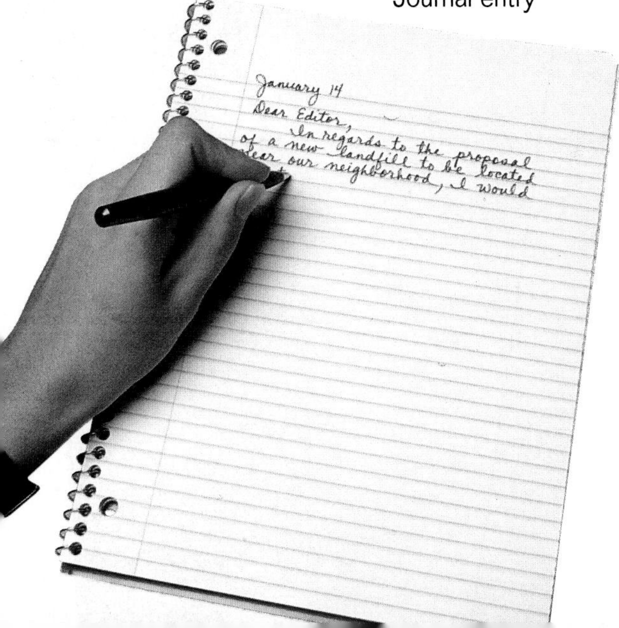

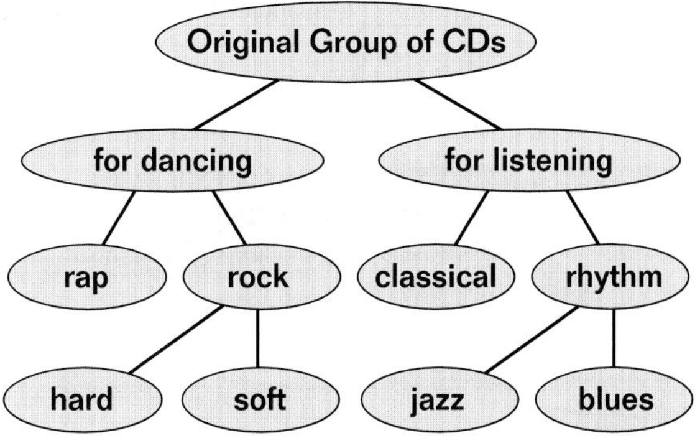

Figure 2 Classifying CDs

Classifying

You may not realize it, but you make things orderly in the world around you. If you hang your shirts together in the closet or if your favorite CDs are stacked together, you have used the skill of classifying.

Classifying is the process of sorting objects or events into groups based on common features. When classifying, first observe the objects or events to be classified. Then, select one feature that is shared by some members in the group, but not by all. Place those members that share that feature into a subgroup. You can classify members into smaller and smaller subgroups based on characteristics.

Remember, when you classify, you are grouping objects or events for a purpose. Keep your purpose in mind as you select the features to form groups and subgroups.

Example How would you classify a collection of CDs? As shown in **Figure 2,** you might classify those you like to dance to in one subgroup and CDs you like to listen to in the next subgroup. The CDs you like to dance to could be subdivided into a rap subgroup and a rock subgroup. Note that for each feature selected, each CD fits into only one subgroup. You would keep selecting features until all the CDs are classified. **Figure 2** shows one possible classification.

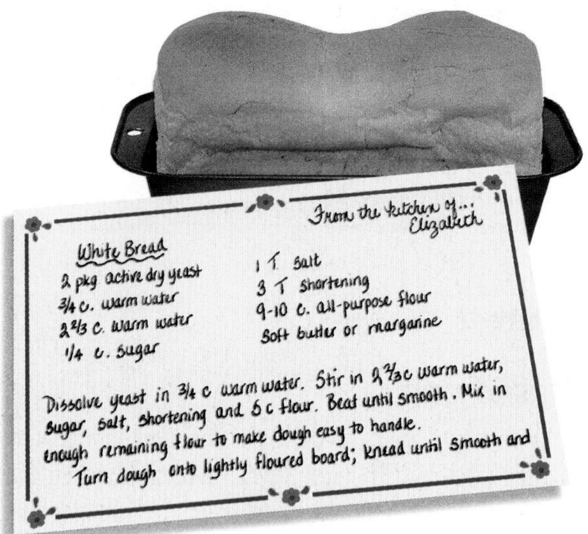

Figure 3 A recipe for bread contains sequenced instructions

Sequencing

A sequence is an arrangement of things or events in a particular order. When you are asked to sequence objects or events within a group, figure out what comes first, then think about what should come second. Continue to choose objects or events until all of the objects you started out with are in order. Then, go back over the sequence to make sure each thing or event in your sequence logically leads to the next.

Example A sequence with which you are most familiar is the use of alphabetical order. Another example of sequence would be the steps in a recipe, as shown in **Figure 3.** Think about baking bread. Steps in the recipe have to be followed in order for the bread to turn out right.

Concept Mapping

If you were taking an automobile trip, you would probably take along a road map. The road map shows your location, your destination, and other places along the way. By looking at the map and finding where you are, you can begin to understand where you are in relation to other locations on the map.

A concept map is similar to a road map. But, a concept map shows relationships among ideas (or concepts) rather than places. A concept map is a diagram that visually shows how concepts are related. Because the concept map shows relationships among ideas, it can make the meanings of ideas and terms clear, and help you understand better what you are studying.

There is usually not one correct way to create a concept map. As you construct one type of map, you may discover other ways to construct the map that show the

Figure 4 Network tree describing U.S. currency

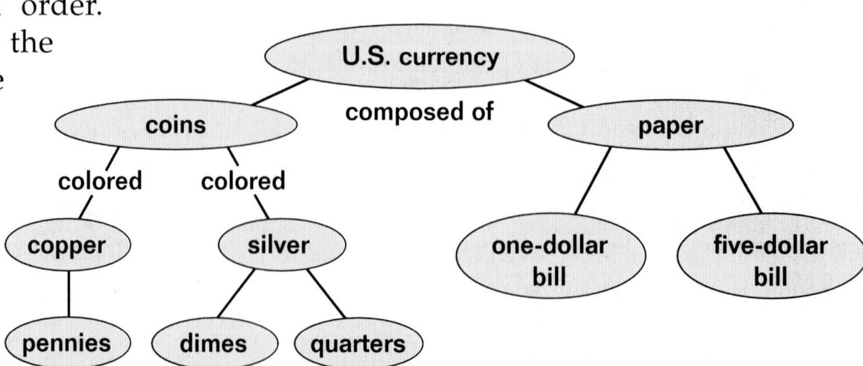

relationships between concepts in a better way. If you do discover what you think is a better way to create a concept map, go ahead and use the new one. Overall, concept maps are useful for breaking a big concept down into smaller parts, making learning easier.

Examples

Network Tree Look at the concept map about U.S. currency in **Figure 4.** This is called a network tree. Notice how some words are in ovals while others are written across connecting lines. The words inside the ovals are science concepts. The lines in the map show related concepts. The words written on the lines describe the relationships between concepts.

When you are asked to construct a network tree, write down the topic and list the major concepts related to that topic on a piece of paper. Then look at your list and begin to put them in order from general to specific. Branch the related concepts from the major concept and describe the relationships on the lines. Continue to write the more specific concepts. Write the relationships between the concepts on the lines until all concepts are mapped. Examine the concept map for relationships that cross branches, and add them to the concept map.

Events Chain An events chain is another type of concept map. An events chain map, such as the one describing a typical morning routine in **Figure 5,** is used to describe ideas in order. In science, an events chain can be used to describe a sequence of events, the steps in a procedure, or the stages of a process.

When making an events chain, first find the one event that starts the chain. This event is called the initiating event. Then, find the next event in the chain and continue until you reach an outcome. Suppose you are asked to describe what happens when your alarm rings. An events chain map describing the steps might look like **Figure 5.** Notice that connecting words are not necessary in an events chain.

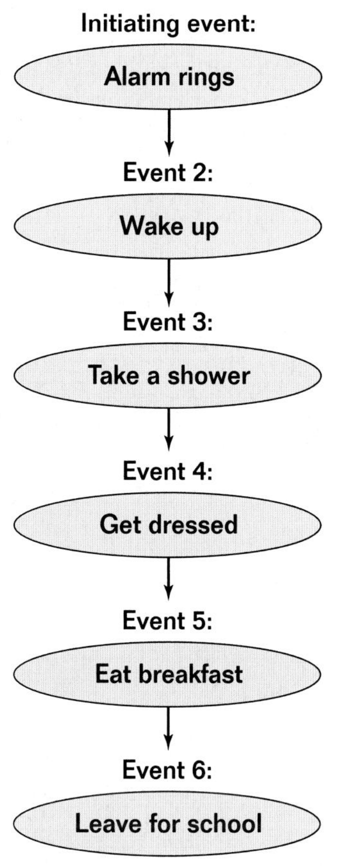

Figure 5 Events chain of a typical morning routine

Cycle Map A cycle concept map is a special type of events chain map. In a cycle concept map, the series of events does not produce a final outcome. Instead, the last event in the chain relates back to the initiating event.

As in the events chain map, you first decide on an initiating event and then list each event in order. Because there is no outcome and the last event relates back to the initiating event, the cycle repeats itself. Look at the cycle map describing the relationship between day and night in **Figure 6.**

Figure 6 Cycle map of day and night.

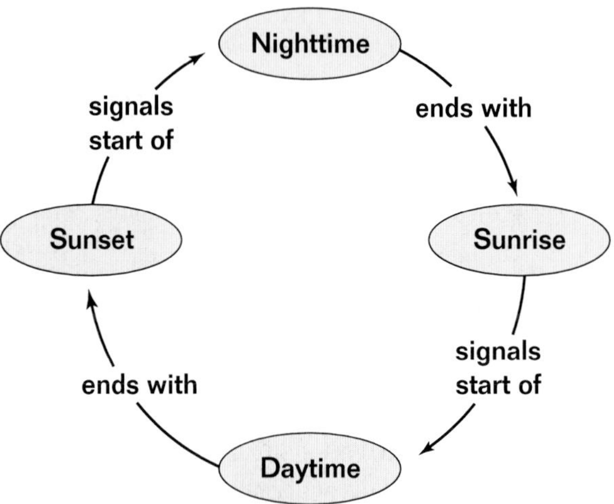

Spider Map A fourth type of concept map is the spider map. This is a map that you can use for brainstorming. Once you have a central idea, you may find you have a jumble of ideas that relate to it, but are not necessarily clearly related to each other. As illustrated by the homework spider map in **Figure 7,** by writing these ideas outside the main concept, you may begin to separate and group unrelated terms so that they become more useful.

Figure 7 Spider map about homework.

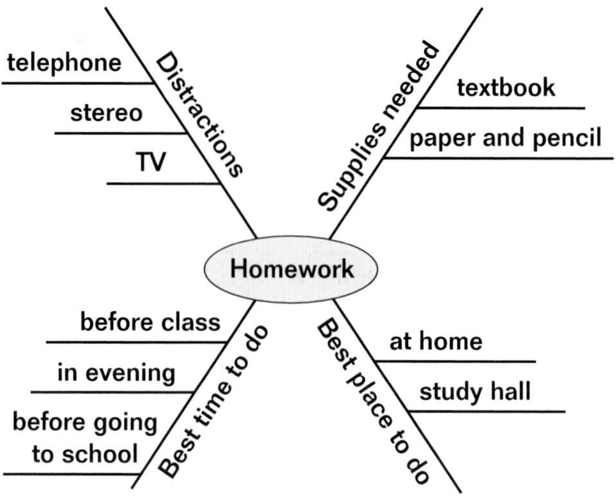

Making and Using Tables

Browse through your textbook and you will notice tables in the text and in the activities. In a table, data or information is arranged in a way that makes it easier for you to understand. Activity tables help organize the data you collect during an activity so that results can be interpreted.

Examples Most tables have a title. At a glance, the title tells you what the table is about. A table is divided into columns and rows. The first column lists items to be compared. In **Figure 8,** the collection of recyclable materials is being compared in a table. The row across the top lists the specific characteristics being compared. Within the grid of the table, the collected data are recorded.

What is the title of the table in **Figure 8?** The title is "Recycled Materials." What is being compared? The different materials being recycled and on which days they are recycled.

Making Tables To make a table, list the items to be compared down in columns and the characteristics to be compared across in rows. The table in

Figure 8 Table of recycled materials

Recycled Materials			
Day of Week	Paper (kg)	Aluminum (kg)	Plastic (kg)
Mon.	4.0	2.0	0.5
Wed.	3.5	1.5	0.5
Fri.	3.0	1.0	1.5

Figure 8 compares the mass of recycled materials collected by a class. On Monday, students turned in 4.0 kg of paper, 2.0 kg of aluminum, and 0.5 kg of plastic. On Wednesday, they turned in 3.5 kg of paper, 1.5 kg of aluminum, and 0.5 kg of plastic. On Friday, the totals were 3.0 kg of paper, 1.0 kg of aluminum, and 1.5 kg of plastic.

Using Tables How much plastic, in kilograms, is being recycled on Wednesday? Locate the column labeled "Plastic (kg)" and the row "Wed." The data in the box where the column and row intersect is the answer. Did you answer "0.5"? How much aluminum, in kilograms, is being recycled on Friday? If you answered "1.0," you understand how to use the parts of the table.

Making and Using Graphs

After scientists organize data in tables, they may display the data in a graph. A graph is a diagram that shows the relationship of one variable to another. A graph makes interpretation and analysis of data easier. There are three basic types of graphs used in science—the line graph, the bar graph, and the circle graph.

Examples

Line Graphs A line graph is used to show the relationship between two variables. The variables being compared go on two axes of the graph. The independent variable always goes on the horizontal axis, called the *x*-axis. The dependent variable always goes on the vertical axis, called the *y*-axis.

Suppose your class started to record the amount of materials they collected in one week for their school to recycle. The collected information is shown in **Figure 9.**

You could make a graph of the materials collected over the three days of the school week. The three weekdays are the independent variables and are placed on the *x*-axis of your graph. The amount of materials collected is the dependent variable and would go on the *y*-axis.

After drawing your axes, label each with a scale. The *x*-axis lists the three weekdays. To make a scale of the amount of materials collected on the *y*-axis, look at the data values. Because the lowest amount collected was 1.0 and the highest was 5.0, you will have to start numbering at least at 1.0 and go through 5.0. You decide to start numbering at 0 and number by ones through 6.0, as shown in **Figure 10.**

Next, plot the data points for collected paper. The first pair of data you want to plot is Monday and 5.0 kg of paper.

Figure 9 Amount of recyclable materials collected during one week

Materials Collected During Week		
Day of Week	Paper (kg)	Aluminum (kg)
Mon.	5.0	4.0
Wed.	4.0	1.0
Fri.	2.5	2.0

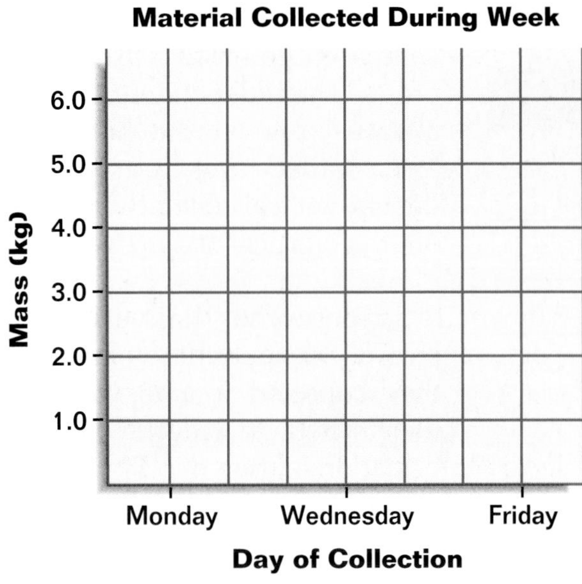

Figure 10 Graph outline for material collected during week

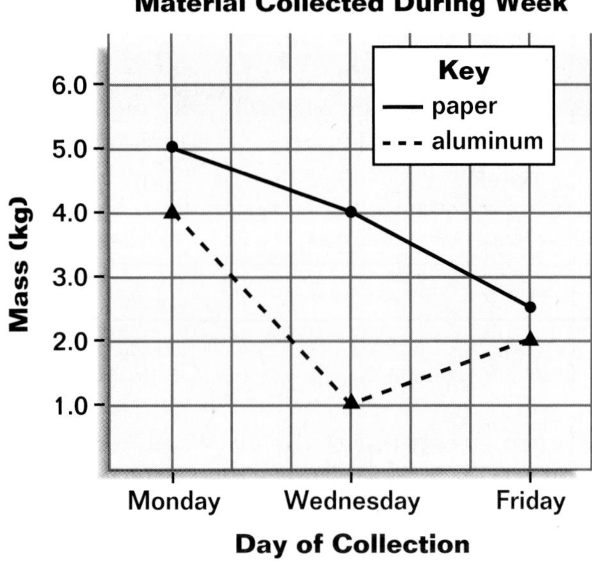

Figure 11 Line graph of materials collected during week

Locate "Monday" on the x-axis and locate "5.0" on the y-axis. Where an imaginary vertical line from the x-axis and an imaginary horizontal line from the y-axis would meet, place the first data point. Place the other data points the same way. After all the points are plotted, connect them with the best smooth curve. Repeat this procedure for the data points for aluminum. Use continuous and dashed lines to distinguish the two line graphs. The resulting graph should look like **Figure 11.**

Bar Graphs Bar graphs are similar to line graphs. They compare data that do not continuously change. In a bar graph, vertical bars show the relationships among data.

To make a bar graph, set up the x-axis and y-axis as you did for the line graph. The data is plotted by drawing vertical bars from the x-axis up to a point where the y-axis would meet the bar if it were extended.

Look at the bar graph in **Figure 12** comparing the mass of aluminum collected over three weekdays. The x-axis is the days on which the aluminum was collected. The y-axis is the mass of aluminum collected, in kilograms.

Circle Graphs A circle graph uses a circle divided into sections to display data. Each section represents part of the whole. All the sections together equal 100 percent.

Suppose you wanted to make a circle graph to show the number of seeds that germinated in a package. You would count the total number of seeds. You find that there are 143 seeds in the package. This represents 100 percent, the whole circle.

You plant the seeds, and 129 seeds germinate. The seeds that germinated will make up one section of the circle graph, and the seeds that did not germinate will make up the remaining section.

To find out how much of the circle each section should take, divide the number of seeds in each section by the total number of seeds. Then, multiply your answer by 360, the number of degrees in a circle, and round to the nearest whole number. The

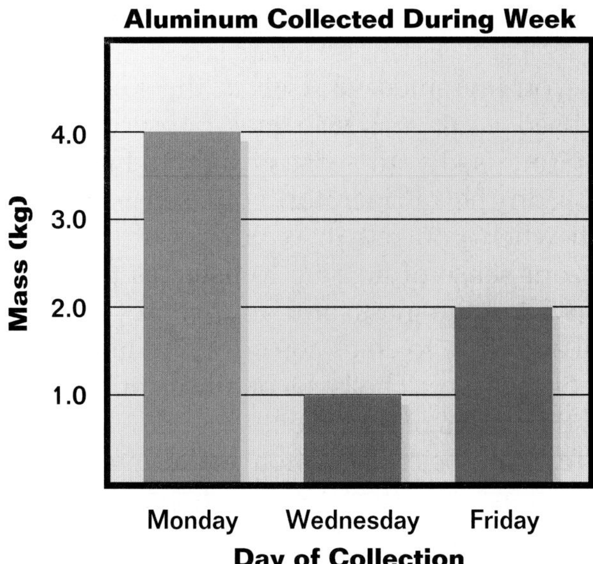

Figure 12 Bar graph of aluminum collected during week

section of the circle graph in degrees that represents the seeds germinated is figured below.

$$\frac{129}{143} \times 360 = 324.75 \text{ or } 325 \text{ degrees (or } 325°\text{)}$$

Plot this group on the circle graph using a compass and a protractor. Use the compass to draw a circle. It will be easier to measure the part of the circle representing the non-germinating seeds, so subtract 325° from 360° to get 35°. Draw a straight line from the center to the edge of the circle. Place your protractor on this line and use it to mark a point at 325°. Use this point to draw a straight line from the center of the circle to the edge. This is the section for the group of seeds that did not germinate. The other section represents the group of 129 seeds that did germinate. Label the sections of your graph and title the graph as shown in **Figure 13.**

Figure 13 Circle graph of germinated seeds

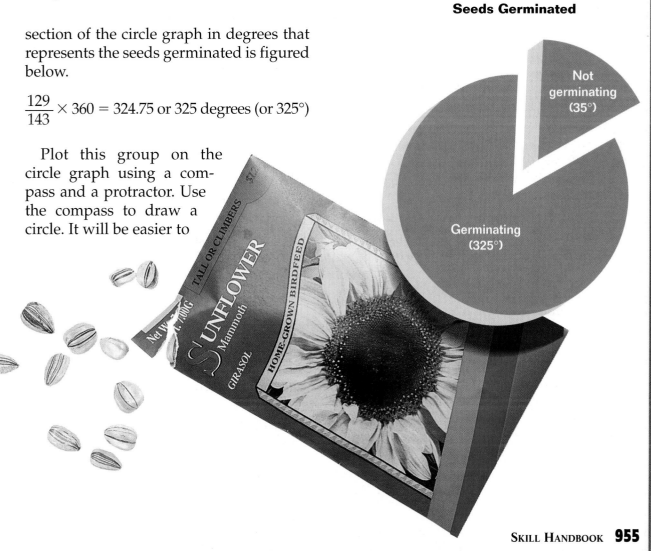

Seeds Germinated

Not germinating (35°)

Germinating (325°)

Thinking Critically

Observing and Inferring

Observing Scientists try to make careful and accurate observations. When possible, they use instruments such as microscopes, thermometers, and balances to make observations. Measurements with a balance or thermometer provide numerical data that can be checked and repeated.

When you make observations in science, you'll find it helpful to examine the entire object or situation first. Then, look carefully for details. Write down everything you observe.

Example Imagine that you have just finished a volleyball game. At home, you open the refrigerator and see a jug of orange juice on the back of the top shelf. The jug, shown in **Figure 14,** feels cold as you grasp it. Then, you drink the juice, smell the oranges, and enjoy the tart taste in your mouth.

Figure 14 Why is this jug of orange juice cold?

As you imagined yourself in the story, you used your senses to make observations. You used your sense of sight to find the jug in the refrigerator, your sense of touch when you felt the coldness of the jug, your sense of hearing to listen as the liquid filled the glass, and your senses of smell and taste to enjoy the odor and tartness of the juice. The basis of all scientific investigation is observation.

Inferring Scientists often make inferences based on their observations. An inference is an attempt to explain or interpret observations or to say what caused what you observed.

When making an inference, be certain to use accurate data and observations. Analyze all of the data that you've collected. Then, based on everything you know, explain or interpret what you've observed.

Example When you drank a glass of orange juice after the volleyball game, you observed that the orange juice was cold as well as refreshing. You might infer that the juice was cold because it had been made much earlier in the day and had been kept in the refrigerator, or you might infer that it had just been made, using both cold water and ice. The only way to be sure which inference is correct is to investigate further.

Comparing and Contrasting

Observations can be analyzed by noting the similarities and differences between two or more objects or events that you observe. When you look at objects or events to see how they are similar, you are comparing them. Contrasting is looking for differences in similar objects or events.

Figure 15 Table comparing the nutritional value of *Cereal A* and *Cereal B*

Nutritional Value		
	Cereal A	Cereal B
Serving size	103 g	105 g
Calories	220	160
Total Fat	10 g	10 g
Protein	2.5 g	2.6 g
Total Carbohydrate	30 g	15 g

Example Suppose you were asked to compare and contrast the nutritional value of two kinds of cereal, *Cereal A* and *Cereal B.* You would start by looking at what is known about these cereals. Arrange this information in a table, like the one in **Figure 15.**

Similarities you might point out are that both cereals have similar serving sizes, amounts of total fat, and protein. Differences include *Cereal A* having a higher calorie value and containing more total carbohydrates than *Cereal B.*

Recognizing Cause and Effect

Have you ever watched something happen and then made suggestions about why it happened? If so, you have observed an effect and inferred a cause. The event is an effect, and the reason for the event is the cause.

Example Suppose that every time your teacher fed the fish in a classroom aquarium, she or he tapped the food container on the edge of the aquarium. Then, one day your teacher just happened to tap the edge of the aquarium with a pencil while making a point. You observed the fish swim to the surface of the aquarium to feed, as shown in **Figure 16.** What is the effect, and what would you infer to be the cause? The effect is the fish swimming to the surface of the aquarium. You might infer the cause to be the teacher tapping on the edge of the aquarium. In determining cause and effect, you have made a logical inference based on your observations.

Perhaps the fish swam to the surface because they reacted to the teacher's waving hand or for some other reason. When scientists are unsure of the cause of a certain event, they design controlled experiments to determine what causes the event. Although you have made a logical conclusion about the behavior of the fish, you would have to perform an experiment to be certain that it was the tapping that caused the effect you observed.

Figure 16 What cause-and-effect situations are occurring in this aquarium?

Science Skill Handbook

Practicing Scientific Processes

You might say that the work of a scientist is to solve problems. But when you decide how to dress on a particular day, you are doing problem solving, too. You may observe what the weather looks like through a window. You may go outside and see whether what you are wearing is heavy or light enough.

Scientists use an orderly approach to learn new information and to solve problems. The methods scientists may use include observing to form a hypothesis, designing an experiment to test a hypothesis, separating and controlling variables, and interpreting data.

Forming Operational Definitions

Operational definitions define an object by showing how it functions, works, or behaves. Such definitions are written in terms of how an object works or how it can be used; that is, what is its job or purpose?

Figure 17 What observations can be made about this dog?

Example Some operational definitions explain how an object can be used.

- A ruler is a tool that measures the size of an object.
- An automobile can move things from one place to another.

Or such a definition may explain how an object works.

- A ruler contains a series of marks that can be used as a standard when measuring.
- An automobile is a vehicle that can move from place to place.

Forming a Hypothesis

Observations You observe all the time. Scientists try to observe as much as possible about the things and events they study so they know that what they say about their observations is reliable.

Some observations describe something using only words. These observations are called qualitative observations. Other observations describe how much of something there is. These are quantitative observations and use numbers, as well as words, in the description. Tools or equipment are used to measure the characteristic being described.

Example If you were making qualitative observations of the dog in **Figure 17,** you might use words such as *furry, yellow,* and *short-haired.* Quantitative observations of this dog might include a mass of 14 kg, a height of 46 cm, ear length of 10 cm, and an age of 150 days.

Hypotheses Hypotheses are tested to help explain observations that have been made. They are often stated as *if* and *then* statements.

Examples Suppose you want to make a perfect score on a spelling test. Begin by thinking of several ways to accomplish this. Base these possibilities on past observations. If you put each of these possibilities into sentence form, using the words *if* and *then,* you can form a hypothesis. All of the following are hypotheses you might consider to explain how you could score 100 percent on your test:

If the test is easy, then I will get a perfect score.

If I am intelligent, then I will get a perfect score.

If I study hard, then I will get a perfect score.

Perhaps a scientist has observed that plants that receive fertilizer grow taller than plants that do not. A scientist may form a hypothesis that says: If plants are fertilized, then their growth will increase.

Designing an Experiment to Test a Hypothesis

In order to test a hypothesis, it's best to write out a procedure. A procedure is the plan that you follow in your experiment. A procedure tells you what materials to use and how to use them. After following the procedure, data are generated. From this generated data, you can then draw a conclusion and make a statement about your results.

If the conclusion you draw from the data supports your hypothesis, then you can say that your hypothesis is reliable. *Reliable* means that you can trust your conclusion. If it did not support your hypothesis, then you would have to make new observations and state a new hypothesis—just make sure that it is one that you can test.

Example Super premium gasoline costs more than regular gasoline. Does super premium gasoline increase the efficiency or fuel mileage of your family car? Let's figure out how to conduct an experiment to test the hypothesis, "*if* premium gas is more efficient, *then* it should increase the fuel mileage of our family car." Then a procedure similar to **Figure 18** must be written to generate data presented in **Figure 19** on the next page.

These data show that premium gasoline is less efficient than regular gasoline. It took more gasoline to travel one mile (0.064) using premium gasoline than it does to travel one mile using regular gasoline (0.059). This conclusion does not support the original hypothesis made.

PROCEDURE

1. Use regular gasoline for two weeks.
2. Record the number of miles between fill-ups and the amount of gasoline used.
3. Switch to premium gasoline for two weeks.
4. Record the number of miles between fill-ups and the amount of gasoline used.

Figure 18 Possible procedural steps

Figure 19 Data generated from procedure steps

Gasoline Data			
	Miles traveled	**Gallons used**	**Gallons per mile**
Regular gasoline	762	45.34	0.059
Premium gasoline	661	42.30	0.064

Separating and Controlling Variables

In any experiment, it is important to keep everything the same except for the item you are testing. The one factor that you change is called the *independent variable.* The factor that changes as a result of the independent variable is called the *dependent variable.* Always make sure that there is only one independent variable. If you allow more than one, you will not know what causes the changes you observe in the independent variable. Many experiments have *controls*—a treatment or an experiment that you can compare with the results of your test groups.

Example In the experiment with the gasoline, you made everything the same except the type of gasoline being used. The driver, the type of automobile, and the weather conditions should remain the same throughout. The gasoline should also be purchased from the same service station. By doing so, you made sure that at the end of the experiment, any differences were the result of the type of fuel being used—regular or premium. The type of gasoline was the *independent factor* and the gas mileage achieved was the *dependent factor.* The use of regular gasoline was the *control.*

Interpreting Data

The word *interpret* means "to explain the meaning of something." Look at the problem originally being explored in the gasoline experiment and find out what the data show. Identify the control group and the test group so you can see whether or not the variable has had an effect. Then, you need to check differences between the control and test groups.

Figure 20 Which gasoline type is most efficient?

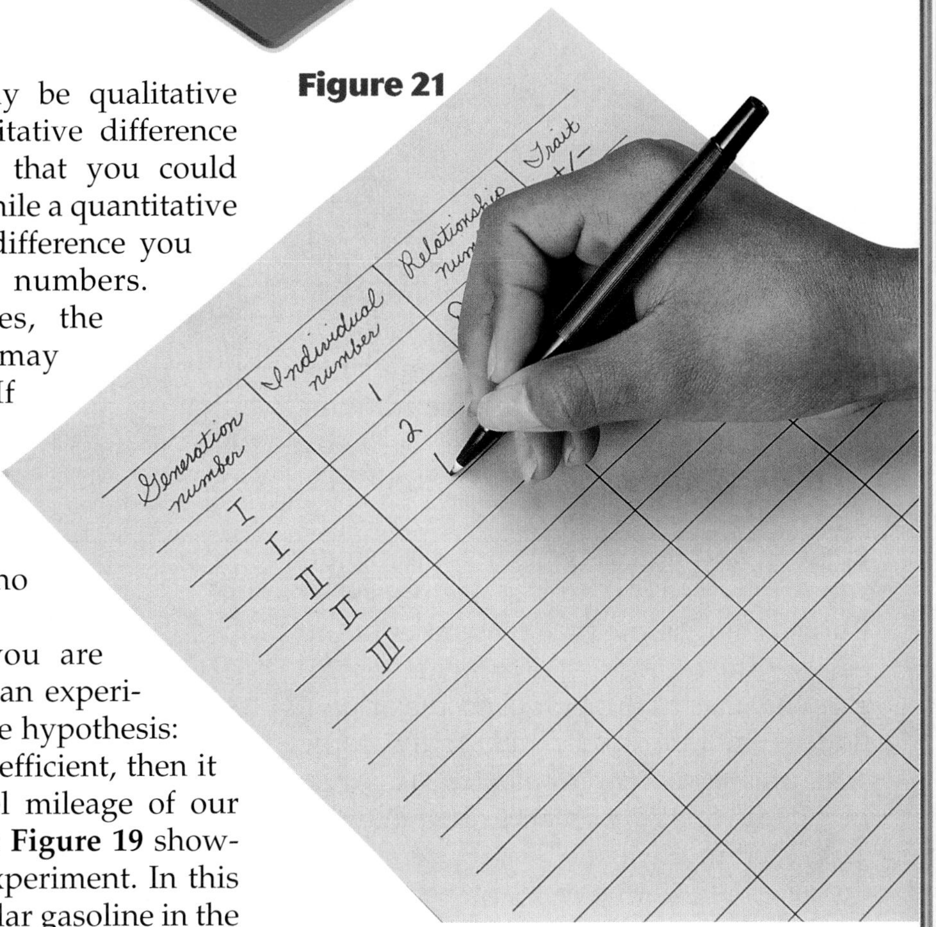

These differences may be qualitative or quantitative. A qualitative difference would be a difference that you could observe and describe, while a quantitative difference would be a difference you can measure using numbers. If there are differences, the variable being tested may have had an effect. If there is no difference between the control and the test groups, the variable being tested apparently has had no effect.

Example Perhaps you are looking at a table from an experiment designed to test the hypothesis: If premium gas is more efficient, then it should increase the fuel mileage of our family car. Look back at **Figure 19** showing the results of this experiment. In this example, the use of regular gasoline in the family car was the control, while the car being fueled by premium gasoline was the test group.

Data showed a quantitative difference in efficiency for gasoline consumption. It took 0.059 gallons of regular gasoline to travel one mile, while it took 0.064 gallons of the premium gasoline to travel the same distance. The regular gasoline was more efficient; it increased the fuel mileage of the family car.

What are data? In the experiment described on these pages, measurements were taken so that at the end of the experiment, you had something concrete to interpret. You had numbers to work with. Not every experiment that you do will give you data in the form of numbers. Sometimes, data will be in the form of a description. At the end of a chemistry experiment, you might have noted that one solution turned yellow when treated with a particular chemical, and another remained colorless, as water, when treated with the same chemical. Data, therefore, are stated in different forms for different types of scientific experiments.

Are all experiments alike? Keep in mind as you perform experiments in science that not every experiment makes use of all of the parts that have been described on these pages. For some, it may be difficult to design an experiment that will always have a control. Other experiments are complex enough that it may be hard to have only one dependent variable. Real scientists encounter many variations in the methods that they use when they perform experiments. The skills in this handbook are here for you to use and practice. In real situations, their uses will vary.

Figure 21

Representing and Applying Data

Interpreting Scientific Illustrations

As you read a science textbook, you will see many drawings, diagrams, and photographs. Illustrations help you to understand what you read. Some illustrations are included to help you understand an idea that you can't see easily by yourself. For instance, we can't see atoms, but we can look at a diagram of an atom and that helps us to understand some things about atoms. Seeing something often helps you remember more easily. Illustrations also provide examples that clarify difficult concepts or give additional information about the topic you are studying. Maps, for example, help you to locate places that may be described in the text.

Examples

Captions and Labels Most illustrations have captions. A caption is a comment that identifies or explains the illustration. Diagrams, such as **Figure 22,** often have labels that identify parts of the organism or the order of steps in a process.

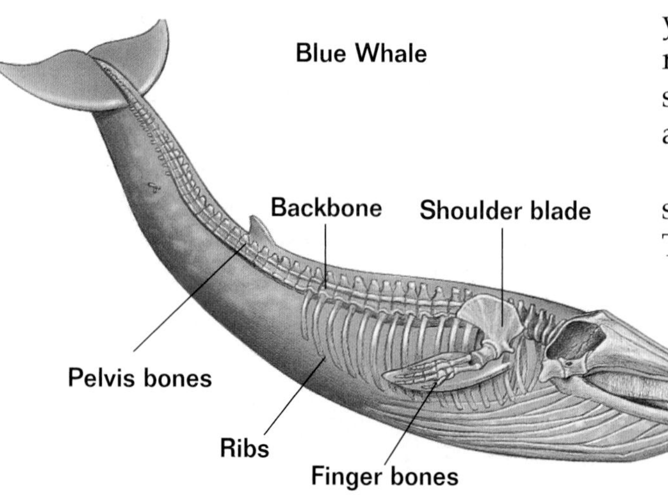

Figure 22 A labeled diagram of a blue whale

Figure 23 The orientation of a dog is shown here.

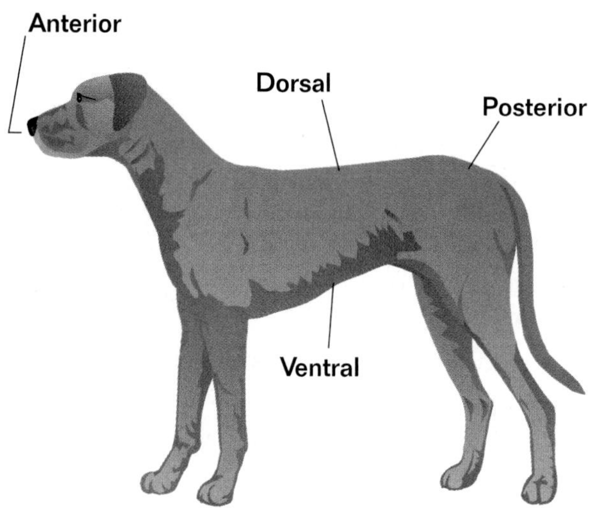

Learning with Illustrations An illustration of an organism shows that organism from a particular view or orientation. In order to understand the illustration, you may need to identify the front (anterior) end, tail (posterior) end, the underside (ventral), and the back (dorsal) side, as shown in **Figure 23.**

You might also check for symmetry. A shark in **Figure 24** has bilateral symmetry. This means that drawing an imaginary line through the center of the animal from the anterior to posterior end forms two mirror images.

Radial symmetry is the arrangement of similar parts around a central point. An object or organism, such as a hydra, can be divided anywhere through the center into similar parts.

Some organisms and objects cannot be divided into two similar parts. If an

Figure 24 A shark (A) illustrating bilateral symmetry and a pear (B) illustrating a longitudinal section and a cross section

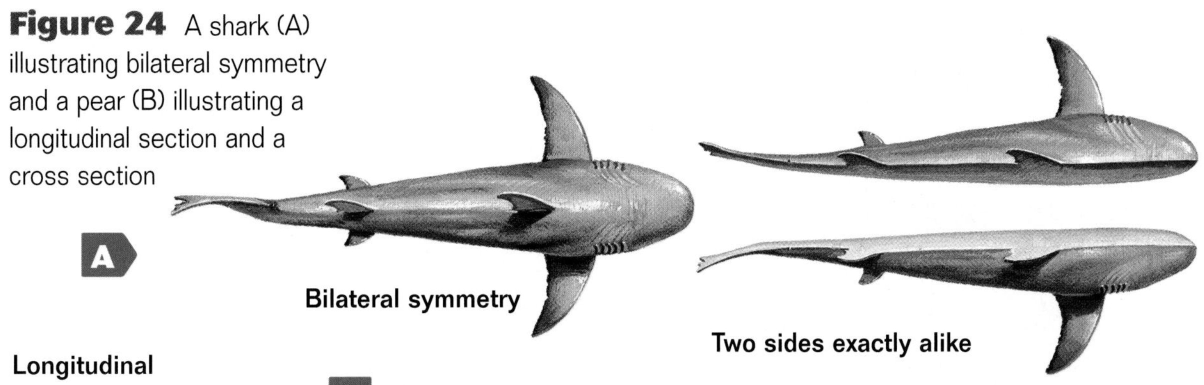

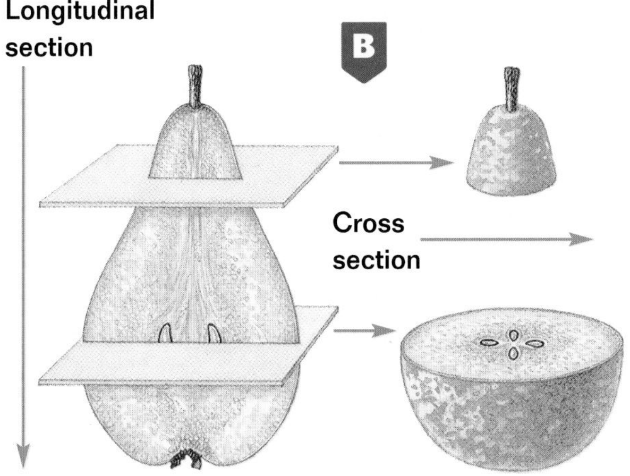

organism or object cannot be divided, it is asymmetrical. Regardless of how you try to divide a natural sponge, you cannot divide it into two parts that look alike.

Some illustrations enable you to see the inside of an organism or object. These illustrations are called sections. **Figure 24** also illustrates some common sections.

Look at all illustrations carefully. Read captions and labels so that you understand exactly what the illustration is showing you.

Making Models

Have you ever worked on a model car, plane, or rocket? These models look, and sometimes work, much like the real thing, but they are often on a different scale than the real thing. In science, models are used to help simplify large or small processes or structures that otherwise would be difficult to see and understand. Your understanding of a structure or process is enhanced when you work with materials to make a model that shows the basic features of the structure or process.

Example In order to make a model, you first have to get a basic idea about the structure or process involved. You decide to make a model to show the differences in size of arteries, veins, and capillaries. First, read about these structures. All three are hollow tubes. Arteries are round and thick. Veins are flat and have thinner walls than arteries. Capillaries are small.

Now, decide what you can use for your model. Common materials are often most useful and cheapest to work with when making models. As illustrated in **Figure 25** on the next page, different kinds and sizes of pasta might work for these models. Different sizes of rubber tubing might do just as well. Cut and glue the different noodles or tubing onto thick paper so the openings can be seen. Then label each. Now you have a simple, easy-to-understand model showing the differences in size of arteries, veins, and capillaries.

What other scientific ideas might a model help you to understand? A model of a molecule can be made from balls of modeling clay (using different colors for the different elements present) and toothpicks (to show different chemical bonds).

Figure 25 Different types of pasta may be used to model blood vessels

A working model of a volcano can be made from clay, a small amount of baking soda, vinegar, and a bottle cap. Other models can be devised on a computer. Some models are mathematical and are represented by equations.

Measuring in SI

The metric system is a system of measurement developed by a group of scientists in 1795. It helps scientists avoid problems by providing standard measurements that all scientists around the world can understand. A modern form of the metric system, called the International System, or SI, was adopted for worldwide use in 1960.

The metric system is convenient because unit sizes vary by multiples of 10. When changing from smaller units to larger units, divide by 10. When changing from larger units to smaller, multiply by 10. For example, to convert millimeters to centimeters, divide the millimeters by 10. To convert 30 millimeters to centimeters, divide 30 by 10 (30 millimeters equal 3 centimeters).

Prefixes are used to name units. Look at **Figure 26** for some common metric prefixes and their meanings. Do you see how the prefix *kilo-* attached to the unit *gram* is *kilogram,* or 1000 grams? The prefix *deci-* attached to the unit *meter* is *decimeter,* or one-tenth (0.1) of a meter.

Examples

Length You have probably measured lengths or distances many times. The meter is the SI unit used to measure length. A baseball bat is about one meter long. When measuring smaller lengths, the meter is divided into smaller units called centimeters and millimeters. A centimeter is one-hundredth (0.01) of a meter, which is about the size of the width of the fingernail on your ring finger. A millimeter is one-thousandth of a meter (0.001), about the thickness of a dime.

Most metric rulers have lines indicating centimeters and millimeters, as shown in

Figure 26 Common metric prefixes

Metric Prefixes

Prefix	Symbol	Meaning	
kilo-	k	1000	thousand
hecto-	h	100	hundred
deca-	da	10	ten
deci-	d	0.1	tenth
centi-	c	0.01	hundredth
milli-	m	0.001	thousandth

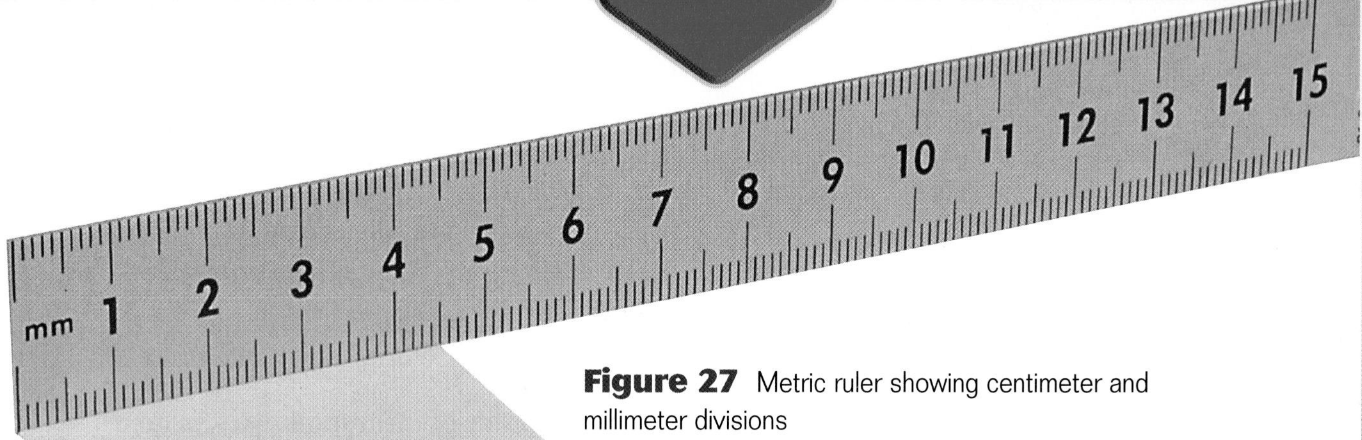

Figure 27 Metric ruler showing centimeter and millimeter divisions

Figure 27. The centimeter lines are the longer, numbered lines; the shorter lines are millimeter lines. When using a metric ruler, line up the 0-centimeter mark with the end of the object being measured, and read the number of the unit where the object ends, in this instance 4.5 cm.

Surface Area Units of length are also used to measure surface area. The standard unit of area is the square meter (m^2). A square that's one meter long on each side has a surface area of one square meter. Similarly, a square centimeter, (cm^2), shown in **Figure 28,** is one centimeter long on each side. The surface area of an object is determined by multiplying the length times the width.

Volume The volume of a rectangular solid is also calculated using units of length. The cubic meter (m^3) is the standard SI unit of volume. A cubic meter is a cube one meter on each side. You can determine the volume of rectangular solids by multiplying length times width times height.

Liquid Volume During science activities, you will measure liquids using beakers and graduated cylinders marked in milliliters, as illustrated in **Figure 29.** A graduated cylinder is a cylindrical container marked with lines from bottom to top.

Liquid volume is measured using a unit called a liter. A liter has the volume of 1000 cubic centimeters. Because the prefix *milli-* means thousandth (0.001), a milliliter equals one cubic centimeter. One milliliter of liquid would completely fill a cube measuring one centimeter on each side.

Figure 28 A square centimeter

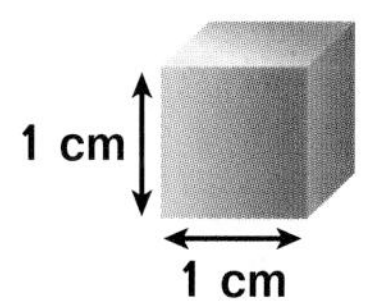

Figure 29 A volume of 79 mL is measured by reading at the lowest point of the curve.

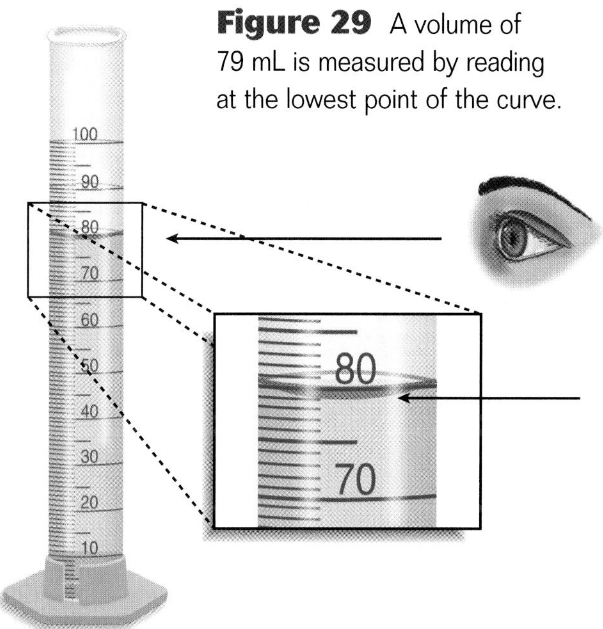

Mass Scientists use balances to find the mass of objects in grams. You might use a beam balance similar to **Figure 30.** Notice that on one side of the balance is a pan and on the other side is a set of beams. Each beam has an object of a known mass called a *rider* that slides on the beam.

Before you find the mass of an object, set the balance to zero by sliding all the riders back to the zero point. Check the pointer on the right to make sure it swings an equal distance above and below the zero point on the scale. If the swing is unequal, find and turn the adjusting screw until you have an equal swing.

Place an object on the pan. Slide the rider with the largest mass along its beam until the pointer drops below zero. Then move it back one notch. Repeat the process on each beam until the pointer swings an equal distance above and below the zero point. Add the masses on each beam to find the mass of the object.

You should never place a hot object or pour chemicals directly onto the pan. Instead, find the mass of a clean beaker or a glass jar. Place the dry or liquid chemicals in the container. Then find the combined mass of the container and the chemicals. Calculate the mass of the chemicals by subtracting the mass of the empty container from the combined mass.

Predicting

When you apply a hypothesis, or general explanation, to a specific situation, you predict something about that situation. First, you must identify which hypothesis fits the situation you are considering.

Examples People use prediction to make everyday decisions. Based on previous observations and experiences, you may form a hypothesis that if it is wintertime, then temperatures will be lower. From past experience in your area, temperatures are lowest in February. You may then use this hypothesis to predict specific temperatures and weather for the month of February in advance. Someone could use these predictions to plan to set aside more money for heating bills during that month.

Figure 30 A beam balance is used to measure mass.

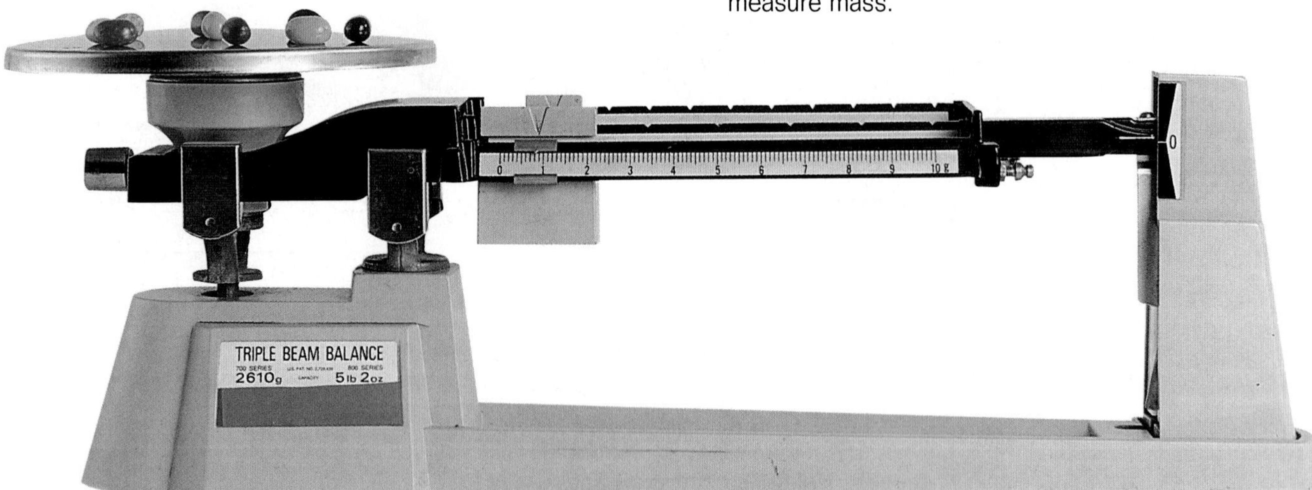

Using Numbers

When working with large populations of organisms, scientists usually cannot observe or study every organism in the population. Instead, they use a sample or a portion of the population. To sample is to take a small representative portion of organisms of a population for research. By making careful observations or manipulating variables within a portion of a group, information is discovered and conclusions are drawn that might then be applied to the whole population.

Scientific work also involves estimating. To estimate is to make a judgment about the size of something or the number of something without actually measuring or counting every member of a population.

Examples Suppose you are trying to determine the effect of a specific nutrient on the growth of black-eyed Susans. It would be impossible to test the entire population of black-eyed Susans, so you would select part of the population for your experiment. Through careful experimentation and observation on a sample of the population, you could generalize the effect of the chemical on the entire population.

Here is a more familiar example. Have you ever tried to guess how many beans were in a sealed jar? If you did, you were estimating. What if you knew the jar of beans held one liter (1000 mL)? If you knew that 30 beans would fit in a 100-milliliter jar, how many beans would you estimate to be in the one-liter jar? If you said about 300 beans, your estimate would be close to the actual number of beans. Can you estimate how many jelly beans are on the cookie sheet in **Figure 31?**

Scientists use a similar process to estimate populations of organisms from bacteria to buffalo. Scientists count the actual number of organisms in a small sample and then estimate the number of organisms in a larger area. For example, if a scientist wanted to count the number of bacterial colonies in a petri dish, a microscope could be used to count the number of organisms in a one-square-centimeter sample. To determine the total population of the culture, the number of organisms in the square-centimeter sample is multiplied by the total number of square centimeters in the culture.

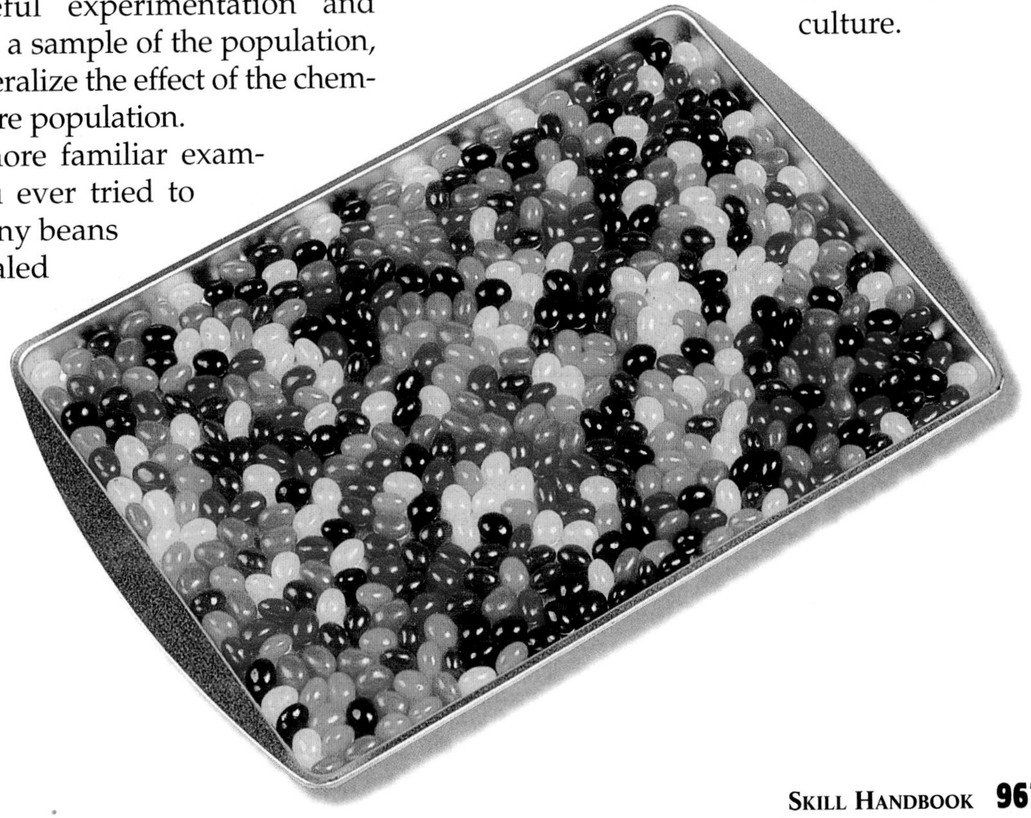

Figure 31
Sampling a group of jelly beans allows for an estimation of the total number of jelly beans in the group.

Using a Word Processor

Suppose your teacher has assigned you to write a report. After you've done your research and decided how you want to write the information, you need to put all that information on paper. The easiest way to do this is with a word processor.

A word processor is a computer program in which you can write your information, change it as many times as you need to, and then print it out so that it looks neat and clean. You can also use a word processor to create tables and columns, add bullets or cartoon art, include page numbers, and even check your spelling.

Example Last week in Science class, your teacher assigned a report on the history of the atom. It has to be double spaced and include at least one table. You've collected all the facts, and you're ready to write your report. Sitting down at your computer, you decide you want to begin by explaining early scientific ideas about the atom and then talk about what scientists think about the atom now.

After you've written the two parts of your report, you decide to put a heading or subtitle above each part and add a title to the paper. To make each of these look different from the rest of your report, you can use a word processor to make the words bigger and bolder. The word processor also can double space your entire report, so that you don't have to add an extra space between each line.

You decide to include a table that lists each scientist that contributed to the theory of the atom along with his or her contribution. Using your word processor, you can create a table with as many rows and columns as you need. And, if you forget to include a scientist in the middle, you can go back and insert a row in the middle of your table without redoing the entire table.

When you've finished with your report, you can tell the word processor to check your spelling. If it finds misspelled words, it often will suggest a word you can use to replace the misspelled word. But, remember that the word processor may not know how to spell all the words in your report. Scan your report and double check your spelling with a dictionary if you're not sure if a word is spelled correctly.

After you've made sure that your report looks just the way you want it on the screen, the word processor will print your report on a printer. With a word processor, your report can look like it was written by a real scientist.

Helpful Hints

- If you aren't sure how to do something using your word processor, look under the help menu. You can look up how to do something, and the word processor will tell you how to do it. Just follow the instructions that the word processor puts on your screen.
- Just because you've spelled checked your report doesn't mean that the spelling is perfect. The spell check can't catch misspelled words that look like other words. So, if you've accidentally typed *mind* instead of *mine,* the spell checker won't know the difference. Always reread your report to make sure you didn't miss any mistakes.

Using a Database

Imagine you're in the middle of research project. You are busily gathering facts and information. But, soon you realize that its becoming harder and harder to organize and keep track of all the information. The tool to solve "information overload" is a database. A database is exactly what it sounds like—a base on which to organize data. Similar to how a file cabinet organizes records, a database also organizes records. However, a database is more powerful than a simple file cabinet because at the click of a mouse, the entire contents can be reshuffled and reorganized. At computer-quick speeds, databases can sort information by any characteristic and filter data into multiple categories. Once you use a database, you will be amazed at how quickly all those facts and bits of information become manageable.

Example For the past few weeks, you have been gathering information on living and extinct primates. A database would be ideal to organize your information. An entry for gorillas might contain fields (categories) for fossil locations, brain size, average height, earliest fossil, and so on. Later on, if you wanted to know which primates have been found in Asia, you could quickly filter all entries using Asia in the field that listed locations. The database will scan all the entries and select the entries containing Asia. If you wanted to rank all the primates by arm length, you would sort all the entries by arm length. By using different combinations of sorting and filtering, you can discover relationships between the data that otherwise might remain hidden.

Helpful Hints

- Before setting up your own database, it's easier to learn the features of your database software by practicing with an established database.
- Entering the data into a database can be time consuming. Learn shortcuts such as tabbing between entry fields and automatic formatting of data that your software may provide.
- Get in the habit of periodically saving your database as you are entering data. That way, if something happens and your computer locks up or the power goes out, you won't lose all of your work. Most databases have specific words you can use to narrow your search.
- AND: If you place an AND between two words in your search, the database will look for any entries that have both the words. For example, "blood AND cell" would give you information about both blood and cells.
- OR: If you place an OR between two words, the database will show entries that have at least one of the words. For example, "bird OR fish" would show you information on either birds or fish.
- NOT: If you place a NOT between two words, the database will look for entries that have the first word but do not have the second word. For example, "reproduction NOT plant" would show you information about reproduction but not about plant reproduction.

Using Graphics Software

Having trouble finding that exact piece of art you're looking for? Do you have a picture in your mind of what you want but can't seem to find the right graphic to represent your ideas? To solve these problems, you can use graphics software. Graphics software allows you to change and create images and diagrams in almost unlimited ways. Typical uses for graphics software include arranging clip-art, changing scanned images, and constructing pictures from scratch. Most graphics-software applications work in similar ways. They use the same basic tools and functions. Once you master one graphics application, you can use any other graphics application relatively easily.

Example For your report on bird adaptations, you want to make a poster displaying a variety of beak and foot types. You have acquired many photos of birds, scanned from magazines and downloaded off the Internet. Using graphics software, you separate the beaks and feet from the birds and enlarge them. Then, you use arrows and text to diagram the particular features that you want to highlight. You also highlight the key features in color, keeping the rest of the graphic in black and white. With graphics software, the possibilities are endless. For the final layout, you place the picture of the bird next to enlarged graphics of the feet and beak. Graphics software allows you to integrate text into your diagrams, which makes your bird poster look clean and professional.

Helpful Hints

- As with any method of drawing, the more you practice using the graphic software, the better your results.
- Start by using the software to manipulate existing drawings. Once you master this, making your own illustrations will be easier.
- Clip art is available on CD-ROMs, and on the Internet. With these resources, finding a piece of clip art to suit your purposes is simple.
- As you work on a drawing, save it often.
- Often you can learn a lot from studying other people's art. Look at other computer illustrations and try to figure out how the artist created it.

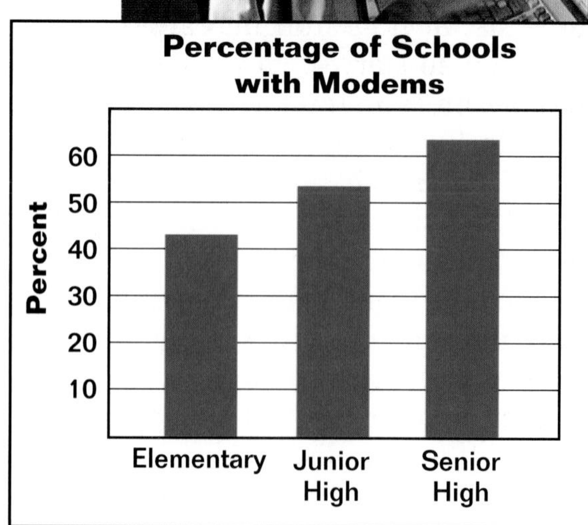

Using a Computerized Card Catalog

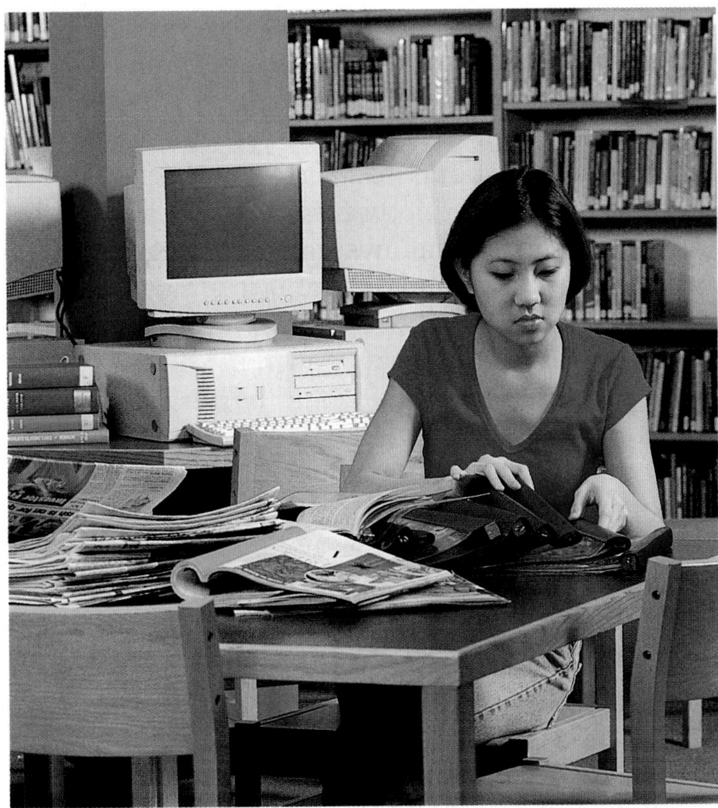

When you have a report or paper to research, you go to the library. To find the information, skill is needed in using a computerized card catalog. You use the computerized card catalog by typing in a subject, the title of a book, or an author's name. The computer will list on the screen all the holdings the library has on the subject, title, or author requested.

A library's holdings include books, magazines, databases, videos, and audio materials. When you have chosen something from this list, the computer will show whether an item is available and where in the library to find it.

Example You have a report due on dinosaurs, and you need to find three books on the subject. In the library, follow the instructions on the computer screen to select the "Subject" heading. You could start by typing in the word *dinosaurs.* This will give you a list of books on that subject. Now you need to narrow your search to the kind of dinosaur you are interested in, for example, *Tyrannosaurus rex.* You can type in *Tyrannosaurus rex* or just look through the list to find titles that you think would have information you need. Once you have selected a short list of books, click on each selection to find out if the library has the books. Then, check on where they are located in the library.

Helpful Hints

- Remember that you can use the computer to search by subject, author, or title. If you know a book's author, but not the title, you can search for all the books the library has by that author.
- When searching by subject, it's often most helpful to narrow your search by using specific search terms. If you don't find enough, you can then broaden your search.
- Pay attention to the type of materials found in your search. If you need a book, you can eliminate any videos or other resources that come up in your search.
- Knowing how your library is arranged can save a lot of time. The librarian will show you where certain types of material are kept and how to find something.

Developing Multimedia Presentations

It's your turn—you have to present your science report to the entire class. How do you do it? You can use many different sources of information to get the class excited about your presentation. Posters, videos, photographs, sound, computers, and the Internet can help show our ideas. First, decide the most important points you want your presentation to make. Then, sketch out what materials and types of media would be best to illustrate those points. Maybe you could start with an outline on an overhead projector, then show a video, followed by something from the Internet or a slide show accompanied by music or recorded voices. Make sure you don't make the presentation too complicated, or you will confuse yourself and the class. Practice your presentation a few times for your parents or brothers and sisters before you present it to the class.

Example Your assignment is to give a presentation on bird-watching. You could have a poster that shows what features you use to identify birds, with a sketch of your favorite bird. A tape of the calls of your favorite bird or a video of birds in your area would work well with the poster. If possible, include an Internet site with illustrations of birds that the class can look at.

Helpful Hints

- Carefully consider what media will best communicate the point you are trying to make.
- Keep your topic and your presentation simple.
- Make sure you learn how to use any equipment you will be using in your presentation.
- Practice the presentation several times.
- If possible, set up all of the equipment ahead of time. Make sure everything is working correctly.

Using E-Mail

It's science fair time and you want to ask a scientist a question about your project, but he or she lives far away. You could write a letter or make a phone call. But you can also use the computer to communicate. You can do this using electronic mail (E-mail). You will need a computer that is connected to an E-mail network. The computer is usually hooked up to the network by a device called a *modem.* A modem works through the telephone lines. Finally, you need an address for the person you want to talk with. The E-mail address works just like a street address to send mail to that person.

Example There are just a few steps needed to send a message to a friend on an E-mail network. First, select Message from the E-mail software menu. Then, enter the E-mail address of your friend. Next, type your message. Make sure you check it for spelling and other errors. Finally, click the Send button to mail your message and off it goes! You will get a reply back in your electronic mailbox. To read your reply, just click on the message and the reply will appear on the screen.

Helpful Hints

- Make sure that you have entered the correct address of the person you're sending the message to.
- Reread your message to make sure it says what you want to say, and check for spelling and grammar.
- If you receive an E-mail message, respond to it as soon as possible.
- If you receive frequent email messages, keep them organized by either deleting them, or saving them in folders according to the subject or sender.

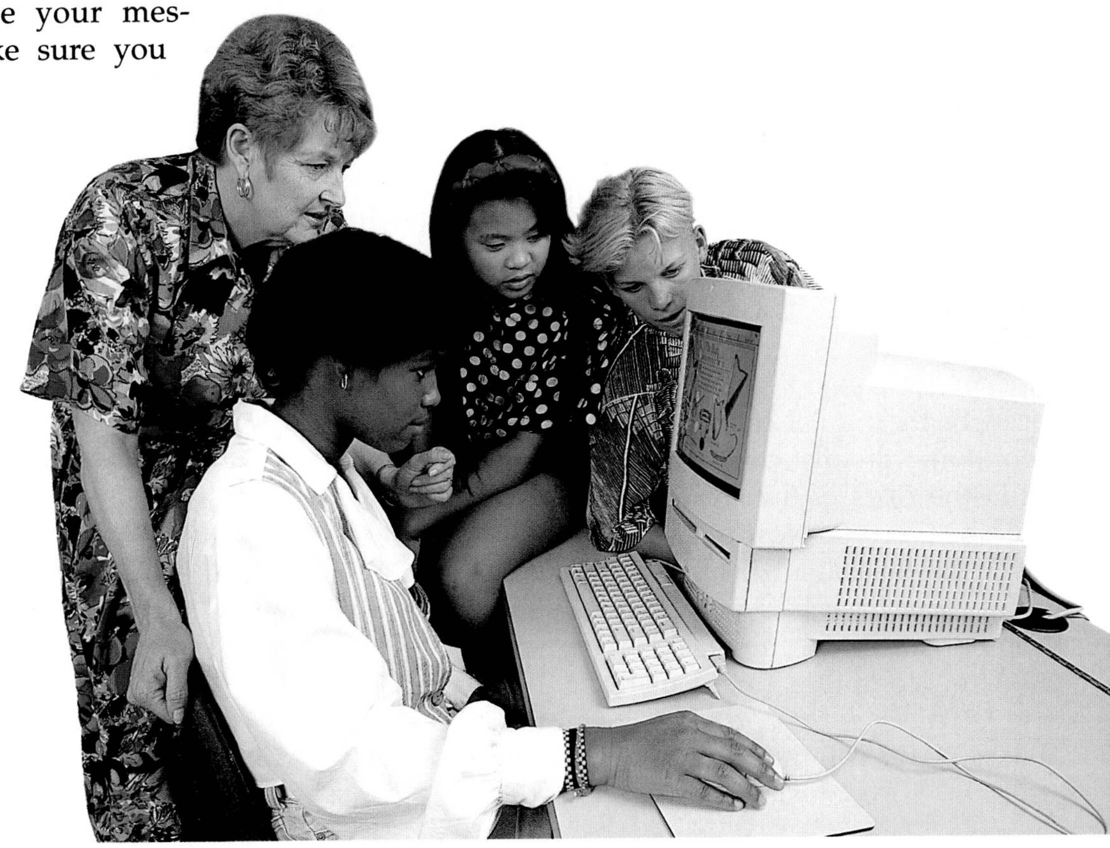

Using an Electronic Spreadsheet

	A	B	C	D
1	Test Runs	Time	Distance	Speed
2	Car 1	5 mins.	5 miles	60 mph
3	Car 2	10 mins.	4 miles	24 mph
4	Car 3	6 mins.	3 miles	30 mph
5				
6				
7				
8				
9				
10				
11				
12				
13				
14				

Your science fair experiment has produced lots of numbers. How do you keep track of all the data, and how can you easily work out all the calculations needed? You can use a computer program called a *spreadsheet* to keep track of data that involve numbers. A spreadsheet is an electronic worksheet. Type in your data in rows and columns, just as in a data table on a sheet of paper. A spreadsheet uses some simple math to do calculations on the data. For example, you could add, subtract, divide, or multiply any of the values in the spreadsheet by another number. Or you can set up a series of math steps you want to apply to the data. If you want to add 12 to all the numbers and then multiply all the numbers by 10, the computer does all the calculations for you in the spreadsheet. Below is an example of a spreadsheet that is a schedule.

Example Let's say that to complete your project, you need to calculate the speed of the model cars in your experiment. Enter the distance traveled by each car in the rows of the spreadsheet. Then enter the time you recorded for each car to travel the measured distance in the column across from each car. To make the formula, just type in the equation you want the computer to calculate; in this case, *speed* = *distance* ÷ *time.* You must make sure the computer knows what data are in the rows and what data are in the columns so the calculation will be correct. Once all the distance and time data and the formula have been entered into the spreadsheet program, the computer will calculate the speed for all the trials you ran. You can even make graphs of the results.

Helpful Hints

- Before you set up the spreadsheet, sketch out how you want to organize the data. Include any formulas you will need to use.
- Make sure you have entered the correct data into the correct rows and columns.
- As you experiment with your particular spreadsheet program you will learn more of its features.
- You can also display your results in a graph. Pick the style of graph that best represents the data you are working with.

Technology Skill Handbook

Using a CD-ROM

What's your favorite music? You probably listen to your favorite music on compact discs (CDs). But, there is another use for compact discs, called CD-ROM. CD-ROM means Compact Disc-Read Only Memory. CD-ROMs hold information. Whole encyclopedias and dictionaries can be stored on CD-ROM discs. This kind of CD-ROM and others are used to research information for reports and papers. The information is accessed by putting the disc in your computer's CD-ROM drive and following the computer's installation instructions. The CD-ROM will have words, pictures, photographs, and maybe even sound and video on a range of topics.

Example Load the CD-ROM into the computer. Find the topic you are interested in by clicking on the Search button. If there is no Search button, try the Help button. Most CD-ROMs are easy to use, but refer to the Help instructions if you have problems. Use the arrow keys to move down through the list of titles on your topic. When you double-click on a title, the article will appear on the screen. You can print the article by clicking on the Print button. Each CD-ROM is different. Click the Help menu to see how to find what you want.

Helpful Hints

- Always open and close the CD-ROM drive on your computer by pushing the button next to the drive. Pushing on the tray to close it will stress the opening mechanism over time.
- Place the disc in the tray so the side with no printing is facing down.
- Read through the installation instructions that come with the CD-ROM.
- Remember to remove the CD-ROM before you shut your computer down.

Using Probeware

Data collecting in an experiment sometimes requires that you take the same measurement over and over again. With probeware, you can hook a probe directly to a computer and have the computer collect the data about temperature, pressure, motion, or pH. Probeware is a combination sensor and software that makes the process of collecting data easier. With probes hooked to computers, you can make many measurements quickly, and you can collect data over a long period of time without needing to be present. Not only will the software record the data, most software will graph the data.

Example Suppose you want to monitor the health of an enclosed ecosystem. You might use an oxygen and a carbon dioxide sensor to monitor the gas concentrations or humidity or temperature. If the gas concentrations remain stable, you could predict that the ecosystem is healthy. After all the data is collected, you can use the software to graph the data and analyze it. With probeware, experimenting is made efficient and precise.

Helpful Hints

- Find out how to properly use each probe before using it.
- Make sure all cables are solidly connected. A loose cable can interrupt the data collection and give you inaccurate results.
- Because probeware makes data collection so easy, do as many trials as possible to strengthen your data.

Using a Graphing Calculator

Science can be thought of as a means to predict the future and explain the past. In other language, if x happens, can we predict y? Can we explain the reason y happened? Simply, is there a relationship between x and y? In nature, a relationship between two events or two quantities, x and y, often occurs. However, the relationship is often complicated and can only be readily seen by making a graph. To analyze a graph, there is no quicker tool than a graphing calculator. The graphing calculator shows the mathematical relationship between two quantities.

Example If you have collected data on the position and time for a migrating whale, you can use the calculator to graph the data. Using the linear regression function on the calculator, you can determine the average migration speed of the whale. The more you use the graphing calculator to solve problems, the more you will discover its power and efficiency.

Graphing calculators have some keys that other calculators do not have. The keys on the bottom half of the calculator are those found on all scientific calculators. The keys located just below the screen are the graphing keys. You will also notice the up, down, left, and right arrow keys. These allow you to move the cursor around on the screen, to "trace" graphs that have been plotted, and to choose items from the menus. The other keys located on the top of the calculator access the special features such as statistical computations and programming features.

A few of the keystrokes that can save you time when using the graphing calculator are listed below.

- The commands above the calculator keys are accessed with the [2nd] or [ALPHA] key. The [2nd] key and its commands are yellow and the [ALPHA] and its commands are green.
- [2nd] [ENTRY] copies the previous calculation so you can edit and use it again.
- Pressing [ON] while the calculator is graphing stops the calculator from completing the graph.
- [2nd] [QUIT] will return you to the home (or text) screen.
- [2nd] [A-LOCK] locks the [ALPHA] key, which is like pressing "shift lock" or "caps lock" on a typewriter or computer. The result is that all letters will be typed and you do not have to repeatedly press the [ALPHA] key. (This is handy for programming.) Stop typing letters by pressing [ALPHA] again.
- [2nd] [OFF] turns the calculator off.

Helpful Hints

- Mastering the graphing calculator takes practice. Don't expect to learn it all in an afternoon.
- Programming a graphing calculator takes a plan. Write out all of the steps before entering them.
- It's easiest to learn how to program the calculator by first using programs that have already been written. As you enter them, figure out what each step is telling the calculator to do.

Skill Activities

Table of Contents

For further explanation and examples of this skill, refer to Using Numbers on page 967 of the **Skill Handbook.**

Teaching Strategies

- Demonstrate some simple rate problems for the students. Even though the numbers in this activity are large, the math is the same as any simple problem that involves distance, time, and velocity.
- Explain that the prefix "geo" means Earth.

Using Numbers

Background

The length of time it takes for a satellite to complete one orbit is called the orbital period. The greater the altitude of a satellite, the longer its orbital period. Satellites that stay above the same spot on Earth's surface are called geostationary satellites. Communication systems for telephone and television use geostationary satellites.

What is the altitude of a geostationary orbit? Try the following procedure to determine the altitude of a geostationary orbit.

Orbital Data

Altitude of orbit (km)	Orbital velocity (km/hr)	Orbital circumference (km)	Orbital period (hr)
10 000	26 470	46 400	1.8
20 000	17 770	103 000	5.8
30 000	11 920	229 000	19.2
40 000	10 560	292 000	27.7
50 000	9575	354 000	37.0

Procedure

1. The Orbital Data table lists the altitude, speed, and circumference of six different orbits. The orbital period can be calculated by dividing the circumference by the speed. Calculate the orbital periods for each altitude and record the data.
2. Make a line graph that compares the altitude and orbital period.

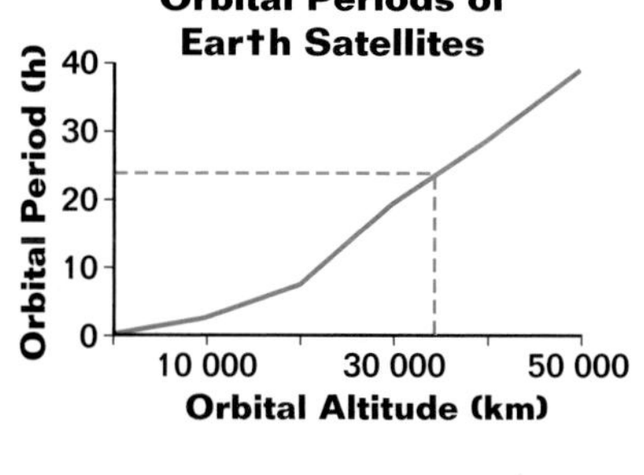

Practicing the SKILL

1. What is the relationship between the altitude and the orbital speed?
2. What is the approximate altitude of a satellite in a geostationary orbit?

For more skill practice, do the Chapter 17 Interactive Exploration on the **Science Voyages Level Blue CD-ROM.**

Practicing the SKILL

1. As altitude increases, the orbital velocity decreases.
2. The approximate altitude of a geostationary satellite is approximately 35 000 km.

Chapter 18

Skill Activity

Use After Section 18-2

Interpreting Scientific Illustrations

Background

During a total solar eclipse, the moon's shadow falls on Earth. The darkest part of the shadow, the umbra, traces a narrow, curved path across Earth's surface. By plotting the moon's orbit and phases, scientists are able to predict the umbra's path for future total solar eclipses. The world map below shows the times and locations of all total solar eclipses until the year 2020.

When and where will future total solar eclipses occur?

Procedure

1. Study the map of future eclipses.
2. Answer the questions in the Practicing the Skill box.

Practicing the SKILL

1. When will the next total solar eclipse occur in the United States? How old will you be at this time?
2. Which eclipse path will be located mostly over the ocean?
3. How many total solar eclipses will occur between the years 1999 and 2020?

For more skill practice, do the Chapter 18 Interactive Exploration on the **Science Voyages Level Blue CD-ROM.**

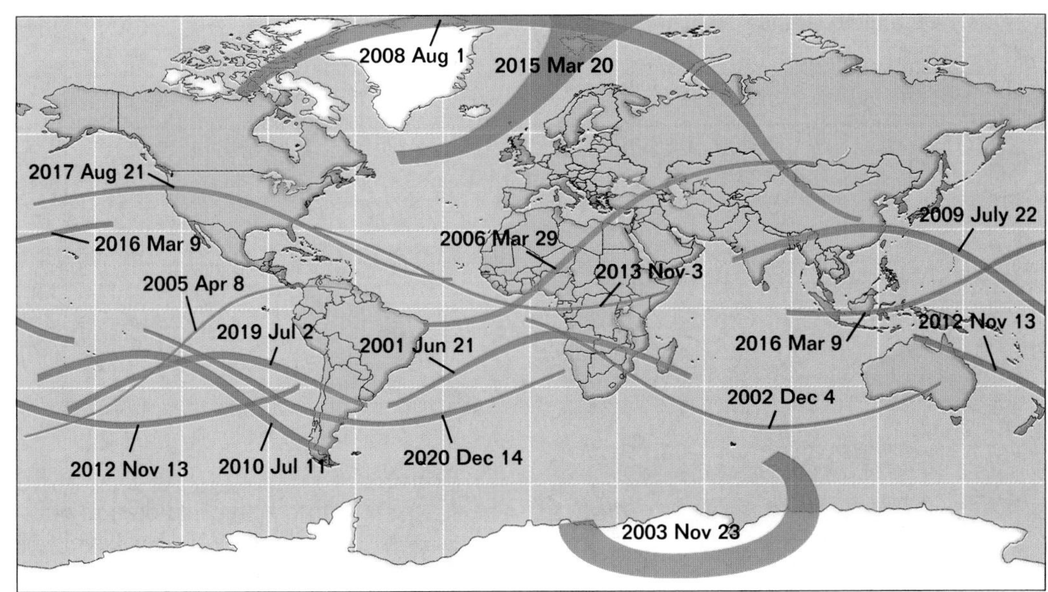

Practicing the SKILL

1. The next total solar eclipse in the United States will be August 21, 2017. Student ages at this time will vary.
2. Answers may vary due to individual interpretation. Answers may include the eclipse path of July 11, 2010 or the eclipse path of November 13, 2012.
3. There will be 19 total solar eclipses between 1999 and 2020.

For further explanation and examples of this skill, refer to Interpreting Scientific Illustrations on page 962 of the **Skill Handbook.**

Teaching Strategies

- Review the positions of the sun, the moon, and Earth during a solar eclipse.
- Use a globe, a light source, and a small ball attached to a wire to illustrate how the path of an eclipse moves across the surface of Earth.

For further explanation and examples of this skill, refer to Predicting on page 966 of the **Skill Handbook.**

Teaching Strategies

- Ask students this question: When we look at the sun, do we see the sun as it is now or as it was? Light takes eight minutes to travel from the sun to Earth. We see the sun as it was eight minutes ago.
- Review astronomical distances and light-years with students.
- Divide the class into groups. Assign each group a star listed in the Star Distances table. Have each group research historic events that took place when the star's light began its journey to Earth. Encourage students to share their research with other groups.

Chapter 19

Skill Activity

Use After Section 19-1

Inferring

Background

The surfaces of Earth's moon, Mercury, and other planetary bodies often are covered with craters. Scientists usually are unable to determine the exact age of the craters because they do not have actual rock samples. However, photographs taken by satellites help scientists determine the rough ages of the craters. For example, if two craters overlap, the crater that appears to be underneath is the older of the two.

Procedure

1. The diagram below shows an area containing several craters. Each crater is labeled by a letter in its center. Study the relationships between the craters and determine their relative ages.

Practicing the SKILL

1. Which crater occurred first, crater A or crater C?
2. Can the rough age of crater J be determined? Why or why not?
3. What is the estimated diameter of crater D?
4. List craters A through I in order of increasing age (youngest crater first).

For more skill practice, do the Chapter 19 Interactive Exploration on the **Science Voyages Level Blue CD-ROM.**

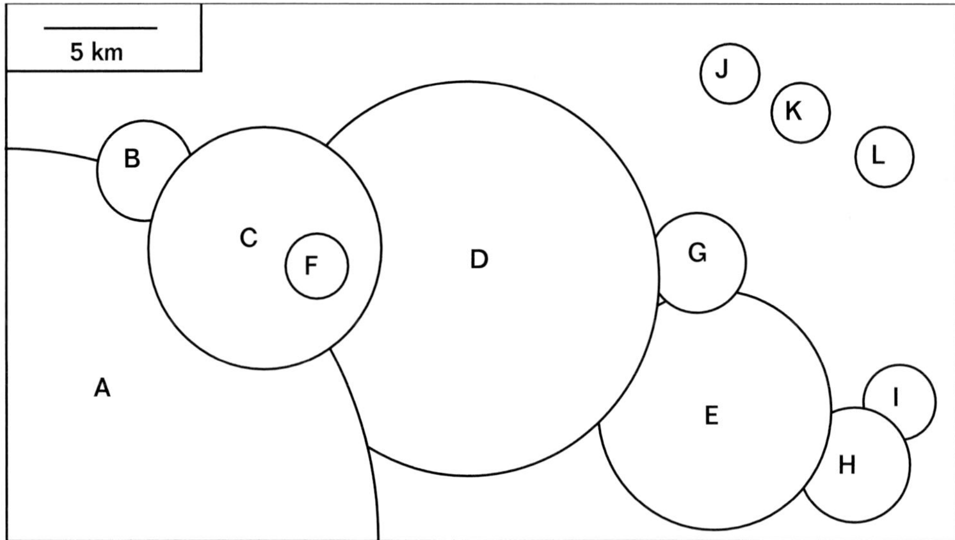

980 SKILL ACTIVITY 19–1

Practicing the SKILL

1. By the year 2000, the television signal would have reached Barnard's Star, Wolf 359, Sirius, Procyon, Altair, and Vega. By 2005, it would have reached Arcturus.
2. Answers will vary depending upon the references used.
3. Arcturus is approximately six times farther from Earth than Bernard's Star.

Predicting

Background

Astronomical distances are measured in light-years. A light-year is the distance that light can travel in one year. Proxima Centauri is a star that is 4.2 light-years away from Earth. When astronomers observe Proxima Centauri, they are seeing what occurred 4.2 years ago. In other words, when you look at the stars, you are looking back in time. The light astronomers observe for Proxima Centauri left the star 4.2 years ago.

What was happening on Earth when a star's light began its journey?

Star Distances

Star	Distance from Earth in light-years	Star	Distance from Earth in light-years
Sirius	8.8	Deneb	1800
Arcturus	36	Barnard's Star	5.9
Rigel	920	Wolf 359	7.6
Betelgeuse	310	Procyon	11
Antares	330	Altair	17
Vega	26	Regulus	85

Procedure

1. The Star Distances table lists the distances to several different stars. Study these distances to determine how long the light has been traveling toward Earth.
2. Using your history references, find a significant event that occurred when light from a particular star began its journey to Earth.
3. Make a data table that lists the significant historical events that occurred when light from the stars began the journey to Earth. Include the historical event, date, and the star in your table. Use at least six of the stars listed.

Practicing the SKILL

1. On July 20, 1969, astronauts landed on the moon. If a television signal showing this landing had been broadcast out to space, which stars would it have reached by the year 2000? by 2005? (Television signals travel at the speed of light, which is 300 000 km/s in a vacuum.)
2. Describe a historic event that took place when light from Rigel began traveling toward Earth.
3. How many times farther is Arcturus from Earth than Barnard's Star is?

For more skill practice, do the Chapter 20 Interactive Exploration on the **Science Voyages Level Blue CD-ROM.**

For further explanation and examples of this skill, refer to Predicting on page 966 of the **Skill Handbook.**

Teaching Strategies

- Ask students this question: When we look at the sun, do we see the sun as it is now or as it was? Light takes eight minutes to travel from the sun to Earth. We see the sun as it was eight minutes ago.
- Review astronomical distances and light-years with students.
- Divide the class into groups. Assign each group a star listed in the Star Distances table. Have each group research historic events that took place when the star's light began its journey to Earth. Encourage students to share their research with other groups.

Practicing the SKILL

1. By the year 2000, the television signal would have reached Barnard's Star, Wolf 359, Sirius, Procyon, Altair, and Vega. By 2005, it would have reached Arcturus.
2. Answers will vary depending upon the references used.
3. Arcturus is approximately six times farther from Earth than Bernard's Star.

For further explanation and examples of this skill, refer to Interpreting Data on page 960 of the **Skill Handbook.**

Teaching Stratagies

- Gather and prepare all materials ahead of time.
- Point out to students that, while most bacteria are quite harmless, some cause diseases. For this reason, people are concerned about their presence on doorknobs, hands, and in food.
- Discuss the use of various liquids people use to disinfect things. Ask students if they believe that all these products really work as claimed by their manufacturers.
- If possible, provide a long class period for Procedure steps 1 and 2. After steps 1 and 2 have been completed, seal all petri dishes with tape.
- Discuss results with the class and ask them what they learned.

Interpreting Data

Background

Bacteriologists are people who study microorganisms, grow bacteria in dishes, and perform experiments on them. Although individual bacteria are too small to see with the naked eye, colonies that contain large numbers of bacteria are visible. The color and shape of the colony can help to identify the type of bacteria.

Scientists often use tables to organize data from experiments. Having data laid out in a logical way makes it easier to interpret. To interpret means to explain why something is the way it is. Interpreting data is determining why you got the results you did. Reading the following procedure and studying the data table will help you learn to interpret data.

Procedure

1. Imagine you are a bacteriologist trying to determine which household item is most effective in preventing the growth of bacteria. You design an experiment in which you have three sterile petri dishes that contain nutrient agar. You rub your finger over the entire surface of the agar in dishes 1 and 2 to introduce bacteria.
2. Next, you cut four small squares of filter paper, soaking them each in one of the following substances: hydrogen peroxide, mouthwash, alcohol, and disinfectant. They are labeled and placed in dish 1, without touching or overlapping. All three petri dishes are covered and placed in a warm, dark place for two days.
3. At the end of two days, you take out each dish to observe any growth. The Bacterial Growth table is a record of your observations.

Bacterial Growth

Dish	Square	Observations
1	hydrogen peroxide	a few colonies are observed
	mouthwash	many colonies are observed
	alcohol	very little growth under square or in surrounding area
	disinfectant	no growth under square or in surrounding area
2	none	hundreds of colonies are present
3	none	no colonies are observed

Practicing the SKILL

1. According to the data above, which substance was most effective in preventing bacterial growth? Which was least effective?
2. In dish 2, bacteria were added but no substance was placed in the dish. What was the purpose of this?
3. Dish 3 contained neither bacteria nor a substance. What purpose did this dish serve?

For more skill practice, do the Chapter 21 Interactive Exploration on the **Science Voyages Level Blue CD-ROM.**

Practicing the SKILL

1. Disinfectant was most effective.
2. Dish 2 shows how the bacteria grow when left undisturbed. Results from Dish 1 can be compared with those of Dish 2.
3. Dish 3 shows the results when no bacteria is present. It proves that the bacteria came from your finger and weren't present in the agar, air, or petri dishes.

Making and Using Tables

Background

Tables are used to record information so that it can be understood easily. Tables help you find information quickly by summarizing information given in the text. A table is similar to a system of classification. Information is grouped in vertical columns so that similarities and differences can be recognized easily. A table has three main parts: a title, vertical columns, and column headings. Sometimes, horizontal lines are used to group the information further.

Procedure

1. Study **Table 22-1** in the Protists and Fungi chapter. Examine the title. Look down the four columns to see if the information is related to the title and to each of the column headings.
2. Examine the information in **Table 22-1.** Notice how all four columns contain information on plantlike protists.
3. Using **Table 22-1,** answer the questions under Practicing the Skill.
4. Make a table of your own, similar to **Table 22-1,** in which you compare the different types of fungi discussed in Section 22-2.

Practicing the SKILL

1. What is the purpose of **Table 22-1?**
2. Which plantlike protist is used to give food a creamy texture?
3. What two plantlike protists have flagella?
4. Which plantlike protist has an eye-spot?
5. What groups of protists contain one-celled organisms, and which contain many-celled organisms?
6. Which plantlike protist can cause red tide?
7. Which has cell walls that contain silica?
8. Which protist is an important food source?
9. Why are tables used?

For more skill practice, do the Chapter 22 Interactive Exploration on the **Science Voyages Level Blue CD-ROM.**

GLENCOE TECHNOLOGY

For further explanation and examples of this skill, refer to Making and Using Tables on page 952 of the **Skill Handbook.**

Teaching Strategies

- Review Table 22-1 with the students. Ask them to describe how tables are different from text in paragraph form. Discuss under what conditions a table might be more useful than written text as well as when written text might be more useful than a table.
- Have students complete the Skill Activity on their own.
- Discuss students' answers to the Practicing the Skill questions.

Practicing the SKILL

1. To give information about plantlike protist.
2. red algae
3. euglenoids and dinoflagellates
4. euglenoids
5. One-celled: euglenoids, diatoms, dinoflagellates, and green algae. Many-celled: green algae, red algae, and brown algae.
6. dinoflagellates
7. diatoms
8. brown algae
9. To display information in a manner that is organized and easy to understand.

23 Skill Activity

For further explanation and examples of this skill, refer to Classifying on page 949 of the **Skill Handbook.**

Teaching Strategies

- Gather a number of samples of gymnosperm branches and distribute sprigs to the students.
- Circulate among the students to assist with decision making. It might be helpful to have field guide to local trees available.
- Discuss the students' answers. Have students point out where they made errors or where the key seemed ambiguous.

Chapter 23 Skill Activity

Use after Section 23-3

Classifying

Background

Keys are used to identify things that are already classified.

In this Skill Activity, you will learn about some trees and how they have been classified. For this activity you need to know that needlelike leaves are shaped like needles and scalelike leaves are like the scales on a fish or a lizard.

How can you use a key to classify plants?

Procedure

1. Look at illustrations or actual examples of gymnosperm leaves.
2. Make a data table and record the number of each leaf down one side.
3. Use the key below to identify the leaves. There may be differences among the leaves. Choose the statement that describes most of the leaves on the branch. By following the key, the numbered steps will lead you to the name of the plant.

Key to Classifying Leaves

1. All leaves are needlelike.
   a. yes, go to 2
   b. no, go to 8
2. Needles are in clusters.
   a. yes, go to 3
   b. no, go to 4
3. Clusters contain 2, 3, or 5 needles.
   a. yes, pine
   b. no, cedar
4. Needles grow on all sides of the stem.
   a. yes, go to 5
   b. no, go to 7
5. Needles grow from a woody peg.
   a. yes, spruce
   b. no, go to 6
6. Needles appear to grow from the branch.
   a. yes, Douglas fir
   b. no, hemlock
7. Most of the needles grow upward.
   a. yes, fir
   b. no, redwood
8. All needles are scalelike but not prickly.
   a. yes, arborvitae
   b. no, juniper

Practicing the SKILL

1. What trait was used to separate the gymnosperm leaves into two groups?
2. What are two traits of a hemlock?
3. What gymnosperms have scalelike leaves?
4. Describe a spruce leaf.
5. How are pine and cedar leaves alike?

For more skill practice, do the Chapter 23 Interactive Exploration on the **Science Voyages Level Blue CD-ROM.**

Practicing the SKILL

1. needlelike or scalelike leaves
2. needlelike leaves and needles grow on all sides of the stem
3. arborvitae and juniper
4. needlelike leaves, needles grow on all sides of the stem, and needles from a woody peg
5. their leaves are needlelike and their needles grow in clusters

Comparing and Contrasting

Background

Determining the type of symmetry an animal has will help you describe the animal, as well as to determine what other animals it might be related to. In this Skill Activity, you will make some decisions about the type of symmetry of several animals.

Procedure

1. Review the discussion of symmetry in Section 24-1 of your textbook. Observe the animals pictured on this page.
2. Decide if the animal has radial symmetry, bilateral symmetry, or no symmetry.
3. Make a copy of the table below and record your answers in this table. If you need additional help, read about the animal's structure in reference books.
4. Explain how you decided what type of symmetry the animal has. Write your explanation in the table column labeled "Reason."

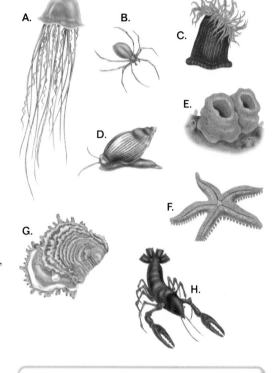

Sample Data

Animal Symmetry

Animal		Symmetry	Reason
jellyfish	(A)	radial	body parts around a central point
crayfish	(H)	bilateral	has two sides and a front and back
sponge	(E)	no symmetry	no definite shape
spider	(B)	bilateral	has two sides and a front and back
sea star	(F)	radial	body parts around a central point
oyster	(G)	bilateral	has two sides and a front and back
snail	(D)	bilateral	has two sides and a front and back
sea anemone	(C)	radial	body parts around a central point

For further explanation and examples of this skill, refer to Comparing and Contrasting on page 956 of the **Skill Handbook.**

Teaching Strategies

- Have the students review the first section of this chapter.
- Allow students to complete the Skill Activity on their own.
- Discuss the students' answers to the activity and Practicing the Skill questions.

Practicing the SKILL

1. Which animals have radial symmetry? Bilateral symmetry? No symmetry?
2. What kind of symmetry do you think most animals have?
3. If an animal has a front and hind end, what kind of symmetry does it have?

For more skill practice, do the Chapter 24 Interactive Exploration on the **Science Voyages Level Blue CD-ROM.**

Practicing the SKILL

1. radial symmetry: jellyfish, sea star, and sea anemone; bilateral symmetry: crayfish, spider, oyster, and snail; no symmetry: sponge
2. Answers may vary, however, students probably are familiar mostly with vertebrates and may answer bilateral symmetry. Also, insects account for the largest number of animals and have bilateral symmetry.
3. bilateral symmetry

For further explanation and examples of this skill, refer to Observing and Inferring on page 956 of the **Skill Handbook.**

Teaching Strategies

- Allow students to complete the Skill Activity individually.
- Discuss the students' answers. to the activity and Practicing the Skill questions.

Observing and Inferring

Background

Have you ever seen an animal track in the snow or mud? If you have, you probably tried to identify what animal left it there. You probably inferred what type of animal left it there based on observations you made about the area you were in.

Scientists also draw conclusions based on observations of the environment. In this activity, you will identify animal tracks and determine which animal made the tracks.

Procedure

1. Look at the figure below.
2. Decide which track belongs to which type of animal.
3. Copy the table in your Science Journal and record your answers.
4. Describe how each animal's foot is adapted to its environment.

Identifying Animal Tracks

Animal	Track	Adaptation
Bear	c	clawed toes
Beaver	a	webbed toes
Cheetah	g	clawed toes
Deer	b	feet for running, support
Horse	d	feet for running
Moose	e	feet for running, support
Raccoon	f	clawed toes

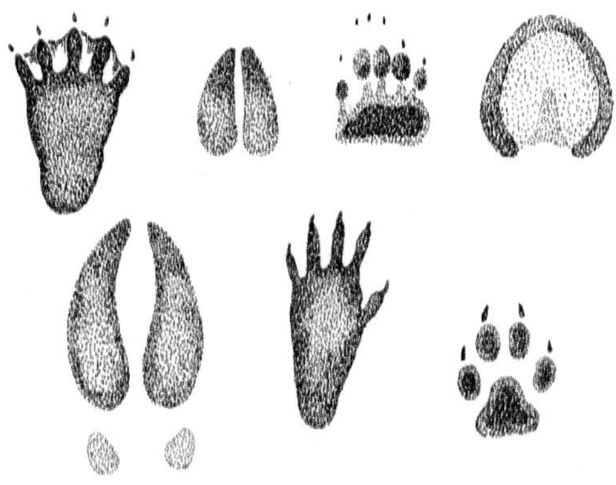

Practicing the SKILL

1. Could you expect to find a raccoon track in the same area you found a cheetah track? Explain.
2. What are the differences between track **b** and **e**? How does that help you identify the track?

For more skill practice, do the Chapter 25 Interactive Exploration on the **Science Voyages Level Blue CD-ROM.**

Practicing the SKILL

1. Yes, because both animals' feet have the same adaptation (clawed toes) which would allow them to function in the same environment.
2. Track e is larger than track b and you can see the impressions of the claws in track e. The differences in tracks help identify them because tracks are unique to each type of animal.

Communicating

Background

Not all of the information that we read is presented honestly or accurately. In order to make informed decisions, you must be able to evaluate critically the information you read to make sure that the information is not only accurate but also that it is not biased or slanted to one particular view. Use the following guidelines to determine if the scientific information you read is reliable.

Procedure

1. Check the background of the author. Most articles written in journals or magazines give a brief biographical sketch of the author. Is the author a professional in the field about which he or she is writing, or is the author trained in another, unrelated field? Has the author earned awards in that field or awards from any of the major scientific societies?
2. Check the source of the article. Has the article been written for a scientific journal or has the article appeared in a popular magazine or local newspaper?
3. Evaluate the emotional level of the information. Scientific information is generally written in a straightforward style. When you read an article, consider the question: Does the headline or title make you angry, sad, or happy?
4. Read the article for how the content is presented. Check to see that concepts are clearly explained and supported by research. Be wary if many conclusions are drawn from only one, limited experiment. Also watch for overuse of such comments as "I think," or "In my opinion."
5. Determine whether the information has been taken out of context. Is the scientist writing the article or has someone reinterpreted the scientist's comments? Is it possible that only parts of the quoted comments are reported?

Practicing the SKILL

1. Read the following headlines. Which one do you think would contain more reliable information?
   - **Strange Fish Kill Has Public Upset**
   - **Scientists Investigate the Death of Fish in Plum River**
2. Which of the following three periodicals would be the best source of information for the situations below?
   - *An environmental periodical*
   - *A consumer periodical*
   - *An encyclopedia*

   a. Which detergent will clean your clothes the best?

   b. What new compounds are being used in making detergents?

   c. What effect do phosphate detergents have on the environment?

For more skill practice, do the Chapter 26 Interactive Exploration on the **Science Voyages Level Blue CD-ROM.**

For further explanation and examples of this skill, refer to Communicating on page 949 of the **Skill Handbook.**

Teaching Strategies

- Allow students to work in small groups to evaluate several articles.
- Have students suggest several other ways in which this skill can be useful in reading other types of material.

Practicing the SKILL

1. The second headline has less emotional appeal and is more straightforward. It would indicate a more reliable source of information.
2. **a.** a consumer periodical
   b. an encyclopedia
   c. an environmental periodical

For further explanation and examples of these skills, refer to Interpreting Scientific Illustrations on page 962 and Interpreting Data on page 960 of the **Skill Handbook.**

Teaching Strategies

- Have students volunteer to explain the effects of excess nitrates and phosphates in lakes and streams.
- Have student groups brainstorm possible sources of nitrate and phosphate pollution.
- Have students look carefully at the picture of the water hyacinth ponds at the water treatment plant, which is in the second section of this chapter. Discuss what chemicals these plants might be removing.

Chapter 27 Skill Activity

Use After Section 27-2

Interpreting Scientific Illustrations and Data

Background

Over the last ten years, people have begun to build houses around Maple Lake. Forty percent of the shoreline now has been developed. Recently, the residents have begun to complain about excessive algae growth and poor fishing. A scientific study indicates high levels of phosphates and nitrates in the lake. In an effort to locate the source of these chemicals, scientists collected and analyzed water samples. The sample locations are shown and the analyses are listed in the table below.

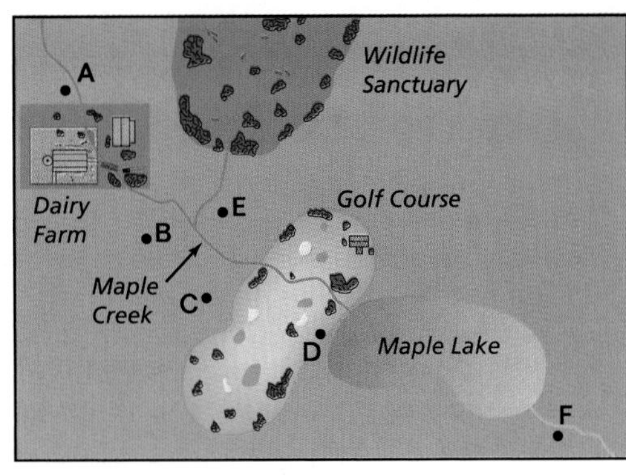

Procedure

1. Study the map of the Maple Lake area.
2. Study the table that lists location by letter and the amount of nitrates and phosphates at each location.
3. Use the map and the table to answer the questions in Practicing the Skill.

Location of Chemicals in Maple Lake

Location	Nitrates	Phosphates
A	2 ppm*	1 ppm
B	16 ppm	2 ppm
C	8 ppm	1 ppm
D	25 ppm	12 ppm
E	<1 ppm	<1 ppm
F	30 ppm	15 ppm

*The abbreviation "ppm" means parts per million. For example, 2 ppm here means 2 parts nitrates per million parts water in Maple Lake.

Practicing the SKILL

1. What might be the source of pollution at B?
2. Why do you think the level of chemicals dropped from B to C?
3. How do you explain the data at D?
4. The level of chemicals at F are higher than D. Where do you think the extra nitrates and phosphates are coming from?
5. A scientist has proposed to create a large water hyacinth pond on the creek between the golf course and Maple Lake. Do you think this will help with the algae problem in the lake? Why or why not?

For more skill practice, do the Chapter 27 Interactive Exploration on the **Science Voyages Level Blue CD-ROM**

GLENCOE TECHNOLOGY

Practicing the SKILL

1. The nitrates probably are coming from the dairy farm. Manure is high in nitrates.
2. The stream from the wildlife sanctuary is unpolluted and this water dilutes the pollution measured at B.
3. Fertilizer runoff from the golf course is adding nitrates and phosphates.
4. The extra nitrates and phosphates could be from residential fertilizer runoff or septic systems.
5. The pond would remove some of the pollution before it reaches the lake. However, the pollution from houses would continue.

English Glossary

This glossary defines each key term that appears in bold type in the text. It also shows the chapter and page number where you can find the word used.

Pronunciation Key

a...b**a**ck (bak)	oh...g**o** (goh)	sh...**sh**elf (shelf)
ay...d**ay** (day)	aw...s**o**ft (sawft)	ch...na**t**ure (nay chur)
ah...f**a**ther (fahth ur)	or...**or**bit (or but)	g...**g**ift (gihft)
ow...fl**ow**er (flow ur)	oy...c**oi**n (coyn)	j...**g**em (jem)
ar...c**ar** (car)	oo...f**oo**t (foot)	ing...s**ing** (sing)
e...l**e**ss (les)	ew...f**oo**d (fewd)	zh...vi**s**ion (vihzh un)
ee...l**ea**f (leef)	yoo...p**u**re (pyoor)	k...ca**k**e (kayk)
ih...tr**i**p (trihp)	yew...f**ew** (fyew)	s...**s**eed, **c**ent (seed, sent)
i (i + con + e)...**i**dea (i dee uh), l**i**fe (life)	uh...comm**a** (cahm uh)	z...**z**one, rai**s**e (zohn, rayz)
	u (+ con)...flow**er** (flo ur)	

A

absolute magnitude: measure of the amount of light a star actually emits. (ch. 20, p. 702)

acid rain: rain, snow, sleet, or hail with a pH below 5.6 that is created when sulfur dioxide or nitrogen oxides combine with moisture in the air; can kill plants, trees, and fish, and damage the surfaces of cars and buildings. (ch. 27, p. 912)

acids: substances that contain hydrogen and produce positively charged hydronium ions when they dissolve in water, forming acidic solutions (ch. 27, p. 912)

aerobes: organisms that require oxygen to survive—for example, humans and most bacteria. (ch. 21, p. 742)

algae (AL gee): one- or many-celled plantlike protists, all of which contain chlorophyll and can make their own food; organized into six main phyla based on their structure, their pigments, and the way they store food. (ch. 23, p. 759)

amphibian: ectothermic vertebrate that spends part of its life in water and part on land. (ch. 25, p. 850)

anaerobes: organisms that are able to live without oxygen—for example, methanogens and thermophiles. (ch. 21, p. 742)

angiosperms (AN jee uh spurmz): vascular plants that flower, have their seeds contained in a fruit, and are the most common form of plant life on Earth. (ch. 23, p. 803)

antibiotic: substance, such as penicillin, produced by one organism that inhibits or kills another organism. (ch. 21, p. 746)

apparent magnitude: measure of the amount of light that is received on Earth from a star. (ch. 20, p. 702)

appendages: jointed structures, such as legs, claws, and antennae, that grow from a body. (ch. 24, p. 832)

arthropod: animals that have jointed appendages, such as an insect or a crustacean, that is classified by the number of body segments and appendages, and that has a protective exoskeleton. (ch. 24, p. 832)

asteroid: piece of rock usually found in the asteroid belt between the orbits of Mars and Jupiter. (ch. 19, p. 691)

astronomical unit: average distance from Earth to the sun (150 million km), which is used to measure distances to objects in the solar system. (ch. 19, p. 676)

axis: imaginary line around which Earth spins. (ch. 18, p. 641)

B

bases: substances that produce negatively charged hydroxide ions when they dissolve in water, forming basic solutions (ch. 27, p. 912)

big bang theory: states that approximately 15 billion years ago, the universe began expanding out of an enormous explosion. (ch. 20, p. 723)

binary system: system in which two stars orbit each other. (ch. 27, p. 708)

bird: endothermic vertebrate with feathers, two legs, two wings, and bills, or beaks, and that lays hard-shelled eggs. (ch. 25, p. 856)

black hole: remnant of a star that is so dense that nothing can escape its gravity. (ch. 20, p. 714)

budding: form of asexual reproduction in which a new organism grows off the side of the parent. (ch. 22, p. 772)

C

cambium (KAM bee um): vascular plant tissue that produces new xylem and phloem cells. (ch. 23, p. 799)

carnivore: flesh-eating animals. (ch. 25, p. 868)

carrying capacity: maximum number of individuals of a particular species that the planet will support. (ch. 26, p. 880)

cartilage: tough, flexible tissue that is similar to bone but is not as hard. (ch. 25, p. 848)

cellulose (SEL yuh lohs): organic compound made of long chains of glucose molecules; forms the rigid cell walls of plants. (ch. 23, p. 786)

chordate: animal with a notochord, a dorsal hollow nerve cord, and gill slits. (ch. 25, p. 846)

chromosphere: layer of the sun's atmosphere above the photosphere and below the corona. (ch. 20, p. 705)

cilia (SIHL ee uh): short, threadlike structures that extend from the cell membrane of ciliates and are used for movement. (ch. 22, p. 765)

Clean Air Act: protects air quality by regulating car manufacturers, coal technologies, and other industries. (ch. 27, p. 914)

Clean Water Act: provides money to states for building sewage and wastewater-treatment facilities and for controlling runoff; also requires states to develop quality standards for their streams. (ch. 27, p. 923)

closed circulatory system: type of blood-circulation system in which blood is carried through blood vessels. (ch. 24, p. 825)

cnidarians (NIH dar ee uns): phylum of hollow-bodied, water-dwelling animals with stinging cells, radial symmetry, a body two layers thick, and both sexual and asexual reproduction. (ch. 24, p. 819)

comet: mass of dust and rock particles mixed in with frozen water, ammonia, and methane; consists of a nucleus, a coma, and a tail. (ch. 19, p. 688)

composting: piling yard wastes where they can gradually decompose. (ch. 26, p. 894)

conservation: careful use of resources to reduce damage to the environment by means such as reducing our use of materials, reusing items, and recycling materials. (ch. 26, p. 893)

constellation: group of stars that forms a pattern that looks like a familiar object, animal, or character. (ch. 20, p. 700)

contour feathers: strong, lightweight feathers that give birds their coloring and streamlined shape and that are used to fly and to steer. (ch. 25, p. 859)

corona: largest layer of the sun's atmosphere that extends millions of miles into space. (ch. 20, p. 705)

cuticle (KYEWT ih kul): waxy, protective layer covering the stems, leaves, and flowers of some land plants; is secreted by the plant's cell walls and slows the evaporation of water. (ch. 23, p. 787)

D

dicot: class of angiosperm that has two seed leaves inside its seeds, vascular bundles that occur in rings, and flower parts in multiples of four or five. (ch. 23, p. 804)

down feathers: soft, fluffy feathers that provide an insulating layer next to the skin of adult birds and that cover the bodies of young birds. (ch. 25, p. 859)

E

Earth: third planet from the sun; surface temperatures allow water to exist as a solid, liquid, and gas and atmosphere protects life from the sun's radiation. (ch. 19, p. 676)

ectotherm: vertebrate whose body temperature changes with the temperature of its surroundings. (ch. 25, p. 846)

electromagnetic spectrum: arrangement of electromagnetic radiation according to wavelength. (ch. 17, p. 613)

ellipse (ee LIHPS): elongated, closed curve that describes Earth's orbit. (ch. 18, p. 643)

endoskeleton: internal system of bones that protects and supports an animal's internal organs and also provides a place for muscle attachment. (ch. 25, p. 846)

endospores: heat-resistant, thick-walled structures many bacteria can produce around themselves when conditions are unfavorable. (ch. 21, p. 747)

endotherm: vertebrate that maintains a constant body temperature. (ch. 25, p. 846)

equinox (EE kwuh nahks): twice-yearly time when the sun is directly above Earth's equator and the number of nighttime hours equals the number of daylight hours worldwide. (ch. 18, p. 645)

estivation: behavioral adaptation for survival during hot, dry summer months, during which an animal becomes inactive; in amphibians, involves hiding in cooler, more humid ground. (ch. 25, p. 851)

exoskeleton: lightweight body covering that protects and supports an arthropod's body, prevents it from drying out, and is shed by molting. (ch. 24, p. 832)

F

fins: fanlike structures of most fish that are used for balancing, steering, and moving, and usually are paired. (ch. 25, p. 847)

first quarter: moon phase in which one-quarter of the moon's surface that faces Earth is lit up; occurs about a week after a new moon. (ch. 18, p. 651)

fish: ectotherm that lives in water and uses gills to get oxygen; usually has fins and scales. (ch. 25, p. 847)

fission: simplest form of asexual reproduction in which two cells are produced with genetic material identical to that of the parent cell; the method by which bacteria reproduce. (ch. 21, p. 742)

flagella: whiplike tails that help many types of bacteria move around in moist environments. (ch. 21, p. 739)

free-living: organism, such as a planarian, that doesn't depend on one particular organism for food or a place to live. (ch. 24, p. 821)

full moon: moon phase in which all of the moon's surface that faces Earth is lit up. (ch. 18, p. 651)

G

galaxy: large group of stars, gas, and dust held together by gravity. (ch. 20, p. 717)

giant: stage in a star's life cycle where hydrogen in the core is used up, the core contracts, and temperatures inside the star increase, causing the outer layers of the star to expand. (ch. 20, p. 713)

gills: organs that exchange oxygen and carbon dioxide with water. (ch. 24, p. 823)

Great Red Spot: high-pressure storm generated by huge thunderstorms in Jupiter's atmosphere. (ch. 19, p. 680)

guard cells: in a plant leaf, the cells that surround the stomata and that open and close them. (ch. 23, p. 801)

gymnosperms (JIHM nuh spurmz): vascular plants that produce seeds on the surface of the female reproductive structures, do not have flowers, and generally have needlelike or scalelike leaves. (ch. 23, p. 802)

H

hazardous wastes: poisonous, cancer-causing, or radioactive wastes that are dangerous to living things. (ch. 26, p. 889)

herbivore: grazing animal that eats only plants. (ch. 25, p. 868)

hibernation: behavioral adaptation for survival during cold, winter months, where an animal becomes inactive and its metabolic needs are lowered; in amphibians, involves burying themselves in mud or leaves until temperatures become warmer. (ch. 25, p. 851)

hyphae (HI fee): mass of many-celled, threadlike tubes that usually make up the body of a fungus. (ch. 22, p. 770)

inner planets: four solid, rocky planets that are closest to the sun—Mercury, Venus, Earth, and Mars. (ch. 19, p. 671)

invertebrates (ihn VURT uh brayts): animals lacking a backbone; about 97 percent of animals are invertebrates. (ch. 24, p. 815)

Jupiter: largest planet and fifth planet from the sun; composed mostly of hydrogen and helium; has continuous storms of high-pressure gas. (ch. 19, p. 680)

L

landfill: area where waste is deposited; the majority of U.S. garbage goes into landfills. (ch. 26, p. 889)

lichen (LI kun): organism that is made up of a fungus and a green alga or a cyanobacterium; an important food source for many animals; used by scientists to monitor pollution levels. (ch. 22, p. 773)

light-year: distance that light travels in one year (9.5 trillion km), which is used to measure distances in space. (ch. 20, p. 703)

lunar eclipse: eclipse that occurs when Earth's shadow falls on the moon. (ch. 18, p. 654)

M

main sequence: in an H-R diagram, the diagonal band of stars that runs from hot, bright stars in the upper-left corner of the diagram to cool, faint stars in the lower-right corner. (ch. 20, p. 710)

mammal: endothermic vertebrate that has hair and produces milk to feed its young. (ch. 25, p. 862)

mantle: thin tissue layer covering a mollusk's soft body; secretes the protective shell of those mollusks having a shell. (ch. 24, p.823)

maria: dark-colored, relatively flat areas of the moon that were formed when ancient lava filled basins on the moon's surface. (ch. 18, p. 655)

Mars: fourth planet from the sun; appears red due to the iron oxide content in its weathered rocks. (ch. 19, p. 676)

marsupial: mammal that gives birth to immature offspring and that has a pouch in which its young complete their development. (ch. 25, p. 864)

mascon: concentration of mass on the moon located beneath an impact basin. (ch. 18, p. 659)

medusa: free-swimming, bell-shaped body plan of a cnidarian, such as a jellyfish, that allows it to drift with the ocean currents. (ch. 24, p. 819)

Mercury: planet closest to the sun; has many craters, low gravitational pull, and is the second-smallest planet in our solar system. (ch. 19, p. 674)

metamorphosis (met uh MOR fuh sus): process in which insects change their body form as they mature; can be complete (egg, larva, pupa, and adult) or incomplete (egg, nymph, and adult). (ch. 24, p. 834)

meteor: meteoroid that burns up in Earth's atmosphere. (ch. 19, p. 690)

meteorite: meteoroid that does not completely burn up in Earth's atmosphere and strikes Earth. (ch. 19, p. 690)

mollusk: soft-bodied invertebrate that has a mantle, a large muscular foot, a complete digestive system with two openings, and usually has a protective shell. (ch. 24, p. 823)

monocot: class of angiosperm that has one seed leaf inside its seeds, vascular tissues arranged as bundles scattered throughout the stem, and flower parts in multiples of three. (ch. 23, p. 804)

monotreme: mammal that lays eggs with tough, leathery shells; the duckbilled platypus and two species of spiny anteaters. (ch. 25, p. 864)

moon phase: changing appearance of the moon as seen from Earth, which depends on the relative positions of the moon, Earth, and sun. (ch. 18, p. 651)

N

nebula: large cloud of gas and dust that can fragment into smaller pieces, each of which will collapse and form stars. (ch. 20, p. 712)

Neptune: large, gaseous planet similar to Uranus; is usually the eighth planet from the sun. (ch. 19, p. 684)

neutron star: collapsed core of a supernova that shrinks to about 10 km to 15 km in diameter and has only neutrons in the dense core. (ch. 20, p. 714)

new moon: moon phase that occurs when the lighted half of the moon faces the sun and the dark side faces Earth. (ch. 18, p. 651)

nitrogen-fixing bacteria: bacteria that live in the root nodules of certain kinds of plants and change nitrogen from the air into forms useful for animals and plants. (ch. 21, p. 746)

nonvascular plant: plant lacking vascular tissue and that absorbs water and other dissolved substances directly through its cell walls. (ch. 23, p. 788)

O

observatory: specially designed building, often with a dome-shaped roof that opens up to admit light; used to house optical telescopes. (ch. 17, p. 614)

omnivore: animals that eat both plants and animals. (ch. 25, p. 868)

Oort Cloud: cloud of comets that completely surrounds the solar system and that is located beyond the orbit of Pluto. (ch. 19, p. 689)

open circulatory system: type of blood-circulation system in which the blood is not contained in vessels but instead surrounds the organs. (ch. 24, p. 824)

orbit: curved path of a satellite as it revolves around an object in space. (ch. 17, p. 620)

outer planets: five planets that are farthest from the sun—Jupiter, Saturn, Uranus, Neptune, and Pluto. (ch. 19, p. 671)

P

parallax: apparent shift in position of an object when it is viewed from two different positions. (ch. 20, p. 703)

parasite: organism, such as a tapeworm, that depends on its host for food and a place to live. (ch. 24, p. 821)

pathogen: any organism that produces disease. (ch. 21, p. 746)

pH scale: scale used to describe how acidic or basic a substance is; ranges from 0 to 14, with 0 being the most acidic and 14 being the most basic. (ch. 27, p. 912)

phloem (FLOH em): vascular plant tissue made up of tubular cells that transport food from where it is made to other parts of the plant where it is used or stored. (ch. 23, p. 799)

photochemical smog: hazy, brown smog that is created when sunlight reacts with pollutants in the air; contains ozone near Earth's surface. (ch. 27, p. 910)

photosphere: lowest layer of the sun's atmosphere and the layer that gives off light. (ch. 20, p. 705)

pioneer species: first plants to grow in new or disturbed environments and that change environmental conditions so that other plant species can grow there. (ch. 23, p. 791)

placental mammal: mammal whose embryo develops in the uterus of the female. (ch. 25, p. 865)

Pluto: smallest planet and considered the ninth planet from the sun; has a thin, changing atmosphere and icy-rock surface. (ch. 19, p. 684)

polyp (PAHL up): vase-shaped body plan of a cnidarian, such as a hydra, that allows it to twist to capture prey and to somersault to a new location. (ch. 24, p. 819)

population: total number of individuals of a particular species in a specific area. (ch. 26, p. 881)

population explosion: rapidly increasing number of humans on Earth due to factors such as modern medicine, better sanitation, better nutrition, and more people surviving to the age when they can have children. (ch. 26, p. 881)

Project Apollo: final stage in the U.S. effort to reach the moon—on July 20, 1969, Neil Armstrong was the first human to set foot on the lunar surface. (ch. 17, p. 625)

Project Gemini: second stage in the U.S. program to reach the moon, in which a team of astronauts met and connected with another spacecraft while in orbit. (ch. 17, p. 624)

Project Mercury: first step in the U.S. effort to reach the moon, in which a piloted spacecraft successfully orbited around Earth and returned safely. (ch. 17, p. 624)

protist: single- or many-celled eukaryotic organism that lives in a moist or wet environment; can be plantlike, animal-like, or funguslike. (ch. 22, p. 758)

protozoans: complex, one-celled, animal-like protists that contain special vacuoles for digesting food and eliminating excess water; classified by their method of movement. (ch. 22, p. 763)

pseudopods (SEWD uh pahdz): temporary, footlike extensions of cytoplasm used by rhizopods for movement and for trapping food. (ch. 22, p. 764)

R

radio telescope: type of telescope that uses a large, curved dish to collect and record radio waves traveling through space and that can be used during the day or at night and during bad weather. (ch. 17, p. 615)

radula (RAJ uh luh): scratchy, tongue-like organ in many mollusks that acts like a file with rows of teeth to break up food into smaller pieces. (ch. 24, p. 823)

recyclable: any item that can be processed and used again in order to conserve natural resources and reduce solid waste. (ch. 26, p. 895)

reflecting telescope: optical telescope that uses a mirror (or mirrors) to focus light and produce an image at the focal point. (ch. 17, p. 614)

refracting telescope: optical telescope that uses a double convex lens to focus light and form an image at the focal point. (ch. 17, p. 614)

reptile: ectothermic vertebrate that has thick, dry, scaly skin, and does not depend on water for reproduction. (ch. 25, p. 853)

revolution: yearly orbit of Earth around the sun. (ch. 18, p. 643)

rhizoids: threadlike roots that are only a few cells in length and that anchor liverworts and mosses in place. (ch. 23, p. 790)

rotation: spinning of Earth on its axis, which causes day and night to occur. (ch. 18, p. 641)

S

Safe Drinking Water Act: strengthens health standards for drinking water; protects rivers, lakes, and streams; gives the public a right to know about contaminants that might be in their tap water. (ch. 27, p.923)

saprophyte: any organism that uses dead material as a food and energy source; sprophytes decompose dead organisms and recycles nutrients so that they are available for use by other organisms; saprophytic bacteria keep dead material from building up over all of Earth. (ch. 21, p. 745)

satellite: any object that revolves around another object; can be natural (Earth's moon) or artificial (*Sputnik I*). (ch. 17, p. 620)

Saturn: sixth planet from the sun; has a complex ring system made of hundreds of ringlets. (ch. 19, p. 681)

scrubber: device used in coal-burning power plants that allows the gases in the smoke to dissolve in water until the pH of the smoke increases to a safe level. (ch. 27, p. 915)

solar eclipse (ih KLIPS): eclipse that occurs when the moon moves directly between the sun and Earth and casts a shadow on part of Earth. (ch. 18, p. 652)

solar system: system of nine planets, including Earth and many smaller objects, that orbit the sun. (ch. 19, p. 669)

solstice: point at which the sun reaches its greatest distance north or south of the equator. (ch. 18, p. 645)

space probe: instrument that travels out into the solar system to gather information and sends the data back to Earth. (ch. 17, p. 621)

space shuttle: reusable spacecraft that carries astronauts, satellites, and other materials to and from space. (ch. 17, p. 628)

space station: large artificial satellite that provides support systems, living quarters, and equipment so that humans can live and work in space and conduct research not possible on Earth. (ch. 17, p. 629)

sphere (SFIHR): round, three-dimensional object whose surface at all points is the same distance from its center. (ch. 18, p. 640)

spore: reproductive cell that forms new organisms without fertilization. (ch. 22, p. 771)

stomata: small pores in the leaf surfaces surrounded by guard cells; allow carbon dioxide, oxygen, and water to enter and leave a leaf. (ch. 23, p. 801)

sulfurous smog: smog formed when burning fuel releases sulfur compounds in the air; may collect in an area where there's little or no wind. (ch. 27, p. 911)

sunspot: dark, relatively cool area on the surface of the sun. (ch. 20, p. 706)

supergiant: late stage in the life cycle of a massive star where the core reaches very high temperatures, heavy elements form by fusion, and the star expands. (ch. 20, p. 714)

symmetry: arrangement of the individual parts of an object; animals with bilateral symmetry have mirror image body parts; animals with radial symmetry have body parts arranged in a circle around a central point; asymmetrical animals have no definite shape. (ch. 24, p. 815)

T

third quarter: moon phase in which only half of the lighted side of the moon is visible. (ch. 18, p. 652)

toxin: poison produced by a bacterial pathogen. (ch. 28, p. 747)

U

Uranus: large, gaseous planet and seventh planet from the sun; has a magnetic pole tilted 60 degrees and rotates on an axis nearly parallel to the plane of its orbit. (ch. 19, p. 683)

V

vaccine: substance that is made from killed bacteria or damaged bacterial particles and can prevent, but not cure, many bacterial diseases. (ch. 21, p. 746)

vascular plant: plant with vascular tissue, a "pipeline" that moves water, food, and dissolved substances to cells throughout the plant. (ch. 23, p. 788)

Venus: second planet from the sun; has a dense atmosphere of carbon dioxide and sulfuric acid. (ch. 19, p. 675)

vertebrates (VURT uh brayts): animals with a backbone; only about 3 percent of animals are vertebrates. (ch. 24, p. 815)

W

waning: occurs after a full moon, when the amount of the moon's lighted side that can be seen becomes smaller. (ch. 18, p. 652)

waxing: occurs shortly after a new moon, when more and more of the moon's lighted side becomes visible. (ch. 20, p. 651)

white dwarf: late stage in a star's life cycle where its core uses up its supply of helium, it contracts, and its outer layers escape into space, leaving behind the hot dense core. (ch. 20, p. 714)

X

xylem (ZI lum): vascular plant tissue made up of tubular vessels that transport water and dissolved substances up from the roots throughout the plant. (ch. 23, p. 799)

Glossary/Glosario

Este glosario define cada término clave que aparece en **negrillas** en el texto. También muestra el número de página donde se usa dicho término.

A

absolute magnitude / magnitud absoluta: Medida de la cantidad de luz que una estrella emite verdaderamente. (Cap. 20, pág. 702)

acid / ácido: Sustancia con un pH menor de 7 en la escala de pH. (Cap. 27 pág. 912)

acid rain / lluvia ácida: Lluvia, nieve, cellisca o granizo con un pH menor que 5.6 que se forma cuando el dióxido sulfuroso o los óxidos de hidrógeno se combinan con la humedad del aire; puede matar plantas, árboles y peces, y además causar daños a las superficies de los carros y edificios. (Cap. 27, pág. 912)

aerobes / aerobios: Organismos que requieren oxigeno para sobrevivir, por ejemplo, los seres humanos y la mayoria de las bacterias. (Cap. 21, pág. 742)

algae / algas: Protistas unicelulares o multicelulares que parecen plantas, contienen clorofila y pueden fabricar su propio alimento; organizadas en seis filos principales con base en sus estructuras, sus pigmentos y la manera en que fabrican alimento. (Cap. 22, pág. 759)

amphibian / anfibio: Vertebrado de sangre fría que pasa parte de su vida en agua y parte sobre tierra. (Cap. 25, pág. 850)

anaerobes / anaerobios: Organismos con variaciones que les permiten vivir sin oxígeno, por ejemplo los metanógenos y los termófilos. (Cap. 21, pág. 742)

angiosperms / angiospermas: Plantas vasculares que florecen y producen frutos que contienen semillas. Son la forma más común de vida vegetal sobre la Tierra. (Cap. 23, pág. 803)

antibiotic / antibiótico: Sustancia producida por un organismo que inhibe o destruye otro organismo. La penicilina es un antibiótico muy conocido, el cual impide que las bacterias produzcan nuevas paredes celulares. (Cap. 21, pág. 746)

apparent magnitude / magnitud aparente: Medida de la cantidad de luz de una estrella que llega hasta la Tierra. (Cap. 20, pág. 702)

appendages / apéndices: Estructuras, tales como garras, patas o incluso antenas que crecen del cuerpo. (Cap. 24, pág. 832)

arthropod / artrópodo: Animal de patas articuladas, tal como un insecto o un crustáceo, que se clasifica de acuerdo con el número de segmentos corporales y apéndices y el cual tiene un exoesqueleto protector. El término artrópodo proviene de la palabra arthros que significa "unido" y de la palabra poda que significa "pata". (Cap. 24, pág. 832)

asteroid / asteroide: Fragmento rocoso semejante al material que formó los planetas. (Cap. 19, pág. 691)

astronomical unit / unidad astronómica: Medida que se usa para medir distancias hacia los objetos en el sistema solar; corresponde a 150 millones de kilómetros, lo cual es la distancia promedio entre la Tierra y el sol. (Cap. 19, pág. 676)

axis / eje: Línea imaginaria alrededor de la cual gira la Tierra. (Cap. 18, pág. 641)

B

bases / bases: Sustancias que producen iones hidroxilos negativos cuando se disuelven en agua, formando soluciones básicas ; sustancias con un pH mayor que siete. (Cap. 27, pág. 912)

big bang theory / teoría de la gran explosión: Teoría que enuncia que hace unos 15 billones de años, el universo comenzó con una enorme explosión. (Cap. 20, pág. 723)

binary system / sistema binario: Sistema en el cual dos estrellas giran una alrededor de la otra. (Cap. 20, pág. 708)

bird / ave: Vertebrado de sangre caliente con plumas, dos patas, dos alas y un pico, que pone huevos con cáscara dura. (Cap. 25, pág. 856)

black hole / agujero negro: Núcleo restante de una estrella de neutrones, el cual es tan denso y masivo que nada puede escapar de su campo de gravedad, ni siquiera la luz. (Cap. 20, pág. 714)

budding / gemación: Es una forma de reproducción asexual en que un nuevo organismo crece de un lado del organismo progenitor. (Cap. 22, pág. 772)

C

cambium / cambium: Tejido que produce nuevas células de xilema y de floema. (Cap. 23, pág. 799)

carnivore / carnívoro: Animal que se alimenta de la carne de otros animales. (Cap. 25, pág. 868)

carrying capacity / capacidad de carga: El mayor número de individuos, de una especie en particular, que el planeta puede soportar y mantener. (Cap. 26, pág. 880)

cartilage / cartílago: Tejido flexible fuerte que se parece al hueso, pero que no es tan duro como el hueso. (Cap. 25, pág. 848)

cellulose / celulosa: Compuesto orgánico hecho de cadenas largas de moléculas de glucosa, del cual están formadas las paredes celulares de las plantas. (Cap. 23, pág. 786)

chordate / cordado: Animal con notocordio, cordón nervioso dorsal hueco en sus espaldas y hendiduras branquiales. (Cap. 25, pág. 846)

chromosphere / cromosfera: Capa que se encuentra encima de la fotosfera y que se extiende por encima de esta unos 2000 km. (Cap. 20, pág. 705)

cilia / cilios: Estructuras cortas que parecen hilos y se extienden desde la membrana celular de los ciliados. (Cap. 22, pág. 765)

Clean Air Act / Ley para el Control de la Contaminación del Aire: Protege la calidad del aire al regular la industria automotriz, las tecnologías del carbón y otras industrias. (Cap. 27, pág. 914)

Clean Water Act / Ley para el Control de la Contaminación del Agua: Otorga fondos a los estados para la construcción de instalaciones de tratamiento de aguas negras y residuales y para el control de las aguas de desagüe. También requiere que los estados desarrollen estándares de calidad para sus corrientes de agua. (Cap. 27, pág. 923)

closed circulatory system / sistema circulatorio cerrado: Sistema circulatorio en que la sangre se transporta por el cuerpo a través de vasos sanguíneos. (Cap. 24, pág. 825)

cnidarians / cnidarios: Filo de animales acuáticos de cuerpo hueco que poseen células urticantes que usan para aturdir o atrapar presas de alimento; también poseen simetría radial. (Cap. 24, pág. 819)

comet / cometa: Objeto compuesto de polvo y partículas rocosas mezclados con agua congelada, metano y amoníaco. (Cap. 19, pág. 688)

composting / abono orgánico: Desechos vegetales que se apilan para que se descompongan paulatinamente. (Cap. 26, pág. 894)

conservation / conservación: Uso cuidadoso de los recursos, lo cual disminuye el daño al ambiente. (Cap. 26, pág. 893)

constellation / constelación: Grupo de estrellas en el firmamento. Las constelaciones recibieron nombres de animales, figuras mitológicas u objetos cotidianos. (Cap. 20, pág. 700)

contour feathers / plumas de contorno: Plumas fuertes y livianas que les dan a las aves sus bellos coloridos y sus perfiles aerodinámicos y las cuales usan para volar y para navegar. (Cap. 25, pág. 859)

corona / corona: La capa más grande de la atmósfera solar, la cual se extiende millones de kilómetros en el espacio. (Cap. 20, pág. 705)

cuticle / cutícula: Capa cerosa protectora que cubre los tallos, hojas y flores de algunas plantas terrestres; es secretada por las paredes celulares de la planta y disminuye la evaporación de agua. (Cap. 23, pág. 787)

D

dicot / dicotiledónea: Tipo de angiosperma que contiene dos cotiledones dentro de sus semillas. (Cap. 23, pág. 804)

E

Earth / la Tierra: El tercer planeta a partir del sol; tiene temperaturas superficiales que permiten que el agua exista como sólido, líquido y gas y una atmósfera que protege la vida de la radiación solar. (Cap. 19, pág. 676)

ectotherm / de sangre fría: Animal vertebrado cuya temperatura corporal cambia con la del ambiente. (Cap. 25, pág. 846)

electromagnetic spectrum / espectro electromagnético: Arreglo de radiación electromagnética, de acuerdo con sus longitudes de onda. (Cap. 17, pág. 613)

ellipse / elipse: Curva cerrada y alargada. La órbita de la Tierra forma un elipse. (Cap. 18, pág. 643)

endoskeleton / endoesqueleto: Sistema óseo interno de los vertebrados que apoya y protege los órganos internos del animal y al cual se adhieren los músculos. (Cap. 25, pág. 846)

endospores / endoesporas: Estructuras con paredes gruesas que rodean a muchas bacterias que producen toxinas, cuando las condiciones son desfavorables. (Cap. 21, pág. 747)

endotherm / de sangre caliente: Animal que mantiene una temperatura corporal constante. (Cap. 25, pág. 846)

equinox / equinoccio: Época del año cuando el sol está directamente encima del ecuador terrestre y las horas de luz solar son iguales a las horas de oscuridad. (Cap. 18, pág. 645)

estivation / estivación: Período de inactividad durante los meses calurosos y secos del verano. (Cap. 25, pág. 851)

exoskeleton / exoesqueleto: Cubierta corporal externa que protege y apoya el cuerpo de los artrópodos y que también impide que se seque el animal. (Cap. 24, pág. 832)

F

fins / aletas: Estructuras en forma de abanico que usan los peces para cambiar de dirección, equilibrarse y moverse. (Cap. 25, pág. 847)

first quarter / cuarto creciente: Fase de la luna cuando, desde la Tierra, se puede observar la mitad de su faz iluminada o un cuarto de la superficie lunar. (Cap. 18, pág. 651)

fish / pez: Animal de sangre fría que usa sus branquias para obtener oxígeno. (Cap. 25, pág. 847)

fission / fisión: La forma más simple de reproducción asexual, en la que se producen dos células con material genético idéntico al de la célula progenitora; es el método de reproducción más común de las bacterias. (Cap. 21, pág. 742)

flagella / flagelos: Estructuras en forma de látigo que poseen algunas bacterias para poder moverse en condiciones húmedas. (Cap. 21, pág. 739)

free-living / de vida libre: Organismo que no depende de otro organismo en particular para su alimentación o morada. (Cap. 24, pág. 821)

full moon / luna llena o plenilunio: Fase lunar durante la cual toda la superficie lunar que da a la Tierra está totalmente iluminada. (Cap. 18, pág. 651)

G

galaxy / galaxia: Grupo inmenso de estrellas, gas y polvo que se mantiene unido gracias a la gravedad. Nuestra galaxia, la Vía Láctea contiene unos 200 billones de estrellas. (Cap. 20, pág. 717)

giant / gigante: Etapa en el ciclo de vida de una estrella en que se agota el hidrógeno del núcleo, el núcleo estelar se contrae y las temperaturas dentro de la estrella aumentan, haciendo que las capas externas de la estrella se expandan. (Cap. 20, pág. 713)

gills / branquias: Órganos de los moluscos que intercambian oxígeno y dióxido de carbono con el agua. (Cap. 24, pág. 823)

Great Red Spot / la Gran Mancha Roja: Espectacular tormenta de gas turbulento y de alta presión que se puede observar continuamente en Júpiter. (Cap. 19, pág. 680)

guard cells / células guardianas: Células alrededor del estoma que lo abren y lo cierran. Junto con la cutícula y los estomas, son adaptaciones que ayudan a las plantas a sobrevivir sobre tierra. (Cap. 23, pág. 801)

gymnosperms / gimnospermas: Plantas vasculares que producen semillas en la superficie de las estructuras reproductoras femeninas. (Cap. 23, pág. 802)

hazardous wastes / desechos peligrosos: Desechos venenosos, cancerígenos o radiactivos que causan daño a los seres vivos. (Cap. 26, pág. 889)

herbivore / herbívoro: Animal de pastoreo que come plantas. (Cap. 25, pág. 868)

hibernation / hibernación: Período de inactividad y bajas necesidades metabólicas durante el invierno. (Cap. 25, pág. 851)

hyphae / hifas: Masas filamentosas multicelulares que, por lo general, componen el cuerpo de los hongos. (Cap. 22, pág. 770)

I

inner planets / planetas interiores: Planetas sólidos rocosos situados más cerca del sol: Mercurio, Venus, la Tierra y Marte. (Cap. 19, pág. 671)

invertebrates / invertebrados: Animal sin columna vertebral. (Cap. 24, pág. 815)

J

Jupiter / Júpiter: El planeta más grande del sistema solar y está ubicado en quinto lugar a partir del sol. (Cap. 19, pág. 680)

L

landfill / vertedero controlado: Área en donde se depositan los residuos. (Cap. 26, pág. 889)

lichen / liquen: Organismo compuesto de un hongo y un alga verde o una cianobacteria. (Cap. 22, pág. 773)

light-year / año luz: Distancia que viaja la luz en un año. Es también la unidad que se usa para medir distancias en el espacio. (Cap. 20, pág. 703)

lunar eclipse / eclipse lunar: Ocurre cuando la sombra de la Tierra cae sobre la luna. (Cap. 18, pág. 654)

M

main sequence / secuencia principal: En el diagrama H-R, la banda diagonal de estrellas que corre desde las estrellas calientes y brillantes, en la parte superior izquierda del diagrama, hasta las estrellas frías y tenues, en la parte inferior derecha. (Cap. 20, pág. 710)

mammal / mamífero: Vertebrado de sangre caliente que tiene pelo y produce leche para amamantar a las crías. (Cap. 25, pág. 862)

mantle / manto: Capa fina de tejido que cubre el cuerpo blando de los moluscos y secreta la concha protectora de los moluscos que poseen concha. (Cap. 24, pág. 823)

maria / maria: Regiones oscuras y relativamente planas de la superficie lunar. (Cap. 18, pág. 655)

Mars / Marte: Denominado el planeta rojo, Marte es el cuarto planeta a partir del sol. (Cap. 19, pág. 676)

marsupial / marsupio: Mamífero con bolsa que tiene crías inmaduras, las cuales completan su desarrollo en dicha bolsa. (Cap. 25, pág. 864)

mascon / concentración de masa: Concentración de masa ubicada debajo de las cuencas de impacto en la Luna. (Cap. 18, pág. 659)

medusa / medusa: Animal de vida libre, con cuerpo en forma de campana. (Cap. 24, pág. 819)

Mercury / Mercurio: El planeta más cercano al sol y es también el segundo planeta más pequeño. (Cap. 19, pág. 674)

metamorphosis / metamorfosis: Cambios por los que pasan muchos insectos y otros animales. Existen dos tipos de metamorfosis: completa e incompleta. (Cap. 24, pág. 834)

meteor / meteoro: Meteoroide que se quema en la atmósfera terrestre. (Cap. 19, pág. 690)

meteorite / meteorito: Meteoroide lo suficientemente grande como para caer sobre la superficie terrestre. (Cap. 19, pág. 690)

mollusk / molusco: Invertebrado de cuerpo blando, generalmente, con concha; posee un manto y una pata muscular grande. (Cap. 24, pág. 823)

monocot / monocotiledónea: Tipo de angiosperma que contiene un cotiledón dentro de sus semillas. (Cap. 23, pág. 804)

monotreme / monotrema: Mamífero que pone huevos con cáscara fuerte y correosa. (Cap. 25, pág. 864)

moon phase / fase lunar: Apariencia cambiante de la luna vista desde la Tierra. La fase que vemos depende de las posiciones relativas de la luna, la Tierra y el sol. (Cap. 18, pág. 651)

N

nebula / nebulosa: Nube extensa de gas y polvo que corresponde a la etapa inicial de formación de una estrella. (Cap. 20, pág. 712)

Neptune / Neptuno: Planeta grande y gaseoso descubierto en 1846; por lo general es el octavo planeta a partir del sol. (Cap. 19, pág. 684)

neutron star / estrella de neutrones: La etapa de una supernova cuando el núcleo denso y colapsado de la estrella se encoge hasta unos 10 a 15 km en diámetro y solo pueden existir neutrones en él. (Cap. 20, pág. 714)

new moon / luna nueva: Ocurre cuando la cara iluminada de la luna mira hacia el Sol y la cara oscura mira hacia la Tierra. La luna se encuentra en el firmamento, pero no podemos verla desde la Tierra. (Cap. 18, pág. 651)

nitrogen-fixing bacteria / bacterias nitrificantes: Bacterias que convierten el nitrógeno del aire en una forma útil para ciertas clases de plantas y animales. (Cap. 21, pág. 746)

nonvascular plant / planta no vascular: Planta que carece de tejido vascular y que usa otros medios para mover agua y sustancias a través de la planta. (Cap. 23, pág. 788)

O

observatory / observatorio: Edificio que alberga la mayoría de los telescopios ópticos usados por astrónomos profesionales. (Cap. 17, pág. 614)

omnivore / omnívoro: Animal que come plantas y también come otros animales. (Cap. 25, pág. 868)

Oort Cloud / Nube de Oort: Nube que, según el astrónomo holandés Jan Oort, está ubicada más allá de la órbita de Plutón y la cual rodea completamente el sistema solar. (Cap. 19, pág. 689)

open circulatory system / sistema circulatorio abierto: Sistema circulatorio que no posee vasos sanguíneos y en el cual la sangre rodea los órganos. (Cap. 24, pág. 824)

orbit / órbita: Trayectoria curva que sigue un objeto a medida que gira alrededor de otro objeto en el espacio. Por ejemplo, los planetas giran, en órbitas, alrededor del Sol. (Cap. 17, pág. 620)

outer planets / planetas exteriores: Planetas más alejados del sol: Júpiter, Neptuno, Saturno, Urano y Plutón. (Cap. 19, pág. 671)

P

parallax / paralaje: Cambio aparente en la posición de un objeto cuando uno lo observa desde dos posiciones diferentes. (Cap. 20, pág. 703)

parasite / parásito: Organismo que depende de su huésped para obtener alimento y morada. (Cap. 24, pág. 821)

pathogen / patógeno: Cualquier organismo causante de enfermedades. (Cap. 21, pág. 746)

pH scale / escala de pH: Escala que describe la acidez o basicidad de una sustancia; varía de 0 a 14, siendo 0 el rango más ácido y 14 el más básico. (Cap. 27, pág. 912)

phloem / floema: Tejido vegetal compuesto de células tubulares. Transporta alimentos desde el lugar en donde se fabrican hasta otras partes de la planta, en donde es usado o almacenado. (Cap. 23, pág. 799)

photochemical smog / smog fotoquímico: Smog color café que se forma cuando la luz solar reacciona con los contaminantes del aire. (Cap. 27, pág. 910)

photosphere / fotosfera: Capa más baja de la atmósfera del sol y desde la cual se emite la luz solar. A menudo llamada superficie solar. (Cap. 20, pág. 705)

pioneer species / especie pionera: Organismos que son los primeros en crecer en áreas nuevas o que han sido alteradas. (Cap. 23, pág. 791)

placental mammal / mamífero placentario: Animal cuyos embriones se desarrollan dentro del útero de la hembra. (Cap. 25, pág. 865)

Pluto / Plutón: El planeta más pequeño del sistema solar y del cual tenemos menos información. Se le considera el noveno planeta a partir del sol. (Cap. 19, pág. 684)

polyp / pólipo: Animal que tiene forma de jarrón y que generalmente es sésil. (Cap. 24, pág. 819)

population / población: Número total de individuos de cierta especie en un área particular. (Cap. 26, pág. 881)

population explosion / explosión demográfica: Rápido crecimiento de la población humana. (Cap. 26, pág. 881)

Project Apollo / Proyecto Apolo: Etapa final del programa americano de viajar a la luna. (Cap. 17, pág. 625)

Project Gemini / Proyecto Gemini: Segunda etapa en la meta de viajar a la luna. (Cap. 17, pág. 624)

Project Mercury / Proyecto Mercurio: Proyecto que inició el programa americano de viajar a la luna. (Cap. 17, pág. 624)

protist / protista: Organismo unicelular o multicelular que vive en ambientes húmedos o lluviosos. (Cap. 22, pág. 758)

protozoans / protozoarios: Protistas unicelulares que parecen animales; son complejos y viven en agua, tierra y tanto en organismos vivos como muertos. (Cap. 22, pág. 763)

pseudopods / seudopodios: Extensiones temporales del citoplasma, o patas falsas, de los Rhizopoda, que usan para moverse y alimentarse. (Cap. 22, pág. 764)

R

radio telescope / radiotelescopio: Tipo de telescopio que se usa para estudiar ondas radiales que viajan a través del espacio. (Cap. 17, pág. 617)

radula / rádula: Órgano de los moluscos que parece una lengua y que actúa como una lima con hileras de dientes para romper los alimentos en pedazos más pequeños. (Cap. 24, pág. 823)

recyclable / reciclable: Cualquier artículo que se puede procesar y volver a usar, para así conservar los recursos naturales y disminuir los desechos sólidos. (Cap. 26, pág. 895)

reflecting telescope / telescopio reflector: Telescopio que usa un espejo como objetivo para enfocar la luz del objeto bajo observación. (Cap. 17, pág. 614)

refracting telescope / telescopio refractor: Telescopio en que la luz del objeto pasa a través de una lente convexa doble, en donde la luz se dobla formando una imagen sobre el punto focal; luego el ocular magnifica la imagen. (Cap. 17, pág. 614)

reptile / reptil: Vertebrado de sangre fría con piel seca y escamosa y el cual no depende del agua para su reproducción. (Cap. 25, pág. 853)

revolution / revolución: Órbita anual de la Tierra alrededor del sol. (Cap. 18, pág. 643)

rhizoids / rizoides: Raíces filamentosas con solo unas cuantas células de grosor que anclan las hepáticas y los musgos en su lugar. (Cap. 23, pág. 790)

rotation / rotación: Movimiento de la Tierra alrededor de su eje, el cual causa el día y la noche. (Cap. 18, pág. 641)

S

Safe Drinking Water Act / Ley sobre la Seguridad del Agua Potable: Fortalece los estándares de salud para el agua potable, protege los ríos, lagos y corrientes de agua y otorga a los ciudadanos el derecho de saber acerca de los contaminantes que pueda contener el agua potable. (Cap. 27, pág. 923)

saprophyte / saprofito: Cualquier organismo que usa materia muerta como su fuente alimenticia y energética; las bacterias saprofitas evitan la acumulación de materias muertas, por todo el mundo. (Cap. 21, pág. 745)

satellite / satélite: Cualquier objeto que gira alrededor de otro objeto. (Cap. 17, pág. 620)

Saturn / Saturno: Conocido como el planeta anular, es el sexto planeta a partir del sol. (Cap. 19, pág. 681)

scrubber / depurador: Dispositivo que hace que los gases en el humo se disuelvan en agua, así como sucedería en la naturaleza, hasta aumentar el pH del humo a un nivel seguro. (Cap. 27, pág. 915)

solar eclipse / eclipse solar: Ocurre cuando la luna se mueve directamente entre el sol y la Tierra y proyecta una sombra sobre parte de la Tierra. (Cap. 18, pág. 652)

solar system / sistema solar: Sistema compuesto de nueve planetas, incluyendo la Tierra, y muchos objetos más pequeños que giran alrededor del sol. (Cap. 19, pág. 669)

solstice / solsticio: Punto en que el sol alcanza su mayor distancia al norte o al sur del ecuador. (Cap. 18, pág. 645)

space probe / sonda espacial: Instrumento que viaja por el sistema solar; reúne información y la envía a la Tierra. (Cap. 17, pág. 621)

space shuttle / transbordador espacial: Nave espacial reutilizable que transporta a astronautas, satélites y otros materiales hacia el espacio y desde el mismo. (Cap. 17, pág. 628)

space station / estación espacial: Estación en el espacio que posee viviendas, áreas de trabajo y de ejercicio, y todo el equipo y sistemas auxiliares que necesitan los seres humanos para vivir y trabajar en el espacio. (Cap. 17, pág. 629)

sphere / esfera: Objeto redondo tridimensional cuya superficie en cualquiera de sus puntos está a la misma distancia de su centro. (Cap. 18, pág. 640)

spore / espora: Célula reproductora que forma nuevos organismos sin ayuda de la fecundación. (Cap. 22, pág. 771)

stomata / estomas: Pequeños poros en la superficie de las hojas de las plantas, que permiten que el dióxido de carbono, el agua y el oxígeno entren y salgan de la hoja. (Cap. 23, pág. 801)

sulfurous smog / smog sulfuroso: Tipo de smog que se forma cuando la quema de combustibles libera compuestos de azufre en el aire; este smog sulfuroso se puede acumular en un área donde no sopla el viento o sopla muy poco. (Cap. 27, pág. 911)

sunspot / mancha solar: Área de la superficie solar que parece oscura porque es más fría que las áreas que la rodean. (Cap. 20, pág. 706)

supergiant / supergigante: Etapa en la formación de una estrella en la cual se forman elementos cada vez más pesados por medio de la fusión, haciendo que a la larga, se forme hierro en su núcleo. (Cap. 20, pág. 714)

symmetry / simetría: Se refiere al arreglo de las partes individuales de un objeto; los animales con simetría bilateral tienen partes corporales que son imágenes especulares una de la otra; los animales con simetría radiada poseen partes corporales arregladas en forma de círculo alrededor de un punto central y los animales asimétricos no tienen una forma corporal definitiva. (Cap. 24, pág. 815)

T

third quarter / cuarto menguante: Cuando se ve solo la mitad de la faz iluminada de la luna. (Cap. 18, pág. 652)

toxin / toxina: Veneno que producen los patógenos bacteriales. (Cap. 21, pág. 747)

U

Uranus / Urano: El séptimo planeta a partir del sol, descubierto en 1781. Es un planeta grande y gaseoso, con 17 satélites y un sistema de anillos oscuros y delgados. (Cap. 19, pág. 683)

V

vaccine / vacuna: Sustancia que se produce a partir de partículas dañadas de las paredes celulares de bacterias o de bacterias muertas; puede prevenir, pero no curar muchas enfermedades causadas por bacterias. (Cap. 21, pág. 746)

vascular plant / planta vascular: Planta con tejidos que forman un sistema que transporta agua, nutrientes y otras sustancias a lo largo de la planta. (Cap. 23, pág. 788)

Venus / Venus: A veces llamado el gemelo de la Tierra, Venus es el segundo planeta a partir del sol; tiene una atmósfera densa de dióxido de carbono y ácido sulfúrico. (Cap. 19, pág. 675)

vertebrates / vertebrados: Animal con columna vertebral; solo un 3 por ciento de todos los animales son vertebrados. (Cap. 24, pág. 815)

W

waning / octante menguante: Cuando la cantidad de la faz iluminada de la luna, que se puede ver desde la Tierra, comienza a disminuir. (Cap. 18, pág. 652)

waxing / octante creciente: Cuando se hace cada vez más visible la cara iluminada de la luna. (Cap. 18, pág. 651)

white dwarf / enana blanca: Etapa tardía en el ciclo de vida de una estrella, en que su núcleo agota su abastecimiento de helio, se contrae y sus capas externas se escapan hacia el espacio, dejando un núcleo denso y caliente. (Cap. 20, pág. 714)

X

xylem / xilema: Tejido compuesto de vasos tubulares que transportan agua y sustancias disueltas desde las raíces, a través de toda la planta. (Cap. 23, pág. 799)

Index

The index for *Science Voyages* will help you locate major topics in the book quickly and easily. Each entry in the index is followed by the numbers of the pages on which the entry is discussed. A page number given in **boldface type** indicates the page on which that entry is defined. A page number given in *italic type* indicates a page on which the entry is used in an illustration or photograph. The abbreviation *act.* indicates a page on which the entry is used in an activity.

A

B

C

R

S

Art Credits

TABLE OF CONTENTS
viii (b)Rolin Graphics; **xi**(l) Barbara Hoopes-Ambler; **xii** Morgan-Cain & Associates.
Chapter 17 - **612-3** Rolin Graphics; **614** George Bucktell; **620 622-3** John Edwards.
Chapter 18 - **641** John Edwards; **642** Rolin Graphics; **643** Bruce Sanders; **644 645** John Edwards; **650** John Edwards/Morgan-Cain & Associates; **651** Morgan-Cain & Associates; **652** John Edwards/Morgan-Cain & Associates; **653 654 656-7** Rolin Graphics; **662** John Edwards; **665** Glencoe/McGraw-Hill.
Chapter 19 - **668-9** Morgan-Cain & Associates; **670 671** Dave Fischer/John Edwards; **673** Dartmouth Publishing; **682** Morgan-Cain & Associates; **683 689** John Edwards; **690-1** (t)Morgan-Cain & Associates; **691** John Edwards; **694** John Edwards; **694** Dave Fischer/John Edwards; **695** Morgan-Cain & Associates; **697** Glencoe/McGraw-Hill.
Chapter 20 - **700** (l)Morgan-Cain & Associates, (r)Precision Graphics; **701 703** John Edwards; **705 710** Morgan-Cain & Associates; **711 712 713** John Edwards; **718** Morgan-Cain & Associates; **719** John Edwards; **720-1** Morgan-Cain & Associates; **721** (b)Jim Shough; **722** John Edwards; **726 727 728 729** Morgan-Cain & Associates; **730** John Edwards; **733** Glencoe/McGraw-Hill.
Chapter 21 - **739 740** Morgan-Cain & Associates; **746-7** Morgan-Cain & Associates/Pond & Giles; **752** Morgan-Cain & Associates; **755** Glencoe/McGraw-Hill.
Chapter 22 - **758** Felipe Passalacqua/Morgan-Cain & Associates; **759** Morgan-Cain & Associates; **763** (t)Felipe Passalacqua, (b)Morgan-Cain & Associates; **765** Morgan-Cain & Associates; **770 771 779** Dave Fischer; **781** Glencoe/McGraw-Hill.
Chapter 23 - **785** Morgan-Cain & Associates; **789** Pond & Giles/Morgan-Cain & Associates; **799** Pond & Giles; **801** Morgan-Cain & Associates; **804 805 809** Pond & Giles; **811** Glencoe/McGraw-Hill.
Chapter 24 - **815** Glencoe/McGraw-Hill; **816** Cende Hill; **817** Glencoe/McGraw-Hill; **819** Cende Hill; **820** Morgan-Cain & Associates; **821** Sarah Woodward; **823** Glencoe/McGraw-Hill; **824** Laurie O'Keefe; **825 826** Sarah Woodward; **832** Glencoe/McGraw-Hill; **834** David Ashby; **837** Sarah Woodward; **840 843** Glencoe/McGraw-Hill.
Chapter 25 - **846 847** Glencoe/McGraw-Hill; **848** Michael Woods; **850** Glencoe/McGraw-Hill; **851** Michael Woods; **852** Robert Hynes; **854** Dave Fischer; **856** Glencoe/McGraw-Hill; **858** David Ashby; **860** Pond & Giles; **862** Glencoe/McGraw-Hill; **864** Morgan-Cain & Associates; **868** Barbara Hoopes-Ambler; **875** Glencoe/McGraw-Hill.
Chapter 26 - **881** Dartmouth Publishing; **885** Glencoe/McGraw-Hill; **888** Tom Kennedy; **889 890** Morgan-Cain & Associates; **891** Glencoe/McGraw-Hill; **895** Tom Kennedy; **904** Dartmouth Publishing; **907** Morgan-Cain & Associates.
Chapter 27 - **911** Thomas Gagliano; **913** John Edwards; **914** Thomas Gagliano, (br)Morgan-Cain & Associates; **915** Morgan-Cain & Associates; **921** John Edwards; **922** Glencoe/McGraw-Hill; **924** Morgan-Cain & Associates; **925** Thomas Gagliano; **927** (l) Dartmouth Publishing; **928** Thomas Gagliano; **931** Glencoe/McGraw-Hill.

Photo Credits

TABLE OF CONTENTS
v Jack Zehrt/FPG International; **viii** (l)Matt Meadows, (r)NASA/Science Source/Photo Researchers; **ix** TSADO/JPL/NASA/Tom Stack & Associates; **x** (t)Jan Hinsch/Science Photo Library/Photo Researchers, (b) Visuals Unlimited; **xi** (r)Jack Wilburn/Animals Animals; **xiii** (r)Nigel Cattlin/Holt Studios International/Photo Researchers, (l)The New Zealand Herald; **xiv** Matt Meadows; **xv** Matt Meadows; **xvi** Kazuaki Iwasaki/The Stock Market; **xvii** (tr)Richard L. Carton/Photo Researchers; **xviii** Matt Meadows.

UNIT 5

Opener - **608-9** NASA; **609** NASA/Corbis Media.

Chapter 17 - **610-1** Jack Zehrt/FPG International; **611** Matt Meadows; **612** (l)Mark Reinstein/FPG International, (r)Mark E. Gibson; **613** (l)Daedalus Enterprises/Peter Arnold, Inc., (c)Rob Atkins/The Image Bank, (r)David M. Dennis/Tom Stack & Associates; **614** Matt Meadows; **615** NASA; **616** (t)Eric Sander/Liaison International, (b)Science Photo Library/Photo Researchers; **618** Matt Meadows; **621** (l)NASA/Science Source/Photo Researchers, (lc)NASA, (rc)NASA/Science Source/Photo Researchers, (r)Martin Marietta Corporation/Science Photo Library/Photo Researchers; **624** NASA; **625** NASA/Mark Marten/Photo Researchers; **626** NASA; **627** International Dark Sky Association; **628-9** Mark M. Lawrence/The Stock Market; **630-1** NASA/Science Photo Library/Photo Researchers; **632** NASA; **633** NASA/Newell Colour Imaging; **634** (t)Rafael Macia/Photo Researchers, (bl)NASA, (br)NASA/Mark Marten/Photo Researchers; **635** (t)NASA, (b)Mark M. Lawrence/The Stock Market.

Chapter 18 - **638-9** NASA/TSADO/Tom Stack & Associates; **639** Matt Meadows; **640** Jerry Schad/Photo Researchers; **643** Skip Comer; **644** (t)Rafael Macia/Photo Researchers, (b)Richard Price/FPG International; **646** NASA/GSFC/Tom Stack & Associates; **647** Tom Croke/Liaison International; **648 649** Matt Meadows; **651** Dr. Fred Espenak/Science Photo Library/Photo Researchers; **653** Bruce Herman/Tony Stone Images; **655** Kazuaki Iwasaki/The Stock Market; **658** NASA; **659** Zuber et al/Johns Hopkins University/NASA/Photo Researchers; **660** BMDO/NRL/LLNL/Science Photo Library/Photo Researchers; **662** (t)Rafael Macia/Photo Researchers, (b)Kazuaki Iwasaki/The Stock Market; **663** (t)NASA, (b)courtesy Gibor Basri.

Chapter 19 - **666-7** Telegraph Colour Library/FPG International; **667** Matt Meadows; **672** Scala/Art Resource, NY; **674** (l)US Geological Survey/Science Photo Library/Photo Researchers, (r)JPL/TSADO/Tom Stack & Associates; **675** JPL/TSADO/Tom Stack & Associates; **676** NASA; **677** (l)USGS/NASA/TASDO/Tom Stack & Associates, (r)NASA/TSADO/Tom Stack & Associates; **678** (l)Science Photo Library/Photo Researchers, (r)TSADO/JPL/NASA/Tom Stack & Associates; **679** USGS/TSADO/Tom Stack & Associates; **680** (t)NASA/Mark Marten/Photo Researchers, (b)NASA/Tom Stack & Associates; **681** (right-1)USGS/TSADO/Tom Stack & Associates, (right-2)TSADO/NASA/Tom Stack & Associates, (right-3)TSADO/NASA/Tom Stack & Associates, (right-4)JPL, (b)Space Telescope Science Institute/NASA/Science Photo Library/Photo Researchers; **683** NASA/JPL/Tom Stack & Associates; **684** (t)NASA, (b)NASA/Photo Researchers; **685** NASA/ESA/Tom Stack & Associates; **687** Tom McHugh/Photo Researchers; **690** David Parker/Science Photo Library/Photo Researchers; **691** Planet Earth Pictures/FPG International; **692** JPL/TSADO/Tom Stack & Associates; **693** NASA; **694** (t)JPL/TSADO/Tom Stack & Associates, (b)NASA; **695** NASA/Mark Marten/Photo Researchers.

Chapter 20 - **698-9** Space Telescope Science Institute/NASA/Science Photo Library/Photo Researchers; **699** Matt Meadows; **701** Bill & Sally Fletcher/Tom Stack & Associates; **702** Tim Courlas; **704** David Parker/Science Photo Library/Photo Researchers; **706** (l)NOAO/TSADO/Tom Stack & Associates, (r)ESA/TSADO/Tom Stack & Associates; **707** (l)Chris Butler/SPL/Photo Researchers, (r)NASA; **708** Bill & Sally Fletcher/Tom Stack & Associates; **709** Tim Courlas; **714** Celestial Image Co./Science Photo Library/Photo Researchers; **715** Bill & Sally Fletcher/Tom Stack & Associates; **716** (l)National Geographic Photographer Sam Abell, (r)David Robert Austen; **717** ©Jerry Lodriguss/Photo Researchers; **718** Telegraph Colour Library; **719** Celestial Image Co./Science Photo Library/Photo Researchers; **723** NASA/Science Source/Photo Researchers; **724** Matt Meadows; **726-9** David S. Addison/Visuals Unlimited; **730** NASA; **731** (t)Celestial Image Co./Science Photo Library/Photo Researchers, (b)©Jerry Lodriguss/Photo Researchers.

UNIT 6

Opener - **734-5** ©Chris Newbert; **735** ©David Young/Tom Stack & Associates.

Chapter 21 - **736-7** Manfred Kage/Peter Arnold, Inc.; **737** Michael Abbey/Photo Researchers; **738** R. Calentine/Visuals Unlimited; **741** Matt Meadows; **742** (t)Tom E. Adams/Peter Arnold, Inc., (b)Visuals Unlimited; **743** D. Foster/Visuals Unlimited; **744** (tl)Michael Abbey/Photo Researchers, (tr)Michael Abbey/Photo Researchers, (bl)Winston Patnode/Photo Researchers, (br)Michael Abbey/Photo Researchers; **745** (t)David R. Frazier/Photo Researchers, (b)Charles Gold/The Stock Market; **748** Alfred Pasieka/Science Photo Library/Photo Researchers; **749** Bryan Hodgson; **750 751** KS Studio; **752** (t)R. Calentine/Visuals Unlimited, (b)Visuals Unlimited; **753** (l)Alfred Pasieka/Science Photo Library/Photo Researchers, (r)Charles Gold/The Stock Market; (b)Daniel Schaefer.

Chapter 22 - **756-7** Amanita Pictures; **757** Mark Burnett; **759** Jan Hinsch/Science Photo Library/Photo Researchers; **760** (t)Dr. David M. Phillips/Photo Researchers, (b)Biophoto Associates/Photo Researchers; **761** (tl)Runk/Schoenberger from Grant Heilman, (tr)Runk/Schoenberger from Grant Heilman, (b)Michael Abbey/Photo Researchers; **762** (t)Walter H. Hodge/Peter Arnold, Inc., (b)Gregory Ochoki/Photo Researchers; **764** (tl)Ronald Gorbutt/Britstock, (tr)Alfred Pasieka/Science Photo Library/Photo Researchers,(b)Oliver Meckes/Photo Researchers; **765** (t)M.I.Walker/Photo Researchers, (b)Sinclair Stammers/Science Photo Library/Photo Researchers; **766** (l)Scott Camazine/Photo Researchers, (c)Amanita Pictures, (r)Matt Meadows; **767** David M. Dennis/Tom Stack & Associates; **768** (l)Nigel Cattlin/Holt Studios International/Photo Reasearchers, Inc., (r)Noble Proctor/Photo Researchers; **769** Paul Johnson/BPS/Tony Stone Images; **770** Amanita Pictures; **771** Ed Reschke/Peter Arnold, Inc.; **772** J. Forsdyke,Gene Cox/Science Photo Library/Photo Researchers; **773** David M. Dennis/Tom Stack & Associates; **774** (l)Stephen J. Krasemann/DRK Photo, (c)Runk/Schoenberger from Grant Heilman, (r)L.West/Photo Researchers; **775** Emory Kristof, (inset)Manfred Kage/Peter Arnold, Inc.; **776** Matt Meadows; **777** Matt Meadows; **778** (t)Jan Hinsch/Science Photo Library/Photo Researchers, (l)Oliver Meckes/Photo Researchers, (r)Runk/Schoenberger from Grant Heilman; **779** The Birmingham News.

Chapter 23 - **782-3** Aaron Haupt; **783** file photo; **784** Michael P. Gadomski/Photo Researchers; **785** (t)Jan Hirsch/Science Photo Library/Photo Researchers, (b)Doug Sokell/Visuals Unlimited, (l)Pat O'Hara/DRK Photo, (r)John Shaw/Tom Stack & Associates; **787** (l)Runk/Schoenberger from Grant Heilman, (c)Harold

Photo Credits

Hofman/Photo Researchers, (r)Kevin Schafer/Peter Arnold, Inc.; **788** David Cavagnaro/DRK Photo; **790** (l)John Kaprielian/Photo Researchers, (r)Barry L. Runk from Grant Heilman; **791** Kevin Schafer/Peter Arnold, Inc.; **792** (tr)Jane Grushow from Grant Heilman, (c)Stephen J. Krasemann/Photo Researchers, (l)Rod Planck/Photo Researchers, (br)David S. Addison/Visuals Unlimited; **793** (t)Runk/Schoenberger from Grant Heilman, (c)Sydney Karp/Photos/NATS, (b)Richard L. Carton/Photo Researchers; **794** Walter H. Hodge/Peter Arnold, Inc.; **795** Ludek Pesek/Science Photo Library/Photo Researchers; **796** Aaron Haupt; **797** (l)John D. Cunningham/Visuals Unlimited, (r)Ira Block, Courtesy Silkeborg Museum, Denmark; **798** Jeff Greenberg/Visuals Unlimited; **800** Runk Schoenberger from Grant Heilman; **802** (l)Richard Shiel/Earth Scenes, (r)Kenneth W. Fink/Photo Researchers; **803** (l)Joyce Photographics/Photo Researchers, (r)M.A. Chappell/Earth Scenes; **804** (l)Photo/NATS, (r)George E. Jones III/Photo Researchers; **805** (t)Mark E. Gibson, (bl)Aaron Haupt, (br)Frank Siteman/Stock Boston; **806** (l)Aaron Haupt, (r)Angelina Lax/Photo Researchers; **807** Matt Meadows; **808** (t)Michael P. Gadomski/Photo Researchers, (b)Walter H. Hodge/Peter Arnold, Inc.; **809** (t)Richard Shiel/Earth Scenes, (b)Aaron Haupt.

Chapter 24 - **812-3** Roger K. Burnard; **813** KS Studio; **814** (l)Mitsuaki Iwago/Minden Pictures, (c)Lynn Stone, (r)Fred Bavendam/Minden Pictures; **817** Fred Bravendam/Minden Pictures; **820** Carolina Biological Supply/Phototake; **821** Breck P. Kent/Animals, Animals; **822** James E. Hayden/Phototake; **823** (l)Zig Leszczynski/Animals, Animals, (r)Andrew J. Martinez/Photo Researchers; **824** (l)William J. Weber, (r)Sharon M. Kurgis; **825** Flip Nicklin/Minden Pictures; **826** Runk/Schoenberger from Grant Heilman; **827** NMSB/Custom Medical Stock Photo; **828** (l)Geri Murphy, (r)Geri Murphy; **829** The New Zealand Herald; **830 831** KS Studio; **832** (l)David M. Dennis, (r)Mark Moffett/Minden Pictures; **833** (t)Frans Lanting/Minden Pictures, (c)Jack Wilburn/Animals, Animals, (b)Sinclair Stammers/Animals, Animals; **834** Lynn Stone; **835** (t)G.I. Bernard/Animals, Animals, (c)E. R. Degginger/Animals, Animals, (b)Fred Bravendam/Minden Pictures; **836** (tr)Ruth Dixon, (l)Fred Bavendam/Minden Pictures, (br)Fred Bavendam/Minden Pictures; **837** Fred Bavendam/Minden Pictures; **838** Dave Fleetham/Tom Stack & Associates; **839** KS Studio; **841** (tl)William J. Weber, (tr)Geri Murphy, (bl)Mark Moffett/Minden Pictures, (br)Frans Lanting/Minden Pictures.

Chapter 25 - **844-5** Roland Seitre/Peter Arnold, Inc.; **845** Dan Rest; **847** (t)Brian Parker/Tom Stack & Associates, (c)David R. Frazier, (b)Jesse Cancelmo; **849** (t)Breck P. Kent/Animals, Animals, (b)Kelvin Aitken/Peter Arnold, Inc.; **850** David M. Dennis; **853** (t)Mark Moffett/Minden Pictures, (lc)Michael Collier, (rc)Alvin R. Staffan, (b)Lynn Stone; **855** Hans Pfletschinger/Peter Arnold, Inc.; **856** (l)Roger K. Burnard, (r)Lynn Stone; **857** (left-1)Don C. Nieman, (left-2)Alan Carey, (left-3)Roy Morsch/The Stock Market, (left-4)Alvin E. Staffan, (right-1)David R. Frazier, (right-2)William J. Weber, (right-3)Alan Nelson, (right-4)William J. Weber; **859** Michael Quinton/Minden Pictures; **861** (l)Mary Evans Picture Library/Photo Researchers, (r)Culver Pictures; **862** Johnny Johnson; **863** Tom McHugh/Photo Researchers; **864** Roger K. Burnard; **865** (t)Sharon Remmen, (b)CNRI/Phototake; **866** (left-1)Tom McHugh/Photo Researchers, (left-2)William J. Weber, (left-3)Stephen Dalton/Animals, Animals, (left-4)Sharon M. Kurgis, (right-1)Sharon Remmen, (right-2)Alvin Staffan, (right-3)V. Berns; **867** (left-1)Tom Pantages, (left-2)Lynn Stone, (left-3)Alvin E. Staffan, (right-1)Alan Carey, (right-2)William J. Weber, (right-3)Frans Lanting/Minden Pictures; **868** (tr)Lynn M. Stone, (l)David R. Frazier, (br)Michael A. Keller/The Stock Market; **869** Gerard Lacz/Peter Arnold, Inc.; **870** Maslowski Photo; **872** (t)Kelvin Aitken/Peter Arnold, Inc., (c)Michael Collier, (b)David M. Dennis; **873** (t)Alan Nelson, (l)William J. Weber, (right-1)Don C. Nieman, (right-2)Stephen Dalton/Animals, Animals, (right-3)V. Berns.

UNIT 7

Opener - **876-7** Sam C. Pierson/Photo Researchers; **877** Keith H. Murakami/Tom Stack & Associates.

Chapter 26 - **878-9** Ray Pfortner/Peter Arnold, Inc.; **879** Mark Burnett; **880** Jon Feingersh/The Stock Market; **882** Matt Meadows; **883** Richard Hutchings; **884** Matt Meadows; **886** (l)Roy Morsch/The Stock Market, (r)Michael Ableman; **887** (t)Jim Wark/Peter Arnold, Inc., (b)Larry Lefever from Grant Heilman; **888** Frans Lanting/Minden Pictures; **891** Mark Burnett; **892** Rick Iwasaki/Tony Stone Images; **893** Jack Dykinga; **896** (l,r)Kenji Kerins, (c)file photo; **898** Matt Meadows; **899** (l)ARS-Banuelos, (r)Nigel Cattlin/Holt Studios International/Photo Researchers; **900** KS Studio; **900-3** file photo; **901** file photos; **902** (tl)Telegraph Colour Library/FPG International, (tr)Hank Morgan/Science Source/Photo Researchers, (bl)file photo, (br)Jose Fuste Raga/The Stock Market; **903** (tl)Mark Burnett, (tr, bl, br)file photos; **904** (l)Jon Feingersh/The Stock Market, (r)Richard Hutchings; **905** (t)Rick Isasaki/Tony Stone Images, (b)Kenji Kerins.

Chapter 27 - **908-9** Mark E. Gibson; **909** Tim Courlas; **910** Rafael Macia/Photo Researchers; **912** Oliver Strewe/Tony Stone Images; **915** Lionel Delevingue/PhotoTake; **916** Mark E. Gibson; **917** University of Montana/Photo by Todd Goodrich; **918** Matt Meadows; **919** file photo; **920** (l)Kenji Kerins, (r)Tom Stack/Tom Stack & Associates; **921** (t)courtesy of the city of San Diego, (b)John Eastcott/Yva Momatiuk/DRK Photo; **923** (l)Tom Ives/The Stock Market, (r)Ian Adams; **926** Doug Martin; **928** Rafael Macia/Photo Researchers; **929** (tl)Kenji Kerins, (tr)Tom Stack/Tom Stack & Associates, (b)Doug Martin.

T.E.1

PERIODIC TABLE OF THE ELEMENTS

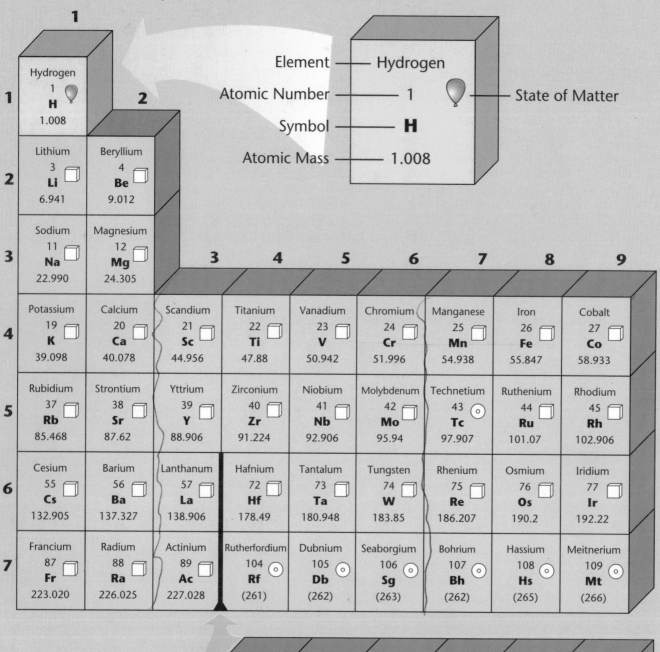

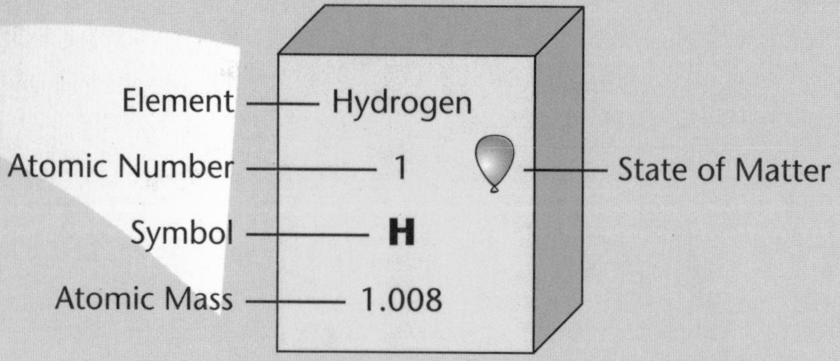

Key:
Element — Hydrogen
Atomic Number — 1
Symbol — **H**
Atomic Mass — 1.008
State of Matter

	1	2	3	4	5	6	7	8	9
1	Hydrogen 1 **H** 1.008								
2	Lithium 3 **Li** 6.941	Beryllium 4 **Be** 9.012							
3	Sodium 11 **Na** 22.990	Magnesium 12 **Mg** 24.305							
4	Potassium 19 **K** 39.098	Calcium 20 **Ca** 40.078	Scandium 21 **Sc** 44.956	Titanium 22 **Ti** 47.88	Vanadium 23 **V** 50.942	Chromium 24 **Cr** 51.996	Manganese 25 **Mn** 54.938	Iron 26 **Fe** 55.847	Cobalt 27 **Co** 58.933
5	Rubidium 37 **Rb** 85.468	Strontium 38 **Sr** 87.62	Yttrium 39 **Y** 88.906	Zirconium 40 **Zr** 91.224	Niobium 41 **Nb** 92.906	Molybdenum 42 **Mo** 95.94	Technetium 43 **Tc** 97.907	Ruthenium 44 **Ru** 101.07	Rhodium 45 **Rh** 102.906
6	Cesium 55 **Cs** 132.905	Barium 56 **Ba** 137.327	Lanthanum 57 **La** 138.906	Hafnium 72 **Hf** 178.49	Tantalum 73 **Ta** 180.948	Tungsten 74 **W** 183.85	Rhenium 75 **Re** 186.207	Osmium 76 **Os** 190.2	Iridium 77 **Ir** 192.22
7	Francium 87 **Fr** 223.020	Radium 88 **Ra** 226.025	Actinium 89 **Ac** 227.028	Rutherfordium 104 **Rf** (261)	Dubnium 105 **Db** (262)	Seaborgium 106 **Sg** (263)	Bohrium 107 **Bh** (262)	Hassium 108 **Hs** (265)	Meitnerium 109 **Mt** (266)

Lanthanide Series	Cerium 58 **Ce** 140.115	Praseodymium 59 **Pr** 140.908	Neodymium 60 **Nd** 144.24	Promethium 61 **Pm** 144.913	Samarium 62 **Sm** 150.36	Europium 63 **Eu** 151.965
Actinide Series	Thorium 90 **Th** 232.038	Protactinium 91 **Pa** 231.036	Uranium 92 **U** 238.029	Neptunium 93 **Np** 237.048	Plutonium 94 **Pu** 244.064	Americium 95 **Am** 243.061